Fishery Products

Edited by

Rudolf Kreuzer

Published by arrangement with the Food and Agriculture Organization of the United Nations

Fishing News (Books) Ltd

23 Rosemount Avenue, West Byfleet

Surrey, England

ISBN 0 85238 065 8

Editorial Team
Associate Editor: C Day

Technical: H Lisac
              M Lindemann

Drawings: A Barcali

Secretarial: K Ellis-Festagallo
              M Ripanti-Aird
              E Schödl

Printed in Great Britain by
The Whitefriars Press Ltd., London and Tonbridge

Contents

Preface

This Technical Conference on Fishery Products was, in a sense, the culmination of FAO's policy and planning in this field for more than two decades. Throughout this period two of our major objectives have been to bring about improvements in standards of hygiene and in quality in fishery products as these are essential if the industry is to make progress throughout the world and, particularly, in the developing countries. In pursuit of these objectives we have held a number of conferences centred on fishery products, of which the chief have been the meetings on: 'Chilling of Fish' (Rotterdam, Netherlands, 1956); 'Fish in Nutrition' (Washington, D.C., U.S.A., 1961); 'Future Developments in the Production and Utilization of Fish Meal' (Rome, Italy, 1961); 'Symposium on the Significance of Fundamental Research in the Utilization of Fish' (Husum, Germany, Fed. Rep. of, 1964); 'Freezing and Irradiation of Fish' (Madrid, Spain, 1967); and 'Fish Inspection and Quality Control' (Halifax, Nova Scotia, Canada, 1969). Each of these meetings dealt with a specific technical aspect of fish as a food product and, I believe, each has contributed to a better understanding of its subject field and has led to progress. The Fishery Products Conference, therefore, followed as a natural culmination of this sequence and came at a critical time for the fishery products industry as a whole.

All of us concerned with fisheries are aware of the many problems confronting us today and in the foreseeable future. While these problems are basically concerned with the world's aquatic resources and their rational exploitation, many are of direct concern to the products industry. These include not only how to make the best and fullest use of all the accepted and traditional fish and other resources, but how to do likewise with those resources which are underutilized or neglected or are not at present exploited at all. The Conference, as was to be expected, dwelt to a considerable extent on this complex subject and, I think, sharpened the focus for all of us on such important newcomers to the market as minced and powdered products. The Conference also reviewed the role of the long-established fish meal and oil industry and stressed its valuable function not only in the utilization of fish which would otherwise remain unexploited but also for its contribution to the foreign exchange earnings of developing countries and for its role in capital accumulation in those countries, thus providing funds for further economic development.

I was especially pleased that the Conference paid a good deal of attention to markets and marketing, subjects which are often neglected at such meetings. As I pointed out in my opening address, people can and will change their food habits given the right kind of products and persuasion. It is largely the task of marketing to ensure that the technologists are guided toward the evolvement of the right kind of products and to persuade the consumers to accept them. In this respect, I should like to quote again a statement made by Mr Hisamune, President of the Japan Marine Fishery Research Centre, at the April 1973 meeting of FAO's Committee on Fisheries. He had described the almost revolutionary changes in the diet of the people of Japan as the result of social and economic reforms during the past two decades, and concluded by saying: 'What I have tried to stress in telling you all this is that tastes and customs, however deep rooted they may be, can still be changed by social or economic factors. This is very important'. Mr Hisamune speaks with the voice of experience as well as hope and what he had to say was echoed and re-echoed in the discussions at the Conference. They confirmed that there is a very bright future for the development of new, and the improvements of existing, fishery products.

There is one other Conference subject I should like to draw attention to in this preface and that is the question of international aid, including joint ventures. The strong participation of developing countries and industry in the Conference lent special significance to discussion of this subject and brought out many useful guidelines concerning the future of such aid. It also showed that FAO, in establishing an international investment and development service in the Fishery Industries Division, is meeting a growing need of both the developing and donor countries, including industry.

Finally, I should like to express on behalf of the Director General of FAO, our great appreciation of all those who contributed to making the Conference so stimulating and rewarding, and to thank, in particular, the Government of Japan for the excellent arrangements made and facilities provided which ensured the smooth and efficient conduct of the Conference.

FAO, Rome   Roy I Jackson,
                                              Deputy Director-General

Introduction

As I indicated in my address at the opening of the FAO Technical Conference on Fishery Products, it was a significant meeting held at a significant time for fisheries. The main groups of traditional food fish stocks appear to be near the limit of exploitation–if not, in some cases, beyond the limit. Yet the world human population continues to increase, therefore the demand for food, especially such protein-rich food as fish, also continues to increase. In view of this situation there is, in particular, an urgent need to exploit the neglected or unfamiliar resources, as well as make more rational use of all the traditional resources. This, as I mentioned in my address, calls for 'international cooperation in developing and preserving the fishery resources of the world and promoting the more effective use of what is already being caught.' This is why I said that the Conference was significant because it provided a rare opportunity to conduct a meaningful exchange of information and views on the pertinent problems that beset the world fisheries situation today and for the foreseeable future. The fact that the participants came from 55 countries, and included a very large number from developing countries and from the fishery industries, increased the significance of the occasion and the meaningfulness of the opportunity to exchange views. My firm impression is that a high degree of success was achieved in this respect, as was evidenced by the considerable number of proposals put forward by the Conference, indicating actions that should be taken by the governments of fishing countries, by industry, and by FAO and other organizations concerned with the development of fisheries. While these suggestions do not provide a blueprint for future activities, they can be regarded as guidelines for all concerned with the welfare and development of fisheries, particularly with regard to handling, preserving, processing and marketing fish and fishery products.

I cannot allow this opportunity to pass without expressing on behalf of the Government of Japan and of all of us concerned with the Conference, our pleasure in being the host of such a gathering. In many ways it was most appropriate to hold the Conference in Japan because not only do we have one of the world's biggest fishery industries, with a production of more than ten million tons a year, but we make the greatest variety of fishery products. This, no doubt, is because fish and other sea foods are traditionally an important part of the Japanese diet. We consume more of such food than any other people, eating all the types of fish, crustaceans and molluscs that are common to man's diet throughout the world and some other kinds, such as whale meat, squid, sea urchins, sea slugs and varieties of seaweed. Many of these are processed into a great range of products, including such relative newcomers as fish sausage and fish ham. And as part of our effort to make the fullest and most rational use of the aquatic resources, we are undertaking extensive and intensive cultivation of fish, shellfish and seaweeds as well as raising fry for release into the sea.

I mention these aspects of the Japanese fisheries scene because they attracted much attention from the participants at the Conference and I think it was generally agreed that they also provided a practical demonstration of the valuable contribution which the fishery products industry can make to the food supply and the national economy.

In concluding, may I say once again how pleased we were to be the host of a Conference attended by such a large and distinguished group of participants.

Tokyo, Japan

I Arakatsu
Chairman
Technical Conference on Fishery Products

List of Authors and Participants in Discussions

Symbols and Abbreviations

Abbr./Symbol	Name of unit	Nom de l'unité (French)	Nombre de la unidad (Spanish)
Bè	The Baume (system of measuring density)	Baumé	Baumé
Btu	British thermal unit	unité thermique britannique	unidad térmica inglesa
cal	calorie	calorie	caloría
	small calorie	petite calorie	caloría pequeña
	gram-calorie	calorie-gramme	caloría-gramo
Cal = kcal	kilocalorie	kilocalorie	kilocaloría
	large calorie	grande calorie	caloría grande
	kilogram-calorie		
ft	foot	pied (anglais)	pie (inglés)
gal	gallon	gallon	galón
ha	hectare	hectare	hectárea
kW	kilowatt	kilowatt	kilovatio
lb	pound (avoirdupois)	livre (avoirdupois)	libra (avoirdupois)
mEq	milliequivalent	milliéquivalent	miliequivalente
	millival	millival	milival
MHz	megahertz	mégahertz	megahertzio
ml	millilitre	millilitre	mililitro
mol	gramme-molecule	molécule-gramme	molécula-gramo
	mole	mole	mol
	gramme-mole		
nm (= mμ)	nanometre (= millimicron)	nanomètre (= millimicron)	nanómetro (= milimicrón)
P	poise	poise	poise
ppm	part per million	partie par million	parte por millón
psi (= lbf/in^2)	pound-force per square inch	livre-force par pouce carré	libra fuerza por pulgada cuadrada
rpm	revolution per minute (= rev/min)	(tour par minute) (= tr/min)	revolución por minuto (= rev/min)
t	metric ton	tonne (métrique)	tonelada métrica
ton [UK]	UK ton (= long ton [USA])[1]	tonne anglaise (= tonne longue)	tonelada inglesa (= tonelada larga)
ton [USA] (= sh tn)	short ton[2]	tonne courte	tonelada corta
USP	Unit of measuring vitamin A activity		
μ [mu] (= μm)	micron (= micrometre)	micron (= micromètre)	micrón, micra (= micrómetro)
μg	microgramme	microgramme	microgramo
μmol	micromole	micromole	micromol
'W' value	Chain length less double bond position from acid end		

[1] [1,016 kg or 2,240 lb (0.454 kg)].
[2] [907 kg or 2,000 lb (0.454 kg)].

Part I

THE INFLUENCE OF TRADITION AND CHANGE

Fish and its Place in Culture *R Kreuzer*

Le poisson et son role Culturel
Alors que la pêche est une activité qui occupe des millions de personnes et que les captures représentent une importante source de nourriture et d'autres produits, les rapports entre l'homme et les poissons sont plus profonds et complexes que ceux qui unissent le prédateur et sa proie. Le présent document vise donc à déterminer l'ampleur et la complexité de ces rapports qui existent depuis les temps préhistoriques et ont influé sur les superstitions, les croyances, les religions, les manifestations artistiques, les coutumes et les moeurs humaines.

La pesca y su lugar en la Cultura
Aunque la pesca es un negocio que ocupa a millones de personas y constituye una fuente importante de alimentos y otros productos, la relación que tiene con el hombre es más profunda y más intrincada que la de un depredador y la presa. Por esto en el documento se trata de indicar el alcance y complejidad de esta relación que ha existido desde tiempos prehistóricos y que ha ejercido una influencia en las supersticiones, creencias, religiones, arte, costumbres y hábitos del hombre.

Some thoughts about the role of fish in human society seem to be relevant as an introduction to a compilation of knowledge on the development of fishery products in all parts of the world. Fish takes a prominent place in the mind of many people as food and, indeed, probably its most beneficial role in many countries is as a source of protein. It is to be hoped, therefore, that in the near future fish will play its full part in eliminating malnutrition in those countries where protein deficiency remains a serious problem in the daily life of many people. In addition, fish holds a prominent place in the economies of a number of countries, particularly those few whose fishery products may account for more than 75 per cent of the total value of their commodity trade. In others, although not so significant, fish still contributes in a variety of ways to their economy and may be important to the export trade, thereby earning valuable foreign exchange. Fisheries also can provide much employment, as in Indonesia where there are more than one million fishermen or the Philippines where they number about seven hundred thousand. There is also the point that fish is increasing in importance in world trade and will continue to do so as developing countries acquire greater skill in modern fish processing.

While it is appropriate to refer to the nutritional and economic importance of fish, its influence on human society is much much broader and more complex. It is to some degree part of the culture of all people and may be related to their religion, mythology and art, and to their songs, dances and hobbies. Indeed, many food habits are linked to, and protected by, religion and are subject to rites and taboos and other measures which have helped maintain food behaviour and patterns through centuries.

All this may justify the linking of fish to the development of civilizations and defining its place in culture.

DAWN OF CIVILIZATION

In the classification system of the many forms of life, man shares with fish the same phylum, both being 'chordata' or vertebrates. When man, however, emerged about 600,000 years ago, the Age of Fishes had already lasted 400 million years and fish had filled the waters of the world with about 40,000 species. While newly arrived man wandered in small groups of 5 to 20 through a hostile world, gathering food, fish had already occupied every conceivable ecological niche in one form or another. The early food gatherers saw fish in all the rivers, lakes and inundation areas and added them to their diet of vegetables, grains, fruits, insects and small animals. This is how man lived during the first 500,000 years of his existence, developing slowly some level of culture and the first food patterns. In the latter phase of this period there is evidence of the first use of fire. A crude

bone industry developed and there are signs of burial rites and simple social institutions. *Homo sapiens*, the modern type of man, appeared in Eurasia as late as 50,000 B.C., and later in Africa, and gave new incentives to culture. The bow and other missile weapons were invented and, with a great deal of imagination, the new men organized skilled collective hunting over steep slopes, and set traps and trained dogs. Such advances supplied the means to hunt large animals. In addition, more fish could be added to the economy of these early hunters because of the invention of harpoons, fish hooks, traps and boats. Meat and fish preservation methods developed, and in this time man changed from eating raw foods to eating them cooked.

The effect on cultural developments was considerable. Food habits and food patterns changed. More important, the abundance of food and the possibility of storing it permitted the development of larger communities and the occupation of sites which provided safety and shelter for considerably longer periods than had been possible before. Bones of seafish found in refuse heaps of communities which lived in caves in western-central France during the Upper Paleolithic period, indicate that trade, including seafish products, was established between the coast and inland settlements.

Improved living conditions led to new cultural patterns. The earliest manifestations of art discovered are in the caves of Altamira and other places in Spain and in France (60,000 B.C. to 10,000 B.C.) and on rocks in the middle of areas rich in game or fish, as in Norway (5,000 B.C. to 1,000 B.C.) where pictures were painted or engraved on the walls of the fjords. These were fish, their heads pointing down to the water. Such pictures were magic-inspired and associated with hunting, fishing and fertility and can be interpreted as aiming at increasing, attracting and catching fish and game. The Meander motif appeared in these drawings and is interpreted as standing for water, and, therefore, being the 'run' of life. The post-glacial culture in Siberia was also one of hunters and fishermen.

Homo sapiens entered North America by way of the Bering Strait about 11,000 B.C. and reached the Magellan Strait by about 9,000 B.C., where they settled in caves. From Eurasia they moved eastward and wandered as far as Oceania and Japan. Fish played a considerable part in the food pattern of all these early cultures. Man's development, however, although similar in its main features, is so complex that it cannot be described in terms of a linear evolution.

AGRICULTURE—THE NEW INCENTIVE

The retreat of the last glaciers in Europe was followed by a warm climate period. The big game disappeared

Fig 1   Reindeer and fish. Magdalenian engraving on a reindeer's horn found in a cave at Lorthet, Hautes-Pyrénés, France.

Fig 2   Men hunting and fishing. Decoration on an Iberian vase from Liria, c. 1000 B.C., Archaeological Museum, Valencia, Spain.

Fig 3   Man carrying fish. Detail of 'The Standard of Ur', Sumerian mosaic, 2600–2400 B.C., British Museum, London

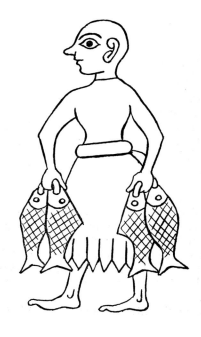

All illustrations in this paper drawn by J. Maxwell.

and people had to explore new sources of food. Grain was collected and horticulture of some kind started. An extensive trade in luxury articles, such as amber and sea shells, was established. However, new incentives and ideas were required to develop a culture above the level of that of the hunting age.

'*Ex oriente lux*', said the Romans and, indeed, a new chapter in the history of man began about 6,000 B.C. in the then warm open landscape and the humid climate of the Middle East. Agriculture, the domestication of animals, and the transition from food collection to food production, caused a significant turning point in man's way and philosophy of life. Increased production of food from a given area of land made a certain food surplus possible, a 'necessary basis for the emergence of civil societies', as a historian puts it. Within the large settlements and stable communities that appeared not all of their members were required for food production. Thus the ground was prepared for the development of religion, law, craftmanship and social life. The volume of trade increased and urbanization began.

Agriculture appeared in Mesopotamia about 6,000 B.C. and on the coast of the Mediterranean and soon also in Egypt. It was practised in southern Europe about 5,000 B.C. but not until about 3,000 B.C. in the northern part of the continent. By that time urbanization had begun in Mesopotamia and Egypt. The first temples were built in Eridu, southern Babylonia (see: Myths), and fish culture began in Mesopotamia and Egypt. Large settlements, with fish pits and effigies of fish in stone, were established in the Lake Baikal area about 4,000 B.C. Some 2,000 years later the population in this area appeared to live mainly by fishing instead of by hunting, to judge from the large number of fish hooks found in their graves.

The transition from nomadic to agricultural life brought about considerable changes in man's food. Flesh and milk and, near water resources, fish, the main staple foods during nomadic times, were supplemented and even replaced by grain so that the use of salt became a physiological necessity. The food patterns of the agricultural societies developed and trade added new commodities to local foods. Salt became more available and salting of fish became widely practised. Salt fish and a quern-ground barley porridge were the main foods in Mesopotamia at about 3,500 B.C. while in Sumeria the staple foods were fresh vegetables with dried, salted and smoked fish. Fresh, salted and dried fish were, with interruptions, important commodities in rural areas of ancient Egypt, but only freshwater fish were eaten because sea fish were considered unclean and were not even touched by the peasants even though their food consisted only of bread, beans and onions. It seems that the priests and nobles then abstained from eating fish but the attitude toward fish frequently changed in ancient Egypt.

Several processing centres for the production of dried and salted fish developed after the sixth century B.C. in the Mediterranean, and a trade in these commodities was established from the mouth of the Dnieper and the south coast of the Black Sea to Cadiz and Malaga in Spain, and from the Indus to the Alps. Smoked fish was a popular dish but was obviously confined to areas of production.

A change in the Mediterranean salt-fish trade came when, after the Second Punic War, Rome's hegemony at sea was undisputed and emphasis shifted to trade. Ostia, Rome's main harbour for the import of grain, became also the trade centre of the salt fish produced in the area between the Black Sea and Spain. This trade attracted heavy private investment in cargo vessels and crews, with large commercial firms being established in Ostia and other ports near Rome, which became the main consumption and distribution centre for fish products.

MYTH, LEGEND AND LORE

Myths, it is said, reflect the thoughts of the people of ancient times about the origin of the world and of man, and seek to explain his position in the world and in relation to gods, heroes and ancestors. Myths are still alive in tribal communities. A tribe, for example, that lives from fishing may attribute this to a supernatural being who taught their ancestors (in mythical times) how to catch and to prepare fish. The myth may reflect the history of a fishery and, at the same time, explains how the traditional food pattern of the tribe came into existence. The cosmogonic myths transfer the knowledge of the tribe on the origin of the world and of their own customs and techniques. Associated with this is, for example, the belief among ancient hunters and fishermen that, for success, they must know the origin of the fish and game they want to catch or to hunt.

Ea, the water god of Mesopotamia, one of the three leading members of the Sumerian pantheon, was probably the first 'fish-like' god in history and was described as a man covered with the body of a fish. He was worshipped in the ancient town of Eridu in a temple on the banks of the river, called the house of 'apsu', the freshwater depths below the earth. There was a sacred pond with many species of fish in the garden of this temple. The water, regarded as the element from which all life originates and to which it returns, was holy to Ea and was used to purify temples, houses and priests.

Knowledge was very difficult to acquire before scripts were evolved so the gods and semi-gods were considered the source of knowledge and wisdom. Wisdom and knowledge in life, with water as the origin of life, formed a symbolic entity, therefore the god of the mysterious waters was venerated as having knowledge and wisdom as deep as the ocean. He transmitted this wisdom and knowledge to the priests. He was also the god of physicians, looked upon as men who 'know water', i.e., the holy water of Ea, the water of life.

Due to their origin in the water, fish stood in the ancient world for fertility and renewal of life. The Sumerians offered them to their water god, and for the Egyptians fish were sacred and were mummified, and were not eaten by priests. A prominent place was occupied by the dolphin, which, in Greek and Roman mythology, was regarded as a fish. It was sacred to deities, was the symbol of the sea, and was regarded as mediator between this and the nether world. The Christians regarded fish as a symbol of Christ and salvation.

In Sumerian and Babylonian mythology the earliest teachers of civilization to men were thought to have come from the sea. The Seven Wise Men of Babylon who lived before the Great Flood were depicted as fish-men and, as the story goes, emerged from the sea

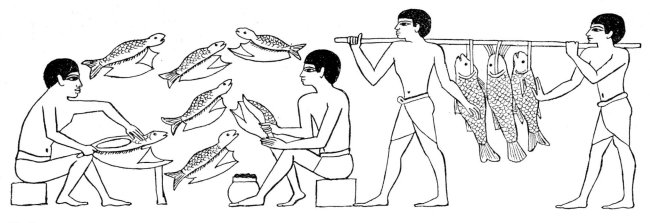

Fig 4

Fig 4   Wall painting in an Egyptian tomb (2500 B.C.) depicting fishermen carrying their catch and splitting fish for drying. Musée Guimet, Paris.

Fig 5   The spinning women of the Cassiti tribe, which conquered Babylonia (1000 B.C.), were held in high esteem. This relief illustrates the point. The slave with a fan attends the spinner, who has before her a dish on which there is a fish – another mark of her social status as fish was the food of the upper and richer classes in Babylonia.

Fig 6   Assyrian soldiers crossing a river. From an Assyrian bas-relief.

Fig 5

Fig 6

25

and brought mankind civilization and wisdom. Oannes, an amphibious being, was described as having the form of a fish but with the head and feet of a man under his fish skin. He is the best known of the Seven Wise Men and the first described by Berosus, a Babylonian historian (about 300 B.C.). Oannes lived in the Persian Gulf and instructed man in writing, in arts and in science during the day, while he dived down into the sea at night.

The Scythian god of horses, Anahita, was originally a fertility demon whose symbol was water, depicted as waves and spirals, and fish were sacred to him. A fish of gold as an amulet on the head of a horse, with engraved waves and other fish, has been found in a Scythian grave.

In Chinese cosmogonic myths the fish appeared in the form of a female deity, Nü Kua, said to have shaped the four pillars supporting heaven out of turtle feet and to have formed man out of earth. She was sometimes the bride or sometimes the sister of Fu-shi, a legendary emperor, who was thought to be the inventor of fishing and hunting. Recognition of the dangerous life of the fishermen and the need to protect them seems to be reflected in the myth of Archer the First, a semi-divine hero who carried out a number of tasks, similar to those of Hercules in Greek mythology, to liberate the world from monsters. One was to fight a giant snake that enjoyed devouring fishermen and their wives. In Chinese mythology, as in that of Mesopotamia, fish were associated with wisdom and teaching. This was reflected in the myth of K'ue hsing, an attendant (follower) of Won-ch'ang, the god of literature. K'ue hsing was brilliant but so ugly that an examiner failed him on that account. In sheer despair he tried to drown himself but was rescued by the Ao fish and was thereafter venerated by gifted candidates in exams who relied on him to see that they were treated fairly.

One of Japan's mythological deities was a god of storm, known as the Shark Man. The role of fishing and hunting in ancient Japan was also reflected in the myth of the brothers Fireshine and Fireshade, great-grandchildren of the sun goddess. While Fireshine caught all kinds of marine animals, Fireshade hunted land animals. When Fireshade tried fishing he had little luck and lost Fireshine's fish hook. He married the daughter of a sea god whom he met when in search of the hook which the fish helped to find and return. The marriage with the 'mermaid' did not last and the hunter returned to hunting. A folk tale of Urashima relates how a fisherman captured a sea turtle which changed into a beautiful maiden with whom he lived happily until his curiosity led him to break a promise and he lost her for ever.

The importance of the sea and the fresh waters to Greeks and Romans is reflected in their mythology and religion. Before commencing a sea voyage the Romans invoked the protection of Oceanus, an ancient sea deity. Dolphins drew his car and he had grapes in his hair and dolphins in his beard. The 3,000 Oceanides and 3,000 river gods were his sons. Nereus, another ancient sea god, was depicted as half man, half fish. He was wise and gave good advice to gods and men. He was the father of the 50 Naiads, those dolphin-riding kindly nymphs of the sea, among whom was Amphitrite. She was the wife of the sea god Neptune who, although a younger god, was supreme in water. He carried a trident and the horse and the dolphin were his sacred animals. No Roman

fisherman would have left the harbour without invoking Neptune's protection. Once, to obtain the favour of Amphitrite, Neptune assumed the form of a dolphin, and therefore the nymph is depicted in a sea-shell car drawn by dolphins. Gay Roman mosaics show dolphins and other fish, putti and tritons happily playing in the water. Pliny the Elder tells many stories of helpful dolphins as, for example, that of a dolphin which used to carry a child at sea. One day the child fell off the dolphin's back during a storm and drowned. The dolphin was so afflicted that it swam to shore and stayed there until it died. According to Pliny, dolphins also helped fishermen by chasing and directing fish toward the nets, then waiting in line for their reward, which consisted of bread dipped in wine. We can therefore understand that in ancient times dolphins became a popular motif in the decoration of floors and walls of houses near the sea.

Fish and the sea were important elements in the cults and ceremonies of the Mochicas, and Chimu of Peru. Sea gods and symbols for fish and water filled their mythological world and were incorporated in tapestries, plates, clay vessels, etc., found in their tombs. Although the significance of these gods and symbols is mostly unknown to us, the pictures and figures are understood to be magic symbols.

Many legends are told in Hawaii about sharks, often disastrous to man. However, the mythological shark has also often guided fishermen to land. An interesting similarity exists in this region with the legend of Jonah. This is the legend about Mutuk, swallowed by a shark, and his miraculous deliverance.

Fish are connected with many Christian legends. Once, when Christ with Peter crossed the Lake of Genezareth, the apostle picked from the water a fish with a coin in its mouth. A black spot remained at each side where Peter's fingers touched the fish which is therefore called 'Peter's fish' or 'Pesce San Pietro', known as John Dory in England. St. Brendan, an Irish monk, went out with three companions on a voyage in 545 A.D. to the West in search of the Land of Promise. Legend has it that in the middle of the ocean they saw what seemed a tiny island but turned out to be a large fish. The fish was converted to Christianity, followed the Saint and allowed him to celebrate Mass on its back in stormy weather. Eventually, it took the monk's ship on its back and brought them all to a beautiful land called the paradise of the birds. It has been assumed that this land was America, so a fish can be said to have had a large share in an earlier discovery of the New World. When, in the seventh century A.D., Bishop Wilfrid, Abbot of Ripon, came for the first time to the pagan Frisians it was a year of particularly large herring catches. The pagans attributed this to the appearance of the holy man and so they welcomed him and he was able to baptize many of them. This even indicates the importance of herring to the coastal people at that time.

As the movement of the sun and its relation to the change of seasons was of the greatest importance to agricultural peoples, astronomy developed with the rise of agriculture. The configurations of the fixed stars were grouped to constellations which were given names of animals and mythological figures. One constellation was called 'Pisces', fish, probably derived from connection with the god of water. It dates back to about 3,000 B.C.

Fig 7

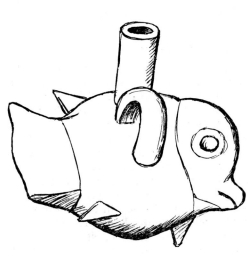

Fig 8

Fig 9

Fig 7   Thor fishing, using a bull's head as bait. In his right hand Thor holds his hammer, and in his left the line. Detail of the bas-reliefs of the Gosforth Cross, Cumberland, England

Fig 8   Dolph n. Indian pottery, Ecuador.

Fig 9   The symbol of the Aldine Press (established 1490)

Fig 10   Ostrogothic jewelled cross, time of Theodoric, flanked by fish, an early Christian symbol. From the Casena treasure, found near Ravenna, Italy.

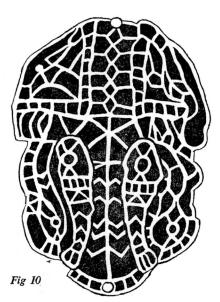

Fig 10

According to Greek mythology, Zeus gave fish a place in the sky to thank them for their help in moving to shore the shell from which Aphrodite rose. As a reference mark for measuring movements in the sky, an imaginary band, the 'Zodiac', also called the circle of animals, was established and divided into 12 equal parts called 'houses'. The twelfth house was called 'Pisces', illustrated by two fishes tied together by their tails, which seems to be the earliest fish symbol. The underlying Greek legend refers to Aphrodite and her son Eros who jumped into the water when surprised by Typhon on the banks of the Euphrates and were turned into fishes. This sign seems to have symbolized originally the fishery of the Nile and the beginning of the rainy season, the season of the fertilizing water. February was also the best season for fishing, the month when the sun starts to pass the house of 'Pisces'. The Zodiac was used as a kind of calendar by the ancient agricultural people, and kept its importance during the Middle Ages as the numerous paintings and sculptures in Christian churches show. It may also be mentioned that other constellations referring to fish are *Piscis australis*, the southern fish, and *Piscis volans*, the flying fish, both in the southern hemisphere. Predicting the future had been an important cult since prehistoric times and astrology was soon linked with astronomy and religion. It aimed at applying the change of the moon, and other movements in the sky, to human life. The Zodiac was accepted unchanged and Pisces refer in astrology to 'limitations', 'troubles' and 'confinement'. In the ancient Roman world astrology became a means of predicting the future.

The fish has appeared in the folklore of fishing communities from very early times and sailors have continuously added new fish tales to the old ones. Fish, fish-like beings and water spirits, even in ancient times, had most generous qualities attributed to them and appeared as obliging and helpful animals. These characteristics must have been preserved in tales and songs transmitted through generations of fishermen as we find similarities in the Mesopotamian and Egyptian myths and in the songs and folklore of communities along the European coast. Poor fisherfolk, with no hope of changing their life for the better, invented stories of fish or mussels which were able to fulfil all their wishes. The fish is held in high regard in folklore because of 'the benefit it brings and has brought to man since prehistoric times', as Franklyn expresses it. Thus, these tales can in effect be seen 'as a monument raised by the simple uncultured people to compliment their heroes and benefactors'. Fishermen love celebrations on rivers, lakes or at the seashore which, in a measure, compensate for their hard life. For example, rituals, such as 'washing the nets' or 'blessing the nets' in England, were celebrated, and are still observed, in most Christian fishing countries – an acknowledgement of man's dependence on God and the sea. Once a year the fishermen of Toyahama celebrate a day of reconciliation when they offer the ocean an immense red fish made from bamboo and linen to compensate for all the fish they have taken out of the sea during the year. The fish is so fantastic that it must influence any kind deity favourably. In China, where fish has always been held in high regard and considered suitable as a present for kings, it stands also for accomplishment, and a wealthy and prosperous district is often honoured as the district of fish and rice. Fish was used as an offering to god and heaven in earlier days.

Reference may be made here to the mermaids, those fanciful half fish and half humans, friendly toward man. They may even marry a man but invariably tragedy follows. Christian sailors dreaded the vision of a mermaid because it meant shipwreck to them. Mermaids appear frequently as figure-heads on sailing vessels and as carvings in churches, indicating their strong association with the life of seagoing people. Melusine, often depicted as a mermaid with two fish tails, was a fairy turned into a snake.

Myths and legends, blended with episodes of the life of the fisherman, have survived in folksongs, plays and dances in many fishing communities around the world showing the strong association of fish with the life, customs and beliefs of the people who depend on the resources of the sea. It can thus be seen that all peoples having a connexion with the sea had fish deities and fish in their myths and legends, generally relative to the more positive aspects of life. They were represented as helpful and dealt with fertility, healing, wisdom and learning. They protected man and even supported his heaven.

FEASTS AND FASTING

Fasting is practised in many religions. In the Christian church Friday became 'fish day' in the eighth century, which increased the importance of fish considerably. In the following centuries numerous fast days were established in England to overcome the shortage of meat. The effect of the Reformation in the 16th century, therefore, was felt by the English fishing industry since fast days were no longer observed. Since the beginning of this decade, Friday has no longer been a meatless day but it still remains the weekly fish day in most Christian countries, which is to the benefit of the fishing industry. Russian Orthodox groups hold pre-Lent festivities in which caviar, smoked salmon, sturgeon and pickled herrings are traditional dishes. From 6th to 18th January, carp, eaten with 'kouting' (porridge, poppy seed, honey and almonds) is a traditional dish to these groups.

Fish is an essential dish at all important Chinese feasts, mainly because it signifies good wishes. The reason is that the pronunciation of the word 'fish' in Chinese is 'Yü' which sounds exactly like the word for 'surplus' or 'plenty'. To say 'have fish' is therefore similar to saying 'have surplus' or 'have plenty', the best wishes one can offer to relatives, friends and superiors. A fish sent as a gift conveys these wishes and when a fish is not available, a wooden model of one is used. The birth of a boy in Japan is celebrated with a ceremonial meal consisting of a cooked fish, with the head on, rice and soup. The lips of the child are moistened with the various dishes. A bamboo pole is erected on the roof of the house or nearby with one or more large paper or cotton fish flying from it, blown up by the wind. Such fish are also flown from poles on 5th May, which is a national 'boys' day'. The fish are often in the shape of a carp which, in Japan, is the symbol of courage, energy and firmness, meaning that the carp swims against the stream of passions and indolence. A traditional fish soup, with a special maize dish, is eaten at a festival called 'homowo' in Accra, Ghana, and its vicinity.

Fig 11 Putti *fishing. Roman mosaic, Piazza Armerina, Sicily.*

Fig 12 Fish and octopus. Greek plate, 5th century B.C., Musée du Louvre, Paris.

Fig 13 Mochica and Chimu fish god holding a tumi knife (Peru). Such deities ruled all sea-spawned creatures and reflected the importance of the sea for these coastal peoples. From V.v. Hagen, The Desert Kingdoms of Peru, *London, 1965*

FISH-SYMBOL AND ART FORM

One of the characteristic cults that evolved with the transition to the agricultural way of life was the mother cult, symbolizing the continuous renewal of life. Water, as the origin of life, and fish, as the symbol of fertility, were attributed to the mother goddess. Death was also associated with the mother cult so that fish became related to the powers of the underworld. It was thought to be a mediator between this and the other life. An amphora from an Etruscan tomb shows a winged female demon, who accompanied the dead on their journey to the underworld, resting on a dolphin. In some of the Etruscan tombs of Tarquinia (Italy) the walls are decorated with paintings of waves in which dolphins and other fish swim and jump. In another tomb dolphins, depicted on a ceiling lamp, swim between the crests of waves. Above them are satyrs and sirens and below them fighting animals, all symbols of the powerful subterranean world. A dolphin is often depicted with Venus to symbolize her relation to the sea. Dolphins played around the ships of the earliest navigators and it is not to be wondered at that they became associated with deities in man's religion, myths and symbolism.

Pachamama, goddess of Lake Titicaca and the town of Tiahuanaco, Peru, had as her symbols fish, the condor and winged human beings. These decorated the walls of the large temple, and on the gate of the moon, which was placed on top of the pyramid of the town, there was a relief covered with fish. In ancient Colombia there were models of fish made of pure gold. These were put into Lake Guatavita on festive occasions as offerings for the gods. Such golden fish were found in the lake in 1652 by Spanish soldiers.

With the transition to Christianity, the old symbols were put to new use. Thus, fish became the symbol of Christ as the bringer of true life and water became the symbol of such life in the baptismal rites. The Greek word for fish, *ichtys*, contains initials emblematical of 'Jesus Christ, Son of God, Saviour'. The fish was a popular symbol of the early Christians and was depicted in the catacombs, together with a bread basket and a cup of red wine. The fish symbol was also depicted in churches and used on seals and rings.

Fish have been widely employed in graphic and applied art of all kinds as a symbol of deities, saints and sovereigns or to symbolize occupations, properties and names. When an Assyrian signed a document he pressed a cylinder seal in a clay tablet on which the facts were written. River gods, gods half men and half fish and fish were represented among other subjects. Dolphins and other sea creatures appear as characteristic features on coins minted in Greek towns of Sicily. So the silver drachma of Syracuse (about 410 B.C.), well known to coin collectors, shows on one side the head of the nymph Arethusa, who was venerated in the town, adorned with dolphins, symbolizing the town's connexion with the sea. Another Greek coin represents Taras, son of Poseidon, riding on a dolphin. As a symbol of a country's association with the sea and fisheries, fish are still used on modern coins, such as the dolphin on the Italian five lire piece and five thousand lire note, and the salmon on the Irish 10 pence coin. FAO is promoting fisheries through coins, such as those issued in Cyprus, Greece, France and Canada in addition to those of Italy. A dolphin is depicted twined around an anchor on a medal from Vespasian, indicating the superiority at sea of Rome under the emperor. A similar design was used by Aldus Manutius, a famous printer and editor, who established the Aldine printing press in 1490. The old seal of Yarmouth shows waves under a fishing boat and three herrings, symbolizing the exclusive right to herring fishing granted to the town by King John.

We find almost all kinds of fish in heraldry, with a special meaning attached to the dolphin. It was considered the chief of all fish and was more frequently depicted than other species. It was used in the coats of arms of noblemen successful in naval affairs, or as a symbol of the sea and of fisheries, as in the coat of arms of the Fishmongers' Company at Billingsgate. Other species of fish in coats of arms symbolize names, sources of revenue and occupations, or recall an event or legend. For example, three herrings decorate the coat of arms of the German family 'Heringh' and three tench that of the French family 'Tanche'. Towns have also tried to find appropriate symbols alluding to their names, as in the case of Aalen and Ahlen which use the eel, called Aal in German, in their coats of arms. In other instances, the most important activities of a city are symbolized, as in Kemi, Finland, where an anchor stands for timber exporting and a fish below it for the fishing industry. Similarly, a net with five herrings entangled in it symbolizes the chief product from Invernay, Scotland. Freshwater fishing is also often represented in heraldry by showing the main species caught. Kingston-upon-Thames bears three silver salmon in its coat of arms and the Russian town of Volgograd has two sturgeons. The two fish in the water beneath a castle, depicted in the arms of Linz, Austria, indicate the environment of the town. The stork eating an eel depicted in the arms of The Hague recalls that the Counts of Holland kept storks at their courts and fed them with eels. The coat of arms of the city of Glasgow has a salmon with a ring in its mouth. Salmon fisheries contributed considerably to the economies of Scotland and England and fishing rights were granted to nobles as a reward for services. Accordingly, the salmon occupied a cardinal position in heraldry. Trout, on the other hand, were more widespread in Germany in the Middle Ages and appear more frequently in the coats of arms there. The flying fish and the shark are the only warm-water fish represented in coats of arms. It was not until Sir Francis Drake's time that the flying fish was accurately described. Until then it was believed to have the wings of a bird.

Fish are well represented on stamps, the collection of which is called 'the hobby of kids and kings'. Stamp collecting started in the USA in the 1850s as an educational project and soon there were hundreds of thousands of collectors there and throughout the world. As the number of new stamps produced yearly vastly increased, collectors specialized on chosen subjects. Most countries produce stamps depicting fish, shellfish, fishing boats and fishing scenes. A recent display of postage stamps on fish and fisheries shown at FAO consisted of some 450 stamps issued by more than 80 countries covering fisheries development, sport fishing, aquaculture and the use of fish as food. Fish stamps are not catalogued so it is difficult for the collector to keep a

Fig 14   Indian fisherman in tortora-reed boat. Mochica and Chimu art, Peru. From V.v. Hagen, The Desert Kingdoms of Peru, *London 1965.*

Fig 15   The dolphin fresco in the bathroom of the Palace of Knossos, Crete. Late Minoan II, c. 1500 B.C.

check on the completeness of his collection of such stamps.

The first representation of fish in art was in the rock and cave paintings of the Upper Paleolithic age. Fish appears again in agricultural civilizations in the zodiacal sign 'Pisces'. During the centuries the fish sign was frequently employed on vases, coins and seals. The zodiac was sculptured in Egyptian temples and, as a kind of agricultural calendar, on Christian churches.

The drawings, paintings and sculpture in tombs show us how fishing was done, how fish was preserved and how it was sold. Egyptian private tombs, first built in the fourth Dynasty (2613 B.C.), contain illustrations of the daily life led by the deceased before he died, as in tombs of Thebe and Nakht, where the dead person is shown standing in a boat fishing or hunting for fowl in the marshes of the Nile, sometimes accompanied by his family. The air is filled with birds and the water with fish. A wall of the 'Tomba della Caccia e Pesca' – tomb of hunting and fishing – (510 B.C.) at the Etruscan necropolis of Tarquinia, Italy, is decorated with a scene of three men fishing from a boat on the coast of the Tyrrhenian Sea.

Vases found in tombs on the coast of Peru are illustrated with drawings of the 'planting of fish' – men walking across a field and making holes in the ground in which they put a grain of corn and a fish. This age-old practice of fertilizing plants with fish goes back to the beginning of agriculture. It was known in Babylonia, apparently as a fertility rite. Indian stone relics and drawings refer to Vishnu's first incarnation as a fish on his way to achieve man's salvation and to his connexion with God.

A dolphin is sculptured at the feet of the most celebrated 'Venus of Medici' in Florence (fourth century B.C.) and a dolphin, holding a small fish in its mouth, supports 'The Venus of Cyrene', a celebrated marble copy of a Greek original (fourth century B.C.) now in the National Museum, Rome. In both sculptures the dolphin is an allusion of the goddess' origin in the sea. Neptune, the god of waters, is shown with his trident and holding a dolphin, sacred to him, in an impressive marble sculpture in the Lateran Museum (Museo Profano Lateranense) in Rome. Mythology and real details are merged in a large mosaic from Constantine, Algeria, in the Musée du Louvre, in Paris. The picture centres around Neptune and Amphitrite standing on a chariot drawn by sea horses. Boats, showing putti as fishermen, and fish, octopus and other sea animals surround the couple. Allegoric themes employing sea gods and Naiads riding on dolphins, or sitting in a sea-shell boat drawn by dolphins, inspired many ancient artists and were eagerly taken up by artists of the Renaissance and later periods. In Raphael's vivacious allegorical picture 'Galatea' in the Palazzo della Farnesina in Rome, forceful dolphins draw the scallop-shell boat of the beautiful nymph trying to escape the Oceanides.

Dolphins, fish and mythological figures decorated the ponds in gardens and parks of Roman villas. The splendour of such decorations is displayed in two exhibits in the National Museum in Naples. One is a charming group of 'Eros on the Dolphin' from a garden pool in Pompeii. The other shows Naiads sitting on fish-like monsters, taken from a swimming pool in ancient Formia,

Gulf of Gaeta. Classic Greek and Roman fish motifs appear more than a thousand years later on Bernini's fountains in Piazza Navona and Piazza Barberini and in many others in Rome and the same motifs were used in fountain decorations all over Europe.

In the first century A.D. art was employed in Roman villas for decorative purposes. It expressed the beauty of nature as seen by the urbanized Romans. A new type of painting appeared at that time in the mosaics and frescoes of villas in Pompeii, Herculaneum and Rome. This was still life, and fish and shellfish had their place in it from the beginning. The art style changed in the sixth century and the pure still life disappeared, to be replaced by symbolic representations. A mosaic in the Basilica of St. Apollinare Nuovo in Ravenna exemplifies this. It shows two fish on a plate at the Last Supper. Still life became an independent art again in the 16th century. This development commenced in the Netherlands and due to the economic importance of herring in that country, this fish appeared in one of the first paintings of this type. It depicts (1560–1570) salted herring on a table, with bread, cheese, a bowl of milk and soup. The variety of sea food in the Netherlands is indicated in the painting 'The Fish Shop' (1739), probably by Joseph Anken. A lively picture of fish on a street market in the 16th century Netherlands is presented by Peter Bruegel's 'Battle between Carnival and Lent' (1559) (Vienna, Kunsthistorisches Museum). An indication of the role of sea food in the French diet may be seen in Chardin's still life 'The Skate' (1728). Fish and the life of fishermen have been the themes of many artists since the Renaissance from Raphæl's 'The Miraculous Draught of Fishes', a tapestry in the Picture Gallery of the Vatican, to Picasso's fish representations.

The art of ornamental initials first introduced by Irish monks is manifested in the illuminated pages of the earliest Irish Gospel manuscripts. It was taken over and further developed by illuminators of ecclesiastical works on the continent of Europe. Fish appear frequently in this important art form. In the famous Book of Kells, written at the end of the eighth century, they are used in ornaments and initials. In the Book of Armagh, another early Irish manuscript, the symbol of John the Evangelist, the eagle, has a fish in its claws. The frequent appearance of fish is explained partly by the place fish had in the monks' diet, partly by the significance of fish as a symbol of Christ in early Christianity.

Today fish appears all over the world in crystal, lead, silver and precious stones and on enamel, chinaware and silk as decorations for our homes.

FISH ON THE ROMAN TABLE

When the Romans had conquered Carthage and had become the supreme sea power in the Mediterranean, they came in direct contact with the Hellenistic and Oriental world. They developed and refined their way of life as a consequence of this contact with a culture influenced by Persian kings and 'the universal outlook of the Greeks'. The simple life, based on traditional customs and on the products of local agriculture, was replaced by a life of surplus and imported luxury. Cato, a farmer and politician, representing the traditional way of life, was concerned about the increasing food imports and the

Fig 16

Fig 16 Etruscan fishermen and dolphin. Detail from painting on a wall of the Tomba della Caccia e Pesca (*Hunting and Fishing Tomb*)*, 510 B.C., Tarquinia, Italy*

Fig 17 A tunny merchant. Decoration on a vase in the Museum at Cefalú, Sicily, 4th century B.C.

Fig 18 Mosaic on the pavement of a fish trader's head office in the Square of the Corporations, at Ostia Antica, the port of Ancient Rome.

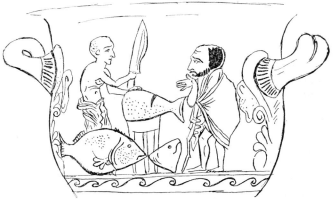

Fig 17

Fig 18

rocketing prices for luxury goods, including imported live fish from Greece and elsewhere in the Mediterranean. 'This State is in a bad way where sea fish costs more than an ox', he complained. Pliny the Elder condemned food trade with foreign countries, including, to a certain extent, the trade with sea fish which was preferred in Rome to beef and pork. Many farmers living close to the sea built fish ponds to supply this good market. According to Pliny, sturgeon was the most appreciated fish on Roman tables although subsequently sea bass found more favour. In his own time the parrotfish was preferred to bass and the demand was such that, under Claudius, the parrotfish was introduced into the waters off Ostia and in Campania. The Senate passed laws against the pleasures of the table in an effort to check luxury living but they were doomed to failure. Lucullus, who was commander in the war against Mithridates, learned in Asia Minor to appreciate the hellenistic/oriental style of life and luxury cooking. He brought the style to Rome where, blended with local cooking, the sophisticated and refined cooking of Imperial Rome emerged. So exotic food items such as cherries, new spices, pheasant, flamingo and new kinds of fish appeared on the table of the rich along with eggs from sea urchins, and oysters and mussels. Food patterns changed and Roman nobles, who sometimes paid as much for a first-class cook as for a country house, indulged in splendid banquets. The art of such cooking included changing the specific flavour of meat and fish by blending the sweet and sour taste, the use of many spices, particularly pepper, and the changing of the appearance of a dish. Thus, grotesque forms often appeared on the table. For example, a piece of meat would appear as a fowl or the highly appreciated teat of a wild sow as a fish. The cookery book of Apicius, a noble Roman gourmet of the time of Tiberius, gives an idea of the new culinary enjoyments. Cooking reached such an overwhelming importance that, with the consent of the Emperor Domitian (A.D. 81 to 96), the Senate was summoned to discuss the best way to prepare a turbot. One new fish preparation of that time was the *garum sociorum*, a product similar to nuoc-mam, prepared by fermenting fish intestines, preferably those of tuna and mackerel. It was widely used for spicing all kinds of food. Another was marinated tuna, prepared by frying the fish in oil, adding salt and spices, and then pouring boiling vinegar over it. This may well be the origin of marinated herring products, such as 'brathering', processed today in northern European countries.

The menu for a dinner in Caesar's time, given for priests, started with the entrée, served with sweet wine, which included sea mussels and oysters, a thrush with asparagus, boiled chicken, chestnuts and a sauce made from mussels and oysters. The next course was mussels, sea fish, birds, boar fillet and paté made from fowl and game. The main course consisted of the teat and head of a sow, fish ragout, duck, hare and roasted fowl. The dessert, unfortunately, is not recorded.

The Roman empire disappeared but the principle or the *ars culinaria*, developed by the blending of oriental and Greek cooking with Roman culinary ideas, survived. However, it was not until the Renaissance that interest in the cooking of classical Roman times was renewed and furthered with great enthusiasm by noble families in the wealthy Italian towns. After 2,000 years, Apicius'

cookery book still seems to be the 'code of practice' for Roman festive cooking. For Christmas Eve festivities, the sophisticated Roman meal starts with an *antipasto di magro*, an entrée consisting of sardines, marinated eel, artichokes, olives and pickled onions and cucumbers. This is followed by spaghetti, with sauce made from anchovies, mussels and small octopus, spiced with red peppers or eaten with tuna. The next course consists of three different kinds of fish, first *dentice* (dentex) or *spigola* (bass), fried in best quality oil from the Sabine Hills and eaten with broccoli or artichokes. Then follows the famous *capitone*, the large eel, preferably from Lake Bolsena, and then sea fish from Ostia, *merluzzo* (hake) or *triglia* (red mullet) in addition to *gamberetti* (shrimps) and *calamari* (squid) fried in oil with broccoli. Then follows the *dolce* (dessert) and *frutta secca* (dried fruit) with nuts.

Catherine de Medici took Italian cooking to France around 1533 and, through the centuries, it has influenced cooking not only in Europe but all over the world.

WAR AND PEACE

Famine, malnourishment and misery racked mediaeval Europe, despite its splendour and power and its magnificent achievements in art and science. Fish was the dominating protein source for rich and poor during times of hunger and during shortages of meat, which often occurred in spring, until agriculture changed the situation by increasing supplies of protein foods. Bacalao, stockfish or salted herring, formed the staple food of explorers on their way to new continents and were the sailor's 'daily bread' on warships. Such food was traded throughout Europe and the expanding world, and was exchanged for precious tropical spices, and because of its economic importance fish was involved in politics and war.

The first move into politics was made by the herrings at the end of the 13th century when they shifted their spawning migrations from the North Sea to the Baltic Sea. This brought them into the area of the Hanseatic League, the commercial union of Lower German towns, and gave rise to two wars between the Hanse and Denmark (1361 to 1362 and 1367 to 1370). As the winners, the Hanse maintained the saltfish monopoly for 150 years, expanding the trade to include Portugal, Russia and Norway. This trade was an addition to the stockfish and cod liver oil trade which the Hanse had controlled since about 1350. Then, in the 16th century, the herring returned to the North Sea, thus contributing substantially to the decline of the Hanse.

The Dutch next became the supreme fishing power in Europe, exploiting the herring grounds off the coast of England and Scotland, and a great deal of their fortune and sea power was ascribed to the herring fishery and trade. A Dutch calvinist writer, according to Cutting, described the situation in 1639 as follows: 'The Dutch catch more herrings, and prepare them better, than any other nation ever will, and the Lord has, through the instrument of herring, made Holland an exchange and staple market for the whole of Europe'. Space does not permit dealing in more detail with this interesting period of the Dutch 'Groote Visschereye', with British attempts under Queen Elizabeth I and King James I to revive their fishery, and with the disputes over Grotius's 'Mare

Fig 19. Dionysius in a fish-shaped boat with a vine twisting around the mast, surrounded by dolphins. Attic cup, signed by the potter Exekios, 550-525 B.C., Antikensammlungen (*Museum of Antiques*), Munich, Federal Republic of Germany.

Fig 20 Fish supporting a vessel in a storm at the command of a saint. Fresco, ceiling of church at Norre Herlev, Denmark, c. 1450-1475.

Librum' (1609) and Selden's 'Mare Clausum' (1635). This was a period when herring played a significant part in the politics of European countries bordering the Atlantic.

In an effort to settle the dispute between Spain and Portugal over their colonies, Pope Alexander VI (1493) divided the world along the 40th latitude W. As one result, the English, in order to avoid war with Spain and Portugal, explored the North Atlantic in their search for the sea route to India where they hoped for huge profits from trade in spices, jewels and gold. Instead of the sea route to India, they discovered the rich fishing grounds off Newfoundland.

There has been much speculation as to whether the discovery and exploration of the Americas and other continents would have occurred with the same speed without salted cod. At least, the salted fish was of great importance in these events. France, Portugal and Spain joined in the exploitation of the Newfoundland fishery between 1505 and 1510 and, due to its economic significance, fish again became involved in war. Vessels with cargoes of salted fish sailing to France from Newfoundland and other grounds were captured by the English. In one year alone, 1541, 25 such ships were taken. Salted fish was not the least reason for the war of the Spanish succession (1701 to 1714). The winner was England, which, in competition with France, then dominated the salt fish trade. The first industrial products, canned fish and meat, were developed in the early 19th century to supply Napoleon's army with fresh food.

The need for international cooperation in fisheries was felt in the 18th century, particularly regarding fishing rights, the safety of fishing vessels and rescue operations. It was not, however, until the end of the 19th century that it became evident that fish do not form an unlimited resource and in 1902 the fear of overfishing of the North Sea led to the creation of the International Council for the Exploration of the Sea (ICES) in Copenhagen. In 1921, an agreement concerning fishing in the Adriatic paved the way for the establishment of international regulatory bodies. Since then, the increasing problems concerned with fishing have led to the establishment of more than 20 regulatory bodies. Some of them have been set up within the framework of the Food and Agriculture Organization of the United Nations (FAO), founded in 1945, which is a leading organization in the promotion of cooperation and the coordination of work among fishery bodies.

In addition to local and regional disputes over fishing rights, developing nations are asserting their right to a larger share of the resources of the waters that wash their shores. The realization that the resources of the sea can provide a rich supply of protein food to meet the nutritional deficiencies of the world population in the future, has awakened many governments to the danger of serious depletion of stocks through overexploitation and pollution and it is to be hoped that international negotiation will replace war in deciding the fate of the sea and its fish.

In recent years pollution, which endangers the fishery resources and may affect the suitability of fish as human food, has attracted international attention. The first world forum for examining these problems was organized by FAO in 1970 in Rome. It was the 'Technical Conference on Marine Pollution and its Effects on Living Resources and Fishing'. The United Nations Conference on the Human Environment followed in 1972, designed to lead to global understanding of the action required to control pollution. But will it be possible to preserve the resources of the oceans as the 'common heritage of mankind' and to prevent the poisoning of the waters which, for thousands of years, have been man's symbol of life? Perhaps an answer will come from the United Nations Conference on the Law of the Sea (which is taking place at the time of this publication going to press). It should be a milestone in man's association with the sea.

SCIENTISTS, BARDS AND PIONEERS

Reference to fish goes back as far as 3000 B.C. when writing was developed. Fish has always been an important subject in man's records. About 600 B.C. fish appears in Persian records. Fish processing was recorded as early as 1500 B.C. in China and the earliest Chinese handbook on fish culture was written by Fan Li about 500 B.C.

Aristotle (about 340 B.C.), one of the greatest philosophers of the ancient western world, grew up among fishermen and, as a boy, observed fish in their environment. These early experiences are obviously reflected in his approach to natural history and in his *Historia Naturalis* he became the first scientist of the West to use personal observation in describing animal life. One fifth of all the animals described in that work are fish. In Roman times, Pliny the Elder devoted two volumes of his 'Natural History' to fish. Book IX is based on the work of 18 authors and deals with taxonomy and biology but also tells charming stories about fish and their association with men. Book XXXII, *Medicinae ex aquatibus*, is about the value of fish and fishery products for medical purposes and describes nearly 1,000 fish, or parts of fish, and pharmaceutical preparations based on fish, supposed to cure all sorts of disease.

With the rise of modern natural science in the 16th century, the range of our knowledge about fish has widened considerably. The wide ecological distribution and adaptability of fish made them attractive objects of natural science. It started with ichthyology, and scientists such as Mangolt (1498), Baldner (1666) and Margrav (1610) in Germany, Rondelet (1507) and Bélon (1517) in France, Salviani (1513) in Italy and Ray (1628) and Willoughby (1635) in England, paved the way for the taxonomic system developed by the Swedish scientists Artedi (1705) and Linnaeus (1707). Fish fascinated the Senator, Minister and Peer of France, the Duke of Lacépède (1756) and inspired him to write his five-volume *Histoire des Poissons*. The largest work about fish is the *Histoire Naturelle des Poissons* by Cuvier (1769) and Valenciennes (1794). The young Swiss scientist Louis Agassiz (1807) was impoverished when he had to meet the expenses for hand-coloured pictures to illustrate his early works on fish. He emigrated to America and his works, published there, attracted for the first time a wide, non-scientific public. His son, Alexander, continued the work. He made his fortune through shares in copper mines and spent the money in support of fishery science. Among many scientists in the 19th century, only a few can be mentioned here. G Günther (1830) investigated the fish collected by the Challenger Expedition (1880), led by Sir Wyville Thomson. The foundation of the laboratory for the study of marine life and the aquarium

Fig 21 *Mermaid on Staffordshire 'slip ware' dish by Thomas Toft, a famous potter, c. 1660-1680. The mermaid was a very popular design. Victoria and Albert Museum, London.*

Fig 22

Fig 22 *The miraculous fishing. Twelfth century fresco from the parish church at Sorpe, Province of Lerida, Spain, Museum of Ancient Art, Barcelona.*

Fig 23 *The legend of Jonah. From a Persian script of the 14th century, Jama at Kawarikh (The History of the World), by Rashid al-Din*

in Naples in 1874, by Anton Dohrn, and setting up similar stations in Plymouth, Liverpool, Bergen and Heligoland advanced marine biology considerably. The Danish zoologist, Johannes Schmidt (1877), revealed the secret of the migration of the eel, a theory which was finally confirmed by the Danish R/V DANA on her circumnavigation of the globe in the years 1928 to 1930. Our knowledge of fish species may not yet be complete. This was dramatically shown in 1938 by the catch off the South African coast of a fish (*Latimeria charumnae*) which belongs to a family thought to have died out 60 million years ago. 'Aquatic Sciences and Fisheries Abstracts', a worldwide information system, which has recently been established, covers over 3,000 journals dealing with all sectors of fishery research and its application. This modern computerized publication is an indication of the importance of fish and fishing today where researchers use hundreds of references when working in one particular field. When Pliny the Elder wrote his comprehensive work, he referred to 18 books, all that existed at that time on the subject.

At the end of the 19th century fisheries exhibitions, such as those of Berlin in 1880 or of London in 1883, stimulated much interest in the development of technology in the fishery industry. As the role of technology in product development and the development of fish product industries are the subject of many papers submitted to this Conference, only a few pioneers may be mentioned in this paper, such as Rudolf Plank, Clarence Birdseye, Rudolf Baader and George Reay.

In the twenties, the science of nutrition demonstrated the influence of the diet on man's health, and the nutritive value of foodstuffs was recognized as a quality factor. This changed significantly man's attitude toward food. In this connexion it is of interest to note that at the request of the German fish industry, physicians, nutritionists and technologists established a Nutritional Advisory Board in 1953 to investigate scientific problems of significance to the fish industry. The first reviews of the place of fish in man's diet were given in the proceedings of the FAO Conference on Fish in Nutrition (1961) and in the four-volume work *Fish as Food* by Borgstrom. Since then, much new knowledge has been added but although numerous publications exist on the importance of fish in man's diet, a comprehensive recent review is still lacking.

Increased fishing efforts, especially after the introduction of steam trawling, caused growing apprehension as to the possible danger to fish stocks. The investigations of Huxley, Prady and McIntosh (1885) proved that a decrease in some fish stocks of the coastal waters of the North Sea was caused by such fishing. McIntosh's book, *Resources of the Sea*, established the need to conserve stocks and Marshall's concept of the inexhaustibility of the oceans was replaced by the idea that the fishery resources of the sea are limited. The term 'overfishing' appeared.

There is a vast literature on fish farming, beginning with the Chinese handbook. In 1763 Ludwig Jacobi wrote about the artificial propagation of trout which he had practised for the first time in man's history and which, 100 years later, gave rise to modern fish farming. In modern times, Claus Schäperclaus carried out pioneer work on fish diseases. There are also countless publications on sport fishing and reference can be made here only to one famous standard work, *The Compleat Angler* by Izaak Walton, who also advised on how to prepare the catch for the table.

The appearance of skippers as novel writers, such as Albert Hutchinson (1938) with *Thrills of the Northern Trawl*, is worth mentioning. Life in fishing communities, which generally have a culture of their own, has inspired many authors such as J C Bertram, *Harvest of the Sea* (1865), E J Mather *Nor'ard of the Dogger* (1888) and W Grenfell *Vikings of Today* (1895) and *Labrador Doctor* (1919). The growing awareness of the public in England in the 1870s is reflected in songs with a strong nautical flavour written for the English music hall and in sentimental ballads such as 'The Three Fishers' by Charles Kingsley. They wrote to create public interest in the dangerous life of fishermen. The cod fishery of the Grand Banks is described in Rudyard Kipling's *Captain Courageous* (1897). Publications on the folklore of fishing communities are numerous, especially in England and Scotland, such as those by Peter Anson, published in many volumes.

There are only a few novels which are well known internationally, such as H Melville's *Moby Dick*, the saga of the hunt for the white whale. N Gunn's *Morning Tide* (1931), and *Silver Darlings* (1941) have a place here, as well as G Carter's *The Smacksmen*, which is about the lives of three generations of East Anglian fishermen. There is also the famous novel *Cannery Row* by J Steinbeck (1945) depicting the life of the people of the fishing fleet and the canning factories of Monterrey, since deserted because of the disappearance of the Californian sardine. Charles Dickens in *David Copperfield* describes the fishing town of Great Yarmouth and in *Pêcheur d'Islande*, P Loti gives a picture of the life of French fishermen on schooners off Iceland. In recent times, public interest in the life and work of those engaged in sea fisheries has been promoted by films, radio and television, the new information media which have added another dimension to the traditional storytelling by script.

FISH FARMING AND SPORT

Fish culture for providing food was apparently practised in China in 2000 B.C. Documents on fish farming exist from the time of the Shan-Jin Dynasty (1766 B.C.), and the practice had become very popular by the time of the Chang Dynasty (1122 B.C.). Ancient documents from the Middle East deal with the exploitation and renting of fish ponds. Rules for the design, construction, stocking and harvesting of fish ponds, as well as for their economic management, were laid down in 475 B.C. by the Chinese expert, Fa Lai, and fish culture flourished until A.D. 68, when the Tang Dynasty came to power. Then there was an unfortunate coincidence which almost caused a complete collapse of fish farming in China. The species farmed at that time was the common carp and there was a similarity between the word for carp and the surname of the Royal family, both being pronounced 'li' although deriving from entirely different words. The common carp became a royal symbol and catching, let alone eating, the fish was considered a sacrilege. It was due only to the skill of the Chinese carp breeders that a catastrophe was avoided. They conducted intensive

Fig 24 The Last Supper. Painting on wood by the Master of Soriguerola, 13th century, Art Museum of Catalonia, Barcelona, Spain

Fig 25 St Brendan celebrating Easter Mass on the back of a big fish. From a sixteenth century etching.

research to replace the common carp by other Cyprinidae of comparable properties. As a result, grass carp and a number of new varieties were bred and fish pond farming in China was saved.

The Romans had fish ponds and tried to rear species with high market value but with little success and their ponds were mainly used for storage of luxury fish. Fish ponds were, without doubt, of great importance in Europe of the Middle Ages in providing fish for fast days and for Lent. Fish culture collapsed in Germany during the Thirty Years War and was revived on a large scale only at the end of the 19th century. England's numerous fish ponds disappeared after the Reformation and today there is limited appreciation of freshwater fish in that country. In Russia, fish farming maintained its importance through the centuries and today produces about 200,000 tons of pond fish. Fish farming has a long history in many countries of Asia and the Far East but was only recently introduced in Africa where about 700,000 tons of farm fish are being produced today. In relation to the future demand for fish and the dwindling supplies of wild fish, it appears that fish farming can increase the availability of food fish considerably in some parts of the world.

As previously mentioned, there was a sacred fish pond in Mesopotamia around 3000 B.C. in one of the oldest temples of the world. The Chinese very early cultivated ornamental fish which could be kept in small containers, and the Romans enjoyed keeping fish in ponds for decorative purposes. Thus, the aquarium has a long history. However, it was not until 1853 that the so-called 'Fish House', the first public aquarium, was established in the Zoological Gardens in Regents Park, London. The breakthrough came only when industry was able to produce sheets of clear glass. Today, the large public aquariums are much appreciated by the people generally and hundreds of thousands of home aquariums give enjoyment to millions. Most of the aquarium fishes used today are tropical species from the Amazons, India and Southeast Asia, and a valuable trade has been established. A later development is the Oceanarium, a large seawater aquarium, such as the Marine Land in Florida and the famous one in Miami, which allow a great variety of different species to be kept in a large tank. These oceanariums are not only spectacular tourist attractions but are also useful for the study of the behaviour and intelligence of sea animals. Here, again, the dolphin is in first place, confirming ancient reports. A still more recent development is the underwater park zones for conserving coastal areas. These parks are of great importance for environmental studies and are a considerable attraction to tourists, especially in tropical areas.

A review of the place of fish in our culture would not be complete without at least a glance at sport fishing. The first sport fisherman, whose name has come down to us from mythical times, was Adapa, a citizen of the Sumerian town Eridu. His wisdom was so immense that the god of heaven considered him worthy of being made immortal. A famous angler, as can be seen in a Pompeian wall painting, was Venus, the beautiful goddess of love, and the favourite pastime of the Roman Emperor, Augustus, was angling. In Europe, fishing as a sport started in the Middle Ages and was mainly developed in Britain. Izaak Walton set the standard in his book *The Compleat Angler*. Fishing is still a growing sport, perhaps especially because it enables people who live and work in cities to spend their free time close to nature. A new sport, underwater fishing, has been made possible through the invention of the aqua lung. Books and films about this new pastime have inspired millions to explore the 'silent world'.

FISH IN MAN'S DIET

Tradition continues to play an important part in our choice of food and in our food behaviour but the modern age is accelerating the pace of change. This increase in pace started with the discovery of the New World and the exploration of other continents. Potatoes appeared in Europe, wheat came to America and cassava to Africa and Asia. Yet most Hindus still do not eat beef, most Moslems still refuse pork and most of the British will not eat horse meat. Dog meat or insects are not considered food by Europeans or Americans. But, why are fish sausages appreciated only by the Japanese and why are marinades preferred only in a few European countries? On the other hand, why are fish sticks accepted in Europe, America, Japan and wherever introduced, and why has FPC not been accepted at all?

Traditional products

In Asia and the Far East rice constitutes the staple food of the people, with fish and fish products most widely used as ingredients. Fish is, therefore, in one form or another eaten every day, the poor eating fish more often than do the better-off. Many of these traditional products, which appear to us to be similar, differ in taste and flavour to those who are accustomed to them. There are strong opinions about the raw material used, and the way of preparation differs from region to region. Sometimes ethnic groups have specific preferences and there are significant differences between the countries.

Fermented fish preparations are the characteristic of the diet in Burma, Thailand, Malaysia, Indo-China, the Philippines and, to a certain extent, Indonesia. Fermented and cured fish products are eaten almost every day by the rural people and the poorer urban population. The small portions in which these are eaten, mostly with rice, can be illustrated by the following: 'balacan', a traditional Malaysian fermented shrimp paste, is mostly eaten in a form called 'sambal-balacan'. A teaspoon of balacan is pounded with four to five fresh red chillies and a couple of onions, and the mixture is sufficient for four to five adults. A similar picture appears in the other countries of this region. Small quantities of salted, smoked or boiled fish, some fish sauce and some fresh fish, such as sardine or scad, are alternative products for the average consumer in rural areas and the poorer population in cities. Meat is a luxury product. In Pakistan, India and Sri Lanka, where fermented fish products are eaten only by some ethnic groups, the main processes used are salting and drying. Many kinds of fish and curing practices are used. The Japanese are great fish eaters and enjoy a wide variety of traditional fish dishes and traditional products, different from those of other countries in the region. The traditional fish products, such as 'kamaboko' and 'katsuobushi' are well known and need not be explained here. A famous traditional dish

Fig 26 *Matsyavatara, Vishnu's first incarnation. Trichinopoly painting, 19th century, from a reproduction in the* New Larousse Encyclopaedia of Mythology.

Fig 27 *Taras, son of Poseidon, riding on a dolphin on his voyage from Crete to Italy. He landed at Taranto, named after him.*

Fig 28 *Silver drachma from Syracuse representing the nymph Arethusa and dolphins, 430 B.C.*

Fig 29 *Seal of the city of Hythe, County of Kent, England. 12th to 13th century A.D.,* Archives Nationales, *Paris.*

consists of pieces of raw fish of different kinds with pickled cucumber slices, lettuce and seaweed.

In tropical Africa, many people of the coastal regions and those living at lake and river shores depend on fish as their main source of protein. In the Congo basin and the lower region of the Niger, fish as food seems to be enjoyed by all tribes. A recent survey in Cameroon indicated that 95 per cent of the population like fish as food. Fish eaters in Ghana amount to some 65 per cent of the population, while the whole life of the Unga tribe in Zambia centres around fish. In some areas of West Africa, fishing is more important than agriculture and fish and fish products are a regular constituent of the diet. Traditionally, fish and fish products are eaten in stews and soups. The main products consumed all over the continent are dried and smoked fish. Salted-dried fish is eaten in only a few countries, such as Zaire, the Congo and Ghana. Fermented fish is used in Ghana as a condiment in their soups, stews and other traditional dishes. In this country fish is usually eaten daily; in the morning, for example, one can eat kenkey with fried fish, and in the afternoon or evening smoked fish in a soup.

In South America fish was traditionally part of the diet in coastal areas and regions near freshwater resources and also today fish is mainly consumed in these regions and in the cities. In general, however, meat is preferred. Some populations live almost entirely on a vegetarian diet as, for example, the Indians in the Andean highlands. There are a few traditional fish products, such as 'cebiche', a product which has been known in Peru since pre-Inca times. Cebiche consists of marinated and heavily spiced flakes of corvina or lenguado. Ancient tribes immersed pieces of raw or cooked fish in an acid extract of wild plants, later replaced by lemon juice when the Spaniards introduced that fruit.

In Europe traditional fish products have changed considerably during the last 40 years and now have a much milder taste and improved texture. The range of such product types has been considerably extended in some countries and a wide variety of specialities has been developed, particularly in the Federal Republic of Germany, the Scandinavian countries, the Netherlands and the USSR. In countries where fresh sea food is preferred, a wide range of recipes has been worked out for frying, baking and grilling fish and shellfish. In this respect the sea food served in Spain, Portugal, Italy, France and Greece is famous.

In North America traditional sea-fish dishes are almost entirely limited to certain provinces. In New England, USA, and the maritime provinces of Canada, one gets superb lobsters and clam chowder. Shrimp dishes of the Gulf States are famous as well as scallops and oysters of the Chesapeake Bay. Freshwater fish are available in most parts of the continent. In general, however, the preference for fish in the USA is low and often fish can be found only in canned and frozen form, mostly in ready-prepared dishes as convenience foods.

Fish avoidance

Fish plays a significant part in the entire diet only in a few countries, such as Norway, Iceland, Japan and the USSR. Fish avoidance, including taboos prohibiting the eating of fish, is known all over the world. It is found in certain economic, social and religious groups as well as in age and sex groups. Such taboos may have social functions or economic effects or may even be of value in the protection of resources, e.g., those prohibiting fishing at certain seasons. Fish avoidance appears prevalent among pastoral populations in the arid and semi-arid areas of North Africa and Asia. For several nomadic peoples in the Sahara, North Africa, eating fish is taboo. Northeast Africa, Sudan, Ethiopia and Somalia, a cultural crossroad where numerous ethnic groups have influenced food behaviour, form another centre of fish avoidance. In the rest of the eastern part of Africa, down to South Africa, fish avoidance is found among Nilo-Hamitic peoples and Bantu groups but most of the agricultural populations will eat fish. Fish is not popular in most countries of the Middle East. The bedouins in Saudi Arabia eat fish only reluctantly and most of the fish caught is still used as fodder for livestock and as fertilizer. Some ethnic and religious groups in India avoid fish entirely. These include the Buddhists, the Vishnavas and most of the Brahmins. Only a few small groups in the Far East avoid fish for religious reasons or because of superstition. Several Indian tribes in the southwest of North America are known to avoid fish, some because they consider fish sacred, a belief connected with totemism. The Andean Indians of South America, on the other hand, seem to avoid fish because they have not been familiar with it since early times.

Often only poor people and low social classes eat fish, as in Somalia and Ethiopia among non-Christian tribes. Thus, fish eating becomes associated with low caste occupational groups, as in India. The influence of various ethnic groups with different religions has created a pattern of fish avoidance and fish acceptance in Ethiopia. The Amharas, largely Christians, inhabiting the central and northern part, accept fish as food but most of the peoples of the southern and southwestern part reject fish. The Dinga of the southern Sudan do not eat fish because they fear to irritate the spirits of the water. Among many tribes in the eastern and southeastern part of Africa, fish avoidance is related to the belief in the transmigration of the soul after death into snakes and because of an assumed similarity between snakes and fish. Canned fish may be accepted while fresh fish is avoided. An interesting field which should be further studied is the relationship between diseases, nutritional requirements and fish avoidance. There are, for example, some fish species considered to cause leprosy or malformation of babies. Kwashiorkor, a nutritional disease, is attributed to non-observance of food taboos rather than to nutritional deficiencies. There are still other forms of fish avoidance, such as the rejection of fish with dark meat, or because of different kinds of superstition. There are physiological and psychological factors, and fish avoidance is by no means a matter of cultural level although education helps to eradicate irrational beliefs.

Fish avoidance due to superstition is disappearing with the growth of nutritional education and the availability of tempting fish products, but some avoidance associated with religions and deep-rooted cultural habits, such as vegetarianism, is likely to persist, as will dislike of fish because of physiological or other biological reasons.

DIERKS, A *Männer Trawler Meere*, Bremerhaven, F.R. Germany,
1961   Verband der deutschen Hochseefischereien, 145 p.
EPPRIGHT, E S Factors influencing food acceptance. *J. Amer. diet.*
1947   *Ass.*, 23:279–587.
FAO Handbook on fish culture in the Indo-Pacific region, based
1962   on the work of Hora, S.L. and T.V.R. Pillay, *FAO Fish.*
        Biol. Tech. Pap., (14):203 p.
FAO Report on regulatory fishery bodies. *FAO Fish. Circ.*,
1972   (138):31 p.
FAO The economic and social effects of the fishing industry – a
1972   comparative study. *FAO Fish. Circ.*, No. 314, 17 p.
FARRER, K T H Historical perspectives of food in Tasmania. *Fd*
1972   *Technol., Australia*, March 1972, p. 116–117, 119, 121, 123,
        125, 126, 128–129, 131.
FOLKERS, K Natural and synthetic nutrients. *Fd Prod. Devel.*,
1972   August-September 1972, p. 61–62.
FOMON, S J Nutrition for a good start. *Fd Prod. Devel.*, August-
1972   September 1972, p. 66.
GERLACH, R *Die Fische*. Hamburg, F.R. Germany, Claasen, 468 p.
1950
GRAUBARD, M Food habits of primitive man. *Scient. Monthly*,
1942   55:342–349; 453–460.
GRIMAL, P *Römische Kulturgeschichte*, Munich, F.R. Germany and
1961   Zurich, Switzerland, Droemer-Knaur, 635 p.
HAGEN, V W VON *The Aztec: man and tribe*. New York, The New
1958   American Library of World Literature, Inc., Mentor
        Books, 222 p.
HAGEN, V M VON *World of the Maya. Ibid.*, 224 p.
1960
HAGEN, V M VON *The Desert Kingdoms of Peru*. London, Weiden-
1965   feld and Nicolson, 191 p.
HARDER, H C Food and Nutrition press information service. *Fd*
1972   *Prod. Devel.*, August-September 1972, p. 66, 68.
HEEN, E and KREUZER, R (ed.) *Fish in Nutrition*. London, Fishing
1962   News (Books) Ltd., 447 p.
HEITMANN, K E *Die Urzeitjäger im technischen Paradies*. Düssel-
1962   dorf, F.R. Germany and Vienna, Austria, 228 p.
HICKLING, C F *Fish Culture*. London, Faber and Faber, 295 p.
1962
HONORÉ, P Ich fand den Weissen Gott. Frankfurt, F.R. Germany,
1965   Heinrich Scheffler, GmbH and Co., 320 p.
HUXSOLL, C C, HOMNICK, D N and DUNLOP, C J Frozen, pre-
1972   cooked rice shapes suitable for all markets. *Fd Prod.*
        Devel., August-September 1972, p. 91–92, 94.
INSALATA, N F The technical microbiological problems in inter-
1972   mediate moisture products. *Ibid.*, August-September
        1972, p. 72.
JENS, H *Mythologisches Lexikon, Gestalten der griechischen,*
1958   *römischen und nordischen Mythologie*. Munich, F.R.
        Germany, W. Goldmann, 173 p.
KELLER, W *Denn sie entzündeten das Licht – Geschichte der Etrusker*
1970   *– die Lösung eines Rätsels*, Munich, F.R. Germany and
        Zurich, Switzerland, Droemer-Knaur, 416 p.
LACHANCE, P A Supplemental protein: does the U.S. diet really
1972   need it? *Fd Prod. Devel.*, August-September 1972, p. 35.
LEMIERE, A Arte giapponese IV. L'incisione, Milan, Italy, Arnoldo
1958   Mondadori *La Tavolazza*, (24):15 p.
LOUDA, J *European Civic Coats of Arms*. London, P. Hamlyn,
1966   265 p.
LÜTZELER, H *Weltgeschichte der Kunst*. Gütersloh, F.R. Germany,
1959   C. Bertelsmann, 320 p.
MCCORMICK, H W, ALLEN, T and YOUNG, W *Shadows in the Sea*.
1963   London, Sidgwick and Jackson, 415 p.
MAIWII, B *Le Musée National – The National Museum – Naples*.
1959   Novara, Italy, Istituto Geografico de Agostini, 165 p.
MALPICA, S S C *Crónica del Hambre en el Perú*. Lima, Perú,
1966   Francisco Moncloa, Editores S.A., 285 p.

MEYER-WAARDEN, P F *Stephan Ludwig Jacobi – Begründer der*
1972   *Kunstlichen Besamung in der Fischzucht*, Berlin, H. Heene-
        mann GmbH, 189 p.
MEYER-WAARDEN, P F (ed.) *Fisch, das Zeitgemässe Lebensmittel*,
1969   Berlin, Westliche Berliner Verlagsgesellschaft Heene-
        mann KG, 225 p.
MORTON, H V *The Waters of Rome*. The Connoisseur and Michael
1966   Joseph, 302 p.
MOULE, TH *Heraldry of Fish – Notices of the Principal Families*
1842   *Bearing Fish in their Arms*. London, John van Voorst,
        Paternoster Row, 252 p.
NICHOLSON, I *Mexican and Central American Mythology*. London,
1968   The Hamlyn Publishing Group, Ltd., 141 p.
NIEHOFF, A H Food habits and the introduction of new foods.
1967   *J. Washington Acad. Sci.*, February 1967: 57 30–37.
PAW, F DE *Grotius and the Law of the Sea*, Brussels, Belgium, Les
1965   Editions de l'Institut de Sociologie de l'Université Libre
        de Bruxelles, 76 p.
PILGRIM, F J What foods do people accept or reject? *J. Amer. diet.*
1961   *Ass.*, 38(5):439–443.
PILLAY, T V R The role of aquaculture in fishery development and
1973   management. Paper submitted to Technical Conference
        on Fishery Management and Development, Vancouver,
        Canada, 13-23 February 1973, *FI:FMD/73/S-47:* 24 p.
PREISLER, R *Der Wohltemperierte Fischesser*. Hamburg-Altona,
        F.R. Germany, Bundesverband der deutschen Fischin-
        dustrie e.V., 127 p.
RADCLIFFE, W Fishing from the Earliest Times, London, John
        Murray, 494 p.
RENNER, H D *The Origin of Food Habits*. London, Faber and
1944   Faber, Ltd., 261 p.
RUIVO, M (ed.) *Marine Pollution and Sea Life*, Fishing News
1972   (Books) Ltd., 624 p.
SIMOONS, F J The geographic approach to food prejudices. *Fd*
1966   *Technol.*, March 1966, p. 42–44.
VOLPICELLI, L *Roma a Tavolo*, Roma, Carlo Colombo, Almanacco
1967   dell'Accademia Italiana della Cucina – Sezione di Roma.

ACKNOWLEDGEMENT

Many persons in Asia and the Far East and Africa have
provided me with information and advice in preparing
this paper. In particular, I wish to thank Mr Tapiador,
FAO Regional Fisheries Officer, Bangkok; Dr S W Ling,
Bangkok, for information on fish in Chinese history;
Dr J Shewan and Dr G H O Burgess, Torry Research
Station, Aberdeen, for assistance with literature on fish;
and Prof Meyer-Waarden, former Director of the Institut
für Küsten und Binnenfischerei, Hamburg, for assistance
with information on developments in the Germany
fishery industry.

A special mention must be made of the highly skillful
work of Mr Jack Maxwell (Art Unit, FAO) who has
made the line drawings which so delightfully illustrate
the text. These are based on paintings, photographs and
other illustrations reproduced in a variety of publications
and documents to which credit is duly given in the
captions.

The Contribution of Fish Technology to the Utilization
of Fish Resources   *G H O Burgess*

**La contribution de la technologie des pêches a l'utilisation des
ressources halieutiques**

Comme l'auteur le souligne, les apports de la recherche technologique aux industries de la pêche du monde entier on pendant longtemps été le fait des hommes de science et des technologues dans de
très nombreux pays. Ce n'est qu'à une époque relativement récente
que les premiers laboratoires consacrés à la technologie des pêches
ont été créés, pour la plupart durant les soixante dernières années.

**La contribucion de la technologia pesquera a la utilizacion de los
recursos icticos**

Como se indica en este documento las contribuciones de la investigación tecnológica a las industrias pesqueras de todo el mundo
proceden de científicos y técnicos de diversos países durante un
largo período de tiempo. No obstante, los primeros laboratorios
dedicados a la tecnología de la pesca han sido creados, hace
relativamente poco tiempo en su mayor parte durante los últimos

En faisant brièvement le point de la contribution apportée par la technologie des pêches à l'utilisation des ressources, l'auteur dégage les leçons du passé et expose les problèmes que les technologues doivent actuellement résoudre et ceux qui se poseront sans doute à eux dans l'avenir. Eu égard au rôle de premier plan que les laboratoires gouvernementaux de technologie halieutique jouent dans la plupart des pays de pêche, l'auteur examine la nature des programmes de travail de ces institutions et formule des conclusions quant au contrôle des activités et aux prestations exigées du personnel qui les exécute.

sesenta años. Al estudiar en general la contribución de la tecnología de la pesca a la utilización de los recursos, el documento saca consecuencias de anteriores hechos y examina los problemas presentes y futuros que habrán de afrontar los tecnólogos. Teniendo en cuenta el papel principal desempeñado por los laboratorios estatales de tecnología de la pesca en la mayoría de los modernos países pesqueros, en el documento se examina la naturaleza de los programas de trabajo de las mencionadas instituciones y se sacan conclusiones con respecto al control de trabajo y los requisitos que se exige al personal que se ocupa de estas cuestiones.

It is tempting to believe that food technology owes its origin to the industrial revolution, but reflection for a moment will show that many of the methods used today in the storage and processing of food were discovered long before recorded history began. What has developed over the past century or so, however, is an understanding of the scientific principles involved in food preservation and processing and with it the capacity to improve existing methods and to develop new ones. Modern fish technology, the application of science to the practice of fish handling, processing, storage and distribution, has been recognized as a separate branch of food technology for perhaps no more than fifty years. Traditional methods of preserving foods have evolved over many centuries to meet the particular needs of generally small communities. As such, and within limitations, they have proved adequate but where industrialization has led to the growth of large urban communities, so these traditional methods have been found incapable of maintaining an adequate food supply for every section of society and the potential rewards for the solution of the supply problems raised by urban growth have hence been great.

Attempts to produce and process food more cheaply, to reduce spoilage and extend shelf life, and to make products more attractive were, in the virtual absence of scientific knowledge about food, often unsuccessful and even dangerous. The United Kingdom, with its large urban development in an industrial society, was one of the earliest countries to encounter problems of adulteration of food. Attention was drawn to widespread adulteration of food early in the nineteenth century but the first legislation was not passed until 1860 (Drummond and Wilbraham 1958). Similar legislation was introduced by other European countries during the nineteenth century (Forbes and Dijksterhuis 1963). The immediate effect of the new food and drugs legislation was to make manufacturers everywhere cautious not to break the law, and as processes became more complex and the chances of mistakes correspondingly greater, so firms began to employ their own chemists. The works chemist was hence one forerunner of the modern food technologist but his role was at first entirely a defensive one. Inevitably he became interested in the processes employed and his training and attitude of mind suggested ways of improving methods that were traditional and unsuited to large-scale operation. Ultimately, the food technologist has become involved in the development of new techniques and products, the utilization of new raw materials, quality assurance and control, and in the meantime his role and training have changed almost beyond recognition. Food and drugs legislation has, however, until recently had little impact on fish industries. A significant feature of the development of sea fisheries in the later nineteenth and early twentieth centuries in both industrial Europe and North America was the slow decline in the consumption, particularly at home, of traditional products and increasing sale of unprocessed fish (Cutting 1955). Most other foods in these industrial countries were at the same time increasingly processed in factories. The opportunities for using additives to 'improve' unprocessed fish have thus been small, even if industry wished to use them. Furthermore, since the product was cheap and plentiful there was little incentive for their use. Because complex processing has not been required, except in the rather specialized field of canning, there has been no obvious advantage merely in large scale of organization and although in very many important respects the situation has changed vastly today, it is still true that small firms handling unprocessed fish can operate quite successfully in many industrialized countries.

As a result of the various factors mentioned, and no doubt others also, there has been no compelling reason for most companies to employ technologists. Various individuals in the last century attempted to improve some of the accepted ways of handling and processing fish, but often they failed because of an imperfect appreciation of the scientific principles involved. The extent of the ignorance of the underlying science on which any effective modern technology must be based, can be gauged by a quotation from C H Stevenson's classic account 'The Preservation of Fishery Products for Food' (1899). He described in some detail the freezing and cold storage of fish and although primarily concerned with practice in the United States, at that time probably the most advanced in the world in the methods used for handling and processing fish; he also mentioned European practice. He dismissed the critical matter of storage temperature, however, in two sentences: 'The temperature in the storage room should be constant, and about 16° to 18°F ($-9°$ to $-8°C$) is considered the most economical. Above 20°F ($-7°C$) the fish are likely to turn yellow about the livers, a result generally attributed to the bursting of the 'gall' '. In many countries industrial cold stores now operate at $-30°C$ and the yellowing about the region of the livers is known to be due to oxidation of the fat, which would be expected to occur rapidly at such high storage temperatures.

It was recognized in many countries before the end of the nineteenth century that improvements in fish industries could only be brought about by application of the results of scientific investigation. At first research was mostly devoted to the biological investigation of fish stocks, life histories and fish farming, though the US Fish Commission, which began publishing information in 1872, gave early attention to some aspects of fish technology including, for instance, Professor W O Atwater's studies of the composition and nutritional value of fish. The first laboratories devoted entirely to the study of fish technology were set up before the end of the nineteenth century. The Norwegian Fiskeri-directoratets Kjemisk-Tekniske Forskningsinstitutt was established in 1892, for example, but it was the problems of food storage and distribution encountered during the 1914–18 war that forced the attention of many governments to the critical lack of scientific information about the handling and storage properties of food. Food shortages brought about by hostilities threw into stark relief the amount of wastage that occurred during normal food handling and processing at that time. Many food research laboratories were founded after 1918 and amongst them were a number for fish technology. Mention may be made, for example, of the Institut Scientifique et Technique des Pêches Maritimes (1918), the Technological Stations at Halifax, NS (1924) and Prince Rupert, B.C., Canada (1925), the Institut für Fischverarbeitung, Germany (1925) and the Torry Research Station, United Kingdom (1929).

It is significant that almost all countries that possess a fish industry now also support one or more technological laboratories, and these are largely or wholly funded by their respective governments. There are many reasons for this state of affairs, but the major one is without doubt that fishing is often a protected or subsidized industry, carried on by many relatively small operators, few of whom would be capable of, or have much incentive for, doing their own research and development. Hence, most of the fish technology researches in the world have been made by, or in collaboration with, government-funded laboratories and it is therefore with their work that we are concerned here.

Tressler (1923) in his comprehensive account of the marine products of commerce, complained that 'A rapid advance in the fishery industries cannot be expected until there is more co-operation among the fishery interests and a more general recognition of the value of scientific researches by the men controlling the organisations.' Tressler was writing about the United States fish industry but his view that insufficient money was spent on research and that industry itself paid little attention to the advantages of applying lessons learned from it was equally valid for fish industries elsewhere at that time. Fifty years later it is right to ask what research in the intervening years has achieved and what it can be expected to contribute to the utilization of fish resources. Further, one may ask how a government fish technology laboratory should go about its job of trying to help industry. In essaying answers to these questions, I am conscious of certain inherent difficulties, partly because what follows must necessarily represent a very personal view based mainly on experience of European and North American technological developments. A more fundamental problem, however, is that of making an assessment of the value of research. I shall not give much attention here to other roles of technological laboratories, such as giving advice to government.

ASSESSING THE VALUE OF RESEARCH

Problems identified by food scientists and technologists and successfully studied by them are generally clearcut and relate to known difficulties in the handling, processing or storage of particular commodities. Solutions when found often, though not always, involve fairly small modifications of an existing process; this is hardly surprising since the manufacturer is usually concerned to make a well known product more uniformly and with less waste. Even today genuinely new products, entirely unknown a century ago, do not represent a large part of most diets and the difficulties of trying to introduce novel products are well known. In other words, the overworked and generally inappropriate expression 'technological break-through' has little application in food research. The scientist or technologist, knowing the problems and the work necessary to find their solution, may see his contribution as the key to the difficulties of the manufacturer. The manufacturer, grappling also with questions of finance and management, may feel that the technological contribution is not necessarily the only key and, since often relatively small changes in processing or production techniques are involved, he may underestimate the value of new findings as these are presented to him and perhaps also feel that he too would have found the proffered solution in due course.

Nevertheless, success in fish technological research can often be seen to have been achieved when work in the laboratory becomes applied in industry. Close collaboration between a government technological laboratory and individual companies is usually a feature of successful application but when some of the successes, for example, the development of the frozen fish industry, or even a more restricted aspect of it such as freezing at sea, are studied years later, it is extremely difficult to separate the individual contribution of technologists and industrialists. Indeed, what the technologist would wish to see done must frequently be modified for a variety of reasons, and the final achievement is a compromise, an amalgam of ideas, to which both he and the industrialist have made their respective contributions. There is even more difficulty in establishing where ideas first originated. Who first recommended low temperature storage of frozen fish? Who first identified *rigor* problems in fish? Scientists and technologists belong to an international fraternity and ideas have no national boundaries. When I began to write this paper it occurred to me to try to trace the origin of some of the major contributions to fish technology, but I reluctantly abandoned the idea. The roll of names soon assumed a massive length and for every key paper quoted there were half a dozen more whose claim to be included was also compelling. Beatty, Tarr, Finn, Reay, Reuter, Planck and Harden Taylor all deserve mention but so do many, many more. Instead, therefore, I shall discuss some contributions of technological research to the development of the world's fish industries without considering from whence ideas first originated. I shall not attempt to cover the whole range of technological researches and shall, for instance, omit all mention of researches into smoking, salting and canning technology, and into fish meal manufacture and by-products generally. In examining the past it is possible that we may obtain guides to ways in which technology can be applied in the future.

LESSONS FROM PAST ACHIEVEMENTS

The widespread distribution of unprocessed fish, whose shelf life was extended merely by packing with ice, was, as mentioned, a development of the nineteenth century and was made possible by the growth of rapid transport systems and improvements in mechanical ice-making plants (Cutting 1955, Burgess 1965). Industrial practice improved during the century and indeed had it not done so exploitation of the more distant fishing grounds of the northern North Sea, and in this century the Northeast Atlantic, would have been virtually impossible. Nevertheless, some of the earliest work in fish technology was concerned with the very practical problems of maintaining the freshness of the catch until it reached the consumer. Workers in the twenties and thirties went to sea on commercial vessels and made observations on current practice. They measured the temperatures of fish as caught, compared the effectiveness of different ways of icing them and suggested improved methods for handling and stowing the catch. Pioneering studies were also made on the sources of heat reaching the fish room. Such work is still a feature today of the programmes of many technological laboratories and is likely to remain so for as long as methods of boat construction and catching continue to change. Although ice has severe limitations, these are not always, or perhaps even often, reached in industrial practice and technologists must continue to show how the properties of ice can be exploited to the full. The users of this information have been primarily vessel builders or their customers, the fishermen and vessel owners. Heat leak into the hold, for example, has a direct bearing on type and thickness of insulation and the design of any additional mechanical cooling plant. There are many instances of information of this kind which has been obtained on one vessel being applied directly in modifying the design of a sistership. This research is not as a whole scientifically very demanding, though some aspects of it are, but requires a certain type of man to carry it through who is able to share and even enjoy the discomforts of commercial fishing, can mix easily with all manner of people, and can continue to make useful observations when suffering the pangs of seasickness in the fishroom during a gale. It is often impossible at sea to follow an experiment in exactly the way designed; fish cannot be caught to order and breakdown of equipment or loss of gear can jeopardize the results from an entire voyage. The man at sea must be able to modify the experiment according to changing situations and hence save something from an otherwise wasted effort. Indeed, this type of man is well suited to carrying out collaborative work with industry on shore; no technological laboratory can, in my view, operate without such people.

Chilling is likely to remain the chosen method of preserving the catch in many fisheries, particularly where vessels are small and voyages short. Most of the world catch is still landed 'fresh' or chilled and there is wide scope therefore for improvement in techniques even in the most advanced fisheries. It would be interesting to know, for instance, what the development of refrigerated sea water has meant to the Pacific salmon and halibut fisheries. Ice in tropical areas is more costly and losses in transport are much greater than in temperate zones but its effects on storage life of fish are more marked. Research may hence be better spent on solving problems of distribution and storage of ice; mere repetition of work done in temperate areas is not what is required.

A difficulty that early confronted technologists was the poor quality of frozen fish. Much of the technology of freezing and cold storage was first developed empirically with results that were very variable and uncertain. Studies in Germany published in 1916 and 1917 drew attention to the effects of slow freezing in greatly altering the histological structure of animal tissues and this observation gave rise to much experiment in many other countries. The original findings have been repeatedly confirmed but it was demonstrated in the thirties that changes in histological structure were not necessarily related to changes in texture and flavour. The key factor in determining the quality of frozen fish, assuming the raw material to be initially fresh and frozen reasonably rapidly, is temperature and time of storage. This was a novel view in the thirties and the temperature recommended of around −30°C was sometimes difficult to achieve and maintain with the refrigeration equipment and insulating materials then available. Steady advances in refrigeration technology and the realization by industry of the advantages of high and more uniform product quality have resulted in a vast improvement in the last decade or two. Cold stores for fish in many countries now operate at temperatures of −30°C or lower, a far cry indeed from the temperatures mentioned by Stevenson. The contribution that technological research has made here has been to specify the conditions that must be satisfied if product quality is to be of a certain defined standard at the conclusion of a specified period of storage. Before this was done nobody knew how to control the quality of products and it is interesting to note in this context that in the United Kingdom food research was first undertaken by the Government in response to requests for such research from the cold storage industry itself (Food Investigation Board 1919). It is difficult to overstate the importance of freezing and cold storage in the development of very many fisheries. A considerable number could not exist without both and many others could exist only by making traditional products. The crayfish or rock lobster industries of the southern hemisphere, for instance, which depend almost entirely on export to the USA, Japan and Europe, would not exist at all and even the well established industries of Iceland and eastern Canada might be forced to preserve a large proportion of their catches by traditional salting or drying.

Warm water species of fish may well have different properties from those of Arctic and temperate areas. What may be required is investigation to determine whether warm water fish have the same demanding requirements for low temperature storage; if they have not, then this may have important economic implications for tropical and subtropical fish industries. In addition, one may ask whether packaging methods and materials developed for one type of marketing system are necessarily appropriate for others. There is here, as in other areas, a need to reinterpret the results obtained elsewhere in the light of different situations.

Nevertheless, every advance requires a combination of circumstances to be successful; lower storage temperatures would have been impossible without corresponding reductions in the costs and improvements in the reliability of refrigeration equipment. Economic considerations, besides technological ones, have played a critical part in the development of freezing at sea. Industry in a number of countries, particularly in the late twenties and early thirties, attempted to develop freezing at sea and some commercial ventures were run for a time. Mainly brine freezing was used, although some vessels employed air freezing. Various quality problems were encountered but more important was the fact that economic forces at that time were unfavourable for the growth of such a development. Technological research after 1945, improvements in refrigeration technology and changes in the biological and economic situation, have all contributed to the successful establishment of the world's fleets of factory trawlers and factory freezers. To say that these are entirely due to the researches of fish technologists would be claiming too much, but it is certain that without research the fleets of highly sophisticated vessels belonging to Japan, the USSR and many European countries could never have been built and operated. The success of freezing at sea has in fact produced a fresh crop of technological problems as vessels have worked new grounds and have had to fish in conditions not originally envisaged.

Technologists have contributed much more, however, than advice on ways of improving specific industrial processes, important though this has been. They have established the scientific foundation on which sound technology must be based. If I have stressed the importance of having men capable of working side by side with industry, it is because I believe this is essential to the success of a technological laboratory; equally important is the ability to do high quality research. Nowhere has this been seen more clearly than in the continuing search for suitable methods for measuring the freshness of fish. This has long been central to the programmes of many technological laboratories. Many possible methods have been examined, physical, chemical and sensory, and most have been rejected because they are insufficiently accurate, too slow or too cumbersome. Some methods remain, accepted as the best we have, but all have some drawbacks. More recently, one or two promising physical methods of measuring the degree of freshness have been proposed but these still remain to be proved in practice. Measuring freshness is, of course, an essential operation in many types of technological investigation, and this in itself would be sufficient justification for carrying out studies to improve the sensitivity of methods. But freshness is an important quality factor for industry and it is interesting to see the way in which industry as adopted and adapted methods to its own needs. It is now, for example, quite usual for upper limits for trimethylamine content to be written into specifications; these can act as a check on buyer and seller and go part of the way toward ensuring the quality of the product. Trimethylamine levels are also used as a check in the Canadian scheme for grading fish (Anderson 1965). It would probably not be difficult to trace the origin and development of the organoleptic scheme proposed for fresh or chilled fish in the European Economic Community (EEC 1970). Technological research has given to industry a variety of possible methods that are now in use, but all are imperfect and none meet entirely the industrial needs. Organoleptic methods, for instance, are rapid and do not require costly equipment and can usually be carried out on quaysides where fish is unloaded or trans-shipped.

Precision of measurement requires rigorous training of a number of people and even when systems are working well the results are likely to be viewed with suspicion by industry, particularly if large sums of money are involved in the results of assessments. Chemical methods, on the other hand, which are independent of the human senses, are destructive, relatively slow, require laboratory facilities and results do not always agree with those of other or organoleptic chemical methods. Physical methods are usually rapid and cheap to carry out and some may have advantages not shared by others, such as being non-destructive.

It would be an interesting point of discussion to consider whether industry has now been provided with as many means of measuring freshness as it really requires. The perfect test for freshness will always be a kind of Philosopher's Stone, for there are certain fundamental reasons why accuracy of measurement is unlikely to be improved much beyond the limits achievable now without a major expenditure of effort in making the measurement whilst any new techniques are likely to suffer in some degree from the disadvantages already listed. Has technological research contributed to industry in this area as much as can reasonably be expected and is further research likely to be decreasingly cost effective? Another point of interest is how decisions are to be taken that enough research has been carried out in this or, indeed, in any other field.

THE ROLE OF A GOVERNMENT FISH TECHNOLOGY LABORATORY

What job is a government fish technology laboratory set up to do? Most laboratories, when first established, have been given a broad indication of the area in which they are to work. For example, the Danish Fisheries Technological Laboratory, when set up in 1931, was given by law the following directions: 'The Laboratory shall carry out investigations and research into the handling, storing, preservation and other industrial utilization of fish. The information obtained shall be made available to the fisheries and fishing industry' (Hansen 1972). The report recommending the establishment of the Torry Research Station said that '. . . research should be instituted with a view to improving the methods of preserving fish from the moment when it has been caught to the moment when it reaches the consumer' (Imperial Economic Committee 1927).

Such statements are clearly of some value but in practice, and as a laboratory develops its programmes of work and conditions in its industry change, so it is necessary to review and redefine the area of work. Furthermore, there is a need to express the objectives of each programme in a great deal more detail and such an exercise has value in clarifying objectives, in establishing priorities and, most difficult of matters, deciding when programmes should be terminated. Some government laboratories are charged with routine, regulatory duties, to inspect and certify fish products, for example, but although routine examination of fish for enforcement purposes may sometimes fit well with research and development work, it is not an essential part of it. Indeed, in many countries enforcement is a responsibility of a separate organization and it can be argued that difficulties can be created by attempting to combine two very different functions.

Although the work of government laboratories is intended to assist the development of the fish industry of the country in question, it is implicit, in the absence of any policy to the contrary, that the interests of the taxpayer are also involved. A flourishing industry, of course, is desirable and will contribute to national wealth, but government also represents consumers and their interests must not be neglected. Although usually the interests of both are the same, they are not necessarily so. For instance, legislation specifying the names under which particular species must be sold, limiting the amount of fish in a fish finger, or prohibiting the use of polyphosphates may be introduced to protect the consumer but may act to the disadvantage of industry. It may prove to be a job for the laboratory to develop methods to detect infractions of the law. Government also has other concerns besides those relating to the consumer and the technological laboratory should also be involved in these. One instance of such a situation is where industry may find it cheaper to buy raw material from abroad rather than attempting to use its own catch. This may occur for reasons of economics or because of the unsuitability or unacceptability of home-caught species for food. It may, however, be national policy to produce more food at home and it then falls to the laboratory to develop methods for utilizing other species and to demonstrate how they should be used. Hence, I believe that the responsibilities of a technological laboratory can be broadly divided into three elements – to the industry, to the consumer and to the government. Government responsibilities extend, of course, beyond domestic issues into the international field, and the laboratory must be able to give advice in its appropriate area of competence. If this view of the responsibilities is accepted, then I believe a number of conclusions can be drawn about the nature of the programme of work and the way in which it should be controlled.

1. Staff must be aware of the way industry works. It is possible to provide sensible answers to industrial problems only if staff are frequently and closely in contact with industrial operations. Unless staff are widely experienced, they cannot be expected to talk on the same terms or perhaps even to understand the nature of the questions asked. The result is likely to be that industry will not seek the advice of the laboratory which will become more and more concerned with other, less relevant, programmes. Perhaps even more important, however, is that staff who have knowledge of industry are enabled to pose critical questions about its operation. Technologists may well see problems in a different way from people in industry and can throw new light on them. The importance of this can be judged from my comments on work on commercial vessels, but many other examples could be given.

2. The research programme must be relevant. It is in many ways easier to choose programmes of research that are laboratory-generated. There is never any shortage of ideas for research topics but these must be judged against the current and possible future problems relating to the fish industry. Those that are merely interesting but without apparent application may be abandoned.

3. The programme must be forward-looking. It is the function of the laboratory to be able to advise on possible new developments and this means that a proportion of the work should probably be devoted to areas that are not of immediate concern to the industry but may be expected to become so. It is, of course, difficult to chart the course between what may become relevant and what will always remain impracticable. The assessment of industry in this regard necessarily tends to be more conservative than that of the technologist who, within reasonable limits, should be adventurous. What is impracticable today often becomes commonplace tomorrow.

4. Nevertheless, most of the work should be directed to answering the current problems of industry. This means that a balance must be maintained between long- and short-term topics. Indeed, without a good programme of work on current problems the question of relevance arises. Some of the work will be *ad hoc* and there are good reasons why it should be so. Scientists and technologists are trained to organize experiments so that they will give meaningful results. The staff of a reasonably well equipped laboratory will have access to equipment not available to industry and which generally industry could not use. They can readily provide answers to problems which do not require prolonged fundamental research for their solution.

5. Staff must be aware of recent developments elsewhere. It is essential that every laboratory should have access to world fisheries literature. It would be an interesting exercise, and perhaps one to be undertaken by FAO, to draw up a list of basic journals for a fish technology library. Perhaps no research should be undertaken until all available sources of information have been exhausted. The library is one of the cheapest places to carry out research. It is worth noting that new fisheries must depend almost entirely on technology borrowed from elsewhere and a new laboratory is not required to start a full programme of innovatory research.

6. Staff must be alert to problems of national concern relating to the fisheries. This is a difficult area but a critical one. The technological laboratory must be able to warn the government of national or internal problems that are likely to arise, for example, in the fields of public health or welfare. This aspect will only be covered adequately, however, if staff are constantly in touch with industry and are actively engaged in research. Furthermore, there must be close collaboration between technologists and those engaged in associated areas of research, such as marine biology and gear development.

7. The laboratory must be able to demonstrate the results of its work. Applied research is only completed when it becomes applied. There is an enormous advantage also for a research worker himself to be able to show industry what he has found. The staff of the laboratory must be prepared to lecture and demonstrate to industry both in the laboratory itself and in fish plants. Furthermore, staff must be prepared to go on giving similar talks over a long period; the facts of freezing and cold storage do not change with time but they are new to many people in industry. In other words, the laboratory, if it is to do its job properly, must do educational work as well as research and development.

8. The laboratory must establish a reputation for discretion, fairness and objectivity. Much of the information collected about industry by a technological laboratory relates to specific operations and individual companies. It can be harmful to firms if this information reaches competitors and it may spoil relations with industry if certain findings are handled in an undiplomatic way. It is difficult to lay down in detail how information should be made available to industry but it is necessary that potentially damaging information, for example, that a particular handling practice results in poor quality fish, should not reach the industry through the popular press. Further, it may be desirable for a laboratory to be able to undertake confidential work, perhaps on repayment, for individual companies. Here commercial secrecy must be maintained. It is important that, if this is to be done, the detailed conditions of the work should be laid down and agreed beforehand. Who owns patents arising from the work? What are the limits of confidentiality? Does the laboratory retain the right to publish if it thinks fit?

Finally, there are two major points to emphasize. First, a technological laboratory can only do its job if it is in constant and close contact not only with industry but also with government. Technology is not something that can be turned on and off like a tap. The laboratory must be kept fully and continuously informed of government policy on fish and food matters, must be able to offer comment and information at any time to policy-makers and particularly must be able to contribute to policy-making by being brought in at an early stage in appropriate discussions.

The second point relates to the role of FAO. In 1945 the following recommendation was made to the UN Interim Commission on Food and Agriculture (UN 1945):

Technological research

'In recent years a great mass of information has been assembled on the technological phases of fish production and processing covering the handling of fish aboard the boat or vessel; the preparation of fish for market by icing, freezing, salting, drying, canning, etc.; and the warehousing, storage and transportation of fishery products. Much work has also been done in the field of fishery by-products, such as fish meal and oil, and in the development of mechanical devices for their preparation. While much still remains to be accomplished in this field, it is believed that existing knowledge is so far in advance of application that the efforts of FAO should be directed toward securing the adoption of these improved methods. This could be achieved through the establishment of some form of clearinghouse for reports covering research done heretofore, thus making the reports available to all research workers interested in obtaining information on the scientific handling of fishery products.

'It is also suggested that FAO sponsor periodic international conferences of fishery technologists to discuss the problems arising in the various countries. This would enable workers who are actively engaged in fishery research to become more widely acquainted with the problems confronting workers in other countries and to exchange ideas that could contribute to the solution of such problems.'

Broadly, this has been the policy followed by FAO in the intervening years and this Conference is one example of many where FAO has been instrumental in bringing together technologists from all over the world to discuss problems of world concern. We have learnt how useful the volumes of papers of past conferences have proved to be as a continuing source of reference. So much of our technology has been developed in relation to the northern hemisphere and is now being applied in warm water fisheries. An increasing amount of information is becoming available about warm water fisheries, but it is scattered and requires to be brought together and properly digested. Has the time come, I wonder, for FAO to sponsor the publication of a handbook of fish technology for warm water fisheries? Such a work would certainly encourage the application of technology to the proper utilization of fish resources.

References

ANDERSON, G G Fish Inspection Service in Canada as it relates to
1966 the inspection of fresh and frozen fish and fish products. *In* R Kreuzer (ed.) *Technology of Fish Utilization*, London, Fishing News (Books) Ltd., p. 144–145.
BURGESS, G H O *Developments in Handling and Processing Fish,*
1965 London, Fishing News (Books) Ltd.
CUTTING, C L *Fish Saving*, London, Leonard Hill.
1955
DRUMMOND, J C and WILBRAHAM, A *The Englishman's Food,*
1958 London, Jonathan Cape.
EEC *Regulation No. 2455/70.*
1970
Food Investigation Board *Report for the year* 1918, London,
1919 H.M.S.O.
FORBES, R J and DIJKSTERHUIS, E J *A History of Science and Technology*,
1963 London, Penguin Books
HANSEN, P The role of the technological laboratory in Danish
1972 fisheries development. *Scand. Refrig.* 1(4)134–137.
Imperial Economics Committee *Report on Marketing and Preparing*
1927 *for Market and Foodstuffs produced within the Empire.* Fifth Report – Fish. London, H.M.S.O.
STEVENSON, C H *The Preservation of fishery products for food,*
1899 Washington, Government Printing Office. Reprinted from *Bull. U.S. Fish. Commn.* XVIII 335–576 1898.
TRESSLER, D K *Marine Products of Commerce*, New York, Chemical
1923 Catalog Co. 1923.
UN *Report of the Technical Committee on Fisheries*, Submitted to
1945 the UN Interim Commission on Food and Agriculture, Washington, U.S.A., April 13, 1945.

Some Dynamics of Fisheries

R Finch

De la dynamique des pêches

Les vingt-cinq dernières années ont été les témoins d'une évolution remarquable dans les activités sociales, économiques, industrielles et agricoles de l'humanité. Les répercussions que cette évolution a eues et continuera d'exercer sur la production et l'utilisation du poisson et des produits de la pêche sont passées en revue. L'auteur examine deux séries de facteurs. La première

Dinamica de la pesca

En los últimos 25 años se han producido cambios y progresos importantes en las actividas sociales, económicas, industriales y agrícolas de la humanidad. Se examinan las repercusiones que estos cambios han tenido y continuarán teniendo sobre la producción y empleo del pescado y de los productos pesqueros. Se toman en consideración dos conjuntos de factores. El primero comprende lo

catégorie comprend les éléments ayant trait à la demande de tout produit alimentaire, par exemple, caractéristiques physiques et sensorielles, coût, disponibilité, innocuité, etc. La seconde englobe les facteurs liés au modifications de l'environnement dans lequel intervient la production des produits de la pêche. Il s'agit des modifications de la quantité et de la composition des mises à terre de poissons, de la croissance de la population, des changements dans la demande de divers produits, des effets de l'expansion agricole et industrielle, et des progrès de la science et de la technologie. L'auteur examine le rôle de ces modifications et procède à une étude comparée des différences qui en ont résulté au cours des deux dernières décennies dans les activités des spécialistes des denrées alimentaires d'origine marine, ainsi que le montre l'évolution des sujets traités dans la documentation publiée. On peut en conclure que la recherche sur les produits de la pêche portera dans l'avenir immédiat sur le renforcement de l'utilisation du poisson et sur la valorisation, en vue de leur emploi direct, d'espèces servant maintenant à la fabrication de farine et d'huile. La qualité et l'innocuité des produits de la pêche recevront aussi une attention accrue. Etant donné les possibilités limitées d'expansion future des disponibilités de poisson, ces activités devraient bénéficier de la priorité absolue.

relativo a la demanda de todo producto alimenticio, como sus características físicas y organolépticas, costo, disponibilidad, seguridad, etc. El segundo se refiere a los cambios en el ambiente en que la preparación de productos pesqueros tiene lugar. Comprende cambios en la cantidad y composición de las descargas de pescado, crecimiento de la población, cambios en la demanda de productos, repercusiones del crecimiento agrícola e industrial y los adelantos de la ciencia y la tecnología. Se examinan los efectos de estos cambios y se compara los resultados de las distintas actividades que en los últimos veinte años, han desempeñado los científicos que se ocupan de los alimentos pesqueros, como lo indica la gama de materias que han constituido la base de los documentos publicados. De ello se llega a la conclusión de que las investigaciones sobre productos pesqueros en un futuro inmediato se ocuparán de mayor utilización del pescado y de fomentar el consumo directo de algunas especies que actualmente se emplean para obtener harina y aceite. También recibirá particular atención la calidad y seguridad de los productos pesqueros. Teniendo en cuenta las posibilidades limitadas de una expansión futura de los suministros de pescado éstas actividades recibirán alta prioridad.

The last 25 years have perhaps constituted the most remarkable period in the history of the world, being marked by an unprecedented increase and diversity of change in almost every aspect of human activity. During this time the world population has increased by nearly 1,500 million, a number which equals the whole population of the earth at the turn of the century. Parallel to this has been a greatly accelerated growth in science, technology, medicine and agriculture, accompanied by profound changes in economic and social patterns and in many other factors which affect the way people live. The harvesting and use of fish have formed an important part of this complex development. The purpose of this paper is to review the factors which influence such growth and change in the world's use of fish. These are considered in two groups: those technical factors which affect the supply and demand of food products, including fish and fishery products, and those broader external factors relating to the growth of the world society which react on these to change the patterns of manufacture and use of fishery products. Past and possible future trends will be reviewed in the light of these factors, and their influence upon the future activities of food scientists considered.

FISHERY PRODUCTS

Fish and shellfish offer a wide range of products to consumers at a wide range of prices. At some times and places fish are luxury foods. For example, live domestic shrimp (*Penaeus japonicus*) sold in May 1972 in Tokyo for US $26.70 to 30.90/kg (Anon. 1972a). The first fresh bluefin tuna (*Thunnus thynnus*) arriving in the Tokyo market in February 1972 sold for the amazing price of US $3,441 for a single fish (Shohara 1972). Such species may be caught for local gourmet markets or for the currency return they bring from foreign markets, but much less commonly as a source of protein food for the producing nation. Less exotic species of fish, such as many demersal species, tunas and salmon, are available at a reasonable cost to a wide spectrum of consumers. In contrast to luxury products, these form part of the normally accepted diet and frequently provide a valuable source of dietary protein. Several species of fish, such as the anchovy (*Engraulis ringens*) of Chile and Peru, and the menhaden (*Brevoortia patronus* and *Brevoortia tyrannus*) of the US Atlantic and Gulf coasts, are usually converted to fish meal for indirect human con-

sumption through feeding to poultry and pigs. In this use they contribute less toward human nutrition than do direct food since it has been estimated that fish meal provides only a 20 per cent dietary protein efficiency as compared to direct consumption (Roels 1969).

The world shortage of protein has led to extensive consideration of fish as a significant source of high-quality protein, the supply of which may be capable of substantial expansion to meet present and growing needs of the undernourished peoples of the world (Finn 1960). Fish provide about one per cent of the world's total food supply. Allowing for processing loss, this is equivalent to an average of about 3.4 g animal protein *per caput* daily for the whole world population, varying from 0.1 to 13 g of protein *per caput* in different countries (Finch 1970). The use of fish protein concentrates (FPC) and fish sausage has been proposed as means by which a large additional supply of inexpensive and high-quality protein can be brought into the food supply (FAO 1968). The important point about the many alternative forms of fish, from conventional fillets to FPC, is that, government subsidies aside, their consumption follows the laws of supply and demand. In a given area, the sale and use of fishery products, whether fish or shellfish, or fresh, frozen, precooked, salted, smoked, pickled, dried, canned, extracted, formulated in complex foods, or whatever, will depend upon three factors: the product characteristics, its availability, and its cost.

Product characteristics

When one considers the many species of fish and shellfish available and the number of ways in which they may be processed, it may be seen that the range and variety of products which may be prepared are immense. Preferences for different types of fishery products are not equal in all areas due to differences in eating customs and experiences. Preferences for certain species of fish have been established in part by their availability (those which can be readily harvested, hence at a reasonable effort or cost, are often preferred), coupled with some of the characteristics of the fish which make them attractive to the consumer. These may include size, a physical conformation which makes them easy to handle and prepare, and a pleasant appearance, odour and flavour. The significance of these factors may vary considerably from country to country, from place to place, and may change in time due to changes in availability, hence familiarity with certain species. Food fish products, in common with other foods, have three characteristics which influence the price the consumer will pay for them. These are the forms in which the products appear, their quality and their safety.

Product form

Traditionally, fish was preserved by drying, salting, smoking and pickling. As man's technological capability increased, iced preservation, canning and then freezing increased the variety of products available, their length of storage and their market range. Further changes have taken place in recent years (Cutting 1962). The conventional unprocessed forms of fish (whole, dressed, filleted, steaked, etc.) require greater or lesser amounts of presale preparation and correspondingly offer greater or lesser levels of convenience to the consumer. In developed countries, as food distribution has grown rapidly more sophisticated, preparation into forms which are convenient for the consumer and packaged for improved display have become important characteristics.

Recent years have seen the development of a major trade in fishsticks or fingers prepared from lean fish fillets, shrimp processed in various ways, and a range of prepared fish foods, including TV-dinners. This development has reached the point where, in some countries, many consumers have become used only to highly prepared forms of fish, such as frozen fillets, fishsticks, and complete fish dinners, and the longer established canned sardines, salmon and tuna. They are now neither capable of, nor interested in, preparation of fish from its original form and are, therefore, willing to pay more for such more convenient products than for the earlier and simpler forms. While these products are only likely to be found in developed countries with elaborate frozen food distribution systems and consumers with a considerable disposable income, they may be produced in part in developing countries to provide a source of income.

Among less conventional forms of fish which have more recently been considered are those made by putting fish through comminuting or flesh-separating machines, followed by subsequent processing. These include a variety of products which may simulate conventional processed products, such as fishsticks, or may be relatively new forms, such as fish sausage. Although a large market has developed for such specialized products in Japan (Amano 1965) their use in other countries is only now commencing. This technique lends itself to some interesting new opportunities for blending and treating fish muscle to make products with a range of different secondary characteristics.

Another new processing method is irradiation-pasteurization or 'radurization' of fish. This also has been the subject of much research, directed mainly to establishing the wholesomeness and safety from *botulinum* hazards of products so processed. An international project is being conducted to establish the wholesomeness of some low-dose irradiated fish products (Hanneson 1972). The objective of this approach is not so much to produce a new form as a conventional product at a lower cost, or better quality through reduced loss and longer shelf life and improved freshness at any given point. In this case, cost rather than form is the factor being modified.

About 35 per cent of the world's fish supply is converted into fishmeal by traditional processes, which is fed to livestock, especially chickens, to provide an indirect source of protein. A relatively new form of fishmeal is solvent-extracted, in which the oil content and oxidized odour are reduced to a very low level, making the meal an acceptable protein supplement for feeding baby pigs and calves for which regular fishmeal is unsuitable (Anon. 1972d).

FPC in various forms is another unconventional fishery product for which a great deal of research has been conducted (Finch 1970) but which, as yet, has achieved little commercial success. This has been attributed to the potentially high cost of food-grade FPC not being matched by correspondingly attractive properties which will persuade the consumer to buy, the consumer in this case being the food manufacturer (PAG 1972a and b). However, it is likely that the reasons are more complex than this and relative in part to the difficulty of introducing new foods and food supplements into diets in developing countries.

Experimentally-produced fish protein isolates are similar to FPC but differ from it in consisting almost solely of pure fish protein and in being capable of a considerable variation in functional properties (Spinelli *et al.* 1973). Protein derivatives, such as succinylates, can be prepared from concentrates and isolates, which have a further range of interesting properties offering new possibilities in food formulation (Groninger 1973). A considerable market in the USA is predicted for protein products with functional properties (Hammonds and Call 1970) and by inference in other developed countries. Fish protein products having suitable properties and price may have a considerable future in this field.

Quality in fishery products

The second factor affecting product demand is quality. Most societies place a premium on quality, but while this is readily apparent in developed countries, it is not limited to them. For example, Van Veen describes the decreasing value of successive extracts of 'nuoc nam' produced in Indochina (Van Veen 1965). The rapidity with which freshly caught fish loses quality and spoils is proverbial. Freezing has brought with it further kinds of spoilage to which fish may be subject. A great many of the earlier studies on preservation of fish were concerned with quality and its companion, spoilage, which represents the terminal stage reached as the quality of fresh fish declines with storage. It is remarkable that, in spite of more than 40 years work, no objective tests have yet been developed which can measure the quality of fishery products accurately, consistently and reliably. Yet the preservation of quality and its measurement, both subjectively and objectively, remain important factors to the producer and the consumer (Soudan 1973).

Safety in fishery products

The third factor influencing the demand for fish is its safety. Fish have shown an almost unique capability to extract some substances, both from their aqueous environment and, in a more concentrated form, through the food chain, and to retain the built up concentrations of these in their muscle and other tissues (FAO 1971). Concern has been expressed about the possible accumulation in fish of pesticides, especially DDT, and its derivatives, mercury, lead, cadmium, arsenic and others. The presence of hydrocarbons, phthalates, viruses, paralytic shellfish poison and other biotoxins, radio-nuclides and other substances, has also recently been the subject of much discussion, study and speculation. Some of these substances may affect the growth and survival of the fish and so imperil fish stocks. Some may affect the colour or flavour of fish products, hence their consumer acceptability. Of greater concern is that some may pose a threat of being injurious to the consumer.

In addition to environmental hazards, dangers may occur through improper processing and storage of fish and fishery products. Public health has suffered due to the growth of *Clostridium botulinum* and other pathogenic organisms, such as *Salmonella* spp. and *Vibrio parahaemolyticus* in fishery products as a result of unsatisfactory processing, storage or handling practices. How-

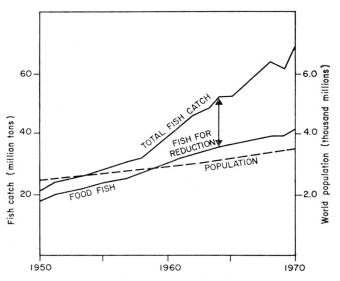

Fig 1 World fish catch and population 1950–1973

ever, it should be said that these microbiological problems are by no means unique to fish. The demand for fish is affected not only by the few incidents which have occurred. Fears arising from uninformed speculation which may follow such incidents can also affect consumer confidence and consequently the sale of fishery products.

THE EFFECT OF EXTERNAL CHANGES ON FISHERY PRODUCTS

The growth of fisheries for the last 20 to 25 years has been conditioned, in addition to the factors which relate to consumer demand, by a series of external changes. These include population growth, changes in the fish supply, advances in science and technology, industrial growth and social changes.

Population and fish supply

At least part of the people of many countries of the world are inadequately nourished and need more food. In addition to this need, the recent rapid growth in world population, partly due to increased life expectancy,

itself the result of improved medical knowledge and services, requires a further corresponding increase in the food supply. The existing supply is frequently also nutritionally unbalanced. Particular attention has been focused on the shortage of protein, especially animal protein, in the food supply (FAO 1970, UN 1968). Although the reality of a world protein shortage, as opposed to a protein-calorie shortage, has recently been called into question, there remains little question that in a number of specific areas the supply of dietary protein is inadequate (Scrimshaw 1972). The addition of relatively small amounts of animal protein to vegetable diets offers, in many cases, a simple and pleasant way to ensure an adequate and balanced protein intake. Increasing the fish catch presents an attractive means to supplement the supply of animal protein. Spurred on by predictions of the boundless wealth of the oceans, many nations have in the last 25 years developed substantial fishery programmes or increased their existing efforts to harvest fish; hence there has been a rapid growth in world fisheries. The resulting overall fish catch has so far largely been achieved through increasing the catch of known species, with a spectacular increase in the amounts of fish used for reduction to fishmeal and oil. Fig. 1 shows the growth of world population and the supply of food fish and fish for reduction for the period 1950 to 1970.

The overall trends shown are important but, as with any generalizations, they obscure a variety of changes in the components, which can be of great local significance. For example, the catch increased from 1948 to 1968 by a factor of about 3.3. The catch of some groups of fish, such as freshwater fish and squid, increased around the same rate. The catch of others, such as blue crab (*Callinectes sapidus*) and European flounder (*Platichthys flesus*), showed no increase or actually decreased. The catch of some major groups, such as prawns and shrimps (*Penaeidae*), Atlantic cod (*Gadus morhua*) and Atlantic herring (*Clupea harengus harengus*) increased, but not as fast as the catch as a whole. Finally, some fisheries showed spectacular increases over the same period, some growing from insignificant to become important contributors to the fish supply. Among the latter species involved were Cape hake (*Merluccius capensis*), South African pilchard (*Sardinops ocellata*), Alaska pollock (*Theragra chalcogramma*) and, of course, Peruvian anchovy (*Engraulis ringens*). The world catch of the latter increased from 1,000 t in 1947, through 777,000 t in 1958 to 11,272,000 t in 1968.

The important questions for the future of fishery products are: (1) can this expansion of the fish catch continue? and (2) will there be changes in the composition of the catch which modify processing needs? Until recently, it was commonly believed that the present annual catch of 70 million t could be increased to 150 to 200 million t without any substantial changes in fishing technology (Anon. 1969). Reviews made in the light of more recent experience are less optimistic. Moiseev predicts a possible increase in the annual world catch of about 20 million t to about 90 million t before a maximum sustainable level is reached (Moiseev 1973). This increase does not include krill as a potential resource, and would be mainly in the form of pelagic species now largely used for reduction rather than food.

Suda recently estimated that an increase of 43 million t in the annual catch was possible (Suda 1973), but indicated that 80 per cent of this would be from species only suitable for reduction. Thus the possible increase in the food fish catch according to Suda's estimate would be only 8.6 million t. It should further be noted that Moiseev's estimate was based on the assumption that effective regulation to avoid overfishing could be developed. Failure to do this, he warned, would be likely to lead to a decrease in the present catch. Although there is some difference between these recent estimates, they both indicate that we are approaching the limit to our food fish resources. If the human population continues to increase as predicted and the fish supply is increased proportionately, the catch will soon reach the maximum sustainable level. The increase in the rate of the food fish catch between 1960 and 1970 was 3.1 per cent annually. The available increase of 8.6 million t food fish indicated by Suda is around 20 per cent of the present catch. If the food fish catch continues to increase at the 3.1 per cent rate, maximum sustainable yield should be reached in 5 to 10 years.

What are the alternatives to increasing the fish supply? One is in the exploitation of krill and other low trophic-level animals. The potential commercial catch of Antarctic krill has been estimated to be 25 to 50 million t (*Lyubimova et al.* 1973). The main problems in using krill are said to be developing improved methods of catch to harvest it in commercial quantities without injury to the carapace, and developing attractive food products. At present also, the logistics and economics of harvesting krill are undefined and may be formidable. A second alternative lies in increasing the fish supply through the development of large-scale commercial aquaculture. The prospects for doing this on a sufficient scale, at a reasonable cost and within a short time, do not appear to be promising. The only remaining alternative is to increase the use of the present catch directly for human food.

Increasing the yield of food from the present fish catch

There are at least three means of increasing the yield from the present or somewhat increased catches. The first is by developing methods of using for food fish now destined for reduction. With some species the development of acceptable product forms would not be difficult but with others, such as menhaden and anchovy, considerable advances in techniques would be needed. This would probably also be largely true of species as yet underutilized, the properties and characteristics of which are unfamiliar to the consumer and the food manufacturer.

The second approach is by developing product forms which use a larger proportion of the raw food fish than is now the case, so that a greater amount of product is obtained from the same catch of landed fish. The use of flesh-separating machines allows the recovery of considerably larger amounts of edible tissue than is available from filleting operations. For example, in the case of Atlantic cod, ordinary filleting yields 30 to 35 per cent of edible tissue, whereas machine flesh separation gives around 50 per cent minced or comminuted muscle tissue. Yield differences vary with the size and the structure of the species (King and Carver 1970), but on the average

the above figures give a good indication of the increases which may be obtained. However, the minced form of tissue which is produced is unfamiliar to the consumer in many countries and considerable research and development will be necessary to make acceptable, stable and economical products which are free from bone fragments. Moreover, a number of questions on standards and nomenclature will have to be resolved before a ready trade in such products can develop. Another means of increasing yield is by processing additional fish into fermented products, such as 'nuoc mam' which are widely consumed in the Orient. This manufacturing process offers an exceptionally complete use of material to give sauces and pastes accepted in several countries. However, the process of fermentation as practised is slow and primitive, and the large amounts of salt added may make the products unsuitable for the diets of small children and pregnant women (Pariser 1967). Means of accelerating the process and reducing the salt level of the end products would be likely to permit its much wider use. Some alternative methods have recently been reviewed (Hale 1972).

A third approach is to improve methods of handling fish at sea and ashore so as to reduce spoilage loss. Considerable research on spoilage has been carried out over the last 25 years and we now know much more about the composition of fish, their physiology and the biochemistry of their *post mortem* changes. Although this knowledge has somewhat improved our understanding of the handling of fish during freezing and thawing, it has so far provided insight to degradative changes rather than means of measuring or arresting them (Farber 1965). Moreover, although the principles of handling and storing fish are by now quite well known, at least for fish caught in temperate waters, their general application in practice is far from perfect. It is likely that more can be done to reduce losses and ensure improved operating systems for handling, processing and distributing fish by putting present knowledge into use than by further extensive research. Action along these lines through more or less elaborate mandatory fisheries inspection systems are in effect in a number of countries (Kreuzer 1971). The adoption and effective application of Codes of Practice being developed under the Codex Alimentarius programme could do much to reduce the loss of fish through spoilage. One particular case of loss is that which occurs with simple sun-dried fishery products produced in considerable amounts in the Oriental developing countries. Poor process control and storage leads to substantial losses through infestation and moulding. Mechanization by present methods using fuel in more than the most limited amounts is frequently not economically feasible. Improved simple means of drying might be developed to reduce losses.

The effects of science and technology

Changes in the fishing industry brought about by advances in science and technology are numerous. Probably the biggest impact has been in harvesting where the development of improved equipment to locate fish and to catch it quickly and efficiently has been matched by that of large and elaborate fleet organizations which can handle the fish at sea in vast amounts. Techniques of freezing on board vessels, little practised 25 years ago, are now widespread and improved equipment has been developed. On a more limited scale, new methods for forecasting the arrival and size of catch for some migratory species, such as has been developed for Pacific albacore (*Thunnus alalunga*), will enable better use to be made of fleets (Laurs 1972). Improved equipment for mechanically preparing and canning fish has been developed and is being continually improved. New materials and designs for containers for handling, processing and packaging fish have come into use. Curiously, although there have been numerous practical advances, no widespread basic impact has been made on fish handling and processing techniques despite intensive research.

FAO classifies the disposition of the catch into fresh, frozen, cured, reduced to meal and oil, and miscellaneous uses. From 1950 to 1970 significant changes have occurred in the pattern of processing. The amount produced in each class has increased. But, while the proportion of the catch canned has remained constant, around 9 per cent, the proportion frozen has grown nearly three-fold and the proportions of the catch which are sold as fresh or cured have dropped substantially. Most dramatic has been the increase in the amount of the catch reduced to oil and meal. It now totals 23.8 million t or about one third of the world catch. The increased exploration of distant fishing waters, coupled with the increasing sophistication of vessel freezing and processing systems, and the spread of frozen food distribution, are likely to maintain or further increase the use of fish in the frozen form. Canned fish can be expected to retain the same consistent proportion held over the last 20 years. It is questionable whether fish reduction will continue the great upward surge of the last 10 years. Over one third of the world supply of fishmeal in 1971 was made from Peruvian anchovy. This resource has recently undergone a serious decline and it is not yet clear to what extent this is a temporary phenomenon.

One important development in the frozen fish field is the increase in prepared and frozen foods, especially fishsticks, fingers or portions, and peeled and deveined shrimp which are frequently converted to breaded, pre-cooked, frozen form for sale in developed countries. Some previously unfamiliar product forms have emerged in association with the development of hitherto unused resources. King crab (*Paralithodes camtschatica*) is one such species which has called for ingenuity in designing preparative equipment.

Work on fishery products in the field of microbiology has advanced our knowledge principally in the area of micro-organisms of public health significance. This work, combined in developed countries with a social change, i.e. the growth of consumer awareness, had led to increased public concern over the possible growth of pathogenic organisms in foods. Such concern has been heightened by yet another change, namely the development and use of new packaging materials which have provided an opportunity for the growth of anaerobic pathogens under certain circumstances. The impact on the fish processing industry has been to increase public health requirements, reflected in equipment design, more elaborate sanitation practices, and a greater reluctance by regulatory authorities to approve new processes which could increase the risks of microbial outgrowth. For example, the practice of pasteurizing picked meat from the blue crab to extend its refrigerated shelf life has developed in recent years. This process mitigates uneven harvests and extends the selling season thus tending to increase the use of the product, reduce waste and stabilize the market. But fears have been expressed recently over possible growth of pathogens in the pasteurized product packed in sealed containers and held under refrigeration. In consequence, the practice may be restricted as a protective measure (Anon. 1972b).

The science of nutrition has seen changes in recent years which may eventually affect the demand for fishery products. Diets in developed countries tend to be high in saturated fats and cholesterol due to the relatively high consumption of meat and dairy products. Evidence is accumulating that the growing incidence of coronary heart disease in the USA is associated in part with such a dietary regime and health authorities have made specific recommendations for dietary modification for persons having a high cholesterol level (Anon. 1973). Fish, with its relatively high level of unsaturated fat and low level of cholesterol, provides an excellent corrective factor in the diet and this can be expected to increase the demand for fish.

The increase in scientific capability has also affected fisheries in a new and alarming way. As the sensitivity of analytical methods has increased, analyses of foods for trace elements and compounds which present possible risks to human health have resulted in them being detected and measured in the food supply. Much public concern has been expressed. For example, several countries have established maximum permitted levels of methyl mercury in their fish supply (FAO/WHO 1972) and anxiety has been expressed over the possible presence of significant amounts of other heavy metals, although there does not appear to be cause for widespread alarm. Some fisheries have already been affected with consequent limitations on supply and increased operating costs due to the need for monitoring.

Agricultural and industrial growth
Agricultural growth is another important factor which has had, and may continue to have, an impact on fisheries. A major advance in the last three decades has been the increase in agricultural yields due to the development and use of agricultural chemicals, including herbicides and pesticides. The spread of many of these into the environment has permitted their uptake by fish leading to concern for the safety of fishery products and to the establishment of maximum levels for some of these substances in foods. One result, for example, has been the temporary banning of chubs (*Salmonidae*) from certain areas of the Great Lakes since their DDT levels have been found excessive.

Industrial growth has been tremendous in the last 30 years and it too has brought problems. Industrial wastes, for instance, have provided major problems to fisheries. The effects can be threefold. First, the reproduction and growth of fish may be impaired, imperilling the stock as a whole (FAO 1971). Second, the fishing and processing industry may be affected by quality changes in the raw material, such as, in colour and flavour which make the fish unacceptable to the consumer, and by the need to meet new operating requirements. Third, the consumer will be affected by a restriction upon the supply of a favourite food, such as has happened with the limitation on swordfish in the USA due to high mercury levels, and subsequent price increases needed to offset increased operating costs.

Changes in fish product research 1952/72

In this review of some of the important changes affecting fisheries, it is interesting to examine changes which have taken place in research on fishery products and processes between 1952 and 1972. Table 1 lists the titles of papers abstracted in *Commercial Fisheries Abstracts* for those two years into principal subject groups (Anon. 1952, Anon. 1972c). Clearly, this comparison is limited since the selection of papers may reflect some editorial bias, the titles may not always reveal the major emphasis of the works, and the abstracts include not only papers on fishery subjects but those on allied subjects which would be of interest to fishery researchers. Nevertheless, any major differences should be apparent. Examination of Table 1 shows several major shifts in the work of food fishery scientists:

1. Vitamin analysis active in 1952 had come to a standstill by 1972. This primarily reflects the replacement of fish liver oils by synthetic vitamins A and D.
2. Work on fishmeal declined to be replaced in part with work on FPC.
3. Work on both nutrition and the properties and utilization of fish oils increased.
4. Irradiation studies, absent in 1952, are shown at a fairly low level in 1972, having reached a peak in the years between.
5. Work on the spoilage and preservation of fish decreased.
6. Work on both pollution and toxicity showed dramatic increases.

TABLE 1. CLASSIFICATION OF SELECTED COMMERCIAL FISHERIES ABSTRACTS

Subject group	Papers abstracted	
	1952	1972
Analysis, vitamins	28	0
Analysis, general	51	82
Antioxidants	12	15
Canned fish	33	20
Composition	35	44
Dried, dehydrated fish	8	17
Fishmeal	50	22
Fish protein concentrate (FPC)	0	30
Frozen fish	51	30
Fresh fish	13	25
Irradiation of fish	0	16
Marine plant products	19	23
Nutrition	16	48
Oils	14	51
Pollution	0	178
Preservation, sanitation	22	12
Smoked fish	5	10
Spoilage	32	12
Salt fish	5	0
Toxicity	1	48

The remaining groups show some minor shifts in emphasis but these are probably not large enough to indicate positive changes of direction. These results agree with the influences and trends discussed previously, except there is no quantitative reflection, other than in irradiation and FPC, of the need to increase process yields and bring new products into use.

CONCLUSIONS

Significant changes in fish processing and products seem likely because of changes in the amounts and composition of fishery resources harvested, increases in population and advances in science and technology, agriculture and industry, and the social structure of the world. Among those which appear likely are:

1. Increased emphasis on devising and improving processes which give a bigger yield from the catch. These will include making minced fish products and improved techniques for fermented and dried fish products.
2. Development of methods and equipment to simplify fishery processing and reduce operating costs and of processes to upgrade small, dark, bony and other fish now reduced to meal.
3. New forms of fish preservation, such as intermediate moisture products, will continue to attract research.
4. An increased study and development of codes of practice for fishery processes and standards for fishery products and continued study of the occurrence and significance of trace elements and compounds, viruses and other micro-organisms, and infestations in fish and fishery products.
5. Continuing studies on improved disposal of fishery production wastes to reduce pollution and ensure more complete and economic production processes.
6. Work on producing functional fish proteins and derivatives will continue to receive attention as they offer new possibilities as protein enhancers, binders and emulsifiers while, in general, studies will be needed to determine nutritive values for many processed fish products.

References

AMANO, K Fish sausage manufacturing. In Borgstrom, G. (ed.),
1965 *Fish as Food*, New York, Academic Press, 3:265–280.
ANON *Comml Fish. Abstracts*, 5:1–12.
1952
ANON *Our Nation and the Sea*. Washington, D.C., U.S.A., U.S.
1969 Govt. Printing Office, p. 88.
ANON *Fishery Market News Report*. Chicago, U.S.A., July 13,
1972a 1972. National Marine Fisheries Service.
ANON FDA is considering new policy on crabmeat controls. *Fd*
1972b *chem. News*, 14(3):13.
ANON *Comml Fish. Abstracts*, 25:1–12.
1972c
ANON *Micronized Protein Concentrate in Milk Replacers*. Bergen,
1972d Norway, Research Farm of the Herring Oil and Meal Industry, 6 p.
ANON Diet and coronary heart disease. *Amer. J. Clin. Nutr.*
1973 26(1):53–54.
CUTTING, C L Historical aspects of fish. In Borgstrom, G (ed.),
1962 *Fish as Food*, New York, Academic Press, 2:1–28.
FAO Fisheries in the food economy. Rome, FAO, *Basic Study*
1968 (19), 78 p.
FAO Pollution, an international problem for fisheries. Rome,
1971 FAO, *World Food Problems* (14), 85 p.
FAO/WHO Lives in peril, protein and the child. Rome, FAO,
1970 *World Food Problems* (12), 52 p.

FAO/WHO   Evaluation of certain food additives and of the con-
1972   taminants mercury, lead, and cadmium. 16th Report of
          the Joint FAO/WHO Expert Committee on Food Addi-
          tives, Geneva, 4–12 April 1972. Rome, FAO, *Nutrition
          Meetings Report Series* (51); Geneva, WHO, *Technical
          Report Series* (505), 32 p.

FARBER, L   Freshness tests. In Borgstrom, G (ed.), *Fish as Food*,
1965   New York, Academic Press, 4:651–26.

FINCH, R   Fish protein for human use. *CRC Critical reviews in
1970   food technology*, 1(4):519–579.

FINN, D B   Fish the great potential food supply. Rome, FAO,
1960   *World Food Problems* (3), 47 p.

GRONINGER, H S   Preparation and properties of succinylated myofi-
1973   brillar protein from fish muscle, to be published in *J. Fd
          Ag. Chem.*

HALE, M B   Making fish protein concentrate by enzymatic hydroly-
1972   sis, Seattle, U.S.A., National Marine Fisheries Service,
          NOAA Technical Report NMFS SSRF-657, 32 p.

HAMMONDS, T M and CALL, D L   Utilization of protein ingredients
1970   in the U.S. food industry, Ithica, New York, Cornell
          University, *A.E. Res.* 321, Part II, 36 p.

HANNESSON, G   Objectives and present status of irradiation of fish
1972   and seafoods. Karlsruhe, F.R. Germany, International
          Project in the Field of Food Irradiation, *Food Irradiation
          Information No.* 1, p. 28–64.

KING, F J and CARVER, J H   How to use nearly all the ocean's food.
1970   *Comml Fish. Rev.*, 32(12):12–21.

KREUZER, R (ed.), *Fish Inspection and Quality Control.* London,
1971   Fishing News (Books) Ltd., 290.

LAURS, R M   *Fishing Information.* La Jolla, Calif., U.S.A., National
1972   Marine Fisheries Service, (5).

LYUBIMOVA, T G, NAUMOV, A G and LAGUNOV, L L   Prospects of
1973   the utilization of krill and other nonconventional resources
          of the world ocean. Paper submitted to the *Technical
          Conference on Fishery Management and Development*,
          Vancouver, Canada, 13–23 February 1973. Rome, FAO,
          (FI:FMD/73/S/46):10 p.

MOISEEV, P A   Development of fisheries for traditionally exploited
1973   species. *Ibid.*, (FI:FMD/73/R-4):20 p.

PAG   The potential of fish protein concentrate for developing
1972a   countries, PAG Statement 16, Part 1, *PAG Bulletin*
          2(2):11–20, New York, Protein Advisory Group, United
          Nations.

PAG   The potential of fish protein concentrate for developing
1972b   countries, PAG Statement 16, Part 2. *Ibid.*, 2(3):24–34.

PARISER, E R   Fish protein concentrate processing methods. In
1967   *Proc. Conference on Fish Protein Concentrates*, Ottawa,
          Federal-Provincial Atlantic Fisheries Committee, p. 69.

ROELS, O   Marine proteins, *Nutrition Reviews*, 27, (2):35–39.
1969

SCRIMSHAW, N S   Statement to the Unicef Executive Board. *PAG
1972   Bulletin*, 2(3):2–8, New York, Protein Advisory Group,
          United Nations.

SHOHARA, J E   "Jumbo" tuna sells for $3 400 in Japan, *Foreign
1972   Fishery Information Release* No. 72–3, Terminal Island,
          Calif., U.S.A., National Marine Fisheries Service (South-
          west Region).

SOUDAN, F   Les exigences de qualité en matière de produits de la
1973   pêche. Paper submitted to the *Technical Conference on
          Fishery Products*, Tokyo, 4–11 December 1973. Rome,
          FAO, (FII:FP/73/R-1):8 p.

SPINELLI, J, GRONINGER, H S Jr and KOURY, B   Preparation and
1973   properties of chemically and enzymatically modified pro-
          tein isolates for use as food ingredients. *Ibid.*, (FII:
          FP/73/E-28):12 p.

SUDA, A   Development of fisheries for nonconventional species.
1973   *FAO Technical Conference on Fishery Management and
          Development*, FI:FMD/73/R-5, Rome, FAO.

VAN VEEN, A G   Fermented and dried seafood products in South-
1965   east Asia. In Borgstrom, G (ed.), *Fish as Food*, New York,
          Academic Press, 3:227–250.

UN   International action to avert the impending protein crisis.
1968   New York, U.N. *Special Report Series of the Advisory
          Committee on the Application of Science and Technology
          to Development*, E/4343/Rev. 1 (Sales No. E.68.XIII.2),
          106.

Discussion on Part I

Historical basis for product and process development

The need to pay attention to cultural patterns and food
behaviour when seeking to modify traditional products
or to introduce new ones was brought to the attention
of the Conference. Influences at work today, that are
significant for the acceptance of products, must be taken
into account. Traditional products maintain their
importance in the nutrition of many countries and their
improvement requires attention.

KREUZER (FAO) pointed out that traditional products
are part of long established food patterns, while industrial products (new types of products) have been
developed in industrial societies to meet particular
requirements. Aspects of health and product quality are
features of the new product concept, and should also
be applied to improve traditional products. Food habits
have changed throughout human history. However, due
recognition should be given to the cultural pattern and
traditional food habits of the countries concerned if it
seems desirable or necessary to accelerate such changes.

FINCH (USA) mentioned the changes that have taken
place with respect to fishery products and the reasons
for these changes. Useful lessons can be learned from
past experience.

BURGESS (UK) pointed out that research staff and technologists should be well acquainted with the industry
and have a good relationship with it. Research and
development should be relevant to the present and future
needs of the industry. He stressed the need for dissemination of information to industry. Information of confidential nature, however, should be available only to
those concerned.

SÁNCHEZ (Peru), referring to Burgess' conclusions, said
that in developing countries development of products
from fish species of low commercial value is most
important.

Promoting product development

The discussion centred on the role of governmental
research institutes in relation to industry, particularly
in promoting the development of new or improved
processes and products.

KOMBOT-NAGUEMON (Central African Republic) found
the comprehensive reviews given in the introduction
instructive because they put product development in the
right perspective to other factors of importance and
influence. In his opinion it would be most useful to bring
together, in an international forum, research workers,
producers, consumers and environmental specialists to
discuss the promotion of such a complex field as is the
adaptation of fish products to the need and taste of different consumers.

SLAVIN (USA) said that the utilization of many species
not commonly used will be of special value in the coastal
fisheries of many countries, both developed and developing. In view of the importance of this matter, he suggested that FAO should set up a working group on
fisheries development to identify: (1) resource potential
for development and (2) problems to be resolved by the
application of technology or by market introduction.
He felt that such action by FAO would provide a valuable
survey of use to all countries concerned with such problems.

FLEAR (UK) explained that research institutes and
industry in Britain maintain a close dialogue on changing

needs and circumstances. For example, as the traditional means of processing small fish no longer apply, high priority is being given to research in this field by the institutes in collaboration with the industry. Similarly, the utilization of unfamiliar species and the development of new products have become increasingly important. As success in these fields is largely dependent on the price of the new products, the research institutes and industry are working closely together with urgency to ensure that the new products meet the demands of the market. Such collaboration includes technical engineering research.

LEARSON (USA) told the Conference that the fishing industry in New England, USA, had appointed representatives to maintain liaison with the research technologists in that State. The two groups meet several times a year to discuss the direction and progress of research programmes concerned with the New England fisheries. This system results in industry obtaining a better understanding of technological research problems and keeps the technologists informed of industry's priorities.

AMANO (Japan) said that there are more than 40 prefectural experimental stations in Japan which provide technological advice to industry. The Japanese Society of Scientific Fisheries, furthermore, has a liaison body for the express purpose of disseminating the results of scientific experiments and programmes to industry. This is done by holding meetings with industry two or three times a year. For example, the industry has been informed of the content of the papers of this Conference through the above-mentioned liaison group.

MUBANGA (Zambia) said that in developing countries it is difficult for the industry to provide research institutions with adequate and accurate information and statistical data. He suggested that when aid for fisheries is provided, the government of developing countries should be encouraged to pay attention to this need and that FAO should assist developing countries in this matter.

GUIZADO (Peru) made the point that development of the fishing industry in developing countries depends largely on the leadership of the governments.

BALASINGAM (Malaysia) mentioned the importance of export to developed markets as a stimulus for the development of the fish product industry.

Basic considerations concerning research
The relation of applied research to fundamental research in the work programmes of technological institutes, a crucial problem, was unfortunately only very briefly discussed.

VAN IJSSELSTEIN (Netherlands) pointed out the danger of research institutes becoming "trouble shooters" for the daily problems of industry and not having enough time left to carry out long-term research and development work. He also referred to the possibility of industry being reluctant to ask the institutes for assistance for fear that their trade secrets should become common knowledge.

BURGESS (UK) stated that there has been no sign of such fear among fishery firms in Britain. Experience in the UK showed that firms, as they become larger, tend to employ their own research technologists. Small firms, however, continue to seek the assistance of the research institutes. When a problem first arises, the institutes assist in solving it free of charge, but if there are subsequent requests for help on the same topic a charge is made for the work done.

DOESBURG (Netherlands) expressed the view that research institutes should serve as a source of technological knowledge to help in developing industrial technology. He added that they should also ensure they retain sufficient time to conduct long-term research.

BRAEKKAN (Norway) stressed that any advancement in food technology must be based on knowledge of the raw material. The chemist and biochemist, therefore, must investigate the properties of the new species to be utilized to enable the food technologist to improve on or develop new techniques for production. Such development would need to cover all aspects, from the preservation of the raw material to the finished product. He underlined the importance of fundamental research in product development and quoted Japan as an example.

Part II
PRESENT PRODUCTS AND PROGRESS IN TECHNIQUES

Development in Bulk Preservation at Sea of Small Whole Fish

P Hansen, K B Olsen and T E Petersen

Developpement de la conservation en vrac des petits poissons entiers a bord des navires

Les anchovetas, capelans, sardines, lançons et petits harengs représentent une part toujours plus importante des captures mondiales de poissons de mer. La teneur en protéines et la valeur nutritionnelle de ces petites espèces sont en général identiques à celles des plus gros poissons. Les petits poissons sont en revanche très délicats et très sensibles à la détérioration oxydative, enzymatique et bactérienne. Dans la pratique, il est souvent mal commode de les éviscérer; or les enzymes viscérales peuvent entraîner de grandes pertes d'huile et de protéine au cours de l'entreposage. La détérioration bactérienne est rapide et comporte la formation d'amines, d'ammoniaque, d'hydrogène sulfuré et d'autres substances volatiles malodorantes et toxiques. Les recherches en laboratoire ont montré qu'on refroidissement rapid à 0°C est indispensable à une bonne conservation. Les petits poissons prédominent dans les captures danoises et de très grandes quantités peuvent être prises à chaque trait de chalut. Des méthodes de manutention incorrectes ont été à l'origine de dangers pour la santé, de cas de pollution et d'une diminution qualitative et quantitative de l'huile et des protéines. Les innovations récentes en matière de manutention et de réfrigération comportent l'emploi d'eau de mer réfrigérée ou de glace pour refroidir rapidement les prises importantes. Le poisson destiné à la consommation humaine devrait être entreposé à bord dans de l'eau de mer réfrigérée ou sous glace, alors que le poisson destiné à la transformation industrielle pourrait être égoutté et entreposé à sec. Dans les deux cas, cependant, il est possible d'utiliser le même équipement de pont et les mêmes cales ou cuves à poisson. Il est proposé un nouveau système pour le dosage et le mélange mécaniques à grande échelle de la glace et du poisson.

Progresos en la Conservacion a bordo de Peces Enteros de Pequeña talla en Grandes Cantidades

La anchoveta, el capelán, la sardina, el lanzón, el espadín y el arenque de pequeña talla constituyen una parte siempre mayor de las capturas mundiales de peces marinos. El contenido proteínico y el valor alimenticio de estas especies de pequeña talla son, en general, iguales a los de los peces de mayor talla. Pero los peces pequeños son muy delicados y están muy expuestos a oxidación y a deterioros causados por acción enzimática y bacteriana. En muy pocos casos resulta práctico exviscerarlos y, por otro lado, las enzimas de las vísceras pueden causar grandes pérdidas de aceite y proteinas durante el almacenamiento. Las bacterias estropean el pescado rápidamente, formando aminas, amoníaco, sulfuro de hidrógeno y otras sustancias volátiles maloliontes y tóxicas. Los estudios hechos en laboratorio han mostrado que para conservar estos peces es esencial enfriarlos rápidamente a 0°C. En las capturas de Dinamarca predominan los peces de pequeña talla y en cada redada se capturan cantidades muy grandes. La falta de eficiencia en la forma de tratar este pescado ha sido causa de peligros para la salud y de contaminación y ha reducido la calidad y el rendimiento en aceite y proteinas. Los últimos progresos en materia de tratamiento y enfriamiento se basan en el empleo de agua de mar refrigerada o de hielo para enfriar rápidamente grandes cantidades de pescado. El pescado destinado al consumo debe almacenarse a bordo en agua de mar refrigerada o en hielo, mientras el pescado destinado a fines industriales puede dejarse escurrir y almacenarse en seco. En ambos casos, sin embargo, puede utilizarse equipo idéntico de cubierta y bodegas o tanques igualmente diseñados. Se sugiere un nuevo sistema para dosificar mecanicamente a gran escala la mezcla de hielo y pescado.

DURING the sixties the world catch of marine fish increased from around 30 to about 70 million tons annually. The herring and mackerel fisheries and the new fisheries for small species such as sand-eel, Norway pout, capeline and anchoveta, account for the major part of the catch increases. Most of these fisheries are seasonal and the individual catches are often large. One hundred tons or more may be taken in one haul in purse seining. A catch of about 25 tons in one haul consists of about one million sand-eels. These have to be stowed into the hold rapidly in order to clear the deck for the next catch a few hours later. The conditions allow no gutting or other elaborate treatment of the individual fish, and the catch must be handled in bulk. The rapid development in the catching technique applied in these fisheries has not yet been followed by appropriate developments in bulk handling and preservation on board. Most of the catches, therefore, are landed in a bruised and decayed state unsuitable for human consumption. About one million tons of small ungutted fish are landed annually for the Danish fish meal industry. The health hazards, pollution problems and losses of fish oil and protein are very serious. The Technological Laboratory of the Danish Ministry of Fisheries has, therefore, undertaken studies in order to develop good bulk handling methods for these catches. The ultimate aim is to improve the handling and chilling to such an extent that the fish landed will be suitable for processing into human food.

FISH COMPOSITION

Table 1 shows examples of the average composition of three species of gadoid and three species of fatty fish. The protein content is in all cases about 17 per cent, while the oil content varies greatly.

TABLE 1. AVERAGE COMPOSITION OF WHOLE FISH

	Protein %	Oil %	Water %	Ash %
Gadoid species				
Whiting—July	16	3	79	3
—November	17	1	78	3
Blue whiting—July	17	5	77	3
—November	17	2	76	3
Norway pout—July	15	7	73	2
—December	18	9	69	3
Fatty species				
Herring—July	18	13	69	2
—November	17	8	72	3
Mackerel—July	18	10	71	2
—November	18	10	70	2
Sand-eel—June	17	8	72	2
—August	17	7	74	2

The viscera show great seasonal variations in quantity and composition. The guts of Norwegian herring make up 10 per cent of the total weight in the summer, but less than 2 per cent in the winter when the fish approach their spawning season and do not feed (Baalsrud 1951). The liver is often used as a lipid depot and may contain 75 per cent or more of oil (Lovern 1962). This is the case with the gadoid species, which contain very little oil in the flesh. The fatty species contain oil in the viscera as well as in the flesh. The subcutaneous lipids may easily oxidize in contact with air. Fish viscera contain proteolytic and lipolytic enzymes. The visceral enzymes in herring are found to be much more powerful than those of the flesh (Baalsrud 1951). The proteolysis and lipolyses leading to "belly burst" and weight loss during storage of wet whole fish (Table 4) are thought to be caused

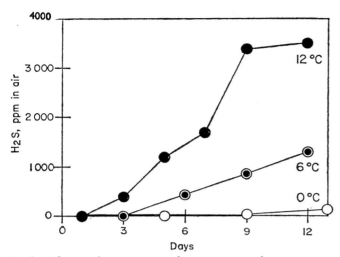

Fig 1   *Influence of storage time and temperature on the concentration of hydrogen sulphide in the air around whole herring being broken*

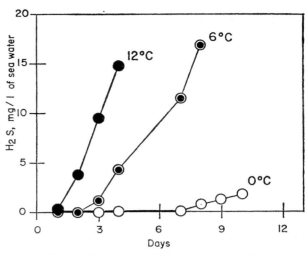

Fig 2   *Influence of storage time and temperature on the concentration of hydrogen sulphide in the sea water around whole herring being tank stored in refrigerated sea water*

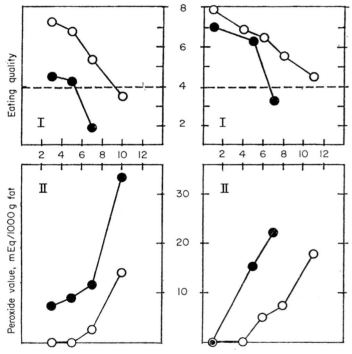

Fig 3   *The storage life of stake net herring iced immediately after catch (○) was 10-12 days. However, herring kept uniced for 4-6 hours after catch (●) had a storage life of only 5-7 days. The peroxide values show that only the former herring had a definite lag phase as regards peroxidation*

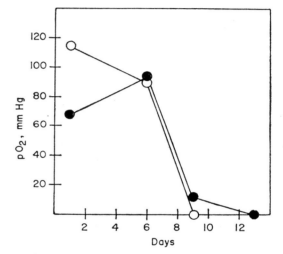

Fig 4   *Influence of storage time on the oxygen pressure around whole herring stored at 0°C. The herring were packed in polyethylene pouches with (●) or without (○) evacuation*

by the visceral enzymes. It is difficult, however, to disentangle the autolysis from the effect of bacterial enzymes. Bacteria are found in the guts and on the skin and gills of fresh fish. During storage they multiply and invade the flesh and other tissues. The bacterial metabolism causes formation of volatile bases and acids, including hydrogen sulphide (Figs 1 and 2).

HANDLING

During handling and storage the number of bacteria will increase greatly if the catch comes into contact with dirty

utensils, deck, and fish hold surfaces. Poor hygienic conditions may be expected to increase the danger of formation of bacterial toxins during subsequent storage at temperatures above 5°C (Cann *et al.* 1965). Close contact between wet fish and dirty wooden surfaces is known to give rise to rapid formation of hydrogen sulphide even at ice temperature (McLean and Castell 1960). Exposure of the catch to sun and wind will increase the rate of subsequent oxidation of fish surfaces. The effect of such exposure is probably insignificant in the case of large catches which are rapidly stowed in the fish hold. On smaller vessels, however, catches may remain unprotected on deck for several hours. In such cases the exposure will significantly reduce their storage life (Fig 3) (Anon. 1963).

STORAGE CONDITIONS

Influence of air

Bulk storage means storage at a high density. Fish may be stored in refrigerated sea water (RSW) in the ratio of

4:1, i.e., a density of about 800 kg of fish per 1 m³ of tank volume. Similar or higher densities may be obtained in bulk icing or in bulk storage without any chilling medium. In all cases of bulk storage in full containers it is characteristic that the quantity of air or oxygen initially present around the fish is very limited. Investigations both in the laboratory and on board show that the composition of the air around wet fish, enclosed at high density, changes, the oxygen gradually being replaced by carbon dioxide (Anon. 1970).

Figure 4 shows the change of the oxygen pressure of small quantities of water enclosed with whole wet herring in polyethylene pouches and stored at 0°C. Although polyethylene does allow some penetration of oxygen, a drastic fall in the oxygen pressure occurred by the end of the first week of storage. The bacterial count at the same time exceeded 1 million per gramme, and the depletion of oxygen appeared to be caused by the bacterial metabolism. The change from aerobic conditions during the first week to anaerobic conditions during the second week of storage will influence bacterial growth and metabolism, the growth rate being smaller in the second week. Fat oxidation and rancidity, which may start in the first week, stagnate after the change to anaerobic storage conditions. The depletion of oxygen shown in Fig 4 is thought to be typical of the bulk storage at 0°C of wet whole fish in full containers with limited access of air. An early change to anaerobic conditions is seen when the fish are stored in RSW in tanks with complete exclusion of air.

Table 2 shows the change in the partial oxygen pressure in sea water packed with whole herring in the ratio of 1:4 and stored in closed 25-litre tanks at 0°, 6° and 12°C, respectively. The oxygen of the tank water is depleted in less than 1 day at 12°C and in less than 1 week at 0°C.

TABLE 2. OXYGEN PRESSURE IN MM HG

Storage temperature	0°C	6°C	12°C
	(mm)	(mm)	(mm)
After 1 day of storage	23	21	0
„ 2 days of storage	18	7	0
„ 3 days of storage	17	0	0
„ 7 days of storage	3	0	0

The atmosphere around industrial fish bulks stored at ambient summer temperature in the holds of Danish fishing vessels has, in many cases, been found to show low oxygen and high carbon dioxide pressures and to present health hazards to the fishermen and the unloading crews involved. Several fatal incidents and a large number of faintings have been recorded (Dalgaard *et al.* 1972).

Influence of storage temperature

The temperature of bulk stored whole fish landed in Danish harbours varies between 0° and 20°C. Fish landed as food fish rarely show temperatures above 10°C, while industrial fish often exceed this in the warm season. The Technological Laboratory of the Danish Ministry of Fisheries has investigated the storage life and changes of whole fish of different species at 0°, 6° and 12°C. Since the occurrence of fatalities great emphasis

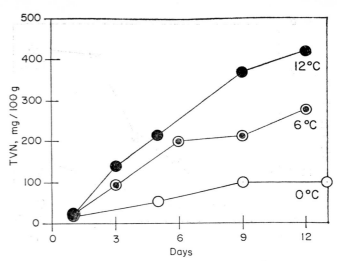

Fig 5 *Influence of storage time and temperature on the contents of total volatile base nitrogen, TVN in whole herring*

has been laid on health aspects. The fatalities in Denmark appear to be due to the replacement of oxygen by carbon dioxide, but it is thought that some incidents abroad were due to lethal concentrations of hydrogen sulphide in the atmosphere around industrial fish. A special technique was developed to measure the emission of hydrogen sulphide from whole fish (Anon. 1971). Figure 7 shows the amount of hydrogen sulphide given off by 1 kg of herring to 1 litre of air. It is seen that lethal concentrations are reached after four days at 12°C and after eight days at 6°C, while the concentrations remain small for more than two weeks when the herring are stored at 0°C. Figure 2 shows the concentration of hydrogen sulphide in the tank water of 25-litre tanks, in which four parts of whole herring were stored with one part of sea water at temperatures of 0°, 6° and 12°C, respectively. These laboratory findings have been supported by the results of large-scale tests in the Danish industrial fisheries. After five days storage of Norway pout in bulk in the fish hold, hydrogen sulphide was emitted from fish stored at 15°C but not from fish stored at 0°C with ice. In practice, hydrogen sulphide will be emitted from unchilled fish both during holding at sea and at unloading. Since hydrogen sulphide is highly

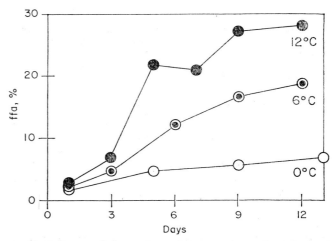

Fig 6 *Influence of storage time and temperature on the contents of free fatty acids in the oil of whole herring*

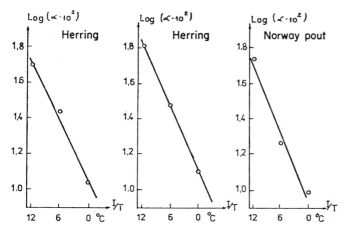

Fig 7   The protein loss during storage of whole fish is probably mainly due to autolysis caused by the digestive enzymes. The protein breakdown is expected to follow a 0-order chemical reaction. This theory agrees well with the findings. At a given temperature, the loss of protein is a linear function of storage time, and the logarithm to the loss per day (α) is a linear function of I/T (°k^{-1}). This figure shows the logarithm to the daily protein loss (α) at three temperatures (0°, 6° and 12°C), for herring caught at different times of the year and for Norway pout. It is interesting to note that the slopes of the straight lines are the same for different species. This indicates that the same enzymatic systems are involved in the autolysis

volatile it is not suitable as an index of the quality of landed fish. Ammonia and volatile amines do not escape as readily as hydrogen sulphide from whole fish and may be used as a quality index. Figure 5 shows the measurements of total volatile base nitrogen in extracts of minced samples of whole herring stored at 0°, 6° and 12°C, respectively. A steady increase is found at all temperatures, but the increase is much faster at 12° and 6°C than at 0°C. The content of free fatty acids in the oil shows a similar spoilage pattern (see Fig. 6).

The storage temperature has a very pronounced effect on the weight loss from whole wet fish in bulk. Table 3 shows the results of laboratory tests on the weight loss from herring and Norway pout stored at 0°, 6° and 12°C.

TABLE 3. DAILY LOSS OF WEIGHT DURING BULK STORAGE

Storage temperature	0°C	6°C	12°C
	%	%	%
Herring	0.3	0.6	1.2
Norway pout	0.4	0.8	2.8

The material lost, the so-called "blood water", contains about 10 per cent protein matter and some oil. While the loss of oil from herring is moderate (Anon. 1971), it is excessive from Norway pout stored at 12° or 15°C (Anon. 1972). Recent Danish tests in connexion with industrial fishing have shown a very drastic effect of iced chilling of Norway pout (Table 4). In the case of gadoid fish, such as Norway pout, the "belly burst" and the subsequent loss of the entrails mean the loss of most of the oil originally present.

Figure 7 is concerned with the temperature effect on the protein loss from herring and Norway pout.

TABLE 4. LOSSES DURING 6 DAYS OF STORAGE ON BOARD

Storage temperature	0°C (iced)	15°C (uniced)
	%	%
Weight loss	6	27
Relative loss of oil	6	74
Relative loss of protein	2	14

CHILLING AND CHILLED STORAGE

The importance of temperature in the bulk storage of wet whole fish. Food fish as well as industrial fish should be chilled to 0°C as soon as possible after catch. In the case of food fish this temperature should be maintained by storing them in RSW or with ice until landing. Industrial fish, i.e., fish intended for fish meal manufacture, may be drained and stored dry after the initial chilling, provided that the fish temperature does not exceed 5°C at landing.

Special techniques are required for the rapid bulk handling and chilling of large catches. The development of such techniques in Denmark is based on the use of ice or RSW or both. In all cases it is necessary that the catch should be chilled immediately. The drainage of melt water, or the sea water circulation, is blocked if the fish soften or break due to delay in chilling. In the case of freshly caught fish, drainage or circulation is possible through fish layers of several metres of thickness (Anon. 1971). It is important, however, that a large part of the bottom of the hold or tank should be perforated. The hold or tank should in all cases have smooth surfaces easy to maintain and clean. The influx of heat should be reduced by appropriate heat insulation of the entire hold or tank.

Ice chilling

When icing small fish in bulk the chilling rate depends on the thoroughness of the mixing of fish and ice in adequate proportions. About 1 kg of ice suffices to chill 100 kg of fish by 1°C. Layers of fish, 11 cm thick, placed between layers of ice are chilled from 15° to about 0°C in 10 h (Anon. 1971). When fish and ice are mixed very thoroughly, chilling to 0°C takes place within a few hours, which is satisfactory for all practical purposes. Full-scale mechanical icing equipment has been designed for use in the Danish industrial fishery. Trials ashore show it to have a capacity of about 1 ton of fish per min. Figure 8 shows the principles in operating such equipment on board large trawlers, i.e., vessels taking 100 tons of fish or more per fishing trip. The system works according to the following main principles (Anon. 1972, Olsen 1972): Ice is loaded into the forehold of the vessel when in port. In the central gangway, which is initially kept free of ice, a horizontal conveyor (10) is built into the floor. The speed of the conveyor is variable, with a capacity up to 250 kg ice per min. It is covered by a safety grid, lengthwise bars with intervals of 80 mm. The quantity of ice required to chill a catch should be placed on top of the ice conveyor before the catch is taken on board. The catch is emptied into deck pounds (3), which are provided with a perforated bottom in order to drain off surplus sea

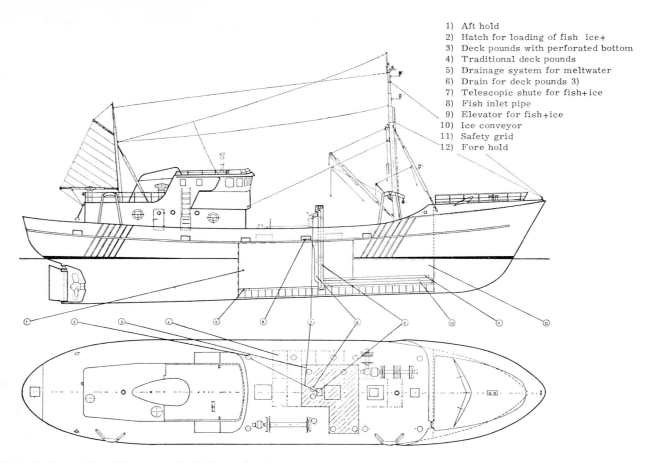

1) Aft hold
2) Hatch for loading of fish ice+
3) Deck pounds with perforated bottom
4) Traditional deck pounds
5) Drainage system for meltwater
6) Drain for deck pounds 3)
7) Telescopic shute for fish+ice
8) Fish inlet pipe
9) Elevator for fish+ice
10) Ice conveyor
11) Safety grid
12) Fore hold

Fig 8   Mechanized ice chilling system for bulk stored catches

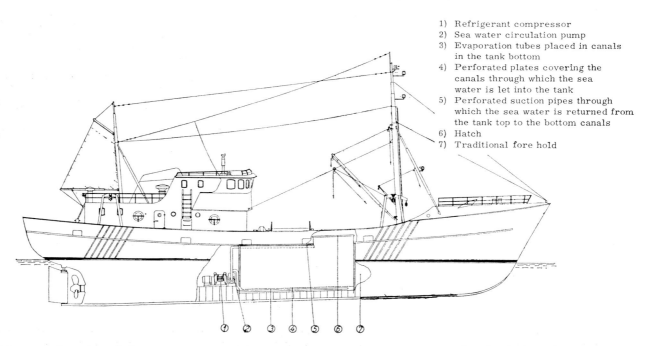

1) Refrigerant compressor
2) Sea water circulation pump
3) Evaporation tubes placed in canals in the tank bottom
4) Perforated plates covering the canals through which the sea water is let into the tank
5) Perforated suction pipes through which the sea water is returned from the tank top to the bottom canals
6) Hatch
7) Traditional fore hold

Fig 9   Danish trawler with three RSW tanks installed in the aft hold. Longitudinal section of the centre tank with installations for circulating and cooling the tank water

water (6). The dry fish then pass into a vertical inlet pipe (8) holding about 350 kg, enough to operate the fish and ice carrying elevator for about 20 sec. The ice conveyor and the fish inlet pipe both empty into the lower part of the elevator (9), with two elevator shovels being loaded with fish and ice in the required proportion. The elevator lifts the mixture of fish and ice to a height of about 2 m above the deck. From this point the mixture falls into a telescopic chute (7), which may be adjusted to lead the mixture into hatches (2) over any part of the fish hold (Olsen 1972). When the system operates with industrial fish, the fish hold can be divided into pounds in the traditional way. Within a few hours after filling the pounds up to deck level, the ice melts and the melt water drains away leaving the chilled fish dry. If more fish and ice are added on top, this should be done as soon as possible and before the fish soften and block further drainage. The system is designed for the chilling of industrial fish, but may operate also with food fish, in which case a surplus of ice should be applied. The design of the fish hold and the method of filling the mixture of ice and food fish into the hold should be modified to avoid crushing and to reduce the mechanical strain on the fish.

Refrigerated sea water (RSW) chilling

According to the present Danish regulations, wet mackerel and herring, which are landed as food fish, should be boxed with ice or stored in RSW. From the fisherman's point of view the RSW technique provides an appreciable saving of labour. The catch can be transferred by means of a pump direct from the net to the tank. In the Scandinavian fishing fleet many purse seiners and a few trawlers have, therefore, installed RSW tanks in recent years. Figure 9 shows an example of an installation combining mechanical refrigeration and forced circulation of the sea water in the tank. Other installations are more primitive, and there are indications that many catches are insufficiently chilled in some RSW tank systems. It would appear that a strict control of the hygiene and temperature of tank-stored fish is essential to safeguard the quality and wholesomeness of the fish.

The main advantages of RSW tank storage are the ease of operation, the rapidity of chilling and the low storage temperature. Crushing of the fish is avoided, because the tank is completely filled with water, which is circulated from the bottom to the top. Oxidation and rancidity of fatty fish can be avoided if air is excluded from the circulation system (Hansen *et al.* 1970). The storage life of whole herring placed in RSW tanks at 0°C is about one week. As shown in Fig 2 hydrogen sulphide appears in the system in the second week of storage. The storage life may be much less than one week if the hygiene and temperature control fails, or if the fish are heavily feeding at catch and, therefore, break up due to the activity of the food enzymes in the gut. Tank-stored fish of low quality are occasionally landed for the fish meal industry which, in such cases, may complain of high water and salt contents in the raw material. The RSW technique, however, may be successfully operated for industrial fish. As mentioned, the sea water may be drained away as soon as the industrial fish are sufficiently chilled if the tanks are heat-insulated sufficiently to protect the bulk-stored fish against excessive temperature rises (Anon. 1971).

References

Anon *Annual Report of the Technological Laboratory of the Danish*
1963 *Ministry of Fisheries*, Lyngby, Denmark, 1962.
Anon *Ibid.*, 1969.
1970
Anon *Ibid.*, 1970.
1971
Anon *Ibid.*, 1971.
1972
Baalsrud, J Proteolytisk nedbryting av sild. *Tidsskrift Kjemi,*
1951 *Bergvesen og Metallurgi*, (5): 71.
Cann, D C *et al* The growth and toxin production of *Clostridium*
1965 *botulinum* type E in certain vacuum packed fish. *The J. appl. Bact.*, 28(3): 431.
Dalgaard, J B *et al* Fatal poisoning and other health hazards
1972 connected with industrial fishing. *Br. J. ind. Med.*, 29:307.
Hansen, P, Ikkala, P and Bjørnum, M Holding fresh fish in
1970 refrigerated sea water. *Bull. int. Inst. Refrig.*, (2):299.
Lovern, J A The lipids of fish and changes occurring in them
1962 during processing and storage. In E Heen and R Kreuzer (ed.) *Fish in Nutrition*, London, Fishing News (Books) Ltd., p. 86.
McLean, N L and Castell, C H Spoilage of fish in vessels at sea.
1960 V. Bilgy fish. In E Hess and G N S Rao (ed.) *Chilling of Fish*, The Hague, Ministry of Agriculture, Fisheries and Food, p. 251.
Olley, J, Ford, J E and Williams, A P Nutritional value of fish
1968 visceral meals. *J. Sci. Fd Agric.*, Vol. 19, May 1968.
Olsen, K Baek Mechanized ice chilling of large catches for subse-
1972 quent bulk storage. *Report to the 3rd Meeting of The European Fish Technology Association, August 14–17, 1972. Technological Laboratory, Danish Ministry of Fisheries, Lyngby, Denmark.*
Petersen, T Ettrup Degradation and loss of oil and proteins from
1972 small ungutted fish during bulk storage at temperatures between 0° and 15°C. *Report to International Congress on Chemical Engineering at the service of Mankind*, Paris, September 2–9, 1972.
Waterman, J J Measures, stowage rates and yields of fishery
1964 products. *Torry Advisory Note No. 17*, (Torry Research Station, Aberdeen Scotland).

Containerized Stowage on Fishing Vessels Using Chilled Sea Water Cooling *G C Eddie and A G Hopper*

Entreposage en conteneurs sur les navires de peche, avec Refroidissement a l'eau de mer réfrigérée

Au Royaume-Uni, on a procédé à des essais en vue de mettre au point une méthode de transport en conteneurs du poisson destiné à la production alimentaire, en utilisant de l'eau de mer réfrigérée pour le refroidissement. Les conteneurs sont des cuves d'aluminium isothermes de 2,1 m³ qui peuvent être remplies à bord des bateaux

Almacenamiento de pescado a bordo en depositos con enfriamientos por agua de mar refrigerada

En el Reino Unido se han hecho experimentos de transporte de pescado para la producción de alimentos en depósitos, utilizando para refrigerarlo agua de mar fría. Los depósitos aislados son de aluminio, de 2,1 m³ de capacidad, que pueden llenarse a bordo y transportarse a las fábricas por carretera.

de pêche et transportées par la route jusqu'aux usines de transformation.

La plupart des travaux ont été axés sur la manutention du hareng en raison de la nature particulière de l'industrie harenguière, où les opérations se déroulent dans des conditions telles, qu'en comparaison avec la mise en caisses et la mise sous glace du poisson, l'emploi d'eau de mer réfrigérée a fortement amélioré la qualité des arrivages de poisson dans les usines.

En soi, le système des conteneurs présente des avantages pour la manutention en mer aussi bien qu'à terre, mais, dans leur conception actuelle, les navires de pêche ne sont pas facilement adaptables à l'emploi de conteneurs et il faut prévoir une certaine réduction de la capacité. On étudie actuellement de nouveaux plans d'aménagement de bateaux de pêches utilisant des conteneurs.

La mayoría de estos trabajos se han concentrado en la manipulación del arenque, debido al carácter especial de esta industria, donde las condiciones de trabajo son tales que el empleo de agua de mar fría ha permitido mejorar notablemente la calidad del pescado que llega a las fábricas, respecto al antiguo sistema de transportarlo en cajas con hielo.

El sistema de depósitos facilita la manipulación tanto a bordo como en tierra, pero el diseño actual de las embarcaciones pesqueras no se adapta fácilmente a su empleo y es de esperar que se reduzca algo la capacidad de aquellos. Pronto tendremos nuevas embarcaciones pesqueras con depósitos.

With the present growth of container handling for freight transport it is natural that the fishing industry should also consider adopting the system in some form and see what benefits can be obtained. The Industrial Development Unit of the British White Fish Authority have made a study of the problem, carrying out extensive field trials in association with two other organizations, the Herring Industry Board and the Torry Research Station of the Ministry of Agriculture, Fisheries and Food. The work so far has been mainly concerned with herring for human consumption which, because of the marketing practices in the United Kingdom and a certain dissatisfaction with the present methods of handling, became a natural choice for the study.

PRESENT METHODS OF HANDLING HERRING

Currently most herring for food are packed into 4-stone (30 kg) boxes with about 11 lb (5 kg) ice. This is done aboard the catching vessels which are relatively small, 65 to 82 ft (20 to 25 m) length overall, and not equipped for freezing or chilling. These boxes are transferred from the fishing grounds to the processing factories. The main food fish processing factories are concentrated in the northeast of Scotland. The fishing grounds change with the seasons and so do the ports of landing. The time of keeping the fish on the fishing vessel is only 25 per cent of the total time from catching to processing, which is about 40 h or so. The remaining time is spent in unloading and overland transport, and in the inevitable delays which exist at the quayside and factory. The processors have become concerned at the sometimes poor quality on receipt at the factory, due to inadequate icing and exposure to high temperatures during the various stages of transport, and also to damage caused by crushing in the boxes. It was felt that a solution to the problem lay in the use of chilled or

FILLING HATCH
DISCHARGE HATCH
ALUMINIUM CONTAINER
50 MM. INSULATION
FIBREGLASS OUTER JACKET
DOUBLE SKINNED ALUMINIUM BASE INSULATION FILLED

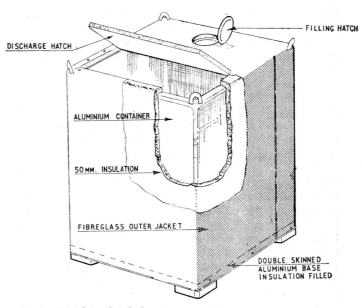

Fig 2 2.1 m³ insulated aluminium container

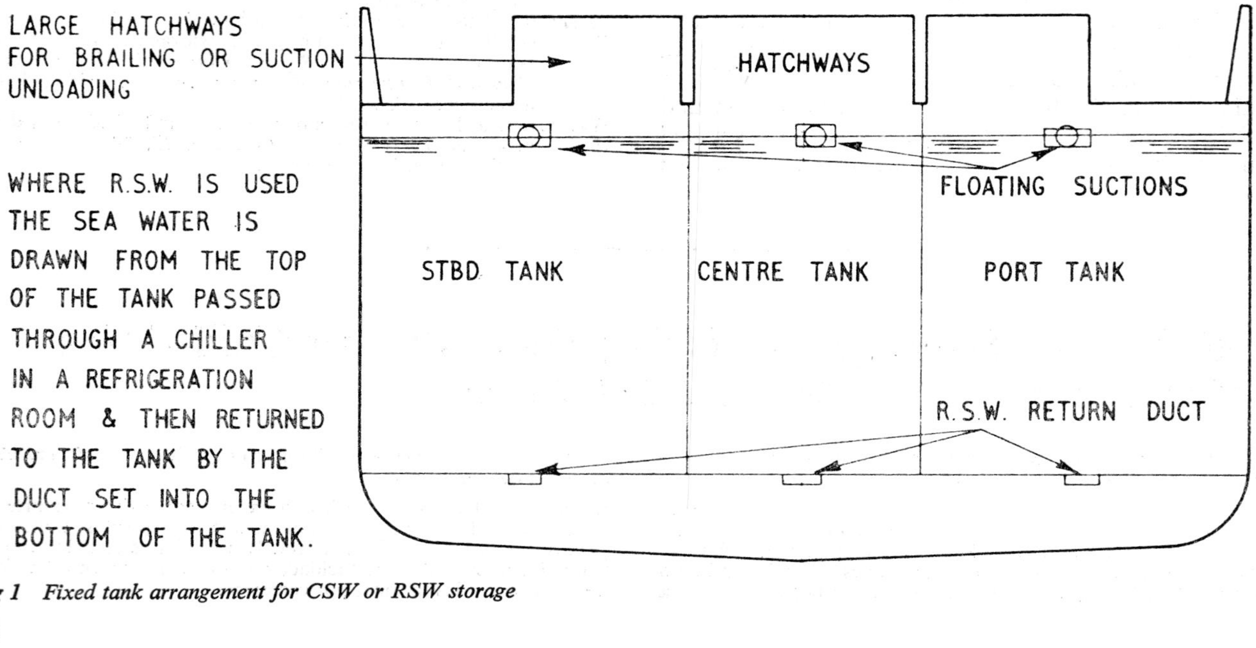

LARGE HATCHWAYS FOR BRAILING OR SUCTION UNLOADING
HATCHWAYS
WHERE R.S.W. IS USED THE SEA WATER IS DRAWN FROM THE TOP OF THE TANK PASSED THROUGH A CHILLER IN A REFRIGERATION ROOM & THEN RETURNED TO THE TANK BY THE DUCT SET INTO THE BOTTOM OF THE TANK.
FLOATING SUCTIONS
STBD TANK
CENTRE TANK
PORT TANK
R.S.W. RETURN DUCT

Fig 1 Fixed tank arrangement for CSW or RSW storage

Fig 3a

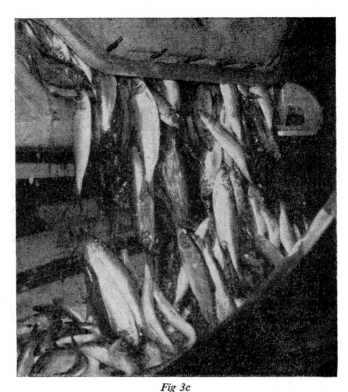

Fig 3c

Fig 3 Discharge sequence using tilt unit

Fig 3b

refrigerated sea water. Chilled sea water (CSW) we define as sea water chilled to about 0°-1°C by the simple addition of fresh water ice. Refrigerated sea water (RSW) is chilled to about −1°C by means of mechanical refrigeration. Both methods are in common use for storage on board fishing vessels in other countries for such species as herring and salmon. In all designs so far the accepted method has been to subdivide the vessel into fixed longitudinal tanks, see Fig 1. This method, whilst being quite suited to vessels which unload directly into a factory, is not so effective in the United Kingdom where there are long road journeys to be made, for which

the fish have to be boxed and iced. With these factors in mind it was decided to experiment with a system in which the fish would be held in the same container and the same cooling medium from catching to processing.

DEVELOPMENT OF THE CONTAINER SYSTEM

It was decided to use chilled sea water as there was a readily available source of ice at the ports and, obviously, it would have been difficult to link the containers to an external refrigeration system either on board or ashore. A standard aluminium transport container of 2.1 m³ (74 ft³) capacity (Fig 2) was selected but modified to suit the particular duties. These modifications included the provision of an insulated outer covering and special filling and discharge arrangements. The containers are placed in the fishroom at the start of the voyage. Each hold at this time 450 kg (1,000 lb) ice. When fishing commences the containers are charged with 500 l (110 UK gal) of sea water and the herring run directly into the containers through a deck scuttle. Each container holds 1,350 kg (210 stone) fish. To ensure that the entire contents of the container are at the same temperature they are agitated by compressed air. On arrival in port the containers are lifted directly on to road vehicles and transported to the processing factories. The vessel can then be equipped immediately with more containers. At the factory, the container, when its contents are required for processing, can be placed in a tilt unit and the contents decanted into a dewatering trough which allows the fish to be admitted to the production line. The tilt unit operation is shown in Fig 3.

TRIALS WORK

Herring

Since a main objective was improving quality on arrival at the processing plant, much work has been done by Torry Research Station on the quality of the herring, using samples from a series of trials carried out between January 1971 and January 1972 by commercial fishing vessels and the research vessel *Sir William Hardy*.

White fish

Stowage of white fish (by which is meant in the United Kingdom demersal species such as cod and haddock) has also been studied. A totally different marketing structure exists in the white fish industry and most of the fish is processed at the port of landing so that long overland transport delays are not part of the problem. The need for the development of such a system is consequently not so important for this fishery, but since the same vessel may be engaged in the herring fishery and the demersal fishery at different times, there is obvious interest in the applicability of the system to demersal species.

RESULTS

Quality results from herring trials

The quality of the containerized CSW herring was compared by Torry Research Station with that of herring stowed and transported by normal boxing and icing practice. It will be appreciated that the intrinsic quality of herring changes with season and fishing grounds. For instance, at certain times of the year when the oil content is high, it is extremely difficult to maintain the herring in good condition. The most popular food product made from herring is the kipper which is a smoke cure. Kippers account for 80 to 90 per cent of herring food products and there is a substantial export market. (See Table 1 for results of kipper production trials, also showing summer and winter oil content of the herring.) In the British industry the most rigorous test of quality is the ability to produce good quality kippers from the fresh herring. The fresh herring are first split along the back by machine and then brined and smoke cured. After passing through the splitting machine, the herring are graded first and second quality according to texture and appearance. Torn or rough kippers and those with split bellies are rejected. The poor results experienced with heavily iced fish on Trial B possibly are accounted for by the bruising effect from crushed block ice used.

On Trial B a number of fish from all three treatments had burst belly walls from autolysis and only sound fish were presented to the splitting machine. The proportions of fish suffering from burst belly walls were as follows:

CSW	13%
Boxed normally iced	41%
Boxed heavily iced	21%

The maximum holding time in these trials was 80 h but holding times of up to 125 h have been tried on other occasions. The safe holding time will vary with the conditions of the fish at the time of catching. All the major processors who have received CSW container fish en-

TABLE 1. KIPPER PRODUCTION TRIALS

	Machine split %	Machine rejects %	First quality %	Second quality %	Kipper rejects %
Trial A					
Winter Herring Oil Content 4–7%					
(i) *36 h after catching*					
CSW	95	5	90	5	0
Boxed normally iced	94	6	84	10	0
Boxed heavily iced	97	3	91	6	0
(ii) *60 h after catching*					
CSW	99	1	97	2	0
Boxed normally iced	98	2	94	4	0
Boxed heavily iced	99	1	95	4	0
Trial B					
Summer Herring Mean Oil Content 21%					
(i) *80 h after catching*					
CSW	100	0	79	19	2
Boxed normally iced	95	5	51	29	15
Boxed heavily iced	90	10	42	39	9

Torry Research Station also measured peroxide value, salt content and water content and carried out taste panel assessment on Trial B. The results are shown in Table 2.

TABLE 2. PEROXIDE VALUE, SALT AND WATER CONTENT AND TASTE VALUES

	Peroxide value	Salt content %	Water content %	Taste max. 5.0
Trial A				
(ii) *60 h after catching*				
CSW	0.14	0.60	75	—
Boxed normally iced	0.71	0.18	75	—
Boxed heavily iced	0.13	0.13	74	—
Trial B				
(i) *80 h after catching*				
CSW	0.20	0.39	61	4.1
Boxed normally iced	0.20	0.21	62	3.5
Boxed heavily iced	0.10	0.23	60	3.7

dorse the Torry results given above but in addition are attaching considerable importance to the reduction in bacteria counts by as much as ten times when the fish is stored in CSW instead of boxes. Cod and haddock have been stored in CSW up to six days with satisfactory results. No firm conclusions can be drawn from the limited trials and more work is planned for 1973.

OPERATIONAL RESULTS

As far as herring for human consumption is concerned, the benefits to quality through using CSW are apparent. Additionally, the containers provide some operational advantages over the boxing system and one notable disadvantage. The work for the crew in loading the vessel on the fishing grounds is substantially reduced by the container method. The crew have simply to pour herring through the deck scuttles into the containers without the need for icing or packing in boxes as at present (Fig 4). Each container requires 4 min loading

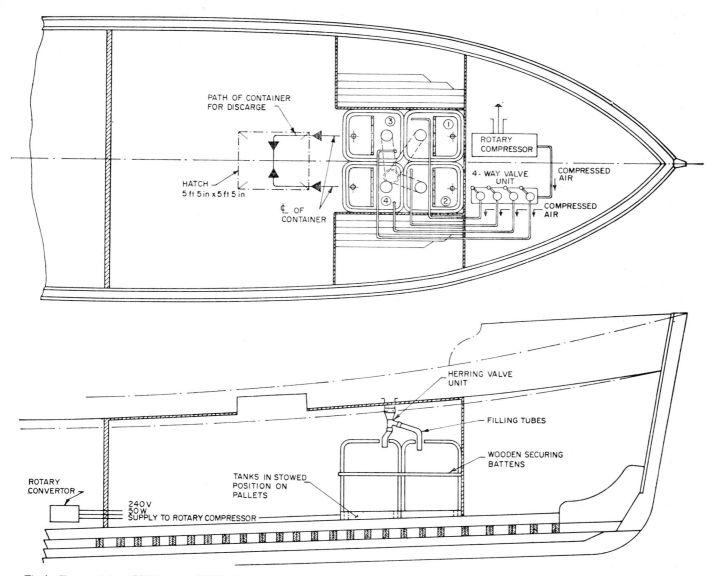

Fig 4 Four container CSW system. MFV Ajax

time, which corresponds roughly to the rate at which fish can be taken aboard from the net. Probably the most significant advantage to the crew is the reduced time and effort in unloading the vessel. The present method of unloading boxes or bulk fish in baskets is very tiring and time-consuming. With containers, only 3 crew are required, compared with the full crew of 8 for the normal methods, and unloading rates are increased from 7.5 tons/h to 24 tons/h. With transport in boxes it is necessary to avoid too much handling of the fish so the road vehicles must be available at the quayside when the vessels are ready to land. Inevitably, this leads to delays and considerable congestion at the quayside. Since containers are relatively easy to handle by crane or fork truck, a planned collection could be made daily from ports allowing the transport organizations to operate in a more efficient manner. As each container is insulated and the fish held in an efficient cooling medium, the safe holding time from catching to processing can be accurately predicted. It is known that this will be greater than in orthodox practice. Present methods preclude the buyer from purchasing fish on Friday for processing on

the following Monday and consequently overtime must be worked at the processing plant at the weekend to clear any remaining raw material. Few factories are therefore able to mount a production operation on herring on Mondays because the vessels are not at sea catching fish on Saturday or Sunday. The new system could be used to allow production on Mondays, thus avoiding the difficulties and expense of weekend working. Since the industry is geographically scattered, the control of boxes is difficult, utilization is low, and losses have been a constant source of discontent for many years. Whilst containers will be subject to the same amount of movement it is believed that they will be far easier to control and that losses will be very small. It is proposed eventually to set up a container pool responsible for washing, servicing and returning the containers to the ports of landing. The notable disadvantage is that the use of containers will reduce the carrying capacity of the vessels. This is not an unexpected problem and all naval architects will be aware that the modern container vessel is much larger than a conventional cargo ship of the same deadweight. With the fishing vessel the reduction in stowage efficiency is much more acute because of the tendency to design very fine hull forms, i.e., with a block coefficient of less than 0.50. In the average 25 m (82 ft) length overall herring trawler the capacity for containers is only about 60 per cent of that for fish stowed in 30-kg boxes. Little can be done with existing vessels or indeed whilst vessels continue to be built along the same lines. Some lost space can be recovered by a mixed stowage of containers and boxes but this is not an ideal situation and inevitably a new design of container trawler must be developed. The White Fish Authority are currently working on design studies of various vessel types which achieve a more efficient stowage factor but do not interfere with the vessel's primary function of catching fish or its sea-keeping ability.

CONCLUSIONS

A system has been developed in which fish for food production is transported from the fishing grounds to the processing plants in chilled sea water in portable containers. This system has been shown to be practicable for the British herring fishery and results in a number of significant operational advantages. These may be summarized as improved quality, a higher proportion of good quality fish products and rationalization of handling between the fishing grounds and the processing plants. Some penalties on carrying capacities must be accepted with existing designs of vessels.

The most impressive result from the point of view of the industry has been that herring stored in this manner are of superior quality to herring of the same type stored by the conventional method of icing in boxes. Very soft fish having high oil content have been of acceptable quality after a storage period of 87 h, and firmer fish have been kept for longer periods. A limited amount of work has been done on the quality of white fish stored in CSW but whilst holding periods of up to six days have given acceptable quality more work has to be done. The structure and marketing methods of the white fish industry do not appear to readily benefit from containerization.

Latest Results in Technology of Preserving and Handling Small Pelagic Fish for Food and Feed

A Mjelde and N Urdahl

Donnees recentes sur la Technologie de la conservation et de la manutention des petits poissons pelagiques destines a l'alimentation humaine et animale

Les auteurs passent brièvement en revue les problèmes associés à l'entreposage en vrac du poisson et à son maintien dans un état acceptable aux fins de transformation en huile et en farine. Ils décrivent les diverses méthodes utilisées pour conserver le poisson entreposé ou, tout au moins, pour inhiber sa détérioration, en particulier l'emploi de plusieurs conservateurs chimiques. Bien que la recherche de nouveaux agents chimiques de conservation se poursuive, les auteurs soulignent que seuls le mêthanal et les nitrates, ou des mélanges de ces substances, se sont jusqu'ici révélés efficaces dans la pratique industrielle.

Resultados mas recientes en la Technologia de la conservacion y manipulacion de peces pelagicos pequeños para la alimentacion humana y para piensos

En este documento se examinan sumariamente los problemas de mantener el pescado almacenado a granel en condiciones aceptables para su elaboración por la industria de aceites y harinas de pescado. Se describen los distintos métodos utilizados para preservar el pescado almacenado, o por lo menos para impedir su deterioro, incluido el empleo de distintas sustancias químicas preservativas. Si bien la búsqueda de nuevos productos químicos preservativos continúa, los autores señalan que sólamente el formaldehido y el nitrito, o combinaciones de ambos, han resultado hasta ahora de uso práctico en la industria.

Winter capelin are caught off the north coast of Norway from January to March when the fish are in their spawning period and are not feeding. This means that they have a low content of digestive enzymes so that spoilage is mainly due to microbiological activity. The landed capelin are stored in bins and tanks in quantities of several thousand tons. This method creates anaerobic conditions in the mass, except for the surface layer. Measurement in the blood-water phase has shown that the oxygen content is low after a relatively short time of storage (<0.1 ppm). The bacteria living under these conditions must, therefore, be able to use anaerobic metabolisms for their energy production.

SPOILAGE

Large numbers of bacteria have been isolated during storage and identified after a model of Shewan et al. (1960). They are all facultative anaerobic organisms and most of them belong to three different types. Type A, which is enterobacter, is usually dominant and accounts for more than 90 per cent of the total when the viable count reaches its maximum. Types B and C belong to the geni *Aeromonas* and *Vibrio*, respectively. They seem to reach their maximum at a somewhat later stage than type A. Figure 1 shows some typical changes that take place during storage of winter capelin under anaerobic conditions. The spoilage pattern may be divided into four phases.

In the lag phase there is little or no bacterial growth and no increase in viable count as the bacteria are adapting themselves to their new environment. They are present on the skin and the gills and it is from here, at the end of this phase, that they start to penetrate the fish. The spoilage activity during this period is low. There is only about 10 to 20 per cent reduction of trimethylaminoxide (TMAO) to trimethylamine (TMA) and no, or little, NH_3 is produced. The temperature is nearly constant. The length of this phase (starting from the catch of the fish) depends much on the temperature. For example, it will last for 1 to 2 days at a temperature of 3° to 4°C. It should be emphasized that the raw material in this phase is in the best condition for the manufacture of high-quality meal and oil.

The exponential phase lasts 1 to 2 days, with active bacterial multiplication. The total viable count increases

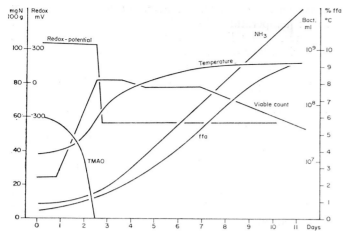

Fig 1 Typical changes taking place during anaerobic storage of unpreserved winter capelin. (ffa = free fatty acids)

from about 5×10^6 bacteria/ml to about 3×10^8 bacteria/ml of blood water. Type A bacteria grows most rapidly with a generation time of 5 to 8 h in temperatures of 2° to 5°C and, at an early stage, becomes dominant. The other types also grow in varying degrees. Figure 1 shows that TMAO is quantitatively reduced to TMA, with the temperature increasing several degrees to the maximum increase per day at the end of the phase. There is some NH_3 production and the start of a rise in free fatty acid. The raw material is, however, still in an acceptable state at the end of the phase. Changes in the fish result from the metabolic processes of the developing bacteria. The substrates for growth are primarily low-molecular weight sugar compounds and, to some extent, lactic acid. The main sugar is ribose produced by conversion of nucleotides, but there are also some hexoses produced by autolytic glycolysis (Kjosbakken 1970; Tarr 1966). It seems now to be well documented (Watson 1939, Tarr 1954, Strøm 1971, Larsen 1971, personal communication) that the bacteria oxidize these substrates, with TMAO acting as a final electron acceptor. This is an energy-providing process similar to the well-known anaerobic respiration with sulphate or nitrate as electron acceptors. The main products of the process are, in addition to TMA, acetic acid and CO_2.

The maximum viable count is reached about the time TMAO is completely reduced to TMA. However, recent work indicates that there is bacterial growth after this time. It has been demonstrated (Fig 1) that quite close to this point, when TMAO is fully reduced, there is a change in the physical condition of the raw material. The redox potential drops sharply to a strongly reducing level. The proposed explanation of this phenomenon is that the bacteria change their metabolism from an anaerobic respiration with TMAO as acceptor to a fermentative one. The energy for continued bacterial growth must now be provided by pure fermentation of residual sugar and probably also of other compounds, such as amino acids.

The following period is called the stationary phase because the viable count has reached its maximum (and sometimes slightly decreases). It is, however, not really stationary because types B and C (*Aeromonas* sp. and *Vibrio* sp.) grow to a maximum in this phase. Since the total viable count does not increase, the number of

type A (the enterobacteria) must decrease. Recent results have shown that types B and C may sometimes outnumber type A in phase 3. Small-scale laboratory experiments have shown that, after a few days of phase 3, type A may completely disappear as types B and C reach a level above 10^8 bacteria/ml. We do not know the reason why the bacterial population sometimes so changes its composition. However, it can be said that the spoilage of fish becomes increasingly due to types B and C as storage continues. The production of NH_3 and the hydrolysis of fat to produce free fatty acids (ffa), which are two of the most unwanted reactions from a preservation point of view, are strong in this and the following phase. NH_3 production is so great that most of it must originate from degradations of aminoacids. As much of this NH_3 is stripped off during processing, there is a loss of protein.

During the decline phase the bacterial count decreases about one order of magnitude. Temperature reaches a maximum, about 5° higher than the starting temperature of the fresh fish. However, NH_3 production continues far into this phase and the ffa increases because of produced extracellular bacterial lipases.

AUTOLYSIS

We have mainly discussed pelagic fish caught in the spawning season, with low digestive activity in the intestine. The changes in the bulk-stored fish are, therefore, mainly caused by micro-organisms. In other seasons the autolytic processes may be more important. This autolysis is caused by enzymes, both from the fish meat and from the digestive tract. The digestive enzymes, proteases and lipases are probably the most important cause of decomposition, especially when the fish have been feeding. The raw material may, in severe cases, be partly "dissolved", and this may cause problems in processing. It should be processed as soon as possible and, consequently, the bacterial decomposition may be of less importance. However, it should be emphasized that the bacterial load of such fish is higher than in non-feeding fish. In addition to bacteria on the surface of the skin and gills, there will usually be high numbers in the digestive tract. The fish are usually caught in the warm season and the higher temperature speeds up spoilage.

METHODS OF HANDLING AND PRESERVATION

What can be done to keep the raw material in an acceptable state until processing? As the cause of much of the decomposition is micro-organisms, it is wise to prevent contamination at all stages. The fish-holds, for example, should be clean before being filled with fish, and transport carriers and tanks and bins at the factories should be cleaned before use because residues of old fish have a very high bacterial count and are often in an active state. Such contamination may start and accelerate decomposition.

The growing rate of bacteria and the reaction rate of enzymes depend on temperature. A reduction of temperature will extend both the lag and growth periods (phases 1 and 2). Roughly speaking, a reduction of temperature by 5° to 6°C will halve the rate of biochemical reactions

TABLE 1. FISH PRESERVATIVES AND PRESERVATION METHODS IN USE OR OF POSSIBLE INTEREST

Preservative method	Comments
Raw material for FPC:	
ice	possible storage time for winter capelin (2° to 5°C) is increased 59 to 100 per cent with 5 per cent ice added.
ice combined with K-sorbate	
RSW	gives meal with a relatively high
RSW combined with K-sorbate and/or CO_2	concentration of NaCl. High concentration of CO_2 has a bacteriostatic effect (Karsti and Grønmyr 1970).
NaCl	relatively high concentration is necessary (> 3 per cent). This gives a whole meal with a high salt content.
Raw material for fish meal:	
formaldehyde	high amounts only moderate may reduce effect when digestibility of used alone the meal.
hexamethylenetetramine	
Na-nitrite	very effective in combination with formaldehyde.
Na-benzoate	useful in combination with
K-sorbate	formaldehyde or hexamethylenetetramine.
Na-metabisulphite	moderate effect.

TABLE 2. LIST OF CHEMICALS TESTED FOR PRESERVING FISH

Tried recently on winter capelin:

formic acid
acetic acid
propionic acid
citric acid
lactic acid
succinic acid
fumaric acid
α – keto – glutaric acid
hydrochloric acid
isopropanol
neomycin (flavomycin)
chlorotetracycline

⎱ tried alone and in combination with formaldehyde

Tried earlier on different types of herring:

sulphuric acid
formic acid
boric acid
borax
urea
hydroxylamine
Na–hydrogen–sulphite
$CaCl_2$
Benzene

and extend possible storage time by about 100 percent. This rule may be used in the temperature range 1°C to 20° or 25°C. Many of the common spoilers of fish are not able to grow in temperatures above 20° to 25°C. The autolytic enzymes and extracellular bacterial enzymes remain active, however, at a considerably higher temperature. Surprising reactions may occur around freezing point. Stimulation of some enzymatic reactions and inhibition of others may take place. Stimulation may cause unwanted reactions. Many enzymes can exist at lower temperatures but with decreasing activity. For instance, many lipolytic enzymes function at $-20°C$. Bacteria will grow at a temperature as low as two degrees below freezing. Reduction of temperature is a good method for preventing rapid decomposition and keeping fish acceptable for the production of fish protein concentrate (FPC) for human consumption. Cooling must be effective. For instance, sufficient ice ought to be mixed with the fish to obtain the wanted temperature decrease. Cooling by mechanical means, as in refrigerated sea water (RSW), is another method. External cooling of bulk-stored fish is of limited effect because of the low heat transfer capacity of the raw material while deep-freezing is economically prohibitive.

Added in sufficient amounts, many chemicals are effective for inhibiting spoilage but most of them have to be used in such high amounts that they reduce the quality of the product, therefore, they are not acceptable. This quality reduction may be due to unwanted changes in the nutritional components or undesirable (or unknown) effects of residual elements on the consumer. The ideal preservative should be able to inhibit the development of bacteria and stop the action of autolytic enzymes. No single preservative has all the desired qualities so combinations of preservatives or of preservatives and cooling, usually offer a better alternative. The application of nitrite and formaldehyde is an example. They act synergistically. The small amounts of nitrite would be of limited value if it were not for the simultaneous addition of formaldehyde which destroys most of the bacteria present in the fish at capture. Some general conclusions may be drawn from Norwegian experience with nitrite and formaldehyde. It is most important that they are used with absolutely fresh fish because, if bacteria have started to increase, they are very difficult to check. Indeed, they may even metabolize the preservative itself (nitrite can be used by many bacteria). Another reason is that extracellular enzymes (proteases and lipases) may already have been produced and may continue to be more or less active even after the addition of preservatives. Higher temperatures, due to bacterial growth, also reduce the effect of late addition of preservatives. Raw material in which there is considerable autolytic activity is more difficult to handle. This is because it takes a relatively long time for the preservatives to pass into the skin and flesh where the enzymes are located. Such diffusion of preservatives is slow and some may even be absorbed at the surface layers of the fish. In such cases, cooling is best (Petersen 1971). Many chemicals have been tested for bulk preservation of fish. Tables 1 and 2 summarize the conclusions of older experiments with herring and more recent work with capelin, and show that only a few preservatives are of practical value and, of these, only two are being put to practical use in the fish meal industry in Norway.

References

KARSTI, O and GRØNMYR, O *Report from the Norwegian Fisheries*
1970 *Research Laboratory.* No. 119/70.
KJOSBAKKEN, J *Lic. techn. thesis.* The Technical University of
1970 Norway, Trondheim, Dept. Biochemistry.
PETERSEN, T E *News Summary IAFMM,* (31):12–33.
1971

SHEWAN, J M, HOBBS, G and HODGKIS, W *J. Appl. Bacteriol.*, 1960 23:379.
STRØM, A *Lic. techn. thesis.* The Technical University of Norway, 1970 Trondheim, Dept. Biochemistry.
STRØM, T *News Summary IAFMM*, (31):78–92. 1971

TARR, H L A *Bacteriol. Rev.*, 18:1–15. 1954
TARR, H L A *J. Fd Sci.*, 31:846. 1966
WATSON, D W *J. Fish. Res. Bd Can.*, 4:252–280. 1939

Initial Treatment of Some Fish Species Caught in the Indian Ocean   *V P Bykov*

Traitement initial de quelques especes de poissons captures dans l'ocean Indien

Le document décrit les résultats d'une étude sur les modifications *post mortem* observées chez les poissons de l'océan Indien. Cette étude, faite en 1966, a porté sur des poissons capturés dans la mer d'Oman, le golfe du Bengale et la mer des Andaman. Les résultats ont montré que, pour obtenir des produits de qualité optimale à partir de ces poissons, il convient de congeler ces derniers avant l'apparition de la *rigor mortis* et de les parer (enlever la tête, les nageoires et les viscères) au lieu de les fileter.

Tratamiento inicial de algunas especies de peces capturadas en el Oceano Indico

En este trabajo se describen los cambios que se producen en los peces del Océano Indico después de la muerte. El estudio se realizó en 1966 con pescado capturado en el Mar de Arabia, la Bahía de Bengala y el Mar de Andaman. La conclusión a que se ha llegado es que para obtener a partir de estos peces un producto de la mejor calidad posible es preciso refrigerarlos antes de que se inicie el *rigor mortis* y limpiarlos (dejar los cuerpos sin cabezas, aletas y vísceras), en vez de cortarlos en filetes.

Over the last decade a number of technological studies of the fish caught in the Indian Ocean have been made by the USSR, mainly by the All-Union Research Institute of Marine Fisheries and Oceanography (VNIRO) and the Azov-Black Sea Research Institute of Marine Fisheries and Oceanography. These investigations were conducted along the following three lines:

(1) Study of the weight composition of different species, i.e., the proportion of the weight of meat, head, bones, skin, fins and viscera, including gonads and liver, the chemical composition of the meat and other body parts, and the organoleptic properties of species likely to be of commercial importance. These investigations resulted in evaluations of the food value of different species and in recommendations as to the most suitable processing method to be applied (canning, drying, smoking, sun-drying, filleting, etc.). Some of the results have been published (Bykov *et al.* 1971, Kovalchuk 1968b, 1969, 1970, 1970b, 1970c, 1970d; Anon 1972).

(2) Development of the processing technology of foods and feeds. For some results, see Anon (1972), Bykov *et al.* (1971) and Kovalchuk (1968a).

(3) Study of changes occurring in the fish after death and their effect on the quality of raw fish. These investigations have been undertaken to find out the optimum conditions for the preliminary treatment of fish on board from the time they are caught until they are sent to be frozen, conditions considered to be very important in view of the high water and air temperatures in the tropical zone of the Indian Ocean.

In the following, studies of changes occurring after death are reported. These were carried out by the author on board the *R/V Akademik Knipovich* during voyages in the Arabian Sea, the Bay of Bengal and the Andaman Sea in January-May 1966 (Bykov *et al.* 1971).

POST MORTEM ALTERATIONS OF MEAT PROPERTIES

So far as the writer knows no data have been published, at least in Soviet literature, on the early *post mortem* alteration in the fish from the Indian Ocean. Yet such data would be of considerable scientific and practical interest in relation to unfavourable temperature conditions during the time after the fish are removed from the net and until they are chilled or frozen. A study was made of the processes occurring in fish when *rigor mortis* sets in and observations were conducted on the changes in the properties of meat during storage. The fish were kept in an ambient air temperature of 28° to 30°C and in refrigerated storage at 0° to 2°C. The following methods were used to observe the onset of *rigor mortis* and the changes in the properties of meat: organoleptic tests and observations on the development of *post mortem* changes; observations on the angle of body curvature showing the degree of muscle contraction (Bykov 1964); tests of elasticity (the ability of a piece of flesh to come back to its original size and shape when no longer exposed to the deforming force) by Nikolaev's tester (Voskresensky 1958); determination of the degree of contraction of a fillet by measuring its size and tracing its contour on paper prior to and after the onset of *rigor mortis;* estimation of the degree of freshness of the fish with the help of a device known as a "Fish Tester"; tests of the water retention capacity of pieces of flesh by centrifuging them for 10 min at 1,500 rpm (Golovin and Pershina 1961).

The catches always contained scores of different species but, naturally, though the state of the whole mass of fish was always observed, only one or two species were selected for a comprehensive examination by the methods referred to above. The observations showed that after removal from the trawl fish which had a body temperature of 23° to 28°C died during a 10 to 15 min period. Within the first hour of storage on deck or below in the processing department most of the fish were in the state of *rigor mortis*, and after two hours all the fish were in the state of *rigor mortis*. Table 1 shows the results of observations on the onset of *rigor mortis* in small croakers (*Otolithes argenteus*) and in Japanese besugo (*Nemipterus japonicus*) during storage at 27° to 28°C. After one hour only 2 specimens out of 8 showed no signs of *rigor mortis* while after two hours all the fish examined were in the state of *rigor mortis*. Japanese besugo were found to be in the state of *rigor mortis* within the first hour of storage. The chilling of fish immediately after capture delays the onset of *rigor mortis* considerably. For example, when large snappers (*Aprion micropteris*) were kept at 26° to 28°C, *rigor mortis* occurred in 1h 10 min, while when they were stored in a refrigerator (0° to 2°C) *rigor mortis* occurred in 2 h 20 min. The use of the "Fish Tester" to observe changes in the degree of freshness of croaker (*Otolithes argenteus*), Japanese besugo (*Nemipterus japonicus*), *Carangoides ferdau* and *Hypoprion palasorrah* stored at 0° to 5°C did not yield satisfactory results (Table 1). This shows that in the case of oceanic fishes the instrument is unsuitable for the assessment of the degree of freshness at different stages of storage.

TABLE 1. ONSET OF *RIGOR MORTIS* AND CHANGES IN DEGREE OF FRESHNESS AS MEASURED BY THE "FISH TESTER" IN TWO SELECTED SPECIES FROM INDIAN OCEAN

Weight of sample (g)	Angle of fish body curvature (degree)			"Fish Tester" readings		
	immediately after capture	after 1 h storage	after 2 h storage	immediately after capture	after 1 h storage	after 2 h storage
Croaker						
350	90	15	29	80	78	88
150	90	90	8	82	80	85
150	90	90	8	86	80	85
120	90		7	80	80	65
110	90	12	15	74	72	82
110	90	75	13	75	75	77
95	90	8	12	86	77	48
80	90	8	8	75	73	65
Japanese besugo						
100	90	4	2	70	70	65
90	90	4	8	70	72	48

In *Muraenesox talabon*, *Aprion micropteris*, *Scoliodon sorrakowah*, *Polynemus xanthonemus*, as in the case of freshwater fishes (Bykov 1964), the elasticity of flesh changes sharply when *rigor mortis* sets in (Table 2).

TABLE 2. CHANGE OF ELASTICITY OF FISH FLESH PRIOR TO AND AT *RIGOR MORTIS*

Fish	Elasticity of flesh (%)	
	prior to *rigor mortis*	at the stage of *rigor mortis*
Muraenesox talabon	70.8	44.5
Aprion micropteris	88.3	60.0
Scoliodon sorrakowah	82.7	52.0
Polynemus xanthonemus	80.0	62.0
Average	80.4	54.6

WATER RETENTION CAPACITY

The determination of the water retention capacity of flesh during storage (in terms of amounts of juice separated by centrifuging pieces of flesh) revealed the following:

(1) As *rigor mortis* sets in during the storage of fresh fish the water holding capacity of the flesh goes down; in fish stored at 0° to 2°C (in contrast to those stored at 30°C) the early drop in the water retention capacity of the flesh is followed by a subsequent rise (Figs 1 and 2).

(2) The degree of reduction in the water holding capacity of muscle tissue is related to storage temperatures, with higher temperatures resulting in lower retention capacity. When whole *Aprion micropteris* were stored at 0° to 2°C the maximum amount of juice separated by centrifuging was 8 ml per 100 g of flesh, but when they were stored at 30°C the amount of juice was 12 ml per 100 g (Fig 1). A similar pattern was observed in the case of fillets: the highest amount of juice separated from fillets stored at 0° to 2°C was 14 ml

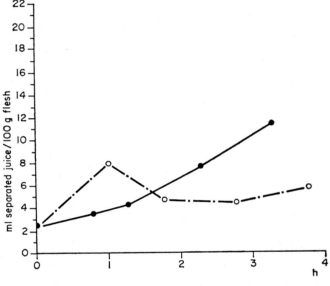

Fig 1 Changes in the water holding capacity of the flesh of whole Aprion micropteris *during storage at 30°C (●——●) and at 0° to 2°C (○·—·○).*

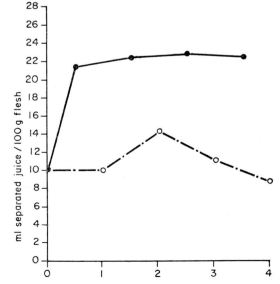

Fig 2 Changes in the water holding capacity of the flesh of fillets of Aprion micropteris *during storage at 30°C (●——●) and at 0° to 2°C (○·—·○).*

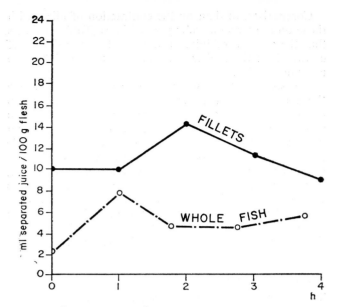

Fig 3   Effect of dressing on the reduction of the water holding capacity of Aprion micropteris during storage at 0° to 2°C.

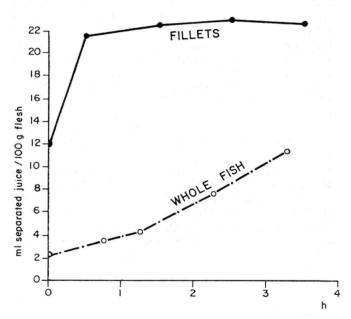

Fig 4   Effect of dressing on the reduction of water holding capacity of Aprion micropteris during storage at 30°C.

while those stored at 30°C yielded as much as 23 ml per 100 g of flesh (Fig 2). Consequently, to obtain a product of the best possible quality and with the highest possible water holding capacity, the fish should be chilled immediately after capture, before *rigor mortis* sets in. This will also reduce losses during subsequent processing. Quick chilling is particularly important when fish are to be filleted.

(3) Changes in the water holding capacity of the flesh during storage depend on the way in which the fish are stored. When they are stored as whole fish, the retention capacity deteriorates to a considerably lesser degree than when they are filleted (Figs 3 and 4). When whole *Aprion micropteris* and their fillets were stored at 0° to 2°C, the maximum amounts of separated juice were 8 ml

per 100 g flesh in the first case and 14 ml in the second (Fig 3). At the storage temperature of 30°C the respective amounts of juice were 11 ml and 23 ml per 100 g of flesh (Fig 4). This seems to indicate a much higher degree of change in the water holding capacity of fillets than in that of whole fish.

The difference in the amounts of juice yielded by whole fish and by fillets was believed to be associated with the muscle contraction at the onset of *rigor mortis*, accompanied by changes in the size of muscles after they are cut away from the backbone. As a consequence, more profound colloidal-chemical changes of flesh properties (due to transformation of proteins of the actomyosin complex) take place in fillets than in whole fish (Bykov 1966). To test this hypothesis observations were made on the contraction of fillets of different species: threadfin (*Polynemus xanthonemus*), butterfish (*Parastromateus niger*), shark (*Scoliodon sorrakowah*), barracuda (*Sphyraena forsteri*), conger pike (*Muraenesox talabon*), captainfish (*Otolithes lateoides*), grouper (*Epinephelus areolatus*), hypoprion (*Hypoprion palasorrah*), scavenger (*Lethrinus nebulosus*) and snapper (*Aprion micropterus*). As soon as the fish were killed the fillets were cut away and their lengths measured. The fillets were left at the ambient air temperature (30°C) until they reached the final stage of contraction in length. Then they were measured again and the contraction was expressed as a percentage of the original length. In addition, the contours of the fillets were traced on paper before and after the contraction to see the changes in their sizes. Results are shown in Table 3 and Figs 5 to 8.

TABLE 3. PERCENTAGE CONTRACTION OF FILLETS OF SELECTED INDIAN OCEAN FISH STORED AT 30°C

| Fish | Contraction (%) | | |
	Sample 1	Sample 2	Average
Threadfin		6	6
Butterfish	10	11	10.5
Shark	11	11	11
Barracuda		11.1	11.1
Conger pike	9.3	13.7	11.5
Captainfish		11	11
Grouper	16	12	14
Hypoprion		14.3	14.3
Scavenger		17	17
Snapper	18	17	17.5

Comparison of data on the contraction of fillets with those on the amounts of separated juice (Table 4) shows that the amount of juice is influenced by the degree of contraction: the higher the contraction, the higher the amount of juice.

TABLE 4. PERCENTAGE CONTRACTION OF FILLETS AND AMOUNT OF SEPARATED JUICE OF SELECTED INDIAN OCEAN FISH

Fish	Contraction (%)	Juice, ml per 100 g of flesh
Threadfin	6	8.3
Barracuda	11.1	9.0
Captainfish	11.5	10.7
Scavenger	17.0	22.7
Snapper	17.5	22.9

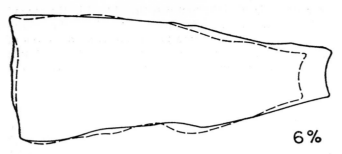

Fig 5 Percentage muscle contraction of threadfin (Polynemus xanthonemus) *at the onset of* rigor mortis. *Shape of fillet before contraction (——) is shown against that after contraction (— —).*

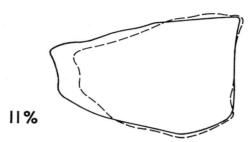

Fig 6 Percentage muscle contraction of captainfish (Otolithes lateoides) *at the onset of* rigor mortis. *Shape of fillet before contraction (——) is shown against that after contraction (— —).*

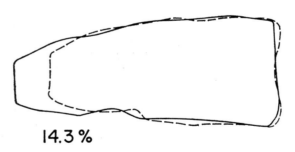

Fig 7 Percentage muscle contraction of Hypoprion palasorrah *at the onset of* rigor mortis. *Shape of fillet before contraction (——) is shown against that after contraction (— —).*

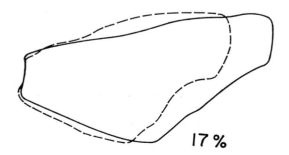

Fig 8 Percentage muscle contraction of scavenger (Lethrinus nebulosis) *at the onset of* rigor mortis. *Shape of fillet before contraction (——) is shown against that after contraction (— —).*

Comparison of data on the contraction of fillets with those on the amounts of separated juice (Table 4) shows that the amount of juice is influenced by the degree of contraction: the higher the contraction, the higher the amount of juice.

The studies of the water holding capacity of muscle tissue and of the contraction of fillets suggest that to obtain a product of the best possible quality the fish should not be filleted but stored whole. However, for a more rational utilization of the edible (flesh) and unedible (heads, viscera, fins, bones) parts it may be required to dress the fish. In this case, it should be dressed, i.e., bodies without heads, fins and viscera. This way permits utilization of most of the offal (heads, fins, viscera) for fish meal production, while the bones, which make up a relatively small part of the body (3.6 to 13.6 per cent depending on the species) are left in the body.

CONCLUSIONS

The study of fish from the Indian Ocean revealed that in their chemical composition and technological properties they did not differ significantly from those of other areas. The exception is *Harpodon nehereus*, which has jelly-like structureless flesh with a rather high moisture content (90.7 per cent) and a low content of protein (8.2 per cent). A typical feature of the catches in the Indian Ocean is the occurrence of many species. This creates difficulties in processing them.

In most species *rigor mortis* sets in within the first hour of capture. It causes considerable reduction in the elasticity and in the water holding capacity of the flesh, the degree of the reduction in the retention capacity being influenced by the temperature to which the fish are exposed and the way of dressing. Flesh stored at the ambient air temperature yields more juice when centrifuged than that of chilled fish; also fillets yield more juice than do whole fish. The fillets cut from the fish immediately after they are killed contract in length by 6 to 17.5 per cent. This high contraction of the muscle tissue is believed to be responsible for the higher amount of juice centrifuged from fillets as compared with that from whole fish.

To obtain a product of the best possible quality, fish should be chilled as soon as they are removed from the net and before *rigor mortis* sets in, and they should be dressed (bodies without heads, fins and viscera) rather than filleted.

References

ANON The technochemical properties of oceanic fishes. Food
1972 Industry Publishing House, 340 p.
BYKOV, V P An objective method of assessing the *post mortem* state
1964 of fish. *Collected papers by the young scientists of VNIRO.* Food Industry Publishing House, p. 190–198.
BYKOV, V P On the *post mortem* contraction of fish muscles.
1966 *VNIRO Bulletin of the scientific and technical information,* (1):136–162.
BYKOV, V P, MAKAROVA, O E, TISHIN, V E and KHVAN, E A Tech-
1971 nological studies on some fish species from the Indian Ocean. *Proceeding of VNIRO,* LXXII:123–142.
GOLOVIN, N A and PERSHINA, L I *Post mortem* mechanical changes
1961 in fish and their role in the preservation of fish by cold. *Proceedings of NIKIMRP,* 1(2):32–33.
KOVALCHUK, G K Maturation of salted products from Indian
1968a Ocean fish. *Rybnoe Khozyaistvo,* (3):65–67.
KOVALCHUK, G K Content of volatile bases in fish from the
1968b Indian Ocean. *Rybnoe Khozyaistvo,* (11):65–67.

KOVALCHUK, G K Some results of the study of the technochemical
1969   properties of teleostomous fishes from the Indian Ocean.
        Rybnoe Khozyaistvo, (10):66–71.
KOVALCHUK, G K The technochemical properties of the yellowfin
1970a   tuna from the Indian Ocean. *Rybnoe Khozyaistvo*, (2):65–
        68.
KOVALCHUK, G K   The technochemical characteristics of the
1970b   bottom fish from the Indian Ocean. *Proceedings of AzCher-
        NIRO*, (29):188–201.

KOVALCHUK, G K The technochemical characteristics of fishes
1970c   from the Antarctic part of the Indian Ocean. *Rybnoe
        Khozyaistvo*, (10):69–72.
KOVALCHUK, G K   The technochemical properties of the bigeye
1970d   tuna from the Indian Ocean. *Rybnoe Khozyaistvo*, (6):71–
        73.
VOSKRESENSKY, N A The technology of salting, smoking and drying
1958   of fish. "Pishchepromizdat", p. 55–65.

The Fishery Products Industries in the Developing World
A Da Costa

Les industries des produits de la pêche dans les pays en voie de developpement

L'auteur du présent document s'efforce de passer en revue la situation actuelle et les perspectives des industries des produits de la
pêche dans les pays en voie de développement, les types de produits
qu'elles fabriquent et leurs méthodes de préparation, ainsi que la
valeur de ces industries pour l'économie des pays intéressés. Etant
donné l'ampleur du domaine sur lequel porte l'examen, on a
groupé les pays en voie de développement en cinq zones de pêche
principales: (1) la région de l'Atlantique Centre-Est au large de
l'Afrique occidentale (COPACE); (2) les eaux intérieures africaines;
(3) l'océan Indien Nord-Ouest (mer d'Oman); (4) l'Amérique latine
(du Mexique à la Patagonie); et (5) l'Extrême-Orient. Un chapitre
est consacré à chacune de ces zones. Le document se termine par
une liste détaillée des produits de certains pays présentée sous forme
de tableau.

**Las industrias de los productos pesqueros del mundo en vias de
desarrollo**

Reseña del estado actual y futuro en el mundo en desarrollo, de la
industria pesquera, sus productos, sus métodos de elaboración, y
su valor en la economía de cada país. Para poder reseñar un área
tan extensa, se dividieron los países en desarrollo en cinco áreas de
pesca principales, a saber: (1) la región de Atlántico centroriental
del Africa Occidental (CPACO); (2) las aguas continentales del
Africa; (3) el noroeste del Océano Indico (Mar Arábigo); (4) la
América Latina (desde México hasta la Patagonia); y (5) el Lejano
Oriente. Se dedica un capítulo a cada una de estas áreas. El trabajo
termina con un cuadro detallado de los productos de algunos
países.

Those countries aware of the value of the fishery resources
are making great efforts to obtain a major share of the
potential fish production. Fish is, however, a highly
perishable food which does not keep for long after it is
caught, particularly in hot climates. This prevents its
distribution and utilization in areas distant from the
catching or landing points if it not properly preserved.
Furthermore, fish caught seasonally or in glut periods
can only be made available for consumption by processing into a product with greater shelf life than fresh, or
even iced, fish. This paper is to provide information on
types of products, their significance to the food economy
of the countries, and the development of the fish product
industries round the developing world, and is based on
statements[1] prepared at FAO's request by the fisheries
authorities of selected countries and on FAO field
reports.

REGIONAL ANALYSIS

For review purposes the developing countries were
grouped in five main fishing areas which have some
similarities in climatic, geographic and socio-economic
conditions.

EASTERN CENTRAL ATLANTIC REGION

The abundant marine fish resources off West Africa,
from the Straits of Gibraltar to the Congo River, have
been intensively exploited by large fishing and processing
fleets from about 15 European, Asian and American
countries. Indeed, more than 50 per cent of the catches
of the whole area have been harvested by such fleets in
recent years. As a result, the productivity of some

grounds has become so low and uneconomic that the
need for proper management of the fisheries in the whole
area has been internationally recognized.

Resource utilization and development of the industry.
The utilization of the catches in the region is indicated
in Table 1. In Morocco, the whole fishery structure has
been determined by the abundance of sardines and
other shoaling pelagic species, which are the basic
material for its long established and rather developed
fish processing industries directed entirely to export
markets. In spite of the abundant marine fish resources
off the coast of Mauritania, not much more than
1,000 t of mullet and seabass are caught by the local
fishermen for domestic consumption. In fact, about
50 per cent of the total Mauritanian fish catch is made
up of freshwater species from the Senegal River
and consumed locally. As a result, the *per caput* consumption in this area averages about 75 kg/year whereas
fish is practically unknown to the people elsewhere in the
country. Mauritania is a peculiar example of unco-
ordinated fishery industries development, with overinvestment in the processing sector. A large fish processing complex has been set up in Nouadhibou (ex
Port Etienne) with modern freezing, salting and drying,
canning and fishmeal facilities for about 300,000 t of raw
material per year while the "domestic" fleet consists
only of three small purse seiners, a trawler and four
lobster boats. The complex, therefore, has to rely on
supplies from foreign vessels fishing in Mauritania's
territorial waters. Senegal's policy in fishery development,
on the other hand, has been to increase fish production
qualitatively and quantitatively, firstly, to provide food
for domestic consumption and, secondly, to earn foreign
exchange. These goals are being achieved through im-

---

[1]Referred to as C.S., followed by the name of the country concerned and the year of publication.

provement in the methods and operations of the artisanal sector and through the modernization of the industrial sector. This has led to the two major successes of the country's commercial fisheries: the integrated tuna fishery and the shrimp fishery. Although the consumption pattern may vary remarkably throughout the country, fish is available in urban and rural areas and consumed at levels roughly double that of all kinds of meat. Artisanal as well as modern industrial processing methods are used in Senegal. In The Gambia, lobster, shrimp, bonga, barracuda and sharks are the most significant resources being utilized by an improved artisanal and processing industry, primarily for export and secondarily to increase the distribution and marketing of such products within the country. Bonga is the species caught and consumed in the greatest quantity. In Sierra Leone, the majority of the fish landed comes from the traditional canoe fishery. Bonga is the main species caught but *Sardinella* (*S. eba*), barracuda (*Caranx* spp.) and mullet are also fished. Fresh fish command the best price, the left-overs being smoked before going stale. In the Ivory Coast more than two thirds of the total catch (74,100 t in 1971) comes from the modern industrial fleet. More than two thirds of the fish are smoked (52,000 t in 1971). Less than 10 per cent of the total catch is canned or frozen, the rest being sold fresh. Abidjan is the major industrial processing centre with a tuna canning plant and a number of large ice, freezing and cold storage plants. The Ghanaian fishery resources are harvested by three fleets: the traditional canoe fleet; the inshore fleet of medium-range motorized fishing vessels; and the deep-sea fleet. The most important resources exploited at present are the *Sardinella*, and mackerels. The abundant tuna resources off Ghana have, so far, been exploited mainly by foreign manned vessels operating under licence. Shrimp resources are currently under investigation for commercial exploitation. In addition, the inland waters of the country, particularly the Lake Volta reservoir, yield some 44,000 t of freshwater fish and molluscs. Being a fish-eating country with a high consumer acceptance for traditional smoked and dried products, and with the demand determined more by what is available than by preference, the *per caput* consumption is remarkably high even in the interior of the country and is, in general, one of the highest in Africa.

About one third of Nigeria's production is from freshwater species caught in the extensive inland waters. The inshore and brackish waters along the length of the coastline of Nigeria provide a seasonal canoe fishery which yields about two thirds of the country's total fish production, mainly bonga and *Sardinella*. In addition, some 54,000 t of frozen fish was landed by chartered vessels of foreign origin. All fish is used for local consumption, except for the small export of shrimp. The general preference is for fresh fish, therefore some of the frozen fish is thawed and marketed as fresh. Over 80 per cent of the fish is smoked (FAO 1970). The pattern of fish production and utilization in the other countries down to the Congo is very much the same with regard to sources, species and utilization.

New products and methods. The introduction of new species and new products in the region has been limited. Smoked bonito (*Orcynopsis unicolor*) fillets are being produced in Morocco but it is too early to evaluate their marketing success. Salted sun-dried fish from Lake Chad in Nigeria has been introduced with Government support, but is considered too expensive, because of the high cost of salt, to compete with traditional fishery products. The quantities produced are, therefore, very small although the product is of acceptable quality, has a longer shelf-life, and is not affected by insects. Wet-salted *Sardinella* and mackerel in barrels are also being reintroduced and test-marketed in Ghana. Some so-called "new products" are no more than variations of existing products groomed to meet particular tastes or special requirements of sophisticated markets. Skinless and boneless sardines and the easy-opening cans introduced by the Moroccan industry are good illustrations. Little has happened to improve the traditional artisanal production and quality of smoked products apart from the introduction of several types of smoking kilns with larger capacities, higher yields and lower running costs. The traditional ones continue, however, to dominate the production. Many modern freezing and cold storage plants, ice factories, distribution cold chains, and a few canneries and fishmeal plants have been set up. With the world demand for frozen tuna and shrimp, refrigeration facilities tend to increase. The SONAFAP plant in Agadir, Morocco, was equipped for the production of solvent-extracted FPC for human consumption but produces extracted fishmeal for animal feed in addition to its bulk production of normal fishmeal. A factory producing fermented fish sauce of the "Nuoc-mam" type, used in the region as a protein-rich additive, was recently established in the Ivory Coast.

Fish inspection and quality control. Fish inspection has not been formally established in the majority of the countries. There is, however, some inspection at the landing places by the Public Health Authorities and the National Fisheries Office in Morocco. The control of the canned fish industry and the inspection of its export products are carried out by the Governmental Export Marketing Office. The Department of Fisheries in Ghana has authority to prevent the sale of spoiled fish for human consumption and the National Standards Board controls the quality standards. In Nigeria, the inspection of the fish landed by trawlers, or imported, is the responsibility of the Federal Ministry of Health while quality control is that of the Nigerian Standards Organization.

Research, training and extension. National facilities for applied research on processing are limited and, with the exception of Morocco, Senegal and Ghana, little or no work has been done in this field. Morocco has research facilities at the Marine Fisheries Institute and at the Canned Fish Research Laboratory of the Moroccan Federation of Canning Industries; experimental work has been carried out at the Fisheries Laboratories of Food Technology Institutes in Dakar, Senegal and in Accra, Ghana, on the improvement of processing and storage methods, with technical assistance from FAO. On-the-job training is still the most common way to acquire the necessary skills in handling and processing. Training in handling and processing technology forms an important part of the "curricula" at the School for Marine Fisheries Administration at Thiaroye, Senegal, for fishery officers at the intermediate and senior levels. This school may eventually become a regional establishment for all French speaking countries of West Africa.

TABLE 1. UTILIZATION OF FISH IN THE EASTERN CENTRAL ATLANTIC REGION

Country	General utilization	Production	Imports	Exports	Total supply	Ex-vessel value of output (U.S. $ million)	Per caput supply (kg/ year)
		1,000 t (live weight)					
Morocco 1970	Food	116.7	—	64.5	52.2	17.0	3.4
	Feed	137.6[a]	—	106.9[a]	30.7[a]	—	—
Mauritania 1970	Food	37.5	—	21.7	15.8	7.0	13.9
	Feed	2.0	—	2.0	—	—	—
Senegal 1970	Food	174.7	—	39.0	135.7	32.0	35.3
Sierra Leone 1971	Food	30.6	7.3[b]	—	37.9	4.3	14.7
Liberia 1970	Food	23.0	3.6	1.0	25.6	6.1	22.2
Ivory Coast 1969	Food	71.0	17.5	3.0	85.5	11.0	17.9
Ghana 1970	Food	187.1	29.6	—	216.7	35.0	24.4
Dahomey 1969	Food	28.0	2.6	0.5	30.1	8.0	11.4
Nigeria 1970	Food	155.8	87.8	0.6	243.0	22.0	3.6
Spanish Guinea 1970	Food	3.8	4.8	0.5	8.1	1.0	27.0
Cameroon 1970	Food	70.8	8.0	2.7	76.1	—	13.1
Gabon 1970	Food	5.1	5.3	0.1	10.3	—	16.6
The Congo 1970	Food	16.2	15.5	0.5	31.2	2.5	28.3

[a] Export fishmeal 1970, 4,500 t
[b] Excludes tuna trans-shipments
Source: FAO 1972

Extension work is carried out within the framework of Governmental Fisheries Institutions, sometimes with foreign technical assistance. Unfortunately, this has not led to general improvement in the artisanal fisheries because the new methods and equipment often involve much higher installation costs than do the traditional ones. In general, the prospective users cannot afford this extra cost, especially if they do not get better prices for the new product.

INLAND WATERS OF AFRICA

The inland waters, composed of large lakes, rivers and swamps, are the major source of fish and fishery products for the landlocked countries as well as for some others, eg, Kenya and Tanzania with extensive marine coasts. Furthermore, man-made lakes are providing new fisheries farther inland, contributing to the improvement of the nutritional pattern of the population of the hinterland.

Resource utilization and development of the industry. Tanzania is one of the largest producers of fish in Africa, total production being about 200,000 t (1971). Of this, only 12 per cent was from the marine fisheries, which are confined to the rather poor inshore waters. Landings are restricted by: lack of infrastructure, irregularity of the catches, and unsuitability of the traditional fishing methods and operations.

The situation in Kenya is somewhat similar. About half of the country's population of about 11 million eat little or no fish, while more than 3.5 million can get freshwater fish cheaper than sea fish. Brief information on fish as a source of animal protein is given in Table 2.

TABLE 2. FISH AS SOURCE OF ANIMAL PROTEIN FOR THE INLAND WATER REGION OF AFRICA

Country	General utilization	Production	Imports	Exports	Total supply	Ex-vessel value of output (U.S. $ million)	Per caput supply (kg/ year)
		1,000 t (live weight)					
Mali 1970	Food	90.0	0.2	20.6	69.6	10.0	14.1
Niger 1970	Food	10.2	0.4	4.0	6.6	1.0	1.6
Sudan 1970	Food	22.0	0.1	0.2	21.9	3.1	1.4
Kenya 1971	Food	35.0	3.4	1.4	37.0	4.1	3.4
	Feed	—	7.0	—	7.0	—	—
Burundi 1970	Food	17.4	1.2	0.5	18.1	1.5	5.1
Uganda 1970	Food	129.0	0.3	1.5	127.8	19.5	15.0
Tanzania 1970	Food	193.7	5.1	25.4	173.4	15.7	13.1
Malawi 1972	Food	43.1	0.6	1.9	41.8	3.9	8.8
Zaire 1971	Food	145.8	66.8	—	212.6	14.6	9.9
	Feed	—	1.5	—	1.5	—	—
Zambia 1970	Food	48.4	23.7	0.6	71.5	4.2	16.5
	Feed	—	24.5	—	24.5	—	—

Source: FAO 1972

Generally, fish processing is still carried out by traditional, often unhygienic and, at times, uneconomic methods, in spite of the success of vigorous fishery administrations with assistance from multi- and bilateral sources, in improving or introducing better techniques to reduce waste, increase returns and produce more wholesome products. Modern industrial facilities are limited to some freezing and cold storage plants, often multi-purpose. Output of frozen fish in Zaire is growing and helping to overcome the problem of transporting fish over long distances.

New products and methods. All fish caught in this area find consumers, including the bony *Haplochromis* sp. and the bitter-tasting *Engraulis cypris* both at present underexploited. Attempts have been made, with FAO assistance, to produce salted and dried products in land-locked countries, mainly to avoid the present heavy losses of smoked and dried products due to insect infestation, but the high cost of salt in the production areas has prevented this development from becoming a commercial operation. The fish processing station of the Department of Fisheries in Uganda is trying to bring about better utilization of *Haplochromis* sp. A major problem encountered in canning *Haplochromis* sp. has been the disintegration of the flesh caused by the extra cooking required to soften the bones. It appears that commercial canning of this species in the foreseeable future will not be feasible. Fishmeal might hold better prospects for development. Experimental work has also been initiated to use *Haplochromis* species to produce powdered products, fish cakes, fish sausages, etc. As a result of the action of the governmental fisheries authorities and the technical assistance received from multi- and bilateral sources, improvements in the traditional processing techniques and equipment have been introduced in some countries with success.

Fish inspection and quality control. The processing of fish, other than by freezing, is done artisanally in this region, essentially in small-scale operations in scattered and often remote fishing villages. Regular fish inspection and quality control, therefore, would not be viable as it would be difficult to enforce it where facilities for proper handling and processing do not exist. However, fisheries personnel carry out periodic checks to ensure that fish is being processed under acceptable hygienic conditions, and assist the fishermen or processors in improving the quality of the products through demonstration of better handling, processing and storage methods. In Tanzania, legislation has already been enacted (Fisheries Act 1970) and the quality standards worked out but it is recognized that their enforcement is not feasible before the planned centralized fish landing and processing sites are established. Tanzania fishery products for export are inspected and approved by the Ministry of Agriculture.

Research, training and extension. Reasonably good facilities for applied research on processing freshwater fish are available in a few countries. The most active is the Freshwater Fisheries Institute in Mwanza, Tanzania, established through bilateral aid from The Netherlands. It also offers training in improved methods of handling, preservation, processing, distribution and marketing. Short courses are also arranged for field staff and fishermen. Training in modern methods of handling, preservation and storage is also given in the fishermen's training centres. In Uganda, the laboratory of the Fish Processing and Marketing Division of the Department of Fisheries is responsible for the introduction of better processing methods and the development of new fishery products. In the latter field, the work has been primarily directed to the utilization of *Haplochromis* sp. The Fisheries Department in Uganda runs also a Fisheries Training Institute where its field workers undergo a two-year course in management and technology, with emphasis on handling and processing. This Institute, from time to time, organizes *ad hoc* courses for artisanal processors, introducing them to new processing developments and equipment. In Zambia, the Central Fisheries Research Institute has been established at Chilanga, with technical assistance provided by the FAO/UNDP project. Work in the Fish Technology Branch of this Institute has been directed to the improvement of the quality and wholesomeness of traditionally handled and processed products and the introduction of light salted, dried or smoked products, mainly to prevent the heavy losses caused by insect infestation. In other countries of this region the applied research facilities in fish processing technology are rudimentary or nonexistent.

NORTHWESTERN INDIAN OCEAN REGION

The coastal waters of the Arabian Sea appear to be potentially very rich fishing grounds, with a great variety of species. The landings of this area already contribute more than two thirds of the total catch of the western Indian Ocean fishing area. Nevertheless, the *per caput* fish consumption in the bordering countries is, with the exception of the People's Democratic Republic of Yemen, Kuwait and Sri Lanka, well below the world average, and the industry's major economic role is not so much to supply animal protein but to earn foreign exchange (Table 3). On the other hand, in spite of the abundance of the marine fishery, the inland waters still supply a good percentage of the landings.

Resource utilization and development of the industry. Landings, both marine and freshwater, are composed of a considerable variety of species. The predominance of a species varies from country to country and is greatly influenced by the fishing methods and operations used, and consumer acceptance and preferences, as well as by the social attitudes to fish and the availability of easy commercial outlets. For a fishing region with a primary productivity comparing favourably with other major upwelling areas of the world, the catches are still modest and, apart from the crustacea (India, Kuwait, Pakistan) and tuna (Somalia), the fisheries are mainly of a subsistence nature. In contrast with the East African countries, where smoked fish is the favoured processed product, the consumer in this area prefers, apart from fresh fish, salted and dried products. In Somalia, consumption of fish is very low and confined to a small sector of the population. Besides tuna, sharks are the major species landed. The tuna catches (mainly yellowfin and skipjack) fluctuate widely. In the People's Democratic Republic of Yemen the predominant species, the sardine, is almost entirely sun-dried on the beaches and sold in the hinterland as fertilizer or animal feed. In some places, sardines are smoked by traditional methods. Considerable quantities of fish are consumed by the coastal population. The first fishmeal plant of the People's Republic of Yemen is being erected, making possible greater utilization of the local sardine stock.

In Iraq, more than 85 per cent of the fish are from inland waters. The bulk of the catch consists mainly of four barbus species. In Iran, the fish come from the two main fishing zones – the Caspian Sea and the inshore waters off the country's southern coast – and are consumed by the domestic market, with the exception of shrimp, sturgeon and caviar and some dried fish, which

TABLE 3. FISH AS SOURCE OF ANIMAL PROTEIN FOR THE NORTH-WESTERN INDIAN OCEAN REGION

Country	General utilization	Production	Imports	Exports	Total supply	Ex-vessel value of output (U.S. $ million)	Per caput consumption (kg/year)
		1,000 t (live weight)					
Somalia 1970	Food	5.0	—	1.7	3.3	—	1.2
People's Democratic Republic of Yemen 1970	Food	40.0	9.3	23.3	26.0	2.4	20.8
	Non-food	75.0	—	—	75.0	—	—
Kuwait 1970	Food	18.0	2.7	7.2	13.5	5.0	18.4
Iraq 1970	Food	23.5	0.2	2.1	17.1	—	2.2
	Non-food	—	5.0ᵃ	—	5.0ᵃ	—	—
Saudi Arabia 1969	Food	29.0	0.2	10.0	19.2	—	3.7
Iran 1970	Food	24.0	0.7	4.5	20.2	—	0.7
	Non-food	—	27.0ᵃ	—	27.0ᵃ	—	—
Pakistan 1971	Food	102.8	—	54.2	48.6	—	0.8
	Non-food	66.5	—	66.5	—	—	—
India 1970	Food	1,617.3	—	70.2	1,547.1	341.0	2.8
	Non-food	128.6	—	—	128.6	—	—
Sri Lanka 1970	Food	141.2	113.2	0.4	254.0	40.0	20.3

ᵃMostly fishmeal; actual weight one fifth of the figure

Source: FAO 1972

are exported. Fish provide very little of the national supply of animal protein, the *per caput* consumption being probably less than 1 kg per year (Table 3). In Pakistan, people are not fish minded, so domestic consumption is only 30 per cent of the total catch, the rest being exported. The consumer prefers freshwater fish, mainly consumed fresh. Elasmobranchs provide the main raw material for fishmeal production.

In India, two thirds of the fish caught are consumed fresh near the point of landing. The greater part of the balance is cured by simple traditional techniques and eaten by the poorer sections of the population. Industrially processed products are mainly for export. Small quantities of sardines and mackerels are canned for sale to institutions and to towns in the northern part of the country. Fishmeal production is seasonal and on a small scale. The utilization of installed capacity in all sectors of the fish processing industry is very low and hampered by the lack of a steady flow of raw material and of profitable markets. Fish in India is, generally speaking, a foodstuff available only to the minority

whose incomes are above average. In Sri Lanka, fish is mainly utilized as food, 90 per cent fresh, with local production supplying more than 50 per cent of the total. Small quantities, especially of the less popular species, are cured, particularly in remote places. The principal product is dry-salted fish. Even with the present improved distribution facilities, there is no indication that the consumption of dry-salted fish is declining, as some experts expected. Industrial-scale operations in this region are mainly for shrimp and tuna. Integrated enterprises (often government-sponsored) have been established with foreign interests and are operating modern fishing vessels, freezing and cold storage plants and, in some cases, canning plants. The products of the latter are mostly exported to developed markets. The average low output of India's fish processing factories, particularly of the canneries, is striking. High production costs hamper utilizing the plants for products of lower unit value. Canning is, therefore, used to pack mainly small shrimp which could not be profitably sold if frozen. Furthermore, the low quality and poor handling and processing practices account for the adverse price differential between products from India and those from some of its competitors in the international market. Compulsory pre-shipment inspection and quality control of products have not yet been able to overcome the problem.

New products and methods. In most of the countries of this region the consumer's preference is for fresh fish. Until the *per caput* consumption of fish is raised substantially, the introduction of new products is likely to be no more than an academic exercise. There are many fish species which could be used in a better and more profitable way than they are at present, as the development work of the fisheries research institutes of India has demonstrated. Improvements in traditional methods of drying, salting, fermenting and smoking have, however, been rather limited. Yet such improvements seem to be the most expedient way to avoid losses due to spoilage and provide products of better quality and nutritional value. Improved fish-curing stations are being set up in different countries, eg, in Somalia, and the People's Democratic Republic of Yemen. In Pakistan, mechanical drying of fish for export is carried out. However, as the plants have been operating at only 40 per cent capacity, the increase in production costs is a constraint to increased trade. As has already been demonstrated in India, when high relative humidity prevents proper drying of salted or unsalted fish, smoking produces a fishery product with better storage life and quality. If cheap fuel is available, the investment required and the production costs should have very little effect on the final price of the product. Acceptance is, however, a matter requiring regional testing.

Fish inspection and quality control. Satisfactory machinery for fish inspection and quality control has not yet been set up in any of the countries of this region. In Pakistan, the Agricultural Marketing Department is responsible for inspection and grading of fish and fishery products, with inspection staff posted at the important production centres. Quality control is carried out by the Marine Fisheries Department, making periodic checks to ascertain that satisfactory handling and processing techniques are followed and that the products conform to satisfactory standards. Pre-shipment quality inspection and laboratory testing of products before export are carried out by these two organizations, which issue certificates of origin and quality. In India, compulsory quality control and pre-shipment inspection of fishery products for export were introduced in 1965 under the Export Act of 1963. The responsibility for implementing them is that of the Central Institute of Fisheries Technology and inspection centres have been established in the eight most important production and shipping areas. Inspection is mostly based on organoleptic and physical characteristics, but bacteriological tests are also made, particularly in the case of canned and cooked-frozen shrimp products. In Sri Lanka, there is legislation to prevent the sale of spoiled and poor quality fish but no effective enforcement. Quality control is exercised generally for export products. The Bureau of Standards, with the assistance of the Ministry of Fisheries, prepares the standard specifications but depends on the Ministry of Fisheries to carry out the quality testing required to issue certificates.

Research, training and extension. Good facilities for both fundamental and applied research in the fields of fish utilization exist in India, particularly at the Central Institute of Fisheries Technology in Ernakulam. Elsewhere, facilities for applied research are limited and are available only in the following countries: In the People's Democratic Republic of Yemen, the state-owned Public Corporation of Fish Wealth is responsible for operating the Fisheries Training and Research Centre in Aden, established with bilateral help from the USSR In Kuwait, the Institute for Scientific Research has not undertaken so far any work in the field of fish utilization. In Iran, technological research is, at present, limited to an institute that supports the operations of the Iran Fisheries Company in the Caspian Sea. But plans are well advanced for setting up a similar marine fisheries institute in Teheran. In Pakistan, the Marine Fisheries Department has a technological section with laboratory facilities and staff, concerned mainly with quality control work. In Sri Lanka, some facilities for fish processing development work are available in the Fisheries Research Station of the Ministry of Fisheries. Specific problems from the industry are also usually referred to this station for advice. Adequate facilities for training high-level personnel in improved methods of fish handling, preservation, processing, distribution and marketing in the region are available perhaps only in India where some fishery research institutes and other organizations have modern equipment and are staffed with experienced technologists. Technical training of extension workers, foremen and those at a lower level is given in the region by on-the-job training or by state training organizations. In Pakistan, there is a vocational training institute, including utilization and marketing. A similar school with identical curricula was established in 1970 in Iraq, providing training in fish handling, preservation and processing at a senior high-school level. Iraq also has a programme for sending trainees abroad for advanced academic education and practical training. As already mentioned, in the People's Democratic Republic of Yemen there are some training facilities in Aden. Extension work is usually the task of the technical units of fisheries administrations. In India, an Extension Division

has been organized at the Central Institute of Fisheries Technology. In Pakistan, there is a technological laboratory in the Marine Fisheries Department which is the central organization entrusted with major research activities. In Sri Lanka, the technical staff of the fisheries administration at district level provide information on developments in handling, preservation and processing techniques to the fishery communities and industries.

LATIN AMERICAN REGION

Considerable scope exists in all the maritime countries of the region for exploiting new resources or for a more efficient utilization of some of the existing ones. For the whole region, the average annual consumption of fish is, at present, well below the world average (Table 4). The variation from country to country correlates to a great extent with local availability and comparative cheapness of meat and other food products. There is a generally favourable attitude toward fish consumption but poor handling and preservation, at sea and ashore, often associated with very low sanitary standards and a lack of quality control throughout the processing cycle, inhibit wider consumption and exports.

Resource utilization and development of the industry. In the food-fish sector, regional production has increased at a fairly constant rate to reach some 1.5 million t in 1971 compared with about 0.9 million t in 1961. Most of the countries are self-sufficient in this respect except Brazil and Cuba. The shellfish output has doubled in 10 years. The by-catch of shrimp trawlers may be 90 per cent of the total catch but only the larger and easily marketable species are utilized. Estimates for the quantities discarded by the Mexican shrimp fleet alone are in the order of half a million t per year.

In Brazil, much of the catch is still taken by artisanal fishermen using the traditional craft and gear, particularly in the northern part of the country and in the lower waters of the Amazon. Freshwater fish, which account for over one fifth of the total landings by weight, are important for the food supply of the inland populations. With the exception of crustacea, largely exported, about 95 per cent of the total catch is consumed domestically. Half of it is processed, such as filleted, frozen, canned, salted and dried, in more than 200 plants, mostly located near the main landing points. Non-diversified canned fish production (98 per cent sardines) is mostly for domestic consumption. Some attempts were recently made to explore export markets but, again, quality problems proved a major handicap. Both Uruguay and Argentina are in an exceptionally favourable geographic position relative to the greatest concentrations of Patagonian hake and anchovy. These resources could supply the existing processing facilities around Montevideo and in Mar del Plata. The anchovy catch in Argentina is used mainly for canning and salt curing, while filleting of hake for the fresh-fish trade and for frozen blocks has increased substantially during the past two years. In Peru, the Government is determined to increase consumption by the development of the food-fish industry, including an expanded and efficient distribution and marketing system (Appleyard 1973). Bonito is the basic species in fresh fish marketing (about 30 per cent of the total) and in the canning industry (about 60 per cent). Dogfish is prime fresh fish in Peru and 90

TABLE 4. FISH AS SOURCE OF ANIMAL PROTEIN FOR LATIN AMERICA

Country	General utilization	Production	Imports	Exports	Total supply	Ex-vessel value of output (U.S. $ million)	Per caput consumption (kg/year)
		1,000 t (live weight)					
Argentina 1970	Food	137.5	13.2	18.1	132.6	20.0	5.5
	Non-food	53.7	19.0	—	72.7	—	—
Barbados 1970	Food	4.0	3.0	0.2	6.8	1.3	26.5
Brazil 1969	Food	493.0	143.3	14.0	622.3	98.0	6.6
	Non-food	—	45.0	—	45.0	—	—
Chile 1970	Food	176.5	0.5	40.4	136.6	34.0	13.9
	Non-food	984.5	—	496.5	488.0	—	—
Colombia 1969	Food	57.8	3.8	3.2	58.4	27.0	2.9
	Non-food	—	17.5	—	17.5	—	—
Costa Rica 1971	Food	8.5	2.2	2.1	8.6	3.1	4.7
Cuba 1970	Food	88.4	59.5	26.2	121.7	—	14.2
	Non-food	17.5	88.5	—	106.0	—	—
Dominican Rep. 1970	Food	5.2	34.9	0.5	39.6	—	9.2
Ecuador 1970	Food	60.7	—	20.7	40.0	10.1	6.6
	Non-food	30.8	—	0.5	30.3	—	—
El Salvador 1970	Food	13.7	1.6	5.6	9.7	4.2	2.3
	Non-food	2.9	—	—	2.9	—	—
Guatemala 1970	Food	5.0	1.5	2.3	4.2	2.7	0.8
Guyana 1969	Food	16.6	7.7	4.4	19.9	14.0	20.2
Haiti 1969	Food	2.6	3.9	0.1	6.4	—	1.3
Honduras 1970	Food	3.8	1.8	3.1	2.5	—	1.0
	Non-food	—	2.5	—	2.5	—	—
Jamaica 1970	Food	18.0	47.8	—	65.8	6.3	33.1
Mexico 1969	Food	234.8	2.3	60.0	177.1	75.0	3.5
	Non-food	89.4	265.8	—	455.2	—	—
Nicaragua 1971	Food	9.6	0.5	4.6	5.5	6.7	2.9
	Non-food	—	4.5	—	4.5	—	—
Panama 1970	Food	17.5	5.5	5.0	18.0	8.0	12.3
	Non-food	24.9	—	24.0	0.9	—	—
Peru 1970	Food	265.4	0.1	27.0	238.5	187.0	17.6
	Non-food	12,295.7	—	10,374.5	—	—	—
Trinidad 1970	Food	13.0	8.5	3.1	18.4	6.8	17.5
Venezuela 1971	Food	139.9	2.4	10.7	102.7	30.0	9.9
	Non-food	29.3	161.0	—	190.3	—	—
Uruguay 1971	Food	14.4	0.3	1.7	13.0	8.0	4.8

per cent of the catch is sold as such, but elsewhere in the region, dogfish and similar species are mainly used as raw material for salting and drying. Shad (*Ethmidium* spp.) which stand up to poor handling without much detriment to quality, have become important raw material for canning. Increased quantities of mackerels (jurel, caballa), sardine (*Sardinops sagax*) and, recently, anchoveta are being used successfully for canning. The exploitation of mussels in this area is quite intensive. It is of interest to note that salting and drying has no significance as a fish processing method in Chile and that half of the landings of food-fish species are still used for fishmeal production, while large quantities of anchoveta are consumed fresh. The industrial fishery activities from Ecuador to Mexico are dominated by the exploitation of crustacea and tuna. However, in some countries, the stocks of clupeoids provide raw material for the canning and/or the fishmeal industry. Most of the shrimp landed is frozen for export. Small quantities of shrimp, often of a lower grade, are sold on the domestic market. The diversion of fishery products to satisfy export priorities adversely affects efforts to achieve better levels of nutrition in the area. Selected species from the by-catches of the shrimp trawlers and dozens of different species from the coastal artisanal fishery provide most of the fish for fresh consumption. Consumption varies from as low as 10 per cent in Honduras to as much as 70 per cent in El Salvador. Salting and drying, the only curing method used, has significant importance only in Mexico, mostly for processing sharks, and in Ecuador for preserving the fish surplus in the Galapagos Islands. Colombia has a big inland-water fishery, the production from which is greater in volume and value than the total marine catches.

In Mexico, the abalone as well as the Pacific lobster and the tuna stocks along the coast of Baja California, supply the specialized processing plants in the area. The stocks of Pacific hake found in deep waters off this area are not exploited commercially so far. Of the great number of finfish species available, only groupers, snappers, mackerels and sharks are caught in quantities of more than 5,000 t per year. The steady increase in sardine catches is being used mostly for fishmeal in an attempt to reduce the present imports of this commodity. The fish resources in the Caribbean and Gulf of Mexico consist of a large number of intermixed species. The most valuable fishery in the region is for shrimp. Spiny lobster is more widely distributed in the Caribbean area and is commercially more important than shrimp.

The stage of development of the fish processing industry in Latin America differs greatly depending on whether it is producing for export or for consumption in domestic markets. Thus, there is to be found the contrast between plants in old, unhygienic and badly kept premises, using obsolete equipment requiring excessive labour, and those which are efficiently managed enterprises in functional and hygienic premises, using modern machinery, equipment and facilities. While technology and know-how have been adopted from developed industries, particularly from the USA and Europe, deficiencies in application are common. In many countries (e.g., Ecuador, Mexico, Costa Rica, Brazil, etc.) attention has been mainly centred on development of export-oriented industries, chiefly frozen crustaceans, tuna and, to some extent, fish fillets. Fish production for local consumption has been somewhat neglected so that the import of canned and cured products, and of fishmeal, is often needed. The efficiency and productivity of the majority of plants in the region are limited by the lack of regular supplies of good quality raw material. On average, less than 50 per cent of the installed capacity is utilized. Handling on board and ashore also requires great improvement throughout Latin America. While imported dry-salted fishery products are readily accepted throughout the region, the local use of the poor quality fish for salting restricts their consumption to the lowest income sector of the domestic market. But, with the present export demand for frozen fish, particularly fish fillets and blocks, Latin American producers are becoming aware of the need to take care of the fish as soon as it comes out of the water.

New products and methods. The industries in Latin America are now attempting to diversify production, and are making various additional products with locally available raw materials. For instance, in Mexico, they are trying to introduce frozen fish products (fish sticks, cakes, steaks, fillets, etc.) but lack of attention to quality has adversely affected these efforts. In Cuba, the production of frozen precooked lobster for export has been started, and in Venezuela production of fish sticks for the domestic market has been successful. It has been reported that only plant capacity limits further expansion. Canned blue crab (*Callinectes sapidus*) and frozen scallops (*Pecten* sp.) are also new Venezuelan products, the entire production being exported to the USA. Peru, with the assistance of FAO, is carrying out the most comprehensive and commercially oriented programme for the introduction of fishery products in both the domestic and export markets. They are applying existing technology to the anchoveta and other underutilized food-fish species. Products for all levels of consumer incomes are being developed. Fish separators are being used in some countries, although still on an experimental basis. Salting of anchoveta in the Mediterranean style, for example, has been introduced and export trials, including canned fillets in vegetable oil, have been successful. Two demersal species, locally known as cod and "rock salmon" (*Polyprion oxigeneios*), are being caught in Chile in increasing quantities. They have a firm texture and good acceptance. A paste is produced from very small shrimp. Headed and gutted fresh hake and frozen hake and "jurel" are vacuum-packed and have found good consumer acceptance. Fish sausages are already on the market. Peru and Chile are active in the production of milk replacers for weaning calves. Hexane extraction of conventional fishmeal is used in Peru while the enzymatic method developed by IFOP (Instituto de Fomento Pesquero), with fresh hake as raw material, is used in Chile. It should be pointed out that multilateral and bilateral technical assistance to Latin American countries will increasingly need to be used to assist in distribution and marketing and for introducing new techniques and processing methods to exploit underutilized species and for establishing quality control systems. The present shortage of other sources of animal protein in Chile has increased the importance of fish and fishery products in human nutrition. In view of the high demand, insufficient attention is being paid to product quality. The improvement of the fish handling and the establishment of quality control systems, both needed for the expansion of the domestic and export markets of food fish, are the main objectives of an FAO-assisted fisheries project recently set up in the country. In Uruguay, too, the emphasis in FAO technical assistance is on improving the efficiency of operations and market development.

Fish inspection and quality control. Throughout Latin America, with perhaps the exception of Cuba, fish inspection and quality control are somewhat ineffective even where they have been officially established. In many countries, sanitary regulations are often treated as simple recommendations, rarely followed and never properly enforced. Many of the regulations are archaic and do not meet modern requirements. Quality standards for export products (frozen shrimp, frozen fish and fillets, etc.) are not strictly observed due to the present high demand and short supply. There are practically no quality grading standards for domestic markets. Fish inspection in the majority of the countries is the responsibility of the institutions charged with inspection of other food products but often not carried out. To help Latin American countries in the establishment of a satisfactory fish inspection and quality control service, FAO is convening regional seminars and training centres.

Research, training and extension. Facilities and trained personnel for undertaking systematically applied research in fish utilization are somewhat limited in Latin America. There is the Technology Branch of IFOP in Chile, set up with the assistance on an FAO/UNDP project, and the Research and Development Section of the Department of Industry in Cuba. Elsewhere, greater emphasis has been placed on technological investigations, the work being mostly carried out by universities, state fishery institutions and private organizations. There has been little coordination of these efforts and dissemination of the results to industry. Only Chile, Peru and Mexico (at the Technology Institute of Monterey) provide formal education in processing technology at university and vocational levels. As the processing centres of the marine fishing countries of Latin America are scattered along the lengthy coasts of two oceans, well trained extension workers could be most effective in providing assistance but the lack of technically skilled staff, the shortage of funds and, sometimes, the unresponsiveness of industry, adversely affect the situation. The effectiveness of such extension work has been demonstrated perhaps only in Chile and Peru. In Cuba, all improvements are tested in one plant and, if found effective, are introduced into all the other plants as far as applicable.

FAR EAST REGION

The fisheries of the developing countries of the Indo-Pacific region, particularly in the West Central Pacific, are characterized by a considerable diversification. Fish protein is much cheaper than any other form of animal protein in the Far East and the *per caput* consumption (Table 5) is well above the world average. In most of the countries the bulk of the catch is consumed by the domestic market but there are valuable exports of frozen crustacea and tuna to developed markets. There are also exports of traditionally salted and dried or fermented products, particularly within the region. Aquaculture

TABLE 5. FISH AS SOURCE OF ANIMAL PROTEIN IN FAR EAST COUNTRIES

Country	General utilization	Production	Imports	Exports	Total supply	Ex-vessel value of output (U.S. $ million)	Per caput consumption (kg/year)
		1,000 t (live weight)					
Australia 1970	Food	101.6	62.3	24.8	139.1	70.0	11.2
	Feed	1.0	133.0	—	134.0	—	—
Burma 1970	Food	432.0	5.4	—	437.8	87.5	15.9
Hong Kong 1970	Food	120.2	82.7	13.3	189.6	51.1	48.1
	Feed	3.3	14.5	2.0	15.8	—	—
Khmer Republic 1969	Food	170.0	—	7.5	162.5	44.0	24.4
Indonesia 1970	Food	1,233.0	3.3	16.0	1,220.3	—	10.2
	Feed	16.0	—	—	16.0	—	—
Republic of Korea 1970	Food	817.0	4.3	96.2	725.1	211.0	22.4
	Feed	—	57.0	—	57.0	—	—
Malaysia 1969	Food	317.3	68.2	119.1	266.4	93.0	25.2
	Feed	54.8	85.5	4.5	135.8	—	—
New Zealand 1971	Food	63.4	7.2	22.8	47.8	23.3	16.7
	Feed	0.3	—	—	0.3	—	—
Philippines 1970	Food	989.8	125.5	2.0	1,113.3	279.0	30.7
	Feed	—	(62.5)	—	(62.5)	—	—
Singapore 1971	Food	10.5	111.8	31.5	90.8	7.2	43.0
	Feed	4.7	147.0	46.0	132.7	—	—
Thailand 1970	Food	917.7	15.2	41.0	891.9	219.0	24.5
	Feed	677.4	—	—	677.4	—	—

has reached a high degree of development and fish from ponds and brackish waters make a significant contribution to production. Seaweed, as human food, is characteristic in this region and the Republic of Korea's cultivated production of laver and dulce seaweeds, for example, amounted to 46,000 tons in 1971.

Resource utilization and development of the industry. More than 2,000 species of marine and freshwater fish occur in and around the countries of the region but only a few dozen support substantial commercial fisheries. Those of economic value are mostly listed in the Appendix. Fish is preferred fresh or alive. Boiled and fermented fish are important products in certain countries (FAO 1967). Since processing such products depends on the quality of salt, they are adversely influenced by the low quality of the solar salt commercially available in the region. Apart from Australia and New Zealand and, perhaps, the Republic of Korea, successful industrial-scale operations in processing are to be found only in the crustacean, mollusc and tuna business and in some fin fish species now in high demand in international markets. For this reason, the fish freezing industry is the most developed in every country and the one operating at or

near to acceptable standards. In spite of the large amounts of suitable species available, the production of canned fish has not expanded much in most of the countries, even as an import replacement item, because of the high price of tinplate, the outdated equipment in the plants, and the low quality of products. These factors, allied to poor management, were the major causes of the failure of this industry in the Philippines, where a regular supply of fish and an outlet for the final products were never assured.

The apparent success of fish canning enterprises in Malaysia seems to indicate that the alternatives for expansion of the industry in the developing countries of this region could be:

(a) A complete vertical integration with a well developed fishing activity – as is the case of the tuna plant associated directly with tuna transhipment at Penang;

(b) An association with the production of other canned food products – as with the plant in Perak which processes fish principally during gluts and is flexible enough to be able to process other food products, such as meat, fruit and vegetables.

Processing of fish by traditional methods is usually a cottage industry carried out with restricted facilities, limited investment in equipment, and little hired labour. But it plays an important socio-economic role by providing full or part-time employment and food in remote areas. The production of salted and dried fish products is, however, declining in Malaysia, the Republic of Korea, and in other countries, where improved infrastructure makes possible the expansion of fresh fish distribution and growth of the frozen fish trade. Nevertheless, traditionally-processed products will remain important for several decades to come and the main effort should, therefore, be to improve the processing techniques, the quality of the raw material and the final cured product, and its shelf life. Small fishmeal plants have been set up in many locations of the region, primarily to utilize fish processing wastes and "trash fish". In Thailand, it has developed into a major industry, utilizing about 20 per cent of the country's total catch, in an excessive number (76) of very small and inefficient plants. There is no recovery of oil or stickwater (FAO 1973).

New products and methods. Many of the so-called new fishery products being processed and marketed are produced by the application of well known techniques to a specific type of resource in order to: (a) present a familiar fish or a commodity in a novel or more convenient way; (b) replace established import items; and (c) produce export products in high demand. An example is the making of "katsuobushi", mainly for the Japanese market. This is done in Thailand by using fillets of bonito (Euthynnus affinis) and in Indonesia by using skipjack. In Australia, snoek fish fingers are being used to replace similar imported commodities. In New Zealand, ghost shark has been successfully used as a substitute for the seasonal elephant fish for "fish and chips". In the Philippines, smoked soft bone "bangos" (Chanos chanos) is in great demand because all the product can be eaten without danger by children. FPC, prepared on a pilot scale from lizard fish and sharks, is being used in school feeding programmes. In addition, fish sausage, manufactured from tuna, tulingan sharks and marlin, has been introduced recently. In the Republic of Korea, besides fish sausage, ready-to-eat fish sticks and various spiced products, e.g., chipped cuttlefish, fried fish fillets and laver chips in convenience packs, are on sale in supermarkets.

The technique developed in Indonesia for salting jellyfish has general interest. Sun-drying plays a key role in traditional fish processing in the region although climatic conditions are in many instances unfavourable. Many attempts, therefore, have been made to use mechanized drying equipment. Thus, in Thailand the traditional method of making boiled-dried shrimp has been replaced by the use of artificial drying and separation of the shell. Artificial dryers are also used to dry squid during the rainy season. Liquid nitrogen freezing is being used in Australia to process prawns and scallops for export. Deboning equipment to prepare minced fish has also been introduced and a large-scale fishmeal plant using whole pilchards rather than conventional processing wastes is in operation. In the Philippines, a line for fish sausage production is now in operation. In the Republic of Korea, an automatic smoking system is on trial in oyster canning and filleting machines are being used on board Alaska pollock trawlers. Changes in the pattern of consumer preferences are developing in this region. Although the demand will continue for the traditional products, especially in rural areas, acceptance of frozen fish and other processed seafoods is steadily growing. Traditional preferences for specific types of fish do exist, but vary from country to country. The utilization of species of limited commercial value may be increased through extensive promotion campaigns such as that carried out by New Zealand's Fishing Industry Board resulting in the acceptance of formerly unpopular species.

Fish inspection and quality control. Fish inspection and quality control are still in the initial stages in most of the region and, where legislation exists, it is not properly enforced in some countries due to lack of organization, trained inspectors and funds. In the Philippines, the Bureau of Standards, the Food and Drug Administration and the Meat and Fish Inspection Board of the Department of Health share responsibility for inspection and quality control of fish and fishery products. An attempt is being made in Thailand to establish an inspection service with FAO assistance. Health certification of shellfish products for export is issued by the Department of Medical Sciences. The Fish Technology Laboratory of the Department of Fisheries operates a frozen fish inspection scheme which includes routine plant inspection, analytic control work and sanitary certification of frozen food products, if required. In spite of the existence in Indonesia of specific regulations issued years ago, inspection and quality control up to now have been limited practically to export products, eg, frozen fish and shellfish. The Fishery Technological Laboratory is providing guidance in control procedures and methods. Inspection laboratories have also been set up near the main export points but have only limited equipment. Under the Korean Fisheries Inspection Law, export items are controlled by the Central Fisheries Inspection Section from raw material to the finished product. In Australia, edible fishery products for export must be prepared in establishments registered under the export regulations administered by the Export Inspection Branch of the Commonwealth Department of Primary Industry. Those for domestic consumption are subject to state health and pure food laws. Many improvements need to be introduced throughout the region, mainly in enforcing regulations, in establishing standards and good technological practices, and in providing the necessary tools for handling, processing and inspecting all fish and fishery products.

Research, training and extension. Technological studies of the proper utilization of the large variety of species available in the region may perhaps be carried out only at the following institutions:

(a) the Fish Technology Laboratory of the Department of Fisheries, Thailand;
(b) the Division of Food Research of CSIRO, Australia, on an *ad hoc* basis, mainly funded by the newly established Fishing Industry Research Fund. At state level, such studies are conducted by the departments responsible for fisheries at several universities;
(c) the Technological Laboratories of the Fisheries Utilization Division of the Philippine Fisheries Commission;
(d) the Utilization and Processing Section of the Korean Fisheries Research and Development Agency, Pusan, where quality improvement of canned shellfish and of traditional products, the utilization of Alaska pollock, and new products from edible seaweeds, are being investigated.

In New Zealand, technological studies and product development work are carried out by Massey University, under Government contract subsidized by the Fishing Industry Board. In Malaysia, the recently created Fisheries Industry Development Authority is giving attention to the expansion of facilities at the Fisheries Research Institute in order to carry out a technological research programme.

The Technical Advisory Service of the Fisheries Division of Australia's Commonwealth Department of Primary Industry, in liaison with the Food Research Division of CSIRO, provides advice and information to industry and issues "Australian Fisheries", a monthly with a circulation of over 15,000 copies. Extension work in Thailand is a task of the Fishery Technology Laboratory of the Department of Fisheries in collaboration with the provincial fishery officers. The Philippine Fisheries Commission is intensifying its extension services to the fishery industry. The Korean Fisheries Research and Development Agency occasionally provides the industry with advice on improved methods of fish utilization. An interesting feature is the annual exhibition of products developed during the year, arranged by the Fisheries Research and Development Agency, which gives technical data to processors and provides on-the-job extension services when needed. In Indonesia, there are extension activities at central and provincial levels to provide guidance and information on the production, utilization and marketing of fish and fishery products. The impact of such extension activities on industry development has, however, been limited, apparently due to lack of appropriate infrastructure and funds.

References

APPLEYARD, W The Requirements for the Establishment of a Food
1973   Fish Industry. In FAO Technical Conference on Fishery
        Products, Tokyo, 4–11 Dec. 1973, Rome, FAO, FII:FP/
        73/E-7, 9 p.

FAO   Fish Processing in the Indo-Pacific Area. Bangkok, Thailand,
1967   FAO Regional Office for Asia and the Far East. *Indo-
        Pacific Fisheries Council—Regional Studies*, (4):231 p.

FAO   Smoke Curing of Fish. *FAO Fish. Rep.*, (88):43 p.
1970

FAO   Fishery Country Profiles. *FAO Fish. Circ.*, (140).
1972

FAO   Report to the Government of Thailand on Fresh Fish Hand-
1973   ling, based on the work of J Graham, *Rep. FAO/UNDP(TA)*
        3187:87 p.

Appendix

Commercially processed fishery products

Abridged information on fishery products of commercial significance made in some of the developing countries is tabulated below:

Fishery Product	Species Used	Remarks
Morocco		
Frozen	Sardines, mackerel, tuna and similar	Whole or eviscerated
Canned		
Sardines in olive oil	Sardine (*Clupea pilchardus*)	Canned mostly by the French raw-pack technique
Sardines in oil, e.g., soy-bean, peanut, refined fish oil		
Sardines in oil and tomato sauce with or without spices		
Sardines skinless and boneless		
Sardines, natural pack		Raw-packed in the cans and processed without precooking
Sardines, paste		
Mackerel fillets in oil	Mackerel (*Scomber* sp.)	Precooked in steam or hot brine solution
Mackerel fillets in oil and tomato sauce		
Mackerel slices, natural pack		Raw-packed and processed without precooking
Anchovies "a la carne" in oil	Anchovy, etc.	Salt cured by traditional Mediterranean techniques
Anchovies filleted flat or rolled with capers in oil		
Anchovies in spicy sauces		Semi-preserved product packed in cans, glass jars, etc.
Tuna in oil	Several species of Thunnidae	Precooked with steam or in hot brine solution
Tuna in oil and tomato sauce		
Tuna fillets		
Tuna, grated		
Tuna, natural pack		Processed without precooking
Tuna paste		
Tuna "Arabic" style		
Fish soups	Various fish species and molluscs	"Bouillabaisse"
Fish soups, natural pack		Main ingredients raw-packed and processed
Fish balls		
Fish paste		
Squid, American style	*Loligo* sp., or *Sepia* sp.	In oil
Squid stew		In special spiced broth
Peeled shrimps		Packed in brine solution
Wet salted		
Sardines	*Clupea pilchardus*	In barrels with salt or in large tanks with saturated brine
Anchovies	*Engraulis* spp.	Raw material for the production of the semi-preserved canned product
Smoked		
Plain bonito	*Orcynopsis unicolor*	Newly developed product being market tested
Fishmeal	Sardines, mackerel, horse mackerel and canneries offal	Protein content 50–70%
FPC		
Extracted fishmeal (for animal feed)	Sardines	80% protein and very low fat content
The Gambia		
Frozen	Sole, ladyfish, mackerel, Spanish mackerel, "cassava", cuttlefish, octopus, shrimps, lobsters	Large species, filleted, small, whole. Very large are processed headless. Other large are semi-dressed, gutted and grilled, e.g., barracuda, meagre. Crab claws and lobster tails frozen. Shrimps headless and shell-on or cooked whole, peeled and deveined
Canned		No product
Dried unsalted	Mullets, shad, catfish, "cassava", ray	Most for consumption in the inland areas where *per caput* income is low
Dried salted	Shark, catfish, mullets, "casava", ray	As above, though bulk of shark product exported

Fishery Product	Species Used	Remarks
The Gambia (continued)		
Wet salted	Catfish, mackerel, snappers	For domestic consumption only
Smoked	Shad or bonga, catfish, herrings, barracuda, bonefish	Shad for the export market, others for domestic consumption
Nigeria		
Frozen	Breams, croakers, red and grey snapper, yellow jack, black jack, horse mackerel, blue mackerel, sardines, hake, lichia, soles	These are not included in Nigeria's production because they are caught by chartered foreign-owned vessels
Dried unsalted	*Alestes* spp., *Lates niloticus, Heterotis niloticus, Distichodus rostratus, Labeo* spp.	The product is prone to insect infestation. Generally the product is inadequately dried and rotting by the time it gets to the market. The odour and peculiar taste make it unpopular except in the north-eastern part of the country
Dried salted	*Lates niloticus, Heterotis niloticus, Distichodus rostratus, Gymnarchus niloticus, Hydrocyon forskali, Labeo* spp., *Citharinus* spp.	Production sponsored by Fisheries Department for acceptability testing. Quite expensive compared with other products, hence demand is very low
Charring drying	*Lates niloticus, Heterotis niloticus, Distichodus rostratus, Labeo* spp.	A product, called Banda, has a distribution all over the country. Generally accepted as a cheap source of animal protein
Smoked	*Ethmalosa fimbriata, Sardinella* spp., *Macrobrachium* spp., *Tilapia* spp., *Chrysichthys* spp., *Gymnarchus niloticus*	Most popular processing method. The smoking kilns vary in the different parts of the country. Product is widely distributed
Pakistan		
Frozen fish	*Sciaena* spp., *Otolithus* spp., *Pomadasys* spp., *Lutjanus* spp., *Acanthopagrus* spp., *Thynnus* spp., *Cybium* spp., *Polynemus* spp., *Cynoglossus* spp.	Quick frozen at $-43°$ to $-46°C$ and stored at $-18°$ to $-23°C$. Packed as whole, gutted, eviscerated or fillets
Frozen shrimps	*Penaeus merguiensis, P. penicillatus, P. indicus, P. semisulcatus, P. monodon, Metapenaeus monoceros, M. stebbingi, M. affinis*	Packed as headless, peeled and deveined in blocks or IQF. Quick frozen and stored at $-18°$ to $-23°C$
Canned shrimps	*Parapenaeopsis stylifera, P. sculptilis*	Packed in brine in 2½- (80-g) and 4½-oz (140-g) cans
Dry-salted fish	*Sciaena* spp., *Otolithus* spp., *Pomadasys* spp., *Lut janus* spp., *Acanthopagrus* spp., *Thynnus* spp., *Cybium* spp., *Polynemus* spp., *Stromateus argenteus, Hilsa* spp., *Carcharius* spp.	Fish cured and dried mechanically or traditionally by sun
Unsalted dried fish	As above	Fish dried mechanically or traditionally by sun
Dry shrimp	*Parapenaeopsis stylifera, P. sculptilis, Metapenaeus affinis, M. stebbingi,* etc.	Shrimps are boiled, sun-dried, deshelled and packed
Fishmeal	*Carcharias acutidens, C. melanoptera, C. ellioti, Myrmillo manazo, J. bleekeri, Triaenodon obesus, Sphryna blochii, Pristis cuspidatus, Rhynchobatus djiddensis*	Raw material is cooked, pressed, dried mechanically or by sun, and ground, sterilized and packed
Fish maws	*Otolithus* spp., *Sciaena* spp.	Air bladders are washed, cleaned and sun-dried
Shark fins	*Carcharias acutidens, C. melanoptera*	Washed properly and dried mechanically or traditionally by sun
Smoked fish	*Otolithus* spp., *Sciaena* spp., *Acanthopagrus* spp., *Carcharias tricuspidatus*	Clean fish dipped into brine solution, drained and smoked
Shark liver oil	*Carcharias acutidens C. melanoptera, C. ellioti, Myrmillo manazo*	Livers are crushed and steam heated. Homogenate is decanted and oil is separated by centrifuge
India		
Frozen shrimps	*Penaeus carinatus, P. indicus, Metapenaeus affinis, M. dobsoni, Parapenaeopsis stylifera*	Frozen shrimps are the most important fishery export products: 68.1% in terms of quantity and 80% in value. There are 92 freezing plants with installed capacity of 500 t/day
Frozen froglegs	*Rana hexadactyla, R. tigrina*	Many of shrimp freezing plants also freeze froglegs for export
Frozen lobsters	*Panulirus homarus, P. ornatus, Puerulus sewelli*	Export mainly to U.S.A.
Frozen fish	Silver pomfret (*Pampus argenteus*), black pomfret, (*Parastromateus niger*), tunnies (*Euthynnus* sp.), seer (*Scomberomorus* sp.)	Export of frozen fish insignificant
Canned shrimp	*Parapenaeopsis stylifera, Metapenaeus affinis, M. dobsoni*	Canned shrimp exported to about 32 world centres. The main export markets are USA, UK, France, DR of Germany, FR of Germany, Bulgaria, Australia. There are at present about 55 canning factories with an installed total capacity of about 95 t/day
Canned fish	Tuna (*Katsuwomus pelamis*), oil sardine (*Sardinella longiceps*), mackerel (*Rastrelliger kanagurta*), seer (*Scomberomorus commersoni*)	Processed mainly for the internal market. Export negligible

Fishery Product	Species Used	Remarks
India (continued)		
Canned lobster tails	*Panulirus homarus, P. ornatus*	
Dried unsalted fish	Whitebait (*Anchoviella* sp.), rainbow sardine (*Dussumieria* sp.), Bombay duck (*Harpodon nehereus*)	Processed mainly in coastal regions for internal and export trade. Exported mainly to Sri Lanka, Mauritius, Singapore, etc. Generally prepared by sun-drying
Dried salted fish	Mackerel (*Rastrelliger kanagurta*), catfish (*Arius* spp.), seer (*Scomberomorus* spp.), flying fish (*Exocoetus* spp.), jewfish (*Sciaena* spp.), shark (*Carcharia* spp.), mullet (*Mugil* spp.), tuna (*Thynnus* sp. and *Katsuwonus pelamis*), barracuda (*Sphyraena* spp.), leather-jacket (*Chroinemus* spp.), cockup (*Lates calcarifer*), black kingfish (*Elacate* spp.), horse mackerel (*Caranx* spp.), big-jawed jumper (*Lactarius* sp.), small caranx (*Caranx* spp.), sailfish (*Istiophorus* spp.), rays and skates (*Trygon* spp. and *Rhynchobatus* spp.), white sardine (*Kowala* and *Thoracata* spp.) garfish (*Hemiramphus* sp.) Indian salmon (*Polynemus* spp.), pomfrets (*Stromateus* sp.), rock cod (*Serranus* spp.), sabrefish (*Chirocentrus* spp.), silver bellies (*Leiognathus* spp.), sea cucumber (*Holothuria* spp.)	Traditionally salted followed by sun-drying for domestic and export fish trade
Salted dried shrimps	*Penaeus indicus, Parapenaeopsi stylifera, Metapenaeus dobsoni, M. affinis*	Produced by sun-drying and exported
Wet salted	Oil sardine (*Sardinella longiceps*), seer (*Scomberomorus* spp.), shark (*Carcharia* spp.)	Produced mainly for internal market
Fermented fish products	Mackerel (*Rastrelliger kanagurta*)	Produced by the special process called 'Colombo curing' mainly for the Sri Lanka market
Smoked fish products		Not produced on commercial scale, only experimentally at the Technology Research Institute from a variety of fishes
Fish sauces		Not produced on commercial scale
FPC		Produced in laboratory at the Technology Research Institute by extraction with an azeotropic mixture of n-hexane and alcohol
Fishmeal	Oil sardines (*Sardinella longiceps*), Bombay duck (*Harpodon nehereus*), jewfish (*Sciaena* spp.), whitebait (*Anchoviella* spp.), silver bellies (*Leiognathus* spp.), horse mackerel (*Caranx* spp.), etc.	Produced by wet and dry reduction methods, the former in commercial plants and the latter by powdering sun-dried fish. Several fishmeal plants have a production capacity of about 40 t/day each
Shark fins and fish maws	Shark fins: fins excluding the caudals of large sharks of different varieties; Fish maws: air bladders of dara (*Polynemus* spp.), jewfish (*Sciaenidae*), catfish (*Arius* spp.), eels (*Muraenesox* spp.)	Produced by sun-drying mainly for export to Hong Kong, Singapore and UK
Fish oils	Oil sardines, sharks and rays (liver)	
Sri Lanka		
Dried salted fish (Karavala)	Scombroids, Carangids, Tunas, Sharks, Lethrinids, Lutjanids, Polynemids, Trichiurids, Clupeids, Leiognathids	The country's principal fishery product
Unsalted dried fish	Anchovies	
Canned fish	Clupeids, Tunas, Scombroids	Initiated recently
Wet-salted and fermented fish (Jadi)	*Rastrelliger* sp., *Selar* sp.	
Smoked fish	*Tilapia* sp., *Cyprinus* sp., *Labeo* sp., *Etroplus* sp.	Good consumer acceptance
Frozen shrimps	*Penaeus monodon, P. semisulcatus, P. indicus*	For export but also available in urban areas
Frozen lobster tails	*Panulirus homarus, P. versicolor, P. ornatus*	For export but also available in urban areas
Shark fins	Sharks	
Shark liver oil	Sharks	
Fishmeal	Fish by-catches and damaged or spoilt fish	
Sea cucumber	*Holothuria scabra*	Produced by drying
Chanks	*Xancus* sp.	
Agar-agar	*Gracilaria* sp.	
Alignic acid	*Sargassum* sp.	

Thailand

Types of products:

1 = Frozen	5 = Wet salted	9 = Fermented	13 = Dried seasoning
2 = Canned	6 = Dried smoked	10 = Shrimp paste	14 = Boiled fish
3 = Dried unsalted	7 = Boiled dry	11 = Fish sauce	
4 = Dried salted	8 = Boiled hard smoked	12 = Fish balls or cakes	

Species Used	Type of Product													
	1	2	3	4	5	6	7	8	9	10	11	12	13	14
Amusium pleuronectes	x													
Anchoviella spp.		x	x								x			
Abalistes stellaris												x		
Caranx spp.				x										
Carcharinus spp.			x									x	x	
Clarias batrachus						x			x					
C. macrocephalus						x			x					
Chirocentrus dorab												x		
Chorinemus sp.				x										
Eleutheronema sp.				x										
Elagatis sp.												x		
Euthynnus affinis		x		x				x						
Holothuria sp.								x						
Johnius sp.				x										
Kryptopterus sp.						x								
Labiobarbus spp.						x			x		x			
Lactarius lactarius														x
Liza spp.														x
Loligo sp.	x	x	x	x							x			
Lutjanus sp.	x													
Metapenaeus spp.	x						x							
Muraenesox spp.												x		
Mussel				x										
Mystus sp.						x								
Mytilus sp.							x							
Nemipterus spp.				x		x			x			x		
Neothunnus sp.		x												
Netuma thalassinus													x	
Notopterus chitata												x		
N. notopterus						x						x		
Octopus sp.	x													
Ompok spp.						x								
Ophicephalus striatus				x					x					
Osteochilus spp.						x			x		x			
Otolithus spp.				x										
Pangasius larnaudii					x				x					
P. pangasius					x				x					
Parastromateus niger				x										
Parathunnus sp.				x										
Penaeus latisulcatus	x						x							
P. merquiensis	x						x							
P. monodon	x						x							
P. semisulcatus	x						x							
Polynemus sp.				x								x		
Priacanthus sp.												x		
Rastrelliger kanagurta														x
R. neglectus		x		x	x						x			x
R. spp.										x				
Sardinella gibbosa											x			
S. spp.		x		x										
Saurida spp.				x		x			x			x		
Scoliodon spp.			x									x	x	
Scolopsis sp.				x		x			x			x		
Scomberomorus spp.				x	x							x		
Sepia sp.	x											x		
Sillago spp.	x		x											
Sphyraena spp.														x
Stolephorus indicus											x			
S. spp.		x	x							x				
Stingray, ray				x										
Thunnus sp.		x												
Tilapia mossambica				x					x					
Trichiurus haumela				x								x		
Trichogaster pectoralis				x										
T. sp.									x					

Source: CS (Thailand 1973)

Remarks:

Fishmeal—All kinds of by-catches   Fish cracker —All kinds of shrimps, fish and squid   Shrimp paste—Planktonic and semi-planktonic crustaceans such as, *Acetes*, Mysis, Copepods and Lucifers

Fishery Product	English Name	Species	Remarks
Indonesia			
Frozen	Shrimps	*Penaeus* spp.	Headless, peeled
		Metapenaeus spp.	Cook and peeled
	Frog	*Rana* spp.	Frog legs
	Skipjack	*Katsuwonus pelamis*	Whole and split
Canned	Milkfish	*Chanos chanos*	Whole and steak
	Sardine-like species	*Sardinella*	Whole
	Skipjack	*Katsuwonus pelamis*	White meat
Dried unsalted	Anchovy	*Stolephorus* spp.	Boiled and unboiled
	Garfish	*Hemirhamphus melanurus*	Boiled and unboiled
		Trichogaster spp.	Whole, headless
		Helostoma temmincki	Butterfly type
	Sharkfin	*Eulamia* spp., etc.	Fin only
	Cuttlefish	*Sepia*	Dressed
	Squids	*Loligo* spp.	Whole and dressed
	Skates/rays	*Cymnura poecilura*, etc.	Slices
	Shrimps (small)	*Penaeus, Metapenaeus*	Boiled, peeled
			Boiled, shell on
	Croakers	*Pseudosciaena* sp.	Belly flaps
	Oyster		Meat only
	Clam		Meat only
	Sea cucumber	*Holothuria* spp.	Dressed
	Fish roe of flying fish	*Cypsilurus* sp.	
Dried salted	Pomfret	*Parastromateus niger*	Drawn and dressed
		Caranx sp.	Whole
	Mackerel	*Scomberomorus* sp.	Dressed and butterfly type
	Croaker	*Pseudosciaena* sp.	Whole
	Hairtail	*Trichiurus* sp.	Whole
	Chub mackerel	*Rastrelliger* sp.	Whole
	Sardine	*Sardinella* spp.	Whole
	Sprat	*Dussumieria* sp.	Whole
	Anchovy	*Stolephorus* spp.	Whole, boiled and unboiled
	Catfish	*Arius thalessinus*, etc.	Butterfly type
	Shrimps	*Penaeus, Metapenaeus*	Peeled
	Squids	*Loligo*	Whole and dressed
	Sharks		Whole and dressed
	Small tuna	*Euthynnus alletteratus*	Dressed
Smoked	Milkfish	*Chanos chanos*	Split
	Skipjack	*Katsuwonus pelamis*	Filleted
	Small tuna	*Euthynnus alletteratus*	Filleted
Fermented	Chub mackerel	*Rastrelliger* spp.	Whole and split
	Catfish	*Arius thalessinus*	Butterfly type
	Threadfins	*Polynemus* sp.	Split
Boiled	Chub mackerel	*Rastrelliger* spp.	Whole
	Scad	*Decapterus* sp.	Whole
	Sardine-like species	*Sardinella* spp.	Whole
	Anchovy	*Stolephorus* spp.	Whole
	Small tuna	*Euthynnus alletteratus*	Whole
	Shark	*Eulamia* sp., etc.	Sticks

Fishery Product	Species Used	Remarks
Australia		
Canned		
Tuna	*Thunnus maccoyii*	Most important commercially produced canned fish
Australian 'salmon'	*Arripis trutta*	Not to be confused with the true salmon of the northern hemisphere
Snoek	*Leionura atun*	
Mullet	*Mugil cephalus*	
Whitebait	*Lovettia sealii*	
Abalone	*Notohaliotis ruber* } *Schismotis laevigata* }	Important export product
Pet food	Various species	
Frozen		
Rock lobster	*Jasus* spp.	Lobster tails are Australia's most important sea-food export
(i) Whole uncooked	*Panulirus cygnus*	
(ii) Whole cooked		
(iii) Uncooked tails		

Fishery Product	Species Used	Remarks
Australia (continued)		
Frozen (continued)		
Shrimps	*Penaeus* spp.	Important export product; no shrimps are canned
Scallop	*Pecten* spp., *Amusium* spp.	Important export product
Mullet	*Mugil cephalus*	
Eel	*Anguilla* spp.	
Abalone	*Notohaliotis ruber, Schismotis laevigata*	
Fish fillets		National market
Fish fingers	Various species	Prepared from frozen blocks of minced or filleted fish
	Leionura atun and other species	
Bait fish	Various species	
Whiting	*Sillago bassensis*	Mainly for export
Tuna	*Thunnus maccoyii*	Mainly for export
Smoked fish	Various species, most important being eel (*Anguilla* spp.)	Small-scale production only
Fish paste	Various species	
Fishmeal	Mainly *Sardinops neopilchardus*	For use in animal feeds
Fish cakes	Various species	
Philippines		
Frozen	Tuna	No. 2 export
	Shrimps	No. 1 export
	Lobsters, milkfish, scallops, swordfish	Usually exported
Canned	Tuna, milkfish, round scad, herrings	For local consumption
Dried with or without salt	Anchovy, slipmouth, round scad, herrings, squids	Local consumption, only small ones are dried without salt
FPC	Lizard fish, sharks	Laboratory scale only
Smoked	Herrings, milkfish, gizzard shad, scad	
Fishmeal	All species of low or no value	
Korea		
Dried	Squid	Mainly dried in the air during winter season
	Alaska pollack	
	"Gouneles"	
	Sharkfin	
	Others	
Salted and dried	Meagre	
	Hairtail	
	Others	
Cooked and dried	Anchovy	
	Oyster	
	Others	
Salted	Hairtail	
	Meagre	
	Mackerel	
	Others	
Pickled	Anchovy	
	Shrimp (Akiami)	
	Squid	
	Oyster	
	Sea urchin	
	Others	
Canned	Saury	Boiled
	Mackerel	Boiled
	Squid	Seasoned
	Others	
Frozen	Mackerel	Round
	Horse mackerel	Round
	Saury	Round
	Squid	Round
	Shrimp	Head off and peeled
	Meagre	Round
	Puffer	Round
	Others	
Dried seaweeds	Laver	
	Dulse	
	Agar-agar	
	Fusiforme	Dried or cooked and dried
	Others	

Fishery Product	Species Used	Remarks
Korea (continued)		
Agar-agar	Agar-agar, ceramium and gracilaria	Stripped Agar-agar Powdered Agar-agar
Fish meat paste	Fish cake	Meagre, file fish, eel and mos
	Others	bottom fish are used
Seasoned and dried	Squid	
	Others	
Fishmeal and oil	Anchovy	
	Squid oil	
	Anchovy oil	
	Shark liver oil	
	Other fish oil	
Other products	Edible	
	Inedible	
Mexico		
Frozen	Shrimps	Gulf of Mexico plants: peeled, deveined, individually frozen shrimp. Pacific Coast plants: headless but mostly unpeeled shrimp in 5-lb (2.25-kg) blocks
	Lobster	Caribbean: fresh tails, domestic. Baja California: cooked tails, export
	Octopus sp. (Pulpo)	Gulf of Mexico (Campeche-Yucatán) domestic market
	Red groupers (Mero)	Filleting (Gulf of Mexico)
	Various species of finfish	Filleting and freezing started on small scale in various shrimp plants
Canned	Sardines and anchoveta	Baja California and Guaymás
	Tuna and similar	Baja California
	Shrimp	Only in special plants, most important Escuinapa near Mazatlán
	Abalone	Exclusively Baja California, mostly for export
	Mackerel, squid, shellfish, mullet pastes	Only small quantities and for local consumption mostly
Salted dried	Shark	Pacific Coast mostly sun-dried. Alvarado, mechanically dried. Both for national market
Smoked	Spanish mackerel (sierra), oysters, mullet	Small quantities, local consumption
Fishmeal	Anchoveta, thread herring, offal	
Peru		
Frozen	Yellowfin tuna (*Thunnus macropterus*)	Round (export)
	Skipjack (*Katsuwomus pelamis*)	Round (export)
	Bonito (*Sarda velox*)	Round (export)
	Merluza (*Merluccius gavi*)	Gutted and headed (export) and Fillets (internal consumption)
	Sardine (*Sardinops sagax*)	Whole (internal consumption)
	Conger eel (*Conger* sp.)	Whole and fillets (internal)
	Sole	Whole (internal consumption)
	Squat lobsters (Langostinos)	Tails, glazed
	Shrimps	Tails, glazed
Canned	Bonito (*Sarda* sp.), skipjack, yellowfin tuna, horse mackerel (*Trachurus murphyi*)	In own juice, in oil, in tomato sauce and other speciality packs
	Shad (*Ethmidium chilcae*), sardine, Pacific mackerel (*Scomber japonicus*)	In own juice, in brine, tomato sauce, in oil and other speciality packs
	Mussels	In own juice with salt added in brine
	Razor clam (Macha)	In brine
	Abalone (*Concholipa concholipa*)	In brine
	Squid	In own juice, in own ink, in oil, in marinated sauce

Fishery Product	Species Used	Remarks
Peru (continued)		
Canned	Smelt (*Austromenidia regia*)	In own juice with salt added, in brine, in tomato sauce and in oil
	Squat lobsters (Langostinos)	In brine
	Clams	In oil, in brine
Salted dried	Bonito (*Sarda* sp.), Pacific mackerel, sea bass (*Serranidae* sp.), horse mackerel, dogfish (*Mustelus* sp.), merluza (Pacific hake)	In pile, by Kench-type cure or pickle cure, sun-drying
Smoked	Pacific mackerel, mullet (*Mugil* sp.) Bonito (*Sarda* sp.), pampanito (*Stromoteus* sp.), king mackerel, others	Hot smoked on small scale
FPC		
(a) for direct consumption	Pacific hake	
(b) extracted fishmeal	Anchoveta (*Engraulis ringens*)	Hexane extraction
Chile (1970)*		
Frozen fish	Hake	Fillets, blocks, whole
	Red conger (*Genypterus reedi*)	Fillets, blocks, whole
	Croakers	Slice
	Pejegallo (*Callorhynchus callorhynchus*)	Slice, fillet
Frozen shellfish	Shrimp	CPD tail: round, blocks
	Squat lobster (Langostino)	CPD tail: round, blocks
	King crab	Round, slabs
	Mussels (Cholga)	Round, slabs
	Mussels (Chorito)	Round, slabs
	Chilean abalone (Loco)	Round, slabs
	Razor clam (Macha)	Round, slabs
	Others	Round, slabs
Canned fish	Hake	Smoked, tomatoes, sauce, spices
	Anchoveta (*Engraulis ringens*)	Cured, brine, oil
	'Machuelo' (Brevoortia *maculata*)	Brine, tomatoes, sauce
	Sardine	Smoked, tomatoes, sauce brine, oil
	Tuna	Brine, oil
	Bonito (*Sarda* sp.)	Brine, oil
	King mackerel (sierra)	Brine, smoked, tomatoes, sauce
	'Cojinova' (*Seriolella* spp.)	Brine, oil
	'Jurel' (*Trachurus* sp.)	Brine, tomatoes, sauce
	'Pejerrey' (*Atherimidae*)	Brine, oil, tomatoes, sauce
	Other	Brine, oil
Canned shellfish	Shrimp	Brine
	King crab	Brine
	Squat lobster (langostino)	Brine
	'Picoroco' (*Pyura chilensis*)	Brine
	Clam (almeja)	Brine, oil
	Mussels (cholga)	Brine, oil
	Mussels (chorito)	Brine, oil
	Chilean abalone (loco)	Brine, oil
	Razor clam (macha)	Brine
	'Erizo' (*Loxechinus albus*)	Oil
	'Piure' (*Pyura tunicata*)	Brine, oil
	Other	Brine, oil
Smoked	King mackerel (sierra)	Hot, cold, smoked
	'Robalo' (*Eleginops maclovinus*)	Hot, cold, smoked
	Horse mackerel (jurel)	Hot, cold, smoked
	Other (shellfish)	Cold smoked
Fishmeal	Hake	
	Anchoveta (*Engraulis ringens*)	
	Sardine	
	Bonito (*Sarda* sp.)	
	King mackerel (sierra)	
	Grunts (cabinza)	

* Source: Fishing Statistics Information, 1969/70. Ministry of Agriculture, Santiago, Chile 1972

Fishery Product	Species Used	Remarks
Chile (continued)		
Fishmeal	'Cojinova' (*Seriolella* spp.)	
	'Jurel' (*Trachurus* sp.)	
	Other	
	Fish waste	Hot gas, drying
	Crustacea waste	Hot gas
	Squids (*Ommastrephes gigas*)	Hot gas and steam drying
Venezuela 1971		
Frozen		
Headless shrimp	*Penaeus schmitti* (white) *P. duorarum* (rosado) and *P. brasiliensis*	About 80 per cent exported in 5-lb (2.25-kg) cartons mainly USA
Finfish	Several species	Small quantities produced for export. Domestic consumption started but still small
Canned		
Sardines	*Sardinella anchovia*	In several filling oils, eg, olive, soya, peanut and tomato sauce. Whole production geared to supply domestic market
Tuna	*Thunnus albacores* (yellowfin), *T. alalunga* (albacora), *T. obesus* (bigeye); also small quantities of *Thunnus thynnus* (bluefin), *T. atlanticus* (blackfin), *Euthynnus pelamis* (bonito), *E. alleteratus* (little tuna)	Practically whole production in oil for domestic market. Sanitary and processing standards of canning industry rather poor. Unless drastic quality improvement is introduced export in quantities is doubtful
Others:		
Mackerel fillets	*Scomber japonicus*	In oil for domestic market
Mussels	*Perna perna*	In own juice or tomato sauce
Arkshells	*Arca occidentalis*	In tomato sauce
Dry salted	Practically all species not sold as fresh or for processing	Traditional techniques of salting and sun-drying – 'green' salted cod is imported for drying in the country and fulfilling internal demand
Fishmeal	*Opisthonema oglinum* (thread herring), *Arius spixii* (marine catfish), *Cetengraulis edentulis* (yellowtail anchovy), Canneries offal (28,700 t) in 1971	

Traditional Stuffed Carp ('Gefilte Fish') *A Herzberg*

La Carpe Farcie Traditionelle ('Gefilte Fish')

L'auteur décrit brièvement les modifications introduites dans la préparation de la carpe farcie – mets juif traditionnel également appelé "gefilte fish" – depuis l'époque où la recette de ce plat était un secret familial jalousement gardé jusqu'à nos jours où la carpe farcie est produite industriellement sous forme d'aliment prêt à l'emploi. Ces développements ont également conduit à la mise au point de produits nouveaux, par exemple les boulettes de poisson (fish balls) fabriquées avec la même matière première et parfois désignées du nom traditionnel de 'gefilte fish'.

Grâce à l'observation de normes rigoureuses de qualité et de saveur, le marché des produits en conserve est en plein essor. Le développement de l'industrie a aussi été benéfique à la pisciculture car elle absorbe les excédents, utilise les petits poissons produits à bas prix et permet le maintien du marché traditionnel de la grosse carpe.

Un Plato Tradicional: la Carpa Rellena ('Gefilte Fish')

El autor presenta brevemente las modificaciones que se han producido en la preparación de un plato judío tradicional, la carpa rellena, desde la época en que la receta se custodiaba celosamente como secreto familiar hasta la producción industrial de este plato como alimento de preparación rápida. Esta evolución ha dado lugar a la preparación de nuevos productos, como albóndigas de carne hecha con la misma materia prima y denominadas con el nombre tradicional de carpa rellena ('gefilte fish').

Como se ha mantenido la buena calidad y sabor del producto, ha sido fácil encontrar mercados y ampliarlos. El desarrollo de esta industria ha sido útil también para la industria piscícola, ya que absorbe los excedentes y utiliza los peces pequeños producidos a bajo precio, permitiendo así mantener el mercado tradicional de carpas de gran talla.

Stuffed carp – that is 'gefilte fish' – is a traditional east European Jewish dish, made with many variations according to taste. It is more or less sweet and spicy, depending on personal taste, origin and, above all, tradition, and is still kept a family secret. The carp is cut open at its head and, after cleaning, the flesh is carefully cut from underneath the skin. This is mixed with the various ingredients and put back into the fish. Slices of the fish are served at the table on festive occasions. A few people still adhere to this traditional way of preparing stuffed carp. A simplified process is that of taking two carps and cleaning them. The belly cavity of one is then stuffed with various ingredients, including the ground-up flesh of the other fish. This recipe probably led to the still easier way of first slicing the fish and filling either the whole cut-out part within the skin or only the belly cavity. Another, still more simplified, method is to make fish balls, of the same raw materials. For the sake of tradition this product is somewhat deceptively called 'gefilte fish'. The raw material for 'gefilte fish' has in the past been any kind of sizable fish. In eastern Europe, these were pike (*Esox lucius*), carp (*Cyprinus carpio*) and other freshwater fish. These were often used together, such as pike stuffed with ground carp, or with the stuffing made up of a mixture of different species of ground-up fish. This tradition has been continued in Israel. Before the development of the fish culture in ponds, grey mullet (*Mugil* sp.) was taken instead of the favourite pike, and used alone or mixed with carp. As most women in Israel now go out to work, they do not have as much time as their grandmothers had to spend hours in the kitchen preparing elaborate dishes. Instead they buy ready-made food products at the grocer's. So they now buy at a relatively low price the canned product which is almost as tasty as the home-made material. About 13,000 acres of fish ponds of Israel produce the raw material required for stuffed fish.

Fish culture has made great progress during the last decennia. The main species grown in polyculture have been carp, *Tilapia* (St. Peter's fish) and grey mullet, but lately silver carp (*Hypophthalmichthys molitrix*) has been successfully introduced. Only carp is used for the production of stuffed fish, as experiments have proved that other species such as silver carp and bleak (*Acanthobrama terrae-sanctae*) are deficient in flavour and texture.

About 12,000 tons of carp are produced annually. Of this quantity, industry takes an increasing quantity. It was about 400 tons in 1969, increasing by 50–100 tons each year since then.

Progress in the fish culture industry has been due to selling carp at a live weight of 0.7–1.0 kg, improved feeding methods, taking advantage of the long growing season and adding non-competing species to the pond stocks. Yield can still be increased by the use of aeration and better feeding. The big fish are sent to the market. The small fish of 230–400 g live weight are supplied to the canning industry and used for stuffed carp and fish balls. The canned fish are low in fat and the meat and bones are soft and tender. They are delivered alive in aerated tanks and are killed and cleaned immediately before processing. Scales, heads, guts, tails and fins and blood spots are removed (Israel Standard 841, Dec. 1972). The fish are cut into slices about one inch thick, just the right portion size for canning. They are packed in natural juice, with a jelling agent (agar) added. This is necessary because the natural jelly is too liquid at room temperature and runs off the plate when the fish is served, even if it has been stored in a refrigerator. Israeli Control Standards do not allow heads to be used for the stuffing or the production of fish balls. The stuffing is made of the tail part of the fish, ground up with fresh eggs, sugar, bread crumbs or crushed unleavened bread (the 'matzo-meal'), onions, carrots, almonds, salt and spices (mainly white pepper). Cornflour may be used instead of bread. Four slices are put into each 300 g (10.5oz) oval can, covered on the inside with an anti-corrosive 'fish-lacquer'. One cannery also uses 385 g (13.5 oz) cans. Fish balls are made in the same way as the stuffing and packed in the same jelly. Sterilization is done at 121°C after the cans are sealed. Products similar to stuffed carp are produced by several American firms but only in the form of fish balls. No genuine stuffed fish are produced outside Israel.

Mechanization of the production line in the canneries includes scaling machines, heading-gutting machines, portion slicers, mixer-grinders and machines to make the balls. The 300 g cans are sold on the local market at about US $0.47 wholesale. The subsidized export wholesale price is about US $0.39 per can for stuffed slices and US $0.36 for fish balls. Standard requirements of the finished product include a drained weight of at least 70 per cent, a minimum nitrogen content of the products of not less than 1.6 per cent, which amounts to about 10 per cent of protein. The starch content must not exceed 1.5 per cent and the pH must be less than 6.5. Also all other requirements concerning freshness and wholesomeness are stipulated in the Israel Standard already mentioned. Control is carried out by inspectors of the Ministry of Health. The industrial products have found a ready and expanding market, especially among working women and in restaurants, and the production of canned stuffed carp has become important to carp culture. It fits into the production scheme as a whole, utilizing surpluses and the cheaply produced small fish.

The Future of Powdered Fish Products   *G M Dreosti*

L'avenir des produits en poudre a base de poisson

On étudie les trois principaux produits en poudre à base de poisson – farine de poisson, concentrés de protéines de poisson (CPP) destinés à la consommation humaine et extraits secs pour la fabrication de produits de remplacement du lait destinés à l'alimentation des veaux.

Il y aura bien une concurrence de plus en plus serrée des industries alimentaires pour la récupération du poisson comestible actuellement utilisé dans les usines de fabrication de farine de poisson, mais celles-ci continueront à faire usage des poissons d'aspect peu plaisant, non-comestibles ou d'un prix de revient trop

Futuro de los productos pesqueros en polvo

Se examinan los tres productos pesqueros en polvo más importantes – harina de pescado, concentrado de proteínas de pescado para consumo humano y sucedáneos sólidos de leche para terneros.

Aunque aumentará la competencia de las industrias alimentarias por absorber el pescado comestible que actualmente se utiliza en las plantas de reducción, la industria de fabricación de harina de pescado continuará utilizando pescado poco atractivo, incomible o demasiado caro para la alimentación. Se utilizarán nuevos tipos de pescado y la industria seguirá creciendo. Sus productos encontrarán fácil mercado, a pesar de posibles competencias. Probable-

élevé à des fins alimentaires. On aura recours à de nouvelles sources de poisson et l'industrie de la farine de poisson continuera à se développer. Ses produits trouveront facilement des marchés, malgré la concurrence possible. Il est probable que l'on apportera des améliorations à la conservation des matières premières, à la cuisson, au dégraissage et au séchage ainsi qu'à l'utilisation des antioxygènes et aux propriétés d'écoulement de la farine de poisson. On prévoit des recherches importantes sur les propriétés chimiques et nutritives, notamment en ce qui concerne le facteur de croissance non identifié.

Un marché considérable pourra peut-être s'offrir à la farine de poisson dans les activités de pisciculture aux fins de l'alimentation humaine ainsi que dans la fabrication d'aliments destinés aux animaux familiers.

Les principales conditions auxquelles doivent satisfaire les matières sèches pour la fabrication de produits de remplacement du lait destinés aux vaeux sont: solubilité, teneur élevée en protéines et faible teneur en graisse et en cendres et, pour la production de viande de veau blanche: très faible teneur en fer. Les recherches devraient aboutir à des améliorations considérables et à une augmentation de la demande commerciale d'extraits secs de poisson pour la fabrication de produits de remplacement du lait.

Les concentrés de protéines de poisson se sont révélés non-toxiques, conformes à l'hygiène, acceptables pour le consommateur et nourrissants, mais les problèmes économiques et les problèmes de commercialisation demandent un examen plus approfondi.

mente se mejorará la conservación de las materias primas, la cocción, la extracción de aceite y el secado, el empleo de antioxidantes y la fluidez de la harina de pescado. Se prevén importantes investigaciones sobre las propiedades químicas y nutritivas, especialmente por lo que se refiere al factor no identificado de crecimiento (UGF).

Es posible que se encuentre un mercado considerable para la harina de pescado en el cultivo de peces para el consumo y en la cría de animales domésticos.

Los principales requisitos de los sucedáneos sólidos de la leche para terneros son que sean solubles, que tengan elevado contenido en proteínas y pocas grasas y cenizas y, si se destinan a la producción de carne blanca de ternera, que el contenido en hierro sea bajísimo. Las investigaciones permitirán probablemente considerables mejoras, incrementando así la demanda de sucedáneos sólidos de la leche procedentes de pescado.

Se ha demostrado que los concentrados proteínicos de pescado no son tóxicos, son higiénicos, aceptables y nutritivos, pero es preciso prestar más atención a los problemas económicos y de mercadeo.

I intend to deal separately with the three main powdered products – fish meal, milk replacer solids and fish protein concentrate – and highlight such aspects regarding raw materials, production, storage and utilization as might have limitations or special advantages in the predictable future. It would seem helpful, in trying to peer into the future, to pinpoint present modern practices and recent developments. Many of these are modifications of old processes. It has been said that if you want new ideas, read old books; if you want old ideas, read new books.

FISH MEAL

Raw materials

Most fish meal is made from pelagic fish such as the Peruvian anchoveta, the Norwegian herring, the American menhaden and the South African pilchard and anchovy, all of which are relatively rich in body oil as compared with the demersal fish. Pelagic fish are relatively less expensive to catch than demersal fish so it would seem that the main fish reduction industries will continue to give preference to them. While some scientists believe that some resources are overfished, other authorities think that the world catch could be doubled in, say, 20 years.

Competition for fish

Some of this fish will undoubtedly be used for human food and there will be increasing competition for edible fish from the producers of other products, particularly for salting, drying, canning and freezing. We should bear in mind, however, that much fish is inedible or unattractive as food, or breaks down rapidly after death or is so seasonal as to render its preservation for food purposes difficult and expensive. Moreover, new raw material such as krill, lampanyctus, cephalopods, etc., will be harvested. There will naturally be good years and lean years of catch, and there will be diversions from the manufacture of fish meal for pigs and poultry (and other birds and animals) to the production of commodities for human consumption. So, on balance, the production and use of fish meal can be expected to grow over the next ten or twenty years.

Competitive products

It may be thought that considerable competition is building up from other protein sources, such as synthetic amino acids (lysine, methionine), unicellular proteins, eg, from oil, plant proteins (eg, field beans, soya, etc.) and specific cereals such as high lysine maize, barley, etc. It seems unlikely that any of these will have any limiting effect on the fish meal market, which is increasing at the rate of about 6 per cent a year.

Preservation

The problem of better preservation of the catch aboard fishing vessels and at the fish reduction plants is one which is occupying the attention of scientists and technologists throughout the world. Chemicals such as formaldehyde and sodium nitrite are used in the fish meal industry with special precautions, and are reasonably effective and without adverse effects on the quality of the meal. Small amounts of formaldehyde, ie, less than 0.02 per cent, based on the weight of the fish, are used in South Africa just before cooking and pressing. This is done occasionally in the early part of the season when the fish are in a biological state difficult to press. Refrigeration has generally been considered too expensive for reduction purposes but experiments tend to indicate that it may today often be feasible and, indeed, profitable. It seems likely, therefore, that refrigeration will be more widely used in preservation of fish for meal.

Production

Modern fish reduction machinery is efficient and well controlled. No major basic changes are foreseen in plant.

Cooking

The fish are mechanically lifted from pits and fed to steam heated rotary cookers to coagulate the proteins and firm them up to the correct degree for pressing (undercooking or overcooking results in difficulty of removing the maximum amount of oil). I foresee improvements in technique, eg, for determining the correct degree of cooking and providing uniformity of cooking for varying raw materials.

101

Pressing

The material is fed to single or double screw rotary presses. The expressed liquor is centrifuged for removal of suspended solids, and pumped to centrifugal separators for removal of the oil. The problem of removing the oil more effectively and more efficiently is being given increased attention. Even with the best screw presses, operating on optimally cooked fish, the fat content is not reduced below about 8 per cent and is usually 10 per cent. Longer dwell times in the press are envisaged. By centrifuging the minced cooked fish, the fat content of the meal can be reduced several per cent lower than is done by presses. Although centrifuging is more expensive, the oil is more valuable on its own than as part of the meal. Centrifugal de-oiling will no doubt be applied on an increasing scale in the industry. Solvent extraction of the oil from fish material, as practised for grains, is too expensive, especially as the extracted oil is of low commercial value, being dark in colour and contaminated with other (partly oxidized) lipid material, eg, phospholipids.

With the present increased scientific effort, fish meal may be put on the market in the next ten years with lower fat content than it has today.

Practically all reduction plants in the world will soon have evaporators for the concentration of de-oiled liquor.

Drying

As moisture is essential for the action of both enzymes and bacteria, it is possible to inhibit both autolysis and putrefaction by removing moisture. At a certain humidity and temperature the action of bacteria is stopped completely. The material is dried in rotary driers heated by oil, coal or gas, or by indirect heating through steam tubes and jacketed heating surfaces. The quality of the protein is unaffected by the type of drier used and is dependent only on the care taken during drying. An increase in the use of two stage drying is foreseen, as this method allows more accurate control. A type of bin drying, as a third stage – similar in effect to the bin driers used during the Second World War for the dehydration of vegetables – will in due course come into use for better drying control and for more economical drying.

Hygiene

The fish meal industry has become increasingly conscious of the need for good housekeeping and hygienic operations. The dwell time of the cooked material in the press is sufficient to destroy most bacteria, including salmonella, and special precautions are now taken – such as recycling the first three quarters of an hour's production while the plant is warming up, and heating the concentrate and decanter solids to 100°C immediately before returning them to the presscake – to ensure freedom from infection at all times. Increased hygiene is being extended to the dry section in factories and to handling plant generally. In the next ten years the microbial precautions at reduction plants will surpass those which a few years ago were current in plants preparing food for human consumption.

Antioxidants

Antioxidant (eg, ethoxyquin or BHT) is now often used to stabilize fish meal. Fish oils are generally much more reactive than oils of plant or land animal origin. The number of unsaturated linkages in some of the long chain polyunsaturated fatty acids of the oil may be as high as 6, in contrast to the 2 or 3 for other oils. Antioxidant is used in many factories (all in South and Southwest Africa and Peru). The advantage to be gained depends on the reactivity of the oil in the fish meal in question. With highly reactive oils the antioxidant prevents the gradual decrease in protein quality during long storage of the meal and retards the loss of vitamins E and A. The antioxidant also minimizes the loss of energy value during long storage. The addition of antioxidant enables reactive fish meal to be stacked and shipped immediately after production, and brings about greater uniformity in the product through stability. Greater use will be made of antioxidants in the fishing industry.

Spontaneous heating

Although antioxidants are useful in permitting the bulking of fish meal as soon as it is cooled, and spontaneous heating is reduced to practically nil, the heating is not completely inhibited. Therefore, the interior of large bulk masses of fish meal can get warm in spite of stabilization or prolonged curing, and this can lead to moisture migration, condensation and mould development, particularly if the periphery of the bulk is cool. The need for internal ventilation, whether in bulk or in bags, cannot therefore be overemphasized. Whilst the present antioxidants are efficacious, further research is required to ensure the arrest of spontaneous heating.

Flavour effects

As the lipids are prevented from oxidation, they are resorbed by the birds or pigs consuming the fish meal, and this may lead to loss of flavour or even taint of the flesh if excessive quantities of meal are used, such as more than about 10 per cent during the last two weeks of feeding poultry or about 7 per cent during the last two months of feeding pigs. The effect is known to be associated with polyunsaturated long chain fatty acids such as clupanodonic and decosohexaenoic acids, and some progress has already been made in finding palliatives, eg, by increasing the vitamin E content or by increasing the proportion of oleic acid to linoleic acid in the diet. This flavour problem may be solved in the not too distant future. There are other ways of avoiding taint such as by extracting all the lipids from the fish meal and using such meal in the last stage feeding of broilers and pigs. As this method is expensive it is more likely that an antioxidant plus a 'corrective factor for flavour' will be the next development.

FFA and peroxides

The belief that high free fatty acids in the residual oil in fish meal and high peroxide values are related to overstorage of raw fish and fish meal, and that they are harmful in the diet, have been disproved by experiments in different parts of the world.

Handling and storing

Fish meal has, until recently, been exported and distributed in woven hessian bags or multiwalled paper sacks. More recently, some has been distributed in woven plastic bags or bags made of solid plastic sheet. Along with advantages, they all have the disadvantage of being time and labour-consuming and expensive in handling. The modern trend is to handle fish meal in bulk as is done with grain. This tendency will undoubtedly expand until practically all fish meal will be handled in this way.

Flow properties

As some fish meals have poor flow properties (eg, from silos) particularly if they have remained static for a long time, many favour the practice of pelletizing the meal. However, considerable quantities of meal will continue to be handled for many years in unpelletized form. Pelletizing for transport requires power, and repowdering involves further power use. Pelletizing is used only when it cannot be avoided conveniently. I can foresee useful further research into improving the flow properties of fish meal.

Uses of fish meal

Fish meal was used as a fertilizer, as a source of nitrogen for the soil. In those early days, production was unhygienic and primitive in contrast to the sophisticated equipment and methods used at present. Fish meal has for many years been used almost entirely as a source of high quality protein for poultry and pigs, fulfilling their needs for essential amino acids. As a result of the excellent body gains achieved and the general health of the birds and animals, the demand for the meal has grown steadily.

Other uses

Fish meal is now being used in increasing amounts for other purposes, eg, as fish food in commercial fish farms. While it requires about 2½ lb of fish protein to build 1 lb of chicken protein, it takes only about 1½ lb of fish protein to produce 1 lb of protein in high quality fish. Present consumption for this purpose is about 4 million tons but it is anticipated that this figure will rise to at least 30 million tons within ten years.

Increasing quantities of fish and fish meal are used in pet foods. Incidentally, experiments were made in Cape Town last year in which fish solids, discharged from decanting centriguges in plants, were compressed into pellets for cat food. The samples were well received by a variety of cats! The protein content of the pellets was about 70 per cent and the fat content about 7 per cent. Although many other uses will undoubtedly be found, fish meal will continue to be used mainly for poultry and pigs and, modified, for calves and humans in due course.

UGF

Fish meal seems to have an unknown growth factor, designated UGF, which promotes growth over and above any expected from its amino acid content. Whether this is merely an "insurance factor" due to a perfect combination and variety of trace elements (fish being derived from the oceans which are the best balanced source of all minerals) or whether it is the physical nature of the protein itself (as distinct from its amino acid composition) or whether there is a specific (UGF) antibiotic or other chemical in fish meal, is not known. Some experiments have tended to support the "minor element" theory and others the "antibiotic" theory. With the improved

facilities and techniques, the next ten years should show us how, and under which circumstances, the UGF operates.

Scientific Advisory Service

I would like to draw your attention to the recent establishment of the Scientific Advisory Service at the Headquarters of the International Association of Fish Meal Manufacturers at 70 Wigmore Street, London, W1H 9DL, to which address any questions may be directed concerning fish meal. The Service is in close touch with scientific research organizations and industries concerned with the production, handling and the use of fish meal, and will answer any questions relating to fish meal.

MILK REPLACERS

Milk replacers are in general use in calf feeding and for human consumption.

For some years the French have been conducting experiments on using fish protein for calf feeding, and have demonstrated that skim milk can be partly substituted by fish products, either in the soluble or insoluble form. There may be a market here in due course for at least a few hundred thousand tons of fish protein annually.

Present requirements by French users are for products with a low odour level, light colour, low fat content, eg, less than 1 per cent and low mineral content, eg, below 10 per cent. A high protein content (more than 70 per cent) and protein quality, and high digestibility are required. As more experience is gained in the use of these products, requirements might be less stringent, such as tolerance of some odour and a darker colour, and a fat content higher than 1 per cent. Milk replacer used for producing white veal must have a very low iron content (below 50 ppm). White fish has a lower iron content than fatty fish, eg, about 50 ppm as compared with several hundred ppm for pelagic fish. There is no unanimity yet as to requirements or, indeed, as to whether fish protein has a bright future in this field. The limitation on the iron content might be dispensed with if and when the production of white-fleshed veal by maintaining calves in a state of anaemia becomes prohibited by law or unpopular as a result of public outcry. At least, the proportion of red- to white-fleshed veal in Europe may increase from the present ratio of approximately 25 per cent to 75 per cent. Three different fish solids for milk replacer in calf feeding are being produced on a small scale, mainly in France and Italy. An insoluble Scandinavian product is marketed which consists of fish material from which the fat is extracted and which is ground very finely and adapted to suspension in water. The iron content is, however, relatively high, eg, a few hundred ppm. Insoluble powders must be milled so finely that they remain suspended in thickened water for at least a few hours.

A soluble product is produced and marketed in France. In another experimental French process enzymes are added to the ground fresh fish aboard the trawlers, and hydrolyzed for segregation and further treatment ashore. The digested mass separates into layers of oil, solubles and sediment. The protein products are concentrated under vacuum, pasteurized and spray-dried. Even the "insoluble" fraction is easily suspendible in water.

However, the fat and iron contents of the latter are relatively high. It is claimed that iron and ash are partly segregated and that the soluble fraction can be used for the production of white veal. Soluble products often have a hydrolysis odour which is unpleasant, and have a lower protein quality than that of extracted insoluble material.

Industrial production of milk replacer for calves and for human consumption may ultimately use appreciable quantities of fish if a sufficient perfection of product is attained and the cost acceptable. In this connexion there is the German experience with Eiweiss, made by solvent extraction, digestion by alkali and neutralization by acid. It was bland and had excellent whipping properties. After the second world war, we made a similar product from South African fishes. The artificial egg-white had excellent whipping qualities and good stability even at high temperatures. However, the cost of production was so high that it became uneconomic as soon as ordinary egg-white became freely available again. Modifications of the German process were developed in the Netherlands and in USSR but both have ceased for the same reason. Although production costs for milk replacer from fish are high, profitability is high. Present fish products for calf milk replacers fetch U.S. $450–600 per ton. In view of this and the attention being given to the problems of manufacturing fully satisfactory milk replacers I foresee a steadily increasing demand for such products for both calves and humans.

FISH PROTEIN CONCENTRATE (FPC)

Hygiene

The manufacture of FPC for human consumption requires totally different standards of fish quality and factory hygiene to those for the manufacture of meal for poultry and pigs, or milk replacers for calves. Only fresh fish must be used for FPC and it has to be processed in factories different from and more expensive than those producing meal. The fish pits would have to be refrigerated or made smaller, as the day's catch would be cooked and dried immediately. All elevators, deboners, cookers, presses and driers would have to be so constructed as to be easily cleaned and washed out after use and then disinfected. After production, FPC has to be stored in sealed containers, such as solid sheet plastic bags, to avoid infection.

Bland FPC

Bland FPC is made by extracting the lipids, and odour and flavour substances under hygienic conditions. It is easier to produce an extracted, bland and stable FPC from white fish than from fatty fish. The solvents generally used for extraction are isopropanol or ethanol. The latter was used in South Africa. Unless all the lipids are extracted as well as the triglycerides by a suitable solvent, such as alcohol, they will tend to "revert" during storage. As part of the flavour components are soluble an even blander and more stable FPC can be made by water extraction. However, this refinement is unnecessary when using FPC in small amounts in the diet, such as in brown bread at a level of 3 per cent which is adequate for considerably enhancing the protein

quality of the diet as a whole. Whatever the solvent, tests show that it is desirable to perform the initial extraction at relatively low temperature to avoid reactions which occur while partly oxidized oil is present in the material. It tends to reduce protein quality and results in a slightly darker colour than when cold extraction is used.

The extraction process can be applied to raw, comminuted fish or to presscake or fish meal. Provided that the fish meal is stored in hermetically sealed containers to prevent oxidation while awaiting extraction, the final product is organoleptically and nutritionally just as good as that made by using fresh fish. It is a less expensive process, both as regards capital and current costs as the extraction plant can be operated regularly and continuously throughout the year. Moreover, the extraction of water by mechanical means (by presses and rotary driers) is far less expensive than extraction by solvents or by azeotropic distillation, involving relatively expensive equipment and processes. It is, therefore, foreseen that extracted FPC will more often be made from hygienically produced and stored fish powder than through direct extraction of fish. When batch extraction was used in our pilot plant, it was necessary (for oily fish such as pilchards, anchovies, etc.) to extract five consecutive times, each for 20 minutes. Extraction was much more rapid and efficient, using far less ethanol, by a countercurrent continuous extraction process in which the fish powder was conveyed upwards and the alcohol percolated downwards. The extracted meal was conveyed beyond the inlet of the ethanol, for draining, and was then dropped into a desolventizer. Continuous countercurrent extraction will probably be used more often in the future than batch extraction.

The used solvent had to be distilled from the extracted oil through an active carbon column in the vapour phase to remove fish odours before re-use. The active carbon had to be cleared of vapours regularly by steaming. The problem of fractional distillation for solvent recovery when ethanol is used was avoided by pre-drying the fish meal to 4 per cent moisture content at which level it is in equilibrium with 92 per cent ethanol – the best strength for optimum results, i.e., the blandest products. The recovered alcohol had to be chemically treated from time to time to remove acetaldehyde which would give the FPC a faint "mousy" odour and flavour and a reddish hue. High acetaldehyde content also restricts the removal of lipids and reduces the available lysine and methionine contents. In our tests the available methionine was reduced by about 40 per cent and the available lysine by about 15 per cent when 200 ppm acetaldehyde were present in the alcohol.

All these steps are expensive, including the desolventizing of the extracted material.

More than 1,000 tons of FPC were used in brown bread in South Africa, a few hundred tons in a product called ProNutro – an enriched porridge powder – and smaller quantities in dehydrated soups. Experimental work showed that the extracted FPC could be incorporated successfully in a variety of other products ranging from stews and sauces to crystallized fruit and biscuits. The National Nutrition Research Institute in Pretoria has developed an excellent protein-enriching medium for the poor to sprinkle over their staple foods.

This product contains about 20 per cent FPC, is highly nutritious and has been well accepted in trials.

A large number of other commodities have been enriched by means of extracted FPC in other countries, including the USA, India and Peru. Amongst the products in which bland FPC has been tested successfully are noodles, flavoured biscuits, cookies, puddings, purees, pretzels, spaghetti and 'angel's hair'. Tests have been described in which FPC has been used in children's hospitals, for school lunch programmes and even for cancer patients. The list of uses will undoubtedly grow in quantity and variety.

When I first made FPC in 1937, the intention was to provide the least expensive source of high quality protein for malnourished babies. In recent times, however, many investigations are concerned with the production of superior products which are suitable for use in highly developed countries. Investigations in the USA, Canada and Chile are aimed at improving the functional properties of FPC, eg, its water retention and swelling properties. It has been reported from Canada, for instance, that by taking two simple steps in the procedure, an FPC can be made which is eminently suitable for incorporation in sausages, as an extender. There are several ways of producing soluble, relatively bland fish protein products. Different products have been made in Chile on a small-scale by enzymic digestion, such as a milk replacer for infants, calf milk replacer and materials for sausages. The Japanese, also using an enzymic process, have produced a product called LFP standing for Liquified Fish Protein, which contains more protein and less minerals than FPC. In the USA, FPC in soluble form has been made by alkalinization at 100°C and subsequent acidification to obtain isoelectric precipitation, and spray drying – a process which seems to me to be similar in principle to the old German Eiweiss process. Dry fish proteins are thermoplastic and may yet be "textured" into fibres for the production of meat-like products of high protein quality with a variety of flavours to suit different palates.

In June 1972, at an International Conference on FPC at the Massachusetts Institute of Technology, Cambridge, USA, all aspects of FPC were discussed. The conclusion was reached that adequate know-how exists in the world for producing FPC, that the products are non-toxic, nutritious and hygienic, and that FPC can be incorporated in a great number of foods and beverages without detection – but that the marketing aspects require further investigation. It seems that we have 'caught the animal' but do not know what to do with it yet.

Non-extracted FPC

The manufacture of extracted FPC requires the installation of more expensive equipment than does the manufacture of unextracted FPC and, moreover, the skills required for operating the plant are greater. It should be further borne in mind that the products are less nutritious because fat, vitamins, and minerals are removed by extraction. The staple diet of the mass of malnourished humans consists largely of cereal dishes with little flavour, and they dislike extracted FPC in their staple foods. Moreover, it is understandable that they are attracted to commodities which can add flavour to

their relatively bland diets. Many of these people live in tropical regions where rancid foods are commonplace and the odour and flavour of fish meal is accepted and desired. For these reasons it is preferable to develop a variety of unextracted FPC products to meet the different requirements.

In tests made in Cape Town, the Bantu taste panel preferred unextracted, unstabilized FPC in their stiff maize porridge (and liked it, provided that sugar was added), to similar unsugared porridge with the addition of neutral extracted FPC. If desired, precautions can be taken to minimize or avoid the development of fishmealy odours and flavours. At the time of production fish meal has a fish odour and flavour, as distinct from a fishmealy one. The odour and flavour can be retained by immediate gas packing or by the addition of an antioxidant or displacing the fish lipids by means of a stable fat and then gas packing, or simply filling containers to the brim and hermetically sealing them for long-term storage. Such store products have proved acceptable not only to test panels representing the Bantu but to other people in the community. The material is preferably made from fish flesh as it can then be made as coarse mince or even shredded as fibres, thus making it possible to tailor the form of product to the intended use. The finely milled bones can be added for mineral content. This type of product – stabilized, unextracted FPC, made from fresh fish under hygienic conditions – is acceptable and useful for the preparation of dishes for all sections of the population. Slight "fishmealiness" of imperfect products can be partly or wholly masked by means of herbs and spices, and especially by curry. A mixture of such FPC and sugar in the proportion of 2:1 is practically free from fishmealiness.

As I see it, the extracted, odourless, tasteless and shapeless FPC upon which so much research work has been done in so many countries for so many years will, in the end, be used in greater measure in developed countries than for malnourished people, while unextracted FPC, upon which so little work has been done to date, is likely to be used in greater measure by those who urgently need good quality protein food. It is amazing to see hundreds of publications on extracted FPC and only isolated publications of unextracted FPC, and these mostly concerning white fish, which is generally more expensive than pelagic fish. More research is urgently required on unextracted FPC for feeding the malnourished millions. I wish to quote the statement made by J A Lovern, Torry Research Station, in 1968: 'I cannot accept that a case has been made out for FPC in the degree of sophistication now envisaged. I feel that if comparable resources had been devoted to studying alternative ways of processing whole fish, something with better commercial prospects would have emerged.'

Different commodities are required in different areas and more time and effort must be spent in investigating the exact requirements, area for area. While unextracted FPC would be acceptable in some regions, others would require salted fish powder, while in others smoked fish powder would be desired. We have found no problem in salting or smoking either extracted or unextracted FPC. The fish can also be salted or smoked before drying. New methods of producing smoke have been developed in recent years, and some further effort will, no doubt, be made. A smoke 'washing' procedure was evolved by me some years ago, which does not affect the flavour of the final product, and this is in regular use in South African fish smokeries. It has been shown that the traces of carcinogens (polycyclic aromatic hydrocarbons (PAH))

eg, 3.4 benzpyrene, etc, in wood smoke are largely removed by this procedure. Briefly, my plea is for closer consultation between those with knowledge of what can be produced and those with knowledge of what is acceptable.

The Role of Fish Meal in Alleviation of Protein Shortage in Human Nutrition *S M Barlow and F W Burton*

Le role de la farine de poisson dans la reduction du deficit proteique en nutrition humaine

Les auteurs exposent brièvement les arguments en faveur du maintien d'un taux maximal d'exploitation des stocks ichtyologiques pour la transformation du poisson en farine. Tout en reconnaissant que la consommation directe du poisson par l'homme permet une utilisation optimale des protéines qu'il contient, ils indiquent les divers facteurs favorables à l'utilisation du poisson sous forme de farine: diversité d'emploi des protéines et de l'huile, apport indirect à la nutrition humaine par la fabrication d'aliments pour animaux et rôle de la pêche industrielle dans le secteur de la farine grâce à l'introduction d'opérations mécanisées dans d'autres secteurs halieutiques des pays en voie de développement, ainsi que l'accumulation de capitaux.

Contribucion de la harina de pescado para aliviar la escasez de proteinas en la nutricion humana

En este documento se examina brevemente las razones que aconsejan mantener al máximo la explotación de las poblaciones de peces, reduciendo el pescado a harina. Aun concediendo que el consumo directo de pescado para la alimentación representa la forma más eficaz de aprovechar su contenido proteínico, se señalan diversos factores favorables al empleo del pescado en forma de harina, entre ellos los diversos usos de las proteínas y el aceite, la contribución indirecta a la alimentación humana mediante los piensos, y la función que desempeña la pesca industrializada propia de la industria harinera en la introducción de las faenas mecanizadas en otros sectores pesqueros de los países en desarrollo y en la acumulación de capital.

Fish meal is a solid product obtained by removing most of the water and some or all of the oil from fish or fish waste. It is generally sold as a powder, and is used mostly in compound feeds for poultry and pigs as a source of high quality protein, essential fat, minerals and vitamins. It is also used in many other forms of livestock feeds, including that for artificially reared fish. Small scale commercial developments of specially prepared fish meal for human food are also taking place. It is far too valuable to be used as a fertilizer. The figures in Table 1 show the relation between the catch for human consumption and the catch for industrial purposes for the years 1966–1972 inclusive. On a number of occasions concern has been expressed at the large quantities of fish caught and not used directly for human consumption. A Polish statement presented to the Food and Agriculture Organization's Committee on Fisheries in 1971 explained that rapidly expanding industrial catches along with rising fish meal production had been anxiously watched by countries whose fleets fished mainly for direct human consumption. In 1972 the Chairman of the United Kingdom Herring Industry Board stated, 'There is an increasing world-wide demand for fish meal and oil for animal feeding. Eastern Europe is expanding its feedingstuffs by 10 per cent per annum. In China, Chairman Mao says that each family must have its own breeding pig, and that the food for it will come from the sea. The sea is full of food for the human race; there is no need to convert it to beef, chicken or bacon.' In the light of such statements it is necessary to review the role of fish meal carefully in order to evaluate its usefulness in a world which is in need of protein.

There are a number of major stocks of fish throughout the world which for very good reasons are almost entirely used for fish meal and oil production, eg menhaden in North America and anchovy in South America and South Africa. Because of the size and nature, includ-

ing palatability to human tastes, of these fish little can be done, at present, to use them directly for human food. Even such areas as the North Sea yield species such as sand-eel and Norway pout which are unusable as human food but can be processed to fish meal and oil. In 1970,

TABLE 1. DISTRIBUTION OF CATCH OF ALL AQUATIC ANIMALS, EXCLUDING WHALES (MILLION TONS)

Year	Catch for human consumption	Catch for industrial purposes[a]	Total catch[b]
1966	38.4	17.9	57.3
	(67.0)[c]	(31.2)	(100.0)
1967	38.9	20.5	60.4
	(64.4)	(33.9)	(100.0)
1968	39.9	23.0	63.9
	(62.4)	(36.0)	(100.0)
1969	40.1	21.5	62.6
	(64.1)	(34.3)	(100.0)
1970	43.1	25.5	69.6
	(61.9)	(36.6)	(100.0)
1971	44.2	24.2	69.4[d]
	(63.7)	(34.9)	(100.0)
1972[e]	44.2	19.4	64.8
	(68.0)	(30.0)	(100.0)

[a]Reduction to meals and oils; whole fish only.
[b]Including small quantities for miscellaneous purposes.
[c]Percentages in brackets.
[d]Revised to 69.7; revision of components not yet available.
[e]Preliminary.

for example, of the 25.5 million tons of whole fish which were converted into fish meal, about nine-tenths was manufactured from species that are currently regarded as unsaleable in any quantity on the human food market. Moreover, some species of fish are extremely prolific (eg menhaden) and if left unharvested increase to a maximum population. To leave them thus would not only be an economic loss, but would also interfere with the harvesting of more desirable edible species. The food and space requirements of these fish could adversely affect the population and ecology of edible species. In these circumstances a properly managed fishery for reduction to meal offers no threat to other fisheries; indeed, it may be an aid to the edible fishery business.

Conflicts of interest can occur over the remaining small proportion of whole fish converted into meal, which are taken from stocks being fished both for human food and meal production. It is on these occasions that critics of fish meal production argue against the use of food fish for animal feed. It is important to make the point, however, that the most efficient exploitation of any fish stock involves fishing up to the optimum sustainable yield or much valuable protein is wasted. If the food fishing industry is not achieving this, it is logical and indeed desirable for the remainder of the yield to be manufactured into meal. Moreover, established food fisheries sometimes result in surpluses of fish which are not sold for human consumption after landing or contain species which are not popular in food shops. These too, should be manufactured into meal.

UTILIZATION EFFICIENCY OF VARIOUS FORMS OF FISH PROTEIN

Pelagic fish left unharvested in the oceans contribute either nothing to the protein available to mankind (in certain circumstances they can have a detrimental effect on the ecology) or, at best, very little by the indirect routes as shown in Fig 1.

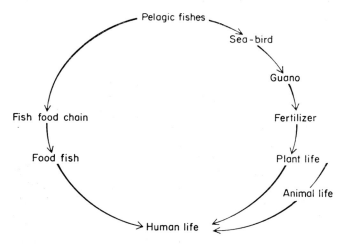

Fig 1   Natural conversion pathways of pelagic fish protein

It is difficult reliably to quantify the efficiency of protein conversion to human food of these alternative pathways. Almost certainly the efficiency of fish protein conversion via the production of guano is less than 1 per cent. The efficiency of fish protein conversion via the food chain depends entirely upon the particular food chain under consideration. To compare any calculated figure with figures for fish-meal protein conversion efficiency to human food is of academic interest only as these two end uses of fish protein from pelagic fish are never exclusively competitive. Even when fishing a stock intensively for fish meal, it is generally regarded that there

are enough fish remaining for the purposes of the food chain.

Most of the fish meal produced in the world is fed to poultry, which in turn is eaten by humans. Three kg of fish protein is required to produce 1 kg of edible chicken protein or, expressing it another way the efficiency of fish protein utilization via production of broilers is about one third. It can be stated, therefore that the efficiency of fish protein utilization by manufacturers of meal is considerably increased compared with leaving the fish unharvested in the oceans. Moreover, it should be borne in mind that the availability of products of high protein content and quality (such as fish meal) mobilizes inferior ingredients for use in animal feedingstuffs which otherwise could not be used. These poorer protein concentrates are often of no direct value as human foods (eg feather meals) or at least little used for direct human consumption (eg cotton seed meal, sunflower meal, etc) and alone would not be useful to many types of livestock. The availability of fish meal makes these products useful in animal nutrition and indirectly in human nutrition. The fish meal contribution to the protein fraction of the diet, therefore, exceeds that of its own amino acid contribution. Furthermore, cereal grains might be wasted or their amino acids inadequately used if it were not possible to supplement them adequately with a product such as fish meal and in doing so convert their proteins into usable and well balanced, attractive chicken or pork protein.

In certain circumstances, some types of human food production could not take place without the availability of fish meal. For example, many of the intensively farmed fish species require a minimum amount of fish protein in the diet. Without the presence of this protein, the fish will not survive. In these cases the development of fish farming is dependent on the availability of adequate supplies of fish protein, mainly in the form of meal. Moreover, the efficiency of fish protein utilization via production of fish (for example, trout) is generally higher than via the production of broilers being of the order of two-fifths.

It is difficult to get consistent data from the literature on the yields from food fish (on a weight basis and a protein basis) after being prepared for the human food market. The differences probably reflect the different practices in different countries and differing processing technology. The two major species of fish which are utilized both by the food industry and the meal industry are herring and pilchard. Therefore, it is worth examining the protein utilization of these two species. Torry gives an average fillet yield from herring as 53 per cent of ungutted landed weight, with a range from 47 per cent to 58 per cent. The Norwegian Fisheries Research Institute collected data indicating a yield on a weight basis of edible meat from herring after various forms of processing from 36 per cent to 65 per cent. The yield of protein in the edible meat expressed as a percentage of the protein in the whole fish can be about 5 units higher. Thus, the efficiency of fish protein utilization by direct human consumption of herring ranges from about 40 to 70 per cent. Turning to pilchards, generally the fish is canned which involves removal of the heads and guts. This leads to a reduction of about 20 to 30 per cent in the weight of the whole fish and a reduction of about 18 to 24 per cent

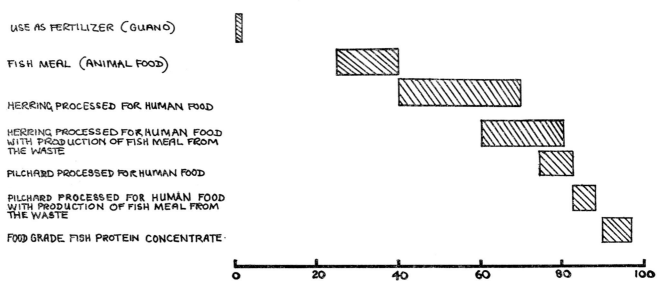

PERCENT EFFECIENCY OF PELAGIC FISH PROTEIN CONVERSION TO HUMAN FOOD BY VARIOUS PROCESSES

USE AS FERTILIZER (GUANO)

FISH MEAL (ANIMAL FOOD)

HERRING PROCESSED FOR HUMAN FOOD

HERRING PROCESSED FOR HUMAN FOOD WITH PRODUCTION OF FISH MEAL FROM THE WASTE

PILCHARD PROCESSED FOR HUMAN FOOD

PILCHARD PROCESSED FOR HUMAN FOOD WITH PRODUCTION OF FISH MEAL FROM THE WASTE

FOOD GRADE FISH PROTEIN CONCENTRATE

Fig 2

in the total protein. Thus the efficiency of fish protein utilization by direct human consumption of pilchard ranges from about 75 to 82 per cent.

A fresh fish operation or canning operation can be made more efficient if it is operated in conjunction with a fish meal process utilizing the waste material. This is done in many countries of the world. The increased efficiency is calculated by adding to the percentage of fish protein utilized directly for human food, the remaining protein as a percentage, divided by a factor of three in order to take into account the efficiency of utilizing fish protein via broiler production of one-third. For example, let it be assumed that 55 per cent of the protein from herring is processed into fillets for direct human consumption. The remaining 45 per cent protein is manufactured into fish meal and one-third of this is eventually presented to the human consumer in the form of chicken flesh, ie, an additional 15 per cent. Thus, in this particular operation 70 per cent of the fish protein eventually finds its way into human food. The most efficient use of fish protein would be obtained by utilizing the whole fish for manufacture of concentrated protein and feeding the resultant product directly to humans. Under these circumstances one would achieve a protein utilization approaching 100 per cent Fig 2. Fish meal manufacturers are aware of the developments in the food grade fish protein concentrate programme and are participating in it. If acceptable products can be produced which are commercially marketable, this development would increase the efficiency of utilization of fish protein to its maximum potential. Small commercial developments are taking place in various countries at the present time, but the tonnages of these products consumed are as yet insignificant compared with the tonnages fed to livestock. This is, nevertheless, a logical step in a continuous improvement in the efficient utilization of marine protein resources. Furthermore, certain aspects of the fish protein concentrate (FPC) programme, particularly FPC grade

B (eg hygienically produced fish meal) offer the possibility of a cheap source of nutritious protein. The intermediaries of expensive freezing, chilling, smoking, or filleting plants are not required, neither are poultry nor pig farms and meat packing stations. Thus capital outlay and qualified manpower are kept to a minimum. The product, being concentrated, is relatively easy to move and has good keeping qualities.

CONCLUSIONS

As the foregoing considerations show, the fish meal industry has a vital role to play. This opinion was expressed in the OECD Review of Fisheries in Member Countries (1972) in which it was stated, 'If the fish meal and oil industry did not exist the raw material it uses would be left in the sea and whatever part it might play in the marine food chain as such would contribute neither protein nor earning to mankind. As in other fisheries, the main motivation is economic and until a better paying outlet becomes available, and at present there are few hopeful signs, the manufacture of meal and oil from fish will continue provided the respective fish stocks remain prolific and, of course, the products remain in demand. In many countries developing their fisheries potential it is easier and more economic to develop a meal industry rather than a large scale food fish industry in the first instance. Once a meal industry has been established, a human food market might develop based on the capital accumulated and the fishery expertise gained during the years of meal production. At the present time substantial quantities of unexploited or under-exploited fish are reported by FAO to lie off the coasts of Argentina, West Africa, Indonesia, in the Arabian Sea and elsewhere. Most of these fish are not suitable for the human food market but could be a valuable addition to the world tonnage of meal produced.

With those species which are used **both** for human

food and fish meal production, the fish protein can be more efficiently utilized by processing the fish for the human food market rather than by manufacturing meal. Even so this improvement in efficiency can be increased if the waste material produced by separating the edible portions of the fish is manufactured into meal. However, having said this, it is important to emphasize a point made by Elliot earlier this year when he spoke to the FAO Technical Conference on Fishery Management and Development. 'Although it is often suggested that certain types of fish 'ought' to be converted into food products rather than fish meal, operators (government or private) have obviously made the best economic calculation they can when they decide in favour of fish meal. Where fish resources are unlimited, operators must surely be left to obtain the best economic return, and for some types and concentration of fish this is likely to come from fish meal. Where fish resources become limited and are controlled by quotas, fish meal operations tend to become uneconomic and a larger proportion of the catch will go to food products anyway. There appears to be no reason why governments should seek to reinforce this trend by banning fish meal operations and allowing food processors into the field instead. Such action is likely to be a misuse of economic resources and the government must then take the responsibility for scrapping existing capital in fish meal plant which otherwise would continue to contribute to the economy.'

The ultimate efficiency of fish protein utilization is achieved by converting whole fish into food grade FPC, certain types of which also offer the possibility of providing a cheap source of nutritious protein. In the next two or three decades much more of this development will be seen.

Utilization of Fish Meal Protein in Modern Integrated System for Domestic Animal Feeding
T E Petersen, B H Christensen and E E Petersen

Utilisation de la proteine de farine de poisson dans un systeme moderne integre pour alimentation des animaux domestiques

Dans la littérature il a souvent été suggéré qu'en cas d'alimentation des animaux domestiques par farine de poisson, l'utilisation de la protéine est d'environs 10 pour cent. Cependant, les taux récemment publiés donnent une utilisation de 25 à 35 pour cent.

Les auteurs ont examiné le NPU pour farine de poisson dans une chaîne alimentaire moderne intégrée pour volaille et ruminants, en tenant compte des possibilités de recyclage des fientes valorisées et d'autres sous-produits, et ont par cela abouti à une utilisation de protéine d'environ 55 pour cent. Ce chiffre est ensuite mis en relation avec l'utilisation des genres de poisson des différents niveaux de la chaîne alimentaire maritime naturelle.

Ci-joint veuillez trouver une discussion de la question de la protéine de poisson concentrée ainsi que de la signification de la farine de poisson pour la production des protéines animales comme nourriture humaine.

Utilizacion de las proteinas de la harina de pescado en un sistema integrado para la alimentacion de animales domesticos

En las publicaciones, frecuentemente es indicado que la utilización de las proteinas para la alimentación de animales domésticos con harina de pescado, es en el orden del 10 por ciento. Sin embargo recientes valores varian entre 25–35 por ciento.

Los autores han investigado el NPU para harina de pescado en una moderna cadena de alimentación integrada para aves de corral y rumiantes, considerando las posibilidades de recircular abono de aves refinado y otros subproductos, resultando en la utilización total de las proteinas de cerca el 55 por ciento. Este valor es referido a la utilización de especies de pescado de diferentes niveles de la cadena natural de alimentación marina.

Una discusión en cuanto a la cuestión del f.p.c. y de la importancia de la harina de pescado en la producción de proteinas animales para la alimentación humana, es incluída.

It is often mentioned in the literature (Roels 1971) that utilization of protein through fish meal in feeding domestic animals leads to waste up to 90 per cent, i.e. only 10 per cent of the added protein is recovered in edible products. However, a figure of about 17 per cent has also been presented (Finch 1970).

Barlow and Burton (1973) recently discussed the protein economy when marine resources are converted into fish meal and further used for edible animal products. They point out that 90 per cent of the 25.5 million tons of raw fish which were used for meal production in 1970 consisted of species which are currently regarded as unsaleable for human food.

Furthermore, they contend that prolific fish species, such as Menhaden, should be fished at a balanced rate, so that they should not interfere with the growth of more desirable species. In any case mankind cannot afford to let such quantities of fish remain unharvested as, for instance, those in the waters of the Argentine, West Africa, Indonesia, and in the Arabian Sea.

PROTEIN CONVERSION EFFICIENCY

The protein conversion efficiency of fish meal in broiler raising is calculated to be 25 per cent, and on a lysine supplementation basis 34 per cent. In making these calculations the authors have considered only the yield of directly edible chicken flesh and have not made any corrections for additional yields obtained by utilization of protein-rich by-products. These yields are compared with those obtained when preparing clupeid species for human consumption, eg

Filleting of Norway herring:	52 per cent
Canning of pilchards:	80 per cent

The authors consider manufacture of fish protein concentrate as the most efficient way of using whole fish for human nutrition as the yield approaches 100 per cent. Commercial developments are taking place in North and South America, India, Africa and Europe in which fish meal manufacturers are participating.

This paper attempts to calculate the total protein

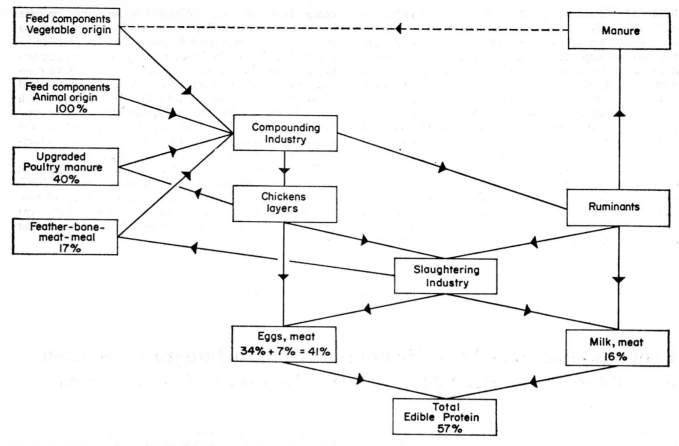

Fig 1   Feed line combined with the possible up-grading and recycling systems for by-products of the kind being introduced in Denmark and England.

utilization of fish meal in a modern integrated production of edible protein, when considering the special ability of fish meal protein to balance vegetable feed proteins and the possibility of recycling by-products. Figure 1 shows a feed line combined with the possible upgrading and recycling systems for by-products, of the kind being introduced in Denmark and England.

Feed components of vegetable and animal origins are compounded into balanced fodder mixtures for poultry. The first by-product is poultry manure, which is dried and sterilized. It contains nitrogen compounds corresponding to about 40 per cent of the protein in the feed. The crude protein concentration in this product is about 35 per cent. This permits 10 per cent recycling into the poultry fodder compound without lowering the growth of the animals. It can also constitute the main protein source for milking cattle or growing calves with a net protein utilization of about 40 per cent (Thomas *et al.*, 1972).

The protein in the edible parts of the slaughtered animals represents some 25 per cent of the total protein fed. The offal from the slaughterhouses (not counting bones in the edible parts) are sterilized and dried into blood-/feather-/meat meal. This recovers about 17 per cent of the feed protein. This by-product too is recycled into domestic fodder compounds with an average protein utilization of around 40 per cent.

Using the figures for protein conversion efficiency established by Barlow and Burton, and adding the

digestible protein derived from by-products, the result is:

Edible flesh protein	34 per cent
Digestible protein from manure protein	16 per cent
Digestible protein from slaughterhouse by-products	7 per cent
Total protein utilization	57 per cent

This result corresponds with Danish experience in large scale feeding of domestic animals.

UTILIZATION OF THE RESOURCES FROM THE OCEAN

Filleting of pelagic fish of the clupeid type results in a yield of some 52 per cent. Corresponding figures (Finch 1970) for the utilization of fish of the cod-type when consumed directly are put at 36 per cent and of the tuna-type at about 33 per cent. Considering the well known feed chain in the sea – phytoplancton, herbivorous (zoo-plancton, anchoveta) 1. carnivorous (clupeids) 2. carnivorous (cod, tuna) 3. carnivorous (tuna) – and accepting the normal assumption of a reduction of 10:1 between successive links, we arrive at the following yield figures for marine protein available for edible purposes (excluding phytoplancton):

Carnivorous 1. (clupeids):	
Filleting and direct consumption	52 per cent
Through fish meal	55–60 per cent

110

Carnivorous 2. (codfish, etc.):
Direct consumption: 0.1 × 36 per cent   3.6 per cent
Carnivorous 3. (tuna, etc.):
Canning: 0.01 × 33 per cent   0.33 per cent

While it has been stated that converting marine protein resources into fish meal incurs a loss of 90 per cent, the above figures indicate the contrary, and that fish meal production is one of the most efficient ways of utilizing marine protein for edible purposes. While it might be argued that balancing the vegetable diets of animals could be done by adding synthetic amino acids, minerals, etc., it seems more logical and economical to use such additives for direct enrichment of human food and to use the fish meal for feed.

The conversion of raw fish into a protein concentrate almost tasteless and odourless has attracted considerable attention, but FPC seems to lack the basic attraction to gain consumer acceptance. So far the majority of attempts to introduce it has been to incorporate it in baked cereal products. But such enrichment of products is questionable. New ideas for its use have to be introduced to justify production of FPC for human consumption. Considering the enormous amount of time, money and resources which have been spent on the development of FPC, such new uses are certainly needed. One attempt

is the use of hygienically produced fish meal as a condiment for soups and stews. Trials of this product under the name of "Joyfish" have been successfully initiated in some African countries by a Norwegian company. In view of these various considerations and of the desire of developing countries to modernize and expand their fishery industries, a first step in such development could be the utilization of small pelagic fish resources for the production of fish meal. This could be a start to the establishment of a modern integrated industry for production of highly acceptable food products of animal origin. As the international market for fish meal is well established and offers good prices, the outlook for such an industry is favourable and production surplus to the need of the local feed industry could easily be exported to earn valuable foreign exchange.

References

BARLOW, S M and BURTON, F W *The Role of Fish Meal in Allevia-*
1973 *tion of Protein Shortages in Human Nutrition.* International Association of Fish Meal Manufacturers.
FINCH, R. Fish protein for human foods. *CRC Critical Reviews in*
1970 *Food Technology,* December, p. 519–580.
ROELS, O A. Fish protein: Its past, present and future. *Nautilus.*
1971 *Documenta Geigy,* (11).
THOMAS, J W, YU YU, TINNIMITT, P and ZINDELL, H C. Dehydrated
1972 poultry waste as a feed for milking cows and growing sheep. *J. Dairy Sci.,* 55(9):1261–65.

Technical Note

Fish Protein Processing: Efficiency of Drying Equipment   *O Myklestad*

The effects of processing on the quality of fishery products and the economy of manufacture have been studied in laboratory tests and in the fish meal industry. These are described briefly in the following text.

Protein lability

A number of chemical changes, e.g. the Maillard reaction and other combinations of reactive groups, have been identified. High temperature processes also may result in significant volatile losses, destruction of amino acids, and burning or charring of protein material. The effects of these adverse changes are manifested by discolorations, decreased solubility and enzymatic cleavability, stronger structural network and, consequently, lower nutritional value.

Laboratory protein tests. Freeze dried herring powders were subjected to variable thermal exposures in a carefully controlled rotary autoclave, some typical results of which are listed in Table 1. Variations in total protein were small and most likely within the experimental error. The other quality criteria (pepsin digestibility, digestibility on the rat, and NPU on the rat and chick) were all adversely affected, the wet powders more than the dry.

Industrial protein tests. A full scale parallel flow rotary dryer, with meal from capelin, was used for these tests. Conditions and results are compiled in Table 2. Total protein in the factory meals were only slightly lower than in the freeze dried reference meals. Pepsin digestibility

(Torry) for meals from unpreserved fish tended to decrease with increasing air temperature. Digestibility of the meal from chemically preserved fish was not affected, a tendency which has been confirmed elsewhere. Feeding trials on rats and chicks revealed that the factory dried meals had decreased growth potential, NPU and PER, but the changes were not consistent with variations in process conditions.

Thermal economy

The marginal profits on fishery products require that all process costs be kept at a minimum. The following few examples illustrate the economic significance of process control. While prominence is given to the drying process, which is particularly rewarding, an analogue discussion of any other thermal process could have been undertaken.

Laboratory measurements. Meals from capelin, herring and mackerel were dried in Torry's wind tunnel at Aberdeen. The drying effect increased with increasing thermal input and decreased with increasing humidity. These findings would be expected in the absence of protein crustation. The influence of air velocity was not immediately predictable. The drying increased with increasing air velocity during the initial stage (wet materials) for all three fish species, but in the final stage (drier material) for only mackerel. These findings give some basis for optimizing the process, while they also

TABLE 1. PROTEIN QUALITY OF AUTOCLAVED HERRING POWDERS

Time min.	Temp. °C	Moist. %	Protein (Total) %[1]	Protein digest. %[2] Torry (dil.)	Protein digest. %[2] Rat (apparent)	NPU, %[2] Rat	NPU, %[2] Chick
0	*	3.1	84.2	100(84.6)[3]	100(82.1)[3]	100(61.2)[3]	100(67.5)[3]
120	96	10.8	85.0	76.0			98.1
120	96	41.0	84.2	66.4	96.0	91.3	89.2
0	*	9.3	85.0	100(85.5)	100(86.9)	100(85.7)	100(66.1)
120	116	6.4	84.0	78.1	97.2	95.3	96.8
120	115	27.0	83.6	43.7	87.7	89.1	85.3
0	*	3.3	83.5	100(87.6)	100(85.8)	100(79.0)	100(65.7)
120	132	2.5	83.0	66.6	95.5	91.8	97.1
120	124	32.0	82.5	33.4	86.1	81.1	76.7

*Freeze dried reference powders   [1]Dry weight basis   [2]Values relative to freeze dried reference powders
[3]Measured values in parenthesis

TABLE 2. PROTEIN QUALITY OF FACTORY DRIED CAPELIN MEALS

Air, °C In	Air, °C Out	Meal, °C In	Meal, °C Max	Meal, °C Out	Meal, % moist In	Meal, % moist Out	Protein, %* (Total)	Protein, %* Digest (Torry)	Rat growth %*	Chick NPU %*	Chick PER %*
790	74	69	79	51	65.1	13.5	97.0	89.8[u]	—	94	83
870	74	70	79	68	69.6	5.2	98.8	87.8[u]	—	—	—
900	78	64	86	59	59.7	12.3	98.6	99.4[p]	93	99	78
950	82	72	76	67	58.4	10.4	98.6	93.5[u]	—	—	—
1,065	78	65	84	54	59.7	14.3	97.3	82.2[u]	98	95	91

*Values relative to freeze dried reference meals   [u]Unpreserved fish   [p]Chemically preserved fish

point out characteristic structural difference within meals from various fish species.

Industrial measurements. The wind tunnel experiments were supplemented by comparative industrial trials (Table 2). The plot of thermal efficiency against the process rate demonstrates the importance of maintaining a high load in the plant. The initial steepness of the temperature and moisture profiles within the drying compartment illustrates a rather vigorous action in the first half of the compartment. These and other findings suggested that an increased hold-up in that region might improve thermal efficiency, and this was tested after a slight plant modification. Two sections of return flights were fitted into the first half of the compartment, and the performance was measured again. The thermal efficiency had increased by about 9 per cent and the load by about 15 per cent. Quality assessments confirmed that the fish meal standard had not suffered by the plant modification.

Marine Lipids and Fatty Acids in Human Nutrition   R G Ackman

Lipides et acides gras d'animaux marins en nutrition humaine
Divers acides entrent dans la composition des graisses des poissons, crustacés et mollusques. Certains d'entre eux, en particulier les acides saturés en C_{16} et C_{18} et les acides mono-insaturés, sont utiles quoique non indispensables en nutrition humaine. Les acides gras "essentiels" connus de la famille de l'acide linoléique sont des constituants mineurs par comparaison avec les acides de la famille de l'acide linolénique qui sont des constituants poly-insaturés caractéristiques des graisses d'animaux marins. Les acides poly-insaturés en C_{20} et C_{22} de la famille de l'acide linolénique peuvent être utiles du point de vue nutritionnel – encore que l'on ne sache pas encore comment – pour les animaux supérieurs.

L'étude de la teneur en cholestérol des produits de la pêche comestibles, en termes de protéines, donne a penser que les poissons gras ne sont pas fortement désavantagés par rapport aux poissons maigres dont les régimes pauvres en stérols. Du fait de leur faible teneur en lipides, les mollusques et crustacés sont indiqués dans de tels régimes, d'autant plus que le cholestérol représente souvent moins de la moitié de la teneur totale en stérols des coquillages.

Lipidos marinos y acidos grasos en la alimentacion del hombre
Las grasas de peces, crustáceos y moluscos contienen diversos ácidos. Algunos de ellos, en especial, los monoácidos no saturados como el C_{16} y C_{18} son útiles aunque no necesarios en la alimentación humana. Los ácidos grasos "esenciales" conocidos de la familia del ácido linoléico son constituyentes menores que los ácidos de la familia linolénica que son los constituyentes poli-insaturados característicos de las grasas marinas. Los ácidos poli-insaturados C_{20} y C_{22} de la familia linolénica pueden ser benéficos en la alimentación en forma hasta el momento indefinida para los animales superiores. El examen del contenido en colesterol de los productos pesqueros comestibles en relación con las proteínas, indica que el pescado graso no es peor que el magro en aquellos regímenes en que el consumo de esterol está contraindicado. La poca grasa de crustáceos y moluscos los hace aptos en las dietas rigurosas, en especial, porque el colesterol es con frecuencia tan mínimo como la mitad del esterol del marisco.

La auto-oxidación del pescado almacenado en frigorífico tiene interés por ser motivo de rancidez y causar reacciones que afectan

L'auto-oxydation du poisson entreposé à l'état congelé revêt de l'importance car elle se traduit par le rancissement du produit et provoque des réactions subtiles qui affectent la texture de la chair. La communication passe brièvement en revue les données disponibles sur les rapports diététiques et nutritionnels qui peuvent exister entre les acides gras poly-insaturés d'animaux aquatiques et l'auto-oxydation, les péroxydes, la saveur, la toxicité, la pisciculture, les antioxygènes naturels et les procédés de maturation.

Les acides gras monoéthyléniques à chaîne en C_{22} se rencontrent dans beaucoup de graisses de dépôt mais leur proportion est faible dans les muscles de poissons maigres, les mollusques et les crustacés. Toutefois, lors de l'hydrogénation partielle des huiles d'animaux marins servant à la fabrication de graisses comestibles, les acides gras polyinsaturés se convertissent en acides monoéthyléniques dans toutes les huiles provenant de la réduction du poisson en farine ou dans les huiles de baleine et de phoque. Récemment, les études sur l'huile de colza ont amené à formuler des critiques à l'encontre de l'emploi de ces acides pour l'alimentation des mammifères. Les effets de différents procédés sont comparés avec ceux de l'huile de colza, et les effets physiologiques observés chez diverses espèces animales sont examinés.

a la textura. Se resumen las relaciones conocidas entre la dieta y la alimentación que pueden ocurrir entre los ácidos grasos poli-insaturados acuáticos y la auto-oxidación, peróxidos, sabor, toxicidad, piscicultura, anti-oxidantes naturales y procesos de envejecimiento.

En muchas grasas de reserva existen ácidos grasos mono-etilénicos de C_{22} que no son importantes en los músculos magros de pescado, moluscos y crustáceos. No obstante, la hidrogenación parcial de los aceites marinos para la producción de grasas comestibles, convierte los ácidos grasos poli-insaturados en ácidos monoetilénicos en todos los aceites producidos mediante la transformación del pescado en harina o de los aceites de ballena y foca. Recientemente los estudios del aceite de colza han sido motivo de críticas del empleo de estos ácidos en la alimentación de los mamíferos. Se comparan los resultados de diferentes experimentos con los efectos del aceite de colza y se examinan los efectos fisiológicos demostrados por diversas especies animales.

The classic work on the desirable dietary role of certain fatty acids, particularly the 'essential' fatty acid linoleic, goes back to 1929 (reviewed by Mead 1968 and Soderhjelm et al. 1970). Even following this development nutritionalists tended to limit their view of fats and oils to one of these being reasonably digestible material providing ca 9,000 cal/g energy, with supplemental benefits from the fat-soluble vitamins A, D and E. Outstanding advances in our understanding of the biochemistry and chemistry of fats required the development of precision small-scale analytical technology (Holman and Rahm 1966; Privett 1966; Ackman 1972; Kuksis 1972) and the impetus provided by the worldwide interest in the relationship between blood cholesterol and cardiovascular diseases in the decade starting about 1955. This technology has now been applied to the fats of many raw fisheries materials and to the partially hydrogenated fats incorporated in margarines and similar edible fats. Discussion can now be based on individual fatty acids in lieu of the former necessarily comprehensive analyses of polyunsaturated fatty acids in terms of numbers of double bonds, which were sometimes misleading in toto due to the varying biological activity of different isomers (Holman 1970). Unfortunately, less attention has been paid to the fats of convenience fishery foods popular in developed countries where substantial proportions of the fat may be of vegetable or other origin and quite different in composition from that of the incorporated raw fishery material.

NATURAL FATTY ACIDS OF MARINE LIPIDS IN NUTRITION

With due care and attention to detail a complete analysis of the fatty acids of a marine lipid by thin-layer and gas-liquid chromatographic techniques can include up to 50 or 60 components. Fewer are necessary (Ackman and Eaton 1971a; Gedam et al. 1971), and only about fourteen need be discussed as important in terms of weight per cent composition. These belong to the four basic series typified by the C_{18} acids of Fig 1. These have no double bonds (18:0 or stearic acid); one double bond removed nine carbon atoms from the methyl end (18:1ω9[1] or oleic acid); two double bonds removed six carbon atoms from the methyl end (18:2ω6 or linoleic acid) and

three double bonds removed three carbon atoms from the methyl end (18:3ω3 or linolenic acid). Most important polyunsaturated fatty acids preserve this relationship to the methyl group even when extra double bonds are introduced. These are listed in Tables 1, 2 and 3 where fatty acid compositions are given for a variety of marine fish, marine invertebrates, and freshwater fish of different origins. The same gross fatty acid compositions are found in marine mammal depot fats (Ackman et al. 1971a), but as these fats are not major elements in the human diet in raw form their significance will be discussed under partially hydrogenated fats.

FAMILIES OF FATTY ACIDS (C_{18})

$$CH_3 - CH_2 - CH_2 - CH_2 - CH_2 - CH_2 - CH_2 - CH_2 - \quad \text{Stearic}$$

$$CH_3 - (CH_2)_7 - CH = CH - \quad \text{Oleic}$$

$$CH_3 - (CH_2)_4 - CH = CH - CH_2 - CH = CH - \quad \text{Linoleic}$$

$$CH_3 - CH_2 - CH = CH - CH_2 - CH = CH - CH_2 - CH = CH - \text{Linolenic}$$

Fig 1 Comparison of critical parts of the structures of common fatty acids. The number of carbon atoms between the terminal methyl group and the center of the nearest double bond identifies the family (saturated, oleic, linoleic or linolenic) but the names themselves apply only to the C_{18} members

Almost all fish, crustacea and molluscs have approximately 0.7 per cent total phospholipids in their muscle. This is a basic cellular pattern and is modified by the inclusion of greater or lesser amounts of triglycerides which may also be cellular lipids at the 0.1 to 0.2 per cent levels, but otherwise are essentially depot fats and may range from 1 to 5 per cent in muscle of flatfish such as flounder to 20 to 30 per cent in fatty fish such as herring and mackerel. The reasons for continued interest in the classes of lipid in aquatic animals are to a certain extent biological as the depot fats can be used as a guide to the nutritional status of the animal. These are also in many cases reflected in pronounced seasonal variations in the depot fat in edible fishery products and hence in gross nutritional value.

Most lipids are completely hydrolyzed in the digestive tracts of humans and other animals (Kifer and Miller 1969, Bour 1971). It is therefore immaterial from a nutritional point of view whether the fatty acids are

---

[1] Chain length: number of double bonds and position relative to terminal methyl group in monoethylenic and methylene-interrupted polyunsaturated fatty acids.

TABLE 1. WEIGHT % OF MAJOR FATTY ACIDS IN AQUATIC TRIGLYCERIDE OILS FROM DIFFERENT GEOGRAPHICAL AREAS PRODUCED BY COMMERCIAL REDUCTION, OR ISOLATED BY LABORATORY EXTRACTIONS, OR ACCEPTED AS OIL BECAUSE OF HIGH LIPID CONTENT

	14:0	16:0	18:0	16:1	18:1	20:1	22:1	18:2ω6	18:3ω3	18:4ω3	20:4ω6	20:5ω3	22:5ω3	22:6ω3
Atlantic														
Herring (Can.)[1]	6.4	12.7	0.9	8.8	12.7	14.1	20.8	1.1	0.6	1.7	0.3	8.4	0.8	4.9
Capelin (Can.)[2]	7.9	11.1	1.0	11.1	17.0	18.9	14.7	1.7	0.4	2.1	0.1	4.6	0.3	3.0
Newfoundland Turbot (Can.)[3]	6.5	12.0	0.9	15.4	17.4	18.6	17.8	0.5	0.2	0.8	0.1	3.0	0.6	1.9
Redfish (Can.)[4]	4.9	13.2	2.2	13.2	13.3	17.2	18.9	0.9	0.5	1.1	0.3	8.0	0.6	8.9
Pacific														
Sablefish (Can.)[3]	6.7	11.1	1.9	6.6	29.0	18.1	14.8	0.7	0.2	0.3	0.3	1.4	0.5	1.0
Saury (Jap.)[5]	6.9	13.4	2.4	5.1	10.1	13.4	13.8	2.3	2.3	5.9	0.9	8.4	1.7	12.0
Indian Ocean														
Pomfret[6]	14.0	28.9	6.1	15.8	13.8	4.6	2.9	2.4	0.7	—	—	3.2	2.8	4.7
Leather jacket[7]	3.3	25.9	7.2	4.2	22.5	trace	—	trace	trace	—	3.3	8.0	trace	24.6
Seer[8]	10.4	26.0	9.3	11.2	15.0	2.0	0.5	2.4	1.5	—	0.3	3.5	0.5	8.2
Freshwater														
Carp oil[9]	3.1	16.8	4.3	17.1	28.3	3.9	—	13.2	2.3	—	2.5	3.2	—	—
Carp muscle[10]	0.7	14.6	4.8	9.4	45.5	—	—	10.8	0.5	—	*	8.7	—	1.9
Sheepshead oil[11]	2.8	16.6	3.3	17.7	26.1	2.4	0.3	4.3	3.6	0.9	2.6	4.7	2.0	2.0
Tullibee oil[11]	4.6	13.8	2.9	21.5	25.2	1.3	0.3	1.9	2.6	1.5	1.7	6.2	1.8	3.8
Trout, cultured[11]	2.7	20.9	8.3	3.9	18.4	—	—	7.3	1.6	3.2	1.7	5.8	trace	7.0
Trout, cultured[12]	2.5	17.1	10.0	7.5	28.4	3.1	—	6.1	trace	trace	2.3	6.4	2.3	11.7
Catfish (low)[13]	1.0	15.2	3.9	2.9	29.7	0.9	—	10.0	0.5	0.4	0.8	0.2	0.2	0.6
Catfish (high)[13]	2.3	22.2	9.3	5.6	49.7	2.0	—	15.7	2.9	1.0	5.5	2.5	1.3	6.1
Marine Mammals														
Finwhale, Arctic[14]	5.0	12.0	1.7	12.0	30.6	12.1	9.7	1.3	0.5	0.7	0.3	3.7	1.6	4.1
Finwhale, Antarctic[15]	12.0	16.1	1.2	11.7	24.3	2.4	1.2	4.0	1.0	1.1	~0.5	5.6	3.7	4.5
Harp seal, Atlantic[16]	4.4	8.2	1.0	18.0	24.7	12.5	4.0	1.4	0.4	1.2	0.5	7.5	3.9	6.7

*Included in 20:5ω3   [1]Ackman and Eaton 1966a   [2]Ackman et al. 1969a   [3]Ackman et al. 1967   [4]Ackman and Ke 1968
[5]Ito and Fukuzumi 1962   [6]Gopakumar and Nair 1967   [7]Khalid et al. 1968   [8]Gopakumar and Nair 1972
[9]Toyomizu and Tomiyasu 1962   [10]Abdel-Hay and Herodek 1968   [11]Veresmaa et al. 1968   [12]Knipprath and Mead 1966
[13]Worthington et al. 1972   [14]Ackman et al. 1965   [15]Ackman and Eaton 1966b   [16]Jangaard and Ke 1968

derived from the phospholipids, triglycerides, sterol esters, glyceryl ethers or even wax esters. Although certain differences among the fourteen fatty acids are apparent in respect to the two basic lipid classes (Tables 2 and 3) even these diminish in significance when it is realized that several of these are produced in the human body in basic amounts adequate for normal physiological functions. Among these are 14:0 (myristic or tetradecanoic), 16:0 (palmitic or hexadecanoic) and 18:0 (stearic or octadecanoic). For the purpose of this discussion these three fatty acids can effectively be disregarded since they are common to most dietary fats. They are desirable in an appropriate balanced diet, and in raw aquatic foodstuffs the totals do not normally exceed about 30 per cent of total fatty acids irrespective of the type of lipid (Tables 1, 2 and 3).

POLYUNSATURATED ACIDS, ATHEROSCLEROSIS, CHOLESTEROL AND PEROXIDES

The polyunsaturated fatty acids of aquatic fats were the basis of the active interest in marine lipids in atherosclerotic studies since, if a lowering of serum cholesterol could be demonstrated with corn oil, then it was reasoned that superior results should be obtained with marine oils, esters of marine fatty acids, or fractions thereof, where the total unsaturation was two or three times that of corn oil. A book review (Enselme 1969) and a short summary (Hodges 1968) may be consulted for authoritative views on the subject of dietary and other factors in atherosclerosis. The tremendous research effort has had little permanent result on consumption of or demand for fishery products beyond some broadening of the basic constituents in recommended diets to include more use of fishery products (Feeley et al. 1972). Notwithstanding this, the image of some fishery products as potentially hazardous, due to "cholesterol" as a high percentage of lipid, has lingered on despite the very valid objection in respect to this problem that the contribution of excess dietary sterol to cholesterol in human plasma may be unimportant (Quintão et al. 1971) except on severe 'overloading' (Connor 1970).

From the data in Tables 4 to 8 it is possible to calculate that one serving of fish (100 g) would contribute about $\frac{1}{10}$th of the daily intake of cholesterol for the North American diet containing 0.5 per cent cholesterol, based on a total intake of either 300 mg/day (Nestel 1970) or 500 mg/day (Connor 1968). In shellfish, etc., cholesterol intake can be ridiculously low even though the sterol is recorded as a high proportion of lipid and in many areas of the world these are luxury foods, not dietary staples. Particular attention should be drawn to the sterol/protein ratios CCPI (Cholesterol Crude Protein Index) which have been extensively studied and tabulated by Koga (1970c) as a basis for dietary and nutritional proposals. A selection of these sterol/protein ratios is included in Table 8 but for further details on many more edible materials, the original publications (Koga 1970a, 1970b, 1970c) should be consulted. However invertebrate sterol ester values (eg oyster) may be too high as

TABLE 2. WEIGHT % OF MAJOR FATTY ACIDS OF PRINCIPAL LIPID TYPES IN MUSCLE TISSUE (EXCEPT FOR WHOLE HERRING) FROM SOME SELECTED SPECIES OF FISH, CRUSTACEANS AND MOLLUSCS

	14:0	16:0	18:0	16:1	18:1	20:1	22:1	18:2ω6	18:3ω3	18:4ω3	20:4ω6	20:5ω3	22:5ω3	22:6ω3
Cod flesh														
Total lipid (Can)[1]	1.4	19.6	3.8	3.5	13.8	3.0	1.0	0.7	0.1	0.4	2.5	17.0	1.3	29.8
Total lipid (Can)[2]	1.0	20.5	3.4	2.2	11.9	1.4	0.6	0.6	—	—	4.7	16.6	1.6	32.9
Phospholipid (UK)[3]	0.5	20.6	4.2	1.6	10.1	1.5	trace	0.8	trace	0.2	2.9	14.6	1.2	35.4
Sole flesh (UK)[3]														
Neutral	4.3	16.5	2.4	14.4	12.2	3.9	trace	0.3	2.0	1.6	4.0	11.9	10.6	7.0
Phospholipid	1.0	20.3	6.1	2.9	9.3	trace	trace	—	—	—	6.4	17.3	9.3	21.2
Halibut flesh (UK)[3]														
Neutral	0.8	9.6	9.0	2.5	12.3	4.0	5.0	trace	trace	—	1.4	13.0	2.5	37.6
Phospholipid	0.4	17.2	6.7	1.5	7.1	—	1.0	trace	—	—	3.4	8.1	trace	45.2
Rockfish flesh (USA)[4]														
Neutral	3.0	16.8	4.4	11.7	28.0	3.9	—	0.9	1.1	—	—	6.4	—	20.0
Phospholipid	0.5	20.0	5.5	2.4	8.9	0.6	—	0.6	0.2	—	—	9.1	—	47.0
Whole herring (Can)[5]														
Neutral	5.6	12.5	1.1	13.6	15.5	13.7	19.4	1.1	0.3	1.2	0.3	6.8	0.2	3.1
Phospholipid	1.8	21.4	3.2	4.6	13.0	2.4	1.6	0.9	0.3	0.2	1.4	12.2	0.8	32.7
Great Lakes coho salmon[6]														
Neutral	3.2	10.3	3.5	10.7	21.2	3.4	0.5	5.6	2.9	0.8	1.6	4.8	4.4	10.6
Phospholipid	3.0	15.6	4.7	8.9	25.3	2.3	0.6	3.6	2.6	1.0	1.3	3.7	4.1	9.9
Dogfish flesh (UK)[3]														
Neutral	1.8	17.0	2.9	4.6	16.1	5.2	4.0	2.2	—	1.3	2.7	8.3	2.7	21.8
Phospholipid	0.4	19.6	8.8	2.8	10.7	3.1	—	0.7	—	—	7.0	5.1	2.3	32.0
Queen crab flesh (Can)[7]														
Neutral	3.8	13.9	2.1	10.4	23.7	11.9	7.7	0.7	0.3	trace	1.7	10.7	1.4	9.2
Phospholipid	3.5	15.4	2.5	5.8	22.4	1.5	—	1.2	0.3	0.1	3.9	31.3	1.0	14.2
King crab whole meat (USA)[8]	1.4	9.2	4.3	5.0	15.0	3.5	3.9	3.2	3.3	2.3	0.6	21.5	1.4	10.2
Shrimp flesh (USA)[9]	2.5	16.0	2.6	5.8	19.0	2.4	1.6	1.5	1.4	1.0	0.4	22.0	1.2	16.0
Squid flesh (Can)[10]	2.2	27.6	4.4	0.4	4.9	4.9	0.5	0.3	0.1	0.1	0.8	15.8	0.3	37.1
Oyster, European (Can)[11]														
Neutral	5.7	36.5	5.0	4.3	10.2	3.3	—	2.3	2.9	3.0	0.7	6.3	trace	4.9
Phospholipid	8.6	28.4	9.5	2.6	8.7	7.8	0.2	1.3	1.5	0.2	1.6	7.1	0.4	3.9
Oyster, American (Can)[11]														
Neutral	3.6	22.5	1.4	4.9	7.7	1.4	—	0.1	3.3	5.0	—	14.1	0.6	14.0
Phospholipid	0.7	5.4	2.9	3.1	4.8	2.9	—	0.3	1.3	2.0	0.4	15.6	1.0	20.3

[1]Addison *et al.* 1968   [2]Jangaard *et al.* 1967   [3]Olley and Duncan 1965   [4]Wood *et al.* 1969   [5]Drozdowski and Ackman 1969
[6]Braddock and Dugan 1972   [7]Addison *et al.* 1972   [8]Krzeczkowski *et al.* 1971   [9]Krzeczkowski 1970
[10]Jangaard and Ackman 1965   [11]Watanabe and Ackman 1972

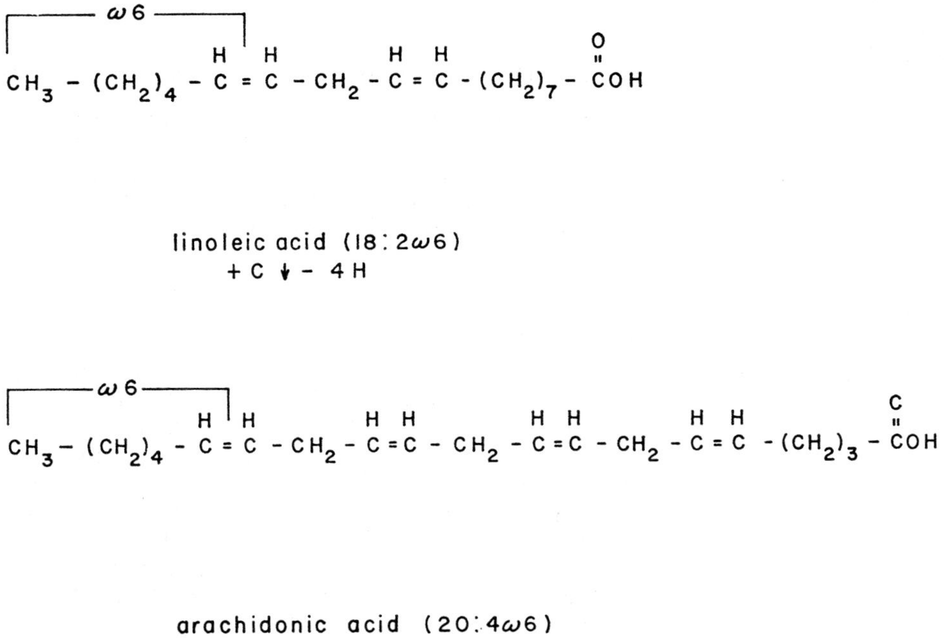

linoleic acid (18:2ω6)
+ C ↓ - 4H

arachidonic acid (20:4ω6)

Fig 2 *Conversion of linoleic acid to arachidonic acid. Note retention of the 'ω6' structure which confers 'essential' fatty acid activity*

Table 3. Comparison among weight per cent composition of major fatty acids from lipids of different types of "mackerel" edible tissues and oils

Fatty Acid / Σ % Lipid, Season, Tissue and Lipid Type	14:0	16:0	18:0	16:1	18:1	20:1	22:1	18:2ω6	18:3ω3	18:4ω3	20:4ω6	20:5ω3	22:5ω3	22:6ω3
Principal Neutral Lipid Acids														
Scomber scombrus Canada, Atlantic[1]														
14.4% Fall, dark meat, triglyceride	4.2	16.9	3.0	5.1	16.4	7.9	12.5	1.6	1.4	2.4	0.4	6.6	1.5	11.1
10.2% Fall, light meat, triglyceride	5.0	15.1	3.9	5.5	23.9	5.9	5.6	1.4	1.3	2.1	0.4	7.6	1.4	13.4
8.7% Spring, dark meat, total lipid	5.7	16.3	3.2	5.9	15.3	8.4	13.0	1.5	0.6	1.3	0.6	7.1	1.3	11.4
2.2% Spring, light meat, total lipid United Kingdom[2]	4.9	16.0	3.5	5.4	13.4	9.1	12.2	1.8	0.9	1.7	0.6	7.6	1.6	14.1
21.6% Fall, body flesh, triglyceride	4.6	16.3	3.7	5.1	24.9	6.3	8.3	2.1	(2.1)	2.9	—	8.3	—	10.9
3.9% Spring, body flesh, triglyceride Italy[3]	5.5	20.1	4.0	6.0	26.0	6.4	8.7	2.2	(2.2)	2.2	—	6.2	—	5.6
~7.3% Fall, triglyceride	4.2	11.5	6.1	8.9	24.3	~4.2	~3.2	1.7	—	1.4	0.7	7.4	1.2	18.2
~1.2% Spring, triglyceride Norway[4]	7.1	25.7	6.7	6.4	18.0	~3.5	~5.7	0.9	—	trace	trace	7.8	0.3	12.4
15.5% Fall, oil	6.6	12.9	2.4	3.8	15.0	11.6	16.6	1.4	1.5	4.8	0.7	6.5	0.9	9.5
Trachurus japonicus, Japan														
17.0% Fall, body flesh, triglyceride[5]	2.8	26.7	8.0	7.8	24.9	0.7	trace	1.2	~1.0	0.7	0.3	5.5	1.7	13.6
2.5% Spring, body flesh, triglyceride[5]	5.6	20.2	6.8	8.4	17.6	3.5	3.9	1.2	~1.4	1.4	1.5	9.4	2.0	8.7
Oil[6]	5.8	17.5	5.0	10.1	16.5	7.5	10.4	1.1	trace	1.8	1.0	7.6	1.7	8.5
Oil[7]	7.8	23.4	8.1	8.6	13.5	3.6	3.0	2.7	1.4	—	—	~2.1	—	7.6
Scomber japonicus, Japan														
Oil[6]	4.4	17.4	6.4	7.1	23.9	—	4.0	2.1	5.4	1.2	0.5	5.8	1.6	11.0
14.1% body oil[8]	6.2	14.1	2.9	6.4	13.7	11.8	14.4	1.6	0.3	3.9	0.5	10.2	0.9	7.3
Principal Polar Lipid Acids														
Scomber scombrus, Canada, Atlantic[1]														
1.6% Fall, dark meat, polar lipid	0.9	14.6	13.1	1.4	14.4	3.4	1.5	3.0	1.2	0.3	1.0	7.2	1.7	29.5
0.5% Fall, light meat, polar lipid United Kingdom[2]	0.5	20.4	7.4	1.8	9.2	1.6	1.0	1.6	0.5	0.2	1.7	10.7	1.6	36.3
1.0% Fall, body flesh, phospholipid	1.9	20.6	6.4	1.8	11.1	1.5	0.8	1.1	(1.1)	0.2	—	12.3	—	34.2
0.8% Spring, body flesh, phospholipid Italy[3]	0.4	18.8	7.3	1.7	9.7	1.1	1.0	1.6	(1.6)	0.3	—	12.5	—	39.8
Fall, body flesh, phospholipid	0.9	12.8	14.4	3.0	14.2	1.1	~3.2	1.5	—	0.4	0.6	7.0	1.4	30.7
Spring, body flesh, phospholipid	1.1	24.2	12.4	2.4	12.7	~0.7	~3.4	1.2	—	trace	trace	7.0	1.1	25.5
Trachurus japonicus, Japan														
0.8% Fall, body flesh, polar lipid[5]	0.3	14.5	13.0	1.1	10.8	0.3	trace	1.2	~0.6	trace	0.3	8.0	2.5	36.6
0.9% Spring, body flesh, polar lipid[5]	0.9	20.8	13.3	1.5	6.2	1.4	0.8	1.0	~0.6	0.3	0.7	9.6	3.0	31.3
1.2% Body flesh, total lipid[9]	2.2	34.0	8.0	6.0	15.6	—	—	1.0	1.1	—	2.1	7.3	2.4	25.3

[1]Ackman and Eaton 1971   [2]Hardy and Keay 1972   [3]Viviani *et al.* 1968   [4]Urdahl and Nygard 1971   [5]Ueda 1972
[6]*Ibid.* 1967   [7]Kajimoto and Yoshida 1970   [8]Yamada 1972   [9]Shono and Toyomizu 1971

'cholesterol' probably includes other sterols (compare Tables 4 and 5 and reviews by Idler and Wiseman 1971, 1972). The CCPI approach corrects for moisture and ash.

The polyunsaturated fatty acids which are relatively plentiful in aquatic lipids, especially those of marine origin, divide into two basic families of which the least plentiful is the linoleic where the ultimate ethylenic double bond is six carbon atoms removed from the terminal methyl group.

Linoleic (9, 12-octadecadienoic) acid is the true 'essential' fatty acid, probably mostly because it can be converted to arachidonic (5, 8, 11, 14-eicosatetraenoic) acid (Fig 2) which is seemingly essential for the function of many phospholipids, especially those of the liver and other vital organs, and certain glands such as the adrenals (Walker and Carney 1971). In most marine lipids linoleic acid itself amounts to 0.5 to 1.5 per cent of total fatty acids while arachidonic acid is somewhat less in depot fats but may be somewhat more in phospholipids (Tables 2 and 3). It is known that stepwise "retroconversion" of long-chain, highly unsaturated, fatty acids (C_{22}) can take place, usually to C_{20} fatty acids (Schlenk *et al.* 1969; Stoffel *et al.* 1970; Kunau 1971). Thus any 22:5ω6 can be altered by animals to the desirable 20:4ω6 via 22:4ω6. Fish may be useful in our diet as

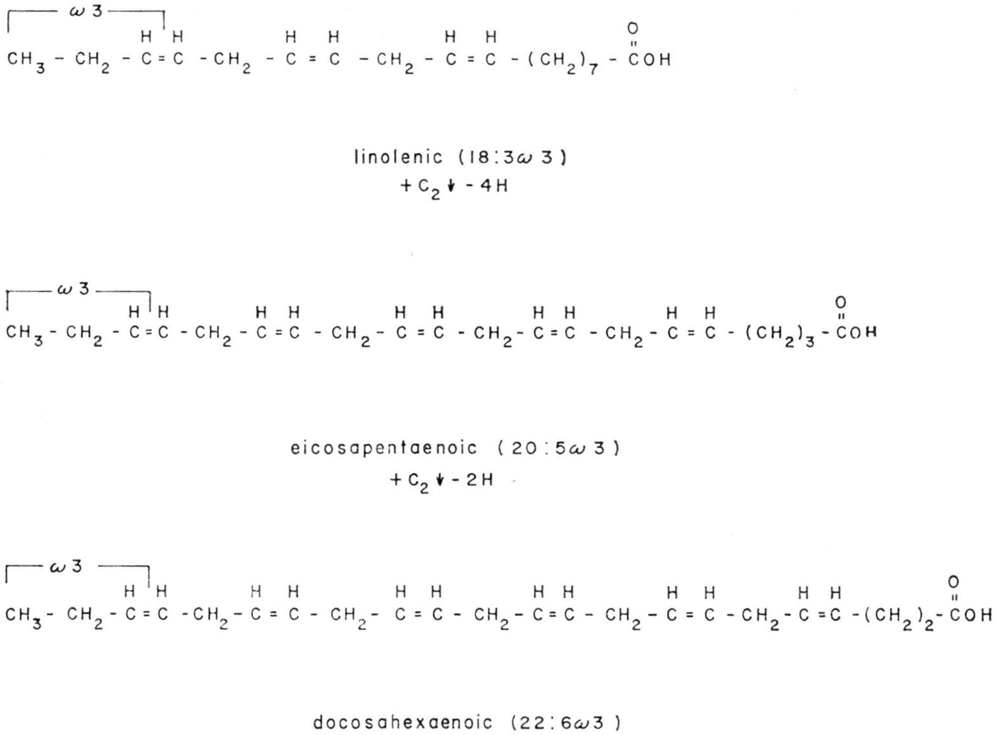

linolenic (18:3ω3)

+C₂ ↓ -4H

eicosapentaenoic (20:5ω3)

+C₂ ↓ -2H

docosahexaenoic (22:6ω3)

Fig 3 *Conversion of linolenic acid to eicosapentaeoic and docosahexaenoic acids. Note retention of "ω3" structure*

22:5ω6 and 22:4ω6 are in fact usually present in most marine lipids although at the trace (<0.1 per cent) level. While the exact daily dosage of linoleic (ω6) fatty acids in man is not very well defined, it is not large and the turnover rate is rather lengthy (Lang and Reimold 1970). These authors indicate that the long-chain aquatic fatty acids fed to rats buffer the short-term fluctuations in 18:2ω6 and 18:3ω6. Thus, even fishery products low in the C₁₈ 'essential' fatty acids could contribute effectively to a balanced diet of both developed and developing countries. It is noteworthy that most freshwater fish and especially commercially cultivated fish (Table 1) tend to have high levels of 18:2ω6 (Ackman 1967; Stickney and Andrews 1971; Worthington *et al.* 1972). This reflects inexpensive terrestrial food sources rich in 18:2ω6, usually accompanied by 18:3ω3 (Albrecht and Breits-precher 1969; Rimsh 1970). The provocative title of a recent scientific paper was 'Evidence for Nonessentiality of Linolenic Acid in the Diet of the Rat' (Tinoco *et al.* 1971). This paper has been criticized. From a fisheries point of view it is, however, necessary to bring into question the whole family of linolenic acids since, while linolenic acid itself is seldom more than a minor (<0.3 per cent) component of marine lipids (excluding certain herbivorous molluscs such as periwinkles, and similarly some fish such as carp, etc., with access to vegetation), the longer-chain more highly unsaturated successor acids of 18:3ω3 with five and six double bonds are the very components which give fish oils and lipids their distinctive character and can total up to 35 to 40 per cent of total fatty acids in some cases (Tables 1, 2 and 3). The two important acids of this type derive from 18:3ω3 (linolenic acid: by chain extension and further desaturation as shown in Fig. 3). The formation of the 20:5ω3 and 22:6ω3 acids from 18:3ω3 by fish is well known and

accepted but the rationale is still uncertain (Stickney and Andrews 1971; Owen *et al.* 1972). Although reduced temperatures are usually invoked to explain this chain extension phenomenon (Andrews and Stickney 1972) it is likely that this may be an oversimplified explanation. Molluscs, for example, appear to be satisfied with mostly 20:5ω3 as their principal long-chain polyunsaturated fatty acid, and this is reflected in their lipids (mostly phospholipids) in increased 22:5ω3 relative to 22:6ω3. The latter acid must then be less necessary to molluscs, while in phospholipids of crustacea and the vertebrates there is increased relative emphasis on 22:6ω3. Nonetheless, 20:5ω3, 22:5ω3 and 22:6ω3 account for the similarities in gross fatty acid compositions of phospholipids from many species where the total is about 40 per cent of all fatty acids (Ackman 1966). Typical examples are illustrated in Table 2. These acids are apparently interconvertible in higher animals, and all equally acceptable in the diet.

The overall impression of the validity of the needs for particular polyunsaturated fatty acids in man and animals is one of confusion (Holman, 1970). Competition between 'linoleic' and 'linolenic' acids exists (Actis Dato and Brenner 1970), even in the brain (Miller *et al.* 1971), and insufficient attention may have been paid to distinctions among muscles and organs (Dvorakova and Bass 1970; Kaunitz 1970), to 'growth factors' (Menge 1971), or to morphological changes, including a decrease in brain size as distinct from other clinical manifestations of fatty acid nutritional problems (Sinclair and Crawford 1971; compare Tinoco *et al.* 1971). It is quite probable that very small amounts of these polyunsaturated acids can be usefully stored even in diluted form against eventual need (Owen *et al.* 1972), and this may have been an original basis for the prominent role of the

TABLE 4. CHOLESTEROL CONTENTS OF MUSCLE FROM EDIBLE FISH AND THE MEATS OF CRUSTACEA AND MOLLUSCS (NORTH AMERICA)

	Per cent sterol in non-saponifiables Cholesterol[1]	Other sterols[1]	Apparent cholesterol content (mg/100 g) calculated on an edible wet weight basis 1	2
Haddock	93.1	5.9	90	—
Pollack	94.1	—	75	—
Salmon	96.1	—	95	—
Lobster meat	99.2	—	170	—
Crab meat	57.4	—	140	52–98
Shrimp meat	95.6	—	200	157
Oyster	41.4	58.6	150	37–58
Clam	36.7	63.3	190	82
Scallop muscle	25.7	74.3	175	60
Alaskan king crab	62.3[3]	37.9[3]	—	—
Atlantic queen crab	93.8[3]	6.3[3]	—	—

[1]Adapted from Kritchevsky, D, Tepper, S A, Ditulla, N W and Holmes, W L *J. Fd Sci.*, 32:64–66, 1967, unless otherwise stipulated.
[2]Adapted from Thompson, M H *Fishery ind. Res.*, 2:11–15, 1964.
[3]Adapted from Idler, D R and Wiseman, P *Comp. Biochem. Physiol.*, 26:1113–1117, 1968.

TABLE 5. STEROL AND FAT CONTENTS OF SOME NORTH AMERICA FISHERY PRODUCTS

	Sterol[1] (mg/100)	Fat (%)
Caviar	300	15
Cod, fresh	50	0.3
Cod, dried	(82)	0.7
Flounder, flesh	50	0.8
Haddock, flesh	60	0.1
Halibut, flesh	50	1.2
Herring, flesh	85	11.3
Mackerel, flesh	95	12.2
Salmon (sockeye or red), flesh	(35)	—
Sardines, canned in oil, drained	140	11.1
Trout, flesh	55	11.4
Tuna, canned in oil, drained	65	8.2
Tuna, canned in water, not drained	(63)	0.8
Clam meat	50[2]	1.6
Oyster meat	50[2]	2.0
Scallop meat	35[3]	0.2
Crab meat	100	1.9
Lobster meat	85	1.5
Shrimp, canned, drained	150	1.1

[1]Fish sterol reported in the total sterol listed is considered to be all cholesterol. The sterols of crustacea are also considered to be all cholesterol, but shellfish sterol figures refer to actual cholesterol determined by gas-liquid chromatography[a][b].
[a]Feeley, et al. 1972
[b]Values in parentheses are imputed values
[2]40 per cent of total sterol
[3]30 per cent of total sterol

TABLE 6. CHOLESTEROL CONTENTS OF MUSCLE FROM EDIBLE FISH FROM EUROPEAN WATERS[1]

Fish	% fat[2]	Cholesterol[3] % in fat	mg/100 g muscle	% in fat-free dry substance
Cod	0.30– 0.57	7.0– 0.3	20.0–40.0	0.11–0.21
Codling	0.21– 0.35	10.0–10.5	22.0–35.0	0.12–0.17
Haddock	0.29– 0.42	6.5–11.1	27.2–35.0	0.15–0.21
Pollack	0.43– 0.45	7.2– 8.0	31.0–36.0	0.15–0.18
White halibut	0.35– 0.60	6.0– 6.9	24.0–34.0	0.11–0.16
Ling	0.34– 0.57	7.4– 9.6	29.0–46.0	0.15–0.24
Coalfish[4]	0.56– 0.83	6.2– 8.2	46.0–53.0	0.26–0.28
Whitefish	0.46– 0.53	8.7–10.7	40.0–50.0	0.23–0.29
Sole	0.60– 2.10	2.8– 8.4	41.5–58.5	0.21–0.29
Catfish	1.05– 4.20	0.8– 4.6	30.2–56.0	0.18–0.29
Red perch	1.30– 7.70	0.5– 1.9	21.3–54.4	0.19–0.29
Dogfish	2.10–16.30	0.4– 1.9	28.4–73.0	0.18–0.45
Herring	10.60–24.20	0.2– 0.6	53.2–66.4	0.33–0.57
Mackerel	17.90–22.50	0.2	34.0–38.8	0.21–0.24
Black halibut	8.90–17.20	0.24– 0.6	43.0–50.0	0.29–0.37

[1]Wurziger and Hensel 1967
[2]Petroleum ether extractable after HCL digestion
[3]Digitonide precipitate from this extract
[4]Saithe or North American Atlantic pollack

TABLE 7. CHOLESTEROL CONTENTS OF MUSCLE FROM EUROPEAN EDIBLE FISH OR PREPARED FOODS[1]

Pack	% fat[2]	Cholesterol % in fat	mg/100 g muscle	% in fat-free dry substance
Cod in bars	0.53	6.6	34.8	0.22
Fishsticks	0.94	6.1	57.0	0.29
Fish steaks	0.58	8.4	48.5	0.25
Breaded cod	0.98	3.3	32.2	0.11
Salmon steak	0.91	5.8	53.0	0.26
Cod fillet	0.41	10.0	41.2	0.22

[1]Wurziger and Hensel 1967
[2]From meat portion only

longer chain polyunsaturated fatty acids in fish fats. When 'retroconversion' occurs in fish, if at all, it is unknown (Yu and Sinnhuber 1972). It is known that in salmonids linolenic acid is superior to linoleic acid in stimulating growth (Castell *et al.* 1972; Yu and Sinnhuber 1972) and that there is mutual interference between the two types of acids in fish lipid metabolism as well as in mammals (Tinsley *et al.* 1971). This may account for

the adverse effect on eggs and egg production, but not on the hens themselves, of menhaden oil as the sole fat in the diet of laying hens (Roland and Edwards 1972). There are broad views that longer-chain fatty acids of both the linoleic type, especially 20:4ω6, and the linolenic type, especially 22:5ω3, may be more desirable in the human diet than is generally accepted because they are relatively more important than other polyunsaturated fatty acids in the muscle of wild game animals (Crawford *et al.* 1969; Crawford and Woodford 1971; Crawford 1972; Crawford and Sinclair 1972a). However, it is important for us to focus attention on the 22:6ω3 of the central nervous system in man and animals (Patriarca *et al.* 1969), and to note that there has been speculation on a link between diet and the lowered incidence of multiple sclerosis in areas where consumption of fish and/or foods rich in linolenic acid is high (Bernsohn and Stephanides 1967). It appears that the postulated 'nonessentiality' of linolenic acid was based on analysis of the whole rat head, and an examination of rat brain, which accounts for only a few per cent of head lipids, showed that $22:6\omega3$ in the vital brain ethanolamine phosphoglycerides made up 22 per cent of the fatty acids (Crawford and Sinclair 1972b). The brains of one-day old chicks contain $22:6\omega3$ which as a proportion of total fatty acids can be increased by feeding menhaden oil rich in linolenic family longer-chain acids, and increased especially in $22:6\omega3$ although $20:5\omega3$ is equal to $22:6\omega3$ in the dietary oil, or decreased by feeding safflower oil deficient in all linolenic type acids (Miller *et al.* 1971).

TABLE 8. CHOLESTEROL CRUDE PROTEIN INDEX (MG CHOLESTEROL IN 100 G CRUDE PROTEIN) FOR SOME FISHERY PRODUCTS AVAILABLE IN JAPAN[1]

Sample	% Crude fat	mg Cholesterol in 100 g fresh sample	CCPI
Bonito	1.96	5	27
Mackerel	5.23	15	74
Gurnet	1.92	25	152
Sole	0.99	51	242
Albacore (dark muscle)	3.72	53	271
Carp	5.74	72	396
Abalone	0.66	121	792
Oyster	1.71	76	1,256
Blue crab	2.22	63	412
Yarika squid body	4.59	345	1,937
Sea urchin ovary	3.12	498	5,491

[1]Koga 1970c

These observations can be combined with other considerations such as the known lowering by half of $22:6\omega3$ in human brain for subjects with multiple sclerosis (Kishimoto *et al.* 1967), to indicate that linolenic-type, longer-chain, highly unsaturated fatty acids may be required by the mammalian nervous system. Hypothesizing from the neonatal brain fatty acid deposition which was observed in rats, a moderate steady replacement of pre-existing $22:6\omega3$ may exist which would be difficult to detect, although $18:3\omega3$ might be required instead of preformed $22:5\omega3$ or $20:5\omega3$. Recently evidence has been adduced that in the rat heart $22:5\omega3$ is apparently conserved when there is an insufficiency of long-chain polyunsaturated acids of the linoleic ($\omega6$) family (Egwim and Kummerow 1972b), so other cellular tissue may also utilize linolenic-type C_{20} and C_{22} acids. If these acids are required in the human diet, then marine or other aquatic fats, including depot fats (Table 1), lean muscle, and whole shellfish (Table 2), can be suitable sources. The normal efficient selectivity of the body protects against temporary excesses of polyunsaturated fatty acids, and even long-term trends can be offset (Imaichi *et al.* 1963; Shorland *et al.* 1969). However, it is necessary to emphasize that adequate vitamin E is essential in all diets involving large amounts of fats rich in highly unsaturated acids of either the linoleic or linolenic families (Boyd 1968).

There are excellent and detailed reviews on oxidative rancidity in fish oils (Aure *et al.* 1967), fish meals (Carpenter 1968), and *in vitro* and *in vivo* studies on the effects of peroxidation of lipids in animals (Artman 1969; Witting 1970). The deposition of the polyunsaturated fatty acids of fish oils in man might be thought to pre-dispose an opinion adverse to the inclusion of fish fats in the diet, but this deposition occurs mostly in depot fats whereas recent research has concentrated on essential membranes which are less influenced by exogenous acids. Recent biochemical research has been stimulated by the 'free radical theory of aging'. In mice, some aging processes can be offset by adding ethoxyquin ('Santoquin') to the diet. Experimental mice outlived controls by nearly 20 per cent (Comfort *et al.* 1971). Modern techniques for studying free radicals in natural systems are available (Roubal 1970; 1971), and supplement observations linking lipid peroxidation with the formation of lipofuscin-like fluorescent pigments in subcellular organelles (Chio *et al.* 1969) or with damage to adenosine triphosphate (ATP) (Roubal and Tappel 1967). The role of antioxidants such as tocopherol (vitamin E) may be to stabilize microsomal membranes from excessive free radical attack (McCay *et al.* 1971) and the levels of natural antioxidants necessary relative to unsaturated acids have been calculated (Gruger and Tappel 1971). The complexity of the possible interrelationships is illustrated by different reports in animal tests on the role of red cell hemolysis versus tocopherol status (Goldstein *et al.* 1969; Alfin-Slater *et al.* 1969a, 1969b). Moreover, although lipid peroxidation is repeatedly implicated in degradation of biological systems, it may not be the major factor when the diet contains lipid antioxidants in amounts normally employed to prevent signs of vitamin E deficiency (Harmon 1971). A definite level of peroxidation *in vivo* has been considered normal (Vladimirov 1972; DiLuzio 1972); but is likely to be influenced by extraneous factors (DiLuzio 1972; Menzel *et al.* 1970). Degradation of peroxides to malonaldehyde is another complex aspect of this problem (Shin *et al.* 1972).

The necessity of adding tocopherol to the diets of cultivated fish (Hashimoto *et al.* 1966; Watanabe *et al.* 1966; Sakaguchi and Hamaguchi 1969; Mann 1970; Watanabe *et al.* 1970a, 1970b; Takeuchi 1972; Aoe *et al.* 1972) probably reflects the heavy deposition of polyunsaturated fatty acids in the muscle and/or livers of these fish and the consequent need for ongoing protection against *in situ* peroxidation. This view is based on the observation that most fish oils and lipids contain about 200 to 300 µg/g lipid of tocopherol, predominantly α-tocopherol (Einset *et al.* 1957; Mega 1965; Ikeda and Taguchi 1966; Ackman and Cormier 1967; Sugii and Kinumaki 1968; Aoe *et al.* 1972; Takeuchi and Ishii 1971). The feeding of low-cost foods such as minced fish or fish scraps is an invitation to autoxidation of the food fatty acids (Shono and Toyomizu 1971). Fresh natural foods would probably prove superior as the composition of synthetic diets may not be that alleged (Albrecht and Breitsprecher 1969) but frozen stored zooplanktons have been found to be inferior to synthetic diets (Brett 1971) In a toxic frozen sand eel fish food substantial losses of polyunsaturated acids were observed (Ueda and Nagaok 1968). This autoxidation may produce factors toxic to the fish (Watanabe and Hashimoto 1968), but in any case will reduce or destroy the tocopherol present in the food. The former process is quite possible although it is reported that lipid peroxides and related materials from oxidized cod liver oil may not be absorbed across the intestinal wall of rats but may

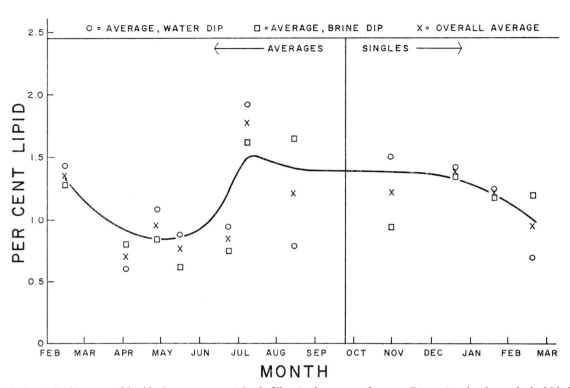

Fig 4   Variation in lipid content of freshly frozen commercial sole fillets in the course of a year. Extractions by the method of Bligh and Dyer, Can. J Biochem. Physiol., *37: 911–917, 1959*

interact with and cause local irritation to membranes (McKay *et al.* 1967). Similarly little peroxide is likely to be directly absorbed by fish without alteration (Takeuchi 1972). An alternative is to suppose that secondary compounds such as 4-hydroperoxy-2-en-1-als of different chain lengths may be responsible for the toxicity (Yoshioka and Kaneda 1972). Among other fatty acid oxidation and fission products associated especially with breakdown of peroxides of marine oil-type fatty acids ($20:5\omega3$ and $22:6\omega3$) are methyl 4-oxobutanoate (Noble and Nawar 1971) and 2-*trans*, 4-*cis*, 7-*cis* decatrienal (Meijboom and Stroink 1972), while the feeding of cod liver oil to rats produced a series of both alkanals and alk-2-enals *in vivo* when tocopherol was not added (Derrick and Wishner 1967). However, reasonable amounts of dietary aldehydes in marine oils such as cod liver oil are tolerated by animals when assessed by the criteria of some biochemical processes (Ziatsev and Maganova 1971). Some of these compounds may be of interest only as objectionable flavour components (Stansby 1971) but others could be toxic and all are potentially unstable and reactive. A possible association of lipids in fish, among other materials, and peroxides with gastric cancer has been suggested (Fukuzumi 1970).

Severe autoxidation of fishery products is usually adequate to prevent their being marketed, or consumed by man if purchased by consumers. Mackerel caught on the Atlantic coast of Canada are one such species where only about 4,500 tons out of 13,600 tons landed are dressed or sold round for human consumption. Several times this catch could be landed if marketing of an attractive frozen product could be improved, but storage life of processed fish is only about three months. Work is under way in laboratories of the Fisheries Research

Board of Canada to develop an acceptable filleted product with a long storage life. The fats and lipids of several so-called 'mackerel' are compared in Table 3. There is little difference in lipids and fatty acids among the mackerel (*Scomber scombrus*) of North Atlantic or Adriatic origin (Table 3), and developments in improved storage techniques would also be generally beneficial to further marketing for food use of catches elsewhere. In Norway substantial amounts of mackerel are reduced for meal and oil (Urdahl and Nygaard 1971). Some work on Spanish mackerel (*Scomberomorus maculatus*) indicates that treatment with antioxidants, chelating agents, and vacuum packaging show promise (Farragut 1972). However, conventional water-soluble antioxidants may be less effective than oil-soluble antioxidants as these reach the tissue depot fats (Tanaka 1967). The major difficulty with this type of fish may be localized effects of heme pigments in the dark (lateral line) muscle because of known pro-oxidant activity of this type of compound (Hirano and Olcott 1971; Kaufmann and Schiller 1971); Nagayama *et al.* 1971) and a generally complex problem associated with trace metals, etc. (Castell 1971). The jack mackerel (*Trachurus japonicus*) may differ in details of lipid fatty acid composition and especially in seasonal extremes for triglyceride lipid (Table 3; Ueda 1972), but as in minced form at 5°C is equally susceptible to oxidative deterioration (Shono and Toyomizu 1971).

The breakdown of mackerel (*Scomber scrombrus*) muscle lipids in frozen storage (−20°C) follows the known process of lipid hydrolyses (Viviani *et al.* 1968). When the fish were lean the hydrolysis over 12 months affected both triglycerides and phospholipids, but in fat fall fish the free fatty acids recovered for identification

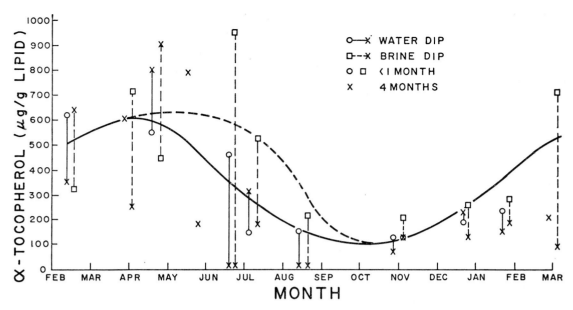

Fig 5 Variations in α-tocopherol content of commercial sole fillets shortly after being freshly frozen and after four months storage at −20°C. 'Dip' refers to pre-packaging treatment

were mostly from the triglycerides. A diminution of *total* fatty acids of nearly 40 per cent was found in the lean fish, and 20 percent in the fat fish. The hydrolysis-oxidation process has recently been compared for *Scomber japonicus* and other species (Takama *et al.* 1972), and other recent developments have been discussed by Braddock and Dugan (1972) in connexion with their studies of frozen coho salmon. The gross oxidation of polyethylenic fatty acids in unfrozen minced fish is easily followed in whole lipids by the gas-liquid chromatographic analysis of 16:0 and 22:6ω3 (Shono and Toyomizu 1971), especially in the liberated acids. On the same basis the loss of 22:6 in blended striped bass (*Roccus* spp.) was 13 per cent at 0°C and an accelerated test for the frozen storage life of fatty species on this basis may perhaps be based on 0°C after further study (Wood and Hintz 1971).

The more subtle changes taking place in frozen stored fish involve liberation of fatty acids from lipids, perhaps mostly from phospholipids, and the interaction of these acids, after peroxidation, with proteins. The reactants necessary for quality changes in frozen muscle include trimethylamine oxide, which breaks down to formaldehyde and dimethylamine. Perhaps with other amines and the peroxides these contribute to the protein aggregation and insolubilization (Castell 1971; Takama *et al.* 1972) used as an index of quality (Dyer 1967; 1968). That some protection against these processes is afforded by the normal *in situ* tocopherol has been shown by a simple experiment (Ackman and Castell, unpublished). A semi-lean fish (largely blackbacked flounder, *Pseudopleuronectes americanus*) from Nova Scotian waters is commercially marketed satisfactorily as frozen fillets. However, rancidity was reported to develop more rapidly in fish caught in June and July than in other times of the year. Each month high quality fillets of commercial origin were dipped in either fresh water or brine and then packaged and frozen by the usual commercial handling. Random packages were selected from the commercial

storage and examined for lipid, tocopherol and susceptibility to Cu^{++} induced rancidity within two or three weeks. These tests were repeated after four months of storage.

Not unexpectedly, total extractable lipid (freshly prepared samples) showed a winter decline and a sharp rise in June and July corresponding to a post-spawning feeding period (Fig 4). Tocopherol in the freshly prepared samples showed an inverse relationship to lipid, being as high as 500 to 600 μg/g lipid in the lean period of the year, and as low as 100 to 200 μg/g lipid when lipid was at its highest in September and October (Fig. 5). However, the notable result is that in June, July and August the tocopherol (about 300 μg/g lipid) tended to be completely destroyed in four months of storage, whereas at other times of the year residual tocopherol was always detected and usually fell no more than about 50 per cent in four months of frozen storage. At present it is not clear whether in summer the tocopherol disappeared due to acceleration of the processes based on breakdown of trimethylamine oxide (TMAO), or due to the presence of some unknown pro-oxidant, but there is thus good reason to suspect that in the fatty fish the typical tocopherol levels of 200 to 300 μg/g lipid, which are adequate to protect the living animal and its fats from normal free radical autoxidants, will at times be inadequate for *post mortem* protection from autoxidation within the frozen muscle. It is not impossible that selenium, which in higher animals is involved with tocopherol transport and/or distribution *in vivo* (Anon. 1972), and otherwise acts in a somewhat obscure role in association with tocopherols (Witting 1970) could also be a factor involved in storage problems.

A SUMMARY OF THE ROLE OF LONG-CHAIN MONOETHYLENIC FATTY ACIDS IN ANIMAL NUTRITION

Four naturally occurring monoethylenic fatty acids are listed in Tables 1, 2 and 3. Of these the 16:1 (hexadecenoic

TABLE 9. PROPORTIONS OF ISOMERS OF MONOETHYLENIC FATTY ACIDS IN EACH OF THE FOUR PRINCIPAL CHAIN LENGTHS OF TYPICAL MARINE LIPIDS

Fatty Acid / Isomer	16:1		18:1		20:1			22:1		
	ω9	ω7	ω9	ω7	ω13−11	ω9	ω7	ω13+11	ω9	ω7
Herring[1]	1	77	70	22	38	57	3	92	6	2
Mackerel[2]	17	78	73	25	8	76	14	73	25	3
Newfoundland Turbot Oil[3]	3	94	72	25	?	~81	8	85	13	2
Sand Launce Oil[4]	2	94	72	23	?	~97	3	92	6	2
Tuna[5]	—	~100	83	17	?	~55	45	93	7	—
American Oyster (Canadian)[6]	44	56	79	17	21	9	62	13	11	76(?)
European Oyster (Canadian)[6]	28	65	64	31	17	15	69	9	11	79(?)
Queen Crab Muscle[7]	4	94	49	48	13	53	31	—	—	—
Finwhale Oil[8]	4	93	87	11	20	76	4	89	10	1
Seal Oil[8]	4	92	84	15	10	82	7	77	20	3

[1]Ackman and Castell 1966   [2]Ackman and Eaton 1971a   [3]Ackman *et al.* 1967   [4]Ackman and Eaton 1971b   [5]Roubal 1963
[6]Watanabe and Ackman 1972   [7]Addison *et al.* 1972   [8]Ackman *et al.* 1971a

or palmitoleic) and 18:1 (octadecenoic or oleic) acids occur in all animal fats and are formed by all animals when required from the corresponding 16:0 (palmitic) and 18:0 (stearic) saturated acids. From a nutritional point of view it is apparent that there are moderately important amounts (10 to 30 per cent) of 18:1 in lipids of all marine animals, while 16:1 is less important (5 to 15 per cent) in depot (triglyceride) fats and of negligible significance (<5 per cent) in most phospholipids. Most lipid workers report 18:1 as "oleic" acid, but in fact although 18:1ω9 (true oleic acid) is usually the dominant isomer, it is always accompanied by a variable proportion (20 to 80 per cent) of 18:1ω7 (*cis*-vaccenic acid). This is formed by the addition of two carbon atoms to 16:1ω7 (palmitoleic acid), which is normally >90 per cent of the 16:1 isomer complex. Typical examples are given in Table 9 although only a few laboratories have studied these details (early work is reviewed by Ackman and Castell 1966). It is unnecessary to discuss these two acids (16:1 and 18:1) in more detail as they are readily digested and assimilated by man, and the dietary contribution from marine lipids is not radically different from that of most desirable foodstuffs, including fats of vegetable origin, in a balanced diet.

The phospholipids of the marine animals listed in Table 2 are typical examples in that only modest amounts of 20:1 (≤5 per cent) and often much less 22:1 (≤3 per cent) are listed (Lambertsen 1972). These acids are much more important in depot fats (triglycerides). The clupeid (herring) family are distinguished (Lambertsen and Braekkan 1965) by very high levels of 22:1 (up to 30 per cent) and correspondingly only slightly less 20:1 (Ackman and Eaton 1966). There is little doubt that in most fish species 20:1 and 22:1 act as depot or energy reserves, but it is possible that they have a supplementary function in clupeids in buoyancy regulation (Ackman and Eaton 1970). These two acids also are made up of several different isomeric forms (Table 9), some formed from pre-existing monoethylenic acids of other chain lengths by chain extension or shortening, and some more directly by desaturation of the corresponding saturated fatty acids, but in fish the ratios among these isomers are relatively constant due to their assimilation from a food web where fats are widely interchanged among different species and trophic levels. In some fish,

especially herring and mackerel, the depot fats accumulate in the muscle and 20:1 and 22:1 can be important nutritional elements in the human diet. In other species such as the gadoids the muscle may be lean and these acids are then found mainly in the liver (Lambertsen 1972) and their dietary importance depends on whether or not the fish is eaten whole. It is not mandatory that fatty fish have high levels of 20:1 and 22:1 as most marine species where the fat is highly unsaturated (e.g., pilchards, Ackman and Sipos 1964; anchoveta, Lambertsen and Braekkan 1965; menhaden, Miller *et al.* 1971) also have very low levels of 20:1 and 22:1. These acids tend to be much less important in freshwater fish than in marine fish (Table 1).

PARTIALLY HYDROGENATED FATS

The naturally occurring monoethylenic fatty acids discussed in the previous section were all of *cis* geometrical configuration. Any monoethylenic double bond can also exist in the *trans* geometrical configuration, but these are not known to be of any significance in natural marine lipids. The principal difference between the *cis* and *trans* acids is the higher melting point of the latter. The process of partial hydrogenation has been applied to marine fats and to terrestrial plant oils for over 60 years to produce modified products possessing more desirable physical properties and having satisfactory storage stability. The liquid fish and whale oils when partially hydrogenated are converted to solid fats with suitable melting points and plasticities which simulate the spreadability and oral attractiveness of butter (ie, they are margarines), or can act as shortenings or cooking fats. When freshly produced such products are free of 'fishy' flavour or taste, but after some months will 'revert' because of the impossibility of completely eliminating the original oxidation-sensitive polyunsaturated fatty acid structures. This is illustrated in Fig 6 where progressive hydrogenation of Peruvian anchoveta oil is shown to not completely eliminate the original 20:5ω3 (eicosapentaenoic) fatty acid until iodine value 107.5 was reached. Moreover the disappearance of an original fatty acid of this type takes place in stages and does not immediately eliminate all parts of the fatty acid molecule capable of flavour reversion. This stepwise

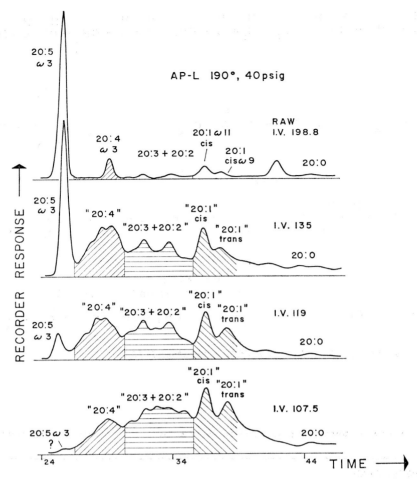

Fig 6 *Progressive changes in the composition of the C₂₀ part of Peruvian anchovy oil hydrogenation*

hydrogenation might hypothetically take place as shown in Fig 7.

After elimination of two out of five ethylenic bonds there still remains a group capable of giving objectionable flavours due to autoxidation. After Step I, some of the '20:4' acids of Fig 6, similar to those in Fig 7, and the residue of original 20:5 can give rise to the formation of 2-*trans*, 4-*cis*, 7 *cis*-decatrienal, which has a strong 'fishy flavour' (Meijboom and Stroink 1972). The basic need (Step II) is the elimination of many of the natural *cis* double bonds (†) with the formation of new saturated fatty acid parts of the chain (at ††). The process of partial hydrogenation is controlled by the use of selective catalysts and conditions to avoid an excess of saturated acids as these have melting points which are too high. This example also shows the isomerization effects affecting the properties of the product. One such effect (Step I) is elimination of two ethylenic bonds (*) to to produce a single one in a new position (**) with, in this example, *trans* configuration. This can remain (Step II) or be converted to *cis* configuration (***) without moving in the chain (Step III). Similarly an original natural *cis* ethylenic bond can become *trans*. At the same time an existing ethylenic bond ‡ can also move along the chain (Step III), in which case it can assume either a *cis* or *trans* configuration in the new position (‡‡). This processing by partial hydrogenation produces a wide range of

fatty acids of continuously varying structure and properties. As a further complication these are bound together in threes in triglycerides each of which originally contained three probably quite different fatty acids (Brockerhoff *et al.* 1968; Bottino 1971). A typical product mixture from partial hydrogenation of anchoveta oil, specifically those fatty acids produced from 20:5ω3 (Fig 6), is thus a mixture of C₂₀ fatty acids with four, three, two and one double bonds which can exist in different positions and configurations. In Fig 6 it will be noted that progressive hydrogenation gradually eliminates separate gas chromatographic peaks visible in the oils of IV 135 and 119 for interim products such as shown in Fig 7 to give an increasingly complex mixture of all possible isomers for each number of residual ethylenic bonds. However, owing to the low proportions of monoethylenic acids formed at these moderate iodine values the ratio of *trans* 20:1 to *cis* 20:1 increases only slowly. In Canadian practice partial hydrogenation to an iodine value of about 78 is usual for herring oils and the *trans* to *cis* ratio is about 1:2 (Ackman *et al.* 1971). Such a mixture has defied complete analysis although partial analyses have been published (Lambertsen *et al.* 1966, 1971; Hølmer and Aaes-Jorgensen 1969a; Ackman *et al.* 1971). The monoethylenic acids are fairly amenable to examination by modern analytical technology and some typical results are given in Table 10. Basically the newly formed

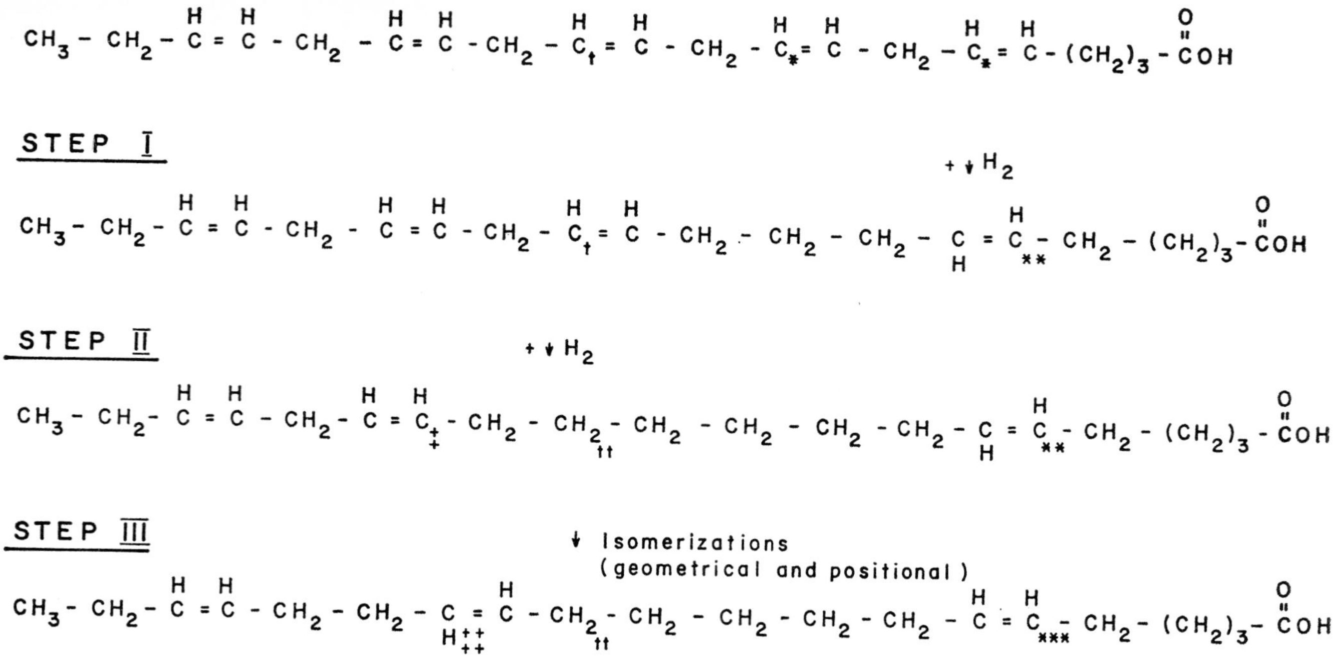

CH$_3$ – CH$_2$ – C=C – CH$_2$ – C=C – CH$_2$ – C$_t$= C – CH$_2$ – C$_*$= C – CH$_2$ – C$_*$= C – (CH$_2$)$_3$ – COH

STEP I

+↓H$_2$

CH$_3$ – CH$_2$ – C=C – CH$_2$ – C=C – CH$_2$ – C$_t$= C – CH$_2$ – CH$_2$ – CH$_2$ – C=C$_{**}$ – CH$_2$ – (CH$_2$)$_3$ – COH

STEP II

+↓H$_2$

CH$_3$ – CH$_2$ – C=C – CH$_2$ – C=C$_+$ – CH$_2$ – CH$_2$ – CH$_2$ – CH$_2$ – CH$_2$ – CH$_2$ – C=C$_{**}$ – CH$_2$ – (CH$_2$)$_3$ – COH

STEP III

↓ Isomerizations
(geometrical and positional)

CH$_3$ – CH$_2$ – C=C – CH$_2$ – CH$_2$ – C=C$_{tt}$ – CH$_2$ – CH$_2$ – CH$_2$ – CH$_2$ – CH$_2$ – C=C$_{***}$ – CH$_2$ – (CH$_2$)$_3$ – COH

Fig 7 *Model of processes typical of a partial hydrogenation of 20:5ω3 as shown in Fig 6*

TABLE 10. PERCENTAGE OF FATTY ACID ISOMERS IN MONOETHYLENIC FATTY ACIDS OF THE FOUR MAJOR CHAIN LENGTHS OF PARTIALLY HYDROGENATED MARINE OILS

'ω' Values (=chain length less double bond position from acid end)	16	15	14	13	12	11	10	9	8	7	6	5	4	3
Original oil and study[1]														
Herring oil, A 22:1 cis	7.7?	7.7?	—	—	—	84.6	—	—	—	—	—	—	—	—
trans	1.2	1.1	2.7	5.5	8.2	57.0	8.9	14.9	—	—	—	—	—	—
Herring oil, B cis	—	—	—	2	3	82	4	9	—	—	—	—	—	—
trans	—	—	—	2	15	57	17	6	2	1	—	—	—	—
Whale oil, B cis	—	—	—	5	10	62	9	11	3	—	—	—	—	—
trans	—	—	1	5	15	47	19	4	3	—	—	—	—	—
Herring oil, A 20:1 cis	—	—	2.6	1.3	3.7	4.6	2.2	85.6	—	—	—	—	—	—
trans	—	—	4.4	3.8	2.9	11.4	15.9	46.0	10.4	4.9	—	—	—	—
Herring oil, B cis	—	—	—	—	1	10	4	75	5	5	—	—	—	—
trans	—	—	—	—	3	9	15	50	15	5	—	—	—	—
Whale oil, B cis	—	—	—	1	4	16	8	53	8	6	3	1	—	—
trans	—	—	—	1	5	12	15	39	15	7	3	2	1	—
Herring oil, A 18:1 cis	—	—	—	—	16.9	8.0	7.7	46.6	6.9	13.8	—	—	—	—
trans	—	—	—	—	3.1	6.2	9.6	41.0	17.1	15.7	4.9	2.3	—	—
Herring oil, B cis	—	—	—	—	—	6	3	66	3	16	3	3	—	—
trans	—	—	—	—	—	5	11	40	17	17	7	3	—	—
Whale oil, B cis	—	—	—	—	—	6	9	57	9	15	3	1	—	—
trans	—	—	—	—	1	5	14	40	18	13	6	3	—	—
Herring oil, A 16:1 cis	—	—	—	—	—	—	6.1	13.6	74.1	6.1	—	—	—	—
trans	—	—	—	—	—	4.8	15.9	5.8	17.3	38.4	7.9	5.1	3.7	1.0
Herring oil, B cis	—	—	—	—	—	—	2	3	5	80	5	4	1	—
trans	—	—	—	—	—	1	12	4	14	45	14	6	3	1
Whale oil, B cis	—	—	—	—	—	—	2	6	8	67	12	3	2	—
trans	—	—	—	—	—	2	6	6	16	44	19	4	3	—

[1]Ackman *et al.* 1971b; Conacher *et al.* 1972

monoethylenic acids from partially hydrogenated fish oil are about two thirds *trans* and one third *cis* (Fig 6), and exist in many probable positions. Initially some tend to remain in groups in which one can often detect the residual positioning of the original *cis* monoethylenic fatty acids in the newly formed geometrical isomers (Tables 9 and 10). Such residual positional effects would be detectable with herring oils and some whale oils originally high in 20:1 and 22:1, but would be less apparent in partially hydrogenated oils originally of high iodine value such as from anchoveta where 20:1 and 22:1 were not originally major components (ie, ≤5 per cent).

The consumption of edible refined partially hydrogenated fats and oils of marine origin has until recently been quite high in many countries. In all oils refined for margarines and shortening in 1968 the proportions of marine oils (fish and whale) were 37 per cent in Japan, 10 per cent in Canada, 53 per cent in the United Kingdom, 63 per cent in Norway and comparably high in Belgium, the Netherlands and Sweden (from FAO statistics). The general fate of partially hydrogenated fats fed to animals with an adequate input of 'essential' fatty acids (see above) is one of some catabolism for energy, some deposition of fatty acids, and a little conversion to other acids. These metabolic changes are discussed by many authors (eg, Aaes-Jorgensen and Hølmer 1969; Hølmer and Aaes-Jorgensen 1969a, 1969b; Munsch *et al.* 1969; Munsch and Pascaud 1969; Beare-Rogers 1970a; Beare-

Rogers 1970b; Bickerstaffe and Annison 1970; Camurati *et al.* 1970; LeBreton 1970; Swindells 1970; Egwim and Kummerow 1972). In the USA partially hydrogenated fats are dominated by soybean oil which contains mostly fatty acids of C_{18} chain length. There has been no usage in edible fats of liquid or partially hydrogenated rapeseed oil, or of partially hydrogenated marine oils. The writer is unaware of reports adversely contrasting public health in western Europe and Japan with that of the USA on the basis of dietary consumption of the monoethylenic fatty acids with chain lengths greater than C_{18}.

There is a large literature dealing with the deposition of the long-chain monoethylenic fatty acids (20:1 or eicosenoic and especially 22:1 or docosenoic) in animal hearts, mostly of weanling rats but including some other species. A selection of important references is presented separately in the Appendix although most of them refer to work carried out with rapeseed oil or 'Canbra' oil. The distinction is that oils from most strains of rapeseed (*Brassica campestris* or *Brassica napus*) contain 25 to 50 per cent of 22:1, specifically Δ^{13} or erucic acid. 'Canbra' oils are produced from rapeseed strains developed in Canada in which the chain extension of most of the $18:1\Delta^9$ to $20:1\Delta^{11}$ and $22:1\Delta^{13}$ is blocked, so that $22:1\Delta^{13}$ is less than 5 per cent of the total fatty acids. This discussion will summarize the work with fish and other marine oils, but to grasp the full implications one should refer to Figs 8, 9, and 10, where the potential for formation of

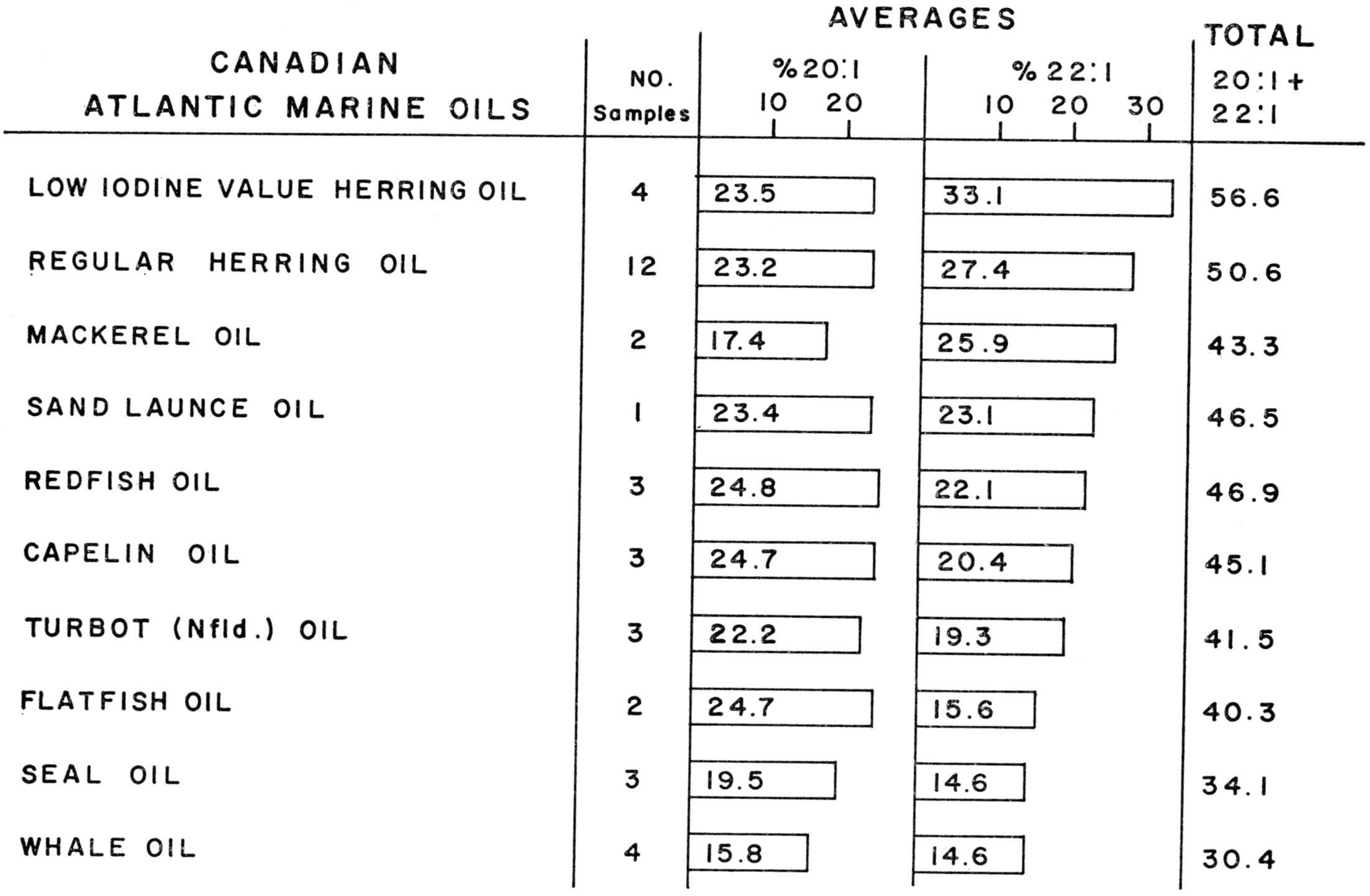

CANADIAN ATLANTIC MARINE OILS	NO. Samples	AVERAGES		TOTAL 20:1 + 22:1
		% 20:1 (10 20)	% 22:1 (10 20 30)	
LOW IODINE VALUE HERRING OIL	4	23.5	33.1	56.6
REGULAR HERRING OIL	12	23.2	27.4	50.6
MACKEREL OIL	2	17.4	25.9	43.3
SAND LAUNCE OIL	1	23.4	23.1	46.5
REDFISH OIL	3	24.8	22.1	46.9
CAPELIN OIL	3	24.7	20.4	45.1
TURBOT (Nfld.) OIL	3	22.2	19.3	41.5
FLATFISH OIL	2	24.7	15.6	40.3
SEAL OIL	3	19.5	14.6	34.1
WHALE OIL	4	15.8	14.6	30.4

Fig 8   Typical proportions of 20:1 and 22:1 which could accumulate in partially hydrogenated marine oils as percentages of total fatty acids

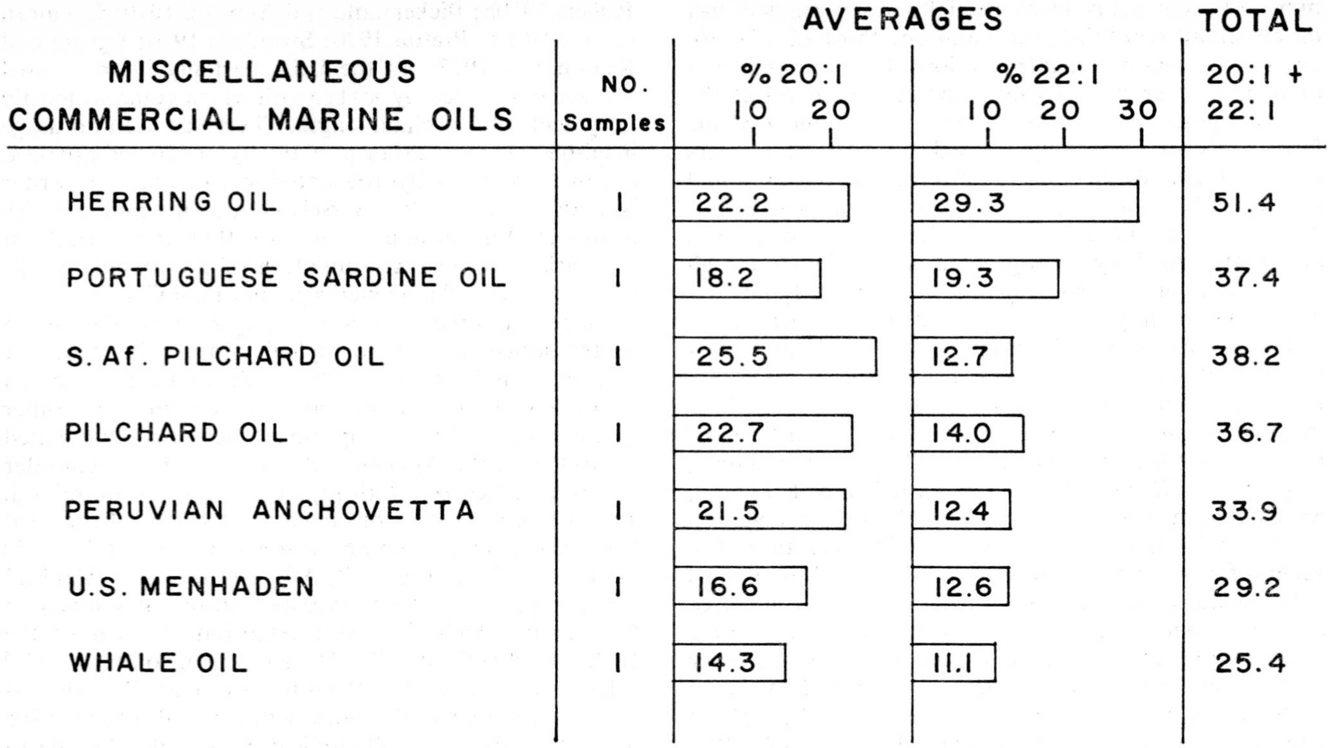

MISCELLANEOUS COMMERCIAL MARINE OILS	NO. Samples	AVERAGES % 20:1 10 20	AVERAGES % 22:1 10 20 30	TOTAL 20:1 + 22:1
HERRING OIL	1	22.2	29.3	51.4
PORTUGUESE SARDINE OIL	1	18.2	19.3	37.4
S. Af. PILCHARD OIL	1	25.5	12.7	38.2
PILCHARD OIL	1	22.7	14.0	36.7
PERUVIAN ANCHOVETTA	1	21.5	12.4	33.9
U.S. MENHADEN	1	16.6	12.6	29.2
WHALE OIL	1	14.3	11.1	25.4

Fig 9 Typical proportions of 20:1 and 22:1 which could accumulate in partially hydrogenated marine oils as percentage of total fatty acids

total 20:1 and 22:1 in hydrogenated oils is presented for many marine oils of different origins. These are calculated from whole oil analyses by converting about 2 per cent each of pre-existing 20:1 and 22:1 to 20:0 and 22:0 and allowing for total conversion of the poly-unsaturated C_{20} and C_{22} acids to 20:1 and 22:1. Neither assumption is strictly correct but comparison between oils may be made with some confidence on the basis of these figures. The totals for potential 20:1 + 22:1 are impressive, but most attention should be given to the potential 22:1 acids. As a proportion of the total fatty acids the range of 22:1 potential acids is not very different from that in various regular rapeseed oils, although very much higher than in 'Canbra' oils where $22:1\Delta^{13}$ is normally under 3.5 per cent of total fatty acids.

Basic experimental design in animal feeding studies with these acids usually involves feeding to weanling male rats a basal diet containing lard and corn oil (or an equivalent source of essential fatty acids) in a 3:1 ratio. The total fat is kept constant at 20 per cent of the diet by weight (= 40 per cent of calories) but part of the fat is replaced by the test fat. When significant amounts of

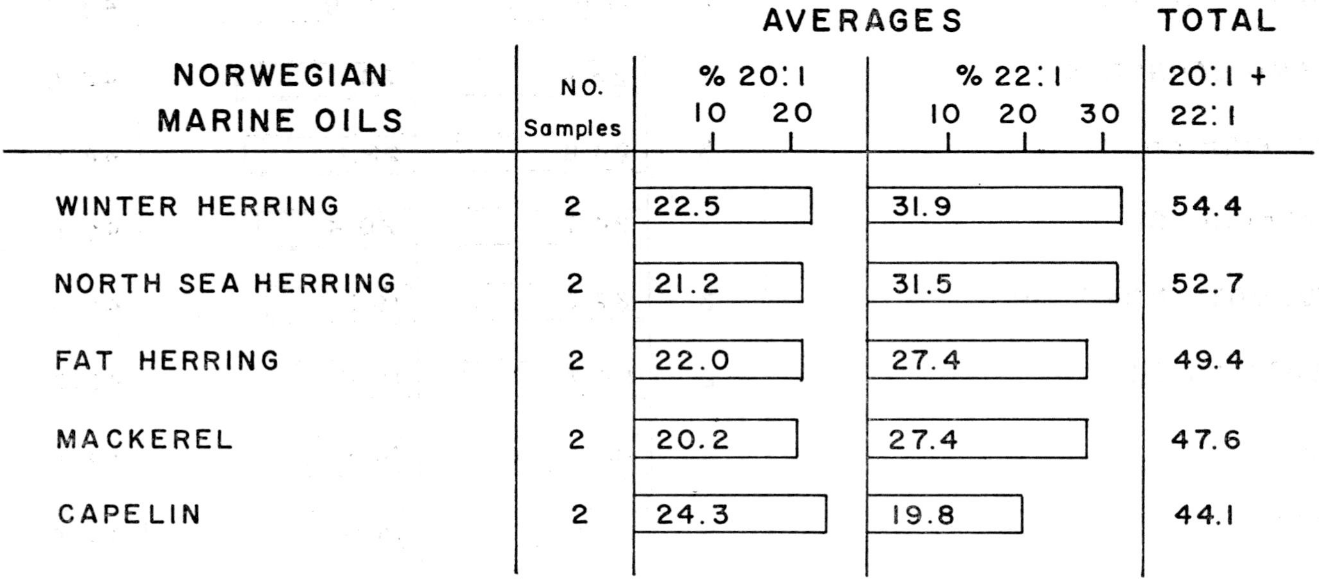

NORWEGIAN MARINE OILS	NO. Samples	AVERAGES % 20:1 10 20	AVERAGES % 22:1 10 20 30	TOTAL 20:1 + 22:1
WINTER HERRING	2	22.5	31.9	54.4
NORTH SEA HERRING	2	21.2	31.5	52.7
FAT HERRING	2	22.0	27.4	49.4
MACKEREL	2	20.2	27.4	47.6
CAPELIN	2	24.3	19.8	44.1

Fig 10 Typical proportions of 20:1 and 22:1 which could accumulate in partially hydrogenated marine oils as percentages of total fatty acids

22:1 acids are fed, visible fat deposits occur after three days in the heart muscle tissue of weanling male rats (depicted by Beare-Rogers *et al.* 1972; at low levels by histopathology). Quantitative fatty acid measurements (Fig 11) show a peak for deposition of 22:1 in rat hearts at seven days (Beare-Rogers *et al.* 1971). This deposit declines markedly after a further week and more slowly thereafter (Fig 11). As shown in Fig 12 the control rats do not show the fat deposition as no 22:1 is in their diet. After several weeks hearts having had fat deposits show histologically detectable damage ranging from mild myocytolysis to necrosis and fibrosis. Some of these changes may occur in control rats.

Fig 11 shows that liquid rapeseed oil deposited 2.7 times as much 22:1 as hydrogenated rapeseed oil, and 4.6 times as much 22:1 as hydrogenated herring oil. The 22:1 acids as percentages of dietary fat were reported as respectively 32.9, 26.3, and 24.1. The inexact correlation of per cent 22:1 in diet with per cent 22:1 in the heart may reflect slightly different responses of the animals to different dietary oils containing 22:1 or possibly reflect

TABLE 11. DEPOSITION OF 22:1 IN CARDIAC FATTY ACIDS OF RATS AFTER ONE WEEK ON 20% FAT DIETS CONTAINING APPROXIMATELY THE SAME LEVEL OF 22:1 FROM PARTIALLY HYDROGENATED MARINE OILS[1]

Oil and iodine value	% 22:1 in oil	% oil in diet	% 22:1 in cardiac fatty acids
Lard-corn oil 3:1	0	20	0
Whale (78)	7.9	20	2.5±0.5
Seal (84)	5.4	20	1.9±0.3
Seal (78)	6.1	20	1.5±0.5
Herring (76)	31.3	2.5	0.7±0.2
Herring (76)	31.3	5.0	1.9±0.3
Herring (76)	31.3	10	4.3±0.5

[1]From: Beare-Rogers and Nera 1972a

isomeric difference in the acid structures which influenced this particular experiment. In a later experiment where the percentage of 22:1 was about the same in liquid and hydrogenated rapeseed oils, the deposits were also nearly the same (Beare-Rogers and Nera 1972a). However, to demonstrate that the effect is usually nominally dependent on total 22:1 with marine oils reference should be made to Table 11. Experimental weanling male rats were fed for one week on a diet incorporating 20 per cent total fat. The deposition of 22:1 in cardiac fatty acids from feeding 20 per cent of a partially hydrogenated seal oil containing 5.4 per cent or 6.1 per cent of 22:1 was essentially the same as from feeding 5.0 per cent of a partially hydrogenated herring oil containing 31.3 per cent of 22:1. A partially hydrogenated whale oil containing more 22:1 (7.9 per cent) than the partially hydrogenated seal oils deposited substantially more 22:1 in the rat cardiac fatty acids. The feeding of up to 16 per cent partially hydrogenated Norwegian capelin oil for one week deposited less 22:1 than 15 per cent partially hydrogenated Canadian herring oil (Teige and Beare-Rogers 1972). Reference to Figs 8 and 10 suggests that this result reflects respective 22:1 levels of about 20 and 30 per cent. In the same experiment raw Peruvian anchoveta oil essentially free of 22:1 led to no significant

cardiac fat deposition. A partially hydrogenated anchoveta oil would of course contain substantial proportion of 22:1 (compare 20:1 in Fig 6).

Female rats show less susceptibility to eventual development of lesions than do males (Rocquelin and Cluzan 1968). Adult rats and gerbils do not show the same cardiac susceptibility to dietary fatty acids as weanling animals. For male rats of three different ages the cardiac deposits of 22:1 as a percentage of total fatty acids after one week of feeding on 20 per cent raw rapeseed oil were: 4 weeks old, 26.3 ± 0.5 per cent; 12 weeks old, 12.2 ± 3.3 per cent; 32 weeks old, 4.5 ± 1.2 per cent. The ages refer to age after the one week of feeding (Beare-Rogers and Nera 1972b). The male adult gerbils in the same study deposited 22.1 as 5.0 ± 0.5 per cent of total cardiac fatty acids in one week of feeding on rapeseed oil, while weanling gerbils deposited 8.6 ± 0.7 per cent after two weeks of feeding. In the gerbils both ages showed a positive response to a fat stain (controls

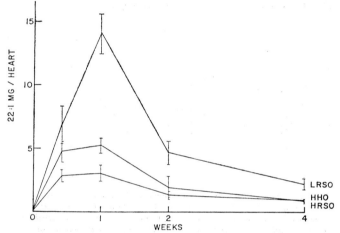

Fig 11   Deposition of 22:1 in hearts of male weanling rats on diets rich in liquid rapeseed oil (LRSO), 32.9% of 22:1; partially hydrogenated rapeseed oil (HRSO), 26.3% of 22:1; or partially hydrogenated herring oil (HHO), 24.1% of 22:1 (Beare-Rogers et al., 1971). Reproduced by permission of Can. Inst. Food Tech. J.

did not) but were negative to histopathological staining and examination techniques. It is essential to realize that in these experiments the diet is not varied and that the maximum cardiac response to dietary 22:1 fatty acids depends on continued 'insult'. To quote from Beare-Rogers and Nera (1972): 'Rats given 20 per cent rapeseed oil for one week and then the control fat for nine weeks were indistinguishable by fatty acid analysis and by histological staining from those of the control rats which had never received rapeseed oil' and 'The effects of rapeseed oil containing erucic acid therefore appeared to be reversible at the stage of greatest lipid accumulation and when other apparent changes in the myocardium were negligible.' Conversely an attempt has been made to 'induce' in weanling rats the natural biochemical processes by which ultimate disposal is made of the longer-chain fatty acids reaching the heart from the bloodstream (Odense and Brockerhoff 1971). In this experiment feeding of two groups of weanling rats started with 1 per cent respectively of partial or raw hydrogenated herring oil and a graduated increase over

12 days reached the same maximum level (18 per cent) as that of groups placed on the maximum levels from the start. On sacrifice at 24 days no definite histopathological effects due to diet could be detected in either group. Unfortunately the lesions which cause concern do not appear until a later stage of continued feeding of 22:1 and it is therefore impossible to evaluate this experiment in the terms applied to most others (ie, short term = fat deposition, or long term = cardiac lesions).

Regrettably due to the pressure to produce results little attention has been paid to the long-term effects of either diets on cardiac lesions. No mortality occurred in an experiment starting with weanling rats and lasting 64 weeks. The dietary factor was extraordinary as 60 per cent of calories were derived from a rapeseed oil containing 45 per cent erucic acid (Abdellatif and Vles 1971b). Moreover despite the cardiac effects of varying degrees of severity detected in a number of animal species under artificial experimental conditions (Beare-Rogers and Nera 1972), a link between 22:1 acids and adverse health effects in man remains to be established.

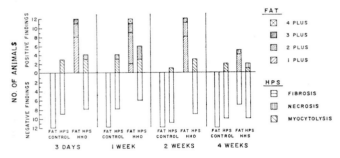

Fig 12   Results of examination of hearts of weanling male rats fed high-fat (20%) diets of either lard plus corn oil (control) or artially hydrogenated herring oil (HHO). "Fat" refers to cardiac at detectable by staining, "HPS" refers to physical changes in tissue detected by histopathological examination after staining, with hematoxylin–phloxine–saffron (Redrawn from Beare-Rogers et al., 1971)

Species other than rats and gerbils which have been studied show detectable cardiac effects in experiments usually designed to maximize these for detailed study. Miniature pigs (fed from ten days after weaning) showed slight deposition of 22:1 on feeding rapeseed oil for one week, and some fat deposition was characterized by histopathological staining techniques. Commercial pigs (fed from three weeks of age) after two weeks on rapeseed oil in a milk formula showed the same results (Beare-Rogers and Nera 1972). Squirrel monkeys fed control and rapeseed oil-rich diets in the same study both showed myocardial fat droplets after one week, suggesting an intolerance to the high-fat diet. After ten weeks experimental animals showed increased deposits of 22:1 over the levels after one week. This response thus differs from those in most other species investigated where 22:1 normally declines. In ducklings various pathological effects, including development of a hydropericardium induced by feeding high levels of erucic acid from rapeseed oil, can be moderated by supplemental feeding of hardened palm oil (Abdellatif and Vles 1971a). Rabbits were also susceptible to cardiac effect from long-term diets high in rapeseed oil, but curiously the pathological

effect observed in the kidneys of rats did not appear in rabbits, while on the other hand rabbits appeared to be susceptible to atherogenic changes (Abdellatif and Vles 1971b).

Weanling rats fed rapeseed oil showed substantial (11.7 per cent) adrenal deposition of 22:1 after 18 weeks (Walker 1972a: see also Carney et al. 1972). On the other hand weanling pigs fed about the same dietary level of 22:1 (as rapeseed oil) for 6 weeks showed markedly less (4.5 per cent) 22:1 in adrenals (Walker 1972b). The heart lipids in these two experiments gave about the same percentage levels of deposition of 20:1 and 22:1. As the ratio of 22:1 to 20:1 was about 1 in the pig adrenals whereas it followed the dietary ratio of 2:1 in the rat adrenals, it is possible that the pig has a considerable resistance to physiological changes due to unusual fatty acids in the diet. The species to species variation in response to dietary 22:1 makes it extremely difficult to extrapolate animal results to man.

It is desirable to refer to Tables 9 and 10 where these isomers of 22:1 of raw and partially hydrogenated marine oils are contrasted. At one time it was hoped that the wider range of isomers available in raw marine oils (Table 9) and especially in partially hydrogenated marine oil (Table 10), would possibly have some beneficial physiological significance. The recent work of Conacher et al. (1973) shows that both cis and trans monoethylenic isomers of a wide range of positions in a partially hydrogenated marine oil are deposited in cardiac lipids of rats with only slight modifications from the dietary composition, mostly due to B-oxidation. Recently a test was carried out in which two isomeric 22:1 acids were compared. The $22:1\Delta^{11}$ (or ω^{11}) isomer characteristic of marine oils and sometimes called cetoleic acid, was deposited in the hearts of weanling rats in proportion equal to the Δ^{13} (or ω^9) isomer, which is the erucic acid of rapeseed oil and accompanies the $22:1\Delta^{11}$ (ω^{11}) in marine oils (Table 9). However the histological assessment showed 'somewhat lesser lesions with the $22:1\Delta^{11}$ isomer' (Beare-Rogers et al. 1972). These are both naturally occurring isomers and the ethylenic bonds are in close proximity. It is possible that some partial rejection of an isomer such as $22:1\Delta^7$ (trans) might mitigate effects from partially hydrogenated oils (see Table 10). In this same study reference is again made to the possible mildly beneficial presence of moderate levels of saturated fatty acids, relative to 22:1, which can sometimes be detected in these experiments. As shown in Tables 1 and 2, marine oils and lipids normally contain appreciable proportions (10 to 30 per cent) of saturated acids, mostly of 16:0 (10 to 15 per cent) with 14:0 (5 to 10 per cent) and 18:0 (<5 per cent), whereas rapeseed oils seldom contain more than 5 per cent 16:0, less 18:0 and very little 14:0. This study also examined the role of 20:1 in weanling male rats and found that after one week cardiac fat droplets could be detected but fatty acid deposition was less severe than for 22:1. This effect is illustrated for an earlier study (Beare-Rogers et al. 1971) in Fig 13. To sum up:

(1) Long-chain monoethylenic fatty acids, especially 22:1 but including 20:1, cause detectable cardiac changes in the young of several animal species due to accumulation of these acids in heart muscle on short-term high-fat feeding.

(2) Continued feeding of high levels of fats rich in these acids can lead to continued accumulation of fat in droplet form (pigs, rabbits, squirrel monkeys), or conversely to a progressive decrease in fat deposits (rats, gerbils), but the ultimate significance is at present unclear for most species.

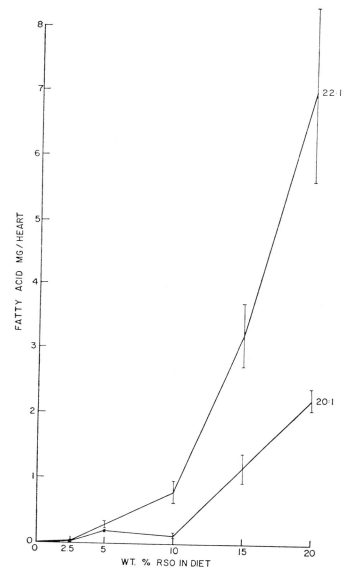

Fig 13   Results of examination for 20:1 and 22:1 of hearts of weanling male rats fed on high-fat (20%) diets containing different levels of liquid rapeseed oil with 12.9% 20:1 and 32.9% 22:1 (Beare–Rogers et al., 1971). Reproduced by permission of Can. Inst. Food Tech. J.

(3) When a dietary oil high in 22:1 is continued fat deposits are ultimately replaced in the hearts of young male rats, gerbils and rabbits by significant numbers of necrotic and fibrotic lesions.

(4) Discontinuance of feeding of fats rich in the 22:1 acids at the time of maximum deposition and continuance of a high-fat diet free of these acids eliminate or reduce eventual appearance of excessive numbers of fibrotic and necrotic lesions in the male rat.

(5) Adult rats and gerbils are relatively resistant to cardiac changes such as the accumulation of 22:1 at dietary levels which show major effects in weanling animals. Female weanling rats deposit fat, but develop fewer lesions than males.

(6) There is no evidence for a 'zero-level' effect as far as accumulation of 22:1 in the hearts of male weanling rats and gerbils is concerned.

(7) The origin of the long-chain fatty acids is relatively unimportant.

(8) Factors of minor, irreproducible, or upproven significance at the time of writing are the precise position and geometrical structure of the mono-ethylenic bond and the inclusion of other types of fatty acids, such as palmitic acid, in the diet.

(9) No correlation of ingestion of these long-chain fatty acids with pathological effects in humans has ever been published.

(10) The present utilization of partially hydrogenated herring oil in edible fats will likely diminish due to lower production and the utilization pattern in Canada will shift to a higher proportion of oils such as redfish, flatfish and other groundfish oils. These generally have lower proportions of C_{22} oils than herring oils.

Despite the lack of evidence for adverse effects of dietary long-chain monoethylenic acids in man, some governments in Europe have imposed limits for 22:1 from 5 to 10 per cent of total fatty acids in edible fats. The Health and Welfare Department of the Government of Canada convened a special committee of independent experts in early 1973 to review the situation. The Department adopted the recommendations of this committee with a limit of 5 per cent for 22:1 in total fatty acids of edible fats and oils effective from December 1973.

References

AAES-JORGENSEN, E and HØLMER, G Lipids, 4:501–506. 1969

ABDEL-HAY and HERODEK, S Annls Inst. biol. Tihany, 33:151–158. 1968

ABDELLATIF, A M M and VLES, R O Nutr. Metab., 13:65–74. 1971a

ABDELLATIF, A M M and VLES, R O Overdruk met Voeding, 1971b 32:602–611.

ACKMAN, R G J. Am. Oil Chem. Soc , 43:385–389. 1966

ACKMAN, R G Comp. Biochem. Physiol., 22:907–922. 1967

ACKMAN, R G In HOLMAN, R T (ed.), Progress in the Chemistry of 1972 Fats and Other Lipids, Oxford, U.K., Pergamon Press, 12:165–284.

ACKMAN, R G and CASTELL, J D Lipids, 1:341–348. 1966

ACKMAN, R G and CORMIER, M G J. Fish. Res. Bd Can., 24:357– 1967 373.

ACKMAN, R G and EATON, C A Ibid., 23:991–1006. 1966a

ACKMAN, R G and EATON, C A Can. J. Biochem., 44:1561–1566. 1966b

ACKMAN, R G and EATON, C A J. Fish. Res. Bd Can., 27:1669–1683. 1970

ACKMAN, R G and EATON, C A Can. Inst. Fd Technol. J., 4:169–174. 1971a

ACKMAN, R G and EATON, C A J. Fish. Res. Bd Can., 28:601–606. 1971b

ACKMAN, R G and KE, P J Ibid., 25:1061–1065. 1968

ACKMAN, R G and SIPOS, J C Ibid., 21:841–843. 1964

ACKMAN, R G, EATON, C A and JANGAARD, P M Can. J. Biochem.,
1965 43:1513–1520.
ACKMAN, R G, EATON, C A and KE, P J J. Fish. Res. Bd Can.,
1967 26:2563–2572.
ACKMAN, R G, EPSTEIN, S and EATON, C A Comp. Biochem.
1971a 40B:683–697.
ACKMAN, R G, HOOPER, S N and HINGLEY, J J. Am. Oil Chem. Soc.,
1971b 48:804–806.
ACKMAN, R G, KE P J, MACCALLUM, W A and ADAMS, D R J.
1969a Fish. Res. Bd Can., 26:2037–2060.
ACTIS DATO, S M and BRENNER, R R Lipids, 5:1014–1015.
1970
ADDISON, R F, ACKMAN, R G and HINGLEY, J J. Fish. Res. Bd Can.,
1968 25:2083–2090.
ADDISON, R F, ACKMAN, R G and HINGLEY, J Ibid., 29:407–411.
1972
ALBRECHT, M L and BREITSPRECHER, B Zeit. für Fischerei, 17:143–
1969 163.
ALFIN-SLATER, R B, HANSEN, H, MORRIS, R S and MELNICK, D
1969a J. Am. Oil Chem. Soc., 46:563–568.
ALFIN-SLATER, R B, MORRIS, R S, AFTERGOOD, L and MELNICK, D
1969b Ibid., 46:657–661.
ANDREWS, J W and STICKNEY, R R Trans. Amer. Fish. Soc.,
1972 101:94–99.
ANON Feedstuffs, Nov. 20, p. 38.
1972
AOE, H, ABE, I, SAITO, T, FUKAWA, H and KOYAMA, H Bull. Jap.
1972 Soc. Sci. Fish., 38:845–851.
ARTMAN, N R In PAOLETTI, R and KRITCHEVSKY, D (ed.), Advances
1969 in Lipid Research, New York, Academic Press, 7:245–330.
AURE, L, OTTESEN, I, FINNE, G and KLØKSTAD, H Fiskeridir. Skr.
1967 Ser. Technol. Unders., 5(3):38 p.
BEARE-ROGERS, J L J. Am. Oil Chem. Soc., 47:487–489.
1970a
BEARE-RODGERS, J L Can. Inst. Fd Technol. J., 3:19–24.
1970b
BEARE-RODGERS, J L and NERA, E A Lipids, 7:548–552.
1972a
BEARE-ROGERS, J L and NERA, E A Comp. Biochem. Physiol.,
1972b 41B:793–800.
BEARE-ROGERS, J L, NERA, E A and CRAIG, B M Lipids, 7:46–50.
1972
BEARE-ROGERS, J L, NERA, E A and HEGGTVEIT, H A Can. Inst. Fd
1971 Technol. J., 4:120–124.
BICKERSTAFFE, R and ANNISON, E F Biochem. J., 118:433–442.
1970
BERNSOHN, J and STEPHANIDES, L M Nature, 215:821–823.
1967
BOYD, J W Br. J. Nutr., 22:411–422.
1968
BOTTINO, N R J. Lipid Res., 12:24–30.
1971
BOUR, H Annls. Hyg. l. fr.-Med. Nutr., 7:15–23.
1971
BRADDOCK, R J and DUGAN, L R, Jr J. Fd Sci., 37:426–429.
1972
BRETT, J R J. Fish. Res. Bd Can., 28:1635–1643.
1971
BROCKERHOFF, H, HOYLE, R J, HUANG, P C and LITCHFIELD, C
1968 Lipids, 3:24–29.
CAMURATI, F, CORTESI, N and FAVINI, G Riv. ital. Sost. grasse,
1970 47:241–247.
CARNEY, J A, LEWIS, A, WALKER, B L and SLINGER, S J Biochem.
1972 Biophys. Acta 280:211–214.
CARPENTER, K J In SWAN, H and LEWIS, D (ed.), Proc. 2nd Nutr.
1968 Conf. for Feed Manufacturers, Nottingham, 1968, London,
       J and A Churchill Ltd., p. 54–74.
CASTELL, C H Ibid, 48:645–649.
1971
CASTELL, J D, SINNHUBER, R O, WALES, J H and LEE, D J J. Nutr.,
1972 102:77–86.
CHIO, K S, REISS, U, FLETCHER, B and TAPPEL, A L Science,
1969 166:1535–1536.
COMFORT, A, YOUHOTSKY-GORE, I and PATHAMANATHON, K Nature,
1971 229:254–255.
CONACHER, H B S, PAGE, B D and CHANDRA, R. K J. Am. Oil Chem.
1972 Soc., 49:520–523.
CONACHER, H B S, PAGE, B D and BEARE-ROGERS, J L Lipids,
1973 8:256–258.
CONNOR, W B J. Am. Diet Ass., 52:202–208.
1968
CONNOR, W E In JONES, R J (ed.), Atheroscler., Proc. Int. Symp.,
1970 2nd 1969, New York, Springer, p. 253–261.
CRAWFORD, M A Nutrition, 26:76–82.
1972
CRAWFORD, M A and SINCLAIR, A J In Lipids, Malnutrition and the
1972a Developing Brain, Amsterdam, Netherlands, ASP (Elsevier
       Excerpta Medica. North Holland), p. 267.

CRAWFORD, M A and SINCLAIR, A J J. Nutr., 102:1315–1322.
1972b
CRAWFORD, M A and WOODFORD, M H Int. J. Biochem., 2:493–496.
1971
CRAWFORD, M A, GALE, M M and WOODFORD, M H Biochem. J.,
1969 115:25–27.
DERRICK, N M and WISHNER, L A Lipids, 2:133–136.
1967
DI LUZIO, N J. Agr. Food Chem., 20:486–490.
1972
DROZDOWSKI, B and ACKMAN, R G J. Am. Oil Chem. Soc., 46:371–
1969 376.
DVORAKOVA, L and BASS, A Phys. Bohemoslav., 19:27–31.
1970
DYER, W J Cryobiology, 3:297–305.
1967
DYER, W J In HAWTHORNE, J (ed.), Low Temperature Biology of
1968 Foodstuffs, New York, Pergamon Press, p. 429–447.
EGWIM, P O and KUMMEROW, F A Lipids, 7:567–571.
1972a
EGWIM, P O and KUMMEROW, F A J. Nutr., 102:783–792.
1972b
EINSET, E, OLCOTT, H S and STANSBY, M E Comm. Fish. Rev., 19,
1957 (Suppl.) (5a):35 p.
ENSELME, J Unsaturated Fatty Acid in Atherosclerosis, Int. Series
1969 of Monographs in Pure and Applied Biology. Division:
       Modern Trends in Physiological Sciences, New York,
       Pergamon Press, 16(2):164 p.
FARRAGUT, R N NOAA Tech. Rep. NMFS SSFR-650, 12 p.
1972
FEELEY, R M, CRINER, P E and WATT, B K J. Am. Diet. Ass.,
1972 61:134–149.
FUKUZUMI, K Fette Seifen AnstrMittel, 72:853–855.
1970
GEDAM, P H, SUBBARAM, M R and AGGARWAL, J S Fette Seifen
1971 AnstrMittel, 73:748–753.
GOLDSTEIN, J R, MENGEL, C E, CAROLLA, R L and EBBERT, L
1969 Aerospace Medicine, 40:132–135.
GOPAKUMAR, K and NAIR, M R Ind. J. Biochem., (4):229–231.
1967
GOPAKUMAR, K and NAIR, M R J. Sci. Fd Agric., 23:493–496.
1972
GRUGER, E H, Jr, and TAPPEL, A L Lipids, 6:147–148.
1971
HARDY, R and KEAY, J N J. Fd Technol., 7:125–137.
1972
HARMON, D J. Gerontology, 26:451–457.
1971
HASHIMOTO, Y, OKAICHI, T, WATANABE, T, FURUKAWA, A and
1966 UMEZU, T Bull. Jap. Soc. Sci. Fish., 32:64–69.
HIRANO, Y and OLCOTT, H S J. Am. Oil Chem. Soc., 48:523–524.
1971
HODGES, R E J. Am. Diet. Ass., 52:198–201.
1968
HOLMAN, R T In HOLMAN, R T (ed.), Progress in the Chemistry of
1970 Fats and Other Lipids, Oxford, U.K., Pergamon Press,
       11(Part 5, Chap. 16):607–682.
HOLMAN, R T and RAHM, J In Progress in the Chemistry of Fats and
1966 Other Lipids, (ed.) HOLMAN, R T, Oxford, U.K., Pergamon
       Press, 11(Part 1):13–90.
HØLMER, G and AAES-JORGENSEN, E Lipids, 4:507–514.
1969a
HØLMER, G and AAES-JORGENSEN, E Lipids, 4:515–521.
1969b
IDLER, D R and WISEMAN, P Intern. J. Biochem., 2:516–528.
1971
IDLER, D R and WISEMAN, P J. Fish. Res. Bd Can., 29:385–398.
1972
IKEDA, S and TAGUCHI, T Bull. Jap. Soc. Sci. Fish., 32:346–351.
1966
IMAICHI, K, MICHAELS, G D, GUNNING, B, GRASSO, S, FUKAYAMA,
1963 G and KINSELL, L W Am. J. Clin. Nutr., 13:158–168.
ITO, S and FUKUZUMI, K J. Chem. Soc. Japan, 65:1963–1968
1962
JANGAARD, P M and ACKMAN, R G J. Fish. Res. Bd Can., 22:131–
1965 137.
JANGAARD, P M and KE, P J Ibid., 25:2419–2426.
1968
JANGAARD, P M, ACKMAN, R G and SIPOS, J C Ibid., 24:613–627.
1967
KAJIMOTO, G and YOSHIDA, H J. Jap. Soc. Fd Nutr., 23:443–446.
1970
KAUFMANN, H P and SCHILLER, H Fette Seifen AnstMittel, 73:209–
1971 216.
KAUNITZ, H Arzneim-Forsch., 20:1500–1505.
1970
KHALID, Q, MIRZA, A S and KHAN, A R J. Am. Oil Chem. Soc.,
1968 45:247–249.

KIFER, R R and MILLER, D *Fishery Ind. Res.*, 5:25–37.
1969

KISHIMOTO, Y, RADIN, N S, TOURTELLOTTE, W W, PARKER, J A
1967 and ITABASHI, H H *Arch. Neurol.*, 16:44–54.

KOGA, Y *J. Jap. Soc. Fd Nutr.*, 23:260–268.
1970a

KOGA, Y *J. Jap. Soc. Fd Nutr.*, 23:269–275.
1970b

KOGA, Y *Nihon Shoku Kenkyu Kai 46 ho* Japanese Food Research
1970c Association, Studies on Japanese Foods, Report No. 46,
23:412–421.

KRZECZKOWSKI, R A *J. Am. Oil Chem. Soc.*, 47:451–452.
1970

KRZECZKOWSKI, R A, TENNEY, R D and KELLEY, C *J. Fd Sci.*,
1971 36:604–606.

KUKSIS, A In HOLMAN, R T (ed.), *Progress in the Chemistry of Fats*
1972 *and Other Lipids*, Oxford, U.K., Pergamon Press, 12:1–163.

KUNAU, W H *FEBS Letters*, 16:54–56.
1971

LAMBERTSEN, G *Fiskeridir. Skr. Ser. Teknol. Unders.*, 5(6):15 p.
1972

LAMBERTSEN, G and BRAEKKAN, O R *Ibid.*, 4:15 p.
1965

LAMBERTSEN, G, MYKLESTAD, H and BRAEKKAN, O R *J. Fd Sci.*,
1966 31:48–52.

LAMBERTSEN, G, MYKLESTAD, H and BRAEKKAN, O R *J. Am. Oil*
1971 *Chem. Soc.*, 48:389–391.

LANG, K and REIMOLD, W V *Z. ErnährWiss.*, 10:137–144.
1970

LEBRETON, E *Riv. ital. Sost. grasse*, 47:231–240.
1970

MANN, H *Fette Seifen AnstrMittel*, 72:1079–1083.
1970

McCAY, P B, POYER, J L, PFEIFER, P U, MAY, H E and GILLIAM,
1971 J M *Lipids*, 6:297–306.

McKAY, D G, KAUNITZ, H, CSAVOSSY, I and JOHNSON, R E *Metab.*
1967 *Clin. Exp.*, 16:111–126.

MEAD, J F In HOLMAN, R T (ed.), *Progress in the Chemistry of Fats*
1968 *and Other Lipids*, Oxford, U.K., Pergamon Press, 9(Part
2):159–192.

MEGA, A *Hokkaido-ritsu Eisei Kenkyushoho* (Rep. Hokkaido Inst.
1965 Pub. Health), (15):93–97.

MEIJBOOM, P W and STROINK, J B A *J. Am. Oil Chem. Soc.*,
1972 49:555–558.

MENGE, H *Poultry Sci.*, 50:261–266.
1971

MENZEL, D B, ROEHM, J M and LEE, SiDuk *J. Agr. Fd Chem.*,
1970 20:481–486.

MILLER, D, SOARES, J H, Jr, CUPPETT, S and WHITE, V *Nutr.*
1971 *Repts., Int.* 4:19–30.

MUNSCH, N and PASCAUD, M *Bull. Soc. Chim. Biol.*, 51:1575–1590.
1969

NAGAYAMA, F, IMANO, S and NAITO, Y *Bull. Jap. Soc. Sci. Fish.*,
1971 37:415–418.

NESTEL, P J In PAOLOTTI, R and KRITCHEVSKY, D (ed.), *Advances*
1970 *in Lipid Research*, New York, Academic Press, 8:1–39.

NOBLE, A C and NAWAR, W W *Can. Inst. Fd Technol. J.*, 4:135.
1971

ODENSE, P H and BROCKERHOFF, H *J. Fish. Res. Bd Can.*, 28:1793–
1971 1795.

OLLEY, J and DUNCAN, W R H *J. Sci. Fd Agric.*, 16:99–104.
1965

OWEN, J N, ADRON, J W, SARGENT, J R and COWEY, C B *Mar. Biol.*,
1972 13:160–166.

PATRIARCA, P, ZATTI, M and GOMPERTZ, D *Biochem. J.*, 115:1079–
1969 1080.

PRIVETT, O In HOLMAN, R T (ed.), *Progress in the Chemistry of Fats*
1966 *and Other Lipids*, Oxford, U.K., Pergamon Press, 9(Part
1):91–117.

QUINTÃO, E, GRUNDY, S M and AHRENS, E H, Jr, *J. Lipid Res.*,
1971 12:233–247.

RIMSH, E Ya *Trudy Vniro*, 74:222–243.
1970

ROCQUELIN, G and CLUZAN, R *Annls. Biol. Anim. Biochem.*
1968 *Biophys.*, 8:395–406.

ROLAND, D A, Sr, EDWARDS, H M, Jr *J. Nutr.*, 102:229–239.
1972

ROUBAL, W T *J. Am. Oil Chem. Soc.*, 40:213–215.
1963

ROUBAL, W T *J. Am. Oil Chem. Soc.*, 47:141–144.
1970

ROUBAL, W T *Fishery Bull.*, 69:371–377.
1971

ROUBAL, W T and TAPPEL, A L *Biochem. Biophys. Acta*, 136:402–
1967 403.

SAKAGUCHI, H and HAMAGUCHI, A *Bull. Jap. Soc. Sci. Fish.*, 35:
1969 1207–1214.

SCHLENK, H, SAND, D M and GELLERMAN, J L *Biochem. Biophys.*
1969 *Acta*, 187:201–207.

SHIN, B C, HUGGINS, J W and CARROWAY, K L *Lipids*, 4:229–233.
1972

SHONO, T and TOYOMIZU, M *Bull. Jap. Soc. Sci. Fish.*, 37:912–918.
1971

SHORLAND, F B, CZOCHANSKA, Z and PRIOR, I A M *Am. J. Clin.*
1969 *Nutr.*, 22:594–605.

SINCLAIR, A J and CRAWFORD, M A *Biochem. J.*, 126:18–19.
1971

SODERHJELM, L, WIESE, H F and HOLMAN, R T In HOLMAN, R T
1970 (ed.), *Progress in the Chemistry of Fats and Other Lipids*,
Oxford, U.K., Pergamon Press, 9(Part 4):555–585.

STANSBY, M E *J. Am. Oil Chem. Soc.*, 48:820–823.
1971

STICKNEY, R R and ANDREWS, J W *J. Nutr.*, 101:1703–1710.
1971

STOFFEL, W, ECKER, W, ASSAD, H and SPRECHER, H *Z Physiol.*
1970 *Chem.*, 351:1545–1554.

SUGII, K and KINUMAKI, T *Bull. Jap. Soc. Sci. Fish.*, 34:420–428.
1968

SWINDELLS, C E *Can. Inst. Fd Technol. J.*, 3:171–175.
1970

TAKAMA, K, ZAMA, K and IGARISHI, H *Bull. Jap. Soc. Sci. Fish.*,
1972 38:607–612.

TAKEUCHI, M *Ibid.*, 38-155–159.
1972

TAKEUCHI, M and ISHII, S *Bull. Tokai Reg. Fish. Lab.*, (68):45–49.
1971

TANAKA, K *Refrig. Japan*, 1–9.
1967

TEIGE, B and BEARE-ROGERS, J L *Proc. Can. Fed. Biol. Soc.*, June
1972 13–16, 1972, Quebec, Abstract No. 233.

TINOCO, J, WILLIAMS, M A, HINCENBERGS, I and LYMAN, R *J.*
1971 *Nutr.*, 101:937–945.

TINSLEY, I J, SADDLER, J B, KREUGER, H M and LOWRY, R R *Int.*
1971 *J. Biochem.*, 2:345–348.

TOYOMIZU, M and TOMIYASU, Y *Bull. Jap. Soc. Sci. Fish.*, 28:526–
1962 533.

UEDA, T *J. Shimonoseki University of Fisheries*, 16:1–10.
1967

UEDA, T *Ibid.*, 20:279–295.
1972

UEDA, T and NAGAOK, T *Ibid.*, 16:51–58.
1968

URDAHL, N and NYGARD, E *Meldinger fra SSF*, (1):3–22.
1971

VERESMAA, E, LAINE, J J and NIINIVAARA, F P *Z. Lebensmittelunters.*
1968 *u Forsch*, 138:150–154.

VIVIANI, R, CORTESI, P, MANCINI, L and BORGATI, A R *Atti Soc.*
1968 *ital. Scienze vet.*, 22:689–694.

VLADIMIROV, Yu A *Izv. Akad. Nauk SSSR Ser. Biol.*, 4:489–501.
1972

WALKER, B L *Nutr. Metab.*, 14:8–16.
1972a

WALKER, B L *Can. J. Anim. Sci.*, 52:713–719.
1972b

WALKER, B L and CARNEY, J A *Lipids*, 6:797–804.
1971

WATANABE, T and ACKMAN, R G *Fish. Res. Bd Techn. Report*, 334.
1972

WATANABE, T and HASHIMOTO, Y *Bull. Jap. Soc. Sci. Fish.*, 34:1131–
1968 1140.

WATANABE, T, MATSUURA, Y and HASHIMOTO, Y *Ibid.*, 32:887–891.
1966

WATANABE, T, TAKASHIMA, F, OGINO, C and HIBIYA, T *Ibid.*,
1970a 36:623–630.

WATANABE, T, TAKASHIMA, F, OGINO, C and HIBIYA, T *Ibid.*,
1970b 36:1231–1234.

WITTING, L A In Holman, R T (ed.), *Progress in the Chemistry of*
1970 *Fats and Other Lipids*, Oxford, U.K., Pergamon Press,
9(Part 4):517–553.

WOOD, G and HINTZ, L *J. Ass. off. Anal. Chem.*, 54:1019–1023.
1971

WOOD, G, HINTZ, L and SALWIN, H *Ibid.*, 52:904–910.
1969

WORTHINGTON, R E, BOGESS, T S, Jr and HEATON, E M *J. Fish.*
1972 *Res. Bd Can.*, 29:113–115.

WURZIGER, J and HENSEL, G *Fette Seifen AnstrMittel*, 70:937–942.
1967

YAMADA, M *Mem. Fac. Fish. Hokkaido Univ.*, 19(1/2):35–136.
1972

YOSHIOKA, M and KANEDA, T *Yukagaku* (Oil Chemistry), 21:316–
1972 321.

YU, T C and SINNHUBER, R O *Lipids*, 7:450–454.
1972

ZAITSEV, A N and MAGANOVA, N B *Voprosy Pitaniya*, 30:52–56.
1971

Application of Fish Oils in the Food Industry
E J Gauglitz, Jr.,
V F Stout and J C Wekell

Emploi des huiles de poisson dans l'industrie alimentaire

Utilisations actuelles et possibles de l'huile de poisson dans les aliments destinés à la consommation humaine, soit comme constituant alimentaire direct sous forme par exemple de margarine ou d'additifs alimentaires (émulsifiants), soit comme constituant indirect sous forme par exemple d eviande d'animaux et de chair de poissons nourris avec des rations contenant de l'huile de poisson. Exposé des problèmes liés à l'acceptation et à l'utilisation de l'huile de poisson dans les denrées alimentaires, notamment élimination des acides gras libres, des composés odorants, des polymères, des toxines et des hydrocarbures chlorés; examen des facteurs intrinsèques et extrinsèques qui limitent l'emploi des huiles de poisson dans les aliments destinés tant à la consommation humaine qu'à l'alimentation animale.

Aplicacion de los aceites de pescado en la industria alimentaria

Este trabajo indica los usos actuales y potenciales del aceite de pescado en alimentos destinados al consumo humano, tanto como elemento directo, por ejemplo, en forma de margarina y aditivos alimentarios (emulsificantes), como en forma de elemento indirecto, como la carne de animales, incluidos peces, criados con raciones que contienen aceite de pescado. Al examinar los factores intrínsecos y extrínsecos que han limitado el empleo de aceites de pescado en los alimentos para el hombre y los animales, se reseñan los diversos problemas que plantea la aceptación y aprovechamiento del aceite de pescado para alimentos, como la eliminación de los ácidos grasos libres, los compuestos olorosos, los polimeros, las toxinas y los hidrocarburos clorinados.

For many years countries throughout the world have recognized the value of oils from marine sources for both edible and industrial purposes and specific segments of the fishing industry have been developed to provide this product. The supply of marine oils has come from two sources: whales and fish. Over the past decade, the tremendous quantities of whale oil have declined to a small fraction of their former volume. It seems likely that whale oil will decline to the point of commercial insignificance. This has placed increased emphasis on fishing for species of oily fish. The major species taken for fish body oil production are pelagic, such as menhaden, anchovy, capelin, herring, mackerel, sardine (pilchard), and saury. Significant quantities of tuna oil are produced as a by-product of tuna canning operations and should also be included. Several other species of lesser importance contribute to the overall world production of fish oil.

World production of fish body oil reached a record level of 1,050,000 tons in 1967 (FAO 1971). Figures are not readily available for the volume of fish oil that goes into food products, but it is reasonable to conclude that the major part of the world production is utilized for that purpose. The remaining portion finds its way into a variety of industrial products. In many European countries where it is necessary to augment the domestic supply of animal and vegetable fats and oils, the demand for oils of marine origin has become significant. These nations, in fact, may import fish oils in order to meet their domestic requirements. The degree of usage in these countries is strongly influenced by the world supply of fats and oils, the economics of the market, and the cultural attitudes of the consumers. Major deterrents to the greater application of fish oils for food purposes, either as triglycerides or fatty derivatives such as emulsifiers, have been associated with quality and undesirable changes in the colour, flavour, and odour of the product. Several factors contribute to the presence and development of undesirable quality characteristics in fish oils. If one is to understand them and their effects on the intended application of the product, he must of necessity begin with a knowledge of the nature of the oil in the living fish. It may be assumed that the fat in any living fish is free of objectionable colour, flavour, or odour constituents. After death, enzymic, bacterial, and oxidative processes begin which ultimately affect both the chemical and physical properties of the oil. The degree of deterioration in quality is initially related to the physical handling of the catch. The length of elapsed time between catching and processing, and the higher temperature of storage, frequently resulting from the lack of refrigeration on the fishing vessels and in holding bins in the processing plants, greatly accelerates the decomposition of the raw material. Good quality raw material may incur a further loss in quality during the reduction process in normal fish meal production using wet or dry reduction (rendering) or by an organic solvent extraction process used for the production of fish protein concentrate. Additional degradation may occur during storage of the product but this is normally a much slower process.

METHODS OF REMOVING UNDESIRABLE COMPONENTS

Among the substances which affect the quality of fish oil are free fatty acids, proteins, carbohydrates, phospholipids, products of autoxidation of oil, naturally occurring toxins, and chlorinated hydrocarbon residues. The concentration of some of these components depends upon the method of production of the fish oil: use of fresh fish and careful processing reduce the amount of deterioration of the oil, which is accompanied by an increase in free fatty acids, autoxidation products, colour bodies, and odoriferous substances. Removal of such deleterious materials is often more difficult than prevention of their formation. Modern processing methods, although expensive and complicated, aid in the production of high quality oil. Gravity separation of oil, meal, and water allows extended contact of the oil with water and proteinaceous materials, which catalyze the formation of free fatty acids and autoxidation products. Centrifugation, on the other hand, gives rapid separation of the oil, prevents degradation, and in addition increases the actual yield of oil by improving the physical separation of the phases (Pigott 1967). The oil which comes from the centrifuge contains small amounts of water and finely divided fish particles (protein) in concentrations high enough to degrade the oil. Polishing by means of steam or hot water and recentrifugation eliminates these undesirable materials and yields an oil stable during long term storage (Pigott 1967).

Subsequent processing of the oil (Chang 1967) is designed further to improve the quality. Degumming and refining involves removal of phosphatides, mucilaginous substances, and free fatty acids by treatment with aqueous alkali. Bleaching by mixing with an adsorbent material such as activated clay, diatomaceous earth, or charcoal, reduces the natural pigments, autoxidized substances, and odorous substances. Hydrogenation or hardening converts the oil into a semisolid substance. Fish oil is thereby converted into shortening and margarine. If a liquid product is desired, this step is omitted. The degree of hydrogenation determines the consistency: the greater the extent of hydrogenation, the harder the product. Hydrogenation is performed by treating heated oil with hydrogen in the presence of a catalyst, most commonly nickel. The final stage of processing is deodorization. Volatile constituents responsible for undesirable odour and flavour are removed. Such substances are often detectable down to 10 ppm or less. By means of vacuum steam distillation a bland product is obtained. Nearly quantitative removal of DDT, DDE, aldrin, dieldrin, heptachlor, and heptachlor epoxide from vegetable oils during deodorization has been reported by Smith et al. (1968) and Saha, et al. (1970) and should also occur in fish oil processing. Simpler methods for removing chlorinated hydrocarbon residues from fish oil have been investigated in this laboratory. They would facilitate use of fish oil in animal feeds. For such uses the oil is not currently deodorized because of the additional cost. Treatment with cold water, hot water, or steam at atmospheric pressure effected no reduction in DDT levels (Stout et al. 1970). Silica gel removes some of the DDT and PCB's but does not reduce the chlorinated hydrocarbon level sufficiently to allow utilization in animal feeds.

NUTRITIVE VALUE OF FISH OILS

Human nutrition

Fish oils have long been a natural constituent of the diet of man since they are a normal component of the edible portion of fish. Although food fish generally contain substantially less fat than land animals, they do represent a source of a markedly different kind of fat from that ingested via plant and animal sources. Fish oils are comprised of fatty acid groups with much more unsaturation than is found in fats of terrestrial origin. This unsaturation is present in the form of methylene interrupted double bonds: that is, the repeating unit is $CH_2CH=CH$. Whereas vegetable oil fatty acid groups contain mainly one and two double bonds with small amounts of three and four double bond components, those from fish oil contain a substantial percentage with five and six double bonds (Gruger 1967). In general, fish oil is metabolized similarly to other lipids although in some cases it may be deposited in fat stores without preliminary breakdown (Karrick 1967). In the human diet fish oil has been utilized mainly in margarine and shortening. Small amounts are consumed directly, especially cod liver oil, which is used as a vitamin supplement, because it contains high concentrations of vitamins A and D. Fish oil has been advocated as a hypocholesterolemic agent in the treatment of atherosclerosis because it has been found to lower elevated serum cholesterol levels (Peifer 1967). Further research suggests that much more complicated changes are involved and that polyunsaturated fats may not effect long term improvement of atherosclerotic lesions (Nestel 1970). Although man has not been shown to possess an essen-

tial fatty acid requirement, fish oils may contribute these vital components to human nutrition.

Animal nutrition

Fish oil is a normal constituent of many animal feeds, which often contain fish meal as a protein source. Fish meal may contain up to 10 per cent fish oil, which seems to be metabolized and utilized as an energy source. As a nutritive component of itself fish oil possesses three potentially beneficial properties. It is a concentrated source of calories, it contains essential fatty acids (Aaes–Jørgensen 1967), and it provides highly unsaturated fat. Up to about five per cent of the total diet, fish oil is metabolized efficiently. It also provides vitamins A, D, and E. Vitamin E must be supplemented further, however, because the high level of polyunsaturation in fish oil increases the requirement for an antioxidant to prevent steatitis or yellow fat disease, nutritional muscular dystrophy (not related to progressive muscular dystrophy in humans), encephalomalacia, and exudative diathesis (Karrick 1967).

The symptoms of essential fatty acid (EFA) deficiency in animals have been delineated in detail, but the exact role they play in metabolism has still not been established. The symptoms include reduced growth rate, dermal lesions, infertility or lack of viability of offspring, and in fish impaired pigmentation (Guarnieri and Johnson 1970). Essential fatty acids in the diet prevent the development of symptoms or, where established, completely and rapidly reverse them. The specific structural requirements for EFA activity will not be known until the exact role of EFA is established, but some empirical evidence for activity has been recognized. Fatty acids which relieve symptoms of EFA deficiency are defined as being active. Their potency is compared to the potency of linoleate. Structures with EFA activity contain two or more double bonds in positions analogous to those in linoleic acid. The relevant feature is the distance of the last double bond from the methyl end of the chain. Full activity is associated with the $\omega6$ system which contains six carbons between the last double bond and the methyl end of the fatty acid chain. Partial EFA activity is associated with the $\omega3$ structure. Linolenic acid promotes growth, but does not prevent or cure dermal symptoms. Thomasson (as reported in Aaes–Jørgensen 1967) defined EFA in relation to linoleic acid, for which the value was set at 100 units/g. He found herring oil to contain 7.9 units/g and menhaden oil 4.4 units/g. Thus when substantial proportions of fish oil are included in animal rations, adequate amounts of EFA are obtained from the oil. The fatty acid composition of most animals reflects the identity of their dietary fat. Inclusion of fish oils in animal foods effects the introduction of polyunsaturation into the animal fat. To the extent that decreased consumption of saturated and monounsaturated fats and increased consumption of polyunsaturated fats is considered beneficial to man, the use of fish oil in animal rations will also implement this alteration in human dietary lipids.

FISH OIL IN HUMAN FOOD

In this section, a brief sketch of the historical uses of fish oils in foods in the United States will be given and the problems and future uses of marine oils will be discussed.

The use of non-hydrogenated fish oils in food is very limited; therefore, the term *fish oil* or *marine oil* will refer to the hydrogenated or hardened oil. Fish or marine oils are hydrogenated to varying degrees depending on their intended use, much like their vegetable counterparts.

Historical

By 1920 hardened fish oils were heavily used in margarine and shortenings in Europe. On the other hand, the edible use of fish oil in the United States was virtually non-existent. Due to shortages of vegetable oils during the first world war, research and development in the United States on edible uses of fish oil were begun. In 1925, 120,000 lb (54 tons) of California sardine oil were hydrogenated and used in margarine; its use reached a peak of 40 million lb (18,000 tons) in 1936 (US Fats and Oils Statistics 1966). Another use of fish oils, which does not appear in the statistics under edible uses, is their conversion to mono and diglycerides for use in superglycerinated shortenings. These glyceride products not only found large markets in the United States but also were shipped abroad. The peak use of sardine oil as glyceride mixtures reached 100 million lb (45,000 tons) annually, going primarily into shortenings. The use of marine oils in food products continued at a high level until 1951 when the mainstay of the fish oil industry, the sardine, was fished out. In the waning years of the sardine fishery, attempts were made to supplement the marine oil glycerides with Alaskan herring oil. Since 1951 the use of fish oils in either margarine or shortening in the United States has been abandoned. Two principal factors have brought about this change:

1. Modifications in the regulations of the Food and Drug Administration.
2. Establishment of a Standard of Identity for margarine which does not permit the use of marine oils.

Food and Drug regulations do not expressly forbid the use of fish oils in food; however, sanitary requirements for raw material going into foods essentially eliminate ordinary commercial fish oil from being used. Within the past 5 years, one manufacturer used imported herring oil in his shortening marketed in the United States. After only a brief exposure, the product was withdrawn from the market, not because of any legal action, but because of fears that labelling requirements indicating the presence of marine oil might cause a reduction in sales volume (Stansby, personal communication).

Since the early fifties the use of fish oils in countries other than the United States has increased dramatically. In 1970 Peru led all countries in the production of fish body oils (310,800 tons), followed by Norway (179,500 tons), and Japan (86,500 tons), (FAO 1971). A substantial part of this production is converted into edible food products (margarine, shortenings, and cooking fats). Prior to 1950 Canada restricted the use of fish oil in margarine, but since 1950 has lifted the ban. In Canada domestic herring oil and imported menhaden oil are used in margarine and to a lesser extent in shortenings.

Problems

The use of fish oils in foods has been limited owing to both *intrinsic* and *extrinsic* problems, but the extrinsic problems create greater barriers to the acceptance of marine oils for human consumption. Intrinsic problems, such as physical and chemical properties of oil, quality, and variability, are easily defined, and over the years methods and technology have been developed to overcome them. Extrinsic problems include economics and aesthetic and cultural preferences, and are far more intangible and difficult to define. Little progress has been made in overcoming them.

Intrinsic problems. Fish oils, unlike vegetable and animal oils and fats, generally contain large amounts of esterified unsaturated fatty acids. Due to the unstable nature of the double bonds the oils have a tendency to undergo oxidation and then become rancid. Hydrogenation or hardening eliminates these problems to some degree. However, all oils (both vegetable and marine) can and do undergo 'reversion' after hydrogenation in storage if they are not properly refined. Two kinds of reversion odour/flavour have been described. In one of these, the hydrogenated oil reverts to the flavour of the original oil. For example, reverted soybean oil is said to have a 'green', 'grassy', or 'beany' flavour. This flavour is generally disliked, at least in the United States. The other kind of odour/flavour results from the hydrogenation process itself. A number of adjectives have been used to describe the particular taste, eg, 'tallowy', 'cardboardy', 'candlelike'. Hannewijk (1967) has shown that this flavour may be due to a slight increase in bound aldehyde content which occurs during storage. The aldehydes result from oxidation of the unsaturated fats remaining after hydrogenation. Hannewijk claims the flavour arises from 6-*trans*-nonenal and has a taste threshold of 0.3 parts per thousand million.

Reversion tastes and odours are a greater problem in shortenings than in margarines. Shortenings tend to be stored at room temperature for long periods of time (one year), whereas margarines are stored in refrigerated condition and used rapidly (within months). Furthermore, the flavour ingredients in margarine (eg, diacetyl) tend to mask any reversion that might occur. The origins or reversion odours and flavours in fish oils are not easily traced since numerous irrelevant substances are extracted along with the triglycerides. The exact nature of these components is not only a function of the particular extraction process, but also depends on the physical condition of the fish at the time of extraction. In order to eliminate the extraneous matter it is mandatory that fish oils undergo refining prior to hydrogenation. Fish oils do not necessarily present more difficult problems in refining as much as different problems, due to methods of extraction (hot or cold pressing in place of solvent extraction) and the nature of the fish themselves. For example, the degree of unsaturation of the original oil plays a part in the tendency of an oil to 'revert', thus menhaden oil would be expected to be less of a problem than sardine oil in regard to reversion. It is felt by European oil refiners that fish oils present fewer problems of reversion than does soybean oil. Because fish oils are obtained from natural sources, and are usually taken from widely different locations, from different species, and at different times of the year, there is a large variation in quality. By quality is meant such factors as colour, fatty acid composition of the triglycerides (chain length and unsaturation), and sulphur content. However, by careful quality control or by blending different batches of oil, these variations can be overcome.

Extrinsic problems. Factors such as economics, marketing, psychology, aesthetics, and social and cultural preferences are much more difficult to identify. Acceptance of flavour depends upon the normal dietary constituents. The *fishy* odour associated with fishery products is generally disliked in the United States for a variety of reasons. In contrast, in northern European and Scandinavian countries fishy flavours and odours appear not only to be tolerated but are actually quite acceptable. Nonetheless, products from these countries find only a limited market in the United States. Similarly, both Europeans and Americans could be expected to dislike some of the fermented fishery products that are acceptable in Asia. Such cultural and psychological bases for acceptance of foods must be recognized when development of foreign markets for a fishery product is being considered.

In the United States and parts of Europe food products containing fish oils have come to be associated by the consumer with low quality and low priced products as compared to those made with vegetable or animal oils and fats. Because of this phenomenon the oil and fat industry is hesitant to market fish oil products where stringent labelling requirements prevail. Probably the most significant factor that has kept fish oil from attaining a greater share of the world oil market is economic. Presently, fish oil is exported to Canada and Europe from the United States. When the difference in market price between vegetable and fish oils is 2 US cents/lb (about 4 US cents/kg) or more, the preference is to use the fish oil since it is usually less expensive. Processors need that differential in order to compensate for the added processing cost of fish oil due to the somewhat different refining procedures required.

Future uses

Past history amply demonstrates the acceptability of fish oils in foods by a vast segment of the world population. Therefore, availability of a food-grade oil would be expected to open the market for use in margarines, shortenings (both solid and liquid), salad oils and dressings, and any other foods requiring the use of oils or fats as an ingredient in the product.

Once its use in food production is more widely accepted, the demand for the oil should continue to increase. Even from the simplistic view of population expansion, the demands for greater food production will also cause increased consumption of fats. For example, fish oil usage in margarine production alone could certainly be expected to return to the levels it once enjoyed, 40 million lb (18,000 tons) in 1936, and possibly surpass that in 10 years in the United States.

FISH OIL IN ANIMAL FEEDS

For many years fish oil has been added to animal feeds. It is an economical source of calories and stimulates growth. The growth enhancement results from the high concentration of linolenic acid homologues (ω3 fatty acids). Whereas tallow, a common component of animal feed, contains less than one per cent of these substances, fish oils, such as menhaden, herring and tuna, contain up to 33 per cent of the active substances (Karrick 1967).

The fish oil used in animal rations must be fresh because autoxidized oils are toxic. The diet must also be supplemented with adequate vitamins, especially vitamin E. The proportion of fish oil must be limited to prevent development of undesirable flavours, which are associated with any polyunsaturated oil and are not unique to fish oil diets. Interestingly, the fish oil in fish flesh and fish meal do not contribute to off-flavours.

Fish oil is very beneficial to laying hens. It increases both egg production and hatchability without causing 'fishy' or other undesirable flavours or odours. In fact, even excessive amounts of fish oil and fish meal do not alter the flavour of eggs. In chicks, menhaden oil has an exceptionally high energy value of 3,700 cal/lb (8,140 cal/kg) compared to 2,900 cal/lb (6,380 cal/kg) for tallow (Karrick 1967). Therefore, extra economy might be obtained in poultry husbandry from menhaden or similar fish oil as a supplement to chick rations. Since herring oil was found to have a substantially lower energy value, 1,502 cal/lb (3,304 cal/kg) March *et al.*, as quoted in Karrick 1967), the high energy value of menhaden oil is probably related to its high proportion of linolenic acid homologues. Other fish oils with equivalent concentrations of these constituents would presumably be equally efficient energy sources. The use of fish oil in the diet of poultry raised for meat does have to be restricted (Karrick 1967). Both the flavour and stability of the flesh are affected adversely at levels above one per cent. Changes in stability during frozen storage are related to the concentration of unsaturated fat laid down in the tissue. To avoid problems, the fish oil is sometimes withdrawn from the diet two to three weeks before marketing. Turkeys are more sensitive to flavour alteration than chickens. At the one per cent level, fish oil causes marked 'fishy' flavour, which could be avoided by removing the fish oil from the diet eight weeks before slaughter (Karrick 1967).

Flavour reversion in pigs develops at levels of fish oil above $\frac{1}{2}$ per cent (Karrick 1967). The fish oil must be removed from the diet two weeks to several months before slaughter to prevent accumulation of polyunsaturated fats in the lard.

Beef cattle rations can include fish oil in moderate amounts. If adequate levels of vitamin E are included, the colour, texture, and flavour of the fat are not affected (Karrick 1967). In dairy cattle, fish oil increases the unsaturated fatty acid composition of the milk and reduces the total butterfat. Up to 26 per cent partially hydrogenated menhaden oil has been fed to new-born calves. Partial hydrogenation and protein encapsulation of the fat overcome the problems of muscular dystrophy associated with feeding non-hydrogenated menhaden oil (Ronning 1970). Prevention of autoxidation of unsaturated entities and adequate levels of vitamin E are requisites to successful utilization of fish oil.

Mink and house cats are often fed diets containing fish. Unless vitamin E is included in the food, steatitis develops. Rancid horse meat causes the same problem. Both mink and cats are susceptible to chlorinated hydrocarbon intoxication. Therefore, fish from contaminated waters must be avoided. Cats are more sensitive to DDT than most mammals. Mink, though not affected by DDT or dieldrin, fail to reproduce at polychlorobiphenyl levels of 5 ppm (Ringer 1972).

Channel catfish reared on artificial diets containing menhaden oil grew more rapidly than fish reared on corresponding diets containing corn oil (Dupree 1970). Fish raised on the menhaden oil diets were less acceptable to taste panels than those raised on corn oil diets (Miyauchi, personal communication). Withdrawal of menhaden oil from the diet in advance of marketing may eliminate the flavour problem. Saltwater pond-reared chinook salmon also grew more rapidly on a menhaden-oil supplemented diet than on the corresponding soybean oil control diet. In addition, the fish on the menhaden oil diet were more resistant to infection by a *Vibrio* organism (Novotny, personal communication). Novotny (personal communication) also found that waste spraying dry pellet rations with menhaden oil stimulated feeding. To avoid autoxidation spraying would have to take place at the time of feeding.

References

AAES-JØRGENSEN, E Fish oils as a source of essential fatty acids.
1967   In M E Stansby (ed.), *Fish oils.*, Westport, Avi., USA, 440 p., Chap. 22.
CHANG, S S Processing of fish oils, *Ibid.*, Chap. 15.
1967
DUPREE, H K Report to US Bureau of Commercial Fisheries.
1970
FAO Yearbook of Fishery Statistics Fishery Commodities, 1970,
1971   Rome, (31):320 p.
GRUGER, E H Fatty acid composition, In M E Stansby (ed.), *Fish*
1967   *oils.* Westport, Avi., USA, 440 p., Chap. 1.

GUARNIERI, M and JOHNSON, R M Essential fatty acids, in R
1970   Paoletti and D Kritchevsky (ed.), *Advances in lipid research*, New York, Academic Press. Vol. 8:469 p., p. 115.
HANNEWIJK, J Use of fish oils in margarine and shortening, In M E
1967   Stansby (ed.), *Fish oils.*, Westport, Avi., USA, 440 p., Chap. 18.
KARRICK, N L Nutritional value as animal feed, *Ibid.*, Chap. 24.
1967
NESTEL, P J Cholesterol turnover in man, In R Paoletti and D
1970   Kritchevsky (ed.), *Advances in lipid research*, New York, Academic Press. Vol. 8:469 p., p. 1.
PEIFER, J J Hypocholesterolemic effects of marine oils, In M E
1967   Stansby (ed.), *Fish oils.* Westport, Avi., USA, 440 p., Chap. 23.
PIGOTT, G M Production of fish oil, *Ibid.*, Chap. 13.
1967
RINGER, R K, AULERICH, R J and ZABIK, M Effect of dietary
1972   polychlorinated biphenyls on growth and reproduction of mink. Am. Chem. Soc., Division of Water, Air and Waste Chemistry, Preprints of Papers Presented at 164th National Meeting, Aug. 28–Sept. 1, 149–154.
RONNING, M Report to US Bureau of Commercial Fisheries.
1970
SAHA, J G, NIELSEN, M A and SUMNER, A K Effect of commercial
1970   processing techniques on lindane-and DDT-^{14}C residues in rapeseed oil. *J. agric. Fd Chem.*, 18(1):43–44.
SMITH, K J, POLEN, P B, VRIES, D M de and COON, F B Removal of
1968   chlorinated pesticides from crude vegetable oil by simulated commercial processing procedures. *J. Am. Oil Chem. Soc.*, 45(12):866–869.
STOUT, V F, BEEZHOLD, F L and HOULE, C R DDT residue levels
1970   in some fishery products and the effectiveness of some treatments in reducing them. *FAO technical conference on marine pollution and its effects on living resources and fishing*, (Rome, 9–18 December), E-106:1–8.
U.S. Fats and Oils Statistics, 1909–65, United States Department
1966   of Agriculture Statistical Bull. No. 376, Washington, DC.

Potential Production of Powdered and Liquid Fish Products for Human Consumption and Animal Feed   *I M Mackie*

Possibilite de fabriquer des produits en poudre et liquides a base de poisson pour la consommation humaine et l'alimentation animale

Préparation de produits liquides par traitement de poisson maigre – poisson entier, filets de poisson ou déchets de filetage – au moyen d'enzymes protéolytiques du commerce. Comparaison de l'efficacité de diverses enzymes protéolytiques pour détacher la chair du squelette des poissons. Utilité de l'adjonction de lipides au début du traitement pour accroître l'aptitude à la suspension des produits en poudre obtenus. Indices d'iode et d'acide thiobarbiturique observés lors d'expériences d'entreposage de produits en poudre préparés avec ou sans antioxygènes.

Produccion potencial de productos pesqueros en polvo y liquidos para e el consumo humano y piensos

Se describe la forma de preparar productos líquidos de pescado tratando pescado magro entero o en filetes o los desechos del fileteado con enzimas proteolíticas que es posible encontrar en el comercio. Se compara la eficacia de diversas enzimas proteolíticas para remover la carne del esqueleto de los peces. Se presentan algunos resultados que muestran el valor que tiene la adición de grasas al principio del tratamiento para mejorar la suspensibilidad del polvo deshidratado obtenido. Se dan también los valores de yodo y ácido tiobarbitúrico obtenidos en experimentos de almacenamiento de los productos deshidratados preparados con y sin antioxidantes.

The dried protein products now prepared for human consumption are called fish protein concentrates (FPC). They are usually prepared from fish fillets by a variety of solvent extractions and drying procedures. They are generally, although not exclusively, tasteless colourless powders with protein contents as high as 80 per cent and fat content of less than 0.2 per cent (Anon. 1970). These products have poor functional properties and, because of this, alternative procedures have been investigated (Fujimaki *et al.* 1971, Rutman 1971, Spinelli *et al.* 1972, Hale 1972, Schmitt and Ploquin 1971 and Fieffé 1966). The use of proteolytic enzymes to liquefy fish muscle has been shown by various workers to be a feasible method of isolating protein from fish. The gritty texture associated with solvent-extraction procedures is not

obtained in these processes. One of the main disadvantages of products obtained by enzymic methods is a bitter flavour believed to be due to low molecular weight peptides during the hydrolysis. There is also uncertainty over the nutritional value of products containing a considerable proportion of free amino acids and peptides and, in particular, some processes are known to depress the content of essential amino acids such as histidine and tryptophan (Hale 1972). Recent work by Fujimaki *et al.* (1971), by Rutman (1972) and Schmitt and Ploquin (1971) suggest that some of these difficulties can be avoided if the time of hydrolysis is kept to a minimum. The work presented in this paper is also based on the principle of keeping hydrolysis time to the minimum required to liquefy but not to dissolve the fish muscle.

EXPERIMENTAL

The fish used were cod (*Gadus morhua*) and haddock (*Gadus aeglefinus*). Hydrolysates were prepared separately from whole fish, skinless fillets and filleting offal (head and skeleton with adhering flesh and belly flaps) respectively. The fillets were minced before being hydrolyzed and the whole fish and filleting offal were diced into cubes (approximately 2 cm³). Commercially available proteolytic enzymes were used. Bacterial proteinase–N (Conc) and Pancreas proteinase (Rohm and Haas); papain (Sigma), Pronase and Bromelain (Koch–Light) and trypsin (BDH).

Digestion without added oil

The raw material (100 g) was homogenized for 3 min in phosphate buffer (500 ml 0.05 µ) in an Atomix blender and the pH of the suspension was adjusted to the optimum for the particular enzyme being used. The mixture was transferred to a flask and the temperature was raised to 50°C by heating in a water bath. A mechanical shaker was used to agitate the contents of the flask. For the digestion with trypsin, 45°C was used and for that with papain and EDTA (0.005 mol) and cysteine (0.001 mol) were added as activators. Hydrolyses were carried out with enzyme to protein ratios varying from 1:40 to 1:400. Digestion was finally stopped by heating at 100°C for 10 minutes. The protein suspension was filtered through a sieve (60 mesh 0.0098 inch), frozen and freeze-dried.

Digestion in presence of added hydrogenated oil containing antioxidants

The raw fish (100 g) with 200 ml of water was added with stirring to 800 ml of an emulsion of hydrogenated oil (melting point 40 to 42°C) preheated to 60°C. Bromelain (0.1 g) was then added and the temperature of the mixture was raised slowly to 60°C. During the time of digestion the mixture was continuously agitated. After 20 min the liquefied mixture was filtered as above and

sterilized in an autoclave at 1.05 kg/cm² (15 psi) for 10 minutes. The hydrolysate was then rehomogenized, cooled and freeze-dried.

Oil-water emulsion (Rutman 1971)

To 10 g of lipid containing antioxidant (0.05 g each of butylated hydroxytoluene BHT and dodecyl gallate) was added 0.15 g of Span 60 (sorbitan minostearate). The mixture was then added to 90 ml water containing 0.35 g Tween 60 (polyoxyethylene 20 sorbitan minostearate). The mixture was blended to form an emulsion and it was used immediately.

Analyses

Nitrogen determination was carried out by the micro-Kjeldahl procedure.

For total α amino acid determination ten ml of the enzymic digest was treated with an equal value of 20 per cent trichloracetic acid solution and after suitable dilution of the supernatant and aliquot was heated at 100°C with 1.2 per cent ninhydrin in methyl-cellosolve-acetate solution. The intensity of the colour produced was measured at 570 namonetres. The concentration is expressed in terms of isoleucine equivalents. The content of the individual amino acids in the final dried products were determined on 24 h hydrolysates obtained after heating samples in 6 N hydrochloric acid *in vacuo* at 110°C (10 mg in 3.0 ml). A Locarte amino-acid analyser was used for the analyses. The lipid was extracted from the final dried protein product by the method of Bligh and Dyer (1959). The iodine value was determined by Wij's method and the thiobarbituric acid value was determined by a modification of the method of Dahle, Hill and Holman (Keay *et al.* 1972).

For determination of specific enzymic activity, the method of Kunitz (1947) with casein as substrate was used.

RESULTS

The results given in this paper are to some extent preliminary. They are intentionally selected to give a general account of our approach to the study of methods of recovering fish protein from white fish offal. Such studies also relate to problems of recovering protein and oil from pelagic species. We have not yet studied this latter problem to any extent but it would appear to be a subject

TABLE 1. OUTLINE OF PROCEDURE FOR LIQUEFYING FISH OR FISH OFFAL WITH PROTEOLYTIC ENZYMES

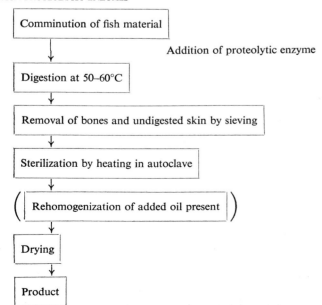

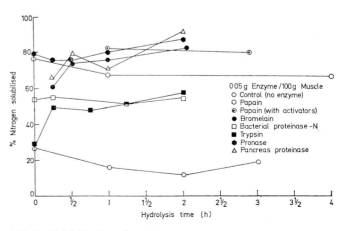

Fig 1   Solubilization of protein

of even greater importance in a worldwide sense and one which clearly merits further attention. We have selected what we consider to be the simpler problem of determining methods of recovering protein from fish processing waste. Also it is of immediate relevance to the fishing industry of the United Kingdom and any results obtained on both basic and applied studies should be a useful base for further research on problems of recovery and utilization of fish proteins. The results presented in Figs 1 and 2 give some indication of the rapidity with which protein nitrogen is solubilized. The 'O time' in Figs 1,

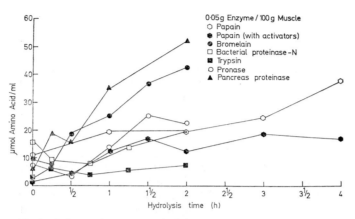

Fig 2   Release of α amino acids

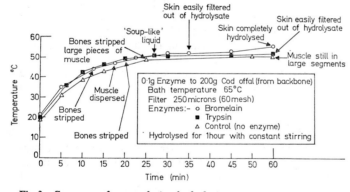

Fig 3   Sequence of events during hydrolysis

2 and 3 is not the time of addition of the enzyme but 10 min later, during which time a homogenized step followed by transfer to the digestion flask has been carried out. The results are presented for comparative purposes only and should be compared with the figures in Table 2 which give the activity of the different enzymes in terms of μg tyrosine released/min/mg casein. Clearly the relative order of activity in casein does not relate either to % nitrogen solubilized or amount/total amino acid released. Such assays are nonetheless useful indices of the changes which are taking place during hydrolysis and they can be used to monitor the course of action of a particular enzyme. It must be concluded that prior to removal of the first aliquot considerable proteolysis has taken place. From previous experiments in which raw and cooked muscle were hydrolyzed it is known that the native proteolytic enzymes of the fish muscle, eg, the cathepsins, contribute to a large extent to the solubilization of fish muscle. It is also clear that differences in

activity of enzymes as determined in artificial substrates, such as casein, do not reflect the effectiveness of action of these enzymes on raw fish muscle. The apparent relative activities of the added proteolytic enzymes are clearly modified by proteolytic enzymes naturally present in the fish muscle.

TABLE 2. ACTIVITY OF ENZYMES IN TERMS OF μG TYROSINE RELEASED/MIN/MG CASEIN

Enzyme	Activity per μg enzyme
Pronase	0.469
Pancreas Proteinase	0.215
Bromelain	0.165
Trypsin	0.077
Bacterial Proteinase–N	0.054
Papain	0.012

For the purpose of the present studies raw fish has been selected because, in addition to proteolysis being more rapid, the simplicity of a method, which is based on the addition of enzymes to raw fish, has much to commend it. By keeping the time of digestion just long enough to disperse the proteins but not long enough to dissolve the skin (see Fig 3) it has been possible to obtain a liquefied 'fish milk' after a digestion time of 30 minutes. During this time all of the enzymes studied remove the muscle tissue from the bones which can be readily removed together with undissolved skin by passing the fish milk through a sieve (60 mesh). Bromelain is more effective than any of the other enzymes studied even when account is taken of the different relative activities of the enzymes as measured by hydrolysis of casein. Trypsin is the least effective and generally a hydrolysis time longer than half an hour is required. When preparations are made with added oil (see Table 1) it is necessary to rehomogenize the protein-oil suspension before freeze-drying or spray-drying. Such products prepared from filleting waste and from fish fillets are off-white in colour but those prepared from whole fish, including viscera, are light brown. All of the products have a slight 'fish meal' smell and in common with all enzymically produced protein preparations they have a bitter flavour, the intensity of which varies with the enzyme used and the time of hydrolysis. This bitter flavour, however, is not nearly so pronounced as in those products obtained after digestion times of several hours. Because of the use of a sieving stage, bones are almost entirely removed and ash contents are generally less than 5 per cent. The protein content of the 'fat added' products vary from 53 to 65 per cent and fat contents from 33 to 37 per cent. The 'fat free' products similarly have ash content of <5 per cent and protein and oil contents of >90 per cent and about 1.0 per cent respectively.

In Table 3 are given the amino acid analyses of 'fat added' products from cod offal and cod fillets. The amino acid analysis of the untreated muscle is also given for comparison. Even with the short digestion times the histidine content of the 'offal' protein is reduced. Similarly, lysine, tyrosine and phenylalanine are less in the hydrolysates but particularly in the offal preparation.

Glycine and proline are correspondingly high in the offal presumably because of hydrolysis of collagen and the connective tissue which are present in greater amount. Compared with fish meal these 'short term' enzymically produced 'fish proteins' disperse well in water, particularly those containing the added oil. In terms of nitrogen recovered in the final dried product, yields of the order of 95 per cent are commonly obtained from the offal. There is no doubt that the addition of oil at the

TABLE 3. AMINO ACID COMPOSITION OF ENZYMIC HYDROLYSATES AND UNTREATED FISH MUSCLE (MG AMINO ACID/G TOTAL N)

Amino acid	Hydrolysate from		Untreated cod muscle
	cod offal	cod fillets	
Aspartic acid	550	632	660
Threonine	243	265	285
Serino	307	277	281
Glutamic acid	777	924	965
Proline	323	273	283
Glycine	569	283	304
Alanine	391	356	376
Cystine/2	56	44	43
Valine	222	233	320
Methionine	181	180	218
Isoleicine	179	200	290
Leucine	392	456	518
Tyrosine	174	209	225
Phenylalanine	203	218	248
Lysine	454	638	752
Histidine	63	157	129
Ammonia	89	79	52
Arginine	398	385	423
Total	5,572	5,809	6,372
Nitrogen recovery	85.2%	86.9%	92.5%

initial stage of the process improves the dispersibility of the dried product. An emulsion stable over periods of hours can readily be obtained but a decision on whether to add oil in the process would depend on the properties required in the final product. Some preliminary measurement of the susceptibility of the products to oxidation on storage up to nine weeks exposed to air at ambient temperatures has been carried out. Data for iodine values of oil and thiobarbituric values extracted from protein products made from cod without

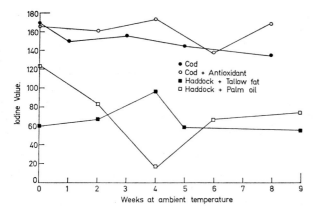

Fig 4 Iodine values of fish hydrolysates

added oil and from haddock with added oil are presented in Figs 4 and 5. Although it is difficult to compare the data for the different products because of the effect of dilution of the added oil, there is a steady decrease in the iodine value of cod (and by inference an increase in oxidation) without antioxidant being present. The thiobarbituric acid values show an increase during the first three weeks, followed by a decrease. Organoleptic properties of the extracted oil changed markedly during the time, particularly the products which did not contain antioxidants – the oil darkened steadily and strong rancid odours were very obvious after two to three weeks storage. It is clear that even in products from non-fatty fish, oxidative rancidity is a problem and some protection of the unsaturated lipids is necessary.

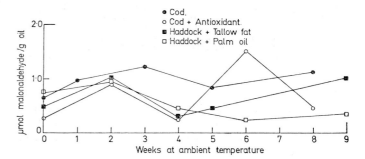

Fig 5   TBA values of fish hydrolysates

GENERAL CONCLUSIONS

The principle of removing fish flesh from raw filleting waste by proteolytic enzymes at relatively high temperatures offers scope for the development of a range of protein products either as sterilized liquid suspensions or as dried powders. The flavour can be influenced by the type of proteolytic enzyme added and the functional properties of these products can be modified by the type of lipid added. The addition of lipid containing antioxidant is a very effective method of distributing antioxidant rapidly throughout the homogenized tissue. Potential products include milk substitutes for both animals and humans. The flavour problem still remains, however, and further research on the mode of action of the different proteolytic enzymes is necessary. As proteolytic processes appear to diminish the amount of some of the essential amino acids, a close check on nutritional value of the various products is being planned.

References

ANON The Economics of Fish Protein Concentrate, Massachusetts
1970   Institute of Technology, USA.
BLIGH, E G and DYER, W G A rapid method of total lipid extraction
1959   and purification. Can. J. Biochem. Physiol., 37:911–917.
FUJIMAKI, M, KATO, H, ARAI, S and YAMASHITA, M Application of
1971   microbial proteases to soybean and other materials to improve acceptability especially through the formation of plactein. J. appl. Bact., 34(1):119–131.
FIEFFÉ, C F Procédé de solubilisation des protéines et produits
1966   alimentaires en résultant. Brevet d'invention No. 1, 439, 936.
HALE, M B Making fish protein concentrates by enzymatic hydroly-
1972   sis. NOAA Tech. Rep. NMFS SSRF-657.

KEAY, J N, RATTAGOOL, P and HARDY, R Chub mackerel of
1972 Thailand (*Rastrelliger neglectus*, Van Kampen). A short study of its chemical composition, cold storage and canning properties. *J. Sci. Fd Agric.*, 23:1359–1368.
KUNITZ, M Crystalline soybean trypsin inhibitor. *J. Gen. Physicol.*,
1947 30:291–320.
RUTMAN, M Process for preparing high energy fish protein con-
1971 centrate. United States Patent Office, 3, 561, 973.

SCHMITT, M and PLOQUIN, J Method of preparing and conditioning
1971 protein-containing foods, applicable notably to the fishing industry. Canadian Patent No. 865668.
SPINELLI, J, KOURY, B and MILLER, R Approaches to the utilization
1972 of fish for the preparation of protein isolates. *J. Fd Sci.*, 37:599–603.

Production of Liquid Fish Silage for Animal Feed   *M L Windsor*

Production d'ensilage liquide de poisson pour l'alimentation animale

Production d'ensilage liquide de poisson par autodigestion à partir de six types de matière, notamment déchets depoissonsde fond et déchets de harengs. Composition des produits obtenus. Modifications survenant au bout d'un an d'entreposage. Modifications observées dans l'huile lorsque l'on utilise des matières premières huileuses. Description d'un système simple de production discontinue par lots de 5 tonnes et d'une méthode de séparation de l'huile.

Produccion de ensilaje de pescado liquido para piensos

Se describe el sistema de producción de ensilaje líquido para peces mediante autodigestión (ensilaje) utilizando seis tipos de materias primas, entre ellos desechos de pescado blanco y de arenque. Se indica la composición de los productos resultantes y los cambios que se producen durante un año de almacenamiento. Se examinan los cambios que se producen en el aceite cuando se utilizan materias primas oleosas. Se describe un sistema sencillo para la producción de partidas de cinco toneladas y un método para la separación del aceite.

'Fish silage' may be defined as a liquid product, made from whole or parts of fish, to which no material has been added other than an acid and in which liquefaction is carried out by enzymes already present in the fish. Fish silage may or may not contain the oil associated with the raw material. Fish silage is normally used as an animal feeding stuff. The preparation of a liquid fish product for this purpose, however, is not a new idea but was developed by Virtanen in Finland in the twenties. There is little published work on the subject but Petersen (1953) reviewed the acid preservation of fish and fish offal in 1953 and McBride *et al.* (1961) carried out a thorough investigation into liquefaction of herring in 1961. Earlier results by Soviet workers Lagunov, Egorova, Rekhina and Eremeeva have also appeared (1958). The preparation of silage products from fish or fish waste by autodigestion is not widespread; such products are made commercially in, for example, Denmark and Poland. The process is little utilized in developing countries. In general, the ensilage of fish to produce a liquid product may be considered a suitable process in areas where: fish waste or excess fish are regularly available; high transport costs and/or material losses would be incurred in sending the material to the nearest fish meal factory; farming (eg pig and poultry production) is carried out locally so that the product need not be transported over great distances; formic acid, or other acids are obtainable.

THE PRODUCTION OF FISH SILAGE

The principle involved in the manufacture of fish silage is that the enzymes already present in the fish are spread throughout the fish mass and the acidity adjusted so as to favour the rapid action of these enzymes and to inhibit bacterial action. The method of preparation is very simple and the equipment consists basically of a strong grinder to produce minced fish, a method of adding and mixing in the required amount of acid, and containers in which to store the material while it is liquefying. This is shown in Fig 1. In the pilot-scale work carried out at the Humber Laboratory the raw material was ground with a hammer mill type disinte-

grator (Scott Reitz RD 12 H. Balfour) using screens with 10 mm holes. This produced a ground fish mass of suitable fineness and enabled a throughput of between 2 and 3 t/h depending upon the method of feeding the grinder. Although mineral acids such as sulphuric acid can be used, the product must then be neutralized before being fed to animals. In this work formic acid has been

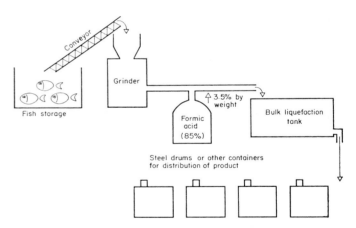

Fig 1   A simple system for the manufacture of fish silage

used. It is rather more expensive than mineral acids but the product may be directly fed to animals. Previous work has established that the addition of approximately 3 per cent by weight of formic acid (98 per cent) is sufficient and, since formic acid (85 per cent) is easier to handle and is commercially available, all fish silages were prepared using an equivalent addition (3.5 per cent) of formic acid (85 per cent). The ground fish and formic acid mixture were well mixed and transferred to a collapsible bulk tank which held about 5 tons of fish silage and measured about 3 m in diameter and 1.2 m high. Formic acid mixtures are mildly corrosive and the tank was constructed from butyl rubber. Liquefaction of the mass proceeds at a rate depending upon the temperature and upon the raw material. In ambient temperatures of about 18 to 20°C liquefaction of herring or herring offal is complete within 24 to 48 hours. Ensilage of white fish offal also proceeds fairly rapidly at this temperature, but due to the very much larger bones present it can take a further 5 to 7 days before the bone material is fine enough to be fed to animals.

Preliminary experiments in separating the oil from the silage have shown that by use of a suitable centrifuge the fish silage may be separated into an aqueous liquid phase, a semi-solid phase and an oil phase. In some instances where there are larger particles a 16 mesh sieve may be utilized before centrifugation to reduce the amount of solids fed to the centrifuge. It is necessary to heat the fish silage to about 50°C prior to centrifugation. In the results described below, however, the oil was not separated from the silage so that changes occurring in the oil during storage could be examined. The six types of fish silage examined were made in the laboratory, using a method similar to that described above but with laboratory scale equipment.

ANALYSIS OF SIX TYPES OF FISH SILAGE

The silages were produced in the laboratory from six types of raw material: whole ungutted sprats (*Sprattus sprattus*), whole ungutted herring (*Clupea harengus*), herring offal, ie, frame and head but not viscera, whole ungutted sand-eels (*Ammodytes tobianus*), white fish offal, ie, cod, haddock and plaice frames and some whole fish but not viscera and whole ungutted mackerel (*Scomber scombrus*). The whole fish were good quality industrial fish and the herring offal and white fish offal were obtained from fish suitable for human consumption. Approximately 8 kg of each silage were produced and these were stored in 10 litre plastic containers covered with loosely fitting lids. The silages were stored in the laboratory at ambient temperature which was 23°C ($\pm$ 3°C) and after the initial preparation were stirred only when samples were taken. Some settling occurs during storage and it is very important that there is adequate mixing prior to sampling. Each silage was analysed when produced and then after storage periods of 2, 4, 7, 14 days and 1, 2, 3, 6, 12 months. When samples were withdrawn, at the above mentioned intervals, the following analyses were carried out.

Moisture

About 10 g of the silage is accurately weighed into a flat glass dish (diameter 100 mm) and dried for 24 h in an oven at 103°C. The moisture content is calculated from the weight loss and expressed as a percentage of the original weight of silage.

Nitrogen

About 5 g of the silage accurately weighed is digested using the Kjeldahl procedure in which 50 ml of concentrated sulphuric acid (nitrogen-free), and 4 mercury catalyst tablets (each containing 1 g of Na_2SO_4 and the equivalent of 0.1 g of mercury) were used. The clear digest is diluted to 500 ml and the nitrogen content measured by autoanalyser using the method of Varley (1966) as modified by Mitchelson and Stowell (1969). The proportion of soluble nitrogen present is determined by quantitatively precipitating the protein in 125 g of silage with 90 ml of 20 per cent trichloracetic acid. After filtering, 50 ml of the filtrate is digested using the procedure outlined above and the nitrogen content determined by the same autoanalyser method.

Oil

Fifty grammes of the silage is dried overnight at 103°C and the dried material quantitatively transferred to a Soxhlet extraction thimble. The material is then extracted using diethyl ether for a period of at least 2 h after the ether appeared colourless. The ether is removed by distillation and the oil remaining in the flask is weighed and expressed as a percentage of the original weight of silage.

Ash

About 5 to 10 g of silage is weighed accurately into a silica basin. The basin contents are placed in an oven at 103°C overnight and then transferred to an oven maintained at 600°C. Heating is continued until the residue is uniformly white. The basin is removed and allowed to cool in a desiccator before weighing. The weight of the ash is calculated as a percentage of the original weight of silage.

The iodine value and free fatty acid content were determined on oil separated from the silage using the following procedure:

Separation of oil from silage

About 100 to 200 g of silage are placed in a pestle and mortar and sufficient anhydrous sodium sulphate added to combine with the water present. About three 100 ml quantities of petroleum ether (40 to 60°C) are added separately and mixed with the material. The petroleum ether extracts are filtered into a conical flask to which a few g of anhydrous sodium sulphate are added. This extract is again filtered and the petroleum then removed on a rotary evaporator at a temperature of 38°C. An oxygen-free nitrogen gas stream is run through the flask to eliminate oxygen and to assist solvent removal.

Iodine value

The iodine value of an oil is defined as the weight of iodine absorbed by 100 parts by weight of the sample. Iodine values are normally determined by Wijs' method and the method described in Pearson (1962) has been used in this work.

Free fatty acids

The estimation of free fatty acids was carried out as outlined in Pearson (1962) using neutral alcohol as the solvent, except that N/10 alcohol KOH was used for the titration. The free fatty acids are expressed as oleic acid as a percentage of the weight of the oil.

RESULTS AND DISCUSSION

Table 1 summarizes some of the analytical results. It is seen that the protein contents of all six samples were within the range 15 to 17 per cent. The four silages made from whole fish contained an average of 16.0 per cent, the others from filleting offal contained an average of 15.2 per cent protein. In other work using commercial white fish offal in pilot scale trials the protein content was normally about 14 per cent.

In order to study the changes in the solubility of the nitrogen which occurs as the proteins are broken down to smaller units, the soluble nitrogen content of the silage was measured at intervals during storage and compared with the total nitrogen content. In the method trichloracetic acid is used and all but low molecular weight peptides and free amino acids would be precipitated, so

TABLE 1. COMPOSITION OF FISH SILAGE

Determination	Whole sprat	Whole herring	Herring offal	Whole sand-eels	White fish offal	Whole mackerel
Crude protein (NX6.25)(%)	16.6	15.4	15.0	15.4	15.5	16.6
Oil content (%)	6.4	4.4	16.3	3.4	0.5	12.0
Moisture content (%)	74.3	77.7	68.1	77.7	78.9	70.2
Ash (%)	2.6	2.0	2.6	2.3	4.1	2.1
Measurements on oil						
Iodine value						
(1) at start	135	147	147	175	—	163
(2) after 12 months	114	104	100	145	—	108
Free fatty acids						
(1) at start	6.6	5.0	2.7	4.2	—	6.1
(2) after 12 months	20.0	21.4	12.6	25.7	—	17.2

that it is a rough measure of the extent of protein solubilization. Figure 2 shows the results obtained for one of the silages (sprat) and is typical of what was found. The soluble nitrogen is plotted as a percentage of total nitrogen and in the freshly prepared silage this amounted to approximately 18 per cent. During the first few days after preparation this percentage rose very sharply to about 75 per cent after 10 days and 85 per cent after 30 days. After about 50 days there was a negligible change in the proportion of soluble nitrogen. No conclusions about nutritional properties can be drawn since there is

no evidence that hydrolyzed protein is more or less valuable nutritionally than protein in its normal form. These chemical changes are, however, accompanied by changes in the physical properties of the silage, which becomes less viscous during storage. The moisture and ash contents of the silages correspond to those of the original raw material and those shown in Table 1 refer to the freshly prepared silage. The moisture content fell by between 2 and 7 per cent during storage of one year.

The oil content varied considerably. The herring offal and herring silages are not made from the same fish samples and there is a considerable difference in the oil content. Commercially it would almost certainly be advisable to remove the oil from the silage before sale but in some situations it might not be possible or desirable and in this experiment the oil was left with the silage and removed for examination at various intervals of time. The result for iodine value and free fatty acids were plotted against storage time and results taken from these curves are given in Table 1 for the start of the experiment and after 12 months storage. In all cases there was a fall in iodine value indicating oxidation of the fat. Sprats showed the least fall in iodine value and mackerel the most. The oil from herring silage and herring offal silage showed a similar decrease in iodine value. The results for sand-eels indicated less oxidation than appeared to have occurred from the physical characteristics of the oil, which was very dark and viscous. It is possible that the extraction procedure with petroleum ether extracted only a less oxidized fraction of the fat.

The free fatty acid content of fish oil is a measure of the extent to which the glycerides in the oil have been decomposed by lipases. It is often used as a criterion for judging the condition and edibility of the fat for com-

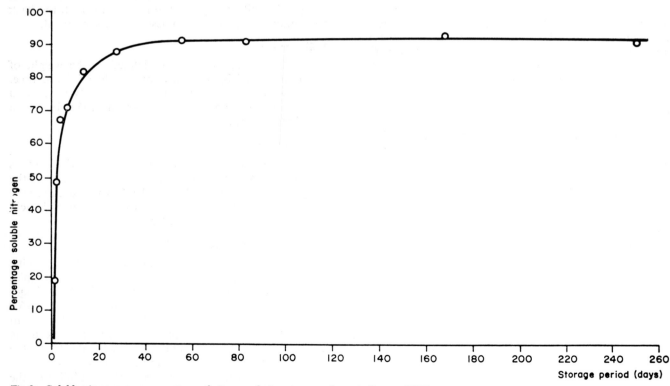

Fig 2   Soluble nitrogen as a percentage of nitrogen during storage of sprat silage at 20°C

mercial purposes. Generally a level of less than 4 per cent free fatty acids is required for high quality fish oils produced in the fish meal industry. The results in Table 1 indicate that in the raw material free fatty acids varied from 2.7 to 6.6 per cent. In all cases however there was a very rapid increase in free fatty acids over the first 100 days and after 12 months the results show that in some cases more than 20 per cent free fatty acids were obtained. Such high figures are presumably due to the presence of lipases in the silage and it is clear that the oil, if it is to be removed, should be separated as soon as possible after manufacture.

NUTRITIONAL VALUE OF FISH SILAGE

Hanson and Lovern (1951) have summarized results of animal feeding trials on fish silage. Most work on the nutritional value of fish silage has been carried out in Denmark. Work has shown that fish silage may be fed to bacon pigs until the animals reach a weight of about 30 kg without the risk of taint. Breeding sows are fed about 0.5 kg fish silage per day, more during lactation, and it has been claimed that fertility is increased as a result. In other experiments with cattle about 1.4 kg fish silage per day has been fed to cows without any taint in the milk or butter. Farm practice involves the feeding of fish silage with beet during the time that the animals are without grass; young cattle will readily eat 20 per cent fish silage in a diet with cereals. Norwegian research has demonstrated that fish silage is equal to herring meal for growth and egg production in hens; superior hatchability is also reported. Laying birds may be fed about 250 g fish silage daily per 12 birds, without producing tainted eggs and breeding fowls may be fed 50 per cent more than this. Swedish work suggests that growing chicks may receive up to 50 per cent of the whole diet as fish silage. Preliminary feeding trials in Britain have been restricted to pigs and the objectives of these trials, carried out at Harper Adams Agricultural College, were: to investigate the performance of pigs when white fish offal silage replaced entirely, or partly, the protein of a commercial ration and to investigate the problem of fish taint in the carcases. Pigs were divided into three groups and each received a different diet as follows: Treatment 1: A control ration which consisted of barley, soybean meal, white fish meal and mineral and vitamin supplements. Treatment 2: A test ration in which the soybean meal and white fish meal were completely replaced by fish silage. Treatment 3: A test ration in which the white fish meal only was replaced by fish silage. The amount of each diet fed was adjusted so as to give equivalent amounts of protein to each group. The pigs were started on these experimental diets when they reached a live weight of about 25 kg. Thereafter the animals were weighed once weekly and the feed intake of each individual pig was noted. The results of this preliminary trial showed no significant differences in food conversion efficiency between the three groups of pigs in daily live weight gain up to 90 kg. When the pigs were graded at the factory for length, shoulder fat, and other measurements there were no significant differences between treatments. The carcases were evaluated by the UK Meat Research Institute who carried out fatty acid analyses, odour tests and tasting tests. Where significant differences were shown between the three treatments they were very small and suggested that the use of fish silage had no deleterious effect on the quality of the meat. The general conclusion reached from this preliminary work was that white fish offal silage is at least equal to conventional protein products in terms of quality.

CONCLUSION

1. The production of an animal feeding stuff from fish or fish wastes by ensilage may be considered as useful in areas where farming is carried out close to fish handling and where there is no outlet for the fish to a fish meal plant.
2. The process needs very simple equipment of low capital cost but formic acid is relatively expensive and a regular supply must be available. Processing is extremely simple and highly trained staff are not necessary. Since the product is not dried there is no effluent air from the process, so there is no air pollution: the product itself does not have an unpleasant odour.
3. Fish silage would be valued mainly for its content of high quality protein and since its protein content averages about 16 per cent its value is likely to be between one quarter and one fifth of that of fish meal, which normally contains up to 70 per cent protein. Fish silage is particularly suited to pig farming and there is evidence that good growth rates and a high quality meat may be obtained.
4. If oily fish are to be utilized it is important to separate the oil as rapidly as possible after ensiling since analysis shows a rapid deterioration in oil quality as measured by free fatty acid content and iodine value. It is, in any case, unwise to feed large quantities of fish oil to pigs or poultry because of the risk of fishy taint.
5. As the product is bulky it is important to utilize it reasonably close to the place of production.
6. Fish silage is not well known and might require an initial marketing effort.
7. It is possible that a human grade dried food can be produced from fish silage, and present work is examining the possibility of evaporating the silage and roller drying it so as to produce a fish protein concentrate.
8. The production of fish silage would be most unlikely to have an effect upon the established fish meal industry since it would probably only be manufactured where there is no outlet for raw material to the fish meal process. It might in some instances be the first step toward producing fish meal since production of fish silage over a period of time would prove the existence of a suitable resource. It is likely that fish silage can provide an answer to the utilization of excess raw material where this is currently discarded or where transport costs are very high and where the liquid product can be utilized locally.

References

HANSON, S W F and LOVERN, J A *Fishing News*, (1988): 11.
1951
LAGUNOV, L L, EGOROVA, L N, REKHINA, N I and EREMEEVA, M N
Rybnoe Khoz., 32(9):78.
LAGUNOV, L L, EGOROVA, L N, REKHINA, N I and EREMEEVA, M N
1958   *Chemical Abstracts*, 52:12263.
McBRIDE, J R, IDLER, D R and MacLEOD, R A *J. Fish. Res. Bd.*
1961   *Can.*, 18(1):93.

MITCHESON, R C and STOWELL, K C *Automation in Analytical*
1969 *Chemistry*, Technicon International Symposium (London).
         London Technicon Instrument Co.
PEARSON, D *The Chemical Analysis of Foods*, London, J & A
1962 Churchill Ltd.

PETERSEN, H *FAO Fish. Bull.*, 6(1–2):18.
1953
VARLEY, J A *Analyst, Lond.*, 91:119.
1966

The Utilization of Small Pelagic Species *E Heen*

Utilisation des especes pelagiques de petite taille

L'auteur décrit brièvement les divers types de produits fabriqués avec les principaux groupes de poissons pelagiques de petite taille, ainsi que les problèmes de manutention, de conservation et d'entreposage. Il examine en particulier l'emploi de conservateurs chimiques et étudie leurs avantages, les difficultés auxquelles ils donnent lieu et leurs limitations.

Aprovechamiento de especies pelagicas de pequeña talla

El autor describe brevemente las diversas clases de productos derivados de los grupos principales de especies pelágicas de pequeña talla y los problemas de la manipulación, conservación y almacenamiento. En particular, se ocupa del empleo de productos químicos como sustancias conservadoras y sus ventajas, dificultades y limitaciones.

There is no clear cut definition of what comprises small pelagic species which include varieties ranging from the herring (*Clupea harengus*) and the sprat (*Clupea sprattus*), the pilchard and the sardine (*Sardinops* spp.), the anchovy (*Engraulis* spp.) and menhaden (*Brevoortia* spp.) to the Indian mackerel, the horse mackerel and the Atlantic mackerel (*Rastrelliger* spp., *Trachurus* spp. and *Scomber scombrus*, respectively) and the capelin (*Mallotus villosus*). All these are predominant in the catch today. Their common characteristics include abundance – they aggregate more than half of the total catch from the oceans today – density of schools, which makes possible efficient mass fishing, and the very different properties of the individual fish during seasons. These properties influence the qualities of the final product. For example, in the feeding season the stomach content apparently induces very high enzymatic activity which affects the belly-tissue and makes it less favourable for some of the products unless corrective action is taken. One remedy is to trap the fish in the net for some time. Another is immediate evisceration.

Another interesting aspect in the utilization of these species is the very broad spectrum of products derived from them. These range from high-cost, luxury products (specialities) to such low cost products as meal and oil. Generally speaking, the limitation in utilization is the small size of some of the species which makes manual handling comparatively costly.

ESTABLISHED PRODUCTS

Most of the catch is used for production of oil and meal. Herring, pilchards and mackerels and, to some extent, capelin are a very suitable basis for reduction as both products may, under certain circumstances, have an equally good market value. The fat content of the fish displaces water which contributes to making the drying operation cheaper, while the requirements for handling and preservation are less demanding than in the case of food products. The catch may be bulk-handled, using pumps, conveyors and trucks, and bruising may be accepted without impairing the value of the raw material. Bulk storage of raw material in bins and silos has also contributed to the big-scale operation of meal and oil industry. In the chilled state (provided by icing, refrigeration, or the arctic climate), the raw material may remain in satisfactory condition even after two weeks of storage. However, the normal 'shelf-life' is much less. Storage of some species caught in the feeding season may be limited to a couple of days.

Chemicals have been used to preserve fish caught in remote waters and to even out supplies of raw material to the factories. But the use of chemical preservatives is a controversial issue. Their use may be limited for economic or other reasons. For instance, an aim in utilization is to produce better products and, with chemical preservatives, there is the potential risk of residues and of possible combination of the chemicals with naturally occurring compounds in the raw material. Such traditional chemical preservatives for herring products as benzoates and hexamethylentetramine, have limited effects. Formaldehyde, which is widely used for preservation and for rendering the raw material more favourable for processing, has also limitations as far as putrefaction and fatty acid formation are concerned. Substances such as sulphites and nitrites are quite efficient in retarding these types of deterioration. Sodium nitrite, in particular, has been studied extensively for this purpose. A prerequisite for successful chemical preservation is full control of the doses used, including their even distribution. This requires the removal of water from the catch, particularly when pumps are used, so there must be good drainage of the cargo.

Canned products

The fully sterilized products are of long standing and are found in most markets of the world. In addition to making the product sterile and thus non-perishable, the advantage of heat treatment to approximately 120°C, is the softening of the bones, which makes them eatable. With Scandinavian canned sardines the intestines are not removed and for this reason the product requires special treatment. The fish, when caught, are left trapped in the net for one to three days to empty their stomachs. This practice is best done in protected waters. Generally speaking, sardine products demand much labour so that most of them are high priced. However, mechanization has been introduced to some extent in the production line. It starts with brining to add a certain amount of salt to the fish and swell the surface area so that subsequent processing gives a desired 'gloss' to the product. Scandinavian sardines are largely smoked, which requires them to be arranged on racks. This operation and beheading, which comes next, have been mechanized.

Handling of the sardines requires care as no bruising can be accepted, nor can the fish be allowed to stick together because that would damage the skin and appearance. Of the species used, the sprat is extremely susceptible to oxidation. This becomes pronounced with bulk freezing. As the species used are very delicate in texture, the nets are emptied by brailing, not pumping, and the fish are put into small-sized boxes with icing. However, bulk handling in tank vessels with refrigerated sea water, or sea water diluted with ice, has been introduced and works successfully when adequate precautions are taken. To even out the supply of raw material, a considerable part of the catch is frozen. As the fish must not be allowed to stick together, they have to be frozen in a liquid medium, ie, water, and the blocks must be protected through glazing.

Semi-conserves

These products, packed in airtight metal boxes, or glass or plastic containers, are semi-preserved with salt, spices and a few chemicals and have a shelf-life of about six months. They may be classified as 'specialities' more than 'commodities' and have a limited market. They require a certain time for 'ripening' in which a complex of chemical reactions results in a specific flavour and texture of the product, depending on the properties of the raw material and its pretreatment. As bony material will not change substantially during this processing, most of the products are made from the boneless part of the fish. The most favoured raw materials are herring and mackerel. The fish may be held full-salted in barrels or bins, and stored at a selected temperature. This gives a good start to the ripening process.

Marinated products

These are also semi-preserved with salt, acid, sugar and a few other ingredients and have a shelf-life up to six months at 0°C. The action of acid makes the bones soft and eatable although backbones are usually removed. Fillets in different forms are generally used to produce a variety of products. The raw materials are held through bulk freezing or in fillet-blocks.

Smoked products

Small pelagic species, with their comparatively high fat content and different properties between species and seasons, are most suitable for making smoked products. The process normally starts with a light salting in brine. The material may be cold or hot smoked, resulting in very different products. The mild-cured type is still perishable and needs cold storage and a refrigerated distribution system. Smoking is normally linked to a drying process. The products are usually based on local traditions with limited marketing possibilities. Advanced drying may result in very stable products, except for the development of rancidity, which limits their acceptability. Constituents of the smoke, in particular some phenols, are efficient anti-oxidants. At the same time, the smoke flavours compensate for the undesired odour and taste resulting from oxidative rancidity. The raw material for these products must be fresh, whether used for immediate processing or frozen. The general trend is toward more use of frozen fish for these products.

Fermented products

Fermented products are traditional in tropical countries, which is to be expected in view of the limited shelf-life of salted and undried fish at high temperatures.

Salted products

Salting is the traditional way of preserving herring in the northern hemisphere. The full-salted fish in saturated brine is protected against rancidity and may be stored for a year in a cold climate. At a temperature above 20°C the fish solubilizes.

TECHNOLOGY

Bulk handling on board

Trawls have been developed for catching small pelagic species, but the standard gears are ring nets or purse seines. The operation may be carried out in minutes and the catch may be anything from a few tons to a hundred tons and more. Such operations have made it more difficult to supply raw material for conventional processing as compared to the old land-nets method in which the catch could be kept alive for weeks until needed for processing. Pumps are used today to empty the nets. This is satisfactory when the catch is for oil and meal production. But for food fish, brailing is recommended because the fish must not be bruised or descaled. Holding fish in the net even a few hours helps to empty their stomachs, which is required for fish used for making canned and mild cured products.

Storage in refrigerated sea water (RSW)

Storage in RSW, introduced some years ago, offers many advantages. It makes a fully mechanized handling system possible, while the temperature in tanks may be lowered below 0°C, which extends shelflife. But the attendant salt uptake limits the use of this method for meal production, especially for meal used for poultry feed. It also affects conventional salted products, such as those made from herring. It seems that the anaerobic conditions in the tank create a reduction system which contributes to a pink colour along the backbone. Diluting the sea water with ice may offset this effect and, at the same time, cool the fish without having to use compressor units. Two parts of ice to one part of sea water reduces the concentration of salt to approximately 1.2 per cent, which is close to the concentration in the tissue of the fish. But there is still an ion exchange – potassium leaks out and sodium enters. Effective chilling requires the liquid to be circulated and evenly distributed throughout the fish. As these tend to sink to the bottom and clog, the movement of the liquid from the bottom and upward offsets this. Even distribution can be obtained by using perforated bottoms and a velocity of the water to prevent the fish from settling. But if the movement is too violent it may increase descaling, which is detrimental.

Icing

This is still the most generally used method of chilling although, up to recently, icing in boxes and bins has been labour-intensive. However, systems for mechanized icing operations have been developed and are now in use. New forms of ice in layers or thin flakes are particularly useful for the delicate small pelagic fishes. 'Caking' of such ice when not sufficiently dry has been a problem, solved by the use of a crusher. Pneumatic tools permit mechanized 'dosage' of ice to each box, bin or container, making the operation competitive.

Freezing

Freezing herring in brine is traditional in many European countries. The extension of this techniques to tuna clippers has contributed to development of the industry, particularly in the USA and Japan. The small, fat pelagic species lend themselves to freezing and thawing, except for their susceptibility to oxidity and rancidity. There is a certain uptake of salt in brine freezing, and even if the salt concentration in the whole fish is insignificant, the surface layer contains sufficient salt to accelerate oxidation reaction and rancidity. This has encouraged airblast freezing, particularly indirect freezing in vertical plate freezers. These are less labour-demanding and the well glazed compact blocks give very good protection to the fish. Some species, such as the delicate and small sprat, require that even minor damage to the skin must be avoided. This means that there must be a minimum of 20 per cent of water in the block to prevent the fish sticking together and full glazing to offset evaporation over a six-month period at a storage temperature of $-35°C$. Thawing the blocks is also demanding and numerous methods have been tried, including microwave and dielectric heating. The trend is to return to spraying with temperate water and steam.

Bulk salting

Salted herring in wooden barrels has for centuries been a staple food in Europe. Barrel-making was an art. For the successful absorption of the salt and formation of brine stirring or circulation is necessary, made possible by rolling the barrels. Salting of round fish may be practicable in only a few cases because of the slow absorption of salt and the risk of deterioration. Different cuts in the fish have been evolved to promote brine development, the simplest being a deep cut in the throat. This opens up a passage for the brine. The more radical method is 'nobbing', in which the intestines are partly removed. It is generally assumed that parts of the intestines, in particular the pyloric cacea, plays a part in the ripening processes in the salted product, developing the desired taste, flavour and texture. Traditional full-salted herring involves handling individual fish in the comparatively small containers. There has been a trend toward bulk salting in tanks or bigger containers and bins. An industrial process starts with drum mixing a calculated amount of salt to herring, facilitating the even distribution of salt and fish. Salting in brine tanks on board the vessels is not widely used although it offers the possibility of a more mechanized process. The main difficulty is to obtain an even absorption of salt and to avoid 'clogging'. In brine salting, this takes place at the top of the tank. A downward movement of the brine is necessary to counteract the tendency to caking. Such movement induced by pumps must not be too violent because it may lead to extensive descaling. The temperature during the salting also influences the properties of the end-product. In this respect there has to be a compromise to govern the desired rate of salt uptake and the risk of bacterial deterioration in the centre part of the fish mass where salt concentration has not reached the necessary level. The most popular 'mild cure' salted herring products, with or without spices and sugar, have a minimum salt content for preservation—15 to 17 per cent of salt in the tissue. The temperature in curing is around 12°C and the process lasts for a few weeks. Storage is at a lower temperature, 4 to 6°C, during which the products 'mature' to the desired extent over several months. While the products are retailed to some extent as the whole fish, they are mostly used for further processing in making 'fine' foods.

Chemical preservation in bulk

Chemical preservation has been used for oil and meal reduction material. Although formaldehyde has been regarded as a bacteriostatic agent, its effect on bacterial and autolytic deterioration in herring in bulk is very limited. This may be due to the slow and incomplete diffusion of the agent into the fish flesh as well as to chemical reactions which take place between formaldehyde and protein. Formaldehyde may be bound and/or oxidized to formic acid through the blood erythrozytes. In spite of this shortcoming, formaldehyde is widely used in oil and meal production because it may give the cooked material better properties in the process of separation. There is a general reluctance to accept formaldehyde in food. However, extensive feeding trials and amino acid distribution analyses have not demonstrated any harmful effect or any noticeable reduction of the feed value of the proteins.

Formaldehyde must be regarded as a promising preservative for short-term storage. For long-term storage, which is of great importance in certain fisheries to even out supplies to the factories, sodium nitrite has proved to be a very efficient means of preservation. It has been used, during the past twenty years, particularly in Norway, although it has been demonstrated that it can be dangerous. The separation process, including different steps of heating, evaporation and drying, should, in principle, provide an opportunity to remove residues of a chemical preservative. But these steps may also facilitate the synthesis of undesired compounds. The nitrous acid is degraded by some of the bacteria present in fish, and molecular nitrogen is liberated. A well calculated dosage of nitrite depending on the time and temperature of storage, should, in principle, make it possible to eliminate the action of the nitrous acid in the synthesis of nitrocompounds. The margin between spoilage and the removal of nitrite is very narrow and a certain residue has to be accepted. Depending upon the condition of the raw material when it enters the process, the available amines from the trimethylamine oxide and process conditions will determine the extent of disethylnitrosamine formation. This toxic and carcinogenic compound is volatile and should be removed in the process. The preservation procedure must be closely followed analytically both as to the amount of nitrite present and possible presence of the nitroso-compounds.

Processing and Utilization of Mackerel *Y Seno*

Transformation et utilisation du maquereau
Exposé succinct de la situation générale des pêcheries de maquereaux
Description des divers produits fabriqués au Japon à partir du
maquereau. Méthodes de transformation utilisées. Brève évaluation
des perspectives d'avenir concernant l'exploitation des ressources
en maquereau et l'expansion de l'utilisation des produits dérivés.

The processing and utilization of mackerel present a
number of technical problems, such as the large variations
in the fat content of the fish, the high enzyme activity and
the large sizes of the catch. However, as the fish are
usually caught in nearby waters and stocks are increasing,
they form a very attractive raw material for processing
and utilization in the future.

FISHING GROUNDS

The mackerel is usually found in inshore waters and is
known by various names (FAO 1972).

The main fishing grounds and species are:

No.	Fishing ground	Species
1	Pacific Northwest	Chub mackerel
2	Atlantic Northeast	Atlantic mackerel
3	Atlantic Northwest	Atlantic mackerel
4	Pacific Western Central	Indo-Pacific mackerel
5	Atlantic Eastern Central	Chub mackerel
6	Indian Ocean Western	Indo-Pacific mackerel
7	Atlantic Southeast	Chub mackerel

CATCH OF MACKEREL

The catch of mackerel has been increasing for the past
10 years – 1.6 million t in 1966, 2.25 million t in 1967,
and 2.79 million t in 1970 (FAO 1972). The percentage
of the catch by country in 1970 was:

No.	Country	%	No.	Country	%
1	Japan	46.6	9	France	1.8
2	USSR	11.3	10	Philippines	1.7
3	Norway	10.3	11	Spain	1.5
4	Malaysia	5.3	12	Korea, Rep of	1.4
5	India	5.0	13	Morocco	1.1
6	Thailand	3.4	14	Taiwan	1.0
7	South Africa	2.7	15	Denmark	0.9
8	Poland	2.7			

(FAO 1972)

UTILIZATION OF MACKEREL

More than 80 per cent of the mackerel catch (FAO 1969a)
was used for food in Japan, India, Spain, the Republic
of Korea, Taiwan and Denmark, while in India, the
Philippines, Spain, the Republic of Korea, Taiwan and
Thailand more than 50 per cent was consumed fresh.
In Canada, Japan and Taiwan much of the mackerel was
frozen while in France, Portugal and Japan a high percentage was canned. In Morocco and Angola much of
the catch was salted and dried. There was decreased consumption of fresh mackerel in Japan, and little change
in that frozen, canned, salted and dried but an increase
in its use for meal and oil as the catches increased in
1968–69 (FAO 1971).

OUTPUT OF PROCESSED MACKEREL

Output of processed mackerel steadily increased from
1958 to 1968, particularly in canned, salted and dried

Elaboración y utilización de la caballa
En este trabajo se trata brevemente de la situación general de la
pesca de la caballa y se dan a conocer varios productos que a partir
de ella se obtienen en el Japón, asi como los métodos de elaboración
empleados. Al final se hace una breve apreciación de las posibilidades de una mayor explotación de los recursos de caballa y del
aumento del consumo de sus productos.

products in Japan (FAO 1969b). Export of the processed
mackerel also increased in all countries. In Sweden, for
example, export of frozen mackerel increased by 1.8 times
during the period while Japan increased the export of
canned products by as much as 47.6 times (FAO 1969b).

PROCESSING CHARACTERISTICS OF MACKEREL

Limited storage time

Mackerel meat has stronger enzymatic activity compared
with other fish and the decomposition of substances related with adenosine triphosphate (ATP) is quick. The
storage of raw mackerel for processing, therefore, is subject to the following limits:

Storage	Temperature	Time limit
Left in room	20°C	6 to 10 hours
Crushed ice or ice water storage	0°C	48 hours
Frozen storage	−18 to −20°C	2 months
	−30°C	3 months

Preparation and quality of products

Frozen, salted and dried products. The freshness quickly
goes from the raw meat, especially of small size containing
a large amount of water and little fat, and the actomyosin
of the muscle protein is largely denaturated at the beginning of the freezing process. Such deterioration makes it
unfit for processed products. The water, therefore, should
be removed by dry salting as soon as possible in order
to prevent loss of freshness and denaturation.

Raw fish rich in fat easily oxidizes during frozen
storage unless it goes through antioxidized processing.
The appearance of the raw fish, even when its fat is
oxidized, does not change except that the gill becomes
yellow but the meat is unfit for processing. Therefore, the
oxidation of its fat is important and the antioxidization
process determines the time the material can be kept in
frozen storage. The oxidizing reaction in the liver is accelerated by haem compounds, while in the case of the
muscle, autoxidation seems the main reaction. In general,
the relative action of oxidation at 0°C is lowered from
20 to 30 per cent of that which takes place at 20°C, but
the repression effect of low temperature seems to be small
if haemoglobin is present. Therefore, the antioxidant process, such as through glazing or packing in thick ice,
should be effected promptly and with great care. The
reaction velocity of hydrolysis at 0, −10 and −20°C is
20 to 30 per cent, 4 to 12 per cent and 0.07 to 2.4 per cent
respectively of that at 20°C. The repression effect of
temperature under −10°C on the reaction seems to be
larger than that of temperatures over 0°C. However, even
with cooling at −20°C, the enzyme reaction is not re-
pressed to any satisfactory extent and the repression effect
differs with the type of enzyme, such as phosphatase,

esterase, glucosidae and protease. Therefore, the temperature of storage determines the length of time raw mackerel may be kept.

Canned products. Raw fish for canning must be as fresh as possible. There is a relationship between the fat content of raw fish and the quality after canning. In general, the relation of the inosinic monophosphate (IMP) ratio of the raw fish, the time of ice storage and the inspection scores judged by organoleptic test of canned mackerel in brine, are as follows:

Canned meat inspection score	IMP ratio of raw fish	Time of storage (h)
9	more than 70	within 24
8	70 ± 15	within 48
7	55 ± 15	within 72
6	less than 40	within 96 ± 12

Remark: $\text{IMP ratio} = \dfrac{\text{IMP}}{\text{IMP} + \text{HxR} + \text{Hx}} \times 100$

where HxR = Inosine and Hx = Hypoxantine

Relation of size of raw fish, fat content and product

Mackerel under 25 cm with little fat content. These are processed into dried sticks (fushi), meal and extract products. Raw fish containing 1 to 2 per cent fat is the best for making dried sticks. If the fat content is 4 to 5 per cent or more the product will become blackish brown, with a soft texture, bitter taste and bad flavour. If the fat content is under 0.5 per cent, it will become red brown, with poor taste and poor flavour.

Fish of 25 to 30 cm with rich fat content. These are processed into salted, salted and dried, smoked, canned and paste products, and feed for fish farming.

Fish of over 30 cm with rich fat content. These are consumed fresh or processed into frozen, salted, salted and dried, smoked and canned products.

Thawing and the quality of products

In general, thawing conditions that do not decompose the substances related with ATP are as follows:

Example – Block size: 370 × 260 × 65 mm

Thawing method	Temp. of thawing	Time of thawing
Running water	+ 8°C	4 h 15 min
Still air	+ 8°C	18 h 30 min
Circulating air	+ 8°C	11 h
High frequency in combination with brine		20 min
Micro-waves continuous system in tunnel		2 to 3 min

Thawing by still or circulating air is the best for canning because the fish skin does not peel off. These methods, however, are unavailable for mass production. In thawing by still or running water it is necessary to break the block, otherwise the fish in the centre remain frozen, while those near the outer edge become over-thawed. With too much water, the substances related with ATP compounds are decomposed.

At a final temperature range of − 1°C to 1.5°C the head and viscera can be removed by machine or hand.

NUTRITIVE VALUE OF MACKEREL

The nutritive value of fresh mackerel and its products is generally as high as that of tuna, bonito and sardine, while canned mackerel in brine has a higher value than that of other canned fish because its subcutaneous fat does not come off the body during preheat preparation (Table 1).

METHODS OF PROCESSING

Chilling up to and during preparation

Usually the fish are chilled to 0°C without delay after being caught, using crushed or flake ice or ice water. With ice, a layer is spread over each 7 cm layer of fish. The weight ratio of fish and ice should be 1:1. The fish are kept in cold store to delay the melting of the ice. During preparation for processing, the fish should be washed with water below 5°C. The water can be kept down to this temperature by putting ice blocks in it.

Salted and dried mackerel

Split-drying (dry-salting method). The fish is split from the ventral or dorsal side, and the head and viscera are removed, and the body washed and drained. Full washing is necessary if the resultant product is to be of light colour. The fish is dry-salted with more than 7 kg salt/100 kg fish. It is left salted overnight and then put on a net or grid to be dried in the sun. The yield is 50 to 70 per cent of the raw fish by weight.

Split-drying (brine-salting method). The fish is soaked in a salt solution of 15 to 20° Be and then dried in the sun for a few hours. The product is slightly salty in taste.

Salted mackerel

Hard-salted mackerel. The American hard-salted mackerel is prepared with split fish on board, the blood being removed in a brine solution of 15 to 18° Bé for 6 to 8 hours. The fish are then temporarily dry-salted, with the meat surface down, the salt amounting to 15 to 17 per cent of the raw fish by weight. When the ambient temperature is over 25°C, the quantity of salt is increased to 20 per cent. Next, the fish are selected by size and weight in the land factory and dry-salted, the salt being 30 to 40 per cent of the weight of the fish. After 10 days the fish become slack and are packed with more salt, amounting to 5 per cent of the weight of the cured fish. Hard, coarse grain salt is used. Impure salt should be avoided as it causes bad penetration, change of colour, and a bitter and rough taste. Fine grain salt tends to form into small lumps which make it hard to spread, and there is also a considerable loss of salt as it flows out with the body liquid. Salt of extra large grain makes its unified penetration hard.

Slack-salted mackerel. The salt should amount to about 20 per cent of the weight of the fish. Slack-salted mackerel cannot be preserved for long; therefore it must be kept in cold storage. Even so, it cannot be stored for more than one month because the fat oxidizes and an objectional odour develops.

Dried mackerel sticks ('fushi')

Dried fish sticks ('fushi') are a special product of Japan, prepared by boiling, smoking and drying fish fillets. It

TABLE 1. NUTRITIVE VALUE OF MACKEREL COMPARED WITH OTHER FISH

	Cal (Cal)	Moisture (g)	Crude protein (g)	Crude fats (g)	Carbohydrate Sugar (g)	Carbohydrate Crude fibre (g)	Ash (g)	Calcium (mg)	Phosphate (mg)	Iron (mg)	Vitamin A (IU)	Vitamin B₁ (mg)	Vitamin B₂ (mg)	Niacin (mg)	C (mg)	Rate of abandon (%)
Fresh																
Mackerel	111	76.0	18.0	4.0	0.7		1.3	5	190	1.8	50	0.15	0.20	8.0	3	46
Horse mackerel	110	75.0	20.0	3.0	0.7		1.3	12	200	0.7	40	0.15	0.08	6.5	2	50
Yellowfin	106	72.7	25.0	0.3	0.8		1.2	2	250	1.0	20	0.10	0.15	4.0	2	35
Bonito	130	70.0	25.0	3.0	0.7		1.3	6	220	1.7	40	0.03	0.15	100.0	2	35
Sardine	125	75.0	17.0	6.0	0.8		1.2	50	240	2.0	60	0.02	0.15	10.0	2	47
Cod	72	81.0	16.6	0.6	0.1		1.7	9	160	0.4	60	0.15	0.10	2.0	0	60
Salted																
Mackerel	142	65.0	25.2	4.2	0.9		4.7	25	240	7.0	0	0.03	0.05	10.0	0	25
Sardine	145	63.6	22.5	5.7	1.0		7.2	73	350	3.0		0.10	0.22		0	25
Cod	87	72.0	20.0	0.7	0.1		7.2	24	150	0.2	0	0.10	0.08	1.6	0	10
Dried sticks (fish – 'fushi')																
Mackerel	366	14.1	74.0	7.4	0.8		3.7	17	650	7.0	0	0.03	0.05		0	0
Bonito	352	14.3	75.6	5.1	1.0		4.0	17	640	5.0	0	0.03	0.55	45.0	0	0
Canned in brine																
Mackerel	190	65.7	17.4	13.4	0.0	0	3.5	290	260	1.6	0	0.02	0.10		0	0
Bonito	119	70.8	28.0	0.8	0.0	0	0.4	17	243	0.3		0.09	0.12			
Sardine	112	72.1	19.6	4.8	0.0	0	3.5	272	355	3.6		0.04	0.13	2.0		

(Suisan Handbook 1972)

is used in soup and broth in thin flakes. Bonito, albacore, bigeye tuna, sardines and mackerel are used as raw material for making this product. The head and viscera of the fish are removed and the body is placed on a tray and put into hot water (70 to 80°C). When it begins to boil, cool water is added and the flesh is cooked at slightly under boiling for 30 to 40 minutes. After it is cooled, the sides are separated from the backbone and the small bones removed. The meat is then put into a steaming-basket in a layer of 6 to 7 pieces, which is hardwood smoke-dried for one hour at 85°C. During this operation, the basket is reversed several times before being cooled overnight. This operation is repeated 5 to 6 times, then the product is dried in the sun for 2 days. When it is dry, it is packed in a box and left for 13 to 14 days. Mould is allowed to develop all over the product, which is then dried in the sun for one day. This operation of developing mould and drying is repeated 1 to 3 times. In making flakes of dried mackerel sticks, the operation of mould development is cut down.

Mackerel paste

The raw mackerel is washed and the head and viscera are removed. After washing and draining, the fish is filleted. In a large-scale operation, the separation of the meat from the fillet is done by machine but in small-scale factories it is done by hand with a large knife. The meat is then cut up and crushed to accelerate defatting and change in colour and to save processing water. The crushed meat is next dipped in water, six times as much water as the quantity of meat, to remove fat, blood, colour and odorous substances. After stirring and settling, the water is changed three or four times. The less fresh the fish, the longer the soaking time required. Ice blocks are put in the water tank, especially in summer. A bi-carbonate solution of 0.2 to 0.3 per cent or a sodium pyrophosphate solution of 0.5 per cent is often used in the water to increase adhesion. After soaking, the meat is dehydrated to 75 per cent moisture by hydraulic press or centrifugal dehydrator and ground with salt (2 to 3 per cent) by a stone grinder for 20 to 30 minutes to make it adhesive.

In the grinding process the pH of the meat tends to drop, the moisture to reduce and the hardness to increase. To prevent this, the following procedures are required:

(a) Addition of some water and cane sugar: this makes grinding easier by lowering the mechanical resistance of meats;

(b) Raise the pH to the range of 7 to 9 to increase the hydrophilic property and solubility of the meat.

Sodium carbonate or sodium phosphate (mono-basic) are used to raise the pH, and sodium pyrophosphate and magnesium chloride are used to dissociate actomyosin into actin and myosin. The meat is ground again with the addition of seasoning materials. These are different according to the product being made but generally include salt, sodium glutamate, sodium 5'-ribonucleotide, spices, milk products and fat, with starch and sodium polyphosphate as adhesive agents. Calcium carbonate or calcium chloride of 0.02 to 0.05 mole are used to strengthen the bond.

Shaping. The seasoned groundfish meat holds the shapes given it through adhesiveness. Examples of shaping are:

(a) Fish paste on the plate: the seasoned ground meat is piled on a thin wooden plate and steamed. This product is called 'itatsuki-kamaboko' in Japanese. The product made from mackerel is of lesser quality because of its colour (not white) and weak adhesiveness.

(b) Frying paste: this is made by frying the seasoned groundfish meat with vegetables. The product is small, flat and easy to fry.

(c) Fish block: this is made with alternate layers of mackerel or other fish fillets and seasoned ground flesh. The product is cut into suitable size, such as a stick or finger. The shaped fresh or thawed meat is heated to more than 90°C by steaming or roasting, and its bondage strengthened. The shape should be such as to make heat penetration easy. As heat of 45 to 70°C activates protease, it is advisable to pass this temperature range as soon as possible.

SMOKED MACKEREL

Ordinary processing

The viscera is removed from the fresh mackerel which is then washed and dry-salted for 5 to 7 days at 0°C. The amount of salt should be 15 to 20 per cent of the weight of the raw fish. After soaking, the fish is desalted in fresh water for 4 h, and smoked for more than 20 days at 18 to 25°C. The moisture content of the product is under 35 per cent.

Electric smoking

The desalted fish is exposed to a corona discharge in order to collect more smoke on its surface. The fish are separately hung on a two-line wire which is used as an electrode. It is charged with direct or indirect current of 10 to 20,000 volts to the corona discharge. The smoke is charged with negative or positive electricity and moves toward the fish which serve as the opposite electrode.

Iron wire-netting can be used for small fish while an endless-wire conveyor is used for the continuous processing of fish of larger size.

Liquid smoking

This is a quick-smoking method. A main component in liquid smoking is wood vinegar obtained by dry distillation of hardwood and separated from wood tar by settling. The liquid is diluted with two parts of water to one of vinegar and an adequate amount of salt is added. The fish is soaked in this solution, at a certain temperature and for a certain time. The fish is then dried in the shade or air-dried until the water content is reduced to about 45 per cent.

CANNED MACKEREL

The fresh mackerel is dressed by splitting and removing the head, tails, fins and viscera by machine or hand. The belly must be carefully washed, especially in the case of small fish. The meat is then cut crosswise into slices that fit in the can and soaked in brine of 15° Bé for 15 to 25 minutes or 18° Bé for 20 minutes at a temperature kept below 5°C by the use of ice. This is done to extract any blood and to prevent the formation of curd and turbid liquid. It is then rinsed in fresh water and packed so that the meat weighs 5 g more than the standard weight. The packed can is weighed. For mackerel in brine, the brine covers the surface of the meat, which prevents adhesion of the meat to the top of the can. The can is then vacuum-sealed. For mackerel in oil, the packed can is cooked by live steam for 20 to 50 minutes at 100 to 150°C. It is then drained and cotton-seed, olive or other vegetable oil is added. The can is exhausted for about 10 minutes at 100°C and then vacuum-sealed. This same method is used to prepare canned mackerel in tomato or white wine sauce.

Canned seasoned mackerel has a good market in Japan. The mackerel meat is packed with soybean sauce and sugar. For mackerel fillet in oil, the raw fish is brined, cooked and is left overnight. After 'di-thio' bond of the fish meat is recombined by air-oxidation and the tissue of the fish is strengthened, the skinless fish is filleted and cleaned. The fillets are packed in oval or square cans with vegetable oil, and sealed and sterilized. All canned mackerel products are packed in lacquered cans to prevent black spot or blackening of the meat, and sulphide stains on the can by the volatile compounds in the meat. After being sterilized and cooled, cans are wiped or dried in hot air, labelled and packed in cartons or wooden boxes. Table 2 gives an example of processing for various canned mackerel products and can sizes.

EXTRACT PRODUCTS

These are of two kinds – food extracts and fish solubles for feed.

Food extracts

These are mostly made from the juice which is a by-product of the cooking procedure for canned products. The extract, therefore, contains much gelatin, and so the taste is diluted. Extract made from washing water and water extract solution in the mackerel paste also contains myoglobin, etc., is unpalatable and unfit for human consumption. The basic extract procedure includes hot water extraction and refining, and the combination of autolysis or added enzymatic digestion and refining. In the hot water method the fish is cut into small pieces and water is added at the rate of 2 times the volume of the raw meat, and is extracted at 80–90°C. This extract is the most tasty. In the autolyzation and enzymatic

TABLE 2. EXAMPLES OF PROCESSING FOR THE CANNED MACKEREL PRODUCTS AND CAN SIZE

	Can size	pH	Initial temp °C	Processing temp °C	Pressure lb/m²	Processing time min	Come-up time min
Canned mackerel							
in brine	1P long	6.0	13.0–15.0	112.6–115.8	8.0–10.5	110	5–20
	½P long	5.7–6.5	10.0–90.0	114.0–115.8	9.0–10.5	80–90	5–25
	1P flat	5.7–6.5	13.0–75.0	115.2–115.8	10.0–10.5	100–120	13–25
	½P flat	5.7–6.5		114.0–115.8	9.0–10.5	90–100	10–30
in oil	½ flat		20.0	112.6	8.0	85	15
Fillet in oil	¼P square		20.0	112.6	7.5	75	
in tomato sauce	½P long	4.2–5.8	50.0–80.0	111.3–115.8	7.0–10.5	70–90	12–30
seasoned	1P long			114.0–115.8	9.0–10.5	90–100	4–30
	½P long	5.7–6.5	21.0–60.0	111.3–115.8	7.0–10.5	70–100	5–20
	1P flat	5.7–6.5	22.0–93.0	112.6–118.2	8.0–12.5	90–120	13–20
	½P flat	5.7–6.5	22.0–90.0	111.3–115.8	7.0–10.5	70–100	13–25

(Canneries Handbook 1972)

digestion methods red-meat fish like mackerel are auto-lyzed by their own hydrolase, and occasionally, with other species, enzymatic digestion is employed, i.e., commercial preparations of enzymes are added at the rate of about 0.2 per cent. The yield is 3 to 5 times that of hot water extraction. For refining, the insoluble matter is removed by centrifuge or strainer, and expeller procedure and diatomaceous earth is added. Then, fats and impure substances are removed by a sludge separator. After preconcentration, the remaining insoluble matter is removed by repeated filtering before concentration.

Fish solubles as feeds

Oil is removed from cooking juices and stickwater obtained in the processing of fish meat and scraps through evaporation. The moisture content is reduced to less than 50 per cent. The head, viscera, backbone and tail of mackerel are put into the digestion tank, to which 0.2 per cent enzymes are added. After stirring vigorously, they are digested for 3 to 5 h at 45 to 55°C. The insoluble matter is removed by decanting and press filtration as soon as possible. The liquid removed by decanting and filtration is heated at more than 80°C, and oil and non-digestible substances are separated and concentrated under vacuum.

FUTURE PROSPECTS

Future of mackerel resources

Mackerel is one of the few species of fish which are gradually increasing at present, and as it feeds on animal plankton, the resource can easily increase ten-fold in comparison with, say, the tuna species which feed on small fish. Plankton feeders may increase suddenly under favourable circumstances but, as they are easily affected by natural circumstances, they may equally decrease at any time; therefore the catch is subject to big changes.

The peak fishing for mackerel is said to last from six or seven to ten years. The catch of mackerel has continued to increase since 1929 in Japan but with some breaks. As of present, there is no trend toward a decline in the resources.

Future of mackerel products

The consumer considers mackerel to be a low-priced fish. Mackerel is sometimes substituted for tuna as a low-calorie food or a dietetic food for hypertension, or a food for religious events. It is also used as pet food.

As the price of mackerel products is lower than that of other fish products, the economy of processing demands mass production. This brings with it certain problems. In connexion with the future use of mackerel, studies should be made of: how to ensure the manufacture of good mackerel products of stabilized quality and uniformity; how to reduce production costs as an aid to expanding sales; how to build up exports of mackerel products. This calls for a longer shelf-life and probably an adjustment of flavours to the taste preferences of the importing countries. The shelf-life of preserved products for export must be over 2 years, and that of semi-preserved products must be at least 3 months.

Canned mackerel, such as that seasoned with vegetable broth, spices or sauces, frying paste and liquid or powdered mackerel (as a tasteless source of protein) seem likely to have the most promising future among the present range of mackerel products.

References

FAO 1969a   *Yb. Fishery Statist., Catches and Landings 1968*, vol. 26:318 p.

FAO 1969b   *Ibid., Fishery Commodities 1968*, vol. 27:337 p.

FAO 1971   *Ibid., Catches and Landings 1970*, vol. 30:476 p.

FAO 1972   *Ibid., Catches and Landings 1971*, vol. 32:558 p.

Opportunities for Improving Fishery Products   *K Amano*

Possibilités d'amélioration des produits de la pêche
L'auteur examine les exigences concernant le développement ou l'amélioration des produits de la pêche, notamment la question des matières premières, le rôle de la technologie, la durée de conservation des produits, les préférences des consommateurs, la production industrielle et l'attrait associé à la nouveauté des produits. Les succès remportés au Japon avec les saucisses de poisson et les produits 'surimi' congelés sont cités comme exemples de telles activités de développement et d'amélioration.

Posibilidad de mejorar los productos pesqueros
En este trabajo se examinan las necesidades de mejorar los productos pesqueros o crear otros nuevos, entrando en cuestiones tales como materias primas, función de la tecnología, vida en almacén de los productos, las preferencias de los consumidores, producción comercial y atractivos comerciales de un producto por su novedad. Como ejemplos de estas mejoras se menciona el éxito logrado en Japón por los embutidos de pescado y los productos congelados 'surimi'.

PRODUCT IMPROVEMENT

The improvement of the fishery products is an essential requirement if better use is to be made of marine resources. In order to achieve such improvement a number of factors have to be considered. These involve the raw material, technology, storage, consumer preference, production and so on.

Raw material

A first requirement for production is the assured supply of raw materials in sufficient quantity to permit economic operation of the processing plant, thereby allowing the technologist to undertake product improvement. Such an assured supply of fish is also important relative to the price. A plentiful supply usually means a reasonable stability in the price of the fish, which is a necessary condition for undertaking a new way of utilizing the raw material. In relation to product development, a careful study should be made of those varieties of fish which can be further utilized.

Technological aspects

The significant role of technology in the product improvement is recognized and food technologists have for many years put in a great deal of effort to improve existing and evolve new processing techniques. However, only a few of the proposed processes are taken up commercially. This may, in part, be due to the fact that human food does not lend itself to changing production as easily as does clothing or housing. Food improvement is generally limited to such matters as its form, flavouring, colouring, cooking, packaging, etc. Again, a technological success in one country may not be suitable for application in another. This is a very important consideration in setting up the production of food items which are unfamiliar in the market concerned, or in introducing improved versions of established products. Careful assessment is also necessary if the improvement requires the use of a sophisticated process, including new machinery.

Storage life

This factor in product improvement may involve technology. When a fish product is to be given wider distribution its storage life usually needs to be extended. In such a case, therefore, the keeping quality of the product must be taken into consideration at the start in relation to the technology involved. Conventional products such as dried, salted or smoked fish may perhaps have been evolved for preservation purposes rather than to enhance their flavour or appeal. As the good keeping quality of a product is so important, this factor should be given priority in the effort to improve fishery products.

Consumers' preference

Consumers' preference is a most critical factor influencing the introduction of a new product into market. Consumers are not always willing to try a new product, because they are conservative in their food habits. This is one reason why there have been so many failures in the past in product improvement and in attempts to introduce new food products. Utmost care, therefore, must be taken to persuade people of the quality and value and nutritiousness of the new or the improved product. This calls for a carefully planned public relations and marketing campaign, including such schemes as involving housewives in tasting panels, giving cookery demonstrations by TV and radio, carrying out marketing tests, and so on. Such a campaign should be continued over a long enough period to reach a realistic assessment of the acceptability of the product before commercial production of it is started.

Commercial production

Where a processing industry is not big enough or financially able to introduce product improvement, financial or technological assistance may be obtained from governmental or international sources. In any case, it is safer to start commercial production on a smaller rather than larger scale until the extent of the market for the product is determined.

Novelty of the product

Attempts have been made in various countries to utilize fish of low market value, but most of them have met with difficulties. Fish protein concentrate and single cell protein from petroleum are examples of such novelty products. An important consideration in respect of novelty products is to establish their wholesomeness. This is an especially serious requirement if the product contains chemicals or if its wholesomeness and quality can be influenced in its processing.

PRODUCT EXAMPLES

Fish sausage and frozen fish 'surimi' are good examples of fishery product development in Japan. The annual production of each is now more than 200,000 tons. The factors mentioned above were considered in relation to these two products (Table 1).

Fish sausage

A sufficient supply of raw materials was assured at a comparatively low price (about US $ 1/kg). Frozen raw material from blue and fin whales was found to give a meaty flavour. Chemical preservatives have helped to make the fish sausage a success, although some countries would not accept them because of public health regulations. However, processing at a temperature a little below 100°C for 30 to 40 min was not sufficient to kill the heat-resistant forms of bacteria so the use of chemicals as preservatives was necessary to enable the product to be distributed under natural conditions. Consumer's reaction was fairly good, because at that time (1954) the standard of living in Japan was not high. So the new fish sausage not only satisfied consumers but helped pave the way to the use of real meat sausages. During the past twenty years, the fish sausage industry concentrated in bigger production companies while small-sized firms have gradually been eliminated.

TABLE 1. MAJOR FACTORS INVOLVED IN THE DEVELOPMENT OF FISH SAUSAGE AND FROZEN 'SURIMI'

Factors	Fish sausage	Frozen 'surimi'
Raw material	Tuna (mostly frozen), frozen whale meat, surimi, and soy protein	Alaska pollock, horse mackerel, croakers
Processing technology	Technology established in kamaboko industry was followed	Freezing of fish meat slurries with sugar addition to avoid protein denaturation
Keeping quality	Heat processing after sealing in plastic film casings together with the use of chemical preservatives	Frozen storage with the aid of sugars and polyphosphates
Consumers'/processors' preference	Impression of consuming meat sausage	Labour-saving for the kamaboko and fish sausage industries
Size of production	Started with small-sized scheme and grew to large production	Medium-sized in shore plants and larger in floating factories
Novelty of the product	A new product among conventional fisheries products, although it imitated the flavour of meat sausage	Essentially new development

Frozen 'surimi'

Again, in the development of frozen 'surimi', the raw material supply was good; the total catch of Alaska pollock at times exceeded 2 million tons. A big role was played by technologists in making the product a commercial proposition. The problem was that the water-holding capacity of 'surimi' was readily destroyed when frozen. But a group of the technologists at Hokkaido Fisheries Experimental Station found that 'surimi', with the addition of cane sugar, could be held in refrigeration and emerge as a good food product. This improvement of the product was based on knowledge acquired about the behaviour of fish muscle protein in frozen form. The 'kamaboko' industry has also greatly benefitted by labour-saving in processing 'surimi'. The heading, de-boning, skinning and evisceration of fish are no longer done. All the workers have to do is to defrost the 'surimi' and throw it into the mixing basins with starch and flavouring agents and cook it. Such a saving is of significant importance to the industry, especially in view of the rising costs of labour.

Before 'surimi' became a mass production product, each variety of kamaboko had a local flavour derived from the fish caught in the sea adjacent to the plant. As 'surimi' is mostly prepared from a single species of fish, the product tends to have a uniform flavour. Some kamaboko plants, therefore, are trying to blend 'surimi' with meat from local fish in an effort to retain some of the traditional characteristics of their product.

Opportunities for Upgrading Fish with Lower Market Value   *V P Bykov*

Possibilités de valoriser le poisson peu prise sur le marché

Le document indique comment l'industrie soviétique de la pêche s'est orientée vers de nouvelles zones de pêches après la deuxième guerre mondiale et a entrepris de capturer nombre d'espèces précédemment inconnues d'elle-même, des savants et du grand public. Devant la résistance manifestée par les consommateurs à l'égard de poissons peu familiers, une grande partie des prises a servi à la fabrication de farine de poisson. Toutefois, l'Union soviétique ayant pour politique de tirer le plus grand parti possible du poisson pour l'alimentation humaine, des recherches et des expériences ont été faites en vue de trouver le moyen d'utiliser ces espèces à cette fin. Pour cela, hommes de science et techniciens ont dû mettre au point des procédés technologiques et des méthodes de transformation permettant de supprimer ou de neutraliser les caractéristiques défavorables de poissons tels que les requins, aloses, silure, etc., et d'utiliser ces espèces et d'autres groupes de poissons difficiles à transformer pour la fabrication de produits alimentaires. Parmi ces poissons se trouvent les poissons pélagiques de petite taille que l'on pêche désormais en abondance. A la suite de recherches plus approfondies, ces petits poissons servent maintenant à la confection de nombreux produits traditionnels et de plusieurs produits nouveaux, par exemple, pâtes protéiques, hydrolysats, poisson haché, puddings, concentrés de protéines de poisson (CPP), potages et bouillons instantanés en poudre, etc.

Posibilidades de mejorar el pescado de poco valor comercial

En este trabajo se describe cómo la industria pesquera soviética entró en nuevos caladeros después de la segunda guerra mundial, capturando muchas especies antes desconocidas para la industria, los científicos y el público en general. La resistencia de los consumidores a estos peces con los que no estaban familiarizados hizo que gran parte de las capturas se transformaran en harina. Pero como el Estado Soviético tiene por norma aprovechar al máximo el pescado para el consumo humano, se realizaron investigaciones y experimentos para ver de hallar posibles maneras de aprovechar estas especies. A tal fin, los científicos y técnicos han preparados métodos tecnológicos y de elaboración que han permitido reducir o suprimir las características poco agradables de peces como el tiburón, alosa, bagre de mar, etc., y preparar productos alimenticios a partir de estos y otros grupos de peces difíciles de elaborar, entre los que encuentran las especies pelágicas de pequeña talla que actualmente se capturan en grandes cantidades. Gracias a las investigaciones realizadas, estos peces de pequeña talla se utilizan actualmente para preparar muchos productos tradicionales y algunos nuevos, como pastas proteínicas, hidrolizados, carne picada, budines, concentrados de proteínas de pescado, sopas y caldos instantáneos deshidratados, etc.

The trend in resource exploitation of the past decade suggests an increase in the landings of typically pelagic fish such as saury, anchovy, sardine, horse mackerel, mackerel, small clupeoids, capelin, poutassou, polar cod and some tunas. This situation would call for the development and improvement of technological methods to process them into various food products.

UTILIZATION OF TRADITIONAL RESOURCES

Before the second world war the Soviet fishing industry depended largely on freshwater, anadromous and semi-anadromous resources such as carp, salmon, sturgeon, perch, etc. Along with a fairly high content of protein, oil and other nutritive substances, these species have a high degree of palatability. Their chemical composition, technological characteristics, high proportion of edible parts and, particularly, their palatability make them a good raw material for making foods and they have long been used to produce such popular products as sun-dried, smoked and salted fish, cured fillets, salted and pasteurized caviar, canned, cooked, live, chilled and frozen fish. Processing of such fish is based on complete utilization of all parts and organs to obtain foods, feeds and technical and medical products. The edible parts and organs provide meat, the developed gonads, roe and milt, and the liver are used for food products. The offal is reduced to fish meal. A schematic representation of such rational utilization is given in Table 1. Rational utilization implies processing in accordance with generally accepted methods, ie, filleting, beheading, and gutting to separate edible parts from offal, with the latter being collected and used. Quick removal of viscera and head (or gills only) contributes to a better preservation of the meat, the most valuable part of fish. Newly caught fish are immediately sent for processing or placed in appropriate storage conditions. When a fishery is in tropical areas quick chilling of the catch in ice or chilled sea water is most important. The catch is processed on board, or is sent to a land-based fish processing plant.

TABLE 1. RATIONAL UTILIZATION OF FISH PARTS

Parts of fish	Main components	Product obtained	Application
Body meat	Complete proteins, oil, non-protein nitrogen	Various food products	Food
Full roe (eggs) and milts	Proteins, oil	Various food products	Food
Head	Proteins, calcium phosphate, oil	Fish meal	Feeds
Skin	Collagen	Raw material for leather and glue	Technical
Scales	Collagen, guanine	Glue, pearl paste	Technical
Swimming bladder	Collagen	Glue	Technical
Liver	Nitrogeneous substances, oil, vitamins A, D, B-12	Vitamin preparations, foods and feeds	Medicinal, food, feeds
Alimentary organs	Nitrogenous substances, oil, enzymes	Fish meal, oil, enzymes	Feeds, technical

In the latter case, the fish are pre-treated on board – dressed, chilled, frozen or salted – to preserve them until the finished product is produced at the processing plant.

UTILIZATION OF NEW RESOURCES

After the second world war the development of fisheries in new areas resulted in catching a number of species previously unknown to Soviet scientists, industry and the general public. These were often of small size, with chemical composition, technological characteristics and taste differing from those of the traditional species. This resulted in certain difficulties in selling food products manufactured from them, therefore a considerable proportion of the catches had to be reduced to fish meal. Reduction to fish meal used to feed animals results in the ultimate loss of as much as 80–85 per cent of the protein in raw fish. In view of the world deficit in animal protein and the high nutritive value of fish proteins, reduction of whole fish to fish meal is not reasonable. As the Soviet fishing industry has always pursued a policy of the maximum utilization of catches for human consumption, the industry and research institutions started studying the chemical composition and technological characteristics of new species and developing methods of processing them into food products. Those used for production of fish meal were termed 'low-grade fish' or 'non-nutritive fish'. However, these terms are usually unwarranted because the chemical composition and nutritive value of the fish are not inferior to many species widely used for human consumption. It would be more appropriate to call them 'fish of lower market value'. Such fish can be divided into four groups:

(1) fish with a peculiar chemical composition of the flesh
(2) fish with a low content of protein and fat which are the main components determining its nutritive value
(3) fish with structureless or infested flesh
(4) small fish which are difficult to process into food products.

Fish with a peculiar chemical composition of the flesh

These are not inferior to other fish in protein content but have a higher content of substances endowing them with a disagreeable flavour. For example, the high content of carbamide (urea) is responsible for the bitterly acid taste of sharks and skates. Carbamide, converted to ammonia during storage, gives off an offensive odour. The meat of such fish as alewife (*Pomolobus mediocris*) and gold-lined grunt (*Bathystoma aurolineatum*) has a sharp iodine flavour. The meat of sea catfish (*Tachysurus filiceps*) has a bad-egg odour which is not noticeable in the finished product. The dark meat of tuna is not used because of the high content of volatile bases. To remedy such natural defects it is necessary to apply processing methods to remove the substances responsible for the offensive flavour. Studies on the use of sharks for food show that cured fillets, culinary products and even canned goods can be produced from them if the carbamide and volatile nitrogenous bases are removed in processing.

Fish with a low content of protein and fat

Fish in the second group include wolffish, grenadier and Bombay duck. Table 2 gives data on the chemical composition of these species. These species, which are usually used for the production of fish meal, can be also used for the production of food if dried to effect the complete or partial removal of moisture.

TABLE 2. CHEMICAL COMPOSITION OF WOLFFISH, GRENADIER AND BOMBAY DUCK

Species	Content (%)	
	protein	fat
Wolffish (*Anarhicas latifrons*)	5.9	1.2
Grenadier (*Macrourus baevis*)	6.6	0.1
Bombay duck (*Harpodon nehereus*)	8.2	0.1

Fish with structureless or infested flesh

The third group includes fish with meat infested by parasites distinguishable by the naked eye (nematodes, cystodes, crustaceans, etc.) and those with structureless meat caused by some micro-organisms harmless to people but which liquefy the fish meat. The latter fish are difficult to detect when caught but the phenomenon shows itself after they are frozen. The structureless meat has a higher content of non-protein nitrogenous matter and, consequently, a lower content of protein. The meat has been found in arrow-toothed halibuts, and in horse mackerels and flounders. Parasite-infested fish are usually detected in the process of dressing but sometimes not before they are ready for the market or for processing into food products. Parasite infestation is observed in Alaska pollack and in porgies, boarfishes, poutassou, etc. Although such infestation interferes with the use of the meat for nutritive purposes, the parasites are harmless to people. The fish, therefore, can be processed not only into fish meal but also into fish protein concentrates, protein hydrolysates, etc.

Small fish which are difficult to process

The fourth group is the most numerous in species, stock abundance and volume of catch. It includes many small pelagic fish that have an adequate content of protein and fat, and a good or at least satisfactory taste, which makes them acceptable for the manufacture of traditional foods, such as canned goods, smoked, salted, sun-dried and cooked products. Included in this group are anchovy, sardine, oil sardine, horse mackerel, mackerel, saury, Caspian sprat, capelin, poutassou, polar cod, Alaska pollack, hake, etc. Large catches are difficult to process by traditional methods such as canning, for example, which involves dressing. Moreover, there may be no market for large quantities and because of this they are partly used for the production of fish meal. The term 'low-grade fish' is particularly wrong for this group because in chemical composition and palatability they are usually not inferior to many large fish which are in great demand.

As Table 3 shows, the small pelagic fish have a high yield of flesh and a high content of protein and fat, and do not differ much from traditional species. It does not seem reasonable, therefore, to use them for fish meal production. Extensive studies are being conducted in the USSR to develop methods of processing small pelagic species into food products. Two lines of research are being followed. One is to try to develop methods whereby small pelagic fish could be used to produce traditional

foods such as frozen, canned, salted, sun-dried, cold smoked, hot smoked, ready-to-eat products and preserves. These attempts have met with fair success. The other is the considerable effort being directed toward finding methods to process the fish into new food products, such as protein paste, hydrolysates, minced meat, puddings, fish protein concentrates, dehydrated instant soups, broths, etc.

The results of investigations on the technological principles of the utilization of raw fish have been summarized by I P Levanidov (TINRO) who proposed a utilization scheme based on the chemical composition of species. This scheme is applicable to freshwater, anadromous, semi-anadromous, large marine demersal and bottom fish, and to small pelagic species. According to Levanidov, all fish can be divided by content of protein and fat into groups for processing as follows:

Fish with a low content of protein (less than 15 per cent)

(a) Lean fish (with fat content less than 2 per cent) to be processed into fish meal

(b) Fatty and extremely fatty fish (fat content from 8 to 16 per cent and more than 15 per cent respectively) to be smoked, sun-dried or frozen

Fish with a medium content of protein (15–20 per cent)

(a) Lean fish (fat content less than 2 per cent) to be frozen

(b) Medium-fatty and extremely fatty fish (fat content 2–8 per cent and 8–15 per cent respectively) to be frozen, smoked, sun-dried or salted

TABLE 3. CHEMICAL COMPOSITION OF SOME FISH SPECIES

Species	Weight of flesh (or gutted and beheaded fish [a]) (%)	Protein Content (Nx 6.25) (%)	Fat Content (%)
Small pelagic fishes			
Round scad (*Decapterus kilishe*)	49–55 / 50	20.6–21.9 / 21.5	1.2–17 / 5.0
Bigeye scad (*Selar crumenophtalmus*)	49–46 / 50	21.5–22.4 / 21.9	2.0–3.2 / 2.8
Crevalle (*Selaroides leptolepis*)	63–65 [a]	21.5	1.2
Maasbanker (*Trachurus trachurus capensis*)	42–63 / 50	19.7	3.9
Round herring (*Etrumeus teres*)	66–70 [a]	21.3	2.8
Thread herring (*Opistonema oglinum*)	69–71 [a]	22.5	5.7
Oil sardine (*Sardinella longiceps*)	59–68 [a]	19.0	7.0
South African pilchard (*Sardinops ocellata*)	61–66 [a]	18.6–21.4	4.2–10.3
Anchovy (*Engraulis encrasicholus*)	61.0	23.0	3.3
Japanese anchovy (*Engraulis japonicus*)	57–64 [a]	13.3–21.0	3.3–18.0
Polar cod (*Boreogadus saida*)	60–71 [a]	16.3–19.1	0.4–0.8
Alaska pollack (*Theragra chalcogramma*)	53–58 [a]	14.6–17.3	0.4–0.9
Capelin (*Mallotus villosus*)	59–72 [a]	12.0–14.8 / 13.1	1.4–11.7 / 5.4
Atlantic mackerel (*Scomber scombrus*)	60–75 [a]	16.5–24.2	0.9–18.8
Spotted mackerel (*Scomber tapeinocephalus*)	64.0 [a]	22.8	7.5
Lantern fish (*Gymnoscopelus* spp)	58	14.7	14.7
Atlantic saury (*Scomberomorus saurus*)	77–79 [a]	23.0–24.6	1.5–11.0
Traditional species			
Pacific herring (*Clupea harengus pallasi*)	64–77 [a]	15–19	2–35
Sprat (*Sprattus sprattus balticus*)	76–80 [a]	13.0–15.2	4.5–13.7
Atlantic cod (*Gadus morhua morhua*)	52–54	16.9–19.4	0.2
Pacific cod (*Gadus morhua macrocephalus*)	41–46	17.1	0.9
Pink salmon (*Oncorhynchus gorbuscha*)	57–60	21.7–14.1	2.6–9.7
Chum salmo (*Oncorhynchus keta*)	73	19–23	4–9
Perch-pike (*Lucioperca lucioperca*)	56.2	19.4	0.6
Carp (*Cyprinus carpio*)	50.6	18.0	4.7

Fish with a high content of protein (more than 20 per cent)

(a) Lean and medium-fatty fish (fat content less than 2 per cent) and 2–8 per cent respectively) to be canned, frozen, smoked or sun-dried

(b) Fatty fish (fat content 8–15 per cent) to be canned, frozen or salted

Fish are directed to processing in the USSR mainly in accordance with this scheme. Small pelagic species are being used for the production of such foods as: canned fish (in oil, tomato sauce, in natural juice or with vegetables); cold, hot and semi-hot smoked fish using common, wet and electric smoking; preserves and salted fish, ready-to-eat and half-finished products. The species being used include Caspian sprat, anchovy, sardine, South African pilchard, oil sardine, saury, Pacific saury, capelin, Alaska pollack, polar cod, hake, horse mackerel, mackerel, etc.

References

Anon. *Technological Properties of Oceanic Species*, Moscow,
1972 Pishtshevaia Promyshlennostj.

BYKOV, V P, MAKAROV, O E, TISHIN, V E and KHVAN E A Tech-
1971 nological studies of some species from the Indian Ocean.
Trudy VNIRO, 72:123–142.

KLEIMENOV, I Y *Chemical and Weight Composition of Fishes from*
1971 *Soviet and Foreign Waters*, Moscow, Pishtshevaia Promyshlennostj.

KOVALCHUK, G K, SKACHKOV V P and VORODIMOVA, A A Tech-
1966 nological composition and food qualities of sharks. *Ryb.
Khoz.*, 42(6):58–60.

LEVANIDOV, I P Classification of fishes by the content of fat and
1968 proteins in their flesh. *Ryb. Khoz.*, (9):50, (10):64–66.

MARTINSEN, G V *Present World Fisheries*, Moscow, Pishtshevaia
1966 Promyshlennostj.

MOISEEV, P A *Biological Resources of the World Ocean*. Ibid.
1969

ZAITSEV, V P, KIZEVETTER, I V, LAGUNOV, L L, *et al.* *Fish Curing*
1969 *and Processing*, Moscow, Mir Publishers.

Upgrading and Adapting Fishery Products of Lower Market Value *H Lisac*

Adaptation et valorisation des produits de la pêche de faible valeur marchande

Le document souligne l'importance que revêt l'amélioration de l'utilisation des ressources halieutiques grâce à la valorisation, à l'adaptation ou à la diversification des produits, en particulier dans les petites ou moyennes entreprises des pays en voie de développement. Quelques formules sont indiquées à ce propos. Un certain nombre d'exemples illustrent diverses activités réalisées dans ce domaine avec des poissons pélagiques, des poissons de fond de faible valeur, des requins, des poissons d'eau douce, des crevettes et des poissons traités. Les procédés technologiques utilisés sont brièvement décrits. Le document énumère les principaux objectifs visés par l'adaptation ou la valorisation des produits de la pêche et signale combien il importe de maintenir l'équilibre entre les coûts à supporter et la valeur escomptée des produits.

Mejoramiento y adaptación de productos pesqueros de escaso valor comercial

En este documento se describe la importancia de mejorar la utilización de los recursos pesqueros y diversas formas de hacerlo, perfeccionando, adaptando o diversificando ciertos productos, especialmente por la industria mediana o de pequeña escala de economías en desarrollo. Diversos ejemplos ilustran parte de los trabajos realizados en esta materia con especies pelágicas, peces demersales de escaso valor, tiburones, peces de agua dulce, camarones y pescado curado. Se hacen breves descripciones de los procesos technológicos empleados. Se enumeran los principales objetivos que han de lograrse mediante la adaptación o mejoramiento de los productos pesqueros y se pone de relieve la importancia que tiene lograr un equilibrio entre los gastos y el precio que se espera lograr con los productos.

The following is an account of selected achievements in field projects and institutes concerning the upgrading of fishery resources of low market value. The examples referred to will indicate some of the many ways in which fishery products may be improved under a variety of conditions in different parts of the world.

ANCHOVY AND SARDINE-LIKE FISH

Dried boiled anchovy

A popular product in Malaysia is dried boiled anchovy (*Stolephorus* sp), known locally as 'ikan bilis'. The traditional method of processing this small fish (its length is 2.5 to 5.0 cm) is to boil it, immediately after landing, in a 10 per cent salt solution for 3 to 5 min then to dry the product in the open air. In dry and sunny weather the product is dried in a day, the moisture content being reduced to 25 per cent. The product, which has a ready market locally, is distributed in baskets or wooden boxes lined with paper and covered by jute cloth. However, unless the anchovy are very fresh when processed, the product becomes soft and reddish and loses much of its market value (Sidaway and Balasingam 1971a). Crushed ice cannot be used to preserve the fish in a fresh state as it damages them. There was a need, therefore, to evolve

a practical method for maintaining the desired quality of the product. On the west coast of Malaysia, the fish is boiled on board and partially dried there. The drying process is then completed when the product is landed. In order to improve the drying technique, catcher boats work with a processing vessel. The catchers transfer their fish to a processing vessel. The fish are boiled on board as soon as possible, in a 10 per cent salt solution and exposed to the air for drying. When the vessel reaches port – usually in the early afternoon – the semi-dried fish are transferred to the shore drying area to complete the process. As a result of this method a high quality product can be produced. It has also eliminated wastage due to spoilage at sea and has led to increased catches because the fishing boats are able to operate longer on the fishing grounds. A further improvement may be achieved through better handling and storage practices and the use of more suitable packaging.

Salted oil sardines

There are large stocks of oil sardines (mainly *Sardinella longiceps* and *S. fimbriata*) in the Gulf of Aden but only a limited commercial exploitation of them, largely because of difficulties in marketing the catch locally. As the Government of the People's Democratic Republic of

Yemen wish to develop the fishery by utilizing the raw material for food products rather than for meal and oil, technological investigations have been started. The objective is to demonstrate the suitability of the fish for processing into various food products, particularly salted products. The work is being carried out by the Fisheries Training and Research Centre, Aden, and the project for Fishery Development in the Gulf of Aden. The Research Centre has experimented in making a product similar to salted herring. It has a moderate salt content and has to be stored at slightly above chill temperature. Some technological problems in this method of salting oil sardine are still being investigated. While the texture of the product is rougher than that of salted herring, it is thought that such a product would be acceptable in the local and in some export markets.

The Development Project has tried to make a product similar to the Mediterranean salted anchovy. Experiments have shown that a product made from headed and gutted fresh fish, with 30 parts of salt to 70 parts of fish packed in small barrels or tin containers and stored in the shade for maturation at the ambient temperature of 30 to 40°C for several weeks, had a reasonable market appeal. Further, fillets of such salted sardines, packed in oil in hermetically sealed, non-sterilized small cans, resembled the Mediterranean salted anchovy. The texture of the sardine products was tougher than that of the anchovy but this may be due to the fact that the sardine used were caught out of the main fishing season when their fat content is low. It is believed that these products can be improved. In addition to the experimental work done so far, the production of heat-processed canned products as a means of upgrading the use of oil sardine is under consideration.

MACKERELS

Chub mackerel

Chub mackerel (*Scomber colias*) is landed in increased quantities by the fishing fleet of the Democratic Republic of Germany. It has been found very suitable for canning (Wagenknecht 1973), and it is already being canned in the USSR, Poland, Japan, Morocco and elsewhere. As the fish soon becomes soft after capture, it should preferably be processed at sea. Heading and eviscerating leaves about 62 per cent of the whole fish while filleting leaves about 41 per cent. The fish are either smoke-flavoured or pre-cooked in cans before being sterilized. The fish can also be packed in brine, oil or sauces. The heat-processed product is similar to canned mackerel. The pre-cooked fish can also be packed in the manner characteristic for 'solid pack' tuna.

Small quantities of chub mackerel (*Rastrelliger* sp) have been canned on the west coast of Malaysia as sardines in tomato sauce (Sidaway and Balasingam 1971b), similar to a product imported from Japan. However, due to the seasonal supplies of the fish and the high price of the imported tomato purée, production has been limited because the local market has a limited price range. The authors have suggested making sauces based on papaya purée, which would suit local taste and replace the tomato purée. Chub mackerel (*Rastrelliger neglectus*) is a fish of high nutritive value and of excellent eating qualities. It is sold fresh on the coast and is taken in bulk, iced, to inland markets but often arrives in a crushed condition. In view of the irregularity of catches, a modest but increasing part is being frozen and stored to even out supplies. Significant quantities are distributed fresh, yet quality problems arise. This is also the case for frozen chub mackerel and there is a need for investigating preservation and processing techniques in order to make the various products more attractive to consumers and to avoid losses.

In this connexion it should be noted that Keat *et al.* (1972) have found in cold storage experiments with commercially frozen chub mackerel of Thailand that the chemical indices of lipid oxidative changes are consistent throughout storage at −14°C. Minimal changes were observed in the case of −30°C storage. It is of practical value to note that vacuum packing apparently compensates for the deficiencies of storage at −14°C. In taste panel evaluations for oxidative rancidity only in the case of unglazed samples stored at −14°C were significant levels of rancidity reported. A difference in the rate of protein denaturation at −14° and −30°C was evident. Limited canning trials carried out with the frozen fish have shown that the best products were those obtained from fillets pickled in 75 per cent saturated sodium chloride brine for 2 min, smoked for 45 min, and from whole fish equally pickled and smoked for 90 minutes. Smoked fillets or whole fish were canned in oil in 225-g oval cans and heat processed for 1 h at 115°C. Smoking and canning appeared to abolish or at least obscure a slightly unpleasant 'metallic' taste which appears to be intrinsic to the species when cooked as wet fish.

Horse mackerel

Horse mackerel (*Trachurus* sp) from the fishing grounds off northwestern Africa can be used to make an acceptable canned product (Wagenknecht 1973). However, it quickly spoils and should be frozen on board as soon after capture as possible. The side line strip of the fish should be removed before canning. Wagenknecht suggests that this could be done by a filleting and skinning machine or by steaming the fish and removing the strip by hand.

LOW-VALUE BOTTOM FISH

More than 80 per cent of the by-catch of shrimp trawlers operating off the west coast of India consist of mostly small and bony varieties of bottom fish. Their market value is low, from 60 to 200 Rs/t compared with 4,000 to 12,000 Rs/t for shrimp. With the use of bigger trawlers fishing in deeper waters, it is expected that the increased landings will result in a bigger by-catch of low value bottom fish. In an effort to make better use of such fish and improve the earnings of the fishermen, the Central Institute of Fisheries Technology, the Indo-Norwegian Project and the State Fisheries College, Mangalore, have been investigating the possibilities of producing frozen fish meat blocks, fish protein concentrate (FPC), fish hydrolysate incorporated in high energy food, fish soup powder, fish flakes and sausages, bacteriological peptone and fish silage (Pillai, communication, 1972).

Experiments by the Indo-Norwegian Project have shown the possibility of separating the flesh from a batch of mixed fish by the use of meat separators and freezing the meat into blocks. For the production of FPC, a modified simple method has been suggested (Ismail *et al.* 1968), using an azeotropic mixture of hexane and alcohol to remove the fat from the press cake obtained after cooking minced meat in an equal volume of water containing 0.5 per cent acetic acid at 70° to 80°C. The dried product has an excellent colour and yields 15 to 18 per cent of the whole fish. The FPC from dressed miscellaneous fish was found to contain 7.5 per cent moisture, 18.11 per cent ash, 0.24 per cent residual fat and 78.17 per cent protein, showing 94.5 pepsin digestibility and 7.84 g of available lysine per 16 g nitrogen.

Fish hydrolysate was prepared from the comminuted and cooked fish muscle that was hydrolyzed by suitable enzymes under controlled conditions. The hydrolysate was concentrated and mixed with sugar, malt and cocoa, the protein content adjusted to around 20 to 25 per cent, and the mixture spray dried. A standard product contained 25 per cent protein, 35 per cent sugar, 5 per cent hydrogenated vegetable fat and 5 per cent cocoa. It was free from fish odour and flavour. A test involving 2,000 persons showed consumer acceptability to be 95 per cent in respect of taste, flavour, colour and odour.

Fish soup powder was prepared from the meat picked from trash fish. The press cake from cooked meat was mixed in suitable proportions with salt, hydrogenated vegetable fat, milk powder, glucose, starch, spices and preservations such as monosodium glutamate, ascorbic acid, etc., and dried under controlled conditions. Fish soup powder prepared from miscellaneous fish contained 5.1 per cent moisture, 19.1 per cent ash, 22.1 per cent protein and 14.6 per cent fat, among other components. The product mixed with boiling water showed consumer acceptability to be 95 per cent.

Fish flakes were also prepared from trash fish according to a standardized method (Anon 1966). Fish press cake was mixed with starch in the proportion of 2:3, the mixture spread into thin layers and dried in the sun, or over steam-heated drum dryers, to a moisture content below 13 per cent. During the process the flakes could be cut in any required shape. According to Kuriyan (communication, 1973), the product is being commercially produced by two firms in the Cochin area and marketed locally.

Work on the preparation of fish sausage from miscellaneous fish at the State Fisheries College, Mangalore, has revealed the possibility of using jew fish, kilimin (*Nemipterus japonicus*) and some other species for this product. Well cooked and finely homogenized fish muscle is suitably blended with starch, sugar, fat, spices and additives. The paste formed is filled into cylindrical casings and pasteurized. Experiments to evolve the most suitable synthetic casings and to extend the shelf life are still in progress.

Bacteriological peptone was prepared from trash fish meal. Cooked fish press cake was enzymatically hydrolyzed, the fat extracted by acetone, acidity adjusted to pH 7 and dried under vacuum. Addition of casein (1 per cent by weight) was necessary to maintain the desired level of free lysine, methionine, tryptophane, leucine and isoleucine. The yield was 5 to 7 per cent of the whole fish weight. The essential analytical and bacterial growth characteristics show that this product was of good quality.

Fish silage for use as a protein supplement to poultry feed was prepared from miscellaneous fish which cannot be economically used for human consumption. The process, described in detail by Arul (1966), involves fermentation of minced fish meat mixed with water and molasses as a carbohydrate source with pure culture of *Lactobacillus plantarum* NCIB 6105. Among other components, the fish silage contained thiamine, riboflavin, pantothenic acid, nicotinic acid and vitamin B_{12}. Feeding trials have shown that the silage added to other feeds improved the egg laying capacity of poultry. Preparation of solid feeds from fish silage is under investigation.

During the past 20 years machines for deboning and filleting fish have been developed, resulting in a greatly increased yield of flesh. In particular, the ability to remove in coarsely minced form the flesh remaining on the carcass after filleting for use in products for human consumption instead of going into fish meal production has upgraded low value raw material, with resultant benefit to the industry as well as the consumer. In this connexion, the production and utilization of minced fish flesh have been carefully investigated, especially in Japan and the USA. Miyauchi and Steinberg (1970) have shown that the total yield of minced flesh from various species of fish ranges from 37 to 60 per cent, based upon round weight. This compares with a yield of 25 to 30 per cent intact flesh by using conventional filleting techniques on the same species.

SHARKS

With the introduction of an inexpensive synthetic vitamin A, there came a rapid decline of commercial shark fishing (Beaumariage 1968). Recently, however, there has been evidence of revived interest in shark as a source of protein food.

In Australia, the 'gumy' shark (*Mystelus antarticus*) and the school shark (*Galeorhinus australis*) are both considered edible, ranking third among the seven principal food fishes reported in the 1960–61 landing statistics (Anon 1962). Fresh and frozen porbeagle shark (*Lamna nasus*) and frozen dogfish (*Squalus* sp) are imported into several European countries, including the United Kingdom, where they are marketed in 'fish and chips' (McCormic *et al.* 1963, Jensen 1967). Sharks and rays have as much as 2.0 to 2.5 per cent urea in their blood, while teleost fishes have only 0.01 to 0.03 per cent (Smith 1953). The deterioration of the urea into ammonia and the reduction of trimethylamine oxide, both immediate results of autolytic and microbial action, are responsible for the pungent shark odour and 'dry taste' characteristics of poorly handled shark meat (Tsachiza *et al.* 1951, Suyama 1960). Therefore, shark carcasses must be rapidly and thoroughly trimmed before being used as food. According to Warfel and Clague (1950) the simplest way to neutralize any residual ammonia is to presoak the fillets in a citric acid solution prior to cooking or freezing. Arundale and Herborg (1971) have described FAO experimental work on the utilization of shark meat for food carried out in Surinam. They suggest gutting and heading sharks and cutting off the tail to accelerate bleeding immediately after catching. Subsequently, the fish should be thoroughly washed and stowed in ice. They recommend processing such shark meat, for example, into frozen fillets, smoked frozen steaks, dried salted fillets, and smoked-salmon substitute. Several tons of these products were successfully test-marketed through a small retail fish shop in Surinam for a number of months in 1970. Frozen fillets were prepared from 3-cm thick shark steaks, from which skin, bone and all red meat was trimmed off. The remaining white meat was washed in running fresh water and wrapped in 500-g units in cellophane. The belly flaps of the shark could not be used for this product. During this preparation the meat was kept chilled by the liberal use of ice. The cellophane-wrapped packages were blast-frozen at − 40°C, placed into polythene bags, sealed, packed in cardboard cartons containing ten 500-g packages each, and stored at below − 18°C. The yield was 30 per cent of frozen fillets and 16 per cent belly flaps for salting, based on the weight of headed, gutted shark. Smoked frozen steaks were prepared in a similar way, but without removal of the red flesh and the backbone. The washed steaks were held in a brine containing 10 per cent salt and 1 per cent vinegar for 30 minutes. Brined steaks were smoked in a non-mechanized smoking oven for 2 h with a clear burning fire and 1 h with a dampened fire. After cooling, they were wrapped in cellophane in 500-g units, blast frozen, packed in polythene bags and cartons, and stored at temperatures lower than − 18°C. Yield was 51 per cent of smoked frozen steaks and 16 per cent belly flaps for salting, based on the weight of headed, gutted shark.

Dried salted fillets were prepared from thoroughly washed fresh shark after belly flaps were removed and skinned. Fillets 1.5 to 2 cm thick and 40 cm long were cut parallel with the backbone and blood spots and skin removed. They were thoroughly washed, left to drip for about 10 min, then salted in perforated plastic containers. The bottom of the container was generously covered with coarse salt and a layer of fillets placed on top. A further layer of salt was added, completely covering the fillets. This process was repeated until the box was filled. The salted fillets were kept in a shaded place for six days. The excess salt was then brushed off and the fillets were sun-dried or dried mechanically. Sun-drying took six days or more. The final product was of poor and inconsistent quality, partly due to unfavourable climatic conditions. In mechanical drying, the most suitable temperature of the air entering the drying chamber was found to be 45°C. This relatively high temperature was believed to contribute to restricting the development of ammonia odour during drying. The relative humidity inside the drier was adjusted to 35 per cent. In this way the 2-cm thick fillets were dried to a moisture content of 35 to 40 per cent within 30 hours. A modified procedure tried out was to run the drier for 6 h and shut it down for the following 18 hours. With this method a total active drying time of 18 h was required to obtain a product equally dry as that obtained by the continuous drying process. The salted dried fillets were packed into polythene pouches of 500 or 1,000 g net content and put into 5-kg cardboard cartons. The yield of the product was 40 per cent of headed, gutted shark.

Smoked salmon substitute 'Seelachs' was prepared from shark by the same salting process described for salted dried fillets. The salted fillets were then cut into slices 1 mm thick and spread on fine-screen frames. The frames were dipped into a colouring solution of 20 kg water and 15 g 'Seelachs-Farbe No. 47761' (colour) for 2 minutes. The slices were smoked for 10 minutes. The product was packed in polythene bags containing 50 g of fish and 25 g of vegetable oil, blast-frozen, and held in cold store. The yield was 30 per cent whole slices and 21 per cent of broken slices and crumbs, based on the weight of headed and gutted shark. Belly flaps cut into long narrow strips, skinned, soaked in 10 per cent salt and 2 per cent vinegar brine for about 10 min, hot-smoked at about 70° to 80°C for up to 1 h, and smoke-flavoured for another 1 to 1½ h, result in a product of particularly attractive appearance. It is called 'Schiller-locken' and is considered a delicacy in some European countries (Biegler 1960).

Shark fins are in great demand as raw material for food specialities. The most valuable fins are those of sharks shorter than 1.5 m, side fins of the sawfish shark (*Pristis pactinatus*), the upper lobe of the tail of all sharks, and all fins of the nurse shark (*Ginglymostoma cirratum*). Those fins have to be cut so that very little skin or meat remains on the fin. It takes fourteen days or more for fins to dry properly. They are then packed in bags, cases or barrels, as mentioned by Beaumariage (1968). This author also describes the quality criteria for cured skins required by the United States market. The skins are generously salt-cured for four to five days, then packed in sisal bags for shipment. The use of shark liver for vitamin A-rich oil, the meat for fish meal and the teeth for novelty items for tourists, make the utilization of the shark complete.

FRESHWATER FISH

Upgrading products made from freshwater fish maybe of practical significance for all countries with substantial inland fisheries. In this connexion the experience of Mali is of interest. In that country, the bulk of such fish has been traditionally sun-dried or smoked, only a small quantity being consumed fresh by the fishermen and their families. Even though the catch includes such species as Nile perch (*Lates niloticus*) and catfish (*Bagrus bayad macropterus*), usually fish of high market value in some countries, the return on fishing was modest. A smoked-salmon substitute from these fish was prepared in a similar way as mentioned above. This product has been so successful that the present supply cannot meet domestic demand. In addition, there is a growing demand from neighbouring countries.

CURED FISH

Smoke-dried fish

While smoke-dried fish is a traditional food in many tropical countries, the production of a product of uniform quality has not been generally achieved. In this respect the work done in Nigeria – and elsewhere – by FAO provides a good example of product upgrading. The smoking of bonga (*Ethmalosa* spp) and some other species in Nigeria was studied by FAO fish processing technologists (1971). They built a non-mechanized Altona-type oven from local materials and tested it. As a result they were able to produce traditional types of smoked products of improved and uniform quality. The process, which has since been introduced in the country on a larger scale, took less labour and consumed less wood than the traditional method. Similarly, in Ghana the traditional smoking methods resulted in products of non-uniform quality and at relatively high cost. The traditional equipment is, therefore, being replaced by the Altona type of oven (Youngs, communication 1972). Such replacement of traditional equipment and methods is gradually spreading in Africa and could, of course, be adapted to the needs of other countries where similar kinds of traditional fish smoking is still done.

Dried salted fish

Sun-drying of fish is a traditional method applied in many countries. In Malaysia, for example, such a method is widespread although the humid climate often makes drying an unsatisfactory process. FAO fish processing technologists working in the Food Technology Research and Development Centre in Malaysia found that the moisture content of the product was sometimes as high as 52 per cent, due to carelessness, impatience to sell the product as quickly as possible, and to obtain the highest profit by keeping as much moisture as possible in it. As a result of their investigations the FAO workers demonstrated that, with a proper ratio of salt to fish and with kiln-drying and storage at chillroom temperature, a much improved product could be made. Further, they proposed the use of suitable protective packaging and optimum storage conditions for increased shelf life.

References

Anon. Australian catch by species and states. *Fish. Newslett. Aust.*
1962   21(3):21.
Anon. *Fish. Technol. Newslett.* CIFT, Cochin, 7(1).
1966
ARUL, J *Fish. Technol.*, *Cochin* 3(1):38–43.
1966

ARUNDALE, J and HERBORG, L Experimental processing of shark,
1971   catfish and small shrimp. *UNDP/FAO Caribbean Fishery Development Project*, report SF/CAR/REG 189 M 18, 23 p. (mimeo).
BEAUMARIAGE, D S Commercial shark fishing and processing in
1968   Florida. *Florida Bd of Conserv. Marine Res. Lab.* St. Petersburg, Educational Series (16):21.
BIEGLER, P *Der Fisch* – Fischwaren-Technologie. Lübeck, F R
1960   Germany, 'Der Fisch' Clara Baader, 5:205.
CARVER, J H and KING, F J Fish scrap offers high quality protein.
1971   *Fd Eng.*, 43(1):75.
CRAWFORD, D L, LAW, D K and BABBITT, J K Yield and acceptability of machine-separated minced flesh from some marine food fish. *J. Fd Sci.* 37:551.
FAO   Equipment and methods for improved smoke-drying of fish
1971   in the tropics. *FAO Fish. Techn. Pap.* (104):27 p.
ISMAIL, P K, MADHAVEN, P and PILLAI, V K *Fish. Technol.*,
1968   *Cochin* 5(1):53.
JENSEN, A C New uses for an old pest. *Sea Frontiers* 13(5):276–285.
1967
KEAY, J N, RATTAGOOL, P and HARDY, R Chub mackerel of
1972   Thailand (*Rastrelliger neglectus* Van Kampen): A short study of its chemical composition, cold storage and canning properties. *J. Sci. Fd Agric.* 23(11):1359–1368.
KING, F J and CARVER, J H How to use nearly all the ocean's
1970   food. *Comml Fish. Rev.* 32(12):12.
McCORMIC, H W, ALLEN, T and YOUNG, W E *Shadows in the Sea*,
1963   Chilton Books, New York, 415 p.
MIYAUCHI, D and STEINBERG, M Machine separation of edible
1970   flesh from fish. *Fish. ind. Res.* 6(4):165.
SIDAWAY, E P and BALASINGAM, M *Fish Processing Industry in*
1971a   *West Malaysia* Food Technology Research and Development Centre of Malaysia, Kuala Lumpur, Publication (42):18–20.
SIDAWAY, E P and BALASINGAM, M *Ibid.* (42):30.
1971b
SMITH, H W *From Fish to Philosopher.* Boston, USA, Little,
1953   Brown and Co.
SUYAMA, M Formation of ammonia and trimethylamine in
1960   elasmobranch fish. *J. Tokyo Univ. Fish.* Spec. Ed. III (1):1–152.
TSACHIZA, Y, TAKAHASHI, I and YOSHIDA, S Formation of ammonia and trimethylamine in shark. *Tohoku J. Agr. Res.*,
1951   2:119–126.
WAGENKNECHT, W Moeglichkeiten der Verarbeitung von Fischarten aus neuen Fanggebieten. *Allg. Fischwztg.* (1):59–60.
1973
WARFEL, H E and CLAGUE, J E Shark fishing potentialities of the
1950   Philippine Seas, *US Fish Wildl. Serv.* Res. Rep. 15:19 p.

New Methods of Shellfish Processing in the United States
R J Learson

Nouveaux procédés de transformation des crustaces et mollusques aux Etats-Unis

L'auteur examine deux domaines de recherche sur la transformation des crustacés et mollusques, dont les résultats pourraient avoir une grande importance pour l'industrie de la pêche. Les procédés étudiés sont les suivants: centrifugation continue pour séparer la chair des coquilles et application des micro-ondes pour ouvrir les bivalves ainsi que pour décongeler les produits de la pêche surgelés. Les recherches sur la centrifugation continue, avec flottation en saumure, montrent qu'il est possible d'utiliser ce procédé pour détacher la chair des crabes et récupérer celle des crustacés et mollusques pendant les opérations de transformation. L'auteur fournit des données sur les rendements ainsi obtenus avec plusieurs espèces de fruits de mer, en particulier les crabes et les mactres. Il a été démontré que les micro-ondes (2,450 Mhz) facilitent l'écaillage manuel des bivalves, le taux de décoquillage augmentant de 30 pour cent. Les micro-ondes dans la bande des fréquences moyennes (915 MHz) semblent offrir de grandes possibilités pour la décongélation des produits de la mer surgelés destinés à d'ultérieures transformations. Des recherches sont en cours sur la décongélation de blocs de poisson et de blocs de crevettes et pétoncles surgelés. Ce procédé augmenterait sensiblement l'efficacité du traitement ainsi que son rendement.

Nuevos metodos para la elaboración de mariscos en los Estados Unidos

Se tratan dos aspectos de la investigación sobre la elaboración de mariscos que pueden tener gran importancia para la industria pesquera. Son la centrifugación continua para separar la carne de la concha, y la aplicación de la energía de las microondas para abrir a los bivalvos y para descongelar y atemperar los productos pesqueros congelados. Las investigaciones sobre la centrifugación continua con flotación en salmuera, revelan las posibles empleos de este método para extraer la carne del cangrejo y recuperar la sobrante de la elaboración de mariscos. Figuran datos de rendimientos de diversas especies de mariscos incluídos cangrejos y almejas. Se ha demostrado que la energía de las microondas (2.450 MHz) facilitan la apertura a mano de los bivalvos, lo cual permite aumentar las aperturas en un 30 por ciento. La energía de las microondas con frecuencias intermedias (915 MHz) parece que tiene un gran potencial para descongelar o atemperar los productos marinos congelados para su posterior elaboración. Se han efectuado investigaciones sobre la atemperación de bloques de pescado y descongelación de camarones y bloques de vieiras. Los resultados indican aumentos importantes en la eficiencia, y en el rendimiento potencial.

There are two areas of research on shellfish processing which may have great potential for the fishing industry.

These are continuous centrifugation for separation of meat from shell and the application of microwave energy for opening bivalves and for thawing and tempering frozen fishery products.

CONTINUOUS CENTRIFUGATION

One of the major problems of the shellfish industry in the United States is the dwindling supply of hand labour. In the crab industry, for example, where nearly all of the meat is picked by hand, the supply of pickers is decreasing, and young people are not entering the industry. Processing plants, therefore, cannot handle all of the raw material that becomes available during peak seasons. The answer to this problem is, of course, automation, and some progress has been made in the development of machines for various phases of the process (Anon. 1967). However, to date, crab processing remains a hand-labour operation, with considerable waste. Laboratory studies indicate potential meat yields up to 30 per cent for many crab species (Learson 1970). At present, the crab industry is achieving meat yields ranging from 14 to 25 per cent, depending upon the species.

Centrifuge process

The purpose of introducing the centrifuge to the processing of shellfish was primarily for the recovery of meats from material that is normally discarded.

Centrifuge operations have been widely used in paper and fishmeal processing operations for many years. Most of these involve the separation of oil and settleable solid materials and dewatering applications. Tretsven (1971) demonstrated the potential for continuous separation of shell and tendon from Dungeness crab meat by a centrifugal process. The machine used was a solid bowl continuous centrifuge designed for separating sediment material. As a result of Tretsven's experiments and subsequent studies, a continuous centrifuge designed specifically for shellfish applications was constructed.

The type used in this research was a solid bowl decanting centrifuge as shown in Fig 1. The operation of the machine is based on the fact that in 15 per cent brine (specific gravity 1.112) shellfish meats float, and shell and cartilage material sink because of their higher specific gravities. In a centrifuge, the separation takes place more rapidly and more completely than in static flotation processes since small differences in specific gravity between materials are magnified by the gravity forces generated in a centrifuge. A diagram of the centrifuge process is shown in Fig 2. Fish material must first be cleaned of all viscera and then chopped or ground to a particle size of less than 3 centimetres. The mixture of meat and bones is then fed into the centrifuge with a continuously circulating brine system. In such operations the centrifuge rotates in the range of 200 to 800 rpm, and the pool of brine, 1 to 3 cm deep, is held to the outside of the bowl by the centrifugal force. The shell material 'sinks' to the outside of the bowl where it is taken away by means of a screw conveyor. The meat, which floats with the brine, is screened out at the exit port. The variables in the machine operation are the specific gravity of the brine, the brine flow rate, the pool depth, and the speed (rpm) of the centrifuge. In the test the crabs and lobsters were first cooked to free the meat from the shell. The samples were then cleaned of all viscera and gill material and divided into sections – bodies, legs and claws – of less

Fig 1 Experimental installation of continuous centrifuge for meat and shell separation

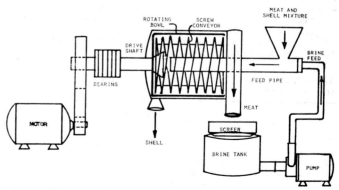

Fig 2 Schematic of continuous centrifuge process

than 3 centimetres. In the lobster experiments only the bodies and walking legs were tested. The samples were chopped or ground prior to processing, depending upon the species and the desired particle size of the finished product. Waste materials from crab-processing plants, surf-clam shucking plants, and fish-filleting operations were tested to determine recovery. In the case of the filleting waste, the fish frames (headed and gutted) were blanched in steam to free the flesh from the bodies prior to centrifugation.

Table 1 shows the species tested and the types of materials used.

Results

The yields obtained from each species using the optimum conditions are shown in Tables 2 and 3.

The crab and lobster meat lost some flavour to the flotation medium and to the water spray used in the

TABLE 1. SPECIES AND TYPES OF RAW MATERIAL PROCESSED BY THE CONTINUOUS CENTRIFUGE

Species	Type of material
Blue crab (*Callinectes sapidus*) Red crab (*Geryon quinquedens*) Rock crab (*Cancer irroratus*) Jonah crab (*Cancer borealis*) Dungeness crab (*Cancer magister*) Snow crab (*Chionoectes tanneri*)	Whole crabs and picking waste
Surf clam (*Spisula solidissima*)	Waste from automatic shucking operation
Spiny lobster (*Panulirus argus*) Northern lobster (*Homarus americanus*)	Cooked bodies and walking legs
Cod (*Gadus morhua*) Haddock (*Melanogrammus aeglefinus*) Ocean perch (*Sebastes marinus*)	Waste frames from filleting operations

TABLE 2. MEAT YIELDS OBTAINED USING THE CENTRIFUGE UNDER THE OPTIMUM CONDITIONS
PER CENT MEAT RECOVERY [a]

Species	Sections			Picking waste
	Claws	Legs	Body	
Blue crab	28.9	30.3	42.4	25.0
Rock crab	17.6	17.6	43.0	11.0
Red crab	31.0	30.5	40.7	—
Tanner crab	36.5	21.5 [b]	56.2	19.5
Dungeness crab		30.0 [c]	48.3	14.7
Jonah crab	22.5	23.5	52.0	—

Per cent meat recovery is based on cooked weight of meat and shell mixture entering machine
Only the last three segments of the leg were used for the test
[c] Claws and legs were not run separately

TABLE 3. CONTINUOUS CENTRIFUGE YIELDS OBTAINED FROM FISH AND SHELLFISH WASTE MATERIALS

Species	Material used	Meat yield (%)
Surf clam	Shucking waste (shell and meat)	50–70
Spiny lobster	Cooked (cleaned) bodies with legs	35–40
Northern lobster	Cooked (cleaned) bodies with legs	28–32
Cod	Headed and gutted frames (cooked)	
Haddock	Headed and gutted frames (cooked)	60–65
Ocean perch	Headed and gutted frames (cooked)	

Note: (a) This yield varies considerably with the efficiency of the shucking operation
(b) Yields are based on cooked weight of headed and gutted frames entering centrifuge

freshening operation. However, the intensity of this effect varied with the particle size of the meat. The small meat particles obtained from small legs and claws retained more brine because of the greater surface area to volume ratio and had to be freshened for a longer time. Conversely, the larger chunks of meat could be freshened more readily, resulting in very little flavour loss. Although all the samples were organoleptically acceptable, the larger chunks of meat were consistently rated higher by the panelists. The quality of clam meats was not affected by the process while the fish flesh recovered resembled cooked fish flakes and was highly acceptable when further processed into chowders or fish cakes.

MICROWAVE APPLICATIONS

The phenomenon of heating objects by means of high frequency electrical fields has been known since the late eighteen-hundreds. Microwave (MCW) ovens first appeared in the nineteen-fifties after the development of radar. However, it was not until the nineteen-sixties, when MCW tubes were developed with sufficient power, that serious attention was given to industrial application. Potential applications of microwave energy for the seafood industry include cooking, blanching, drying, thawing and pasteurization.

Microwave opening of bivalves

Research carried out at the National Marine Fisheries Atlantic Fishery Products Technology Center in Gloucester, Massachusetts, USA, has shown that microwave energy (2 450 MHz) can be used to increase the productivity of shucking oysters and other bivalves (Mendelsohn *et al.* 1969). A short microwave treatment relaxes the muscle of the bivalve without cooking the meat, resulting in a visible loosening or opening of the shell halves (gaping). This allows easy separation with a shucking knife and greatly facilitates the shucking process. Microwave treatment of oysters prior to shucking had no effect on the processing and storage characteristics of the meats (Learson and Stone 1969), and it did not affect their water

TABLE 4. EFFECT OF MICROWAVE TREATMENT ON LABOUR COSTS OF SHUCKING OYSTERS

	Hand-shucking [a]	Hand-shucking [b]	Hand-shucking with microwave [b]
Shucking rate, oysters/man/h	462	502	660
Oysters/1, average	72	72	72
1/man/h	6.43	6.96	9.20
Man/h/year	720	720	720
1/man/year	4,632	5,015	6,624
Wages [c]	2.72	2.94	3.00 [d]
Cost, US$/year	1,958	2,177	2,160
Cost, US$/h	0.423	0.423	0.325 [e]

[a] Data developed by University of Maryland (Wheaton 1969)
[b] Data obtained from in-plant test described in this report
[c] Standard rate for shuckers is US$0.42/1
[d] Estimated hourly wage for expert shucker eliminating piecework system
[e] Exclusive of microwave processing costs

TABLE 5. COMPARATIVE COSTS OF NORMAL AND MICROWAVE SHUCKING PROCESSES

	Normal process	Microwave process
Litres per year	91,000	91,000
Cost, US$/1 [a]	0.423	0.325
Cost/year	38,500	29,600
Annual cost of 10 kW Unit amortized over 5 years, US$		5 000
Direct costs, US$ [b]		1 700
Total costs, US$	38,500	36,300
No. of shuckers required	20	14

Net savings: US$2,200 plus 6 shuckers

[a] Data from previous table
[b] Costs of installation, interest and auxiliary equipment estimated at 1/3 capital cost

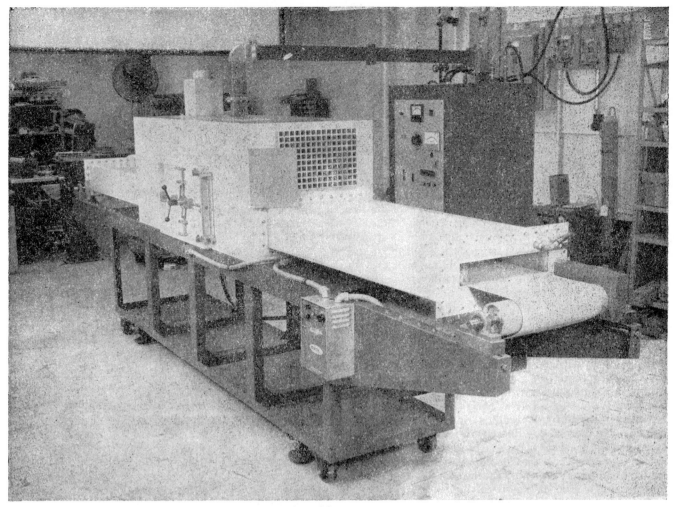

Fig 3 Conveyorized 5 kW microwave applicator (2450 MHz) used for oyster processing

Fig 4 Laboratory-scale 5 kW microwave applicator (915 MHz) used for thawing and tempering experiments

uptake during the washing process ('blowing'). There were no significant differences between microwave-treated oysters and untreated meats regarding pH, drip, bacterial numbers, and organoleptic quality, either immediately after shucking or during refrigerated storage. These results indicated that the microwave process could represent a major breakthrough for the shellfish industry.

Tests were carried out under commercial conditions in order to determine necessary power requirements for commercial equipment and to establish data for economic analysis of the microwave process. Fig 3 shows the 5-kW conveyorized microwave tunnel used in these studies. Data obtained from oyster plants indicate an average throughput (80 per cent gaping) of 120 1/h/kW for Chesapeake Bay oysters (*Crassostrea virginica*). Time study data obtained demonstrated an average increase in shucking efficiency of 30 per cent. Table 4 shows the effect of microwave treatment on the labour costs of shucking oysters, and Table 5 shows a cost comparison of the microwave process versus the normal hand shucking process for an oyster plant averaging 91,000 1 of shucked meats per year (Learson *et al.* 1970).

Data obtained from tests in commercial shucking of ocean quahogs (*Arctica islandica*) and hard clams (*Mercenaria mercenaria*) demonstrated similar results. Shucking productivity increased approximately 30 per cent on average. Throughputs ranged from 90 to 140 1/h/kW for maximum efficiency. Recent laboratory studies indicate greater efficiency with bivalves harvested from relatively deeper waters. It appears that the pressure of the environment affects bivalves to some extent.

In summary, the use of microwave energy for bivalve shucking appears to be economical from a commercial standpoint. The microwave process eliminates the need for highly skilled shuckers and should ease the problems of recruiting and training shuckers.

Microwave tempering and thawing

Very little has been done on the defrosting process, and procedures developed many years ago are still used. Much of the United States seafood production is from defrosted bulk products processed into consumer items. Fish portion and fish stick processors generally temper frozen fish blocks by raising the temperature to about 7°C for cutting operations. Layer-packed fillets must be partially defrosted to permit their separation prior to processing, and scallops and shrimp must be completely defrosted for peeling and breading. These operations are usually carried out using tempering rooms, water defrosting systems, warm air systems and ambient air. In general, all of these require a large amount of labour and a great deal of time and space, creating problems in production scheduling and leading to quality losses and bacterial contamination problems.

The most common defrosting procedure used in the shrimp industry is water defrosting. The frozen shrimp, in 2.25-kg boxes, are immersed from 1 to 3 h in tanks which are continuously overflowing with 27°C water. This system often leads to product losses, high labour costs and sanitation problems. When heat is applied to frozen fish, either by warm air or water or by radiant heat, the surface thaws first. The remaining frozen fish is then surrounded by thawed material having only about one third the thermal conductivity of the frozen material; consequently, the time necessary to thaw fish completely is much greater than that necessary to freeze it under similar conditions of surface heat transfer. Unfortunately, thawing time cannot be shortened by subjecting the surface to high temperatures, for this could produce cooking, drying, or deleterious effects upon quality. For these reasons much research has been carried out on electronic methods of defrosting, such as dielectric and microwave heating. In both cases, the frozen material is placed in a field of alternating electrical energy which causes individual polar molecules within the frozen material to oscillate. This results in molecular friction within the material, generating heat. Since the heating is uniform throughout, great precision in heating can be achieved, and since thermal conductivity is not a factor, the time of defrosting can be greatly reduced.

Workers at Torry Research Station in Aberdeen (Jason and Sanders 1962) have carried out extensive testing with fish at 35 MHz, and Bengtsson (1963) has demonstrated the defrosting of both meat and fish at 35 and 2,450 MHz. The results of these experiments indicated marked advantages over common defrosting procedures and some disadvantages concerning runaway heating and high capital cost for equipment. In general, the lower frequencies are associated with slower heating rates and 'arcing' which causes spot burning of the product. At the higher frequency, the depth penetration is limited, restricting product thickness. In 1969, the Bureau of Commercial Fisheries, now the National Marine Fisheries Service (NMFS), with the cooperation of Raytheon Company carried out a series of defrosting and tempering experiments using 915 MHz (Learson and Stone, unpublished). Results of these tests indicated that this inter-

mediate frequency eliminated many of the problems previously reported for electronic defrosting. Using a 5-kW conveyorized microwave tunnel (Fig 4), frozen blocks of clam meats, scallops, flounder and shrimp were uniformly heated to internal temperatures of − 2°C to 1°C, allowing separation of the block for further processing. The most promising uses for the microwave system appeared to be for the tempering of frozen fish blocks and the defrosting of shrimp blocks.

TABLE 6. LABORATORY TEST BACTERIOLOGICAL RESULTS – MICROWAVE VS. WATER DEFROSTING OF RAW, HEADLESS SHRIMP – 31–35/LB (68–77/KG)

Sample	Total plate count (Number per gramme)
Frozen control	1.8×10^5
Microwave-defrosted, no wash	1.8×10^5
Microwave-defrosted, spray wash	1.7×10^4
Water-thawed for one hour	7.7×10^4
Water-thawed for two hours	1.8×10^5
Water-thawed, peeled	7.2×10^4
Microwave-thawed, peeled	5.7×10^4

TABLE 7. LABORATORY TEST – PROXIMATE COMPOSITION – MICROWAVE VS. WATER DEFROSTING – RAW, HEADLESS SHRIMP – 31–35/LB (68–77/KG) [a]

	Frozen control	Microwave-defrosted	Water-defrosted 1 h	Water-defrosted 2 h
% protein	18.70	18.60	16.05	16.55
% moisture	80.68	80.72	81.91	82.35
% fat	0.134	0.217	0.220	0.178
% ash	1.05	1.01	1.00	0.80
Moisture to protein ratio	4.32	4.34	5.10	4.97

[a] For analysis purposes, the compositions are based on peeled meats

TABLE 8. LABORATORY TEST – PEELED AND COOKED YIELD – MICROWAVE VS. WATER DEFROSTING – RAW, HEADLESS SHRIMP 31–35/LB (68–77/KG)

	Water-defrosted	Microwave-defrosted
Frozen raw, headless weight (g)	2,267	2,267
Peeled weight (g)	1,828	1,788
Peeled yield (%)	80.6	78.9
Cooked weight (g)	1,468	1,517
Cooked/peeled yield (%)	80.2	84.7
Cooked/frozen yield (%)	64.8	67.0

The temperature is critical for proper cutting and slicing of frozen fish blocks. If too high, it results in smearing the product during cutting; and if too low, it can result in shattering the portions and excessive wear on cutting equipment. Tests on commercial 16.5-lb (7.5-kg) fish blocks using a 25-kW conveyorized microwave tunnel (915 MHz) demonstrated uniform heating from an initial temperature of − 18° to 7°C with a temperature range of ± 2°C throughout the fish block. Production rates depend on the initial product temperature. Fig 5 shows production rate curves for tempering fish blocks derived from enthalpy data and confirmed experimentally. Advantages of microwave tempering systems include elimination of tempering rooms, more efficient production scheduling, less handling and more uniform cutting. Estimated tempering costs for a microwave system capable of tempering 1,800 kg/h are about US$0.0066/kg over eight years of operation (Bezanson, private communication).

Experiments comparing commercial water defrosting of shrimp with microwave defrosting were carried out on a laboratory scale in cooperation with the Raytheon Company New Products Center in Waltham, Massachusetts. Raw, headless brown shrimp (*Penaeus aztecus*) of known history were used for the laboratory experiments. These were shipped in ice to the Gloucester laboratory, where they were frozen and glazed in 5-lb (2.25-kg) cartons. They were held at −18°C for 30 days prior to defrosting. A stainless steel tank holding approximately 23 kg of 18°C water was used to defrost 4.5-kg batches of shrimp. Hot or warm water was added periodically to maintain the temperature of the water in the tank at approximately 18°C throughout the defrosting process. The microwave defrosting was carried out in a 915-MHz conveyorized multimode applicator (Fig 4). Duplicate samples were defrosted by both methods and were analysed and compared with a frozen control sample for total plate counts, proximate composition, and organoleptic quality. The frozen control had a total plate count of 1.8 × 10⁵. At the conclusion of microwave defrosting and of a 2-h water defrost, the counts were identical to that of the control. A rapid spray wash with tap water reduced the count by one log cycle to 1.7 × 10⁴ on the microwave-defrosted shrimp. Total plate counts on peeled meats defrosted by the two methods did not differ significantly from each other. These data are summarized in Table 6. Proximate analyses (Table 7) showed that the water-defrosted shrimp contained an average of 16.30 per cent protein as compared with 18.70 per cent in the frozen control and the microwave-defrosted sample. The moisture/protein ratio of the water-defrosted samples averaged 5.05 versus 4.32 for the frozen control and 4.34 for the microwave-defrosted. Batches of shrimp defrosted by both methods were hand-peeled, then cooked for a yield determination. These data are summarized in Table 8. The yield of peeled water-defrosted shrimp was 1.7 per cent greater than that of the microwave-defrosted samples. However, the yield was 4.5 per cent greater for the cooked microwave-defrosted shrimp. This result is attributed to the improved protein retention associated with microwave-defrosting. Triangle tests indicated that no significant quality difference could be attributed to the defrosting method.

The 5-kW microwave system used in the laboratory tests was installed in a shrimp breading plant and operated for eleven days. During this time 7,270 kg of raw, headless shrimp of various sizes were microwave-defrosted. The optimum throughput rate was found to be 159 kg/h at 5 kW. Typical shrimp temperatures at the tunnel exit ranged from −2.5° to 1.1°C, while input temperatures ranged from −15° to −8°C. It was possible to achieve separation of individual shrimp at flow rates up to 204 kg/h at 3.5°C, but the shrimp required considerable additional heat input before they became suitable for peeling.

Conversely, flow rates as low as 114 kg/h were tested in order to try to raise the temperature of the shrimp above 1°C. However, this resulted in some spot over-

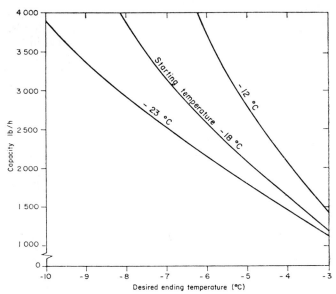

Fig 5 *Capacity curves based on enthalpy data for tempering lean fish (80% moisture, 20% protein) using a 25 kW microwave tunnel (915 MHz)*

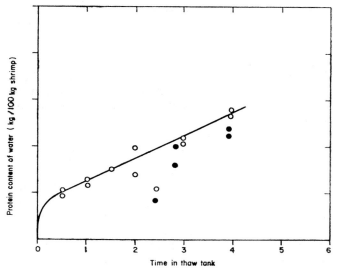

Fig 6 *Protein losses during water defrosting (17°C). Raw headless brown shrimp, 40–50 count per pound*

heating. This condition was attributed to three factors: (a) defrosted shrimp absorbs microwave energy faster than frozen shrimp, (b) substantial temperature gradients existed in shrimp blocks entering the tunnel, and (c) the tunnel used in the tests was subsequently found to have an energy gradient, so that more energy was applied to the sides of the shrimp blocks than to the centre portion. As was expected, the microwave energy had little effect on the glaze ice. At all flow rates a matrix of ice surrounded the partially defrosted shrimp upon exit from the tunnel. This matrix could be easily broken into small fragments by impacting the carton on a flat solid surface. Careful inspections showed that this impact did not cause physical damage to the shrimp. Shrimp that were lightly glazed (Colombian, poly-lined cartons) could be separated without impacting. Shrimp mixed with as much as 0.91 kg of glaze ice (Mexican, pan-frozen) could be separated effectively after impacting the carton on its large side.

165

Proximate analyses were carried out on samples defrosted under production conditions by both methods. These results are set forth in Table 9. As reported in the laboratory tests, the water-defrosted shrimp consistently contained less protein than the microwave-defrosted. Moisture/protein ratios were also higher in the water-defrosted samples.

TABLE 9. PRODUCTION TEST – PROXIMATE COMPOSITION – MICROWAVE VS. WATER-DEFROSTING – RAW, HEADLESS SHRIMP [a]

	Louisiana brown – 40–50 count	Louisiana brown – 40–50 count	Colombia white – 41–50 count	Colombia white – 36–40 count
% Protein (water-defrosted)	16.57	17.13	16.68	15.54
% Protein (microwave-defrosted)	18.66	17.80	17.49	16.36
Protein difference (% of total weight)	2.09	0.67	0.81	0.82
Moisture/protein ratio (water-defrosted)	4.97	4.76	4.93	—
Moisture protein ratio (microwave-defrosted)	4.28	4.53	4.65	—

[a] For analysis purposes the compositions were determined from peeled meats

Loss of protein during water-defrosting was further investigated by sampling the defrosting water. Fig 6 shows this protein leaching effect. Soluble protein in the water was found to increase steadily throughout the 4-h test.

During the production tests a number of attempts were made to obtain comparative yield data for the two defrosting methods. Based on composition difference, one might expect that microwave-defrosting would improve yield at least 1 per cent over water-defrosting, the value of which could exceed US$150,000 per year in a large shrimp-breeding plant. Conclusive data were not obtained, however, because of excessive variables and difficulties encountered in making accurate measurements under production conditions. For example, successive tests on shrimp from the same lot, defrosted and handled under identical conditions, showed production yield differences of 3 per cent.

The only significant measure of yield relevant for this analysis would compare the weight of the frozen, raw, headless shrimp versus peeled or breaded weight. However, frozen weight is indeterminate because all frozen, raw, headless shrimp contain glaze. Therefore, label weights must be used. Accordingly, an experiment was conducted to determine true frozen weights in one lot of Mexican, pan-frozen shrimp. Individual 2.25-kg boxes were microwave-defrosted, drained, and weighed under uniform conditions. The standard deviation in the individual weights was 3.3 per cent, and distribution was not normal in the sample measured (28 boxes). Therefore, a large number of comparative tests would be required to establish statistical validity.

Drained weight of raw, headless shrimp is also of little significance, since it was shown that defrosted shrimp lose weight continuously with time. Also, since water-defrosting significantly alters the composition, there may be differences in the physical properties of water-defrosted

and microwave-defrosted shrimp. These could affect the subsequent peeled yield, especially when machine peeling is employed. In similar studies on herring, Jason and Sanders (1962) reported yields of 88 per cent for electronic-defrosted herring versus 68 per cent for water-defrosted samples.

It proved to be very difficult to follow individual lots of shrimp through the peeling stage and obtain accurate weight measurements under commercial conditions. Mechanical adjustments of the peeling machine and variable residence time of peeled shrimp in water were two variables contributing to differences in peeled yield. If an attempt had been made to measure yield differences on the basis of breaded weights, even more variables, such as breading percentage, would be introduced. When these factors became apparent, no further attempts were made to measure comparative production yields.

CONCLUSIONS

It is concluded that microwave defrosting is particularly suited to the defrosting of raw headless shrimp for the following reasons:

(1) microwave defrosting would allow compliance with the present GMP[1] guideline for raw headless shrimp regarding the requirements of temperature and packaging removal
(2) there is improved production control resulting from rapid in-line processing
(3) water usage is reduced substantially, alleviating waste disposal problems
(4) defrosting takes place within the carton, eliminating the need to remove the carton and increasing handling efficiency after thawing
(5) ice requirements are reduced because there is no 'temperature overshoot'
(6) bacteriological control and quality control are improved
(7) nutritional value, as evidenced by moisture/protein ratio is retained.

References

Anon. Resumé of current status of oyster shucking devices. Special
1967 Report. Oyster Institute of North America. 29 Sept. 1967, 2 p.
BENGTSSON, N E Electronic defrosting of meat and fish at 35 and
1963 2,450 MCS – A laboratory comparison. Fd Technol. 17(10):97.
JASON, A C and SANDERS, H R Dielectric thawing of fish, Parts 1
1962 and 2. Fd Technol. 16(6):101.
LEARSON, R J Report of a workshop meeting with members of
1970 the blue crab industry, Atlanta, Georgia, April 21. Gloucester, Mass., USA, NMFS Atlantic Fishery Products Technology Center.
LEARSON, R J and STONE, W R Microwave opening of oysters –
1969 some economic considerations. Microwave Energy Appl. Newsl. 2(5):9–12.
LEARSON, R J, SPRACKLIN, B W and JONES, K A The effects of
1970 microwave treatment on the processing and storage characteristics of Chesapeake oysters. Microwave Energy Appl. Newsl. 3(4):8–11.
MENDELSOHN, J M, RONSIVALLI, L J, KING, F J, CARVER, J H,
1969 LEARSON, R J, SPRACKLIN, B W and KENYON, E M Opening oysters and other bivalves using microwave energy. Fish. ind. Res. 4(7):241–248.
TRETSVEN, W L The separation of crab meat from shell and tendon
1971 by a centrifugal process. Comm. Fish. Rev. 33(5):48.

[1] Good Manufacturing Practice.

WHEATON, F Engineering approach to oyster processing, presented at the Annual Meeting of the American Society of Agricultural Engineering, Purdue University, Maryland, USA, 22–25 June 1969, Paper No. 69–520.
1969

Acknowledgement

The author thanks Alan F Bezanson and William R Stone of Raytheon Company, and Glenn Reierstad of the Bird Machine Company for advice and assistance.

Handling and Processing the Deep-Sea Shrimp *Pandalus borealis* for the Freezing Industry   *J Aagaard*

Manutention et transformation de la crevette de grand fond *Pandalus borealis* destinée à l'industrie de la congelation

Les crevettes de grand fond *Pandalus borealis* sont parmi les plus petites des espèces marines exploitées commercialement pour l'alimentation humaine. Elles sont transformées en produits de prix élevé à la suite d'une série complexe d'opérations au moyen d'un équipement spécialement conçu à cet effet. En raison de leur structure délicate, il faut les manipuler et les traiter avec grand soin afin de préserver leurs qualités gastronomiques. L'auteur fait le point des connaissances actuelles sur l'utilisation des crevettes. Il décrit les méthodes et le matériel utilisés dans l'industrie de la congélation des crevettes pour montrer comment de nombreux problèmes sont résolus dans la pratique.

Manipulación y elaboración del camarón de agua profunda *Pandalus borealis* destinado a la industria de congelación

El camarón de agua profunda *Pandalus borealis* figura entre los más pequeños animales marinos explotados comercialmente. Estos camarones se transforman en productos de alto precio mediante una compleja cadena de operaciones, utilizando equipo especialmente diseñado. Debido a la delicadeza de su estructura, es preciso proceder con atención durante la manipulación y tratamiento, para conservar sus cualidades gastronómicas. En este trabajo se resume la situación actual de los conocimientos sobre el aprovechamiento de este camarón. Se describen los métodos y el equipo introducidos en la industria de congelación de camarones, para mostrar cómo se afrontan en la práctica los numerosos problemas que se plantean.

Processing the deep-sea shrimp *Pandalus borealis* industrially requires a high level of know-how and specialized equipment. The shrimps, also known as the pink or northern shrimp, are among the smallest of the commercially exploited sea-foods, are highly perishable and easily lose their gastronomical qualities. Within the last 15 years a modern shrimp-freezing industry has been developed in Denmark and Greenland, based on a close cooperation between the shrimp industry, the Technological Laboratory of the Danish Ministry of Fisheries, and suppliers of equipment for the fishing industry. This paper summarizes the present state of knowledge on handling and processing the shrimps into frozen products, based mainly on experience gained from the development of the Danish/Greenland shrimp-freezing industry.

SHRIMP AS RAW MATERIAL

Types of quality deterioration

When the trawl is emptied on board some of the shrimp may still be alive, but they will die within a few hours. The rate of the deterioration is determined by many factors and the symptoms are as follows: The bright red colour of the tail fades and becomes pale. Green, brown, and finally black, discolorations develop in the carapace. The texture loses its firmness and elasticity and becomes soft. The connexion between the carapace and the tail is loosened. The content of total solids decreases, and the yield of peeled cooked meat is lowered. The sweet, rich flavour of fresh shrimp is gradually lost, staleness develops and finally putrefaction. Odour changes from fresh and seaweedy into ammoniacal and putrid. The bacterial count rises, as do the contents of volatile bases and the pH. The ability of shrimp in shell to curl on cooking gradually disappears.

Handling on board vessels

Handling procedures on board vary dependent on the lengths of the trips, the size of the catches etc, and on local practice. The three major aims of handling shrimp on board should be to diminish bruising, to obtain the maximum degree of cleanliness and to keep the temperature of the shrimp between 0° and −1.5°C. In a Danish shrimp trawler the catch is emptied directly from the net into a tank of cold water. In this way the shrimp are kept cool and moist and are partly cleaned of mud. Separating the by-catch is facilitated, as the shrimp drop to the bottom, while some of the fish float on the surface. From the tank the catch passes a sorting table, where the by-catch and debris are removed. The shrimp are then transferred into another tank where circulating chilled sea water (ice and sea water) quickly cools and cleans them before they are packed in polyethylene boxes with a top and bottom layer of ice and placed in the refrigerated hold. This procedure is an example of careful handling. Such treatment is of major importance to processing plants striving for high quality products and high yields. While storage of shrimp in chilled sea water prevents fading of the astaxanthin and discoloration, it does not seem to prolong storage life compared to iced storage. Yields of cooked, peeled meat for the first two days of storage are equal to that of iced shrimp. After prolonged storage, however, there are increasing losses of yield from shrimp kept in chilled sea water (James 1972).

Landing the shrimp

There is no auction system in Greenland because of the lack of competing buyers. The fishermen are paid according to quality, size and weight of the shrimp. Prime quality shrimp are clean and free of mud. Texture is crisp and colour is bright red. Temperature is below 6°C and above freezing. Few shrimp are bruised or with loose heads. The boxes are stored in the hold or on deck protected by insulated pallet hoods. About 90 per cent of the catch are today landed as prime quality. Shrimp weighing above 7 g each obtain a higher price than those weighing less. This pricing is to stimulate the fishermen to search for grounds with larger shrimp, which can be processed at lower costs. Samples of the catch are there-

167

Fig 1   Equipment for size-grading of shrimp into 3 to 5 categories with a capacity of 1000–1500 kg shrimp per hour (Atlas/E H Matthiesen, Copenhagen)

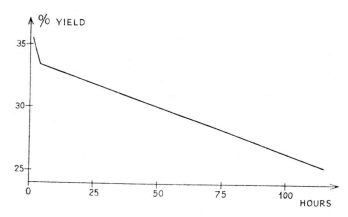

Fig 2   Yields of cooked, peeled meats from 8 days old shrimp depending on how many hours after catching the shrimp were cooked

fore graded to determine the proportions between the size categories. During chilled storage the shrimp may pick up water and increase the tissue weight by up to 10 per cent. Likewise, surface moisture may add variable amounts of water up to 10 per cent to the weight. These facts call for standardized procedures in estimating and comparing yields in processing.

Size grading

Some customers call for specified counts of shrimp per weight unit, for which they are willing to pay a higher price. In plants employing machine peeling as well as

hand peeling, the larger shrimp should be peeled by hand. The size categories may be varied according to the supply of raw material and processing capacity. In RGTD[1] plants size grading is done immediately after landing, while the shrimp are still robust. Heavy objects like pieces of stone, which could damage the peeling machinery, are removed in the same operation. Washing may be done with the grading. If the necessary precautions are taken, the water can simultaneously act as a chilling agent. The size-graded, cleaned and chilled shrimp are then ready for transfer into chilled storage.

Chilled raw material

In traditional storage raw shrimp are placed in a chilled store in boxes with ice. Chilling and washing the shrimp prior to boxing are recommended. To reduce loss of quality and yield in storage, RGTD cook the shrimp as quickly as possible after landing and keep them in the chilled store. Cooking stabilizes colour, texture, flavour and yield of the shrimp at the level determined by the age of the raw material. Fig 2 shows the yields of eight day-old raw material, dependent on when cooked. The extraordinarily high yields obtained by such cooking immediately after death are attended by a tough, rubbery texture of the meat. It is important that the shrimp be chilled immediately and effectively after cooking (Fig 3). A delay accelerates the oxidation of astaxanthin into the orange-coloured astacin. Ineffective chilling detracts from the chilled storage life. Cold water chilling is recom-

[1] The Royal Greenland Trade Department.

168

Fig 3 *Small size equipment for batch-wise water cooking and cooling 600 kg shrimp per hour. After the loading/unloading section the shrimp pass a cooking bath and two chilling vats where the shrimp are chilled in a counter-flow of cold water. The second chilling vat contains an ice-water mixture (E H Matthiesen, Copenhagen)*

mended, but after chilling there should be no direct contact between the shrimp and melting ice due to its leaching effects (Anon. 1969). With sanitary handling, the storage life of cooked shrimp has been prolonged by 40 per cent compared to the storage life of raw shrimp (Legaspi and Khiang 1972).

Frozen raw material

Daily and seasonal fluctuations in fresh shrimp landings

Fig 4 *Hand-peeling of shrimp. The upper conveyor brings whole, cooked shrimp to the peelers. On the lower conveyor peeled meat is returned for control of weight and cleanliness. Heads and shells are flushed down a chute beneath the table and pumped away from a sump (E H Matthiesen, Copenhagen)*

may be levelled out by freezing shrimp shell-on and keeping them in buffer storage. Thawed raw material of cooked shrimp is much more difficult to peel than are raw shrimp. A short heat treatment (blanching) prior to freezing seems only to deteriorate peeling characteristics. Whether the shrimp are frozen after or without heat treatment does not seem to influence the quality of the end-products, apart from their appearance (Aagaard 1968). Fresh shrimp frozen as raw material should be of a perfect quality, whether frozen raw or cooked. Freezing and frozen storage should be so arranged as to lower the temperature of the shrimp quickly and keep it at a low level, preferably below $-25°C$. Frozen raw shrimp are especially susceptible to temperature fluctuations, due to the still active enzymes.

Different thawing methods are available (Aagaard 1968, Lorentzen 1969). The use of water as a thawing medium facilitates a quick and even thawing because of the many interspaces between the shrimps. RGTD uses the pasteurizing apparatus shown in Fig 7 for thawing 100-kg batches of single frozen shrimp. A fixed amount of water is circulated. Within a thawing period of 3 min the temperature of the water drops from 35°C to 8–10°C, while the temperature of the shrimp rises to 0°–5°C. A very effective heat transfer is obtained, and excessive heating of the shrimp is prevented. After thawing, the shrimp should be immediately processed. Excessive heat treatment in cooking tends to give a dry texture and brittle meats, which easily break into pieces when peeled. This is a problem whether cooking is performed before freezing or after thawing.

PROCESSING

The shrimp are processed into a variety of frozen products. They are marketed shell-on or shucked, head-on or beheaded, heat-treated or raw. They are sold in retail and catering packs or in blocks for further processing into battered, breaded products. The technique of processing into comminuted meats by means of separators has been introduced, the meat being put into block production. A complex chain of operations is involved in the manufacture of the different products. As an example this paper will concentrate on describing procedures in processing a ready-to-use product of cooked, peeled meat in retail or catering packs. The description will be illustrated by the processing practices of RGTD.

Cooking

Cooking coagulates the proteins and firms the meat. If the shrimp are peeled raw, they lose much of their colour in the peeling operation. RGTD therefore always peels the shrimp after cooking. During cooking there is a loss of weight dependent on temperature as well as cooking time (Tables 1 and 2). As a rule of thumb a heat treatment of 1½–2 min at 99°–100°C or 3–3½ min at 91°–94°C will give a satisfactory texture, according to Danish taste. Temperatures below about 90°C will not firm the meat enough, even if cooking times are prolonged. By cooling the shrimp in cold water immediately after cooking exactly determined conditions are obtained. Moreover, the astaxanthin will not so easily oxidize to astacin. Also, there will be a smaller degree of recontamination in later handling as growth conditions for bacteria are reduced. Finally, cooling is inevitable if the shrimp are to be stored between cooking and processing. Fig 3 shows a simple cooking-cooling device. Recent investigations indicate that cooking in 2 per cent salt water improves the yield of peeled meat compared to cooking in fresh water or heavier salt brines (Hansen 1972). Adding polyphosphates to the cooking water does not seem to influence yield figures.

TABLE 1. LOSS OF WEIGHT BY STEAM COOKING SHRIMP SHELL-ON

Cooking time in min	2	4	6
Per cent loss of weight	10–11	19–20	about 22

TABLE 2. LOSS OF WEIGHT BY 2-MIN HEAT TREATMENT OF RAW SHRIMP MEAT

Water temperature	60°C	80°C	90°C	100°C
Per cent loss of weight	25	41	46	50

Peeling

Hand peeling involves great labour costs but smaller investments. The labour costs increase as the size of the shrimp decreases. The advantage of hand peeling is a higher yield of meat of a better quality, especially as regards colour and smoothness of the meat surface. The techniques of operating peeling machines have been refined since the first were introduced in Greenland in 1959. At the start, the shrimp were peeled raw after 2–4 days storage in ice water mixtures. Low yields and pale broken meats with a rough surface were for many years the characteristics of machine peeling. Today shrimp can be peeled by machine with almost the same yield and quality as by hand peeling. This change results from:

    Improved and uniform raw material
    Peeling as quickly as possible after landing
    Peeling of cooked shrimp
    Even feed rate
    Low rates of dosage
    Quick passage through the peeler section
    Strict yield control at short intervals
    Changed design of machinery
    Improved maintenance and cleaning of machinery

Cleaning

The shrimp meat, whether peeled by hand or machine, should pass a cleaning operation before packaging to remove any remaining pieces of shell, antennae, entrails, etc. Machine-peeled meats, especially, call for a cleaning operation. Peeling the shrimp perfectly in the machines would be too rough and injure the quality as well as detract from the yield. Cleaning may be done by an air current blowing the light pieces of shell, etc, away from the heavier meats. Manual cleaning is common in Greenland. The cleaning-washing machine shown in Fig 5 is also used. It is effective, but washes some of the colour away.

Brine-dipping

Brine-dipping prior to packaging enhances the flavour. The desirable salt content varies from country to country. In RGTD we find that a light salt concentration of 1.5

Fig 5 Cleaning and washing machine for peeled shrimp-meat (E H Matthiesen, Copenhagen)

per cent in the meat gives a definite enhancement of flavour without offending any consumer's sense of taste. It should be remembered that salt may catalyze the development of off-flavours if the frozen meat is insufficiently protected against oxidation by the package (Anon. 1961). The salt content of raw shrimp meat is about 0.8 per cent. This salt content can be raised, for instance, by cooking in brine. It seems much simpler, however, to control the salt content in the finished product by introducing brine-dipping. Batch as well as flow processes are used in brine-dipping. A batch equipment is shown in Fig 6. For hygienic reasons, a steady or frequent change of the brine should take place. Citric acid is sometimes added to the brine in order to control the pH of the meats. Prior to packaging the brine-dipped meats should be allowed to drain to avoid excessive thaw drip of the frozen product.

Pasteurization

The delicacy and size of the deep-sea shrimp and the large number of handling operations call for strict hygienic procedures in processing (Hansen and Aagaard 1969). Furthermore, precooked meat which is ready for consumption after thawing without further heat treatment, is often used with mayonnaise which is an excellent growth media for bacteria. Consequently, special care should be taken to eliminate any latent health hazards. RGTD therefore in 1967 introduced a pasteurizing treatment of the meat prior to freezing. The procedures were developed by a team from RGTD, the Technological Laboratory of the Danish Ministry of Fisheries and Danish Health Authorities (Anon. 1966, 1967, 1968,

1969; Fredebo-Thomsen 1968). Pasteurization is today obligatory in all frozen shrimp processing in Denmark and Greenland. The pasteurization is performed as a heat treatment, which raises the temperature of the meat to 70°C. This causes a very sharp reduction in the total bacterial count and eliminates harmful bacteria such as staphylococci and salmonellae. Heat treatment should be reduced as much as possible to minimize quality deterioration. Two types of pasteurizing procedures are used. One pasteurizes pre-packed shrimp meat in evacuated plastic pouches. If the maximum thickness of the shrimp layers in the pouch is 15 mm and there is effective heat transfer, a centre temperature of 70°C is obtained after five minutes with 80°C warm water. After heat-treatment the meat is effectively chilled. The apparatus shown in Fig 7 is used. Individually quick frozen shrimp have to be pasteurized prior to packaging with consequent risk of recontamination. RGTD uses the equipment shown in Fig 8. In a continuous process, the shrimp pass through a water bath at 85°C for 25 seconds. In the next section they are chilled and brine-dipped, using 8 per cent brine. The brine is kept cool by continuous circulation through a heat exchanger and passes a UV sterilizing tube. The shrimp are taken directly to the freezer by an elevator.

Packaging

Peeled frozen meats are marketed in such packaging materials as tins, waxboard cartons, plastic wraps and

Fig 7   Equipment for batch-wise pasteurization of pre-packed shrimp-meat in evacuated plastic pouches. A 5 minutes heat-treatment in 80°C warm water is followed by an 8 minutes chilling period. In a modified operation the apparatus may be used to thaw frozen raw material of individually frozen shrimp shell-on (E H Matthiesen, Copenhagen)

Fig 6   Equipment for batch-wise brine dipping of peeled shrimp-meat. The brine passes in a counter-flow to the shrimp in three dipping sections. Fresh brine is steadily added and used brine removed by overflow. Each of the four stainless steel baskets contains about 5 kg of shrimp-meat (E H Matthiesen, Copenhagen)

Fig 8   Equipment for continuous pasteurization of shrimp-meat prior to IQF freezing and packaging. In the background a pasteurizing bath, a chilling section and an elevator leading the shrimp directly to a continuous freezer. In front hot water reservoir, U.V. sterilizing tube and cold brine reservoir. From the cold brine reservoir the brine passes a heat-exchanger (not seen in the picture) on its way to the chilling section.

plastic pouches. The types of packaging (blockfrozen or IQF[1], dry or wet pack, glazed or unglazed, with or without vacuum) as well as the material determine the appropriateness of the package. The main objects of packaging are to protect the meat against deterioration. This means that the packaging materials should be impermeable to oxygen and water vapour and fit tightly around the shrimp meat to avoid desiccation. Individually quick frozen shrimp are, of course, packed after freezing. Vacuum-packaging, therefore, is less protective so RGTD has found it necessary to glaze the IQF shrimp prior to vacuum-packaging. Current investigations indicate a frozen storage life of glazed IQF shrimp in heat-sealed plastic pouches at —20°C of about two months if packed without vacuum, about three months if semi-evacuated, and about five months if fully evacuated. Automatic weighing and vacuum-packaging equipment is used in packaging IQF shrimp. Apart from saving labour costs, the equipment reduces the manual handling of the shrimp after pasteurization and consequently minimizes the risks of recontamination.

Freezing

Pre-packed shrimp meat is normally frozen in plate or air-blast freezers. For IQF shrimp the variety of freezing equipment available includes traditional air-blast freezers, fluidized bed freezers, belt freezers, drum freezers, liquid nitrogen or liquid freon freezers. The freezing rates vary according to the equipment and method (pre-packed or IQF). Variations in the freezing rates are of minor importance to quality compared to the handling of the raw material and the pre-freezing processing. Dehydration losses in freezing, however, are of economic importance and may play a role in the design of appropriate freezing equipment for IQF shrimp. It should be remembered, however, that frozen shrimp meat is able to compensate

for dehydration by reabsorption of water, for instance from a glazing layer. The well known influence of time and temperature on quality deterioration during frozen storage applies to frozen shrimp. Lowering the temperature is of special importance if the package does not protect the meat effectively against oxidation and desiccation. RGTD therefore reserves the best storage conditions, ie, the lowest storage temperatures, for its IQF products.

References

AAGAARD, J Frozen raw material. Freezing, storage, thawing. In
1968   *The deep sea shrimp (Pandalus borealis)*. Technological Laboratory of the Danish Ministry of Fisheries, Copenhagen, 1968, 24 p.
Anon.   Annual Report 1960. Technological Laboratory of the
1961   Danish Ministry of Fisheries, Copenhagen, Denmark.
Anon.   *Ibid.*, 1965.
1966
Anon.   *Ibid.*, 1966.
1967
Anon.   *Ibid.*, 1967.
1968
Anon.   *Ibid.*, 1968.
1969
FREDEBO-THOMSEN, B Pasteurization of shrimps before freezing.
1968   In *The deep sea shrimp (Pandalus borealis)*. Technological Laboratory of the Danish Ministry of Fisheries, Copenhagen, Denmark, 59 p.
HANSEN, P Pre-treatment of the deep sea shrimp *Pandalus borealis*
1972   for the canning industry. *Proceedings of the 6th International Congress on Canned Foods*, Paris (in Press).
HANSEN, P and AAGAARD, J Freezing of shellfish. In *Freezing*
1969   *and Irradiation of Fish*, London, 147 p.
JAMES, D Unpublished report. The technological Laboratory of
1972   the Danish Ministry of Fisheries, Copenhagen, Denmark.
LEGASPI, A S and KHIANG, Y W Unpublished report, *Ibid.*
1972
LORENTZEN, G Thawing of Fish and Doublefreezing – New Ex-
1969   perimental Results (in Norwegian). *Kjöleteknikk og Fryserinæring* 21(1):3.

[1] Individually Quick Frozen

The Catches and Utilization of Shellfish in Japan   *T Motohiro*

Capture et Utilization des crustaces et mollusques au Japon

Description de la préparation de nombreux produits à base de crustacés et de mollusques: crabes en conserve de divers types, huîtres fumées, crevettes conditionnées avec ou sans milieu de couverture, clams bouillis, fumés et assaisonnés, pétoncles bouillis, ormeaux séchés, divers types de crevettes séchées et décortiquées, bêche-de-mer (holothuries) et produits fermentés tels qu'oursins et viscères de bêche-de-mer.

Captura y utilización de los mariscos en el Japón

En este documento se describe la preparación de diversos mariscos, tales como las diversas clases de cangrejos enlatados, ostras ahumadas, camarones envasados con o sin líquido, almejas hervidas, ahumadas o aderezadas, vieiras hervidas, abulones secos, diversas clases de camarones secos y pelados, cohombros y productos fermentados, como erizos y vísceras de cohombro.

Shellfish include crustaceans and molluscs and other invertebrates. The principal commercial shellfish are crabs, oysters, scallops, abalones, clams and shrimps which are usually consumed fresh or frozen. However, they are now being increasingly processed in other forms of food products. Large crabs are used as raw material for canning in Japan while some are sold, fresh or frozen, on the domestic market. King crab (*Paralithodes camtschatica*), horse-hair crab (*Erimacrus isenbeckii*), *Chionecetes phalangium* and *Paralithodes brevipes* are used for commercial packs. King crab and *P. brevipes* are caught in the waters of northern Hokkaido, the Kuril Islands and the Okhotsk Sea. *E. isenbeckii* are caught in northern

Hokkaido waters and *C. phalangium* in the Japan Sea. *Crassostrea laperousei*, *C. rivularis*, *C. denselamellosa* and *C. gigas* are important species of oysters used in Japan for canning and freezing. They are mainly caught in Hiroshima and Matsushima Bays. Clams are one of the most popular shellfish in Japan and, among the species being used are *Corbicula leana*, hard clam (*Meretrix lusoria*), hen clam (*Spisula sachalinensis*), little-neck clam (*Venerupis japonica*) and *Anadara subcrenata*. All of these are found along the coast of Japan. The little-neck clams are particularly abundant in the Ariake Sea. The clams are processed into various kinds of sea food products.

Shrimps are generally consumed fresh, frozen and

dried. *Pandalus borealis* is packed as canned product. The increase in demand in Japan for shrimp has led to a substantial rise in their import. Among sea food products made for export is a boiled-dried one prepared from sea cucumber (*Stichopus japonicus*) while, another type, a fermented product prepared from sea urchins (*Strongylocentrotus pulcherrimus*, *Pseudocentrotus depressus* and *Haliocidaris crassispina*), is produced for the domestic market. They are mentioned as specialized types of sea food products.

CANNED PRODUCTS

Crabs

King crab was canned for the first time in 1892–93 in the neighbourhood of Otaru in Hokkaido.

Crabs are captured by tangle nets (bottom gillnets) and the carapace is removed on board while the vessel is returning to the cannery (floating or on shore). The shelled carcasses are put into netting bags of about 38 mm mesh and boiled in sea water for about 18 to 20 min; afterwards being cooled in sea water for about 10 min. After this process, the meat is easy to separate by knife or scissors from the remainder of the shell. The meat is divided into body meat (shoulder meat), first-leg meat, joint meat, second-leg meat and claw meat and put into separate pans where it is kept until packed in the cans. It is placed in bamboo cages and washed in a tank of sea water. After washing, the body (shoulder) meat usually holds its shape but any that loses its shape is degraded to 'flake meat'. The joint and second-leg meat also usually hold their shape but any that does not is used for the ornamental meat of 'third-grade' canned crab. As flake meat absorbs considerable sea water, it is graded into 'fancy', 'fair', and 'third' (graded in each case A or B). The meat is usually packed in parchment-lined C-enamelled ½-lb (227-g) flat cans the net weight being about 230 g. In the best quality cans, 2 to 4 large pieces of first-leg meat form the top and bottom layers for good appearance, the shaped-shoulder meat, joint meat, and claw meat being placed at the sides. Flake meat is placed in the centre. Since sea water is used for washing and boiling in floating canneries, the addition of salt is not necessary, but when fresh water is used in land canneries, salt must be added, about 2 g per ½-lb (227-g) can. The cans are vacuum-sealed and are heated in a retort at 108° to 109°C for 80 min. The cans are then cooled quickly by a cold water spray.

Horse-hair crab is processed at land canneries. The removal of the carapace is done in the same way as with the Alaska king crab and the carcasses are cooked in fresh water with salt added or in sea water for 15 to 18 min then quickly cooled. The shell of each leg is cut at three places with a knife. The first leg is chipped by the knife and the meat is removed by shaking. The meat of the second leg is removed by using a roller press. This meat breaks and becomes 'red-flake meat'. Misshapen shoulder meat becomes 'white-flake meat'. Horse-hair crab meat must be more carefully washed than that of the king crab in order to prevent blue discoloration and the muscle fibre is thinner and more likely to crumble. The shaped and broken meats must be separated and the off-colour parts removed. The meat is generally packed in parchment-lined C-enamelled ½-lb (227-g) or

¼-lb (114-g) flat tins, the net weight being about 230 g in the ½-lb cans. From 4 to 6 pieces of the first-leg meat are placed on the top and bottom with the white-flake meat placed outside and red-flake meat inside. The ratio of white- and red-flake meats is 6:4. When fresh water is used for washing and cooking, salt must be added in packing the meat. The heat process takes 90 min at 108° to 109°C. The product is graded as 'fancy' and 'choice'.

Precautions in canned crab. In the early days of crab canning, the product often suffered from blackening of the meat, until it was found that this discoloration could be prevented by the addition of tartaric or citric acids in the can or by the use of parchment paper lining and C-enamel cans. (Fellers and Parks, 1926; Legendre, 1928; Shima, 1927.) Blue discoloration in canned crab meat has also caused trouble until recently. Its appearance is undoubtedly due to the copper contained in haemocyanin, a component of the blood of molluscs or arthropods. (Inoue and Motohiro, 1970b.) When the copper content is above 2 mg% blueing occurs, caused by the haemocyanin-sulphide complex. (Inoue and Motohiro, 1970a.) Osakabe (1958) has succeeded in preventing the appearance of blue meat by 'low temperature and fractional heating'. This method is based on the difference of the coagulating temperatures between blood protein (69° to 70°C) and meat protein (59° to 60°C) of crabs. 'Dead' colour is a greyish brown discoloration of the white meat of canned crab caused by copper and iron. Boiling the carapace at sea and mechanical shucking on land often leaves the copper and iron levels of the meat too high. They can be reduced by extra washing after boiling, thus preventing or restricting the development of the off-colour (Motohiro *et al.* 1972).

The pH value of canned crab is between 6.8 and 7.4, but may occasionally be as high as 7.4 to 7.8, although produced by a standard process from very fresh material within 3 h of catching. If paper-shell crab (a stage in the moulting cycle) is packed in cans, the pH is invariably higher than 7.6, while hard crab (a later stage) normally has a pH of 6.8. (Motohiro and Inoue, 1970.) The buffering capacity of crab muscle is related to the abnormally higher pH value. Such capacity varies throughout the intermoult stages. It is strong in paper crab muscle and weak in hard crab muscle. The organic and inorganic reserves effect the buffering capacity, so that washing results in a weakening of the capacity, therefore, such washing should be carefully controlled. (Motohiro and Inoue, 1971.)

Oysters

Only large, fat and well-shaped specimens of *Crassostrea gigas*, *C. denselamellosa*, and *C. rivularis* are used in Japanese oyster packs. The oysters are shucked raw and are generally washed with 2 to 3 per cent salt solution, drained and steamed 10 to 15 min at 100°C. After inspection and grading, they are packed in cans with 1 to 2 per cent brine added. For the smoked oyster in oil product, the oysters are shucked by hand. The meats are placed in barrels and taken to the cannery. The mucus substance on the surface of the body is removed by sprinkling it with 3 to 6 per cent salt, left to stand about 2 h. The oysters are carefully washed in fresh water, agitated by air pressure, then boiled for 3 min to make the meat firm. The next step is to steam them for 20 min at 100°C or 10 to 20 min at 101.8°C. Cooled, they are smoked for 20 to 40 min at 50° to 80°C. Various sized cans are used. The heat process is generally for 60 min at 109.9°C.

Shrimps

Pandalus borealis is used for canned shrimp, picked or peeled by hand after being put in a brine (6 to 9 Bé) for 2 to 3 min. The black streak tissue attached to the upper side of the meat is removed. The meat is then soaked in an acid solution (1 kg tartaric acid dissolved in 100 l of water) for about 15 min, washed, drained and steamed for 15 to 30 min. Steaming makes the meat red and the product comma-shaped. Next the meat is partially dried in the shade. This procedure is important as it ensures that the shrimp do not stick together in the can. They are graded for size and packed in parchment-lined C-enamelled cans. Dry-pack shrimp are processed for 90 min at 108°C. For wet packs, a small quantity of brine of 6°Bé is added to each can. The cans are processed for 18 to 20 min at 108°C, depending on size.

Clams

Boiled whole clams. Hard and little-neck clams for canning should be fresh and of even grain. They are placed in a basket and washed with fresh water then heated in boiling water from 4 to 5 min. They are spread in a thin layer on the filling table to cool and to permit removal of the broken pieces and parts unfit for canning. The meat is removed from the shells by hand. They are packed into cans of various sizes. For example, the net weight of the tall 1-lb (454-g) can is at least 227 g, with salt (5.6 g), to which tartaric acid has been added in the proportion of 1/1 000. Hot water is added to the packed cans, which are then exhausted and sealed. The 1-lb (454-g) cans are processed for 90 min at 120°C.

Seasoned clams. Hard- and little-neck clams are marketed as 'Tsukuda-ni' or 'Shigure-ni' with soya sauce and sugar. For the first product, the clam meat removed from the shell is first boiled in a diluted seasoning juice made from soya sauce and sugar (soya sauce 2 l, sugar 58 to 640 g) for 50 to 60 min. Then it is boiled for 30 min in a stronger concentrated seasoning juice and finally boiled again in a still more concentrated juice. The meat is packed in cans, sealed and processed at 107°C for 60 to 70 min. For the second product, the boiled clams are placed on skewers and roasted over a charcoal fire and are then packed, still skewed.

Smoked little-neck clams in oil. Short-neck clams, removed from the shell, are processed on a wire tray in a smoke house. They are packed in cans with vegetable oil and heated at 110°C for 60 min.

Boiled hen clams. There are two products: (1) raw and (2) boiled.

For the raw product, shucked hen clams are washed and the siphon cut to remove the sand. The visceral matter is squeezed out by hand. The base of the black mantle is removed and washed with a dilute brine, and drained. The raw material is packed in 1-lb (454-g) flat cans of about 250 g with 3.5 g of salt added. The cans are exhausted and sealed or vacuum sealed and heated for 90 min at 106°C. The ½-lb (227-g) cans are processed

for 70 min at the same temperature. For the boiled product, after being washed and having the mantle removed, the clams are boiled. The boiled meat is packed in 1-lb (454-g) flat cans (about 300 g per can).

Precautions in canned clams. The live clams must be induced to expel any sand in their digestive organs in sea water or in dilute brine solution in which the pH value is adjusted to about 4.8. (Tanikawa, unpublished data.) Blackening of canned clams often occurs. The presence of copper and of iron transferred to the intestine from the mud is involved in blackening in combination with hydrogen sulphide given off during the process of canning. The content of hydrogen sulphide is usually below 50 mg%, which is possibly the minimum amount necessary to cause blackening. However, if the level is higher, perhaps when the raw material is not fresh, the development of blackening may occur. (Tanikawa *et al.* 1966.) Furthermore, certain bacterial spores surviving the heating process can, on growth, cause blackening or both blackening and can-swelling. (Tanikawa *et al.* 1967a.) Thus both meat-blackening and can-swelling may occur in the same pack. A method proposed for preventing this is to remove some of the bacteria from the digestive tract by electrophoresis. (Tanikawa *et al.* 1967b.) The application of 15V for 30 min can make clams, of low bacterial contamination, relatively bacteria-free reducing numbers from 10^5 to 10^3. Some phosphate compounds (0.2%) and C-enamel-lined cans are also effective in decreasing the blackening.

Scallop

Boiled scallop. When raw scallops are unloaded at the cannery, the shells, 10 at a time, are put into a basket which is heated for 3 min in boiling water. This opens the shells which facilitates the removal of the body. The ligament (adductor muscle) is taken out because it is the only part of the scallop which is valuable as food. It is the part which is packed in cans. The remainder (mantle and visceral sack) is utilized in other ways. The thin membrane which surrounds the ligament must not be removed in washing otherwise the muscle fibre of the ligament will break up. After washing, the ligament is boiled in a dilute salt solution for 15 min and cooled before being packed in 1-lb or ½-lb (454- or 227-g) flat cans with 2 per cent salt solution. The 1-lb (454-g) cans must have a net drained weight of more than 260 g while the ½-lb (227-g) cans weigh at least 130 g. The cans are vacuum sealed and heat processed (70 min at 110°C for the 1-lb (454-g) cans). Other species resembling the scallop are processed in the same way.

Smoked or seasoned scallop. The ligaments of the scallop are also smoked and packed in cans with vegetable oil or seasoned with juice of soya sauce and sugar.

Other shellfish

Other shellfish are processed for canning but the production is small and economically unimportant. For example, 'bai' (*Babylonia japonicus*) or 'mategai' (*Solen gouldis*) are canned as seasoned products. The former is a kind of coil shell and the latter is a long cylindrical shell, also called a razor shell. Both are widely distributed in Japan.

DRIED PRODUCTS

Abalone

The body meat is removed, leaving the visceral mass in the shell and avoiding injury to the lamella (gill). After grading by size, 3.75 kg of meat of the large size, abalones are treated with 360 g of salt for 2 to 3 days. The meat is then carefully cleansed with fresh water in a tank, the surface of the body being scrubbed with a brush. Next, the meat is put in a basket and heated in a pot. After boiling, it is soaked in hot water at 50°C, the temperature being controlled by adding cold water. After 1 to 2 h of this treatment the meat becomes so soft that a straw can be stuck through it. The meat still in the baskets, is dried in the shade for about an hour and then roasted over a charcoal fire at about 70°C. They are then dried again in the shade. If the abalones are large they are boiled again the next day for 20 to 40 min. Thereafter, the roasting and drying are repeated for 5 to 10 days depending on size. On the last day they are only dried. The whole operation may take a month for large abalone and half that time for the small abalone.

Shrimps

Shrimp peeled after drying. The species used for this product are *Metapenaeus joyneri*, *Palaemon nipponensis*, *Sergestes lucens* and *Pasiphaea sivado*. The shrimp are washed and boiled in large kettles (about 20 l each) to which about 360 g of salt are added. When the water boils, about 4 kg of shrimp are dumped into each kettle and boiled for 30 to 40 min until the bodies become curved. They are then put on bamboo-blinds and dried. The heads and shells of the dried shrimp are separated from the meat by various means. The simplest process is to head the shrimp with a bamboo or wooden stick but recently the meats have been mechanically separated. The mechanical device used in Japan is a barrel-like arrangement having many revolving short blades. As dried shrimp, separated from the shell, lose their colour in prolonged storage, they should be kept in their shell until marketed.

Dried peeled shrimp. Penaeus japonicus is the main raw material for this product. The heads and shells are removed by hand and the meat boiled and dried. This dried shrimp is considered to be of the best quality.

Dried shrimp with shell. This product is prepared from *Metapenaeus joyneri*, *Penaeus japonicus*, *Palaemon nipponensis* and *Sergestes lucens*. The process is the same as that for shrimp peeled after drying except that, in this case, the shrimp are not peeled. The best quality of product is light red in colour, of good curve-shape and of uniform size.

Scallop

Fresh scallops are boiled in sea water to open the shell and the body removed. Usually the mantle and viscera are removed to obtain the ligament but, if it is desired to remove the ligament in the raw condition, the shell is opened with a knife. The ligaments are placed in a basket which is put into boiling sea water or salt solution (1.4 kg of salt in 20 l of water) for 20 min. Afterwards, the ligaments are put into another basket and placed outdoors to dry for about a week. Sometimes they are dried over a charcoal fire for a short time before being put in the sun. Yellowish-white products are considered to be superior in quality. They are called 'white-dried ligaments'. The product yield is 3.5 to 5.0 per cent of the total raw shellfish. Ligaments dried with the mantle and visceral mass are called 'black-dried'. They are prepared by reboiling the shellfish bodies and smoked. A strand of cotton is run through ligaments and they are then dried. The yield of 'black-dried' product is 7.5 to 8.5 per cent of the total raw shellfish.

Sea cucumber

The living sea cucumber is placed in fresh water for a short time to clean the intestinal tract. The intestine from the anus is removed in diluted salt water by a deviscerating apparatus and the abdominal cavity is cleaned with a thin brush and drained. The body is put into boiling salt water of 3° Bé, and is boiled for 1 to 1½ h. If a body swells by the expansion of air in the abdominal cavity, it is deflated with a needle. After boiling, any adhering form is removed and the body is straightened and placed in a basket. When cool, the flesh is roasted at 70°C then dried in the shade for 5 days. The product is then put in a straw bag for 2 to 3 days to equalize the moisture content and afterwards again dried for 2 to 3 days. The yield is 5 per cent of the weight of the raw sea cucumber.

FERMENTED PRODUCTS

Sea urchin

Of the sea urchins, *Strongylocentrotus pulcherrimus*, *Pseudocentrotus depressus* and *Heliocidaris crassispina* from the waters surrounding Japan are used for preparing fermented products. The shell is split with a hammer and the reproductive organs are removed. They are placed in a small tub or into an open bamboo basket to be washed. Floating extraneous substances are removed. The basket is then taken from the water and carefully drained. Then the organs are spread on a table and covered with salt by means of a bamboo spatula. The amount of salt used differs according to its quality, the season and the freshness of the raw material, usually being about 20 to 30 per cent of the weight of the organ. The organs are put on a bamboo blind to drain thoroughly for several hours, are then placed in a barrel or vessel and shut in with a lid. When the product is sold, it is kneaded to a paste with a bamboo spatula. Any foreign material found in the paste is removed and the paste is put into glass bottles of 75, 188 or 375 g net weight. A recent modification introduced is to knead the material in a mixer, then season it with sugar without 'sake' or with sweet 'sake', in a barrel where the fermentation is continued.

Fermented sea urchin paste is the most expensive of the fermented marine products in Japan.

Sea cucumber viscera

This product is prepared by fermenting the visceral mass, especially the intestine of sea cucumber (*Stichopus japonicus*). This product is liked by drinkers and is very expensive. The season for production is December to March. The respiratory organ is yellowish and distasteful, so it is removed from the visceral mass with a knife. The longer the alimentary canal, the more expensive the product. The visceral mass (alimentary canal and reproductive organs) is washed thoroughly in sea water and the contents of the alimentary canal are pulled out by hand without breaking the canal. Sometimes the alimentary canal is split carefully with a knife. The material is drained in a bamboo basket with one third of the total amount of fine-ground salt to be used in the process. After draining, the remaining two thirds of the salt is added. The total amount of salt used is 10 to 15 per cent of the weight of the raw visceral mass. The mixture is stirred frequently with a thin stick for $5\frac{1}{2}$ h. When it stops dripping, it is put into a barrel and covered with a lid. If the stirring is continued for a week, the fermentation will advance moderately, and the resultant product is of the best taste. The mixture can be stored for 2 to 3 weeks without spoiling. The finished product is sold in small glass bottles.

References

FELLERS, C R and PARKS, C F Biological study and proximate
1926   composition of Pacific coast crabs. *Univ. Wash. Publ. Fisher.* 1(7):139.
INOUE, N and MOTOHIRO, T A cause and mechanism of blue
1970a   discoloration of canned crab meat. I. Chemical analysis and histological observation of blue meat. *Bull. Japan. Soc. Sci. Fish.* 36(6):588.

INOUE, N and MOTOHIRO, T A cause and mechanism of blue
1970b   discoloration of canned crab meat. II. Detection of haemocyanin in the blue meat. *Ibid.* 36(7):692.
LEGENDRE, R Industrial application of pH: Cure for the blackening of canned crustaceae. *Office Natl des Recherches et
1928   Inventions, Chimie et Industrie.* (842).
MOTOHIRO, T and INOUE, N pH of canned crab meat. I. Stages in
1970   the molting cycle in relation to pH. *Fd Technol.* 24(12):71.
MOTOHIRO, T and INOUE, N pH of canned crab meat. II. Effect of
1971   some chemical compounds on the buffering capacity of horsehair crab (*Erimacrus isenbeckii*) muscle during intermolt stages. *Jr. Fd Sci.* 36(1):51.
MOTOHIRO, T. NUMAKURA, T and ISEYA, Z A cause of dead color
1972   discoloration in the meat of canned Tanner crab (*Chionecetes opilio elongatus*). *Canners' J.* 51(3):75.
OSAKABE, I Studies on the prevention of blue meat in canned crab
1958   by 'Fractional and low temperature cooking methods'. *Ibid.* 37(9):72.
SHIMA, K Studies on the prevention of 'blackening' of canned
1927   crab, shrimp, shellfish and corn. *Chem. Abstr. Japan.* 1(10):460.
TANIKAWA, E, MOTOHIRO, T and AKIBA, M Cause of can swelling
1966   and blackening of canned baby clams. I. Chemical factors involved in blackening. *J. Fd Sci.* 31(3):400.
TANIKAWA, E, MOTOHIRO, T and AKIBA, M Cause of can swelling
1967a   and blackening of canned baby clams. II. Bacterial action involved in can swelling and blackening canned baby clams. *Ibid.* 32(2):231.
TANIKAWA, E, MOTOHIRO, T and AKIBA, M Removal of bacteria
1967b   from food raw materials by electrophoresis. *Fd Technol.* p. 21(3A), 121A.

Technical Note

Analytical Indications of a More Rational Approach to Accelerated Fish Sauce Production   *G E Howard and J Dougan*

In recent years, some of the principal producing countries have shown considerable interest in the development of rapid methods of fish sauce manufacture which could also use species of fish not suitable for the traditional process. These rapid processes usually involve the addition of proteolytic enzymes of vegetable origin, such as papain, but acid hydrolysis and increased temperatures have also been tried. Generally, the products have satisfactory nitrogen contents but their flavour differs from that of the traditional product and is often unacceptable.

Several workers have investigated the flavouring constituents of fish sauces but there are considerable qualitative and quantitative discrepancies between their results. Van Veen stated that the flavour was due to methyl ketones and that volatile acids were relatively unimportant. Nguyen-An-Cu and Vialard-Goudou found that the total volatile acid content of Vietnamese sauces (calculated as acetic acid) varied from 7 to 14 g/l (ie, 117–234 mEq/l) and the ratio of *n*-butyric acid to acetic acid varied from 1:1 to 1:20. Troung-van-Chom considered that the aroma was due to the fatty acids but obtained much lower results than the earlier workers. Saisithi *et al.* working on Thai fish sauces identified formic acid, acetic acid, propionic acid and *iso*-butyric acid in contrast to other workers who had reported *n*-butyric acid. The Thai sauces contained a maximum of 87 mEq/l of volatile acids and, as the authors were unable to detect any carbonyls, they concluded that fatty acids played an important part in the flavour.

The present investigation was begun to clarify and

extend our knowledge of the flavouring constituents of fish sauces for the guidance of those who are engaged in devising new methods of manufacture.

Samples of fish sauces produced in China, Hong Kong, the Philippines and Thailand were analysed for carbonyl compounds and in each case the total concentration of carbonyl compounds (excluding keto-acids) was only about 0.1 mmol/l. The principal carbonyl compound was acetone; acetaldehyde was also found together with traces of butau -2- one and *n*-valeraldehyde. These compounds appeared to make no contribution to the odour. The volatile acids were isolated, and when restored to their original dilution in water, they gave a distinct, sharp, cheesy odour. The volatile acids were identified as formic acid, acetic acid, propionic acid, *iso*-butyric acid, *n*-butyric acid and *iso*-valeric acid. Traces of higher acids were found in a few samples. In a series of mature samples from Thailand the total fatty acid content ranged from 40 to 98 mEq/l (median value 78 mEq/l). The most abundant volatile acid was acetic acid (210 to 530 mg/100 ml, median value 420 mg/100 ml) followed by propionic acid (11 to 47 mg/100 ml, median value 27 mg/100 ml), *n*-butyric acid (6 to 43 mg/100 ml, median value 16 mg/100 ml), and *iso*-valeric acid (3 to 30 mg/100 ml, median value 4 mg/100 ml). Only one of these samples contained a measurable amount of *iso*-butyric acid, namely 1 mg/100 ml.

The determination of fatty acids in a series of samples taken from vats at different stages of fermentation showed that the acids were formed almost entirely during the third month after which no significant increase was observed. Oxidative deamination of the amino-acids of fish protein would not be expected to produce *n*-butyric acid. The oxidation of fats on the other hand, would be expected to produce all of the straight chain acids but little, if any, of the branched chain acids that were also found. It seems probable, therefore, that most of the fatty acids arose from the oxidation of fats, which suggests that modified methods of fish sauce production concentrated upon rapid proteolysis are unlikely to give products with the traditional flavour unless they also encourage the formation of fatty acids. Investigation of the meaty aroma showed that it contained at least fifty constituents (which were not identified) and was probably formed by the oxidation of precursors that were still present in mature sauces. The volatile bases, which consisted mainly of ammonia with traces of amines, also contribute to the odours, but their effect depends upon both their concentration and the pH value of the sauce, which was usually between 5.6 and 6.1.

Acknowledgement

The authors gratefully acknowledge help received from Dr Sman Vardhanabhuti of the Applied Scientific Research Corporation of Thailand in collecting samples of Thai fish sauce used.

Discussion on Part II

Handling and chilling of fish

The discussion focussed on new research findings concerning the bulk preservation of small pelagic fish and on the use of mobile containers which is a new approach to fish preservation. It was the consensus of opinion that chilling the catch should be a rule for all fishing vessels and for all purposes. Containerization was the thread which ran through the entire discussion dealing with small pelagic fish, with freshwater and with tropical fish. In future planning of fishing vessels and transport facilities the use of containers should be taken into account. The use of containers on board larger vessels was mainly discussed.

BLIGH (Canada) expressed the view that the greatest challenge facing fishery technologists is to improve the use of, and economic return from, the available resources, both traditional and new. It is necessary to add value to products through better processing and to eliminate wastage as a result of inefficient handling in land plants and at sea. As an example he stated that the Canadian fishing industry discards at sea a large part of the catch, sometimes as much as 50 per cent.

HANSEN (FAO), referring to bulk preservation of small whole fish at sea, said that there had been many instances of men killed by hydrogen sulphide or carbon dioxide emitted by whole fish stored in bulk in vessels. However, it now seemed clear that simple ice packing provides a solution to the problem of bulk storage as it maintains the quality of the fish and avoids waste and health hazards in handling large catches of such small fish at sea. But there is still a long way to go before proper chilling and handling become daily practice in the world's

fisheries, and to achieve this it will be necessary for all concerned: government authorities, research workers, fishing boat designers and builders, fishermen and the fish processing industries, to work together to this end.

BYKOV (USSR), reporting on Soviet experience in storing small fish, said that they have found it essential to put catches of small pelagic fish into chilled water as quickly as possible after they are hauled on board. This practice is an important aid to achieving a high quality in the finished products. In some cases, he added, they use ice instead of chilled water. Referring to experiments in the maturation of fish, Bykov said these had been done with the use of microbiological ferments (Terrazin and Orizin) and with the natural enzymes from fish. They had experimented with such fish as horse mackerel, mackerel and sardine, with good results. This fermenting practice can be used commercially in the USSR as it has been approved by the health authority.

HOPPER (UK) explained that the containerization experiments described in the relevant paper had been limited to herring because of the special circumstances of the trade in the UK They wished to develop a system in which the herring is held undisturbed in the same condition of chilling whether in the fishing vessel, on the quayside or in road transport. The experiments had indicated a way of making better use of the resource by reducing wastage from spoilage. However, he pointed out that, no matter how beneficial a new system may be, it may make very heavy demands on the industry, requiring the adoption of a series of new practices, some of which may at first cause such inconvenience as to outweigh the benefits to be derived from less spoilage and better quality. It often takes a lot of time and hard work to make such an innovation commercially attractive and acceptable.

HJUL (UK) pointed out that the introduction of containerization into the fishing industry will require special handling facilities at the ports. The present design of ports and markets might be a constraint on the use of the new system, therefore planners should now take these factors into account, and so should the designers of fishing vessels. Hjul expressed the view that containerization may bring about a change in the traditional patterns of fish landing and distribution, with vessels some day bringing fish direct to major distribution centres. As there is a great future for containerization in the fishing industry, he suggested that FAO should consider ways of helping port and fish market authorities to plan for such developments.

HOPPER (UK) pointed out that in the interest of development of processing industries in developing countries, consideration must be given to provide more refrigerated cargo space at $-20°C$ which at present is almost impossible to obtain, and could prove a barrier to free trade in fish products.

HJUL (UK) replied to Hopper's remark about refrigerated shipping service to move fish from developing countries. He said that as provision of refrigeration on board is very costly, shipping companies will provide it only if there is the certainty of regular and substantial traffic. He suggested that a practical alternative is the use of self-refrigerated containers, such as the Japanese industry uses for shipping tuna to the USA.

AMANO (Japan) confirmed that such containers are used to export frozen tuna, the temperature inside them being kept about −20°C.

The use of preservatives in fishery products

The use of preservatives in fishery products was discussed without reaching a particular conclusion. The consensus of opinion was that chemicals will be needed for many years to come in the effort to reduce waste and losses due to deterioration. Chemical preservation should be used as a secondary method, and should not be relied upon as a single means of preserving raw materials and products. It should not reduce efforts to develop improved systems for applied refrigeration, for example, to secure supplies for the reduction industry.

COLE (UK) took the view that it may be advisable to use chemicals but under careful control.

MEYBOOM (Netherlands) said that even after pasteurization the keeping time of products such as fish sausage is limited in the high ambient temperatures of tropical countries. In the absence of a cold chain, preservatives should be used. The dangers involved are minimal if the use is limited to those processors who will strictly observe the permitted levels. He suggested that the Conference should urge that developing countries use food preservation as long as alternative means of extending the storage life of products are not available.

CLARKE (Guyana) said that the use of preservatives in Guyana depends on the product and the socio-economic need for it.

JAYARAJ (India) reported that Japanese experts had helped produce a fish sausage to suit Indian taste. This could now be produced commercially but the product has a keeping time of only three to five weeks without a cold chain.

SAND (Norway) said that most studies of fish spoilage are done on individual fish exposed to air and very few on bulk fish stored under anaerobic conditions. More knowledge of microflora and enzymes and their mode of action and the effect of physical and chemical factors, is indispensable if the breakdown processes are to be effectively inhibited. Referring to chemical preservatives, he said they had their merits, provided their limitations and hazards are known and controlled. Chemicals could be useful because of their general bactericidal activity and because of their selective effect on microflora, depressing undesirable bacteria and stimulating useful ones, such as lactobacilli.

DREOSTI (IAFMM) stated that both refrigeration and chemical treatment have advantages and difficulties in storing fish for reduction purposes. An important factor is the proper drainage of such stored fish. This, in itself, is almost as effective as refrigeration. The use of formaldehyde, he said, is necessary at certain times of the year for pressing certain pelagic fish which then have active enzymes. If the fish are not 'firmed up' in this way, they cannot be pressed at all. As long as the formaldehyde is kept down to a low level of 0.05 per cent, based on the weight of the fish, there is no adverse effect on the protein and fish quality.

HANSEN (FAO) and SAND (Norway), in reply to a question by SÁNCHEZ (Peru) as to whether Danish and Norwegian experience in preservation of fish, with the help of chemicals, could be applied in Peru and elsewhere, said it was inadvisable as such practices should be 'tailor-made' to meet the specific requirements of the fishery and the conditions concerned. Hansen suggested that in Peruvian conditions chilling would be the advisable way to prevent spoilage. Sand stressed that the use of chemical preservatives must be carefully supervised by a public quality control service. Without such strict supervision they should not be used.

Fish protein, meal and oil

Fish protein

A large part of the discussion was concentrated on problems related to fish protein concentrate (FPC) and functional proteins. The consensus seemed to be that the best use of less sophisticated FPC products lies in the developing countries. The commercial use of functional fish protein is still subject to further technical and economic research.

BLIGH (Canada) reported that the Canadian FPC programme at the Halifax Laboratory, Nova Scotia, has been closed down after several years of research which produced the Halifax IPA Process for a Type A FPC and later a patented preparation of a functional fish protein (FFP). They turned to FFP in 1969 since there appeared to be in North America a greater market potential for this type of product than for a type A FPC. By retaining many of the characteristics of the protein of fresh fish muscle they wanted to prepare a dry protein concentrate which would function as an emulsifier and could be used as a binder in, for example, such foods as luncheon meats. However, so far no company has shown interest in the commercial use of the product although several larger companies in Canada have studied the question of production and marketing of both FPC and FFP. The Canadian Cardinal Protein Plant at Canso, NS, designed to produce 200 tons of raw material a day, never got into full production and has been closed down due to cost and limited availability of raw materials, lack of markets and competition from other sources of protein. The outlook for FPC type A products is not optimistic, particularly in technically advanced countries.

SAND (Norway) expressed a more optimistic view about the Norwegian FPC type B, known as Norse Fish Powder. The idea is based on the fact that consumers in many countries enjoy dried fishery products and that a dried powder would fit into their dietary picture. So every effort has been made since 1968 to investigate problems, covering raw materials, handling and quality control, hygiene, processing techniques, chemical and bacteriological standards, nutritional value and so on, in order to evolve a product which meets the most exacting demands. Only mechanical extraction of fat has been applied, leaving a residue of 5 to 10 per cent in the end product. Sample tests in selected countries in need of protein in their diet yielded very encouraging results, including an improvement in the general health of the consumers. In fact, the powder has been favourably received in 13 countries, some tests being conducted with the cooperation of FAO and the World Food Programme (WFP). On the question of quality, he stated that so far the powder has been made exclusively from whole edible fish. The hygiene and quality standards met in production are those of instant soups. The powder has so far been produced at a few selected plants but for the continuous production of such a food item there is a need to design and lay out a special plant for this purpose.

TALABI (Nigeria) said that investigations into new possibilities in FPC were based on the successful introduction of the Norwegian fish powder. Experiments were conducted to investigate the possibilities of using stickwater for the production of a suitable FPC product. Bigeye (*Brachydeuterus* sp.) was used as raw material. This fish is one of the most important by-catches in the Nigerian shrimping operations.

DAVIS (Australia) mentioned that a US company has patented a process to prepare a beef-flavoured solution from fish stickwater and cookwater. This solution is spray-dried to give a high protein stable powder which can be used in soups and stews as a substitute for meat gravy. This may be a better way of marketing powdered fish protein as a beef substitute.

ACKMAN (Canada) referred to the comment on the addition of fish protein to other foods. He observed that two problems had not been mentioned: the adverse factor for the manufacturer in detailed labelling of constituents, and the question of allergy to undergraded fish protein. Regarding the first question, if a labelling law requires details of the constituents of a product, manufacturers may find such information adverse to their 'corporate image', that is to say, they would prefer to print 'vegetable protein' on the label than 'fish protein' which has an unfavourable impact on the public. Regarding the second question, he stressed that there are very few genuine cases of allergy to undergraded fish protein and that 99.9 per cent of such claims do not stand up to clinical investigation but the public are easily excited by the remote possibility of allergy. He said that the degree of degradation of FPC and FFP relative to the starting protein has not, as far as he knows, been researched clinically from this point of view. It may be that the destruction of protein structure is adequate but he suggested that research on this subject should be made.

OKADA (Japan) stated that there is a need to develop new and economic processes for production of FFP. He suggested the application of sugars and amino acids or oxy- or poly-basic organic acids, which inhibit protein denaturation during solvent extraction and during storage. He also suggested the application of ammoniacal (NH_3) atmospheres which keep the pH of products at the weak alkaline level during storage, preventing the aggregation of proteins.

SPINELLI (USA) said with regard to competitive protein sources that could exert an influence on the price of fish protein, we should keep in mind that in a few years we will see the emergence of a new protein source, ie, single-cell protein. This protein will undoubtedly be used as feed material which, in return, will influence the price of both plant proteins and fish meal. This development, therefore, should give us further impetus on the development of fish protein for human consumption.

CHRISTIANSEN (Sweden) contended that from the marketing viewpoint the cost estimates of FPC have often been too optimistic. He suggested that the commercial selling price for a bland FPC without sophisticated functional properties should reflect the following calculations:

	US$/lb
Raw material (filleting waste)	0.02
Raw material equivalent (yield factor 10:1)	0.20
Processing costs	0.16
Corporate overhead	0.12
Advertising and sales expenses	0.10
Profit	0.12
Total	0.72

He referred to the fact that many western countries doubt the value of protein enrichment as their people do not need such fortification of the diet. As a consequence, there is increased emphasis in developed countries on the functional properties of fish protein. It also follows that more consideration should be given to socio-economic factors in studying the potential uses of FPC in developing countries where, it would seem, there is a need for other types of FPC products than those produced by means of solvent extraction.

ARATA (Chile) described tests being carried out to utilize shrimp heads for other than meal production, including production of chitin and hydrolyzed protein. Concentrated protein of high nutritive value have been obtained, utilizing proteolytic enzymes, such as pepsin and fisin. The concentrate has been spray-dried and used as an additive, eg, to spaghetti. It has been favourably received. A by-product of the concentrate is a cake which was used as fertilizer.

Fish meal

The discussion on fish meal was wide ranging, with several participants urging the importance of using as much as possible of the world's fishery resources for direct human consumption, while other speakers stressed the importance of fish meal production in the full utilization of resources which would otherwise not be used at all.

PETERKIN (Guyana), ALLSOPP (IDRC) and CONSTANTINIDES (USA) expressed views along the former line. The latter stressed that there are no generally recognized criteria to determine which fish are unwanted or unpalatable because those considered so by one group of people may be thought highly desirable by another group. He suggested that the Japanese example of making the fullest use of marine resources for human food is the one which should be followed, especially by the developing nations.

KAMAKAWA (Japan) said that all the by-catch in the pollock fishing was processed into fish meal in the Japanese factory ships.

BYKOV (USSR) stated that all offal from dressed fish and all fish worthless as food are reduced to meal on board Soviet vessels.

KARNICKI (Poland) said that all Polish long-distance trawlers are equipped with fish meal plants. Offal and fish unsuitable for direct human consumption are made into meal. Small catcher boats are used to deliver such material to the processing vessels.

BURTON (IAFMM) said that conversion of fish to meal and oil is a major factor in preventing waste and ensuring the beneficial use of fish which cannot be used gainfully for direct human consumption. About 90 per cent of the raw material, being converted to meal, is comprised of species which cannot at present be utilized for any other purpose. This situation is likely to continue and it is expected that some 80 per cent of the increased marine catch in future will be converted to meal and oil. Burton also pointed out that for some of the developing countries the establishment of a fish meal and oil industry is a first step toward modernization and industrialization of their fisheries. In addition to earning foreign exchange through exports of meal and oil and acquiring capital for development, the countries benefit from the industrial training resulting from the establishment of the meal and oil industry. They also benefit from the availability of the meal for replacing imports. Chile and Peru are two examples of countries going through this development process.

BARLOW (IAFMM) and CHRISTENSEN (Denmark) elaborated on the amount of animal protein which results from using fish meal for livestock feed. The former mentioned that the figure calculated by him for utilization of fish protein via fish meal production for animal feed is 34 per cent. Although this is much higher than figures quoted by others during this Conference, he believes that this figure is correct. This figure is infinitely greater than it would be if the fish were unharvested. The manufacture of fish meal under these circumstances is both desirable and profitable. Another viewpoint is that a foodfish industry may follow an established fishmeal industry based on capital accumulated and expertise gained.

FINCH (USA) concluded the discussion on the use of fishery resources which aroused much interest and stated that the Conference noted a concern that fish converted to meal and oil is not directly available for human consumption. However, it noted also that fish meal itself provides a valuable source of protein to humans and that fish meal is generally made from waste fishery materials and from fish for which there is no other use and which would otherwise be wasted in the oceans. In view of the worldwide interest in this whole question, the Conference suggested that where fish and other marine resources cannot be gainfully used for direct human consumption, they should be converted into meal and oil until research and development have established products and markets which will permit their direct use as human food.

Fish oil

ACKMAN (Canada) said that no doubt linoleic acid is essential not only in rats but also in man. He added that Dr U A Crawford of the Nuffield Institute of Comparative Medicine (UK) had informed him that there is evidence that linoleic acid and its relatives may be especially important in primates. Marine fats are important sources of fatty acids of the linoleic family in normal human diets in many parts of the world.

SÁNCHEZ and GUIZADO (Peru) explained that the oil from the Peruvian anchoveta has the chemical characteristics of high saturation. It is made up of fatty acids of which more than 60 per cent are highly unsaturated, showing an iodine index of 200 to 210, the value depending on the state of sexual maturity of the fish. The domestic market is now taking the oil, mixed with cotton seed and soya oil, for edible purposes. When used in the production of margarine, the taste of it tends to return after a period of about 18 days.

ACKMAN (Canada) commented on this and said that success in using mixtures of partially hydrogenated marine and vegetable oils in products depends on their rapid distribution and consumption, relative to local conditions. For example, in European conditions the 'shelf-life' of such products would be at least several weeks and in Canada several months. He added that the flavour reversion problem is notorious with the product and virtually inescapable.

Liquid fish silage

Production of fish silage is one of the alternative methods of utilizing fish waste. The process offers advantages in some areas, but more investigations and experiments are required as to the end use, storage and distribution of the silage and of products which could be developed using fish silage as protein component.

MACKIE (UK) said the process is of value in areas where it is uneconomic to operate a fishmeal plant. The silage is useful as feed for pigs but not for humans because of the high concentration of formic acid used. He explained that his paper on powdered and liquid fish products illustrates one of a number of alternative methods of utilizing fish waste now converted to meal. A milk substitute is an example of a product with superior functional properties to fish meal. The process involves the use of proteolytic enzymes to disperse but not to dissolve the protein of the fish from the bones. A fish protein preparation is obtained which can be pumped and treated as a liquid. This is advantageous from a processing point of view.

JAMES (Australia) presented some results of feeding trials made with a silage produced from the viscera of abalone which contains a wide range of enzymes while the hepato-pancreas contains powerful glycosidases. When a source of free sugar is added, ensiling is very rapid. Silages prepared with 10 per cent added carbohydrate contain 28 to 35 per cent solids, 11 to 13 per cent protein, 2 to 3 per cent fat, 2 per cent salt and 0.1 to 0.3 per cent calcium. In pig feeding trials, 40 per cent of the diet was replaced by silage. Pork patties made from the loins of the pigs so fed had a bland odour and flavour. He added that as the establishment of a fish meal industry requires substantial capital and large stocks of fish, the interests of developing countries may best be served by adopting silage production for local animal feed.

DISNEY (FAO) mentioned that the Tropical Products Institute (UK) has produced fish silage from waste in such countries as Ghana and Malawi. They have experimented with adding cassava and maize meal to the liquid silage. The resultant paste can be sun-dried without spoilage even under humid conditions. The results of feeding trials with rats suggest that the product is equivalent to a casein-controlled diet but trials with chicks have shown that it does not perform as well as a commercial chick starter diet. However, a trial with lysine and methionine added gave results comparable to those of commercial chick feeds.

Value of new equipment in the preparation of new products
Much attention was attracted by the development of equipment which facilitates the preparation of new products and the better exploitation of underexploited fish resources. The introduction of meat separators or deboning machines have changed the picture of the white fish industry in the whole world. The use of this new equipment facilitated the development of a range of new products based on similar raw materials and it enabled the better utilization and upgrading of small pelagic fish species. The development of a filleting machine which allows filleting of tropical fish species considerably facilitates the exploitation of warm water fish resources, as it will enable tropical fisheries to produce products such as fillet blocks and fish portions for export. The centrifuge floating technique for separating edible from non-edible parts and microwave irradiation for opening bi-valves are two new processes for handling shellfish. Most important would be the development of heading and gutting machines for small fish.

BLACKWOOD (Canada) referred to Canadian experiences in the utilization of deboning machines. The new equipment makes possible the utilization of species not suitable for processing in traditional ways: the recovery of fish flesh by it exceeds substantially the yield from conventional filleting; and the minced flesh, perhaps derived from mixed species of similar flesh colour, texture, odour and flavour, can be prepared in the form of a wide range of new, high quality fishery products. Blackwood said that the demand in Canada for minced fish flesh products exceeds the supply. One company's sales had increased by more than 50 per cent in 1972 and are still going up. The products in popular demand include fish cakes and fingers, party starters with shrimp and crab added, fish and chips, and salmon croquettes.

MOSS (Canada) related how his company, with the use of new deboning machines and other equipment, have been able to utilize freshwater species of fish that are not suitable for processing by traditional methods because of excessive numbers of bones, size and flavour. The use of the new equipment also resulted in yields of meat that are considerably higher than can be obtained by conventional filleting.

KARNICKI (Poland) mentioned, with regard to the importance of developing new machinery for processing, that developing machines for heading and gutting small fish is a most important item as it would enable such species to be processed into minced products.

LEARSON (USA), with reference to the value of new equipment, said that continuous centrifugation and microwave energy applications are now being operated commercially, primarily on the West Coast of the USA and in the Canadian Maritime provinces. They are mostly being used for the recovery of crab meat. While the quality of the meat does not approach that of the hand-picked product, it is a very valuable raw material for speciality products. Microwave energy is being used in the USA beef and poultry industry for defrosting frozen material. Recent laboratory tests under commercial conditions indicate potential use for microwave energy for defrosting salmon and tuna loins, and tempering fish blocks and bulk frozen raw material used for pet food. While the cost of such centrifuge and microwave equipment is high, the increase in processing efficiency and retention of quality in the raw material appear to make the investment worthwhile for large-scale operations.

DREWS (Germany, Fed Rep of) said that in view of the processing and marketing problems, especially in developing tropical countries, it may be the best approach to process from suitable fish species 'neutral' products such as fillet blocks and fish portions which are in high demand in industrialized countries. This approach is now possible as recently machines have been developed to fillet a mixed variety of tropical fish, mainly of the sea-bream type.

HOPPER (UK) added to the suggestion made by Drews in saying that many developing countries have both the wish and capacity to develop such trade. They should continue to catch fish by means of unsophisticated vessels and methods within the technical competence of the fishermen, with the processing plants located ashore where they can be more easily maintained and where a high level of employment can be provided. There is a need to determine the most acceptable form of product, in particular for export, eg, frozen whole fish, fillet blocks or consumer packs.

OKADA (Japan) pointed out that the development of frozen surimi has accelerated the growth of the Alaska pollock fishery. The very large increase in surimi production is due mainly to the demand for kamaboko, a traditional Japanese fishery product. In this connexion, it should be mentioned that much research has been done to keep up the quality of Alaska pollock in cold storage and to develop various types of machines and equipment to help increase the production of frozen surimi.

GUIZADO (Peru), in reply to a question about the use of pumps for unloading fish, said that they were successfully used in unloading anchoveta for meal but he did not recommend their use for fish for direct human consumption.

Part III

PROBLEMS AND TRENDS IN THE UTILIZATION OF SPECIFIC RESOURCES

183

The Requirements for the Establishment of a Food Fish Industry   *W P Appleyard*

Specifications relatives a la creation d'une industrie du poisson pour la consommation humaine.

Faisant essentiellement appel à l'expérience acquise au Pérou, le document décrit les progrès réalisés au cours des trois dernières années dans l'implantation de l'industrie des poissons comestibles: création tout d'abord d'un Ministère des pêches distinct; importance et situation quelque peu paradoxale de l'industrie péruvienen de l'anchoveta; rôle et rapports présents et futurs du secteur public et du secteur privé; solution apportée à chaque problème rencontré de la capture jusqu'à la consommation finale à mesure du développement de l'effort de pêche, de l'infrastructure, de la formation professionnelle, de l'inspection du poisson, des usines de transformation, du système de commercialisation et des programmes d'éducation des consommateurs; méthodes de financement, fonction des organisations multilatérales et bilatérales, politiques concernant les coopératives de pêcheurs et la pêche artisanale, rôle des chalutiers-usines étrangers; possibilités d'avenir; besoins, problèmes, solutions possibles et perspectives de l'industrie des poissons comestibles dans un pays en voie de développement.

Requisitos para el establecimiento de una industria de alimentos pesqueros.

Este trabajo se basa en buena parte en la experiencia peruana y describe los progresos realizados durante los últimos tres años en el establecimiento de industrias pesqueras para la alimentación. Se hace referencia a la decisión inicial del Gobierno de crear un Ministerio de Pesca independiente, examinando al mismo tiempo la situación, decisiva y bastante paradójica, de la industria peruana de la anchoveta. Se examinan la función y la relación actuales y futuras entre el Gobierno y el sector privado. Se trata de los diversos aspectos de la industria de elaboración de pescado para alimentación, desde la captura hasta el consumo, analizando sucesivamente el esfuerzo de captura, la infraestructura, las actividades de capacitación, los servicios de inspección del pescado, las instalaciones de elaboración, el sistema comercial y el programa de educación de los consumidores. Se examinan los métodos de financiación, las funciones de los organismos multilaterales y bilaterales, la política frente a las cooperativas pesqueras y los pescadores artesanales, y el lugar que ocupan en el sector pesquero los arrastreros-factoría extranjeros. Se pasan en revista brevemente las oportunidades para el futuro. El trabajo ilustra las necesidades, problemas, posibles métodos y oportunidades de la industria de elaboración de pescado para alimentación en un país en desarrollo.

There is no known formula by which food fish industries can be established in developing countries, although much basic criteria are common to all. Much depends on such considerations as funds available; the political and social climates; the historical association with fishing; local attitudes and aptitudes; and the need for protein and foreign exchange. Above all, the whole structure must depend on the fishery resource and an accurate knowledge of it, and how it can best be managed and exploited. In ideal circumstances, with no pressures, it would be preferable to spread such development over many years but this is rarely possible. In the following example, the case of Peru is discussed because the experiences of the past few years coupled with the plans for the future combine to illustrate the intricacies of the programme necessary for a food fish development.

BACKGROUND

The Peruvian fishing industry is above all characterized by the anchoveta which accounts for over 98 per cent of the total catch and represents the largest single species catch in the world, averaging about 10 million tons annually. The fishery is essentially coastal, the most important areas being off Chimbote and Callao-Pisco. In addition to the predominant anchoveta industry, there is a trawl fishery by approximately 60 vessels for demersal species, including hake, and a bonito fishery employing some 80 seiners. Both fleets consist largely of converted anchoveta vessesls and are based mainly at Paita. Skipjack and yellowfin tuna fishing is carried out by a few local boats and some foreign vessels operating under contract. Over 3,000 smaller craft are engaged in traditional fishing for a variety of species, including crustacea and molluscs. The overall food fish catch from the sea is about 200,000 tons. Freshwater fisheries, yielding between 30,000 and 80,000 tons annually, are exploited by some hundreds of small craft and thousands of canoes, notably on the River Amazon and Lake Titicaca.

Over 120 plants along the Peruvian coast convert anchoveta into fish meal and oil. Of the other fish, the bonito are either canned, mainly for export, or consumed fresh or chilled locally, while most of the tuna is frozen whole for export. Domestic supplies of fish are provided mainly by the coastal fisheries and demersal trawling. The freshwater catch is also consumed locally. Although domestic consumption is only two per cent of the total catch, this amounts to more than 10 kg per head annually, which is relatively high by both regional and international standards. The explosive development of the Peruvian anchoveta industry is one of the most remarkable of post-war phenomena in fisheries. High initial profits combined with an enormous resource potential and excellent market prospects resulted in the prompt injection of capital and technology, creating an industry earning more than US$300 million annually in foreign exchange and, providing 38 per cent of such earnings in 1971. The extensive processing infrastructure and ancillary activities have provided much employment, especially in areas where work opportunities were previously limited. Fisheries development has also led to the establishment of associated industries, such as shipbuilding, net and gear factories, and mechanical workshops.

THE IMMEDIATE PICTURE

It is important to appreciate the unique position of Peru which allowed the Government to take vigorous action to establish the food fish industry on a bigger scale. This situation included a fishery-oriented economy, a substantial cash flow, a measure of technical competence, a local desire to exploit the anchoveta and a resource capable of great exploitation, the desire for additional foreign earnings and the need to provide more animal protein in the diet of the people. Thus, there existed a remarkable development climate and opportunity. Paradoxically, the sheer size and importance of the present-day anchoveta industry has made it difficult to appreciate the somewhat different problems and value of the much smaller food fish industry. It was in these circumstances that fishery activities were divorced from agriculture in February 1970 and a separate Ministry of Fisheries was established – a significant and far-sighted policy step. This Ministry, apart from establishing an organizational structure covering all aspects of the industry, took over the long-established Instituto del Mar, created the parastatal bodies of Empresa Pública de Servicios Pesqueros (EPSEP) and Empresa Pública de Comercialización de Harina y Aceite de Pescado (EPCHAP). In principle, the role of the Ministry is to do the planning, EPSEP to implement the plans relative to food fish and EPCHAP to control the selling of fish meal and oil. The objective of EPSEP at this stage was to give the State a participation in the food fish industry whereby influence could be brought to bear on pricing and distribution policies, the infrastructure developed and assistance given to the cooperatives. EPSEP could also represent the State in any fishery enterprise in which there was Government participation because development by involvement with both the local and foreign private sectors was envisaged. The concept of a State Food Fish Company operating in tandem with the private sector is interesting whether viewed as the thin end of the wedge in nationalization or as having a stimulating effect on the private sector by way of example or competition. Whatever the view, such a state enterprise can be the vehicle for activities which may be either unattractive to the private sector (eg, setting up a sales and distribution organization in the mountain region) or inappropriate for the private sector (eg, the provision of coastal fishing terminals or inland fish markets). Naturally, such activities may require subsidies, particularly during the start-up period, but such a policy can be justified on social grounds.

One of the immediate acts of the Ministry was to develop a Five-Year Plan (1971–1976) within the framework of the National Plan. While it is easy to criticize plans, particularly new ones, they provide a focus for national effort and are necessary even if they become at times a mixture of hopes, aspirations and bids to secure a share of the national economy. Such plans, if reviewed regularly and realistically, provide the necessary guidance for the action required. Obviously, the first questions concern the size of the resource available and how it can be best exploited. Peru was fortunate in having an Instituto del Mar with ten years of experience. However, practically all its budget and talent, supported by multilateral and bilateral assistance, had been dedicated to the exploitation of the anchoveta resource, not to the food fish sector. There is a danger at the early stage of planning of over-optimism on the part of Government officials and some time may elapse before realistic targets emerge. In this respect, Peruvian officials have estimated a sustainable yield of 600,000 tons per annum and lower estimate of 400,000 tons. Both are sufficiently above the existing harvest of around 200,000 tons to give time for further research or investigation. The main danger to avoid is that of allowing infrastructure and vessel development and investment to outstrip the real resource base. This cannot be over-emphasized. At this stage, too, the danger of utilizing hastily compiled data which might

throw up convenient answers must be constantly borne in mind. In developing such plans the improvements that can be effected in harvesting and handling the existing catch must be kept in mind as, no doubt, the existing fleet can catch more fish if given the benefit of improved techniques and supported by more adequate infrastructure. Also, too, wastage – once estimated as high as 25 per cent – can be substantially reduced through improved distribution.

In any developing country, the method of funding fishery development needs very early consideration. The availability of such funds needs to be seen in relation to the overall economy. From then on, the administration of such funds is a matter of policy decision. Apart from traditional private banking sources, a Fishery Division of the Industrial Bank has been created in Peru which provides funds to both the public and private sectors. It is interesting to note that EPSEP has a role in recovering advances made to the fishery cooperatives as it contracts to buy the catch from cooperatives and deducts from the proceeds the repayment due for the new vessels being built. Eventually, this Division might become the Fisheries Development Bank. Another source of finance developed in Peru is Corporación Financiera de Desarrollo (COFIDE), the State Investment Corporation. COFIDE will finance pre-feasibility and feasibility studies and loan money on terms varying from those obtained from international and foreign sources by taking an equity position in companies. This type of financial involvement is already in evidence in Peruana de Pesca SA (PEPESCA) – a company having COFIDE as the major shareholder, with the Industrial Bank, EPSEP and a private Peruvian fishing company as the other shareholders. PEPESCA will operate a five-vessel international tuna fishing fleet.

In looking at the local funding arrangements, it is perhaps relevant to consider the philosophy behind borrowing money from overseas. The fact that money is available is not sufficient reason to borrow it. It is all too easy to incur such a debt, doubly unfortunate if it means obtaining unsuitable or uneconomical equipment. Too frequently, tied loans only benefit the lender. It is also of practical value to relate the expertise of the lender to the funding. Many food fish industries have foundered almost before starting because of inappropriate funding arrangements, although today there is little trouble in obtaining good funding for well conceived and realistic projects. The question of the necessity or otherwise of the foreign investor is a vexing one. His capital, his technical expertise and his international experience make his participation in a developing food fish industry desirable, but there has to be a critical examination of his motives. Quite rightly, his prime interest is his shareholders, and he is not usually motivated by any patriotic or pioneering spirit. He wants a reasonable return on his capital (higher than he would get in his country because of the risk factor) and often seeks products, sales commissions, management fees, and tax benefits. He may be utilizing locked-in funds or taking an opportunity to expand. Although there are many solid companies of high reputation and proven performance, it must be remembered that fishing operations, particularly new ones, attract the promotor and the speculator. But, of course, the latter category can sometimes serve a purpose in identifying an opportunity and making a start. Peru is attempting to develop a food fish industry of coexistence but, even if the parastatal bodies, the Peruvian private sector and the foreign investor develop together, there must be problems of conflicting interests, different management philosophies, and diverse aims and considerations. Although difficult, such problems are by no means irreconcilable. In funding, the role of multilateral and bilateral assistance needs to be examined. Too often, assistance is pressed on a developing country in the hope of securing influence or equipment orders, and in such cases the well-being of the recipient Government or the ultimate usefulness or result of the project is the least consideration. Similarly, hurriedly conceived requests for assistance frequently result in duplication, competition and misuse of money and talent. There is a great need for well prepared and coordinated assistance programmes, but all those concerned must appreciate that expertise of a satisfactory level cannot be turned off and on like a tap. Both recipient and donor need to exercise tolerance and develop understanding if they are to obtain the full benefits of an assistance programme. Over the past two years a significant programme of bilateral and multilateral aid has been developed for the Peruvian food fish industry which should materially assist the implementation of plans.

Three years is, of course, a short time for any government in any country to set up organizations, develop the policies and plans, and to commence the physical process of implementing them. Both political and social considerations warranted speedy action in Peru and inevitably some lessons will be learned the hard way. If a perfect study was made of every problem, it is doubtful if there could be any progress. To hurry matters along, the Ministry has made extensive use of outside consultants and, if there is a lesson to be learned from this, it is that terms of reference need to be well defined. There is always a risk that such experts and consultants will work over the data of others and come up with a more handsome report than the previous one. But with well defined terms of reference, foreign experts can speed up implementation and make a substantial, practical contribution to progress, albeit often at a high cost. The Ministry started with a three-year programme to construct 16 fish terminals and 12 inland fish distribution depots. This programme has developed some of the infrastructure necessary to service the artisanal fishermen and the fishery cooperatives, and to establish a sales network in the Sierra so as to improve the protein content of the local diet. The coastal terminals include simple processing facilities, refrigerated storage space and ice-making plants. Some have quay space, others beach haul-out equipment. The inland distribution depots sell to local wholesalers and retailers. These depots have storage space for frozen and other processed fish, processing space, vehicle parking lots, and office accommodation for sales staff. This US$3 million programme sounds to be a relatively simple exercise but, by the remote location of the installations, it has involved a variety of civil engineering problems. With these solved, the problems of training the human resources arise. These are perhaps the most difficult because there is no background or tradition to this type of activity. (The writer incidentally encountered similar problems in developing a national network of sales and distribution depots in the United Kingdom in the fifties.)

In addition to these developments, the Ministry has replaced the antiquated fish pier at Callao with a modern US$1 million terminal modelled on that of Esbjerg, Denmark. At the same time, the Lima Wholesale Fish Market has been completely rebuilt, resulting in a complex with ice-making and cold storage facilities, processing facilities, and hygienic sales areas. With the ability to handle up to 400 tons per day at both the Callao Terminal and the Lima Market, the Lima Metropolitan Area is now well served, although active consideration is being given to the development of smaller and decentralized wholesale markets to relieve congestion and allow for future growth. A major effort has also been made to introduce the distribution of fresh fish in 42-litre boxes. EPSEP has some 100,000 in circulation which, at a cost of US$5 each, represents a major investment – and a management headache in controlling their whereabouts. In developing the coastal terminals, the Ministry has acknowledged the important role which the artisanal fishermen and the fishery cooperatives can play in fishery development. It is easy – but wrong – to dismiss the artisanal fisherman as a person who contributes little to the economy. In a coastal fishery such as Peru the artisanal fishermen and the fishery cooperatives can become the most economic fishing unit if the yardstick of dividing expenses (including depreciation and interest on investment) by total catch is used. By providing the infrastructure and encouraging the cooperatives to build new vessels, the Ministry is fulfilling a social obligation as well as meeting an economic need. In respect of small vessel design and construction, a sustained effort is needed to develop standard designs. This calls for realization that badly designed vessels remain a liability for many years. Furthermore, it must be recognized that the building of food fish vessels is a specialist business and not one that can be readily developed despite the previous years of experience in building anchoveta vessels. A promising programme has been initiated whereby surplus purse seiners from the anchoveta fleet are being converted to food fishing. There is probably a surplus capacity of some 500 vessels in the anchoveta fleet but, because of age, size, condition or lack of power, perhaps less than 100 can be considered for this programme. To purchase and convert such a vessel to a 30-ton capacity food fish boat with a five to seven-year life expectancy costs about US$70,000. In 1972, the Ministry purchased and converted six bolicheras, with eight more in an early 1973 programme. The failure of the 1972 anchoveta catch has broadened the thinking of the private sector who have a 1973 programme in excess of 50 vessels. A major company (OYSSA) has purchased a factory vessel that has a brine freezing capacity of 200 tons/24 hours and a storage capacity of 2,000 tons. This vessel will be supported by about 30 converted bolicheras which are mainly concerned with the catching of bonito, machete, caballa and other pelagic species. Much of the catch will be utilized for canning.

There can be little doubt that the major problem to be faced in developing the food fish industry of Peru is to upgrade the quality of the product. As in many developing countries, fish has not hitherto been gutted or bled nor has it been stowed in ice. The increasing availability of ice is a big step forward but it takes a revolution to change the fishing habits of centuries. It is hoped that the domestic market will develop a taste for good fish. However, the only way in which the fisherman will learn to handle his catch better is if it can be demonstrated that fish of good quality will give him a better return on a continuing basis than fish of poor quality. Unless fish of good quality can be landed, all the trappings of a modern food fish industry are almost a waste of time. In the rapidly developing Peruvian food fish industry, the teaching of correct handling of fish at sea has become a major problem. If fishermen see the crews of other vessels earning a living by working less, they want to do the same. It is becoming increasingly evident that machine gutting at sea will probably be the solution to this particular problem. It will apply especially in the case of the efficient handling of such export items as merluza. Space considerations on the decks of vessels also influence this thinking. Whilst mechanization for its own sake is rarely justified in a developing fishery, it must be kept in mind that what appears to be cheap labour per hour does not necessarily mean cheap production per ton of product. To improve quality standards, the Ministry has established the mechanics of a fish inspection service which deals with fresh fish at the coast and inland, processed fish, fish for export and processing plants. The establishment of such a service in a country having a 3,000 km coast line is a tremendous task and it will take several years before it can be made truly effective. Nevertheless, a start has been made in a few major areas of activity, eg the new terminal at Callao and the new Lima Wholesale Fish Market. Training courses are in being which concentrate on the parctical aspects of fish inspection. At the same time, an effort is being made in improving handling and internal quality control procedures in the processing plants. This in-plant training has made a good start. Here again, Peru had an advantage in having an established fish meal inspection service, Empresa Pública de Certificaciones Pesqueras del Perú (CERPER) which, with the exception of plant inspection, handles the food fish inspection service. However, convenient as it may be to have the organizational support of CERPER, the need to develop a new approach has become evident – not the least problem being to avoid the fish inspection service becoming branded as some sort of police force.

The next stage is to examine the fate of that fish. Until the improved infrastructure and domestic distribution facilities, backed by consumer education programmes, take effect, there will be wastage and an unequal distribution of supplies as the coastal populations are so much more readily accessible. These aspects can be remedied slowly. In this respect it is encouraging to note the progress in the sales of frozen hake in the Sierra cities and towns – fish delivered by Hercules aircraft in 18-ton parcels. This method of delivery is proving to be more economical than is road transport. Peru is fortunate in having a hake resource with an estimated annual sustainable yield of 100,000 to 300,000 tons. At present the catch exceeds 20,000 tons, which is converted into fish meal. A processing industry is to be based on this resource. Essentially export-oriented, the concentration will be on frozen fillet products, although salting and drying processes are also being developed. Detailed plans for a major processing complex at Paita capable of

handling 50,000 tons a year are being prepared. While it is not yet clear as to how the complex will be developed, seemingly, it would be logical for the Government to develop the infrastructure (eg the quays, discharging facilities, ice-making and storing installations, repair yards, cold storage) and prepare an industrial park upon which EPSEP and the private sector can develop various processing factories. If this is the case, the next step in rationalized planning would be to license the production capacity of the proposed factories and the supporting fleets so that the resource is not overexploited and the investment maximized. As other export opportunities for frozen fish are occurring, it will become necessary eventually to determine priorities for the market. For instance, frozen gutted bonito currently has a profitable market in Europe whereas the domestic consumer can buy the fish at the artificially fixed low price of US$0.07 per pound. Such a price gives little inducement to the fishermen to catch bonito. In future marketing, therefore, the emphasis might well be on the export of frozen and canned bonito, allowing other species, eg jurel or machete, to develop the domestic demand.

In examining the frozen food fish scene, reference must be made to tuna. A foreign company has operated about ten vessels out of Paita for several years. No doubt, this has brought advantages to Peru by way of foreign exchange, employment and social benefits, as well as profits to the company concerned. However, both the public and private sector are now entering the tuna catching industry with ambitious plans for freezing and canning. The sensible involvement of foreign expertise by way of management and selling will, no doubt, contribute. In developing frozen fish export markets, the need to define opportunities and priorities is essential. One has to be quite clear on such points as what and how much can be caught. Is there an established market? What can it absorb? What share of that market can be captured? Can quality and packing specifications be achieved? Can continuity of supply be ensured? It is easy enough to become enthusiastic about possibilities for exploiting interesting local resources, eg sea urchin or giant oysters, but it is necessary to see when the potential cannot justify the proposed enterprise.

The Peruvian fish canning industry flourished during the 1939–1945 war but has diminished significantly in recent years, and much of the equipment is either outdated or operating in plants incapable of producing the high quality of products needed today. Improved supplies and reviving export markets are encouraging the more efficient of the companies to expand and, at the same time, a new EPSEP plant is contemplated for the canning of anchoveta as food fish, but this development is still at the pilot plant stage. In this so-called frozen food age, it is all too easy to forget the opportunities afforded by the earlier methods of fish processing, eg, canning, salting, drying and pickling. The emphasis is too often on more sophisticated products and it is as well to ask what such sophistication achieves. In this respect, it might well be noted that foreign advisers are inclined to rely on their own product experience rather than attempt to determine the best process for the developing countries concerned. Apart from the traditional food fish resource, at least some of the 10 million ton anchoveta resource might be used for food. In addition to canning, possibilities are being explored for freezing, drying and salting the fish and a food target of several thousand tons of anchoveta should be achievable within the next two or three years. But, as with all food fish, very careful steps need to be taken in handling the fish at all stages and, in particular, at sea. However, in the initial stages and while modern processing facilities are being constructed, there are possibilities for exporting frozen anchoveta for subsequent reprocessing. There is, too, the huge pet food markets of USA and Europe which, no doubt, will eventually have to turn to Peruvian anchoveta as a raw material, despite the freight cost disadvantages. And Peru, like any other pet food supplier, must realize that this market is most discriminating. The markets (notably USA) open to the anchoveta are limited unless the product can be marketed in its own right – that is to say, as anchoveta rather than under established sardine labels. It has already been demonstrated that there is customer acceptance of Peruvian anchoveta if gutted or starved and packed in a sauce or oil. World shortages of protein or changes in taste should encourage the development of comminuted products manufactured from anchoveta. Peru is already active in this field, producing such items as a fish sausage. As a basic raw material for fish protein concentrate, Peruvian anchoveta offers quantity and availability as well as fish meal manufacturing experience and technology. However, development in this direction has been almost nil because of the lack of a market, ie, those who need it cannot afford it or those that can afford it do not need it. In common with several other countries, Peru is involved in upgrading fish meal for use as a milk replacer. This should ensure Peru being well placed to exploit any marketing breakthrough in regard to edible fish meal. It is perhaps appropriate to comment at this juncture what can be achieved at pilot plant level in product development and formulation. For example, at a cost of less than US$100,000 EPSEP/FAO have developed laboratory facilities and a pilot plant which can smoke, salt, dry, freeze, can, vacuum-pack, and mechanically gut and fillet fish of most types – certainly those of commercial interest. A new detailed product preparation programme – largely involving merluza, caballa, machete, tollo, bonito, anchoveta, squid and sardine in a range of 40 product types – has been evolved to see the product through the commercial sampling stage. The work will include product specification and costings. It is a practical and commercially-oriented programme, applying or modify existing technnology to Peruvian food fish and converting that fish into an acceptable and, hopefully, profitable form.

A profound change is under way in the field of inland distribution and marketing. The Government provision of infrastructure, the EPSEP intervention into wholesaling and retailing (EPSEP operates over 100 retail selling points in Lima alone), the consumer education programmes at all levels, the increasing price of meat coupled with a 15-day per month ban on beef selling, and larger supplies of fish are all combining to induce far greater awareness of food fish. The increasing role of EPSEP and the apparent lack of return on capital are features of this situation. Because of the gap between the prices to the fishermen and the consumer – mostly caused by inadequate turnover, wastage and inefficiency – and the need to establish a national marketing system, the Government has decided to give EPSEP the State food fish monopoly. It will have to be a gradual process, involving the collaboration of the private sector with a number of wholesalers/transporters becoming only transporters. Already, EPSEP has acquired more than 25 per cent of the Lima area market. Such effort cannot succeed on a long-term basis unless the consumer can be convinced of the value and attraction of fish. There is evidence that this is being achieved and that progress can be accelerated through better handling of the catch at sea and ashore, supported by adequate infrastructure, distribution facilities, marketing programmes and educational campaigns. Incidentally, it is interesting to note in this connexion that sophisticated advertising techniques such as joint campaigns with other products, eg, beer and matches, have proved very effective. In any country, the development of significant physical resources takes time. For example, it might well take at least a year to identify an opportunity, eg, hake freezing, then a year to develop the feasibility of the project, and another year to do the detailing planning and seek out funds, after which it may take two more years to construct the factory – a total of at least five years. One Peruvian approach to this problem is to license foreign factory trawlers to fish in Peruvian waters for limited periods for a fee or as a joint venture. Thus, an operation can be arranged in such a manner that much needed fishing experience is gained, some training is acquired, Peruvian products are introduced to export markets, shipping opportunities are developed, additional fish is made available for the expanding domestic market and foreign exchange is earned. A joint venture involving two Polish B15 freezer trawlers is under way and valuable commercial experience is being gained. While all this is going on shore-based installations can be built, perhaps even adjusted in the light of experience. There is, of course, the risk that the highly intensive fishing effort of large foreign trawlers could damage the resource but, if licensed prudently with a constant monitoring of the resource by the Instituto del Mar, overfishing can be avoided. Indeed, the experience gained should help to avoid overinvestment and overexpansion and help to guide and augment the development of a shore based programme.

Little mention has been made of aquaculture. An active programme, particularly for trout farming, is under development but significant results are a distance away. It is easy to become overoptimistic in planning fish culture without paying due consideration to the problems of disease, location, management and markets. The development of the Amazon Region is a major problem on its own. With a resource of, say, 30,000 to 80,000 tons, the food contribution locally is great and could be developed extensively. An initial but significant step forward is the provision of limited infrastructure in Iquitos. Further, the pilot scheme of EPSEP, whereby canoe fishermen are provided with ice, thus allowing them greater fishing time until refrigerated motor barges can collect their catches, can have far-reaching effects. There is a flourishing trade in the export of ornamental fishes and there seems no reason why this luxury industry should not continue to grow. Above all, the discovery of oil in the Amazon Region will change the whole economy of the area, bringing new opportunities to the fishing community.

In establishing a fish industry, an underlying theme is the need for training in all fields at all levels. However, training simply for the sake of training is not enough and there is a constant need to determine the human requirements. For example, a too ambitious fishermen's training centre in Peru could over-supply the market quite quickly. Rather than a highly sophisticated training centre, training in the field by extension workers can be most effective. Peru is also benefiting from fellowships and study tours provided by multilateral and bilateral sources. Efficiently organized study tours, tailored to the capacity and need of the participants, are proving to be a rapid way of training at decision-making and other levels. Constructive work is being achieved in Peru by universities with fishery faculties. But the need for co-ordination is always there. The same observation goes for work at technical centres and laboratories. Their programmes need to be slanted toward applying internationally known techniques to the local problems and opportunities of Peru. Overall, in looking at training programmes, it must be remembered the fishing industry is labour intensive and, in many countries, it should probably be kept so. The best use, therefore, must be made of labour if Peru's food fish products are to remain competitive in international markets.

THE FUTURE

It is worth briefly considering the future as Peru strives to establish a more substantial food fishery. What, for instance, will be the opportunities opened up by the Andean Pact? What about other regional possibilities, such as technical centres? If the future is promising in these respects, Peru is certainly well placed to take advantage of them and, indeed, in some instances, to take the initiative. Also, as the food fish industry develops, there will be a greater need for the inclusion of fish in the trading agreements Peru has with other countries. For example, in this way substantial exports could be sold to the Japanese market. The development of fishery complexes at La Puntilla, Samanco and Meca Grande is in the detailed planning stage. The projects will include docking and processing facilities for shellfish, tuna freezing and anchoveta. The role of Peru in the international fishing scene has yet to be defined. An indication of hopes in this respect is that the joint company PEPESCA SA envisages five 1,000-ton tuna vessels to operate in the international tuna fisheries. As in other fields, assuming economic criteria are used, any major development, eg, fishing the Atlantic, hardly seems likely or viable. But in all efforts in development it should be realised that while policies of governments may change, the ingredients and problems of developing a food fish industry do not.

Trends in the Utilization of Alaska Pollack in Japan
M Okada and E Noguchi

Tendances de l'utilisation de la morue du pacifique Occidental au Japon.

L'accroissement remarquable des captures de morue du Pacifique occidental par l'industrie japonaise de la pêche – qui sont passées d'environ 300,000 tonnes avant 1960 à 2,360,000 tonnes en 1970 – est allé de pair avec une forte expansion de l'utilisation de ce poisson. Le document traite de cette évolution. Les produits pour la fabrication desquels cette ressource jusqu'ici sous-exploitée est de plus en plus utilisée comprennent le sukimi (filets séchés fumés), le mintai (poisson séché congelé), l'oyakozuke (tranches de filets marinées), le tarako (rogue salée), les blocs de poisson, la farine de poisson et, plus particulièrement, la gelée de poisson, notamment à base de surimi congelé préparé à bord des bateaux de pêche à partir de morue du Pacifique occidental.

Utilisation del colin de Alaska en Japon.

El notable aumento de las capturas de colín de Alaska por los pescadores japoneses – de unas 300,000 toneladas antes de 1960 a 2,360,000 toneladas en 1970 – ha ido acompañado por una gran expansión de la utilización de este pescado. En el presente trabajo se describe esta evolución. Entre los productos para los que cada vez se utilizan más estos peces, hasta ahora poco explotados, figuran los siguientes: sukimi (filetes salados secos), mintai (pescado congelado seco), oyakozuke (trozos de filetes en escabeche), tarako (huevas saladas), bloques, harina y, sobre todo, gelatina de pescado, utilizando sobre todo surimi congelado a bordo.

The big expansion in the catch of Alaska pollack has been accompanied by the growth of the fish reduction and fish jelly industries. The fish meal expansion is largely due to the recent growth of the poultry, pig and fish farming industries in Japan.

PRODUCTION OF ALASKA POLLACK

Alaska pollack, *Teragra chalcogramma*, is a mid-water fish known as sukesodara in Japan and walleye pollack or whiting in Canada and the USA. It is a member of the Gadoid family and is found widely in the northern Pacific Ocean where the water temperature ranges between 0° and 12°C. The fish grows for 6 or more years to a length of about 65 centimetres. Its life span is up to 14 years. The main fishing grounds are North Korean Bay, the sea around Hokkaido, the Okhotsk Sea and the Bering Sea. The annual catch by Japan used to be about 300,000 tons but has increased remarkably since early 1960, reaching 2,360,000 tons in 1970. It accounts for 25 per cent of the total Japanese catch (Table 1).

The increased production of fish jelly from 509,000 tons in 1960 to 1,081,000 tons in 1970 is also largely due to the supply of Alaska pollack in the form of frozen

TABLE 1. CATCH OF ALASKA POLLACK BY TYPE OF FISHERY (in thousand tons)

	1960	1965	1967	1968	1969	1970
Total	380	691	1,247	1,606	1,944	2,360
Trawling in Bering Sea	26	230	562	686	878	1,266
Trawling off Kamchatka		36	253	547	670	711
Offshore fishing	354	425	432	373	396	383

surimi (Table 2). In 1970 more than one million tons of the pollack was used by the fish jelly industry which produces kamaboko, fish sausage or other products, which are favoured foods in Japan. Frozen surimi, evolved in 1959, is the most significant new food utilization of Alaska pollack. In 1970, 317,000 tons of pollack (16 per cent of the total catch) were taken from the waters of Hokkaido and Sakhalin (the Japan Sea, the northern Pacific and the Okhotsk Sea) by trawling, gillnetting and longlining by boats of less than 100 tons. In 1970, 711,000 tons of pollack (31 per cent of the total catch) were caught off the Kamchatka Peninsula by stern trawlers in the 350-ton class, based on Hokkaido and the northern part of Japan. Trawlers, with a big mother ship as a large floating processing plant, and with large stern trawling factory boats of 3,000 to 5,000 tons caught 1,320,000 tons of Alaska pollack on the Continental shelf of the south eastern Bering Sea (53 per cent of the total catch in 1970).

TABLE 2. JELLY AND SURIMI FROM ALASKA POLLACK (in thousand tons)

	1960	1965	1967	1968	1969	1970
Fish jelly products	509	797	912	999	1,077	1,081
Frozen surimi						
Total		32	84	145	196	261
Shore plants		24	45	70	93	119
Factory boats		8	39	75	103	142

TABLE 3. DISPOSITION OF THE CATCH OF ALASKA POLLACK IN 1970

	Total catch	Catch for factory boats	Catch for shore plants
Quantity (000 t)	2,360	1,335	1,011
Disposition			
Marketing fresh	8%	0%	18%
Processing to fish jelly and frozen surimi	55%	52%	61%
Curing	7%	0%	15%
Reduction to meal	30%	48%	6%

TABLE 4. GENERAL COMPOSITION OF ALASKA POLLACK FLESH (IN PERCENTAGES)

Moisture	Total nitrogen	Non protein nitrogen	Crude fat	Ash
82.1	2.62	0.32	0.32	1.28

DISPOSITION OF THE CATCH

About 70 per cent of the total catch was used for food purposes in 1970. The remainder was processed into fish meal used to feed poultry and fish. Eight per cent of the catch was marketed as fresh fish, 7 per cent used to make cured products, while more than 50 per cent was supplied to fish jelly industry as whole fish or frozen surimi (Table 3). More than half the catch, 1,335,000 tons, was processed in factory ships in the Bering Sea in 1970 within 24 hours of being caught, 645,000 tons being processed into fish meal and 690,000 tons to frozen surimi. This produced 148,000 tons of fish meal, 20,000 tons of fish oil and 138,000 tons of frozen surimi. The shore processing plants, mostly located in the fishing ports in

Hokkaido and the northern Pacific coast of Japan, process fish from near and distant waters. It takes 1 to 3 days to land the fish from the coastal fisheries and 5 to 9 days to land the Kamtchatka catch. Icing in boxes is used only for fish destined for the fresh fish market. Crushed ice is used. The distant water trawlers have refrigerated fish rooms. Only 6 per cent of the one million tons of pollack landed in 1970 was processed into non-food products, 76 per cent being used to make food products and 18 per cent being marketed fresh. The quantity of frozen packaged fillets has recently increased rapidly. Some 14,000 tons of frozen block Alaska pollack were exported to the USA. Fish processed into fish jelly and frozen surimi accounted for 61 per cent of the total landed. About 23,000 tons of cured foods, such as dried frozen or dried salted fish, were produced from 15 per cent of the landed catch. An important process in the shore plants is salting the roe. This is one of the luxury fish foods in Japan and in 1970 37,000 tons were produced, worth 12,000 million yen. Production of fish meal in shore plants was about 120,000 tons, mostly from offal and surplus fish.

QUALITY CHARACTERISTICS OF ALASKA POLLACK

Chemical characteristics

The edible part amounts to about 40 per cent of the total weight of the fish. The tissue of dark muscle immediately under the skin amounts to only 4 per cent of the total weight of the muscle tissue. The colour of the flesh varies from grey-white to pink. It is moist, tender and very lean. Table 4 shows the main composition of the flesh. The moisture content varies according to the season. The limit, 80 to 85 per cent, is smaller than with most fish. It reaches its highest level immediately after spawning (spring to early summer). During the feeding migration, the moisture content decreases to a range of 80 to 82 per cent. The oil is found almost entirely in the liver and rises from about 17 per cent in spring to more than 60 per cent in autumn. Vitamin A content of the oil ranges from 3,000 to 30,000 IU. Low keeping quality is the biggest defect of Alaska pollack from a commercial standpoint.

Keeping quality of iced fish

The raw flesh has a bland neutral odour. The fish, however, develops a strong, over-powering surface or skin odour in less than one day if uniced. Immediate icing aboard is, therefore, essential. The odours develop gradually after a week of ice storage and reduce acceptability as fresh fish.

The rate of *post mortem* breakdown of adenosine triphosphate (ATP) is much faster than in other species. In 1 to 2 days of iced storage 75 per cent of ATP in the pollack breaks down to hypoxanthine (Hy). Such decomposition takes more than 7 days with ocean perch, English sole and skipjack. Trimethylamine oxide (TMAO) is converted enzymatically to dimethylamine (DMA) and formic acid (HCHO) in the Alaska pollack as well as in those of other members of the Gadoid family (Amano et al. 1963, Amano and Yamada 1964). This particular enzymatic breakdown does not permit the application of Dyer's method (Dyer 1945) for trimethylamine (TMA) determination when TMA is used as an index of freshness, because the value obtained by Dyer's method consists of both TMA and DMA. The method improved by Hashimoto *et al.* (1957) should be applied for TMA determination in the flesh of the Gadoids. The jelly forming property of fish flesh is a very important factor from a technological standpoint in fish jelly and frozen surimi production. Alaska pollack loses this property in ice storage. For instance, the decrease is noticeable after 4 days storage.

Keeping quality of frozen fish

Freezing is at present the only method for preserving the fresh fish characteristics during long storage but the fish deteriorates more rapidly than other species even in frozen storage. Within 6 months storage at $-20°C$, the flesh becomes tough and dry, and releases a large amount of drip when thawed. Its jelly forming property is lost after only 3 months storage at $-20°C$. This low keeping characteristic of frozen Alaska pollack may be related to its high moisture and very low fat content (Tanaka 1965), very low stability of the myofibrillar proteins (Arai 1971), accumulation of HCHO (Tokunaga 1972), which is the enzymatic degradation product of TMAO and has a drastic denaturing effect on proteins, and so on. The Alaska pollack cannot be treated as a conventional bottom fish. The need for rapid chilling and of techniques to prevent deterioration in frozen storage is a serious consideration from a quality standpoint.

PRODUCTS FROM ALASKA POLLACK

Many cured products are produced from Alaska pollack at the shore plants, such as dried salted, dried unsalted, salted and pickled fish and so on.

Annual production of sukimi, which is a dried salted fillet of Alaska pollack, amounts to 10,000 tons. Fresh and large fish are needed to make first class products. After being headed and gutted, the fish is soaked overnight in cold water to remove the blood, and then filleted. The fillets are skinned by hand and washed again, and then laid in layers of salt, some 5 to 12 per cent of the weight of the fillets. After 2 or 3 days salting with frequent restacking, the fillets are washed lightly to clean their surface and then dried. Sun drying is commonly used, but recently drying chambers have been installed. The moisture content of the final product varies from 25 to 45 per cent depending on the extent of drying.

Mintai is dried frozen fish. It is a kind of stockfish and is produced – about 25,000 tons yearly – only in midwinter in Hokkaido. It has a characteristic texture – spongy, very fibrous and as light as balsa wood. This texture is attributed to the denaturing of myofibrillar proteins during freezing and in the drying operation. The fish is headed, gutted and soaked in cold water for 2 to 5 days to remove blood and inorganic substances. Such washing accelerates the formation of large ice crystals during the freezing operation, resulting in the spongy texture of the product. The fish is put on an outdoor shelf and allowed to freeze naturally. In early spring, when partially thawed, the water is drained off and the fish is gradually dried. The moisture content of the final product is about 10 per cent.

Oyakozuke, made from slices of marinated fish, is produced from the skinned fillet of Alaska pollack. It is salted in a dry state for one day, the salt being 7 to 9 per cent of its weight. After washing, the fillet is cut into small slices of about $50 \times 5 \times 20$ mm, soaked in vinegar overnight and then dewatered by light pressing. The slices are then placed in a mixture made of sugar, monosodium glutamate and cooked pieces of Alaska pollack egg.

Tarako is salted fish roe, which is very popular in Japan. With the increased catch of Alaska pollack, production of tarako has been increasing and reached 37,000 tons in 1970. It is said that the commercial value of the Alaska pollack landed is determined by the quality of the roe. Roe must be handled very carefully before salting to avoid bursting its delicate skin. Roes are washed in diluted brine and mixed with dry salt, 10 to 25 per cent of their weight. The amount of salt varies with the ripeness of the egg as well as the temperature. Roes are usually salted in layers for 5 to 15 h with frequent restacking. Dye is often added with the salt. After salting, the roes are washed in their own brine and laid on wire mesh trays to shape them as well as to drain out the water. Moisture content of the final product is about 60 per cent. The fish supplying the roes are, of course, processed to make various foods.

Alaska pollack is the most important material for fish jelly production in Hokkaido and the northern Honshu. Output in 1970 amounted to 150,000 tons of kamaboko, deep fat fried kamaboko and chikuwa. The fish jelly process involves the following steps: heading and gutting – washing – flesh separation – washing the flesh – dewatering – grinding – mixing of ingredients with the flesh – shaping – cooking – cooling – final product. After being headed and gutted, the fish is put in a fish washer and then through a flesh separator. The deboned flesh is washed or bleached with cold water to remove blood, mucus or fat. Such washing improves significantly the colour and odour as well as the texture of the final product. The flesh is washed in a tank equipped with a stirrer. After being treated with 5 to 7 times the amount of water, the flesh is allowed to settle. The washing operation is repeated several times. Machines for continuous washing have been generally introduced recently. The flesh is dewatered by a press or a centrifuge machine. After passing through a chopper, the minced flesh is ground into a paste with salt and other ingredients in a stone mortar or a silent cutter. Salt is an essential ingredient, the amount ranging from 2.5 to 4 per cent. Sugar, monosodium glutamate and sodium inosinate are commonly used as flavouring ingredients. Various kinds of spices, small pieces of vegetables, such as carrot or onion, or slices of squid meat or cheese, are often added, especially for deep fat fried kamaboko. Potato or corn starch are used to improve the texture of the products. The paste, after shaping, is cooked and changes the texture from a paste to a jelly and inactivates the microorganisms present in the flesh. Steaming is applied to common kamaboko, placed on an oblong wood plate. Broiling is used for chikuwa, a tubular kamaboko, and deep fat frying for fried kamaboko and satsumaage. Immersion in hot water is used for fish sausage. Continuous operating cookers are now being widely used. The jelly is rapidly cooled in the cold air.

Frozen surimi is a newly developed raw material for preparing fish jelly, the production of which has so expanded that it exceeded one million tons in 1970. This growth is largely due to the appeal of fish jelly as a ready-to-eat food. Furthermore, its appearance and flavour can be easily modified to meet consumer preferences and it can be made from any species of fish. These favourable factors, together with the development of frozen surimi and the supply of a huge amount of Alaska pollack, made possible the remarkable growth of the fish jelly industry. Myofibrillar proteins of Alaska pollack, once frozen, are denatured rapidly and cannot be used for fish jelly production. But the Hokkaido Experimental Fisheries Station discovered in 1959 that the denaturing can be prevented for a long period if the fish is processed into frozen surimi (Nishiya et al. 1962). As a result, the demand for and the production of frozen surimi has grown spectacularly. Making frozen surimi follows the initial procedure for making fish jelly. There are two types of frozen surimi, one with and one without salt. In the salted type, kaen surimi, 2.5 per cent of salt and 10 per cent of sugar are added to the washed flesh. In the salt-free type, muen surimi, 0.2 per cent of polyphosphates and 5 to 8 per cent of sugar (sucrose, glucose or sorbitol) are used. The flesh is mixed with the additives and shaped to a block of 10 kg weight packed into a polyethylene bag. It is quick frozen and stored under −20°C. The product is conveyed in refrigerated cars to the jelly plants. There it is sliced and thawed in still air, although recently microwave thawers are being increasingly used.

Twenty thousand tons of fish block were produced from Alaska pollack in 1970 at shore plants, most of which were exported to the USA. For this product, large, very fresh fish are washed thoroughly and filleted by hand or machine. The fillets are skinned, washed to remove slime, blood or debris, inspected and drained. They are then placed in metal trays in layers and frozen in a contact plate or a blast freezer, given ice glaze, and packed in a waxed carton. In another type of fish block prepared for the domestic market, the minced fish is ground with salt, chemical seasonings and pork fat to paste. This mixture is placed between layers of skinless fillets and frozen in a block.

Surplus fish and offal are reduced to fish meal. Just under 50 per cent of the Bering Sea catch is reduced to fish meal by the factory ships. The shore plants rely chiefly on offal. After being cooked, fish or offal are put through a continuous screw press, the cake being dried usually in a rotating kiln but indirect dryers, with steam jacketed kilns, have been installed to many new plants. The liquid pressed out is fed into a continuous centrifuge. The stickwater, the aqueous part of the liquid freed from oil, is concentrated as a syrup containing 30 to 50 per cent of solids by a multiple effect evaporator. This syrup can be marketed as a fish soluble or can be mixed and dried with the pressed cake to produce wholemeal.

UTILIZATION OF NEGLECTED SPECIES AS FROZEN 'SURIMI'

The possibility of using under-utilized species as frozen 'surimi' is now under study at many research laboratories in North and South America as well as in Southeast Asia. These efforts are largely concentrated on two possibilities. One is to adapt the raw material for processing into foods by controlling their appearance, flavour and texture. As the people in each country have their own tastes, these studies are very important. The other is to study the characteristics of species for jelly-

TABLE 5. JELLY-FORMING CAPABILITY OF AMERICAN AND NEW ZEALAND FISH[a]

Fish		Area of catch	Treatment	Score
Common name	Scientific name			
Pacific hake	Merluccius productus	North Pacific coast of USA	iced, 2 days	6
			iced, 2 days (parasitic)	1
Chilean hake	M. gayi	Chilean coast	iced, 2 days	8
			iced, 6 days	4
			−20°C, 4 months	8
Argentine hake	M. hubbsi	Argentine coast	−40°C, 5 months	7
New Zealand hake	M. australis	ibid.	ibid.	7
Merluza de cola	Macruronus magellanicus	Chilean coast	iced, 2 days	8
			−20°C, 4 months	6
		Argentine coast	−40°C, 5 months	6
Hoki	Macruronus novae-zelandiae	New Zeland coast	−20°C, 4 months	9
	Micromesistius australis	Argentine coast	−40°C, 5 months	6
Rockfishes	Sebastodes brevispniis	North Pacific coast of USA	iced, 4 days	8
silvergray			iced, 10 days	6
Black	S. melanops	ibid.	iced, 4 days	7
Yellowtail	S. flavidus	ibid.	ibid.	7
Ling cod	Ophiodon elongatus	ibid.	iced, 10 days	9
Pacific cod	Gadus macrocephalus	ibid.	iced, 1 day	9
			iced, 9 days	7
Croaker	—	Gulf of Mexico	−20°C, 1 month	10
Baracuda	Thyrsites atun	New Zealand coast	−20°C, 3 months	1
Sierra	ibid.	Chilean coast	−20°C, 4 months	5
		Argentine coast	−40°C, 5 months	1

[a]Jelly-forming capability was evaluated by elasticity and texture of kamaboko prepared from the fish and scored by the 10-point system (very superior: 9–10; very low: 0–1).

forming capability. This capacity is the determining factor for the quality of frozen 'surimi' and the elasticity of 'kamaboko' prepared from it. The jelly-forming quality of species varies widely and is, in addition, influenced by the freshness of the fish, the fishing grounds, the time of the year and other factors.

Characteristics of some under-utilized species from American and New Zealand waters were studied from the viewpoint of their jelly-forming capabilities by the staff of Tokai Regional Fisheries Research Laboratory. Some of the results are shown in Table 5. For the purpose, the fish might be conveniently divided into three groups: superior, intermediate, and inferior. Fish of the superior group, which produce jelly that is elastic even after iced or cold storage for a long period, are many; species of croakers in Asian and American waters, 'blanquillo' in Chilean waters, 'hoki' of New Zealand waters and so on. Small pelagic fish, such as mackerel and anchovy, have very low jelly-forming capability. Most demersal fish belong to the intermediate groups. Hakes of the genus *Merluccius* and rockfishes of the genus *Sebastodes* retain a good jelly-forming capability after a few days of iced storage or several months of cold storage. The rate of decrease in jelly-forming capability during storage varies among species. Hake from the Pacific coast of USA produced very poor 'kamaboko' with mushy texture, due

to infection by protozoan parasites having an active proteolytic enzyme. Myxosporidian parasites are relatively common in various species of fish caught in certain parts of the world. A high incidence of infection in a catch would preclude its use not only for 'surimi' but also for fresh or frozen fish.

References

AMANO, K, YAMADA, K, and BITO, M, *Bull. Jap. Soc. Sci. Fish.* 1963   29(9): 860–864.
AMANO, K and YAMADA, K, *Ibid.*, 30(5):430–443, 30(8):639–645., 1964
ARAI, K *New Food Ind. (Japan)*, 13(12):48. 1971
DYER, W J *J. Fish. Res. Bd. Can.*, 6:351. 1945
HASHIMOTO, Y and OKAICHI, T, *Bull. Jap. Soc. Sci. Fish.*, 23:269. 1957
IWATA, K and YAMADA, J, *Bull. Tokai Reg. Fish Lab.* 58:147–153. 1969
IWATA, K, CHANDRASEKHAR, T C, IIDA, H, SUZUKI, T and 1970   NOGUCHI, E, *Ibid.* 61:43–51.
NISHIYA, K *et al.* Jap. Patent 306, 857. 1962
OKADA, M and SUZUKI, A, *Ibid.* 65:67–73. 1971
TANAKA, T *Reito*, (447):3. 1965
TOKUNAGA, T *Jap. Soc. Sci. Fish. Cong. Kochi.* 1972

The Commercial Utilization of Cape Hake   J R Burt

L'utilisation commerciale du merlu du Cap.

Au Royaume-Uni, le marché du merlu du Cap est important et varié. On l'étudie sous trois aspects: en tant que secteur spécifique du merlu du Cap, en tant qu'élément d'un secteur général du merlu et en tant qu'élément de l'ensemble du marché du poisson de chalut. On présente des arguments démontrant que les produits dérivés de ce poisson sont susceptibles d'être bien accueillis et ont une valeur intéressante.

La manutention et la transformation de cette espèce présentent des caractéristiques analogues à celles d'autres poissons de chalut, cependant qu'une certaine mollesse de la chair du merlu et sa tendance à se défaire sont probablement les facteurs critiques essentiels qu'il convient de prendre en considération au cours de la préparation de produits congelés de bonne qualité. On discute l'importance d'une réfrigération prompte, rapide et continue des captures, ainsi que la nécessité de vider le poisson aussitôt que possible après sa prise. On étudie les effets de la température et ceux de retards intervenant à divers moments du processus de manutention aussi bien pour les opérations de congélation effectuées en mer que pour celles qui ont lieu à terre et on décrit les procédés utilisés – traitement avec des solutions de sel et de polyphosphate effectué avant la congélation – pour empêcher la chair d'exsuder et de se défaire lors de la décongélation.

Pour finir, on examine brièvement les types d'équipement requis pour mécaniser la plupart des opérations unitaires intervenant au cours de la transformation du merlu du Cap.

Aprovechamiento comercial de la merluza del Cabo.

El mercado de merluza del Cabo en el Reino Unido es importante y variado, y se estudia en tres formas: como sector específico, como parte del sector genérico de la merluza, y como parte del mercado general del pescado blanco. Se dan prueba de que los productos derivados de este pescado encuentran amplia aceptación y son económicamente valiosos.

Las características de esta especie por lo que se refiere a tratamiento y elaboración son análogas a las de otras especies de pescado blanco; para la preparación de productos congelados de buena calidad, los factores más críticos son probablemente cierta blandura de la carne y la tendencia de ésta a abrirse. Se examina la importancia de una refrigeración tempestiva, rápida y sostenida del pescado, y la necesidad de eviscerar los peces tan pronto como sea posible. Se examinan los efectos de la temperatura y de los retrasos en diversos momentos del proceso de congelación, tanto a bordo como en tierra, y se explica como reducir la exudación al descongelar y la abertura de la carne tratándola antes de congelarla con soluciones de sal y polifosfatos.

Por último, se examina brevemente el equipo necesario para mecanizar la mayoría de las diversas operaciones por que pasa la merluza del Cabo en el proceso de elaboración.

The main difficulty inherent in consideration of a topic such as this lies both in the unavailability of certain essential items of information as well as in the possible non-applicability of much of what is available because of its being outdated. Many assumptions have to be made and data have often to be extrapolated beyond the limits of strict validity. Since there would be little point in utilizing or exploiting a resource if there were not a market for products derived from it, this paper starts with some observations on the market for Cape hake in the United Kingdom which can be considered as a model for the

resource outlet. However, the commercial fishery makes no distinction between the two species, *Merluccius capensis* and *Merluccius paradoxus* (Pshenichnyy and Assorov 1969; Jones and Mackie 1970; Botha 1971; Botha and Mombeck 1971; FAO, 1968). Both species will be treated together throughout the rest of this paper.

THE MARKET

A substantial and varied market exists for the Cape hake. It would be impossible to analyse this market in detail because it is very seldom an entity in itself: at times it can be considered in its own right, and at others as part of a more general hake segment. However, in terms of total quantities involved it is probably more logical to consider it as just a part, which cannot be separately quantified, of the non-specific white fish market. Some statistics are available, though, which will illustrate the size in the United Kingdom of these three types of market and these will serve as frames of reference or as guidelines. The total estimated supplies of demersal fish available for human consumption in the United Kingdom in 1971 was approximately 760,000 tons (landed weight equivalent) and this was worth some £85 million. In that year 134,000 tons of white fish were sold on the retail and catering markets in the frozen state (WFA 1972). It is appreciated that the bulk of this would consist of products from designated species but a substantial portion, including some of the material which is species designated, could have been produced from any of a wide range of species. In particular, laminated blocks which are to be used for the production of fish fingers and fish portions would fall into this category. The demand for laminated blocks is unsatisfied. Furthermore, the quick-frozen sector is that segment of the fish products market which has expanded most in recent years and it has been predicted that this is a major growth area coming as it does into the category of convenience foods. It can be deduced that Cape hake accounts for a very small proportion of the total of frozen white fish sold in this country. Imports of quick-frozen white fish from South Africa, virtually all of which would be hake, amounted to only 2,000 tons (landed weight equivalent: worth £280,000) in 1971 (WFA 1972), but this is not a true estimate for the potential market. In 1967, for instance, 6,000 tons were imported from South Africa and to each of these figures can be added a fraction of the 2,000 tons of frozen fish which Japan exports annually to the United Kingdom (Birds Eye 1972). As far back as 1928 a consignment of frozen hake from South Africa was received enthusiastically in Fleetwood (Anon. 1928) and it was stated then that large and regular supplies would follow. More definite indications of acceptability have been published recently. A commercial assessment of the acceptability of Cape hake was obtained after the return of the British trawler KIRKELLA from the Southeast Atlantic. This sea-frozen material was judged to be very acceptable and was found to attract a premium over and above the price of sea-frozen cod. It was concluded that fish of this good quality could be sold without difficulty in the United Kingdom (WFA 1968). This emphasis on quality and its importance in this discriminating market had also appeared in a report relating to the sale of sea-frozen Cape hake at a good price in Fleetwood (Anon. 1966a). Despite this it must be remembered that there are differences between the various markets for Cape hake. The mass home market for hake in Spain, for instance, has been described as 'generally poor' (Anon. 1966b), but it is nonetheless very important because of its size. On the other hand, some Cape hake fillets were reportedly difficult to market in Germany and such fish would be used there to 'make up production at the end of the year' (Anon. 1967a). Despite this, German trawler operators have been reported as finding fishing on these grounds profitable (Anon. 1967b). This brings us finally to a consideration of what has been regarded as the traditional market for hake in Britain: the western parts of England and Wales and, in particular, the regions adjacent to the fishing ports of Milford Haven and Fleetwood. These two ports were the ones which handled the bulk of the landings of European hake in the days before the slump of that fishery and a large hake eating public still persists in those areas. It is largely demand from there which causes hake to have such a high intrinsic value and to be classed as a 'quality' fish. In 1971, just under 2,500 tons of hake (worth £686,000) were landed in the United Kingdom (WFA 1972). At the prices prevailing then, this made hake over twice as valuable as cod in terms of price per unit weight. Considerable quantities of Cape hake are sold in these areas by friers, who use thawed fillets, or by fishmongers, who cut steaks on demand from whole fish. Each of these outlets has a preference for large fish and this was confirmed with the KIRKELLA fish (WFA 1968).

HANDLING AND PROCESSING

All the tenets of good handling and processing practices apply to Cape hake and it would be pointless to reiterate all of them here. However, where limits peculiar to this species for certain processes have been determined they will be presented. Also, some of the more characteristic technologically important properties of Cape hake will be discussed. This discussion will also be restricted to those products which are of interest to British industry and British consumers. Before considering in greater detail the various patterns of handling and processing which are imposed on this fishery, mention ought to be made of a few general factors which are known to be of technological importance. The one which has the greatest individual influence on how Cape hake should be handled and on the quality of the end products is the environmental temperature. Living as they do in the cooler bottom waters of the Benguela current, these fish are acclimatized to subantarctic or, at the worst, temperate conditions but after capture they are exposed to conditions which might be described as nearing subtropical. Surface water temperatures of 14° to 21°C and air temperatures of 13° to 24°C have been reported (Wagenknecht and Horn 1967, Kordyl and Karnicki 1969, Burt et al. 1974a, b). Fish temperatures will accordingly be affected by these and by the times taken to bring the catch inboard once the codend has surfaced and to stow the catch. Levels in the fish of 10°C to 19°C were recorded in the studies quoted above. For most species of fish even fairly short exposure to high temperatures at this stage is known to affect adversely the quality of the end product and Cape hake is no exception. In common with other species of hake, this fish has a reputation of being easily damaged and soft. The softness increases with time in the unfrozen state after death and its extent is related to holding temperatures. Just how serious this is commercially can be gauged from the fact that Cape hake is often completely soft long before any off-odour or flavour develops (Rowan and Marks 1951). This generalized softness is not believed to be associated with protozoan infestation (Rowan 1952) in this species, although a more positive correlation between softness and parasites is reported for *Merluccius merluccius* (Fletcher et al. 1951) and *M. productus* (Dassow et al.

1970). However, for further information on the extent of occurrence in Cape hake flesh of the myxosporidian parasite, *Chloromyxum thyristes*, the literature should be consulted (Davies and Beyers 1947; Rowan 1956; Patashnik and Groninger 1964; Grimols and Tillman 1970). Size and size distribution are two further biological factors which govern the ways in which fish can be processed commercially but for the purposes of this paper it would be superfluous to reproduce detailed statistics already published (Jones 1967; Pshenichnyy and Assorov 1969; Mombeck 1970, 1971; Botha 1971; Smit and Rushburne 1971).

Handling on board

Pinkness in the flesh, due to blood, is associated with delay in heading and gutting (Pienaar 1961) and during freezing, cold storage and thawing this pinkness changes to a brown discolouration. Increasing delays, even at chill temperatures, before gutting lead to increasing amounts of discolouration (Burt *et al.* 1968, 1974a) while delays before chilling have effects on quality (Gilberg 1954) and on gaping (Burt *et al.* 1974a). Delays prior to freezing also lead to progressive losses in quality. Significant amounts of softness and gaping result from as short a period as five days in ice before freezing (Dreosti and Pienaar 1961, Peinaar 1962, Burt *et al.* 1974a) and the normal flavour and odour changes become more significant after then. Cape hake have been known to remain in prime condition under experimental control for nine to ten days in ice (Gilberg 1964) although this may be an overestimate for commercial purposes. The manner in which the fish are stowed in ice also has an effect on the rate of deterioration of quality (Gilberg 1954, Dreosti and Simmonds 1962) although shallow bulking does not appear to be any worse than boxing in ice as far as gaping and colour are concerned (Burt *et al.* 1974a). Chilled storage of guts-in fish in refrigerated sea water (RSW) is used on board some trawlers in this fishery and this system of stowage has certain advantages over icing: there is a shorter delay between capture and chilling, chilling is more rapid and the penetration of salt causes the flesh to become firmer. On the debit side, though, prolonged storage with guts-in can accelerate the production of off-odours and flavours and can exacerbate the colour problem, while salt in the flesh accelerates the production of cold storage flavours and odours (Burt *et al.* 1968). For short periods, say up to three or four days, the advantages of RSW would tend to outweigh its disadvantages while icing would be the method of choice for longer times. On this point, salt can be tasted in the flesh after immersion of whole fish in RSW for less than one day. The quality of sea-frozen Cape hake is affected by much the same factors as are known to affect other species of fish (Jones 1969, Burt *et al.* 1969). Where Cape hake differ from cod, for instance, is in the relative importance of *rigor mortis* which is comparatively weak in the former species (Wagenknecht and Horn 1967; Burt *et al.* 1968, 1974b). In spite of this advantage, it is difficult to produce a sea-frozen fillet which is acceptable to the trade and poor colour is the main reason for rejection (Burt *et al.* 1974b). However, if a fillet freezing at sea operation is selected, discolourations can be reduced by maintaining the fish in a chilled environment right through till freezing, by early

gutting, by imposing a 30 to 60 minute bleeding delay before filleting and by freezing immediately after filleting. Such sea-frozen fillets will have an excellent flavour and texture and will not exhibit any significant amount of gaping. Despite the fact that freezing at sea as fillets would appear to be the logical process to adopt in this as in any fishery, only a small proportion of the Cape hake which enters the United Kingdom market has been so processed. Where sea-frozen fish is concerned the United Kingdom trade appears to prefer material that has been frozen on the bone and filleted ashore after thawing. In this instance the main defect which the producer has to prevent is gaping and not discolouration. Recommendations similar to those made above would also be made here: the fish should be held chilled all the time before freezing, gutting should be carried out as soon as possible and a bleeding delay of 30 min or so is desirable. Colour is seldom limiting but is occasionally where gutting has been delayed and to keep the amount of gaping down to an acceptable level the fish should be in the freezers within four to five hours (Burt *et al.* 1974b) Apart from being more efficient than cold air or ice in chilling fish (Dreosti and Simmonds 1962), RSW is the only practical method available for chilling fish in bulk on board freezer trawlers. An apparent contradiction exists between the limits which have been mentioned for producing good quality sea-frozen (four to five hours) and shore-frozen (seven days) Cape hake, but further consideration will show that this is not a valid comparison. In the former instance the fish is being assessed for its suitability as a raw material for filleting and further processing, while the latter is being judged as an end product in itself. The long-term chilled material has a colour advantage which is not lost when it is filleted and frozen. Were it to be frozen on the bone it would not bear comparison with the sea-frozen fish on the grounds of flavour, gaping and, perhaps, even colour. A third form in which Cape hake can be frozen at sea is as steaks, or cutlets (Flechtenmacher 1967, Burt *et al.* 1974b). Gaping in this product is contained by the skin and discolourations can be kept to a minimum by following the regime recommended for sea-frozen fillets. Such a commodity should find an outlet in that sector of the United Kingdom market which prefers its hake streaked.

Processing ashore

Where the raw material has been frozen at sea on the bone, thawing is the obvious first step. Provided overheating and mechanical damage are avoided, normal commercial thawing procedures are applicable and the thawed fish can be treated subsequently along with material which is to be frozen for the first time. Two cautionary points need to be interpolated here: it is advisable to fillet thawed fish as soon as, but not before, thawing is complete. If too long a delay, even at chill temperatures, occurs before filleting, discoloured fillets will be produced (Burt *et al.* 1974b). On the other hand, if any ice remains in the flesh when the fillets are cut, gaping will be aggravated. Filleting and freezing, either as fillets or as laminated blocks, are the most important procedures in terms of amounts of fish involved and colour, softness and gaping are the critical properties at these stages. Softness governs the ease of filleting; if the fish are too soft, mechanical filleting leads to unacceptable wastage and hand filleting is then essential. Provided colour is acceptable, the extent of gaping usually determines the final end product, fillets which are more broken going into laminated blocks. Dipping procedures can be introduced after filleting and the use of brine and tripolyphosphate solutions can be of twofold benefit in reducing thaw drip as well as gaping (Pienaar 1963, 1964). Conditions for obtaining the maximum benefits have been determined. Immersion for 2 min in each of 26 per cent brine and 12.5 per cent sodium tripolyphosphate before freezing will reduce thaw drip to a minimum but will at the same time introduce what may be unacceptable levels of salt into the flesh. On the other hand, immersion for 2 min in 6 per cent salt followed by a half to two min in 12 per cent sodium tripolyphosphate solutions are the minimum treatments required to produce significant improvements in appearance by causing the flakes of even the most broken fillets to adhere to each other. Salt concentrations in the flesh resulting from treatment under the latter set of conditions are acceptable. Fillets of hake can be smoked to give a very pleasant product but two points are worth bearing in mind. The presence of *Chloromyxum* in appreciable numbers in smoked fillets causes the flesh to go white and opaque in spots or patches which have a soft mushy texture. The second concerns the suitability of sea-frozen fillets for smoking. While smoke uptake, colour and eating quality can all be satisfactory it has been found that smoked sea-frozen fillets are not commercially acceptable because of lack of surface gloss (Burt *et al.* 1974b).

Cold storage

Conditions of storage will have an effect on all types of frozen Cape hake products. Whilst the usual time and temperature induced changes in succulence and other textural parameters occur to a greater or lesser extent in common with all types of white fish during cold storage, flavour and odour changes are probably the most critical from the point of view of consumer acceptance. The flesh of Cape hake can contain an average of up to 1.4 per cent fat (Van Wyk 1944), but the brown muscle which lies just under the skin will account for the major part of this. This is particularly important in the case of products where the skin has been stripped away and access of atmospheric oxygen to the fatty tissues is thus made more easy. 'Cold store' flavours appear more quickly in laminated blocks and skin-off fillets of Cape hake than they do in skin-on fillets or whole fish.

Equipment

For the most part Cape hake is amenable, despite its softness, to mechanical handling on board or ashore and unit operations are becoming increasingly mechanized here as in other fisheries. However, a decrease in the proportion of good quality fillets obtained by mechanical filleting will result from delays before handling on board and particularly if these are at temperatures above 0°C (Wagenknecht and Horn 1967). Machines for heading, gutting, descaling, filleting, skinning and dipping are available and applicable to this species with no, or only slight, adjustment and it follows from the accounts given above of how defects arise that efficient systems for pre- and post-gutting chilling are essential on board freezer trawlers. Freezing equipment, be it vertical plate, horizontal plate or air blast, should be capable of operation according to the normal codes of practice devised for white fish in general: temperatures of −30°C should be maintainable throughout cold storage; and the thawing equipment used should not produce mechanical or thermal damage.

CONCLUSION

In conclusion, it is obvious from the variety of patterns of commercial involvement that no single formula leads to successful exploitation of this fishery. Examples of almost every type of fishing operation can be found, eg, wet fish trawlers landing fish in ice or in RSW for freshing, freezing, smoking, canning or salting and drying; wet fish trawlers supplying factory ships; freezer trawlers trans-shipping, at sea or in port, their production of frozen fillets or whole fish; freezer trawlers landing fish on the bone for thawing and subsequent processing as above. In addition the number of fishing vessels involved gives an indication of the intensity of effort. South African and South West African firms operate 18 freezer and over 60 wet fish trawlers, and it has been estimated that up to 50 Soviet, 50 to 70 Spanish, 18 Cuban, 6 Japanese, 3 Israeli and an unknown number of Polish vessels are fishing in the Southeast Atlantic (Anon. 1967b). These factors are partly indicative of declining catches in other fisheries, of increasing demand for white fish and of the acceptability of Cape hake.

References

Anon. *Cold Storage*, Dec. 1928, p. 385.
1928

Anon. *S. Afr. Shipping News and Fishg Indust. Rev.*, Feb. 1966, p. 85.
1966a

Anon. *Ibid.*, Sept. 1966, p. 121.
1966b

Anon. *Ibid.*, Apr. 1967, p. 89.
1967a

Anon. *Ibid.*, Aug. 1967, p. 89.
1967b

Birds Eye. *Annual Review*, 1972. Birds Eye Foods Ltd., Walton on
1972   Thames, UK, p. 35–39.

BOTHA, L Growth and otolith morphology of the Cape hakes
1971   *Merluccius capensis* Cast. and *M. paradoxus* Franca. Republic of South Africa, Department of Industries, *Division of Sea Fisheries Investigational Report*, No. 97, 32 p.

BOTHA, L and MOMBECK, F Research and conservation on the Cape
1971   hake. *S. Afr. Shipping News and Fishg Indust. Rev.*, 26(12): 59–63.

BURT, J R, DREOSTI, G M, JONES, N R, KELMAN, J H, McDONALD I,
1968   MURRAY, J, SIMMONDS, C K and STROUD, G D The handling of Cape hake. *Fishg News int.*, 7(6):39–42.

BURT, J R, CONNELL, J J, EARLY, J C and LOVE, R M Factors
1969   affecting the quality of frozen fish. In C. Dexter (ed.) *Marketing fish*, London, World Fishing, p. 11–13.

BURT, J R, DREOSTI, G M, JONES, N R, SIMMONDS, C K and
1974a   STROUD G D Technological investigations into Cape hake. I. Freezing ashore of fish chill stored at sea. *J. Fd Technol.* In press.

BURT, J R, DREOSTI, G M, JONES, N R, KELMAN, J H, McDONALD, I,
1974b   MURRAY, J and SIMMONDS, C K Technological investigations into Cape hake. II. Freezing at sea. *J. Fd Technol.* In press.

DASSOW, J A, PATASHNIK, M, and KOURY, B J Characteristics of
1970   Pacific hake, *Merluccius productus*, that affect its suitability for food. US Fish and Wildlife Service, *Bureau of Commercial Fisheries*, Circular 332, p. 127–136.

DAVIES, R and BEYERS, E A protozoal disease of South African
1947   trawled fish and its routine detection by fluorescence. *Nature, Lond.*, 159:174.

DREOSTI, G M and PIENAAR, A G Effect of delay in freezing hake.
1961   *Fishing Industry Research Institute, Cape Town, 15th Annual Report*, p. 16.

DREOSTI, G M and SIMMONDS, C K Rapid chilling of hake. *Fishing
1962   Industry Research Institute, Cape Town, 16th Annual Report*, p. 14–16.

FAO Report of the ACMRR/ICES working party on the fishery
1968   resources of the eastern Central and Southeast Atlantic. Supplement 1 to the report of the fifth session of the Advisory Committee on Marine Resources Research. *FAO Fisheries Reports* No. 56, Suppl. 1, 59 p.

FLECHTENMACHER, W Seehecht-Verarbeitung an Bord. *Inform. für*
1967   *die Fischwirtschaft*, 14(3):131–139.

FLETCHER, L I, Hodgkiss, W and Shewan, J M The milkiness of
1951   Mauretanean hake and its probable cause. *Fishing News*, (2007):11–12.

GILBERG, Y Fresh hake: storage of chilled fish. *Fishing Industry*
1954   *Research Institute, Cape Town, 7th Annual Report*, p. 9–10.

GRIMOLS, R B and TILLMAN, M F Importance of the worldwide
1970   hake, *Merluccius*, resource. US Fish and Wildlife Service, *Bureau of Commercial Fisheries, Circular 332*, p. 1–21.

JONES, B W S. African hake prospects. *Wld Fishg*, 16(10):60–62.

JONES, B W and MACKIE, I M An application of electrophoretic
1970   analysis of muscle myogens to taxonomic studies in the genus *Merluccius*. *Comp. Biochem. Physiol.*, 32:267–273.

JONES, N R Fish as a raw material for freezing: factors influencing
1969   the quality of products frozen at sea. *Freezing and irradiation of fish*, London, Fishing News (Books) Ltd., p. 31–39.

KORDYL, E and KARNICKI, Z Factors influencing quality of frozen
1969   fish at sea in subtropical and tropical areas. *Freezing and irradiation of fish*, London, Fishing News (Books) Ltd., p. 189–195.

MOMBECK, F Weitere Mitteilungen über den Seehecht im süda-
1970   frikanischen Raum. *Arch. Fisch Wiss.*, 21(1):62–66.

MOMBECK, F. 3. Mitteilung über die Seehecht im SO-Atlantik:
1971   Alter und Wachstum. *Arch. Fisch Wiss.*, 22(1):34–40..,

PATASHNIK, M and GRONINGER, H S Jr. Observations on the milky
1964   condition in some Pacific coast fishes. *J. Fish. Res. Bd Can.*, 21(2):335–346.

PIENAAR, A G Discolouration of hake flesh. *Fishing Industry*
1961   *Research Institute, Cape Town, 15th Annual Report*, p· 20–22.

PIENAAR, A G Effect of delay in freezing hake. *Fishing Industry*
1962   *Research Institute, Cape Town, 16th Annual Report*, p. 19.

PIENAAR, A. G. Drip from frozen hake fillets on thawing. *Fishing*
1963   *Industry Research Institute, Cape Town, 17th Annual Report*, p. 15–17.

PIENAAR, A G Drip from frozen hake fillets on thawing. *Fishing*
1964   *Industry Research Institute, Cape Town, 18th Annual Report*, p. 18–19.

PSHENICHNYY, B P and ASSOROV, V V Some biological features of
1969   the Atlantic Ocean hake (*Merluccius*) along the Southwest African coast. *Vop. Ikhtiol.* 9(3):331–338 (of translation journal produced by the Amer. Fish. Soc.).

ROWAN, A N Fresh stockfish. *Fishing Industry Research Institute*,
1952   *Cape Town, 5th Annual Report*, p. 7–8.

ROWAN, A N and MARKS, R H Fresh stockfish: softening of flesh.
1951   *Fishing Industry Research Institute, Cape Town, 4th Annual Report*, p. 11.

ROWAN, M K *Chloromyxum thyrsites* in various South African
1956   fishes. *Fishing Industry Research Institute, Cape Town, 9th Annual Report*, p. 7–8.

SMIT, P G and RUSHBURNE, J L *A survey of the fishing industry in*
1971   *South Africa and South West Africa*. Statsinform (Pty) Limited, South Africa, No. 4, April 1971, p. 71–86.

VAN WYK, G F South African Fish Products. Part VIII. Composi-
1944   tion of the flesh of Cape fishes. *J. Soc. chem. Ind.*, 63:367–371.

WAGENKNECHT, W and HORN, R Lagerungseigenschaften von
1967   Seehecht und anderen bedeutsamen Nutzfischarten der südwestafrikanischen Gewässer. *Fisch.-Forsch.*, 5(3):97–104.

WFA Acceptability of S. Atlantic hake. *White Fish Authority*,
1968   London, *Bull.*, (29):3 p.

WFA Fish Industry Review. *Quarterly Journal of the White Fish*
1972   *Authority, London*, 2(2):40 p.

Problems in the Industrial Utilization of Hake in South Africa   *K A Oettle*

Exploitation commerciale du merlu de l'Afrique du sud.

Examen des effets des activités de chalutage en Afrique du Sud sur l'exploitation des fonds de pêche traditionnels, entre autres la réduction des quantités capturées et la diminution de la taille moyenne du poisson débarqué. Etude succincte de l'historique de cette industrie du chalutage et description des mesures à prendre pour lui conserver sa position, ainsi que les difficultés qui se posent aux transformateurs. Analyse des efforts accomplis pour produire du poisson congelé de bonne qualité, ainsi que des procédés les plus récents utilisés dans la transformation du merlu.

Exploitacion commercial de la merluza de Sudafrica.

Se examinan los efectos que tiene en la industria arrastrera de Sudáfrica la explotación de los caladeros tradicionales, la disminución de las capturas y la reducción de la talla media de los peces descargados. Se pasa en revista brevemente a los antecedentes de esta industria y se describen las medidas que será preciso tomar para que mantenga su posición, junto con las dificultades que encuentran los elaboradores. Se explica lo que se está haciendo por producir pescado congelado de buena calidad y las innovaciones en la elaboración de merluza.

Jones and Van Eck reported that the 1965 level of hake catch represented about 95 per cent of the maximum sustainable yield. This catch was exceeded the following year and was doubled three years later (Table 1). The catch decreased in 1969 for the first time since 1961.

TABLE 1. CATCHES OF HAKE LANDED FROM THE SOUTHEAST ATLANTIC 1961–70 (THOUSANDS OF TONS, LIVE WEIGHT)

1961	1962	1963	1964	1965	1966	1967	1968	1969	1970
95	98	111	170	332	478	505	712	629	663

The catch rates per unit of effort on the Southwest African fishing grounds decreased from 1.1 tons per hour in 1966 to 0.6 tons in 1967. Research has shown that there has been a corresponding decline in the abundance of large fish and an increase in small fish. Table 2 indicates

TABLE 2. LENGTH COMPOSITION OF HAKE LANDINGS FROM 1966 TO 1971 (THOUSANDS OF FISH PER 100 HOURS FISHING) LENGTH MEASURED FROM TIP OF SNOUT TO END OF TAIL

Length group (cm)	1966	1967	1968	1969	1970	1971
30–39	7.9	10.1	11.3	12.7	18.7	15.1
40–59	57.5	53.4	53.4	39.1	39.1	38.7
59–99	22.9	12.0	15.1	13.6	11.3	17.2

the length distribution on Cape grounds from 1966 to 1971. Thus, the South African trawling industry faces a continuing period of declining catches. Technological optimism alone will not solve the basic problem of a dwindling natural resource and an improvement will not be possible until the overexploitation of the resource is either halted or vigourously restricted.

197

THE INDUSTRY

Quality problems

The majority of South African hake live and feed in the cool waters of the Benguela current. Therefore, it is to be expected that the flesh of the fish will deteriorate during catching and handling, particularly in the high environmental temperatures prevailing off the South-west African coast where fishing operations are concentrated for most of the year. As a result, the shore-based facilities can at best expect to receive a raw material of variable and, at times, doubtful quality. The storage life of hake in ice has been found to be ten days. The duration of the fishing trips, therefore, has to be kept within the above limit if the catch is to be utilized as edible fish and the economics of extended fishing trips have to take second place to the necessity for landing an acceptable product. The processing industry's chief problem has been the control of quality of raw material from wet fish trawlers, with particular reference to texture and size of fish. In view of this situation, it was logical that attention would be directed toward freezing at sea. Thus, the South African trawling fleet has, since 1966, been supplemented by stern freezer trawlers. Thirteen vessels of this type are now in operation, freezing fish at sea.

Facilities to ensure good quality hake frozen at sea

In designing the modern fleet of freezer trawlers cognizance was taken of the necessity for chilling the catch immediately it was brought on to the factory deck. Four chill tanks are therefore provided, communicating with the main deck, each tank capable of holding 5 tons of fish and 1.25 tons of Refrigerated Sea Water and a Chilled Sea Water storage tank with a capacity of 5 tons beneath the chill tanks. Four pumps enable the Refrigerated Sea Water (RSW) to be circulated through each tank. Design calculations estimated the chilling load on the tanks at 83,000 kcal/h on the assumption that the fish from the codend would, at the designed sorting, scaling, heading and gutting rate, remain in the chill tanks for a minimum period of 30 minutes and a maximum of 360 minutes.

It was calculated that, after heading and gutting, the fish would be flumed to four smaller bleeding chill tanks each capable of holding 3 tons of fish for one hour prior to the fish being size-graded, packed into the freezing moulds and frozen in the four horizontal plate freezers. The chilling load on these tanks was estimated at 33,000 kcal/h. In practice, however, it has been found that due to the smaller drags than anticipated, these loads were unrealistic. Loads have approached 41,000 kcal/h and 75,000 kcal/h respectively, due to the freshly caught fish not being held in the chill tanks for any length of time. Cooling of the RSW is effected in three shell and tube evaporators and a sophisticated control system of the direct expansion F.22 prevents the evaporation temperature of the refrigerant falling below a predetermined minimum to chill the water to 2°C. Should either the refrigerant-evaporation temperature or the chilled-water temperature happen to fall below the predetermined minimum temperature, the compressor plant is automatically stopped thereby preventing any possibility of freezing up the coolers. As an additional safety precaution a flow switch is installed at the outlet of each cooler in order to stop the compressor plant should there be no flow of sea water through the cooler due to pump failure or blockage of pipes.

The importance of immediately chilling the catch after releasing it from the codend has been stressed by the investigations into the processing of Cape hake and the resulting high quality of the frozen product has certainly justified the expense of providing this facility.

Processing developments

South African hake is presently processed into smoked and quick frozen fillets, skinless and boneless fish blocks for subsequent production of fish portions, etc, and fish cakes and canned spiced (curried) fish. Until a few years ago all operations, with the exception of skinning, were manual. Mainly because of difficulties in maintaining a permanent labour force, mechanization of filleting had to be undertaken and further mechanization will follow to maintain continuity of production, particularly when the flow of raw material is stabilized at a reasonably high level. If the proportion of small fish increases, additional filleting machines will have to be installed to maintain the required tonnage throughput. The rate of filleting, whether by hand or by machine, cannot be increased beyond a set maximum whatever the size of the fish, so coping with smaller fish inescapably calls for more men or machines. Also inevitable is the fact that processing costs must increase in direct proportion to the number of small fish processed and yields will suffer due to the higher bone/flesh ratio in small as compared with large fish. Softness of the raw material from distant fishing grounds has caused concern because a break-up of fillets occurs, perhaps due to extended delays at chill temperatures prior to filleting and freezing. Treatment with sodium tripolyphosphate (TPP) has effected a vast improvement experimentally, even where short dip times were used and the commercial application of the TPP treatment to alleviate the defect is being investigated.

Thawing of sea-frozen whole fish

Sea-frozen round hake is of superb quality, with no problems due to *rigor mortis*, so the solution to the problem of maintaining supplies to the factories lies in the thawing of this fish.

Considerable capital expenditure will be involved in providing the equipment required to thaw sufficient sea-frozen fish to supplement the diminishing supply of chilled fish and processing costs will be further increased in operating the thawing plant. There appears, however, to be no other solution if the present fishing pattern persists.

Market problems

The local fish trade has traditionally been in the wet (chilled) form with certain sections demanding a specific size of fish, usually large. Quick frozen fillets have made inroads into this market but fillet sizes are specified and demanded. A similar position prevails in the export markets for quick frozen fillets. The effect of diminished supplies of wet fish suitable for the local trade has been countered by persuading the market to accept sea-frozen whole hake. The supplies of smaller chilled fish have necessitated the finding of new outlets for the smaller fillets derived from this fish. The use of boning machines, particularly valuable in the case of small fish, necessitated the development of products with which the market is not familiar.

CONCLUSION

While it is recognized that catches of fish can also be affected by natural phenomena over which we have no control, there is a general consensus that it is essential to introduce adequate and effective conservation measures if the industry is to survive. Setting up the Commission for the Conservation of Marine Resources of the Southeast Atlantic Ocean is therefore timely and the implementation of its recommendations is a matter of urgency.

LITERATURE USED

BOTHA, L. Research and conservation on the Cape Hake. *S. African Ship News and Fishing Industry Review*, Dec. 1971.

BOTHA, L. S.A. Trawlfish landings from 1955 to 1968 with special reference to Hake. *S. African Ship News and Fishing Industry Review*, Jan. 1970.

BOTHA, L Unpublished data.

BURT, J R *et al.* The handling of Cape Hake. *Fishing News International*, 7(6)

Eddie, G C The expansion of the fisheries. *The Institute of Mech. Engineers, Proceedings* 1970/71.

FAO *Yearbooks of Fishery Statistics*.

Fish Trades Gazette, 24 June 1972.

Massachussets Institute of Technology *'The limits to Growth'*.

RANKEN, M B F Evaluation of modern techniques and equipment for freezing whole fish at sea. In R Kreuzer (ed.). *Freezing and irradiation of fish*, Fishing News (Books) Ltd., London, 1969, p. 1–23.

The United States Experience with Pacific Hake
(*Merluccius productus*) *J A Dassow and A J Beardsley*

Le merlu du Pacifique (*Merluccius productus*): **experience Americaine.**

L'aire de distribution du merlu du Pacifique (*Merluccius productus*) occupe une vaste étendue du plateau continental de l'océan Pacifiques de l'Alaska à la Baja-Californie. Un stock biologiquement analogue, mais génétiquement distinct de merlus du Pacifique se recontre dans les eaux côtières du Puget Sound, dans l'Etat de Washington. Ce stock est exploité depuis 1966 et a donné des mises à terre relativement stables de 3,600 à 4,500 tonnes par an. Selon le document, l'expérience et l'activité commerciale ont démontré, de 1965 à 1971, la rentabilité d'une pêcherie exploitant le merlu de haute mer par chalutage pélagique. Il ressort d'études techniques antérieures que l'on pourrait utiliser un pourcentage élevé des merlus du Pacifique pour fabriquer des blocs de filets congelés, à condition que le poisson soit réfrigéré convenablement à bord. La présence d'un parasite protozoaire protéolytique (myxosporidien) dans les muscles de certains poissons a donné à la chair une texture spongieuse qui a freiné l'exploitation de cette espèce aux Etats-Unis à des fins alimentaires dans les années soixante. Toutefois, l'incidence du myxosporidien a diminué de manière notable à mesure qu'augmentait l'effort de pêche et l'utilisation du merlu par l'industrie alimentaire semble donc offrir des perspectives favorables. En 1966–67, des essais ont porté sur l'exploitation commerciale du merlu océanique pour la fabrication de farine et d'huile de poisson, mais ces essais n'ont pas été couronnés de succès étant donné les couts d'exploitation, plus élevés que prévu, et le marasme du marché. Une pêcherie industrielle s'est créée pour utiliser le merlu dans les rations de poisson en boulettes et dans les aliments des animaux d'agrément; elle pourrait se développer, car les ressources le permettent. En 1971, le National Marine Fisheries Service a évalué la production de concentrés protéiques de poisson dans une usine de démonstration d'une capacité de 50 tonnes de poisson cru par jour. Les études en cours indiquent que l'emploi du merlu par l'industrie de transformation alimentaire devrait permettre d'utiliser pleinement ce poisson dans l'avenir.

La experiencia de los Estados Unidos con la merluza del Pacifico (*Merluccius productus*)

La merluza del Pacífico (*Merluccius productus*) está distribuida ampliamente en la plataforma continental del Océano Pacífico que se extiende desde Alaska hasta la Baja California. También hay una población aislada genéticamente pero de características biológicas similares de la merluza del Pacifico en las aguas de Puget Sound en el estado de Washington. Esta población se explota desde 1966 y las descargas anuales, relativamente estables, son del orden de 3,600 a 4,500 toneladas. En el documento se describe cómo la posibilidad de una pesca de arrastre pelágica de la merluza de media altura se ha demostrado experimental y comercialmente desde 1965 hasta 1971. Los primeros estudios tecnológicos indicaban que un gran porcentaje de merluza del Pacífico podría emplearse para hacer bloques de filetes congelados, caso de que el pescado pudiera enfriarse convenientemente a bordo. La presencia de un parásito protozoario proteolítico (mixosporidios) en el tejido muscular de algunas merluzas causaba una textura pulposa y fue el factor limitante de la pesca de esta especie con destino a la alimentación en los Estados Unidos en el decenio de 1960. Desde entonces ha disminuido mucho la incidencia del parásito a medida que ha aumentado la pesca y por lo tanto el futuro empleo de la merluza para productos destinados a la alimentación tiene buen porvenir. El empleo de la merluza oceánica para la producción de harina y aceite se ensayó comercialmente en 1966 y 1967 pero no tuvo éxito debido a que los costos de explotación eran mayores de los previstos y el mercado estaba deprimido. La pesca industrial para fabricar comprimidos de merluza con los cuales alimentar peces y animales caseros ha ido prosperando y podrá ampliarse a medida que la disponibilidad de recursos lo permita. La fabricación de concentrados de proteínas de pescado (CPP) en un establecimiento de demostración de una capacidad de 50 toneladas por día (pescado en bruto) fue evaluada por el Servicio Nacional de Pesca Marina en 1971. Los estudios indican que en lo futuro su empleo en los alimentos elaborados permitirán la completa utilización de la merluza del Pacífico.

Hake are cod-like fish, *Merluccius* spp., *Urophycis* spp., harvested commercially in both the Atlantic and Pacific Oceans. Important Atlantic species are the silver hake or whiting, *M. bilinearis* of New England, and the European hake, *M. merluccius* of the North Atlantic, also common in the Mediterranean and Adriatic; the South African hake, *M. capensis;* and the Argentine hake, *M. hubbsi*. In the Pacific the main commercial species are the Chilean hake, *M. gayi*, and the Pacific hake, *M. productus*. The North Atlantic hake has long been an important and valuable food fish. In the South Atlantic both Argentina and South Africa have developed substantial hake fisheries during the past decade, primarily for export as frozen fillet blocks, while South Pacific hake has been used to some extent for food by Chile but more extensively in fish meal production. Pacific hake, *M. productus*, is fished for food locally in California and is taken occasionally by trawlers in California and Oregon for animal feed and industrial purposes. Hake has been regarded generally as an incidental industrial fish and was not considered of commercial importance by most fishermen in the Pacific Northwest until 1964 and 1965. In this report we review the developments in the Pacific hake fishery.

TECHNOLOGICAL EXPERIENCE WITH PACIFIC HAKE

The first task of the technologist in the development of a fishery for a little-utilized species is to establish its physical and technological characteristics. The second task is evaluation for utilization as food or industrial products. Both fishermen and processors may have fixed ideas about the feasibility of various uses depending on practical considerations. These include availability of fish in relation to port and process facilities, expected landing volume, size and keeping quality of the fish, time and duration of the fishing season, and the probable price of the landed fish as determined by all factors. The Pacific coast hake survey of 1965 was planned by the Exploratory Fishing Unit of the Bureau of Commercial Fisheries in Seattle. At that time most people considered hake an undesirable food fish and its greatest potential seemed to be for conversion to fish meal and pet food. But trends showed clearly that a worldwide market existed for additional species of fish suitable for frozen fillet block production to meet the growing demand for breaded fish sticks and fish portions. Such demand seemed certain to improve the price for fish and to make it practical for the trawler to sort and ice the hake catch. To provide for complete utilization of Pacific hake, technological studies were planned on the characteristics and composition of whole fish and the edible portion and their use for both food and industrial products. The technical feasibility of using hake for production of fish protein concentrate (FPC) was evaluated in both small- and large-scale tests during 1970 and 1971. As ocean hake were available during the summer and autumn and Puget Sound hake during the winter and spring, fish were obtained from both sources.

Characteristics and composition

Hake has fairly lean meat with a grey-white-to-pink colouration and a mild-to-neutral odour when fresh. A comparison of the composition of whole hake with Pacific herring (Table 1) shows that hake has slightly less protein and much less oil. Table 2 shows that the protein content of hake fillet is comparable with Pacific cod but that the oil content is significantly higher (although hake is still a moderately lean fish). Fillet yields of hake in one commercial trial with fish of an average weight of 1.1 kg were about 25 per cent, an acceptable commercial yield.

TABLE 1. COMPARISON OF COMPOSITION RANGE OF WHOLE PACIFIC HERRING (*Clupea pallasii*) AND PACIFIC HAKE (*Merluccius productus*), IN PERCENTAGES

| | Pacific herring[a] | | Pacific hake[b] | |
	Minimum	Maximum	Minimum	Maximum
Protein	14.3	17.8	13.4	16.0
Oil	4.9	24.3	1.4	6.0
Moisture	57.7	74.8	72.9	82.9
Ash (total mineral content)	2.3	2.8	2.8	3.8

[a]McBride et al., 1959
[b]Patashnik et al., 1970

Hake meat texture is highly variable but tends to be soft and the fillets may fall apart when handled. If the fish is not iced or refrigerated soon after catch, it develops a strong persistent odour and, in some fish, a mushy meat texture. If cooked while really fresh, Pacific hake is tender and moist, has a mild flavour similar to

TABLE 2. COMPARISON OF COMPOSITION OF PACIFIC HAKE AND COD FILLETS, IN PERCENTAGES

| | Pacific cod[a] | | | Pacific hake[b] | | |
	Minimum	Maximum	Average	Minimum	Maximum	Average
Protein	15.8	19.1	17.9	14.0	17.8	16.1
Oil	0.3	0.8	0.6	0.5	3.1	2.5
Moisture	79.7	83.2	81.5	79.4	84.0	81.3
Ash	1.1	1.3	1.2	1.0	1.5	1.1

[a]Thurston, 1961
[b]Patashnik et al., 1970

some species of sole and flounder, and is suitable for a variety of uses requiring lean white meat.

Abnormal texture of some hake

The completely unacceptable mushy texture was observed in a high percentage of fish from some catches in 1965–66. It usually developed as milky pockets in the meat about four hours after the fish were caught. Investigation (Dassow et al. 1970) showed that the condition was usually associated with the presence of a microscopic myxosporidian parasite, *Kudoa* sp., in the muscle and was similar to that reported in other Pacific fish species (Patashnik and Groninger 1964). The mushy texture was caused by development of a high level of *post mortem* proteolytic activity in meat infected with the parasite. The meat that appeared to be heavily parasitized was discoloured by the metabolic products and had a significantly lower protein content than that of normal hake (Dassow et al. 1970). The incidence of the parasite in Pacific hake catches observed during 1965–66 ranged from 20 to 40 per cent, which precluded use of the fish for fresh or frozen fillets at that time. It was believed, however, that commercial harvesting and normal replacement of the stock would reduce the incidence as had happened with other species (Forrester 1956). This did take place, notably, in the ocean hake harvested during 1971 for the Government's FPC plant at Aberdeen, Washington, when the abnormal texture was not a significant problem in the 1,325 tons of fresh, chilled hake landed. There is no evidence that the myxosporidia can cause illness or infection in man. The problem, therefore, relates primarily to the effect on keeping quality and acceptability of the hake. Cooking readily destroys the organism although it is tolerant to environmental changes in salinity and temperature and appears to remain viable in frozen stored fish. The development of proteolytic activity and mushy texture was observed in parasitized fillets that were frozen, thawed and then held for several hours. For this reason the effective utilization of Pacific hake for high-quality fresh and frozen fish products must be predicated on a hake population in which the incidence of myxosporidian is low.

Evaluation for food use

Keeping quality. During the exploratory fishing of 1965–66, a number of tests were made in which the whole hake were iced immediately aboard the vessel. Fish of the same catch were also held at 15°C ambient temperature and iced six hours or more later. The results showed that Pacific hake should be iced or processed without delay, mainly because of the rapid autolytic (chemical) changes in the meat and skin. If chilled and iced quickly, whole hake remained *in rigor* up to three days. Fillets from hake not over 24 hours out of water were stored in metal fillet containers at 1°C and remained in acceptable condition as long as two weeks. These tests demonstrated that if the fish are chilled properly after catching, their keeping quality is about the same as that of most trawl fish species. During 1971 three trawlers equipped with mechanically-refrigerated sea-water tanks were used to obtain hake for the FPC plant at Aberdeen, Washington. The whole hake were transferred to the pre-chilled sea water after catch and held at 0±1°C during the two to five days required for the vessel to obtain a load and return to the plant. Depending on the operation of the plant, the hake were transferred and held in refrigerated brine tanks (made up with 6 per cent salt by weight) at −1°C for an additional one to four days. Under these conditions whole hake generally remained of food-grade quality for a minimum of seven days. In one instance, hake examined after nine days under refrigeration showed no signs of decomposition although transfers and handling had caused considerable physical damage. Hake showed considerable absorption of sodium chloride during brine storage, depending on storage time and physical damage, and a significant decrease in the protein and non-protein nitrogenous contents. Analysis of fresh whole hake in September 1971 showed an average of 14.7 per cent total protein compared with an average of 12.1 per cent in fish used at the plant. During the same period, fresh, whole hake had an average ash or mineral content of 3.0 per cent compared with 4.9 per cent ash in stored fish, an increase of almost 2 per cent from salt absorption. The moisture content of stored fish was 80.5 per cent, which is in the range noted for whole hake (Table 1).

Both laboratory and commercial tests were made of the feasibility of filleting and freezing hake as individually quick-frozen (IQF) fillets or as frozen fillet blocks. In addition to the incidence of soft fish from myxosporidian infection, there were two problems in producing a high-quality frozen product: (1) excessively soft texture and (2) oxidative rancidity of hake meat during storage. Hake fillets of otherwise good quality that have been stored in the frozen state lose considerable liquid (drip) during thawing which tends to make them soft. However, when dipped briefly, prior to freezing, in a solution containing 2 per cent sodium chloride and 7.5 per cent sodium tripolyphosphate, both the water-holding capacity and the firmness of the fillets were improved to an acceptable level (Dassow *et al.* 1970). In one acceptability trial, portions from frozen blocks of treated hake were seasoned and served as breaded cooked portions. Results showed good acceptability. Oxidative rancidity occurred in the fatty surface meat of frozen hake fillets stored unglazed for only two weeks at −18°C. Lower temperature of storage markedly slowed the rate of oxidation and at −29°C the fillets were not organoleptically rancid until after 18 weeks. The tests showed that the fillets should be well glazed or packaged tightly with a moisture-vapour proof film and stored at the temperature of −29°C to minimize rancidity development. In a study to evaluate the frozen shelf-life and acceptance of portions prepared from frozen hake fillet blocks, Crawford and Law (1972) found that the application of antioxidants

reduced the level of oxidative rancidity during 12 months' storage at −26°C. They concluded that portions prepared from frozen blocks of Pacific hake fillets possessed a relatively high degree of frozen shelf-life stability and acceptance when stored under vacuum in moisture-vapour proof film.

The potential development of FPC as a protein food supplement was reviewed adequately for the first time at the FAO Conference on Fish in Nutrition held in Washington, D.C., in September 1961 (Heen and Kreuzer 1962). Finch (1970) reviewed the later research and developments in the production, safety and nutritional value of FPC. In the United States, research and the initial pilot studies of the production of FPC were based on the processing of red hake (*Urophycis chuss*) by a three-stage counter-current extraction (Knobl *et al.* 1971). The feasibility of commercially producing FPC by a four-stage counter-current IPA extraction from Pacific hake was tested in 1971 by the National Marine Fisheries Service at Aberdeen, Washington (Finch 1969; Ernst 1971). Approximately 450 tons of Puget Sound hake and 1,325 tons of ocean hake were processed from March to September 1971, the highest monthly yield of FPC being 8.1 per cent based on weight of whole fish landed during August. The main reasons for the relatively low yield were the losses in soluble protein and non-protein nitrogenous constituents during brine storage, removal of some protein in deboning prior to extraction, and some losses during extraction primarily in the IPA/water miscella and suspended fines. By deboning, the final protein content was increased and the total mineral (ash) and fluoride contents of the FPC were reduced. Following is the composition of the FPC produced from Pacific ocean hake during the first-phase operation of the plant (Ocean Harvesters 1971):

Protein content	95.6%
Moisture	3.2%
Lipids	0.15%
Ash	3.9%
Fluoride	48 ppm
Residual isopropanol	146 ppm
Total bacterial plate count	3,100 bacteria/g
Sieve analysis	92% finer than US 200-mesh screen

Samples of this FPC were compared organoleptically with that produced in the laboratory from Atlantic red hake. The colour, odour, flavour and physical characteristics were similar. Ten representative samples of the plant FPC were evaluated for protein efficiency ratio (PER) by the standard method and found to be on the average 112 per cent of the casein control. Later, quantities of Pacific hake FPC were made available for larger-scale food supplement studies. Detailed reports of the various studies and the engineering reports of the plant operation are being prepared and published by the National Marine Fisheries Service.

Evaluation for industrial products

Early estimates of the abundance and availability of Pacific hake off the Washington coast indicated that the resource could support an industry for production of fish meal and animal feeds.

The laboratory undertook during 1964–65 cooperative

tests with industrial reduction plants to determine the yield and value of meal and oil from Pacific hake. Early tests with dry-rendering were not successful since the oil in the hake was sufficiently high to produce a meal with an excessive oil content (Nelson and Dyer 1970). Other tests with the wet reduction process were successful and showed that hake could be used to produce high-quality meal, oil and solubles. A commercial wet-reduction plant with a 25 t/h capacity was constructed and began operation late in 1966, and a high-quality hake meal was produced during 1966 and 1967. Berg (1970) reported the average composition of three lots of the meal used for a study of nutritive value in poultry rations as 74.6 per cent protein, 5.7 per cent fat, 14.6 per cent ash, and 4.5 per cent moisture. Berg found that the product compared favourably with herring meal produced in British Columbia. The hake meal promoted good growth when added at the 5 per cent level to a basal ration for broilers. Arscott and Crawford (1969) reported that up to 7.5 per cent hake meal can replace a similar amount of soybean meal protein in a broiler ration with a significant improvement in feed conversion. The hake-meal plant came into operation in July 1966 when fish meal prices were relatively high but declining. During 1967 the development of the industrial hake fishery was supported partly through technical assistance grants, but with declining prices, the costs of harvest proved to be too high for commercial production. This, together with a decreased availability of ocean hake, precluded the success of a high-volume industrial fishery for Pacific hake and the plant was not operated after 1967.

Pacific hake was shown to be useful as an ingredient in low-cost animal foods and continues to be harvested on a moderate scale for use in pet food, mink rations and fish hatchery diets. For these products, the hake is taken as needed and when available in both the Puget Sound and ocean fisheries. The fish is delivered within a day or two of being caught. It is ground, packed into 50-lb (22.7 kg) bags, frozen and stored for later use. For pet food production, frozen ground hake is shipped to a central processing plant where many raw materials are used for processing into a pet food of uniform composition. For fish hatchery diets, hake does not provide energy at a level comparable to accepted wet-fish ingredients in the Oregon Moist Pellet (Crawford et al. 1969). But pasteurized wet hake, supplemented by 28 per cent additional fat and used to replace the 40 per cent turbot-tuna viscera fraction of the pellet, obtained comparable growth responses and conversions for chinook salmon. For use in mink rations, 20 per cent of wet hake could be substituted in the diet provided it was heat processed. Stout et al. (1970) showed that it was essential to inactivate a heat-labile factor in raw hake that interfered with iron metabolism in mink and caused a pelt condition called 'cotton-fur'. Feeding tests in which a 20-per cent level of hake meal was added to the mink diet indicated that growth was somewhat less and not as satisfactory as with diets using the heat-processed wet hake. The use of fresh-ground hake has been considered for other processed feeds in which one or more species may be blended with additives to produce a feed with specified texture and flavour. Patashnik and Kangas (1971) developed a pasteurized whole fish ration for captured marine mammals in which herring is the main ingredient. Hake and other fish may be included in this ration.

DEVELOPMENTS FOR FUTURE HAKE UTILIZATION

The use of Pacific hake for production of fillets poses the problem, as with other trawl fish, that the yield is considerably less than the total amount of edible meat that might be recovered. Our laboratory has investigated methods of mechanically separating the edible meat from headed and gutted fish of various species (Miyauchi and Steinberg 1970). This study showed that 49 per cent edible meat based on the weight of the whole hake could be recovered by utilizing a meat-separating machine developed and used in Japan for the manufacture of fish sausage and kamaboko. Subsequent tests (Teeny and Miyauchi 1972) showed that the minced meat of black rockfish could be treated to produce a satisfactory frozen block suitable for breaded fish stick production. In the future we believe that hake and other lesser-utilized species may be used to produce a variety of the convenience-type foods favoured by US consumers, including breaded fish sticks, fish portions, flavoured fish spreads and fish sausages. In other tests, it was shown that the minced meat may be incorporated as a protein ingredient in other processed fish, meat and cereal foods. Research is continuing in this field to broaden the potential use of Pacific hake as well as many other species. Another development for future hake utilization resulted from our continuing research at Seattle on modified processes for producing FPC and protein isolates from a wide variety of fish species by aqueous extraction procedures. The objective of these processes is to produce FPC and protein isolates in which the desirable functional characteristics of the protein are retained as well as the nutritional value. Spinelli et al. (1972) have reported on methods for preparation of enzymic modifications of myofibrillar fish proteins and the effect of process variables on functional properties of the modified proteins. The potential application of such modified proteins in food systems is being reviewed in a separate report at this Conference. The importance of these and other protein developments to the future of Pacific hake utilization lies in the high value of the products compared to fish meal and animal feeds. Most of the less desirable and little-utilized species are excellent raw materials for either minced meat or protein isolate production. The US experience with Pacific hake has demonstrated again that both availability and assurance of a substantial resource are essential for a successful commercial fishery in which the final product must be produced in large volume at a low price. The development of minced meat products and modified protein isolates from hake and other fish may well provide the versatility and high value that will enable the USA to expand the Pacific trawl fishery and develop the broader utilization of the hake for food.

References

Arscott, T G and Crawford, D L The effect of hake meal in
1969   broiler rations. *Poultry Science*, 48:1123–1125.
Berg, L R Preliminary studies of the nutritive value of hake meal
1970   for poultry. *US Fish. Wildl. Serv. Circ.*, 322:143–148.

CRAWFORD, D L and LAW, D K Shelf life stability and acceptance
1972 of frozen Pacific hake (*Merluccius productus*) fillet portions. *Jour. Fd Sci.*, 37:801–802.

CRAWFORD, D L, LAW, D K, McKEE, T B and MILLS, D E Hake a
1969 source of protein for hatchery fish nutrition. *Proceedings of the Twelfth Annual Northwest Fish Culture Conference*, 76 p.

DASSOW, J A, PATASHNIK, M and KOURY, B Characteristics of Pacific
1970 hake, *Merluccius productus*, that affect its suitability for food. *US Fish. Wildl. Serv. Circ.*, 322:127–136.

ERNST, R C Jr. FPC: The NMFS experiment and demonstration
1971 plant process. *Com. Fish. Rev.*, 33(2):22–28.

FINCH, R The US fish protein concentrate program. *Ibid.* 31(1):
1969 25–30.

FINCH, R Fish proteins for human foods. *Critical Reviews on Food*
1970 *Technology*, 1:519–580.

FORRESTER, C R The relation of stock density to 'milkiness' of
1956 lemon sole in Union Bay, B.C. *Fish. Res. Bd Can. Prog. Rept. Pac. Coast Sta.*, 105:11.

HEEN, E and KREUZER, R Fish in Nutrition, London, *Fishing News*
1962 (*Books*) Ltd., 445 p.

KNOBL, G M Jr., STILLINGS, B R, Fox, W R and HALE, M B Fish
1971 protein concentrates. *Com. Fish. Rev.*, 33(7–8):54–63.

MIYAUCHI, D and STEINBERG, M Machine separation of edible flesh
1970 from fish. *Fish. Ind. Res.* 6(4):165P171.

NELSON, R W and DYER, J A Production of meal and oil from hake.
1970 *Ibid.* 332:127–142.

Ocean Harvesters, Inc. Summary Report of the Hake Run 1971.
1971 *Contract No. 14–17–0007–980.* (Natl. Mar. Fish. Serv., US Dept. of Commerce, Washington, D.C.), 47 p.

PATASHNIK, M and KANGAS, P 'Tek-Food', A pasteurized whole
1971 fish ration for captive marine mammals. *Laboratory Animal Sci.* 21(3):406–409.

PATASHNIK, M and GRONINGER, H S Jr. Observations on the milky
1964 condition in some Pacific coast fishes. *J. Fish. Res. Bd Can.* 21:335–346.

SPINELLI, J, B KOURY and MILLER, R Approaches to the utilization
1972 of fish for the preparation of protein isolates. Enzymic modifications of myofibrillar fish proteins. *J. Fd Sc.* 37:604–608.

STOUT, F M, ADAIR, J and OLDFIELD, J E Feeding Pacific hake to
1970 mink. *US Fish. Wildl. Serv. Circ.* 332:149–152.

TEENY, F M and MIYAUCHI, D Preparation and utilization of frozen
1972 blocks of minced black rockfish muscle. *J. Milk and Fd Tech.* 35(7):414–417.

Prospects for Utilizing Capelin (*Mallotus villosus*) for Human Consumption   *P M Jangaard*

Perspectives de l'utilisation du capelan (*Mallotus villosus*) pour l'alimentation humaine.

Le capelan est un petit poisson pélagique (15–20 cm) se trouvant en grandes quantités dans les régions septentrionales de l'Atlantique et du Pacifique. En 1972, les prises mondiales de capelan ont atteint de 1,9 à 2 millions de tonnes, la Norvège en ayant capturé à elle seule 1,6 million de tonnes. Mais 8–10,000 tonnes seulement ont servi à l'alimentation humaine, la plus grande partie ayant été transformée en huile et en farine de poisson.

Le capelan est considéré depuis des siècles comme une source importante de matière première pour la fabrication de denrées alimentaires, d'appâts, de produits pour l'alimentation animale et d'engrais dans les régions où ce poisson est facilement capturable à l'époque du frai.

On estime que le capelan frais est un excellent poisson comestible. Diverses études ont révélé que le capelan capturé au cours des migrations de reproduction se conserve bien sous congélation et que l'équipement de transformation que l'on trouve dans le commerce peut, moyennant de légères modifications, servir à préparer le poisson pour une ultérieure congélation ou mise en conserve. Le mâle, plus grand que la femelle, convient particulièrement bien à cet effet; les femelles grainées sont exportées au Japon à l'état congelé. Plusieurs produits en conserve à base de capelan présentent de bonnes possibilitités commerciales. Divers concentrés de protéines de capelan ont été préparés et évalués du point de vue nutritionnel.

Perspectivas del aprovechamiento del capelan (*Mallotus villosus* Para el consumo humano.

El capelán es un pequeño pez pelágico (15–20 cm) que se encuentra en grandes cantidades en la parte septentrional del Atlántico y del Pacífico. Las capturas mundiales en 1970 ascendieron a 1,9–2 millones de toneladas, de las cuales 1,6 millones correspondieron a Noruega. Sólo de 8–10,000 toneladas de este total se utilizaron para el consumo humano, transformándose el resto en harina y aceite.

En las zonas en que es fácil pescar el capelán durante la temporada de desove, este pez ha sido considerado durante siglos una fuente importante de alimentos, cebo, piensos y a bonos.

El capelán fresco es excelente para el consumo. Los estudios realizados han demostrado que el capturado durante sus movimientos migratorios para desovar se conserva bien en frigorífico y que es posible utilizar equipo de elaboración que se encuentra en el mercado, modificándolo ligeramente, para elaborarlo con vistas) a su congelación o envasado posteriores. Para estos productos son especialmente adecuados los capelanes machos de gran talla, mientras las hembras con huevas se exportan congeladas al Japón. Se ha mostrado que el capelán questo en conserva de distintas maneras ofrece buenas posibilidades comerciales. Se han preparado y evaluado nutricionalmente varios concentrados de proteínas de capelán.

The capelin, *Mallotus villosus* (Müller 1777), has a circumpolar distribution and can be found in the northern regions of the Atlantic and the Pacific. In the eastern Atlantic capelin are most abundant in winter and spring off Finmark, northern Norway, and northern USSR They are widely distributed throughout the Barents Sea and occur sporadically in the White Sea and the Kara Sea. Capelin are abundant in waters off Iceland, Greenland, Newfoundland and Labrador, and are also found in the northern Pacific. During the spawning migration, to the coasts of Newfoundland and Labrador, Iceland, Norway and Greenland, the schools of capelin are followed by cod and salmon, and seals and whales also feed heavily on the fish at other times of the year. The famous Newfoundland inshore cod fishery developed as a result of this migration, contributing to the early settling of Newfoundland. Capelin belong to the suborder Salmonoidea and, with the smelts, comprise the family

Osmeridae. Mature specimens are generally 13–20 cm in length, although fish up to 24.5 cm have been recorded. During the first year both the male and female are the same size, but during the second year the differential growth rate favours the male which is 1.0–2.5 cm larger than the female at maturity (Winters 1969). Since most capelin spawn only once, the size of the stock is dependent on each year-class for success and, therefore, large variations in abundance can occur. The route of the spawning migration and the area of spawning can also change, causing local failures in the fishery.

COMPOSITION

Capelin show large seasonal variations in fat and water content. The Newfoundland and Labrador capelin, which spawn in June–July, reach a minimum fat content and maximum water content at the end of this period. The fish move offshore and feed in summer and autumn and by November the fat content can be as high as 20 per cent. During winter this drops slowly and, as the gonads develop in the spring, a further decline occurs as shown in Fig. 1. The Barents Sea–Norwegian capelin spawn earlier in the spring and reach a minimum fat content in April. The fish then migrate to the Bear Island–Spitzbergen area for feeding.

WORLD CATCH AND FISHING METHODS

The world catch of capelin is listed in Table 1.

TABLE 1. WORLD CATCH OF CAPELIN (METRIC TONS)

	1972	1971	1970	1969	1968	1967
Norway	1,600,000	1,371,000	1,301,000	678,900	522,200	402,800
Iceland	270,000	182,900	188,600	171,000	78,200	97,200
USSR	N.A.	20,800	15,400	900	19,100	5,700
Canada	4,400	2,600	3,500	3,600	3,400	3,800
Greenland	N.A.	2,500	3,100	200	200	3,700
Total	—	1,579,900	1,511,600	854,600	623,100	513,200

In Norway the chief fishery is carried out during the spawning migration, but considerable quantities of feeding capelin are taken in August–October in some years. The whole of the Icelandic catch consists of pre-spawning capelin. The capelin off Newfoundland and Labrador differ in schooling behaviour from those in the Barents Sea and most of the small catch is taken with traps or nets close to shore, but midwater trawls appear to be the most efficient gear for coastal and offshore areas.

METHODS OF UTILIZATION

In Greenland the 'angmagssat' have always been very important in the life of the Eskimos. In May–June the Greenlanders travelled to the spawning areas in the fjords where at low tide the fish were taken in dipnets and placed on rocks to dry. If wet weather coincided with the fishing season, the catch could be ruined. The dried capelin were stored in sacks for winter provisions. Capelin has been called the 'Greenlander's daily bread' since it was used daily in the winter. Capelin is still important as a food fish there and quantities are also used to feed dogs and sheep (Hansen and Hermann 1953). In Newfoundland the 'caplin' has traditionally been used fresh or salted and dried for human consumption and fed to dogs and other animals. Capelin were also spread on the fields as a fertilizer. Fresh capelin have always been considered an excellent bait for cod. In Norway some 'lodde' was traditionally used fresh for human consumption and fresh and salted for animal feed. The same uses were made of the 'loona' in Iceland and the 'moiva' in northern USSR.

More than 99 per cent of the present world catch is used for the production of meal and oil. Capelin meal has been subjected to extensive analyses and feeding tests and has been shown to have excellent nutritional qualities (Jangaard et al. 1973). Several batches of meal were recently produced in Norway and evaluated as a

protein supplement for human consumption. The results were good and the product appeared to be highly acceptable in several African and Asian countries. The protein content of the meals ranges from 67 to 72 per cent with a fat content of 7–12 per cent, ash 8–11 per cent and moisture 6–12 per cent. Table 2 lists the nutritional composition of meals from Newfoundland and Norway.

Capelin oil has been widely used in the production of margarines and shortenings after hydrogenation and refining. It has a relatively low iodine value which varies with fishing area and season. Typical analytical data are given in Table 3.

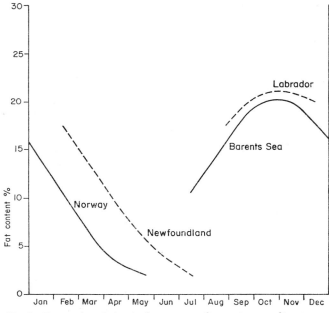

Fig 1   Seasonal variation in fat content of maturing capelin

PROSPECTS FOR INCREASED UTILIZATION FOR HUMAN CONSUMPTION

Consumption of fresh capelin is limited to the area where the fish are landed and increased utilization must be based on frozen raw material. The comparatively lean capelin (1–8 per cent fat) have been shown to stand up exceptionally well in frozen storage. Reports indicate that, quick frozen, it can be stored for at least a year without objectionable deterioration in eating quality. Few, if any, controlled studies have been carried out and little information is available on the storage stability of fat capelin (Jangaard 1973). Although the reason for the

TABLE 2. NUTRITIONAL COMPOSITION OF CAPELIN MEALS

Amino acid	g/100 g protein		Vitamin	ppm	
	Canadian[a]	Norwegian[b]		Canadian	Norwegian
Lysine	8.23	7.77	Thiamine	1,20	—
Methionine	3.10	2.83	Riboflavin	7.55	—
Cystine	1.32	1.29	Panthothenic acid	19.6	—
Tryptophan	1.17	1.15	Niacin	54.1	—
Histidine	2.50	2.03	Choline chloride	6.100	—
Arginine	6.18	5.69	Biotin	0.469	—
Threonine	4.61	4.28	Folic acid	0.408	—
Valine	4.87	5.24	Vitamin B_{12}	0.107	—
Isoleucine	4.27	4.51			
Leucine	9.66	7.56		% of meal	
Phenylalanine	4.18	3.81			
Tyrosine	3.67	3.64	Protein	72.2	70.2
Aspartic acid	9.01	9.18	Fat (soxhlet)	9.3	8.8
Serine	4.30	4.05	Water	8.0	7.9
Glutamic acid	13.86	13.43	Ash	8.8	9.8
Proline	3.63	3.07	Calcium—Ca	2.0	1.72
Glycine	5.25	4.98	Phosphorus—P	1.7	1.75
Alanine	4.95	6.12	Magnesium	0.25	0.13
Available lysine	6.2	6.6			

[a]Jangaard et al. 1973
[b]Opstvedt et al. 1970

good frozen storage stability has not been studied, it could be due partly to the low iodine value of the depot fat. Herring, however, are susceptible to rancidity in frozen storage, even though the iodine value of their oil in some cases is as low as that of capelin (100–110). The distribution of depot fat globules in muscle tissues of capelin is probably different, since it is often difficult to press enough oil from them. Cooking at lower temperatures (60°C) seems to assist in liberating the oil globules. It is also possible that natural antioxidants are present in capelin.

The difference in size between female and male capelin during the spawning migration makes it possible to a certain extent to segregate them in commercial grading machines. The roe-containing females have been frozen whole in recent years and exported to Japan where they are further processed by drying, in some caser preceded by salting or smoking. Norway and Iceland supplied most of this product in 1972 (7–8,000 tons). The larger

male capelin, averaging 18.5 cm in length in catches taken off Newfoundland, have been shown to make good frozen products. Eviscerated capelin with the head removed appear to be the most promising product for the North American market. Freshwater smelt, a fish belonging to the same family as capelin and similar in eating quality, are being marketed successfully in Canada and the United States. They are gutted and cleaned and the heads removed mechanically. They are then marketed, plain or breaded, frozen in plastic bags. Frozen and thawed capelin were successfull processed in this equipment and taste panel evaluations were favourable. Capelin can be fried, baked or broiled. The bones are then so soft that even the backbone can be eaten. Similar experiments carried out on Greenland capelin included an attractive product in puffed batter. On a smaller scale the gutting and heading can be done with scissors or shears (Sepic and MacCallum 1969). Two major manufacturers of fish-processing equipment have experimented

TABLE 3. MAJOR FATTY ACIDS IN SAMPLES OF CAPELINE LIPIDS AND COMMERCIAL OILS (IN WEIGHT PER CENT)

Fatty acid	Canada				Norway		
	Total lipids[a]		Total lipids[b]		Oil[b]		Commercial oil[a]
14:0	9.3	7.4	6.7	7.6	8.1	8.2	7.9
16:0	8.5	11.1	11.3	14.9	9.0	13.5	11.1
16:1	15.1	15.0	8.2	7.4	8.7	7.6	11.1
18:0	1.8	1.5	1.3	1.6	1.1	1.3	1.0
18:1	7.6	10.7	17.3	20.3	17.4	22.9	17.0
18:2	0.4	0.8	1.2	1.6	1.2	1.5	1.7
18:4	0.9	1.5	0.9	2.5	1.0	2.5	2.1
20:1	22.7	14.8	20.5	13.0	24.9	14.7	18.9
20:5	6.1	10.1	5.3	6.1	2.9	4.6	4.6
22:1	19.6	12.7	15.6	12.2	19.5	13.9	14.7
22:6	2.6	7.3	7.4	7.0	1.7	3.7	3.0
Total lipids in fish	1.9	3.9	6.8	10.3	—	—	—
Phospholipids in lipids	8.8	24.1	15.7	6.5	—	—	—
Iodine value	113	154	125.4	130.7	96.7	110.5	109

[a]Ackman et al. 1969
[b]Urdahl and Nygard 1971

by using machines designed for handling small herring or sprats. Some modifications may have to be introduced due to the slightly different shape and the larger fins found in male capelin, but individual fillets, butterfly fillets and headed and 'nobbed' (viscera pulled out) capelin were produced for evaluation. Although little work appears to have been carried out on the processing of fat capelin, reports indicate that the eating quality is excellent. A Soviet author (Prokhorov 1967) points out that fat capelin would be a better raw material for frozen and canned products than those caught during the spawning migration. Recent reports indicate that Soviet factory vessels are indeed taking considerable quantities of fat capelin off Labrador.

Acceptable canned products have been produced in several countries, although only minor quantities have been marketed in western countries. Frozen raw material can be used and the fish should be gutted and thoroughly cleaned to prevent off-flavours developing. The most successful canned pack tested has been a lightly smoked product in vegetable oil (Lantz 1966). Due to the high water content of spawning capelin, the fish must be subjected to extra drying before being placed in the cans. A modified process using smoke oil flavouring has given good results (Iredale, D. G. 1972, *Fish. Res. Bd. Can., Winnipeg, Man.,* personal communication), and capelin frozen for two, four and six months before canning were rated equal to fresh canned capelin (Horne 1961). A Soviet publication (Zaitsev *et al.* 1969) indicates that the fish are being used as a raw material for several canned products in that country. Especially mentioned are fried capelin packed in oil, fried in vegetable garnish and marinade and lightly smoked in oil. The Research Laboratory of the Norwegian Canning Industry in Stavanger has also carried out a number of canning experiments with both lean and fat capelin. Several products, especially smoked, were of good quality. Fat capelin packed in salt and spices on the fishing vessel resulted in a good quality anchovy product, and a paste with added tomato purée and spices was also rated as successful.

Dried fresh or dried salted capelin are still being produced in some areas where capelin are caught, few being consumed outside these areas. The only exception is the dried female capelin exported to Japan. Small quantities of both lightly and heavily smoked capelin are produced, especially in the provinces of Newfoundland and Quebec. The use of capelin in minced fish products has not yet been extensively studied and no published reports

are available. The high moisture content of the fish in the spawning season might necessitate draining off the excess water. The black lining in the gut cavity will give paste an unappetizing grey colour if it passes through the holes of the separator. If these problems could be solved, minced fish products, such as fish cakes and fish sticks, could become important. Capelin are well suited as a raw material for fish protein concentrate production and quantities have been experimentally prepared by the Halifax Isopropanol Process and evaluated nutritionally. Pilot plant studies are also underway to produce a functional fish protein (FFP) from capelin.

References

ACKMAN, R G, KE, P J, MACCALLUM, W A and ADAMS, D R New-
1969 foundland capelin lipids: fatty acid composition and alterations during frozen storage. *J. Fish. Res. Bd. Canada,* 26:2037–2060.

HANSEN, P M and HERMANN, F Capelin. In *Fish and ocean at*
1953 *Greenland,* p. 85–88.

HORNE, D C Canning of capelin. *Ann. Rep. Tech. Unit, Fish. Res.*
1961 *Bd. Canada, St. John's 1960–61.* M.S., p. 28–31.

JANGAARD, P M Capelin. *Fish. Res. Bd. Can. Bull.,* In preparation.
1973

JANGAARD, P M, REGIER, L W, CLAGGETT, F G, MARCH, B E and
1973 BIELY, J Nutrient composition of experimentally produced meals from whole argentine, capelin, sand lance and from flounder and redfish filleting scrap. *J. Fish. Res. Bd. Can.,* Submitted.

LANTZ, A W Special products from freshwater fish. *Fish. Res. Bd.*
1966 *Can. Bull.,* 151:45 p.

MACCALLUM, W A, ADAMS, D R, ACKMAN, R G, KE, P J, DYER, W J
1969 FRASER, D I and PUNJAMAPIRON, S Newfoundland capelin: Proximate composition. *J. Fish. Res. Bd. Can.,* 26:2027–2035.

OPSTVEDT, J, OLSEN, S, URDAHL, N, LAKSESVELA, B and BJÖRNSTAD J
1970 The nutritive value of fish meal produced from different species of fish. *Meldinger fra SSF,* (4), Dec. 1970: 117–167

PITT, T K Distribution, spawning and racial studies of the capelin,
1958 *Mallotus villosus* (Müller), in the offshore Newfoundland area. *J. Fish. Res. Bd. Can.,* 15:275–293.

PROKHOROV, V S Ecology of the Barents Sea capelin (*Mallotus*
1965 *villosus villosus* (Müller)) and prospects for its commercial utilization. Tr. PINRO 19:1–70. (*Fish. Res. Bd. Can. Transl. Ser.,* (813), 1967).

SEPIC, K and MACCALLUM, W A Heading and gutting of capelin
1969 with special hand shears. *J. Fish. Res. Bd. Can.,* 26:2257–2259.

TEMPLEMAN, W The life history of the capelin (*Mallotus villosus*
1948 O F Müller) in Newfoundland waters. *Res. Bull. Nfld. Govt. Lab.,* 17:151 p.

URDAHL, N and NYGÅRD, E Fat composition and distribution from
1971 raw material to end-product meal and oil. *Meldinger fra SSF,* (1), April 1971, p. 3-22.

WINTERS, G H Capelin (*Mallotus villosus*). In F E Firth, (ed.)
1969 Encyclopedia of Marine Resources. Van Nostrand Reinhold Co., N Y. p. 94–101.

ZAITSEV, V, KIZEVETTER, I, LAGUNOV, L, MAKAROVA, T, MINDER, L
1969 and PODSEVALOV, V Fish curing and processing. MIR Publ. Moscow. 722 p.

Technology of Processing of Atlantic Sardine   *M Bidenko, V Shenderyuk and L Agzhitova*

Technologie de la transformation de la sardine de l'Atlantique.

Le document passe brièvement en revue les caractéristiques biologiques de quatre espèces de sardine de l'Atlantique appartenant au genre *Sardinella* qui constituent le gros des captures de ce poisson par l'URSS Il fournit des données expérimentales sur les propriétés technologiques et chimiques des sardines, ainsi que les résultats d'observations sur leurs modifications qualitatives dans différentes conditions d'entreposage. Il prête une attention considérable au problème de la production de diverses denrées ali-

Technologia de la elaboracion de la sardina del Atlantico.

En este documento se describen brevemente las características biológicas de las cuatro especies de sardina del Atlántico pertenecientes al género *Sardinella* que representan el grueso de las capturas de estas especies por parte de la URSS Se dan a conocer datos experimentales sobre las propiedades técnicas y químicas de las sardinas y los resultados de observaciones acerca de sus cambios cualitativos, según sean las condiciones de su almacenamiento. Se presta especial atención al problema de la producción de diversos

mentaires à base de sardine de l'Atlantique. Le document décrit aussi des méthodes permettant d'accélérer le processus de maturation des produits légèrement salés, et des moyens d'en améliorer la qualité.

The genus *Sardinella* includes many species inhabiting the tropical and subtropical waters of the Atlantic and Indian Oceans, as well as the western parts of the Pacific Ocean and adjacent seas. The USSR mainly fish sardines of the genus *Sardinella* in the Central East Atlantic where four species occur: *Sardinella aurita* (including *Sardinella aurita terrasae*), *S. eba*, *S. maderensis* and *S. cameronensis*. The Soviet sardine fishery based on *S. aurita* and *S. eba* is worked by trawls and purse seines. The trawlers freeze their catch while the seiners deliver theirs to factory ships to be frozen or salted to make salted, spiced products. Land-based plants also produce salted, spiced, cured and various canned products. 'Sardines in oil', as well as spiced, salted and cured products, made mainly from *S. aurita terrasae*, are in popular demand.

TECHNOLOGICAL PROPERTIES OF THE RAW MATERIAL

In view of the importance of the fishery, the AtlantNIRO laboratories give a good deal of attention to investigation of the stocks and their possible utilization for fish products. Sampling at sea has been carried out through the fishing season to determine the technochemical characteristics of the Atlantic sardine. Investigations have covered commercial length of fish, weight, fat content and weight ratio of separate parts of the fish (head, body, internal organs). Mean values of these are given in Table 1. The fat content in sardine flesh may vary not only with the month, but also within one catch. This is due to the different stages of maturity of the fish. An attempt has been made to relate fat content to length, depth, thickness and girth of the fish body. However, it was found that there is no strict relationship between the above parameters.

TABLE 1. SEASONAL DATA ON CERTAIN CHARACTERISTICS OF ATLANTIC SARDINE

Fishing period	Size (cm)	Weight (g)	Fat content in flesh (%)
January	28	373	9.1
February	29	408	6.8
March	29	440	9.1
April	26	279	10.6
May	26	278	9.5
June	27	300	8.0
July	26	291	5.1
August	25	273	3.8
September	27	343	7.5
October	28	379	9.8
November	29	391	7.3
December	28	354	7.4

HANDLING BEFORE PROCESSING

As catches are irregular and often small it is necessary to accumulate raw material to give even loading of processing equipment. Investigations into the variation of fish quality under different conditions and at different temperatures of storage have been conducted, with the

objective of determining the optimum storage conditions before processing. The ambient temperature at the fishing grounds is about 22° to 27°C, with the water temperature at 18° to 22°C. Sardine taken by purse seine were used for these investigations (see Table 2).

TABLE 2. THE DURATION OF *rigor mortis* IN ATLANTIC SARDINE WHEN HELD WITHOUT COOLING, IN ICE AND IN COOLED SEA WATER

Storage conditions	Temperature of fish (°C)	Duration of rigor mortis (h)
40 cm layer without cooling	17–20	6–8
40 cm layer after cooling with fine granular ice	2–4	40–48
In cooled sea water at ratio of fish weight and water 2:1	2–4	48

Cooling of fish immediately after catch and storing them in cooled sea water allows the accumulation of raw material for full and economic operation of the processing plant. As a rule, such cooled material is not kept on board the factory ships for more than 6 to 8 h before being processed to provide frozen, salted and spiced fish products of high quality.

PROCESSING

The raw material

Most of the sardine caught is frozen on board and then processed ashore. Automatic quick freezers of various designs are used. Freezing temperature is between −28° and −35°C. The freezing time for a block of 10 cm thickness is 2.5 to 4 h, with the final temperature of the frozen fish being −18° to −20°C. The fish is glazed to reduce desiccation and fat oxidation. The total storage time of the frozen fish from freezing until its arrival at the processing plants in different parts of the USSR is 60 to 90 days. Yellowing of the fish surface is a characteristic of frozen sardine as well as of other marine species. The yellow colour is frequently attributed to oxidation when assessing quality by the organoleptic method. However, investigations carried out on marine and fresh-water fish, including sardines, indicate that yellowing in the subsurface layer is not always associated with fat oxidation. This frequently appears in the course of refrigeration even in the first days of storage of high quality fish. As is known, most fish species possess fat-soluble carotenoid pigments in the skin of the dorsal and lateral parts. The investigations have shown that the colouring of the subsurface layer in the early period of storage is due to the migration of the carotenoid pigments from the skin into the subsurface layer. This has been confirmed by the identification of carotenoids in the skin and subsurface layer by spectrophotometric examination. Such yellowing is not accompanied by a noticeable loss of quality, as might be expected in the case of fat oxidation. This, for example, can be seen from the data on pilchard fat analysis (Table 3). Carotenoids from the kin can be detected in muscle tissue (Fig. 1). The movement of carotenoids into the subsurface layer is associated with the initial dehydration of the skin during freezing or shortly after, especially under the influence of sunlight. Subsurface yellowing in the sardine is usually slight and mainly near the head or the dorsal fin. However, in some cases the colour is more intense on the dorsal and lateral surfaces. The degree of discolouration depends on the

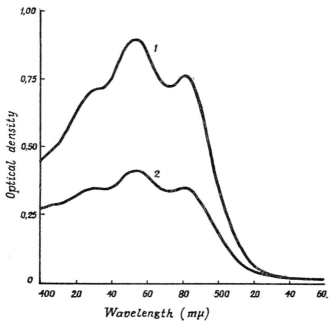

Fig 1 *A spectrum of carotenoid intake in Atlantic sardine: 1—from the skid; 2—from the subsurface layer*

fat content of the fish, the amount of carotenoids in the fat, and the physiological condition and other properties of the fish. Carotenoids act as weak antioxidants during storage of the frozen fish. They tend to stabilize non-oxidated and weakly oxidated fat. Thus, in sardines with or without slight subsurface yellowing, the intensity of the fat oxidation varies. Table 4 gives the aldehyde number

TABLE 3. ANALYSIS OF FAT FROM FROZEN PILCHARD AFTER VARIOUS PERIODS OF COLD STORAGE

Duration of fish storage h	Acid number mg KOH	Peroxide number iodine (%)	Aldehyde number (mg%)	Iodine number ioidne (%)	Carote-noids
0	3.5	0.02	0	180	traces
5 (yellowing appeared)	3.5	0.03	0.12	180	0.3
120	3.8	0.3	0.20	174	1.9

TABLE 4. THE ALDEHYDE NUMBER (MG% CINNAMON ALDEHYDE) FOR FISH MUSCLE TISSUE WITH AND WITHOUT CAROTENOIDS AFTER DIFFERENT PERIODS OF STORAGE

Storage duration days	Aldehyde number (mg%)	
	with carotenoids	without carotenoids
50	0.58	0.75
65	0.63	0.78
80	1.04	0.82

in fish muscle tissue. After 50 days storage, when slight signs of rancidity appeared, the aldehyde number was greater in the fish without carotenoids. However, with increased storage periods the antioxidant effect was lost. Thus the antioxidant properties of carotenoid can be extended by strict adherence to technological rules for handling during freezing and cold storage, and in particular by lowering the storage temperature.

Production of some spiced and salted products

Production of spiced products from sardines has been developed considerably in the USSR. Chilled sardines are mainly used for this purpose. The heads are first removed along with the viscera by special machines. This process, whilst removing inedible material, assists in the removal of blood which discolours the flesh if allowed to remain, especially in the area of the backbone. The beheaded fish is then washed in cool water to prevent excessive temperature rise, mixed with a salt/sugar mixture and packed into 3,033-ml cans. Afterwards the required amount of saturated solution of NaCl and C_6H_5COONa is added and the can is hermetically sealed and stored at temperatures of $-2°$ to $-4°C$ to allow maturation. The following amounts of ingredients (in g) are recommended for producing semi-spiced products: fish – 2,560, common salt – 171, saturated solution of sodium chloride – 235, sugar – 30.4, C_6H_5COONa – 2.6. For spiced products: fish – 2,600, spices and salt – 233, saturated solution of sodium chloride – 167. The use of mixed salting accelerates the salting process and assists in obtaining products of high quality. The dynamics of sardine salting and changes in fish weight during the process of storage are given in Table 5.

TABLE 5. CHANGES IN FISH AND BRINE DURING STORAGE

Storage time (days)	Technological and chemical indices of spiced products		
	Salt content (%)	Fish weight (% of the weight of packed fish)	Specific gravity of brine (g/cm³)
1	4.3	91.1	1.147
2	5.3	92.0	1.131
3	6.2	92.2	1.222
4	6.6	92.0	1.122
6	7.6	93.4	1.110
10	7.8	94.1	1.106
15	7.6	95.2	1.106
20	8.3	95.6	1.105
30	8.3	96.3	1.111
60	8.1	99.7	1.110
90	8.0	100.2	1.112

The data indicate that the salting process is practically completed after 6 to 10 days of storage while changes in fish weight owing to diffusion processes take place throughout the period. We can judge that the salting process ends when the specific gravity of the brine reaches 1.106 to 1.110. The dynamics of the maturation of the semi-spiced products made from sardine caught in September can be seen in Table 6. It is expressed according to the indices adopted in the USSR (ie, buffer capacity in degrees and nitrogen of free amino groups, in mg%).

According to organoleptic tests, the product was ready

TABLE 6. CHANGES OF MATURATION INDICES, BUFFER CAPACITY AND FREE AMINO NITROGEN

Maturation after (days)	Values of maturation indices	
	Buffer capacity (degree)	Nitrogen of free amino groups (mg %)
30	126	176
60	184	201
120	206	317

for eating after three months of storage. It is worthwhile noting that though sardine belongs to Clupeidae, the taste and smell of mature sardines differ from those of herring, eg, Atlantic herring, to a considerable extent. This difference may be explained by certain peculiarities of the basic maturing process which create the flavour and odour due to biochemical reactions during fermentation. Fig. 2 shows typical pH characteristics of raw proteinase which is responsible at least in part for these maturation changes. Curve 1 describes the activity of proteolytic enzyme systems measured by the accumulation

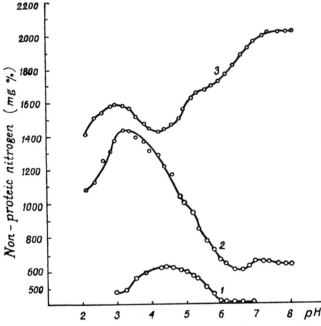

Fig 2 A dependence of the proteolyric ferment activity on pH of reaction mixture: 1—in muscle tissue; 2—in round fish with empty stomachs; 3 in round fish with filled stomachs

of non-protein nitrogen during the hydrolysis of muscle tissue at 30°C; curve 2 gives the same index for round fish with the stomach empty; curve 3 for round fish with the stomach full. As can be seen, the optimum pH for muscle proteinase activity is 4 to 5; round fish with the stomach empty is characterized by 2 complexes of proteinase – one active in acid medium (optimum pH 3 to 4) and one active in alkaline conditions (optimum pH 7.5). Food in the digestive tract greatly affects the activity of the alkaline ferment complex. Gutting the fish has a great influence upon the composition of the ferments involved in maturation, and upon the speed of the process as well as on the quality of the final product. The USSR and other countries are carrying out work on the utilization of ferment preparations to speed up the maturation process.

It is possible that the maturation of salted fish products may be accelerated by using either microbiological enzymes and/or proteinase preparations obtained from natural raw materials, such as the internal organs of fish which have a highly active complex of proteolytic ferments. When using enzyme preparations in such a way, it is a basic necessity to consider their properties, including their ability to catalyze certain reactions. The enzyme preparation should be chosen according to the processing technique involved and the required characteristics and eating quality of the final product. The experimental data collected by the USSR indicate that microbial enzyme preparations differ from the proteinase enzyme system of the raw material and cannot imitate the natural maturation process in salted fish brought about by their own proteinase complex. To accelerate the maturation process of salted sardine products the microbial enzyme preparation, terrizyme, was used, obtained from *Aspergillus terricola*, and a preparation of proteolytic enzymes obtained from the internal organs of marine fish. All the experiments were based on chilled sardines. The fat content in the fish flesh was 2 to 5 per cent. Prior to salting, the fish was gutted and washed in cold water. The process mixtures were prepared according to the recipes and enzyme preparations and brine were added. Fish enzymes were used in solution and terrizyme in the dry condition. Salting and maturation of the products took place at temperatures from −2° to −4°C. The results of technological and chemical analysis during the process are given in Table 7.

TABLE 7. ANALYSIS OF SALTED SARDINE DURING MATURATION

Product	Maturing duration (days)	Maturing indices	
		'Bufferness' degree	Nitrogen of free amino groups (mg %)
Without ferment preparations	30	126	176
	60	184	201
	90	188	218
	120	206	317
Without ferment preparation of fish raw material	30	141	211
	60	234	286
	90	288	334
	120	258	412
With the use of terrizyme	30	168	232
	60	282	342
	90	312	377
	120	302	470

These data and the results of organoleptic assessment strongly indicate that a considerable acceleration of maturing takes place and that the quality of the product improves under the influence of added proteolytic enzymes. In this case the use of proteinase preparations made from the raw material resulted in products of higher quality than those processed by means of terrizyme. The former products were tender and attractive in appearance, with an oily surface to the fish and with characteristic flavour and odour. Those made with terrizyme were tender also but were characterized by irregular softening of the flesh all over the body of the fish and had a specific flavour. Small packs of herring, mackerel and other fish in various sauces are in great demand in the USSR and other European countries. Such products, as a rule, are prepared from frozen fish in shore plants. They require a lot of time for maturation, which raises the price of production. Investigations, therefore, have been carried out on the use of enzyme preparations to speed up the process and improve the quality of such products. Products have been made using sardine fillets frozen at the fishing ground. The fillets were thawed in air at a temperature of 2° to 4°C and salted according to the following recipe:

fillet	..	..	..	..	..	100.00 kg
salt	..	..	..	..	..	7.70 kg
sugar	..	..	..	..	..	1.15 kg
12% salt solution		..	..	..	10.10 kg

Enzyme preparations were dissolved in brine, resulting in various proteinase activities. This activity can be determined by the increase in free amino nitrogen (AN) in 1 g of sardine per hour at 30°C and is termed the activity index. Maturing of sardine fillets took place at temperatures from −2°C to −4°C. The maturing indices of mild salted sardine fillets are given in Table 8.

TABLE 8. MATURATION OF SALTED SARDINE FILLETS UNDER THE INFLUENCE OF ADDED PROTEOLYTIC ENZYMES FROM RAW MATERIAL AND *A. terricola* OF VARIOUS ACTIVITIES

| Activity index of proteinase (mg AN/g.h) | Duration of maturing (days) | Maturing indices | |
		'Bufferness' degree	Nitrogen of free amino groups (mg %)
Mild salted sardine fillets without ferment preparations			
1.31	17	74	89
	31	91	91
	46	94	95
	60	103	111
Mild salted sardine fillets with the preparation of proteolytic enzymes from raw material			
3.47	17	95	92
	31	100	108
	46	113	111
	60	129	132
8.10	17	101	108
	31	115	119
	46	118	128
	60	139	154
10.82	17	108	138
	31	136	148
	46	142	176
	60	150	191
Mild salted sardine fillets with terrizyme			
4.81	17	100	108
	31	111	117
	46	147	162
	60	157	184

Organoleptic assessment demonstrated that mild salted fillets of sardine without enzyme preparation failed to mature by the end of the storage period. The fillet samples with enzyme preparation matured but at different rates, depending on the summary activity index value of the enzyme added. In this case, as in previous experiments, proteolytic enzymes of raw material gave products of high quality. With added enzyme preparation, mild salted fillet ripened irrespective of the dosage, the free

amino nitrogen in all cases reaching 110 to 140 mg%. When the index exceeded 140 mg% over-ripening of products was noted. It is possible by graphing summary activity against time (to give a value of 135 mg% free amino nitrogen) to determine the required summary activity of enzyme preparation depending on the desired time of maturation.

It should be noted that the dynamics of the maturing process for mild salt fillet with terrizyme added are not as predictable as with the enzyme preparation from raw material. This fact would appear to support the theory that there are certain differences in the maturation of salted fish products assisted by microbiological preparations. As salted fillet in consumer packs should be mature after a certain fixed shelf-life, unripe fillet after only seven days storage with added ferment preparation was used. The mild salted fillet was washed in brine of 1.05 g/cm³ specific gravity for 1 min. After the brine had dripped off, the fillets were cut transversely into pieces according to the height of the can selected for packaging. The fillets were packed in lacquered cans. The cans were then filled with apple sauce and closed. Maturing took place in the temperature range of 0° to −2°C and 15 days later the product acquired characteristic maturation indices. Thus, ferment preparations may be used to accelerate the ripening of mild salted sardine fillet and provide a means of utilizing this species for a fish product which is in great demand. The composition of the liquors can be varied according to the customers' eating habits.

In the USSR, a considerable amount of sardine is used for salted and spiced products in barrels produced both on the fishing grounds and ashore when frozen fish is used. Products are made both of undressed and dressed sardine. High quality salted and spiced sardine products are made from precooled raw material. Even if the raw material is of adequate quality, it is important to cool to 4° to 6°C before salting. This temperature is favourable for fish salting and retards *post mortem* alterations. The salting treatment can be changed according to taste to give products of a particular salt content. A mixture of spices, salt and sugar is prepared according to the following recipe (amounts in kg to treat 100 kg of sardines):

Black pepper	..	..	..	0.120
Sweet pepper	..	..	..	0.210
Cinnamon	..	..	..	..	0.075
Clove	..	..	..	..	0.085
Coriander	..	..	..	..	0.058
Bay leaf	..	..	..	..	0.025
Nutmeg	..	..	..	..	0.034
Mace	..	..	..	..	0.020
Ginger	..	..	..	..	0.040
Sugar	..	..	..	..	0.260
Salt	..	..	..	..	8–10

The fish is packed in rows and the spice/salt mixture is added to fill the barrels. A temperature range from −2° to −4°C is recommended for storage during the maturation of salted and spiced sardine.

Production of smoke-cured sardine

A large amount of raw material in the USSR is used to prepare smoke-cured sardine, which is in great demand.

The basic factors affecting the quality of cured sardine are as follows: the duration of their storage before processing, salt content of semi-finished products, and the conditions of smoking, drying and curing. Experiments were carried out at AtlantNIRO to determine the effects of different initial salt content and periods of storage of salted semi-finished products on the quality of smoke-cured sardine, all given the same smoking treatment. Salted semi-finished products were prepared with salt contents of 6, 8, 11, 14 per cent, and storage periods before smoke-curing of 7, 14, 40, 95 days. Before curing, salted semi-finished products with a salt content above 7 per cent were soaked in water at a temperature of 10°C. The soaking period was determined by the salt content in the product. Fish were dried at an air temperature of 23°C for 2 h. Smoking was carried out in a mechanical smoking chamber at an air temperature of 23° to 25°C for 24 to 30 h. An organoleptic assessment of the smoke-cured sardine was made according to a 35-point system.

Estimate in points

Appearance	..	..	..	1–5
Colour	..	..	..	..	1–5
Texture	..	..	..	..	1–5
Taste ..	..	..	..	..	3–10
Odour	..	..	..	..	3–10

The highest score was given to smoke-cured sardine prepared from a mild salted semi-finished product without soaking when the storage period was minimal. With an increase of storage period and salt content, the quality of the final product decreased. Thus, the duration of storage of the semi-finished material before final processing has an influence on the quality of the final smoke-cured product. Hence, salted semi-finished material should be landed and smoked as soon as possible after salting. In the USSR, the bulk of this kind of product is being made from frozen raw material.

CANNED PRODUCTS

The manufacture of various canned products from this kind of raw material, for instance sardines in oil, in flavoured oil, or in tomato sauce, etc., has been widely developed in the USSR and these products, together with frozen, salted spiced and cured products and preserves, are in great demand. Sardines of all the species listed in the fresh and frozen states are used to prepare canned products and are called 'Atlantic sardines in oil'. Frozen raw material is canned as 'Atlantic sardines in tomato sauce'. In both cases only first grade raw material should be used and the standards and technological requirements adopted should be met. The fish intended for canned products are immediately sorted out from the by-catch and from damaged fish and then washed with sea water. When preparing canned products aboard on the fishing grounds, fresh fish are delivered for immediate gutting and subsequent storage in tanks. The raw material is stored in tanks in cooled sea water at around, but not exceeding, −1°. The ratio of fish to water should be 1:2. The duration of storage possible in such reservoirs depends on the quality and size of fish but should not exceed 5 h. Before gutting, the frozen sardines are allowed to defrost in the air at a temperature not exceeding 20°C. They are sometimes defrosted in running water or in static water which is frequently changed. In such cases the water temperature should not exceed 15°C. The ratio of fish to water should be 1:2. The fish are gutted and beheaded by machine or by hand. The dressed fish are carefully washed to remove remnants of intestines and blood clots with clean sea or fresh water at a temperature not exceeding 15°C. The ratio of fish to water should be 1:2. The washed fish are then either cut transversely to the appropriate size for canning, or may be salted immediately and later cut to size. In either case the fish are then salted in a solution of specific gravity 1.17 to 1.20, at a temperature not exceeding 15°C. The ratio of fish weight to solution is 1:3. The salt content of the flesh after the process should be 1.5 per cent. When salting fish at sea during fishing, the salt solution may be based on sea water. Alternatively salt may be added directly into the cans at a level of 1.5 per cent of the net weight. Fried fish for canning is initially subjected to warm-air drying in special apparatuses. Drying lasts 40 min. The fish is then sprinkled with a thin layer of rusk and fried in seed oil at between 140° and 170°C. The frying period is determined by the size of fish pieces, the type of frier and the oil temperature. A smooth golden crust is indicative of adequate treatment. At the conclusion of frying it should be possible to remove the flesh from the bones when breaking the fried pieces. The fried fish is cooled to 40°C.

The blanching of sardines for inclusion in canned products either in oil or tomato sauce is carried out in special apparatuses. Moisture loss during thermal processing should be 18 to 20 per cent. Blanching in the cans is usual. In blanchers of the ISS-6 type, the first stage of processing consists of direct steam boiling at 100°C for 24 to 26 min (in the first compartment). The second stage consists of drying the fish by hot air or a mixture of hot air and steam at 120° to 130°C for 12 to 18 min, depending on the size of fish and cans. In the 'Mazer Platt' line of thermal apparatus, fish is subjected to direct steam boiling at 120°C for 10 to 16 min. When producing canned 'Atlantic sardines in oil', small fish are packed in printed 245-ml cans and sardine slices are packed in 250-ml cylindrical cans. When preparing products such as 'sardines fried in tomato sauce' or 'sardines blanched in tomato sauce' cans up to 350-ml capacity are used, the slices being packed flat with the cut surfaces toward the top and bottom of the can. The filled cans are topped up with refined deodorized olive or seed oil or tomato sauce. Olive oil should be previously heated to 80°C. Oil added to each can should be 20 per cent of the net weight of the product. Tomato sauce should be added to cans at a temperature in excess of 85°C. The dry matter content of the tomato sauce (without oil) used should be 22 to 23 per cent in canned products of fried fish and 27 to 28 per cent in those of blanched fish. Filled cans are covered with clean marked tops, closed, washed, sterilized, then cooled in water to a temperature of 40° to 45°C, and dried before storage.

The sterilization of canned products in oil is based on the following formula:

$$\text{235 and 250-ml can} \; \frac{\text{5–15–80–20 min}}{112°C}$$

The sterilization of canned products in tomato sauce is based on:

235-ml can
$$\frac{5-15-80-20 \text{ min}}{112°C}$$

350-ml can:

for small fish
$$\frac{5-15-90-20 \text{ min}}{112°C}$$

for large fish
$$\frac{5-15-110-20 \text{ min}}{112°C}$$

Experience has shown that the formulae for sterilization times do not give a high quality product when large fish are used. An increase in sterilization time to 110 min results in poor texture and flavour and a darkening of tomato sauce. Increased time, of course, also reduces the throughput of the plant. Investigations carried out at AtlantNIRO showed that it is possible to sterilize larger fish and successfully overcome these problems. The treatment applied is based on: 5–15–50–20 min/120°C for 350-ml cans. The USSR fleet makes a big catch of large sardines. Hitherto, these fish were of little use for canning. The preparation of such material for canned products requires a special method of slicing.

The Government Standard for 'Atlantic sardine in oil' requires a compulsory period of ripening of not less than six months. During the ripening period the organoleptic properties of canned products improve considerably: a pleasant taste and odour develop and the flesh becomes soft and succulent. The scales soften. Prolonged storage, however, gives rise to ageing and a loss of these desirable characteristics. Comparative investigations of quality variability in canned sardine made from small fish bodies or slices of larger fish show the stages of ripening and ageing. Careful observations of changes in the protein and fat content in storage, as well as regular organoleptic assessment, have demonstrated that 'Atlantic sardines in oil (sliced)' ripen in three months. Thus, the application resulting from these investigations has led to the rational utilization of Atlantic sardine in the USSR through the manufacture of various notable food products of high gastronomical quality.

LITERATURE USED

ARTYUKHOVA, S A and PRASOL, S N Some results of the test and
1973 specification of the actual formulas of sterilization of fish preserves. *Rybochozjaistvennye issledovanija v Atlanticheskom okeane*, v. 52.
KARPECHENKO, YU. L. Sardine of West Africa. *Rybnoe khoz'* (2).
POSTEL, E General information about Clupeidae of West Africa.
1955 West Africa *Rapp. Proc. Verb.* 137.
PROSVIROV, E S Some results of the research and scouting works in
1962 equatorial Atlantic from November 1960 to March 1961. *Trudy BaltNIRO* v. 8.
ROSSIGNOL, M Premières observations sur la biologie des sardinelles
1955 dans la région de Pointe-Noire. *Rapp. Proc. Verb.* 137.

Utilization of Sardinella Resources in India   *V K Pillai*

Utilisation des ressources de sardinelles en Inde.

Sardinella longiceps, principale espèce exploitée par les pêcheries indiennes de sardinelles, sert principalement à la fabrication d'huile de qualité inférieure et comme engrais. La consommation humaine est restreinte en raison des difficultés présentées par la transformation du poisson, du caractère saisonnier des captures et de leur saveur particulière due à l'huile qu'elles contiennent. Le présent document décrit l'utilisation actuelle de ce poisson: congélation, conserve et salage. Grâce à la congélation, il sera peut-être possible de transformer de plus grandes quantités de ce poisson dans les conserveries, bien que la production de sardines en boites ait diminué au cours des dernières années. Des recherches ont montré que le conditionnement 'au naturel'—consistant à présenter le poisson dans son propre jus—constitue une méthode prometteuse de mise en conserve. Le produit ainsi préparé est plaisant et a une saveur trés agréable. On a également normalisé des méthodes de conditionnement du poisson en sauce tomate et en sauce blanche. On décrit les utilisations actuelles et possibles de l'huile de sardinelle.

Aprovechamiento de la sardinilla de la India.

La sardinella *Sardinella longiceps*, que es la especie más importante de la pesquería india de sardinilla, se utiliza principalmente para producir aceite de mala calidad y como fertilizante. Su empleo para al consumo es limitado, debido a las dificultades que plantea su elaboración, al carácter estacional de las capturas y a su peculiar sabor aceitoso. Se describen las diversas formas en que se approvecha est especie en la actualidad, congelándola evasóndola y curándola. Tal vez la congelación permita incrementar el empleo de este pescado en las fábricas de conservas, aunque la producción de sardinas en conserva ha disminuido en los últimos años. Los estudios han mostrado que un método prometedor de conserva es al natural, en su propio jugo. El producto asi preparado tiene excelente sabor y buena presencia. Se han preparado tambièn métodos uniformes de envasado con tomate y salsa blanca. Se describen los usos actuales y otros posibles empleos.

The apparent world shortage of sardines of the *Pilchardus* spp. has generated interest in *Sardinella* spp. from tropical countries. Of the 16 known species belonging to the group, the *Sardinella longiceps* or 'oil sardine' is the most important and widely distributed in the tropical environment. In India the sardine fishery is the largest single one, accounting for 25–30 per cent of total marine landings. In 1971, total landings amounted to 1.154 million tons, of which sardines provided over 272,000 tons. Of this, the oil sardine accounted for more than 208,000 tons. Although the fishery is common to both the west and east coasts of India, the heaviest concentration is along the coastal regions of Mysore and Kerala States. Sporadic catches of *S. longiceps* are made on the east coast but the main sardine fishery there depends on lesser known species. The fishery has exhibited wide fluctuations. Fishing for the oil sardine has been restricted, commencing with the pre-monsoon showers and becoming regular during July/August, with the peak season from October to January. Thereafter, it dwindles and ends by March. Irrespective of the fact that in nutritive value (Table 1) the sardine compares well with any other fish, it remains cheap because of the lack of means of disposal and probably because of its peculiar flavour resulting from the high oil content. An industry based on the fish has not been developed for various reasons – the high capital cost involved, the short duration of the fishery, the unsteady supply, the lack of infrastructure and, above all, the technological problems involved in handling, preservation, processing and transport. Increased production through the use of more sophisticated fishing methods, such as purse seining, has not appealed to the private sector for the same reasons. The legitimate place of sardine in the future of India's fisheries development has, however, been fully recognized by the Central and State Governments and massive efforts have recently been launched to find solutions to many of the problems. The Indo-Norwegian Project and the Central Institute of Fisheries Technology, both based in Cochin, have been, in particular, engaged in solving technological problems involved in commercial catching, preservation, processing and transport.

TABLE 1. PROXIMATE COMPOSITION OF SARDINE

Moisture	65.28
Fat	14.34%
Crude protein	18.10%
Ash	1.65%
Inorganic phosphorous	175 mg %
α-amino nitrogen	105 mg %

ICING AND STORAGE

As the fish is landed all along the coast and the potential markets are generally thousands of kilometres away, quick transport of the fish in fresh state is not easy. Even the introduction of refrigerated trucks and rail wagons has not been able to solve the problem to any significant extent. The conventional method of preservation by icing also is not as effective as with other fish because of the high oil content. Some of the problems encountered in low temperature preservation and transport of oil sardines are highlighted below. During ice storage as well as during freezing and thawing the belly flaps break and the viscera protrude, reducing the consumer appeal even though the fish is of prime quality and the organoleptic properties are not affected (Perigreen and Govindan 1969). The incidence of belly bursting in certain cases ranges up to 30 per cent depending on maturity, fat content and nature of stomach contents. With an oil content as high as 17 per cent (wet weight basis) during peak seasons, with a high degree of unsaturation due to the presence of poly-unsaturated fatty acids, the incidence of oxidative rancidity is very high.

Several trials with iced sardines have shown that loss occurs in the weight, up to 5 per cent during a storage period of five days. There is also loss in nutritive value due to the leaching away of soluble protein components by melting ice and development of rancidity. In the case of S. longiceps it has been observed that during chill storage considerable changes occur in the major protein fractions – viz, sarcoplasmic, myofibrillar and stroma proteins (Devadasan and Rajendranathan 1970). Reduction in sarcoplasmic protein was as much as 6 per cent in two weeks' storage. Organoleptic, physical and chemical changes occuring in sardines held in ice storage for more than two or three days are such that canned or frozen products prepared from them are substandard (Madhavan et al. 1970; Vasanth and Pillai 1971).

FREEZING

Here again belly bursting was found to be a serious problem (Rao and Perigreen 1964; Anon. 1965).

Tests have been made in India by freezing oil sardines in bulk and transporting them over long distances involving three to five days' journey by rail. The containers used were plywood boxes – tea chests lined on the inside with 2.5 cm thickness of thermocole covered in polythene. When deep frozen at −40°C with a 25 per cent water glaze, the fish showed no apparent loss in quality after 72 hours. The temperature of the transported material rarely went above −1°C. The maximum loss of weight due to thaw drip noticed during these trials was less than 5 per cent. It has been demonstrated that the oxidative rancidity could be controlled and storage life extended considerably by dipping the fish in an 0.05 per cent solution of hydroquinone for 5 minutes or in 0.1 per cent agar-agar solution (Cyriac et al. 1966). The influence of different prefreezing ice storage periods on the biochemical and organoleptic qualities in the individually quick frozen and block frozen forms has been investigated. There is no significant difference in organoleptic and biochemical characteristics between individually quick frozen and block frozen sardines (Vasanth and Pillai 1971).

CANNING

Canning of the fish for export has not so far been attempted seriously in India. The few existing canneries cater mainly for the domestic market. The main reasons for slow development of the sardine canning industry in the country are the seasonal nature of fishery which results in the plants lying idle for most part of the year; the non-availability of olive oil in India; and the abnormally high cost of tin containers for packing the fish. The discovery that frozen sardine can be kept in processable condition for periods of two to three months and that sardine can be caught in the offshore waters during the non-traditional seasons may help to dispel fears on the first count. The Indian canners use deodourized groundnut oil as the filling medium in sardine packs. Experience shows that this pack can find only a very restricted entry into export markets, perhaps because of the general preference for sardines in olive or soybean oil. The Indian packer has not attempted to diversify his products, such as the 'skinless and boneless' types produced by Portugal and Morocco, the smoked type by Norway and the sauce packs by South Africa. The Indian packer cannot provide the variety of containers as are used elsewhere. In addition, the cans account for nearly 40 per cent of the total cost of the finished product. Recent investigations have, however, shown that there are economical alternate methods of canning. The most promising appears to be the 'sardine natural pack', in which the fish is packed in its own juice. The product is very attractive and has an excellent flavour. Methods have also been standardized for packing the fish in tomato and white sauces.

CURING

Until recently a good part of the catch used to be preserved by salt-curing – wet curing or dry curing. With the development of better transport and storage facilities and the introduction of more sophisticated methods of preservation, such as freezing and canning, the quantity of cured sardines has dropped year after year. So has the export of cured sardines. However, the practice will remain in use for many years to come because it is the cheapest method of preservation and the taste of the product is liked by many people in India and nearby countries. Susceptibility to attack by fungus and red halophilic bacteria and occurrence of rancidity are the most important problems in this field. Mixed preservatives consisting of salt, sodium propionate and BHA (butylated hydroxyanisole) have been found efficient in controlling most of these (Valsan 1963). Further improvements by using sodium benzoate, dip treatment in sodium propionate, etc, have also been successfully demonstrated.

SARDINE OIL INDUSTRY

The modern sardine oil industry developed in India in the twenties although the fishery dates back to 1320 A.D. (Sundar 1968). The extraction is done on a cottage scale near the landing centres and is not well organized. The method of extraction is by cooking the fish in iron vessels, often without adding sufficient quantity of water. The oil thus extracted is of very poor quality, of undesirable colour and odour and of inferior chemical characteristics.

TABLE 2. COMPARISON OF THE INDIAN SARDINE OIL WITH OTHER SIMILAR OILS

Property	Indian sardine oil	British Columbia herring oil	Canadian pilchard oil	North American menhaden oil
Specific gravity at 15.5°C	0.9218	0.9228 0.9265	0.9290– 0.9370	0.9311
Colour Lovbond units in 1 inch cell				
(i) Yellow	70	20–35	40–75	—
(ii) Red	1	1.8–3.4	3.5–6.0	—
Refractive index at 25°C	1.4755	1.4730– 1.4775	1.4785– 1.4802	—
Iodine value	152–175	118–160	170–188	160
Free fatty acids as percentage of oleic acid	0.56– 3.89	0.2–5.0	0.1–13.0	7.57
Saponification value	192–195	182–189	188–199	189.3
Non-saponifiable matter %	1.3	0.5–1.7	0.1–1.25	1.6

TABLE 3. COMPARISON OF THE QUALITIES OF COMMERCIAL OIL TO THAT PREPARED BY THE IMPROVED METHOD

	Commercial oil	Oil prepared by improved methods
Colour	Deep brown to black	Light yellow to brown
Clarity at room temperature	Turbid	Clear
Odour	Rancid	No rancid odour
Refractive index	1.4780	1.4755
Specific gravity	0.9250	0.9219
Moisture %	0.25–0.62	0.20–0.40
Nitrogen	0.02–0.10	Nill
Saponification value	190–198	192–195
Iodine value	99–161	152–175
Peroxide value	0.4382–7.2	0.3–2.7
Unsaponifiable matter %	0.84–1.55	0.83–1.55
Free fatty acids %	5.8–49.58	0.56–3.89

Methods have now been worked out for extraction of oil comparable with those in other countries (Table 2) giving an average yield of oil of 12 per cent during the season (Madhavan and Kaimal 1968). The improvements in the chemical characteristics of the oil in this method can be seen from Table 3. The fatty acid composition of the lipids of oil sardine has revealed that they contain a high amount of poly-unsaturated fatty acids constituted by decosahexaenoic and eicosapentaenoic acids (Gopakumar and Rajendranathan 1966). Poly-unsaturated fatty acids are known to be of pharmacological importance as they may be used to keep the cholesterol content in blood low (Velankar 1968).

Utilization of sardine oil

An age-old practice of fishermen is to use sardine oil for painting the bottom of their fishing crafts while they use some of the better grade oil for edible purposes (Aggarwal 1968). Other important applications of low grade oil produced commercially are for fat liquoring of leather, tempering of metals, batching of jute and in insecticidal soaps (Anon. 1962). Fish oils employed as fungicides and insecticides are sometimes modified in minor ways to improve their natural fungicidal activity. Such preparations are less potent than organic insecticides but, unlike the latter, they are non-toxic to man (Velankar 1968). The high unsaturation, easy susceptibility to oxidation, flavour reversion and related changes create technological problems in its use in hydrogenated products, soap manufacture and domestic consumption (Madhavan and Kaimal 1968). It has been reported that cold cleared and winterized sardine oil as such, or in admixture with groundnut oil in varying proportions, can be successfully used as the medium in canning sardines (Sen and Revenkar 1968). Hydrogenation done at atmospheric pressure is quite rapid and can bring down the iodine value (IV) to 100, when the typical rancid and fishy odour is removed and the oil is stabilized. Controlled direct interesterification of the hydrogenated oil then prepared gives a butter-like consistency (Sen and Revenkar 1968). Refined sardine oil could be used in the manufacture of hard soaps after hydrogenation at about 100 psi (7 kg/ cm²) and at temperatures of 150° to 170°C using 2 per cent Rufert Nickel catalyst for 5 hours when the oil becomes a hard pale white solid having IV 10 (Aggarwal 1968). The neutral sardine oil can be split into fatty acids by fractional distillation into three groups (Kotwal and Pai 1968):

(a) Fraction resembling fatty acids having IV ranging from 65 to 82 with a yield of 47 to 58 per cent, constituting both saturated and unsaturated fatty acids up to and including C 18, with comparatively low fishy odour, which, if properly mixed with other oils, can be used in the manufacture of laundry soaps;

(b) A low yield of 5 to 20 per cent of poly-unsaturated fractions with IV or about 220, comprising mainly archidonic, clupanodonic and other unidentified fatty acids, useful in paints;

(c) A non-distillable polymerized unsaturated fatty acid, neutral and unsaponifiable, which has found acceptance in varnish manufacture.

Use of fish-oil fatty acids in the manufacture of oil modified alkyl resins using pentaerythrytol and phthalic anhydride has been attempted (Ahluwallah 1962). 'Distilled fatty acids' (painty type), a mixture of poly-unsaturated fatty acids arachidonic and clupanodonic, which is claimed to have high unsaturation (IV in the range 230 to 250), of the conugated type, have also been introduced along with a lower grade fish oil called 'Polymerized oil' suitable for dark colour varnishes.

TABLE 4. QUANTITY IN TONS OF DIFFERENT BY-PRODUCTS PRODUCED IN KERALA STATE (KERALA FISHERIES ADMINISTRATIVE REPORTS)

By-product	1964–65	1965–66	1966–67	1967–68	1968–69	Average
Sardine oil	2,073.13	1,079.88	85.17	5.35	671.26	782.96
Fish guano	7,031.35	613.50 ⎤		12.00	197.80	1,963.66
Fish		⎬ 85.00				
manure	5,909.18	433.00 ⎦		3,882.48	8,808.10	4,758.19
Fish meal			6.08	84.73	22.08	37.63

A further breakthrough in the possible application of sardine oil for industrial purposes was achieved as a result of the investigations carried out at the Central Institute of Fisheries Technology, Cochin. Conversion of sardine oil into factice, a filler in rubber compounding industry (Kaimal and Madhavan 1967), and for use as a vehicle in surface coating material (Kaimal et al. 1968), as a printing ink base, as an additive in lubricating oil (Madhaven and Kaimal 1968), etc., have been success-fully tried.

Fertilizer

During glut seasons the fish are sometimes used as manure. The most common form is the guano, the residue left after oil extraction by the crude method. This is generally beach-dried and is found to contain 8 to 10 per cent nitrogen and a good amount of phosphates. Being well cooked, it disintegrates easily and mixes with soil quickly and is believed to be 15 to 20 times richer than ordinary cattle manure. Trimmings and wastes from the sardine-canning factories, when canning is taken up on a large scale, will constitute a good source of manure. Methods have already been suggested for preparing a liquid fertilizer from fish and shrimp wastes with two different NPK ratios, 8:8:16 and 7:10:15, suitable for common crops like coconut, arecanut, ginger, tapioca, pepper and vegetables (Ismail and Madhavan 1970).

References

AGGARWAL, J S Paintindia, 18(4):43–45.
1968
AHLUWALLAH, A J Paintindia, 18(4):46–49.
1968
Anon. The Wealth of India—Raw Materials—4 (Council of
1962 Scientific and Industrial Research, New Delhi), p. 111.
Anon. Fish Technology Newsletter, 6(2):4.
1965
CYRIAC MATHEN, CHOUDHURI, D R and PILLAI, V K Fish. Technol.,
1966 India, 3(1):30–37.
DEVADASAN, K and RAJENDRANATHAN NAIR, M Fish. Technol.,
1970 India, 7(2):195–197.
GOPAKUMAR, K and RAJENDRANATHAN NAIR, M Fish. Technol.,
1966 India, 3(1):21–25.
ISMAIL, P K and MADHAVAN, P Fish. Technol., India, 7(2):216–217.
1970
KAIMAL, M N N and MADHAVAN, P Res and Ind., 12(4):251–252.
1967
KAIMAL, M N N, GOPALAKRISHNA PILLAI, A G and MADHAVAN, P
1968 Res. and Ind., 13(1):24–26.
KOTWAL, K F and PAI, V M Paintindia, 18(4):54–55.
1968
MADHAVAN, P and KAIMAL, M N Paintindia, 18(4):50–53.
1968
MADHAVAN, P, BALACHANDRAN, K K and CHOUDHURI, D R Fish.
1970 Technol., India, 7(1):67–72.
PERIGREEN, P A and GOVINDAN, T K Fish. Technol., India, 6(2):74–
1969 78.
PERIGREEN, P A, GOVINDAN, T K and PILLAI, V K Fish. Technol.,
1969 India, 6(1):55–58.
RAO, C V N and PERIGREEN, P A Fish. Technol., Inda, 1(1):68–75.
1964
SEN, D P and REVENKAR, G D Paintindia, 18(4):42.
1968
SUNDAR KINI, U Seminar on Marine Oils—9 June 1968, Special
1968 Supplement to Paintindia, 18(4):31–34.
VALSAN, A P Indian J. Fish. 10(2), Section B, 9–10.
1963
VASANTH SHENOY, A and PILLAI, V K Fish. Technol., India, 8(1):
1971 37–41.
VELANKAR, N K Paintindia, 18(4):35–38.
1968

Aprovechamiento de la Anchoveta para Consumo Humano en el Perú   E Loayza S

Anchoveta utilization for human consumption in Peru.

The enormously rich anchoveta resource of the Peruvian sea invites diversification of its use from traditional conversion into fish meal and oil to utilization for direct human consumption. The record of its utilization, though very poor because of the shadow cast by the fabulous meal industry, has been boosted by the dynamic policy of the new Ministry of Fisheries, and there has been steadily mounting interest in utilization of part of the resource in a more direct form. Current foreign market prospects and the growing need for protein on the domestic market are combining to move the Government and Peruvian and foreign industrialists to advance from research on the possibilities of the anchoveta to the establishment of enter-prises to turn out a variety of products, notably anchovetas packed in the sardine and anchovy styles and in frozen blocks, which would involve an investment estimated at US$3.5 million. The paper reviews past and present efforts to prepare the anchoveta for direct human consumption, the different approaches made to ensure that the raw material meets consumer quality standards, and attempts to produce a variety of new anchoveta products.

Utilisation de l'anchoveta pour la consommation humaine au Perou

L'abondance des ressources en anchoveta que recèlent les eaux péruviennes incite à les utiliser pour la consommation humaine directe au lieu de se borner comme auparavant à les employer pour fabriquer de la farine et de l'huile de poisson. Les premiers essais d'une telle utilisation, bien que timides en comparaison de l'ampleur colossale de l'industrie de la farine, ont été encouragés par la politique dynamique du nouveau Ministère des pêches et il convient de noter que l'on s'intéresse de plus en plus à employer de façon plus directe une partie de ces ressources. Les perspectives actuelles que présente le marché d'exportation et le besoin croissant de protéines sur le marché intérieur sont deux raisons qui poussent le Gouverne-ment et les industriels péruviens et étrangers non seulement à explorer les possibilités qu'offre l'anchoveta, mais encore à créer des usines pour la fabrication de divers produits, notamment conserves du type sardine, blocs congelés et anchois, le montant des investisse-ments y afférents étant estimé à 3,5 millions de \$EU Le document décrit les efforts déployés par le passé comme à l'heure actuelle en vue d'utiliser directement l'anchoveta pour la consommation humaine, les différents essais entrepris pour obtenir une matière première de la qualité exigée par le consommateur et les activités réalisées afin de mettre au point divers produits nouveaux à base d'anchoveta.

El mar del Perú, con su inmensa riqueza de anchoveta, presenta un enorme estímulo para el empleo de dicho recurso en la alimentación humana y no solamente para la producción de harina y aceite de pescado que en poco tiempo ha hecho nacer en el país una potente industria. Los varios intentos realizados en el pasado para su utilización en otra forma que no fuese la elaboración de harina y aceite de pescado, no tuvieron éxito. Sin embargo, con la dinámica política del nuevo Ministerio de Pesquería, se están multiplicando los esfuerzos para derivar hacia el consumo humano parte de esta grandísima riqueza ictiológica, orientándolos asimismo, hacia el mercado exterior para, con el ingreso de divisas y apoyándose en ellas, desarrollar el consumo interno de sus productos pesqueros tan importantes para resolver el problema de la desnutrición.

ANTECEDENTES

El consumo de anchoveta secada al sol ha sido característico de ciertos núcleos de población, como caletas de pescadores y poblaciones aledañas de las costas sur y central. Allí era común observar tendales de anchoveta secándose al sol, que después se envasaba en sacos para su empleo como parte de la dieta. Con la industria harinera esta costumbre ha desaparecido surgiendo en su lugar grandes fábricas para la reducción del recurso.

La preparación de anchoveta salada, tipo anchoa, se ejecutaba a nivel familiar, pero en estos últimos años se han realizado esfuerzos para la producción comercial de este tipo de preparado.

La anchoveta, a pesar de su abundancia, no significó jamás un elementos importante en la alimentación del peruano. Solamente a partir de la década del setenta empezaron a surgir intentos de aprovecharla en la alimentación humana para mejorar el nivel nutricional de la población, particularmente la del interior del país, y en los últimos tres años, gracias al impulso del nuevo Gobierno se han tomado acciones orientadas al aprovechamiento industrial de la anchoveta en distintas formas de preparación, con objeto de captar el mercado exterior capaz de absorber volúmenes que justifiquen la inversión requerida.

MANIPULEO DE ANCHOVETA A BORDO

Cualquier intento de utilización de la anchoveta para el consumo humano directo está regido por un común denominador: 'adecuado manipuleo a bordo'. Muy poca experiencia se tiene en nuestro medio referente al correcto manejo de la anchoveta en las embarcaciones, capaz de permitir un inmediato uso a nivel de una actividad comercial. Es por esta razón y dada la urgencia de resolver el problema en vista de las inversiones, que se avecinan en términos de instalaciones fabriles que más adelante se detallan, que el Proyecto PNUD PER/69/535 conjuntamente con la Empresa Pública de Servicios Pesqueros (EPSEP), ha llevado y está llevando a cabo una serie de pruebas orientadas a establecer la forma más adecuada de manipuleo a bordo que satisfaga los requerimientos de orden técnico-económico. El conocimiento y práctica actual de actividades semejantes, llevadas a cabo en otras latitudes ha servido de base para canalizar las experiencias que más adelante se indican,

paralelamente con otros planteamientos que han surgido en vista de la realidad de nuestro mar y nuestra pesquería, a las cuales necesariamente deben adecuarse las experiencias extranjeras para lograr ser viables.

Anchoveta viva con ayuno forzado

En base a la práctica común de la pesquería noruega, consistente en recluir las sardinas vivas en ciertas zonas de los fiordos de bajo contenido planctónico para que evacúen su contenido intestinal, se han realizado varias pruebas que en realidad han representado nuestro mayor esfuerzo orientado al manipuleo a bordo de anchoveta. El especial interés que se ha puesto en estas pruebas es en razón del producto que se desea obtener luego del procesamiento: 'Brisling Sardine' y que, como es bien sabido, el pescado se envasa con vísceras previamente evacuadas.

Tres tipos de pruebas experimentales fueron llevad as a cabo:

(a) **Tanques de fibra de vidrio.** Los tanques fueron acondicionados en cubierta de la embarcación, circulando el agua mediante una bomba y un filtro. Una vez en muelle fueron transportados en camión y la anchoveta vertida en unas pozas de concreto. Lamentablemente, el sistema resultaba muy moroso y, debido a la falta de aereación en el transporte, muy pocas anchovetas se lograron mantener vivas. Aparte de ello, demás está decir el elevado costo que representa esta operación.

(b) **Tanques de fibra y descarga por bombeo.** Dados los problemas de descarga de la prueba anterior, se experimentó la utilización de un absorbente convencional de anchoveta para harina y que a través de tubería dirigía el producto a una poza de concreto en tierra. Las características de la bomba y los excesivos cambios de dirección de la tubería se tradujo en una supervivencia de tan solo el 10 por ciento de la anchoveta así transportada. A pesar de ello sin embargo, creemos que este sistema, con las modificaciones del caso, no debe ser descartado, por la simplicidad que representa para la descarga de anchoveta viva conservada a bordo en tanques con circulación de agua.

(c) **Redes flotantes.** Las pruebas fueron realizadas en la zona sur debido a las facilidades disponibles en puerto y a la menor contaminación del agua. Se preparó una red flotante de 11 × 3.5 × 3 m en la que se permitía que la anchoveta nadara libremente del boliche hacia ella. La red era luego halada por la bolicher a baja velocidad hasta el puerto, donde bajo vigilancia era dejada hasta el día siguiente.

Si bien este sistema da buenos resultados en Noruega, con el spratt y el arenque, no ha dado un resultado adecuado en nuestro medio, debido principalmente a las razones siguientes:

- los peces son constantemente atacados por aves marinas y lobos, que asustan a la anchoveta provocando que se dañen entre ellas
- la acción de las olas es muy marcada, traduciéndose en daños mecánicos de los peces, los que al cabo de dos días han perdido prácticamente todas sus escamas y parcialmente la piel
- el agua contiene demasiado plancton, lo que impide una apropiada evacuación de los intestinos.

De las diferentes pruebas mencionadas, hemos concluído que para obtener anchoveta con el intestino limpio, bajo las condiciones propias de nuestro medio, lo más adecuado resultaría ser la utilización de tanques a bordo, con agua filtrada circulante e inyección de oxígeno, en los que debería manternerse los peces hasta quedar totalmente limpios antes del desembarque. Las pruebas que a este respecto se vienen realizando nos permitirán conocer cuán efectivo resulta este sistema desde el punto de vista de supervivencia de los peces y cuán económica resulta ser la operación.

En cajas con hielo

Desde el punto de vista práctico y de acuerdo con la experiencia que al respecto se tiene, en nuestro medio, la forma más viable de manipular el recurso a bordo resulta ser el de 'cajas con hielo'. Especial cuidado se debe poner en el tipo de caja para que la altura de anchoveta y hielo no resulte perjudicial por efecto de la presión sobre las capas inferiores. El problema principal, sin embargo, no estriba en el acondicionamiento a bordo, la descarga o la calidad del producto, sino en la necesidad de eviscerar en tierra, tanto para la elaboración de anchoveta tipo sardina, como para otra clase de preparados. La evisceración de un pescado tan pequeño requiere por un lado, de una elevada cantidad de mano de obra, incrementando en consecuencia los costos de producción y, por otro, la mecanización del proceso no es una tarea sencilla dado que aún no se cuenta con la máquina apropiada capaz de realizar esta tarea con la eficacia y velocidad requeridas. El Proyecto PER/69/535 y la EPSEP están seriamente abocados a esta tarea que, a no dudarlo, es un aspecto de primordial importancia para el éxito de cualquier empresa orientada al procesamiento de anchoveta. Cabe hacer resaltar que, aparte de las pruebas que se vienen realizando con distintos tipos de maquinaria para eviscerar, una fábrica de Alemania está desarrollando una máquina capaz de satisfacer nuestros requerimientos sobre la base de muestras congeladas de anchoveta que les han sido enviadas. En conclusión, podemos decir que es fundamental continuar llevando a cabo una serie de pruebas más, que permitan establecer definitivamente la forma más adecuada de manipular a bordo cantidades comerciales de anchoveta para consumo humano y, paralelamente, realizar las pruebas pertinentes para establecer el sistema más adecuado de evisceración. Estos dos aspectos, en realidad, constituyen los pilares del éxito o fracaso de la utilización de este importante, recurso en el consumo humano directo.

EXPERIENCIAS EN EL APROVECHAMIENTO DE ANCHOVETA PARA CONSUMO HUMANO

Anchoveta seca

Una de las primeras acciones orientadas al aprovechamiento comercial de anchoveta para consumo humano ha sido el seco-salado. El procesamiento consistía en acondicionar en barricas con salmuera saturada la anchoveta recién capturada. Luego del desembarque eran transportadas a una localidad distante 45 km al este y a una altitud de 800 m SNM. Una vez allí, el pescado era retirado de las barricas, lavado con agua dulce para eliminar el exceso de sal y extendido en tendales elevados unos 0.80 m sobre la superficie del suelo. Dada la altitud de la localidad (800 m SNM alta radiación y baja humedad relativa), el producto quedaba seco en cuestión de pocos días. La anchoveta así elaborada se envasaba en bolsitas plásticas de 100 g cada una, destinándose a las poblaciones del interior del país. La aceptabilidad del producto en la serranía era bastante bueno, dado que en esa región existe la costumbre de consumir carnes secas. Lamentablemente, su alto contenido de aceite de rápida oxidación, tendía a producir en algunos casos disturbios de carácter gastrointestinal (tal situación podía haber sido obviada con un ligero proceso de ahumado). La falta de apoyo (hace 10 a 12 años) al entonces Servicio de Pesquería, que llevaba a cabo este trabajo, derivó en el abandono de la operación que presentaba perspectivas interesantes.

Tratada con agua caliente y secada al sol

Como una derivación del procedimiento anterior, en el del país, dentro del marco de una actividad lateral ligada a la fabricación prioritaria de harina de pescado, se inició la producción de anchoveta secada al sol, en volúmenes comerciales bajo la modalidad de tratarla previo al secado con agua de mar caliente, durante unos minutos; el propósito entre otros era el de eliminar parte del aceite y reducir los efectos de enranciamiento en el producto final. Lamentablemente, a pesar de ser un producto con buenas perspectivas en el mercado local y ciertos países asiáticos, su elaboración fue descontinuada.

Secada artificialmente

En la actualidad, a través de la EPSEP y el Proyecto PER/69/535 se están elaborando muestras de anchoveta seca, preparadas en diferentes formas y empleando la deshidratación artificial para su envío a los distintos mercados potenciales del exterior. A la fecha, se han obtenido respuestas halagadoras de dichos mercados que han motivado la elaboración de planes concretos para su preparación a nivel comerical. Los estudios técnicos económicos pertinentes que se están llevando a cabo serán el indicativo si la operación se pone o no en marcha.

Anchoveta tipo anchoa

Sin lugar a dudas, este tipo de producto es el que más se tuvo en mente desde los albores de la explotación comercial de la anchoveta. Ello era lógico ya que la anchoa era y es ampliamente conocida en los distintos mercados mundiales, alcanzando altas cotizaciones por tratarse de un producto sofisticado. Sin embargo, han tenido que transcurrir varios años y un esfuerzo significativo, especialmente a través de la empresa privada, cuyo renglón principal es la harina de pescado, para solventar los problemas inherentes a su elaboración y lograr un producto que satisfaga las exigencias del mercado exterior. Hoy en día se están realizando gestiones tendientes a la formación de una Empresa Estatal Asociada (capital privado peruano y capital estatal), orientada hacia la elaboración de anchoveta tipo anchoa, con un capital de 1.5 millones de $EE.UU.

Bloques de anchoveta congelada

Una de las formas de elaboración de anchoveta para consumo humano, que en los dos últimos años ha adquirido cierta importancia aunque aún no ha ingresado a la fase de producción comercial, ha sido la de bloques congelados. La escasez del recurso anchoa, en los países que tradicionalmente elaboran este producto, ha servido de base para tentar la utilización de anchoveta peruana congelada, como materia prima para esta industria. Hasta el momento han sido enviados lotes de 10 y 20 t a mercados europeos, quienes parecen haber reaccionado favorablemente a la calidad del producto. Por la relativa simplicidad del proceso, es muy probable que los bloques congelados se conviertan a corto plazo en el renglón más importante de utilización de este recurso en el consumo humano.

Anchoveta en conserva tipo sardina

De los diferentes productos que se mencionan en este trabajo, la anchoveta en conserva 'tipo sardina' es probablemente la que ha sido tratada con más cuidado y dedicación. La Empresa Pública de Servicios Pesqueros, el Proyecto PER/69/535 e industriales europeos, han conducido una serie de pruebas preliminares a nivel de planta piloto para probar la bondad de la anchoveta en sus distintas formas de preparación (en aceite, en salsa tomate, en salsa mostaza; sin cabeza y sin vísceras, con el intestino limpio, etc.). Los resultados obtenidos hasta el momento han sido muy halagadores, habiendo pasado las pruebas de calidad exigidas por los productores europeos, con larga experiencia en la elaboración de sardinas en conserva. Es así que al presente se encuentra en proceso de formación una Empresa Mixta (capital privado extranjero y capital estatal peruano), destinada a la elaboración de anchoveta en conserva, tanto para el mercado exterior como doméstico, con una inversión inicial del orden de los 2 millones de $EE.UU.

Hidrolizado de anchoveta

Un producto nuevo que ha sido lanzado al mercado peruano con cierto grado de éxito es el hidrolizado de anchoveta. A través de un proceso convencional, la anchoveta es hidrolizada conjuntamente con una proteína vegetal. El producto resultante es posteriormente concentrado obteniéndose un líquido viscoso, oscuro, aromático, sin olor ni sabor a pescado, muy semejante al concentrado de carne. El producto, se ofrece en el mercado en frascos de vidrio, acompañado de un recetario bien elaborado que muestra diversas formas de preparación utilizándolo como ingrediente principal, y mostrando el valor nutritivo de estos platos com-parativamente con los productos tradicionales ricos en proteínas.

Concentrado protéico de pescado

No puede dejar de mencionarse el concentrado protéico de pescado, que a pesar de los problemas de comercialización y de otra índole, que a nivel mundial es de todos conocidos, también ha tenido en el Perú sus defensores. El proceso de elaboración es un sistema patentado que emplea vapores de hexano en una cámara de vacío, provocado por una bomba de anillo de agua. La extracción del aceite sólo es parcial y el producto final tiene un ligero olor a camarón chino, como su mismo inventor así lo califica. La empresa durante varios años ha elaborado este producto, cuya principal salida la ha encontrado en las plantas de alimentos balanceados, las que progresivamente están incrementando el empleo de la denominada 'upgraded fish meal'. Sin embargo, el productor no ha cejado en sus intentos de emplear este concentrado en la alimentación humana y al presente se encuentra abocada en la conducción de un proyecto que conjuntamente con el Ministerio de Salud pretende introducir en el programa de desayunos escolares, un tipo de galleta enriquecida con proteínas de pescado. También el producto fue utilizado en producción de sopas. El éxito o fracaso del programa, dependerá en gran medida del apoyo que decida proporcionarle el Ministerio respectivo, el costo del producto y la aceptación de la niñez en edad escolar.

CONCLUSIONES

Los distintos productos a base de anchoveta que han sido mencionados, más otra serie que están en proceso de experimentación, representan los primeros pasos que está dando el Perú en un esfuerzo por diversificar la utilización de un abundante recurso que hasta hoy se ha empleado única y exclusivamente en la elaboración de harina y aceite de pescado. Es preciso hacer hincapié en el aspecto de que no es tan importante lo que se pueda hacer con el recurso sino lo que realmente se haga y en ese sentido el Perú, tal como se desprende de lo descrito anteriormente, ha tomado ya una serie de medidas concretas orientadas hacia la industrialización para el consumo humano de parte de su inmensa riqueza anchovetera. A no dudarlo, el éxito que puedan tener estas actividades serán el imán que atraiga una utilización cada vez mayor de la anchoveta en la alimentación directa del hombre.

Technical Note

Processing of Lake Tanganyika Sardines in Burundi   *H J Horn*

In the Burundi sector of Lake Tanganyika fish production reached 16,800 tons (1972) and averaged 12,610 tons between 1962 and 1971. At present 70 to 80 per cent of the catch consists of the sardines *Stolothrissa tanganicae* and *Limnothrissa miodon*. These are true clupeids growing to a length of 6 to 9 cm. An estimated 35 per cent of the total catch is consumed fresh and the remainder is sun-dried on sandy beaches. The product is poor and does not keep well. During the rainy season, when catches are relatively high, sun-drying is often difficult and some 10 per cent wastage occurs. If stored for more than a few weeks, bacterial deterioration and infestation by the beetles *Dermestes* and *Nicrobia* cause further loss. Relatively little of the catch reaches the mountainous interior of Burundi where most of the population lives. This is due mainly to poor roads and lack of suitable

Fig 1   Fish drying plant at the Fishing Centre Kitaza

processing and distribution. Since protein deficiency and 'kwashiorkor' are acute in much of the country, the Government places a high priority on developing the fishery and has recently set up, with the assistance of UNDP and FAO, a fishery project at Kitaza, 25 km from the capital. This is a model fishing centre where fishermen are trained in the use of mechanized catamaran lift-net units which they obtain by hire-purchase. The catches of the boats of this school are processed by the brining/sun-drying/smoking method developed by Cabrita and Watanabe (1971) for Lake Tanganyika sardines in Zambia. The product lasts for six months without significant deterioration at tropical temperatures. The method has

Fig 2   Weighing of sardines before brining and drying

been adapted to the different climate of Burundi and this paper describes it and the results of marketing trials in Burundi in 1972/73.

METHODS

Sardines

The plant (Fig 1) consists of a roofed shed, open at the sides, and a covered cement floor of 8 by 15 m. Brine tanks, smoke ovens and packing tables constitute the processing equipment. Drying racks are placed around the shed, each 1.5 m wide, about 20 m long and 0.7 m above ground. They are constructed of metal frames on which galvanized wire netting is stretched. At one end of each rack there is a roll of synthetic tarpaulin which

Fig 3   Smoked sardines leaving the oven

can be pulled over the rack to protect drying fish from rain. There are four 500 litre metal brine tanks, coated with corrosion resistant paint. The two brick-walled smoke ovens contain racks of galvanized mesh and each oven has a capacity of 1,000 kg fresh sardines. The ovens are served by separate fire boxes, and smoke is introduced through channels in the floor and regulated by damper flaps. The construction is simple and requires little maintenance.

Catches are landed at six o'clock in the morning and, after weighing, the sardines are placed in saturated brine for 12 to 15 min (Fig 2). They are then spread on the drying racks for up to six hours, depending on sun intensity, wind, cloud cover or rain. Smoking takes four hours at temperatures of 40° to 60°C, gradually increased, and for the final 0.5 h temperature is raised to 100°C (Fig 3). After cooling in air, the sardines are sealed in printed polyethylene packs of 200 g and stored in cardboard cartons (Fig 4). Brining results in 8 to 10 per cent salt in the product. Sun-drying results in 30 to 35 per cent reduction of fresh weight, and smoking reduces it a further 5 per cent. The process kills bacterial and beetle egg infection. The present capacity of the plant is 5,000 kg fresh sardines per day, which could be increased to an estimated 10,000 kg by doubling the number of drying racks and smoke ovens.

Other species

Other fish caught with sardines are their predators *Luciolates stappersii*, a herringlike fish, with a usual length

Fig 4 Sealing of polyethylene bags and packing in printed cardboard containers

from estimates of bulk production costs at 15 Burundi Francs (US$0.192) per 200 g ex-factory. This is slightly higher on a weight-for-weight basis than the price of local beef; nevertheless it was considered acceptable by the population because of taste and ease of conservation. Beef is, in any case, in short supply. Also, in considering the price, it should be remembered that the product has the additional value of being concentrated by dehydration in a country where transportation is difficult and costly.

Basing the price paid to fishermen for fresh sardines at the lake shore on the average price of the previous five years (10 Bu.F./kg), preliminary monthly production costs and profit at the low daily average factory intake of 1,000 kg were as follows:

Cost	Fresh sardines, 1,000 kg/day for 26 days at 10 Bu.F.k/g	260,000 Bu.F.
	Labour	13,000 Bu.F.
	Salt, 4,000 kg	23,000 Bu.F.
	Plastic bags, wood and small general costs, also amortization	44,000 Bu.F.
	Total	340,000 Bu.F.
Sale	Processed sardines 7,800 kg (30 % yield) at 50 Bu.F./kg	390,000 Bu.F.
Profit	Ex-factory per month = 50,000 Bu.F. (US$641)	

A principal marketing problem still unsolved concerns the role of distributors. Uncontrolled activity by middlemen could readily increase the retail price to the point of reducing the quantity that the peasant market could afford and largely negate the value of this resource in present economic circumstances.

SOCIAL EFFECTS OF IMPROVED PROCESSING AND MARKETING

Certain socio-economic effects have become apparent in the small Model Fishing Centre. For example, the routine daily fishing for profit as distinct from subsistence, means the introduction of new work habits. Acceptance of the discipline of regular work has varied considerably with individuals, and the most successful are generally those who respond best in this regard. While subsistence fishermen are at present dispersed along the shore, such centres will tend to concentrate them. Most are also farmers, but the better economic opportunities provided by the Centre have encouraged some of them to place more emphasis on fishing than farming. In any case, being located away from their land makes farming more difficult. On the negative side, drunkenness has increased markedly, presumably due to the availability of cash.

of 7 to 29 cm, and *Lates mariae*, *L. angustifrons*, and *L. microlepis*, Nile perch species, with a usual length of 40 to 70 cm. With the exception of *L. microlepis*, the flesh of these species is of excellent quality. *Luciolates* has been successfully made into pickled fillets which, by hot-smoking, can be made into a 'bueckling'-type product (hot-smoked products). *L. mariae* and *L. angustifrons* may be sliced, dyed and lightly smoked to make a 'smoked salmon' substitute product. These items are highly priced in relation to the brined/dried/smoked sardines, and are therefore of lower priority in the present context of fishery development in Burundi. However, by supplying them to the limited local high-income market, they can be used to increase profits and subsidize or lower the sale price of the sardines.

MARKETING

Acceptability trials were first made in areas where people rarely eat fish. Taste and price were critical factors. More than 10,000 packs of 200 g processed sardines were sold at village markets. At the first visit to a market sales were generally slow, but at the second visit the batch sold quickly. From the point of view of taste, the product was highly appreciated, and because of its tastiness a small amount, mixed with the usual staples of cassava porridge or maize, is sufficient to make the meal much more attractive. So the sardines appear to be used as a 'relish' as well as food. The retail price was determined

References

CABRITA, F J and WATANABE, K Design, construction and economic
1971   consideration of fish dry-smoking plant in Zambia. Special
        publ. Ministry of Lands and Natural Resources, Zambia
        and UNDP/FAO.
HALING, A   Développement de la pêche artisanale et la com-
1972   mercialisation du poisson. *UNDP/FAO Rapport au
        Gouvernement du Burundi.*
COLLART, A   Pêche artisanale et pêche industrielle au Lac Tan-
1958   ganyika. Publication de direction de l'Agriculture, des
        Forêts et de l'Elevage, Bruxelles.

WATANABE, K Improved method of preparing dried sardine from
1971   Lake Tanganyika. Special publ. Ministry of Lands and
        Natural Resources, Zambia and UNDP/FAO.

Acknowledgement

Thanks are given to M Ngomirakiza, Directeur du Département des
Eaux et Forêts, Ministère de l'Agriculture et de l'Elevage, Burundi,
and his department for kind cooperation.

Utilization of Barracudina as a Source of Wax Esters and Proteins   *R C Ackman, C A Eaton and P J Ke*

Utilisation du barracoudina comme source de cires esterifiees et de proteines.

Au cours du printemps de 1971, on a observé la présence de grandes quantités de barracoudina blanc, *Paralepis rissoi Krøyeri* Bonaparte 1840, dans le Golfe du Saint-Laurent. Bien que les difficultés techniques liées aux reáctions d'évitement jugées inhabituelles de ce poisson aient empêché son exploitation à grande échelle, encore au moment de la rédaction du présent article (1972), nous avons procédé à une évaluation de la ressource. Une attention particulière a été accordée à la récupération des lipides, qui sont riches en cires estérifiées, ainsi qu'à l'évaluation des protéines ayant une teneur modérée en lipides (farine de poisson) et des protéines essentiellement exemptes de lipides (concentré de protéines de posson).

Aprovechamiento de la barracudina para la obtencion de esteres cereos u proteinas.

En la primavera de 1971 se encontraron cantidades considerables de barracudina blanca, *Paralepis rissol* Krøyeri Bonaparte 1840, en el Golfo de San Lorenzo. Aunque al momento de escribir esta nota (1972) no ha sido posible explotarla a gran escala debido a dificultades técnicas planteadas, según se cree, por el desusual comportamiento de fuga en estos animales, se ha podido evaluar desde el punto de vista de los recursos. Se ha prestado especial atención a la recuperación de los lípidos, que son ricos en ésteres céreos, a la evaluación de las proteínas, que contienen una cantidad moderada de lípidos (harina de pescado) y de proteínas esencialmente exentas de lípidos (concentrado de proteína de pescado).

The resources of the sea available to man for animal protein and lipid are the subject of controversy even as regards quantity (Ryther 1969, 1970; Alverson *et al.* 1970) while quality has received only passing mention. It is certain that among the animals which will eventually be exploited when economics and technology permit, are small fish such as the myctophids. These mid-water fish school in reasonably dense concentrations (Backus *et al.* 1968, Barham 1971) at least on occasion, although for unknown reasons, and are thought to be one of the sources of scattering layers in the ocean (Butler and Pearcy 1972). In common with many other speculative marine animal resources these fish are often found at considerable depth (> 100 m) and their commercial potential, particularly as foodstuffs for man, has received little technological evaluation. An accessible fish species sharing similar technological problems, the white barracudina, *Paralepis rissoi Krøyeri*, has been studied from a resource utilization point of view. Basic information has been obtained pertinent to the eventual utilization of myctophids and other fish or crustaceans, with lipids rich in wax esters, for industrial fats, and for protein recovery and evaluation.

PRELIMINARY EVALUATION

The first fish brought to our attention were a few specimens caught as incidentals to exploratory mid-water trawling for redfish being carried out by the Industrial Development Branch, Fisheries Service, Canada Department of the Environment. These were caught off Cape Breton Island in April of 1971. After identification by the St. Andrews Laboratory of the Fisheries Research Board, the lipids group of the Halifax Laboratory of the Fisheries Research Board examined the lipid (Ackman *et al.* 1972) and found it to be predominantly wax esters (Table 1). As these resembled the wax esters of sperm oil in composition (Table 2) the possibility arose of substituting barracudina oil for the sperm oil which had been included in the whale products banned from entry to the

United States of America (US General Services Administration, Federal Register, December 2, 1970, p. 18319). A preliminary analysis of uncooked whole fish (1 kg) ground and defatted with methylene chloride (1.6 l), yielded 7 per cent oil and indicated that production of meal and protein for nutrition should be feasible as the fish solids had suitable properties (Table 3).

TECHNOLOGICAL EVALUATION

In 1972, despite considerable efforts to obtain large amounts of barracudina, only about 140 kg became available for reasons discussed below. Fortunately these were obtained in small lots over the spring, summer and autumn seasons from different locations in the Gulf of St. Lawrence area and showed that total lipid was always predominantly wax ester, although lipid ranged from 7.0 to 17.7 per cent on a wet weight basis. The available fish were divided randomly into a lot of 81 kg for fish meal production and evaluation and a lot of 40 kg for fish protein concentrate production by extraction with isopropyl alcohol (IPA) (Power 1962). Study of the recovery and properties of the oil was a major consideration in both instances.

FISH MEAL AND OIL PROPERTIES

The barracudina were processed in a small-scale reduction plant (Chemical Research Organization Model 25, Esbjerg, Denmark) at the Fisheries Research Board Laboratory in Vancouver, B.C. (Claggett 1968). Cooking was at 60°C and the presscake was steam dried (operating temperature 110°C, outlet meal temperature 71°C). The oil was separated by floatation and subsequently cleaned by putting it through a continuous centrifuge with hot water. The yields are described in Table 4. The stickwater was not returned to the meal resulting in a 'presscake' meal rather than a whole meal. Ethoxyquin, 250 ppm, was added to the meal. Feeding tests for meal evaluation were carried out as described by Power *et al.*

(1969), by Mrs. B E March, University of British Columbia, and included a nutritional study on the oil. Other analyses were carried out under contract by the Wisconsin Alumni Research Foundation (WARF) Institute Inc., Madison, Wisconsin. Many of the fish used for reduction were full of small crustaceans (euphausids) and this resulted in a dark red oil. This coloration had not been observed in fish muscle extracts and would probably be a seasonal factor and dependent on diet.

minuting mill, Model D, with a few litres of isopropyl alcohol (Shell Chem. Co., 99.9 per cent) for local cooling and to facilitate handling. The ground fish were cooked with a total of 136 l of IPA at 65°C for 20 minutes. The slurry was transferred by pump to a basket centrifuge and the liquid separated (Extract A). Subsequently the protein was re-extracted with fresh isopropyl alcohol, 136 l, to give Extract B, and again with 136 l to give Extract C which was not examined for lipid. The protein was vacuum dried at 60°C in an Abbé Rota-Cone

TABLE 1. COMPARISON OF LIPID YIELD AND PROPERTIES FOR VARIOUS CATCHES OF BARRACUDINA

Year	1971	1972	1972	1972
Month	April	May	July	October
Average length of fish, cm	25.4	23.5	24.1	19–24[a]
Average weight of fish, g	27.0	18.9	23.8	10–24[a]
%Lipid recovery[b]	17.7 (body)	7 (body)[c]	14 (whole)	8.1–14.8[a] (whole)
%Wax ester in lipid	85	89	79	70
%Triglyceride in lipid	10	7	16	21
Total lipid iodine value (Wijs)	126	122	124	135
Wax ester fatty acid iodine value[d]	136 (calc.)	153	129	166
Triglyceride iodine value[d]	48 (calc.)	78	80	98

[a]Ranges are minimum and maximum
[b]Bligh and Dyer (1964) method, wet weight basis
[c]Solitary fish
[d]Calculated from GLC analysis of TLC isolates

TABLE 2. WEIGHT PERCENTAGES OF IMPORTANT COMPONENTS OF WAX ESTERS OF BARRACUDINA AND SPERM WHALE BODY AND HEAD OILS

Ester	Fatty acids			Fatty alcohols		
	Barracudina	Sperm body[a]	Sperm head[a]	Barracudina	Sperm body[a]	Sperm head[a]
14:0	6.2	3.3	14.4	3.8	3.2	11.0
14:1	0.3	2.4	33.3	—	—	—
16:0	6.3	8.1	2.8	40.2	24.9	49.7
16:1	15.7	26.9	9.5	0.5	9.6	4.4
18:0	0.4	1.1	0.2	7.0	4.3	3.5
18:1	34.2	33.3	4.9	29.6	44.9	27.3
20:1	4.3	10.9	0.9	8.3	5.0	0.5
20:5ω3	8.5	1.7	—	—	0.3	Trace
22:1	5.3	2.2	—	5.5	0.2	—
22:5ω3	0.4	0.8	0.2	—	0.6	Trace
22:6ω3	8.9	2.1	0.3	—	—	—

[a]Date from Challinor, C J, Hamilton, R J and Simpson, K, Chem. Phys. Lipids, 3:145–151, 1969

TABLE 3. PROXIMATE ANALYSIS OF BARRACUDINA PRESSCAKE MEAL, BARRACUDINA FISH PROTEIN CONCENTRATE AND METHYLENE CHLORIDE DEFATTED BARRACUDINA (%)

	Fish Meal (Presscake)	Fish Protein Concentrate	Defatted Fish
Moisture	6.3	3.0	4.1
Ether Extract (Fat)	17.8	0.5	8.2
Protein	67.0	89.1	77.5
Ash	7.9	11.2	10.2
Fibre	0.4	0.5	ND
	99.4	104.3	100.0

vacuum rotary drier at 2 cm Hg pressure for 23 h and ground to 200 mesh in a Rietz mill. Chemical analyses of presscake and FPC are given in Tables 5 to 7.

ISOPROPANOL FRACTIONATION OF LIPID

The compositions of the lipids recovered from Extracts A and B and fractions prepared therefrom are described in Table 8. The process is illustrated in flow diagrams (Figs. 1 and 2). Preliminary isopropanol solubility data (Ke and Ackman, unpublished results) had indicated that a considerable proportion of lipid would be thrown out of solution on cooling Extract A to ambient temperature (about 20°C). Because of the higher specific gravity of the oil relative to the IPA-water phase, oil A_2 sank. To facilitate handling at room temperature and to obtain additional oil as a major product fraction, the IPA phase from Extract A_2 (the upper layer at 20°C) was concentrated in a flash evaporator to 10 litres. The oil thrown out of solution (Top oil A^3) now appeared as the

FISH PROTEIN CONCENTRATE (FPC) AND LIPID RECOVERY

The solvent extraction procedure was designed to produce a regular grade of fish protein concentrate similar to that produced from whole herring or capelin (Power 1964). The fish, 40 kg ,were ground in a Fitzpatrick com-

TABLE 4. YIELDS FROM PILOT PLANT REDUCTIONS OF WHOLE BARRACUDINA

Weight of raw material processed, kg	81.0
Recovery of presscake meal, kg	16.3
Recovery of presscake meal, %	20.1
Recovery of oil, kg	2.72
Recovery of oil, %	3.4
Press liquor (stickwater) data:	
Weight, kg	48.0
Oil content, %	0.8
Solid content, %	3.0
Theoretical meal yield, %	21.9
Theoretical oil yield, %	3.8

TABLE 5. VITAMIN ANALYSIS OF BARRACUDINA PRODUCTS (PPM)

	Fish Meal (Presscake)	Fish Protein Concentrate
Thiamin	0.5	0.4
Riboflavin	3.9	4.25
Pantothenic acid	7.37	8.22
Niacin	32.2	15.9
Choline Chloride	4,870.0	277.0
Biotin	0.346	0.236
Folic acid	0.92	0.46
Vitamin B-12	0.0262	0.0215

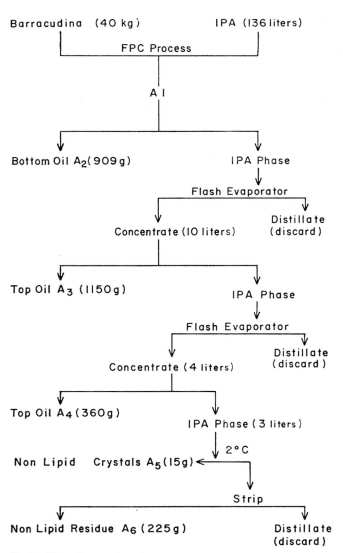

Fig 1   Flow diagram for oil recovery from initial extraction of barracudina with 99.9% IPA

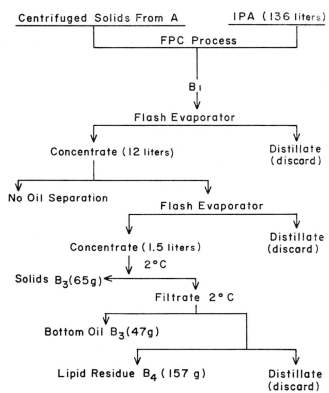

Fig 2   Flow diagram for oil recovery from second extraction of barracudina with 99.9% IPA

upper phase because of the density change, as IPA was preferentially lost from the IPA/H₂O solution on flash distillation. Further separations were carried out at 2°C to maximize oil recovery. The separated oils were found to differ from the lipid dissolved from the fish owing to the preferential solubility in isopropyl alcohol of phospholipids, free fatty acids, sterols, etc., as had been previously observed for herring lipids (Drozdowski and Ackman 1969). The partitioning and solubility had a dual role as the ratio of wax esters to triglycerides was slightly altered (Table 8). In addition, it was expected that the wax esters containing polyunsaturated fatty acids (Ackman *et al.* 1972) would partition into the isopropyl alcohol phase, with a consequent lowering of the iodine value and preparation of a product closer to the iodine value of commercial sperm oil (about 70 to 96).

PROBLEMS IN FISHING BARRACUDINA

The barracudina first brought to our attention had been retrieved from a mid-water trawl fishing for cod (or redfish) off Cape Breton Island in April 1971. The barracudina were mostly entangled in the net, a fact which received little notice as the cod-end mesh was about 12 cm and it was thought that most of the barra-

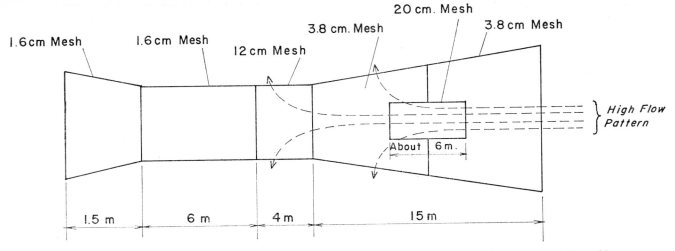

Fig 3 *A cod-end designed by the Industrial Development Branch, Fisheries Service, Department of the Environment (Canada), or exploratory mid-water trawling for barracudina*

cudina had escaped through the mesh. The cod were presumed to be feeding on the barracudina and echo-sounding traces for the schools extended for 60 kilometres. Barracudina were at one time thought to be rare (Leim and Scott 1966, cf. Scott and Tibbo 1968, Bakkala 1971). In June of the same year thousands of barracudina were caught the same way off Anticosti Island but in association with mid-water catches of redfish (*Sebastes marinus*). Reports from fishermen which suggested that large schools of barracudina were available off Anticosti Island were supported by the distribution data of Leim and Scott (1966). In 1972 these were located by echo-sounder and fished with an IDS net Diamond V-B mid-water trawl in which the cod-end mesh was reduced to about 2 cm, a size found suitable for sand launce (*Ammodytes* spp.), a fish similar in size to the barracudina. It was quickly realized that the cod-end was again empty, that the few barracudina caught were in the upper part of the net as it surfaced. This information seems to relate to visual observations on the behaviour of the barracudina (cited as *Paralepis rissoi*) discussed by Barham (1971). Although these particular barracudina (in the Mediterranean and adjacent Atlantic) 'darted away' horizontally, the numerous observations cited by Barham (1971) on the vertical mid-water orientation of the members of the Paralepidid family (see also Scott and Tibbo 1968) suggest that the white barracudina may also orient vertically. If, then, they flee from the water pressure build-up in advance of the cod-end, very rapidly and initially in a vertical direction, this would explain the poor catches and distribution in the net. The Industrial Development Branch of the Fisheries Service, who have carried out most of these trials, consider that barracudina may be encouraged in this escape manoeuvre by the wash of water ahead of the net in general and in particular due to the resistance of the fine mesh cod-end to water flow. Accordingly W. W. Johnson and J. R. Trimm designed modified truncated cod-ends, with vent panels and a coarse exhaust ring, for use with Diamond III or V-B trawls. These modifications should reduce trawl drag as well as displacement of water from in front of the net (Fig. 3). The balance of the exploratory fishing, carried out without a netsonde,

using a Diamond III mid-water trawl off Cape Breton Island in May of 1972 and in the Cabot Strait in October of 1972 collected a few kg of fish on most trials, indicating that barracudina occur widely in the Gulf of St. Lawrence/Cabot Strait area. Although barracudina have been caught in mid-water at about 100 m depth, it is noteworthy that all catches have come from locations where the bottom drops off steeply from about 50 m to as much as 250 m depth. The stomach contents observed have been exclusively *Meganyctiphanes norvegica* or *Thysanoessa inermis* (in agreement with Leim and Scott 1966). The smallest fish (about 10 cm) came from the Cabot Strait. We have not observed ripe gonads in fish up to 25 cm in length and believe these to be immature. The same sizes have been taken from swordfish stomachs (Scott and Tibbo 1968).

PROTEIN AND METABOLIZABLE ENERGY RESULTS

There seems to be little doubt that the protein of barracudina is similar to that of most fish commercially exploited for meal production. The meal composition data of Tables 3 and 5 to 7 closely resemble that tabulated in a study of meals from a variety of North Atlantic species (Opstvedt *et al.* 1970) or of meal from herring (Kifer *et al.* 1969a, Power *et al.* 1969), menhaden (Kifer *et al.* 1968a) or anchoveta (Kifer *et al.* 1968b, 1969b). The bioassay data (Table 9) also compare favourable in protein quality with that for meals from other species (Power *et al.* 1969, Opstvedt *et al.* 1970, Sparre 1971). Data for a menhaden presscake meal prepared at the same time as the barracudina presscake meal have been included in Table 9 to facilitate comparison, along with a regular commercial herring meal. All three meals were evaluated in the same feeding tests. These tests showed that the metabolizable energy value of barracudina meal was 4,360 cal/grammes. The metabolizable energy of the barracudina oil in the meal was calculated at 8,515 cal/g versus 9,235 for the menhaden oil in the same bioassay. The digestibility of the barracudina lipid in the meal must therefore have been at least 90 per cent despite the high wax ester content. Thus there is then no reason to keep barracudina meal separate from other meals in a plant reducing more than one species. The protein in the fish protein concentrate (Tables 3 and 9) is also similar to the products from other species (Power 1964, Weinberg 1967). The available lysine was 9.60 per cent of crude protein. The two-week protein efficiency ratio was 2.92 versus 2.50 for casein, and the four-week values were 2.81 and 2.50. The IPA-defatted protein product (fish protein concentrate) was similar in odour, taste and appearance to similar products made from whole fish of types regularly eaten in Canada. Barracudina, and probably other mid-water fish species, therefore appear capable of exploitation as high quality protein sources.

WAX ESTERS AND FUTURE FISHERIES

Exploratory work on the technology of exploitation of the accessible surface zooplankters has already begun. The smaller species such as copepods are unlikely to be economically harvested except in special circumstances such as in the swarms found in the fjords of Norway (Wiborg and Bjørke 1968, 1969). Up to 10 t of *Calanus* sp. have been harvested in a year at a rate of 500–700 kg/h by trawl, or in traps. These are acceptable as

TABLE 6. MINERAL ANALYSIS OF BARRACUDINA PRODUCTS

	Fish Meal (Presscake)	Fish Protein Concentrate
	(%)	(%)
Calcium	2.02	2.36
Magnesium	0.17	0.232
Phosphorus	1.55	1.79
Potassium	0.725	1.12
Sodium	0.377	0.722
	(ppm)	(ppm)
Aluminium	598.0	44.5
Arsenic	1.2	0.33
Barium	2.54	<2.0
Boron	23.5	5.23
Cadmium	0.4	0.2
Chromium	13.1	6.44
Cobalt	0.6	<0.05
Copper	42.5	11.1
Iodine	1.1	1.1
Iron	2,220.0	75.5
Lead	17.0	1.4
Manganese	23.4	4.74
Mercury	0.1	0.12
Molybdenum	0.4	0.1
Selenium	2.15	1.54
Strontium	92.0	118.0
Zinc	425.0	125.0

TABLE 7. AMINO ACID ANALYSES OF BARRACUDINA PRODUCTS (G/100 PRODUCT)

	Fish Meal (Presscake	Fish Protein Concentrate
Lysine	5.29	7.30
Histidine	1.92	2.19
Arginine	3.85	5.24
Aspartic acid	7.10	10.10
Threonine	3.19	4.13
Serine	2.83	3.98
Glutamic acid	9.92	14.60
Proline	2.63	3.81
Glycine	3.28	5.69
Alanine	4.23	6.32
Valine	3.90	4.85
Methionine	2.37	3.13
Isoleucine	3.53	4.27
Leucine	5.84	7.78
Tyrosine	2.68	3.55
Phenylalanine	3.29	4.07
Tryptophan	0.78	1.02
Cystine	0.88	1.37
Ammonia	0.45	0.60

trout and salmon food in commercial rearing operations. *Meganyctiphanes norvegica* and *Thysanoessa inermis* (Raymont *et al.* 1969, Ackman *et al.* 1970) and *Euphausia pacifica* (Pierce *et al.* 1969) are representative euphausids suitable for technological exploitation in the northern hemisphere and an alternative is the crab *Pleuroncodes planipes* (Pierce *et al.* 1969). The krill *Euphausia superba* has not only been examined for basic composition (Pierce *et al.* 1969, Sidhu *et al.* 1970) but is already being exploited to make a 'paste' with shrimplike flavour (Nikolayeva 1971, Kryuchkova and Makarov 1969, Egorova *et al.* 1970, Krjuchkova 1971). This is possible because the fat is predominantly in the form of glyceryl esters, and therefore perfectly acceptable nutritionally, although it is somewhat susceptible to autoxidation (Maksimov 1968[1]). Our concern as to potential adverse dietary effects originating in wax esters of marine fish (Sato and Tsuchiya 1969, 1970) appears to be unfounded. The metabolizable energy and feeding studies indicate that barracudina wax esters had no untoward dietary effect when fed as the lipid component of fish meal. Our results are a guide to the exploitation and technological utilization of several mid-water animal species. Many of these are myctophids which are known to have lipids rich in wax esters (Nevenzel *et al.* 1969). Some *Lampanyctus*

[1] As printed there is an error in this paper and 'quantity saponifiable' should read 'quantity not-saponifiable'.

TABLE 8. PROPERTIES OF LIPID FRACTIONS FROM ISOPROPYL ALCOHOL EXTRACTION OF BARRACUDINA

	Total A₁	Bottom Oil A₂	Top Oil A₃	Top Oil A₄	Total B₁	Solids B₃	Bottom Oil B₃
Per cent wax ester	71	70	43	68	68	58	62
Per cent triglyceride	12	28	22	3	23	37	37
Ratio waz ester/triglyceride	5.9	2.5	3.2	14.3	3.0	1.6	1.7
Iodine value oil or lipid (Wijs)	133	121	125	115	134	115	131
Iodine value wax ester (Wijs)	118	110	116	112	109	93	94
Iodine value triglyceride[a]	72	91	105	63	88	63	96
Per cent free fatty acid	7	1	2	26	4	2	Trace
Per cent: sterols, mono and di-glycerides, phospholipids	10	1	6	28[b]	5	3	1

[a]Calculated from GLC analysis
[b]Major portion of this fraction non-lipd

TABLE 9. PEPSIN DIGESTIBILITY, AVAILABLE LYSINE, SUPPLEMENTARY PROTEIN VALUES AND FEED CONVERSION FOR FISH MEALS

	Barracudina Fish Meal (Presscake)	Menhaden Fish Meal (Prescake)	British Columbia Herring Meal
Pepsin digestibility[a] as % of crude protein	83.56	91.78	—
Available lysine as % of total protein	6.04	6.11	5.97
Supplementary protein values[b] 4% of protein	126.00	132.00	146.00
Feed conversion, g gain/g feed consumed	0.38	0.39	0.40
Supplementary protein values[b] 8% of protein	102.00	109.00	113.00
Feed conversion, g gain/g feed consumed	0.50	0.51	0.52

[a]Pepsin (activity 1:20,000) at a concentration of 0.02 per cent
[b]Chicks four weeks on test

sp. and *Myctophum* sp. were taken along with barracudina off Cape Breton Island indicating the association of wax esters and depth in fish. Wax esters also occur widely in many crustacean zooplankters which might be considered for future exploitation as a food source (Nevenzel 1970, Benson *et al.* in press, Lee *et al.* 1971, Morris 1971a, 1971b, 1972; Lee and Hirota 1972, Yamada 1972). Assuming that fishing could be made practical for densities as low as 1 g of animal/m³ (Barraclough *et al.* 1969, Wiborg 1971) then the small individual sizes in both potential resources, perhaps 1 to 5 cm in length for euphausids and 1 to 10 or 2 to 15 cm in length for mesopelagic fishes (Marshall 1971, McCartney and Stubbs 1971), and the frequent juxtaposition of various animal species in mid-water (Ebeling *et al.* 1971, Marshall 1971, Donaldson 1972), would dictate handling *en masse*. These resources could be used for fish meal but fishing costs are likely to be high, suggesting that it would be better to produce a defatted protein product such as we have demonstrated to be practical for the more accessible barracudina.

References

ACKMAN, R G, EATON, C A, SIPOS, J C, HOOPER, S N and CASTELL,
1970   J D *J. Fish. Res. Bd. Can.*, (27):513–533.
ACKMAN, R G, HOOPER, S N. EPSTEIN, S and KELLEHER, M *J. Am.*
1972   *Oil Chem. Soc.*, (49):378–382.
ALVERSON, D L, LONGHURST, A R and GULLAND, J A *Science*,
1970   (168):503–505.
BACKUS, R H, CRADDOCK, J E, HAEDRICH, R L, SHORES, D L, TEAL,
1968   J M, WING, A S, MEAD, G W and CLARKE, E D *Ibid.*, (160):
991–993.
BAKKALA, R G *Fishery Bull.*, (69):881.
BARHAM, E G In Farquhar G Brook (ed.), *Proc. Int. Symp. Biol.*
1971   *Sound Scattering Ocean, Warrenton, Virginia, March 31–
April 2, 1970*, US Gov. Print. Office, Washington, MC
Report 005, p. 100–118.
BARRACLOUGH, W E, LeBRASSEUR, R J and KENNEDY, O D *Science*,
1969   (166):611–613.
BENSON, A A, LEE, R F and NEVENZEL, J C In *Proc. Int. Symp.
Lipids, Bangalore, Dec. 2–7, 1971*, London and New York,
Academic Press, (in press, 1972).
BUTLER, J L and PEARCY, W F *J. Fish. Res. Bd. Can.*, (29):1145–
1972   1150.
CLAGGETT, F G *Fish. Can.*, 21(1):14–16.
1968
DONALDSON, H S *J. Fish. Res. Bd. Can.*, (29):1419–1423.
1972
DROZDOWSKI, B and ACKMAN, R G *J. Am. Oil Chem. Soc.*, (46):
1969   371–376.
EBELING, A W, CAILLIET, G M, IBARA, R M and DeWITT, F A Jr. In
1971   Farquhar G Brook (ed.), *Proc. Int. Symp. Biol. Sound
Scattering Ocean, Warrenton, Virginia, March 31–April 2,
1970*, US Gov. Print. Office, Washington, MC Report 005,
p. 1–19.

EGOROVA, L N, KOPYLENKO, L R, MASLENNIKOVA, N V and
1970   SIDOROVA, E M *Trudy Vses. Mauch. Issl. Inst. Morsk. Ryb.
Khoz. Okean.* (*VNIRO*), Moscow (73):179–187.
KIFER, R R, PAYNE, W L, MILLER, D and AMBROSE, M E *Feedstuffs*,
1968a   40(20):36 *et seq.*
KIFER, R R, PAYNE, W L, BAUERSFELD, P E and AMBROSE, M E *Ibid.*
1968b   40(35):32 *et seq.*
KIFER, R R, MILLER, D, PAYNE, W L and AMBROSE, M E *Ibid.*, 41(39):
1969a   18 *et seq.*
KIFER, R R, PAYNE, W L, MILLER, D and AMBROSE, M E *Ibid.*, 41(31):
1969b   24 *et seq.*
KRJUCHKOVA, M I German Patent 1936258, 8 pages. Disclosed
Feb. 11, 1971.
KRYUCHKOVA, M I and MAKAROV, O E *Trudy VNIRO* (66):295–298.
1969
LEE, R F and HIROTA, J *Limnol. and Oceanog.*, (in press, 1972).
LEE, R F, HIROTA, J and BARNETT, A M *Deep-Sea Research*, (18):
1971   1147–1165.
LEIM, A H and SCOTT, W B Fishes of the Atlantic Coast of Canada,
1966   *Fish. Res. Bd. Can. Bull.*, (185):485 p.
MAKSIMOV, S I *Ryb Khoz.*, 44(6):68–69.
1968
MARSHALL, N B In Farquhar G Brook (ed.), *Proc. Int. Symp. Biol.*
1971   *Sound Scattering Ocean, Warrenton, Virginia, March 31–
April 2, 1970*, U.S. Gov. Print. Office, Washington, MC
Report 005, p. 69–73.
McCARTNEY, B S and Stubbs, A R *Ibid.*, p. 180–211.
1971
MORRIS, R J *Deep-Sea Research*, (18):525–529.
1971a
MORRIS, R J *Comp. Biochem. Physiol.*, (40B):275–281.
1971b
MORRIS, R J *Marine Biology*, (16):102–107.
1972
NEVENZEL, J C *Lipids*, (5):308–319.
1970
NEVENZEL, J C, RODEGKER, W, ROBINSON, J S and KAYAMA, M.
1969   *Comp. Biochem. Physiol.*, (31):25–36.
NIKOLAYEVA, N Ye In Rerepletchick, R R and Rzhavskaya, F M
1967   (ed.), Technology of Fats, Oils and Food Products, *VNIRO
Proceedings*, LXIII, p. 161–164.
OPSTVEDT, OHLSEN, J, S URDAHL, N, LAKESVELA. B and BJØRNSTAD, J
Meldinger fra S.S.F., (4):118–166.
PIERCE, R W, VAN DER VEEN, J and OLCOTT, H S *J. Agric. and Food
1969   Chem.*, (17):367–369.
POWER, H E *J. Fish. Res. Bd. Can.*, (19):1039–1045.
1962
POWER, H E *Ibid.*, (21):1489–1504.
1964
POWER, H E, Savagaon, K A, MARCH. B E and BIELY, J *Feedstuffs*,
1969   41(47):48 *et seq.*
RAYMONT, J E G, SRINIVASAGAM, R T and RAYMONT, J K B *Deep-
1969   Sea Research*, (16):141–156.
RYTHER, J H *Science*, (166):72–76.
1969
RYTHER, J H *Ibid.*, (168):503–505.
1970
SATO, Y and TSUCHIYA, Y *Tohoku J. of Agric. Res.*, (20): 89–95.
1969
SATO, Y and TSUCHIYA, Y *Ibid.*, (21):176–182.
1970
SCOTT, W B and TIBBO, S N *J. Fish. Res. Bd. Can.*, (25):903–919.
1968
SIDHU, G S, MONTGOMERY, W A, HOLLOWAY, G L. JOHNSON, A R
1970   and WALKER, D M *J. Sci. Fd Agric.*, (21):293–296.
SPARRE, T *Norsildmel Bulletin*, (2), May, 20 p.
1971
WEINBERG, B *Fishing News International*, (6) (Jan.): 18 *et seq.*
1967
WIBORG, K F *FiskDir. Skr. Ser. HavUnders.*, (16):10–35.
1971
WIBORG, K F and BJØRKE, H *Fiskets Gang*, (42):727–730.
1968
WIBORG, K T and BJØRKE, H *Ibid.*, (48):819–822.
1969
YAMADA, M *Mem. Fac. Fish. Hokkaido Univ.*, 19(1/2):35–136.
1972

Acknowledgements

Cooperating technicians of the Industrial Development Branch, Fisheries Service, were J R Trimm, D A Peeling and W D'Entremont. The advice of L W Regier, Halifax Laboratory, Fisheries Research Board of Canada, has been most helpful. The fish protein concentrate was prepared by R Legendre of the same laboratory. We are also grateful to the Vancouver Laboratory, Fisheries Research Board of Canada, for the use of their reduction unit. The meals were prepared by F G Claggett. J Hingley assisted with lipid analyses.

Alternative Uses of Bonito in Peru   *P W de Haan*

Utilisations nouvelles de la bonite au Perou

La présente communication décrit un 'modèle' élaboré pour étudier les activités de l'industrie péruvienne de la conserve de bonites, en vue de déterminer les obstacles à une expansion rentable de cette industrie. L'analyse montre que le potentiel de l'industrie est important mais qu'il importe de réaliser un programme majeur portant sur la reconstruction, la modernisation et la rationalisation de l'industrie dans son ensemble, y compris le secteur de la pêche, si le potentiel doit être utilisé pleinement. L'une des conditions fondamentales requises pour assurer la santé et la prospérité de l'industrie réside dans la certitude de l'approvisionnement en matières premières; or, à l'heure actuelle, cet approvisionnement n'est pas continu, en dépit de l'abondance des ressources.

Otros posibles empleos del bonito en el Peru

En este trabajo se describe un 'modelo' preparado para estudiar las actividades de la industria conservera de bonito del Perú con vistas a determinar los obstáculos que se oponen a la expansión rentable de la industria. El análisis ha mostrado que el potencial de la industria es may grande, pero que para aprovecharlo es esencial iniciar un programa a gran escala de reconstrucción, modernización y racionalización de toda la industria, incluido el sector pesquero. En especial, un requisito fundamental para la solidez y prosperidad de esta industria es garantizar loss suministros de materia prima, que en la actualidad no son continuos, a pesar de la abundancia de los recursos.

A study was made in Peru to determine the economic consequences of utilizing the bonito catches in various ways. Such a study was needed in order to acquire some knowledge on basic economic relationships of the bonito processing industry, to assess the economic feasibility of new forms of utilization, and to look into some socio-economic aspects of producing these products.

THE FRAME OF REFERENCE
Characteristics of the species

The bonito is the smallest and lowest priced of the tuna family and is generally known by this Spanish name. The type generally found in the waters of Peru has the following characteristics:

Species:	Mainly *Sarda chiliensis* (Pacific bonito)
Mean Length:	65 cm
Mean Weight:	2,750 g
Size Grading:	2.5 to 5.0 kg/fish (73%)
	1.5 to 2.5 kg/fish (23%)
	Under 1.5 kg/fish (4%)
Edible part:	58%
Chemical composition of edible part (averages):	
Water:	73%
Fat:	4.5%
Protein:	21%
Minerals:	1.5%
Range of fat content:	1.6 to 11.2%
Spawning time:	November to February

Resource and landings

Years ago the annual sustainable catch of bonito in the waters of Peru was estimated to be about 80,000 tons. Such a large catch has not been obtained since 1966 and it is therefore assumed that total resource has diminished. As the fish is mainly dependent on anchoveta for its food, the depletion of total anchoveta stock has probably had this adverse effect on the bonito resource but no serious scientific assessment of it has yet been made. The main landings take place from around November to February all along the coast, the principal ports being Callao, Chimbote and Sechura. On an average, catches amount to 30 per cent of the total weight as well as value of all the foodfish landings of Peru, thus making it the most important single species in that sector.

Utilization

Bonito has been traditionally used in four ways: fresh, frozen, canned and dry-salted. In general, about 50 per cent is consumed fresh, and 35 per cent used for canning, the rest being split in a rather erratic way between dry-salted and frozen.

Fresh bonito seems to be the most favoured fish of the lower and medium income groups. This market buys the better quality fish and provides the fishermen with his best return on catches.

The canning industry was started during the second world war and became a main supplier to the allied forces. The importance of Peru as a world supplier of canned bonito can be evaluated from Table 1. Unfortunately the table does not give the figures for a presumed large producer, Japan, probably because its production is included in the 'canned tuna' category. The amount of frozen bonito fluctuates wildly from year to year. Most of the freezing is done by two or three canning plants to provide buffer stocks of raw material. Around 15 per cent of the Peruvian bonito catch is sold in a dry-salted form, mostly carried out on board of small vessels, with no other means of preserving the catch.

TABLE 1. WORLD PRODUCTION OF CANNED BONITO (THOUSAND TONS)

	1958	1966	1970
Peru	14.4	10.1	7.8
Spain	12.1	12.4	8.4[a]
USA	0.9	2.0	1.3
Argentina	—	3.2	2.2[a]
Others	1.8	3.1	0.4
Total	29.2	20.8	20.1
% Production share Peru	49	49	39

[a] 1969 data

Source: FAO (1971) Yearbook of Fishery Statistics, Fishery commodities, 1970, (31): 320 p.

The markets

The demand for a number of bonito products is quite large and the market can certainly absorb the current supply at prevailing prices. For example, domestic consumption of canned bonito is claimed[1] to have been around 16,500 tons gross weight in 1971 (70 per cent of the production that year). The export market is believed to have space for around 8,000 tons of the Peruvian product annually. While the home market is growing

[1] By Sociedad Nacional de Pesquería (SNP), the Association of Peruvian Fisheries enterprises. Figures from this source are in serious disharmony with those published by FAO in the Yearbook of Fishery Statistics, e.g., Production of canned bonito 1969:
FAO: 5,100 tons net weight = 6,100 tons gross weight
SNP: 8,500 tons gross weight.

steadily, the export market also offers excellent growth prospects, ie, around 15 per cent annually for the European market.

Frozen bonito exports cannot be estimated because no sizable quantity of product has yet been produced. But it is certain that there exists an initial demand of around 2,000 to 5,000 tons per year, attractive enough at prevailing prices to induce production. The same strong demand conditions prevail for dry-salted bonito, although prices are probably not high enough to stimulate additional production above that undertaken for catch preservation reasons.

The state of the industry

During and after the second world war, the canning industry expanded and reached its highest production level toward the end of the fifties, the peak year being 1961 with a production of 24,000 tons (source: Sociedad Nacional de Pesquería) gross weight. Production then started to decline, reaching a low of about 11,000 tons in 1969. Much higher figures have been reported for the last two years, but dependable statistics are not yet available. Table 2 gives some economic characteristics of the fish canning industry in Peru.

This conflicting situation seems to justify some further investigation into the economics of utilizing the bonito resources of Peru in different ways.

ECONOMIC ANALYSIS OF A BONITO CANNING OPERATION

The model

The advantage of a theoretical and unbiased investigation into the workings of a settled industry is that such an approach tends to throw new light on well established facts and positions. Bearing this objective in mind, it was decided to build and operate theoretically a plant with a canning capacity of 1,100 cases of $48\frac{1}{2}$ lb (225 g) tuna cans daily. This plant capacity was chosen in order to remain as close as possible to existing capacity figures in Peru, of which Table 4 gives a frequency distribution.

For calculation of the annual total output, it was assumed that a year consists of 220 working days, thus making ample allowance for shutdown time due to lack of fish and other reasons. Yearly production would then amount to 242,000 cases.

The *total investment* was estimated at US $560,000 and *yearly fixed costs* at US $80,000 (the exchange rate

TABLE 2. PERUVIAN CANNING INDUSTRY

	1965	1966	1967	1968	1969	1970
Number of canneries in operation	20	21	19	19	20	27
Average production per cannery (t/year)	970	690	690	690	660	650
Total persons employed	2,280	1,760	1,450	1,800	1,870	1,470
Average production per person employed (t/year)	8.5	8.2	9.1	7.3	7.1	12.0

Source: Diagnóstico del Sector Pesquero 1971 – Ministerio de Pesquería

In general, it must be admitted that the canneries of Peru are in a poor state. Their equipment is old and run down, they are operating on a small scale, work organization and management are often of low standard, and hygiene is frequently extremely bad. Many plants close down when the bonito becomes seasonally scarce because diversification of production is not yet commonly practised. Only two plants freeze a small working stock of raw material. Labour has to be laid off, and there occur unwanted fluctuations in adjacent economic sectors. Table 3 shows the average incomes of the Peruvian fishing companies. Although all the requisities for a sound industry seem to be available (a stock which can support the activity, and availability of capital equipment and management, which ought to have the required experience), the picture drawn is not a very bright one.

TABLE 3. AVERAGE NET INCOME OF FISHING COMPANIES IN PERU FOR 1971

Sector	No. of Companies	Total net Income (US $)	Average net Income (US $/ company)
Fish meal	76	36,816,400	490,900
Freezing and canning	18	409,100	22,700
Independent boat owners	54	1,181,100	21,900

Source: Peruvian Times, 29 September 1972

TABLE 4. FREQUENCY DISTRIBUTION OF CANNING CAPACITIES IN PERU

Canning capacity per 8 h working day (Cases of 48 cans)	Number of Plants
0 – 500	8
501 – 1,000	6
1,001 – 2,000	7
2,000 –	5

Source: Sociedad Nacional de Pesquería

used here and in subsequent calculations is 40 Peruvian soles to US $1). For the calculation of *raw material costs*, the starting point must evidently be the physical relationship between input and output. The Instituto del Mar del Perú has collected these yield figures from various canning plants and gives the average percentages in Table 5. Table 5 shows that there are four product varieties to be made out of the raw material: solid, chunk, flakes, and grated. The total yield obtained when producing a certain combination of varieties is given in the last column, showing an average of, say, 32 per cent. It must be kept in mind that this is an average figure making use of the contributions, from many small and inefficient canning factories. It is thus presumably negatively biased and efficiently run operations must be able to achieve much higher figures. However, for the sake of staying in line with existing conditions, these

TABLE 5. YIELD PERCENTAGE FOR CONVERSION OF FRESH TO CANNED BONITO ($\frac{1}{2}$ LB (225 G) TUNA CAN)

Solid Pack	Chunk	Flakes	Grated	Total
20.5 – 21.5	2.3 – 2.5	3.2 – 3.5	4.9 – 5.5	31.0 – 33.0
19.5	—	5.3	6.2	31.0
22.0	—	—	10.0	32.0

Source: IMARPE, Informe No. 33, Page 66 – Instituto del Mar del Perú

average yields were used as a base for the subsequent calculations.

Although it is possible to make all four products simultaneously, for sake of simplicity it was opted to produce only the combination of 'solid' and 'grated' varieties in the model operation. Working at the chosen capacity rate produces 242,000 cases a year (11,616,000 of $\frac{1}{2}$ lb (225 g) cans), part of which is 'solid' and part 'grated'. The size of these proportions must be determined by the physical proportions of the raw material (yield percentages of Table 5) as well as by the manufacturer's convention of filling the different variety packs (grated and solid) with different amounts of raw material. In the Peruvian case, it is common practice to fill a can of 'solid' with 170 g and a can of 'grated' with 142 g of fish. Output proportion for the two varieties are thus: solid:grated = 65:35.5. The average raw material input per average can (65 per cent solid and 35 per cent grated) can be calculated to amount to 500 g of bonito. We are now in a position to calculate the cost price on a 'per case' basis so as to be able to look into the sensitivity of the operation towards changes in output, raw material prices and production programme choice. Variable costs per average case were calculated at: 4.60 + 24 X. The symbol 'X' represents the buying price per kg of fish used as raw material. This symbol has been introduced in order to be able to establish a set of cost and revenue relationships which will enable one to assess the dependability of the profitability of the operation on the buying price of raw material.

In order to obtain some insight into the structure of the cost components, Table 6 has been prepared on the assumption of a 220 day full capacity output and on a raw material buying price of US $140/ton, a price realistic at the time of writing. The US bonito packers are currently paying around US $150 to 210/ton bonito ex-vessel. The build-up of the cost price shows the canning operation to be 'raw material intensive'. With this characteristic and the knowledge that buying prices of raw material tend to fluctuate, it seems useful to look into some consequences of such price changes on the profitability of the canning operation. Before doing this, however, the relationship between total output and profitability of the operation, the so-called break-even analysis, needs to be established.

TABLE 6. COST COMPONENTS PER CASE OF 48$\frac{1}{2}$ LB (225 G) CANS OF BONITO AS PERCENTAGE OF TOTAL COST

Raw material	41
Cans and ingredients	35
Labour	14
Energy, services, etc.	6
Fixed costs	4

The break-even analysis

The break-even analysis in its strict sense estimates how many units of a product will have to be sold in order to cover costs. The number of units is called the break-even volume. This volume is estimated by analysing how total revenue and total cost vary at different sales volumes. Total revenue at any particular sales volume is that volume times the unit price received. It will therefore be necessary, before the analysis can be carried out, to obtain an indication of the ex-factory prices for canned bonito. For the home market sales these prices are: solid, per case US $11 and grated, per case US $6. Comparable ex-factory prices in case of export can be calculated at: solid, per case US $12.50 and grated, per case US $7. The difference in prices between the home and the export market is partially attributable to a 22 per cent government export bonus issued for 'non traditional manufactured export items' (Certex). The cost function can be drawn up from the figures obtained in the foregoing paragraph, although assumption must be made of linearity in the production function, ie, one assumes that output and per unit costs move in the same proportion at the normal range of output variation. Buying and selling circumstances, as follow, will have to be assumed before break-even volumes can be calculated.

Buying:
Raw material can be obtained at US $140/ton so that variable costs amount to US $7.96 per case.

Selling:
(a) If solid and grated are sold on the home market, the average price per case (Ph) is US $9.25.
(b) If solid is sold on the export market and grated on the home market, the average price per case (Pc) becomes US $10.20.
(c) If both products are sold on the export market, the average price (Pe) is US $10.55.

Remembering that the fixed yearly cost of the plant amounts to US $80,000, the break-even volumes for the three cases are:

(a) 62,000 cases or 56 production days.
(b) 36,000 cases or 33 production days.
(c) 31,000 cases or 28 production days.

These three cases have been brought into graphical illustration in Fig. 1 in which total yearly profit is shown as a dependant of yearly production, always under the assumption of a buying price of US $140/ton. The vertical axis of the figure displays the total profit before taxes in thousands of US dollars whilst the horizontal axis shows the number of production days (bottom axis) or the number of produced cases (top axis) which are necessary to obtain the corresponding amount of profit. Under these circumstances, the obtainable levels of profit seem to be encouraging, to say the least. Although many canneries might not be able to reach the proposed 220 full capacity production days, an average of 150 days can be expected. Even the least profitable selling position (home market) would then be able to provide the investor with a 24 per cent extra interest above the going rate, chosen at 10 per cent. The most profitable case (220 production days, export market) would even provide for a return on capital of around 110 per cent (before taxes).

Sensitivity to changes in bonito prices

Around 40 per cent of the cost price of a can of bonito is attributable to the fish if bought at US $140/ton (Table 6). Under normal circumstances, this price tends to fluctuate and it therefore seems useful to analyse the effects such changes would have on total profitability of the operation. Even if fixed buying prices for landed fish may prevail (in Peru bonito is bought by the state food-fish enterprise and sold to the canneries at US $140/ ton), such an analysis holds its value as it can determine to what extent it would be profitable for the cannery operator to fish for bonito and/or to smooth out irregularities in supply by freezing a working stock of raw material. Assuming that the operator has only bonito as a production option, one can calculate the maximum price he would be willing to pay for his raw material to maximize profits or minimize losses. Using the break-even relationship, one finds these maximum prices to be:

(a) US $190/ton (home market).
(b) US $235/ton (combination)
(c) US $250/ton (export market)

This means that the operator who is able to sell his product on the export market would be willing to pay up to US $250/ton in order to achieve greater production. Due to certain technical limitations (fishing season), not all the production days (220) are to be expected. Under existing circumstances, the operation would break even if the average buying price of raw material was:

(a) US $160/ton (home market)
(b) US $220/ton (combination)
(c) US $235/ton (export market)

Fig. 2 plots the relationship between raw material price (horizontal axis) and the number of production days required to break even (vertical axis). The graph shows that as buying prices become higher (and the contribution margin to fixed costs becomes smaller), a proportionally greater number of production days are required to earn back the fixed costs. This means that once the price has reached a certain point, it becomes more desirable for the operator to start making other products with higher contribution margins so as to make better use of his production capacity. Taking case 'a' as an example, one could expect that the operator would seriously look for alternative production possibilities once the bonito price approaches the US $140/ton mark. At this point the contribution margin (ie, the difference between revenue and variable costs per unit) lies around US $1.30 per case. By applying the same reasoning to positions 'b' and 'c', ie, looking for the unit elasticity point on the curve, one finds the US $1.30 contribution margin to be the point where the operator should seriously start to look for a more profitable production and/or sales programme. What are the alternatives? Evidently the making of different products. These could be found by systematic analysis of the economic characteristic of different opportunities, paying attention to markets, volume, seasonal variation, etc., in order to select a programme giving a maximum synergistic effect toward the original bonito line.

Choice of variety pack or production programme

Up to this point production was assumed to consist of both the 'solid' and the 'grated' variety, the proportion between outputs of the products being stipulated by physical proportions of the raw material. However, it may well be possible that, under certain conditions, production of only the more expensive 'solid' may be more profitable. These conditions could occur when there is a temporary abundance of raw material, thus perhaps forcing prices down and making production capacity a scarce factor. Assuming such a period of glut the operator would want to know about the economic consequences of discarding (or selling as fish meal) part of the fish he would otherwise use for production of 'grated'. Raw material input per case of output (now only 'solid') would be 37 kg and from this around 10 per cent would be discarded that would have been used for production of grated. As a consequence of limited capacity in certain stages, output would probably come down, the lowest production limit being 65 per cent of 1,100 = 715 cases and the highest are 1,100 cases.

Table 7 has been drawn up in order to be able to compare the contribution margins to fixed costs of the two programmes at two selling positions. The last two columns show the percentual fraction of the initial production time needed to break even (or to maintain the same profit level) with the new programmes. If, eg, at US $100/ton of raw material the producer selling on the home market managed to produce only 'solid' at an output level of more than 83 per cent of 1,100 cases per day, it would be more profitable for him to do so.

TABLE 7. CONTRIBUTION MARGINS TO FIXED COSTS OF TWO PROGRAMMES AT TWO SELLING POSITIONS

Raw material price (US $/t)	Both solid and grated		Solid only		H_1/H_2 (%)	E_1/E_2 (%)
	H_1	E_2	H_1	E_2		
100	225	355	270	420	83	85
110	201	331	233	383	86	87
120	177	307	196	346	90	89
130	153	283	159	309	96	92
140	129	259	122	272	106	95
150	105	235	85	235	124	100

H = Home market selling   1 = Solid and grated production
E = Export market selling   2 = Solid only production

Changes in yield factor

As already stated, the average yield factors as given in Table 5 were in many cases found to be on the low side. One factory, eg, claims to need only 27 kg of fish to make a case of solid, which amounts to having a yield factor of 30 per cent instead of the average 22 per cent of Table 5.

Table 8 shows the difference in cost price due to yield alterations in absolute figures. The last column shows the gain in cents per case from raising the yield one per cent.

Raising the yield from, eg, 22 to 30 per cent for solid production would thus lower the cost price per case by around US $1.36. Any additional costs incurred in raising the yield would have to be deducted from this amount. Such a rise in yield would also influence the choice of production programme, causing a shift in favour of producing solid only.

TABLE 8. YIELD AND COST PRICE

Yield (%)	Raw material cost per case of solid (US $)	Difference in cost price per case (US $)
20	5.61	—
21	5.34	0.27
22	5.10	0.25
23	4.88	0.22
24	4.68	0.20
25	4.49	0.19
30	3.74	0.16

Some preliminary conclusions

What conclusions can be made from the foregoing analysis? In the first place, it should be stressed that the price and profit relations found are only applicable in the micro-economic sense, ie, they lose their validity if applied to the economy on the whole. However, they can well be used by the individual operator as a guide to production programming and they do give some insight into the profitability of the process. The model operation seems to show quite a high level of profitability. Taking the most favourable example, the high yield process and export markets, one finds a total profit of around US $800,000 after 220 days of operation. From this amount, around 30 per cent would be deducted in taxes, thus leaving US $560,000 in profits, equal to 100 per cent of the investment. This figure might very well be surpassed if one takes into consideration that export prices for canned bonito are still rising, the latest figures being: US $12.90 per case of solid in oil and US $7.70 per case of grated in oil. Even if one looks at the most pessimistic case assumed (low yield, 150 days, home market) this would still give the entrepreneur an extra interest of 7 per cent after taxes above the 10 per cent he may be paying for borrowed funds. Partly responsible for this high return on capital percentage is the fact that the canning operation needs a relatively small investment. Under normal circumstances, high profits would immediately attract new entrances into the field, who, by their competition, would start to skim off the profit margin. Thus, if the foregoing analysis holds true, one should expect to find in Peru a rapidly expanding and still very profitable canning industry. But this does not seem to be the case. Indeed, one can encounter exactly the opposite scene: plants closing, offered for sale or running at a fraction of their capacity. What could be the reasons for this contradiction between theory and reality? Although a thorough inquiry into this problem is too extensive a task for the scope of this paper, a number of plausible reasons can be given. First of all smallness of scale impedes efficiency. Many small plants use antiquated machinery and their hygienic standards are extremely low, thus keeping them out of major export markets. Their location has often been badly chosen so that no profitable production alternatives are available. Little systematic research or market development have been done to facilitiate production of other products besides bonito. But the most serious problem seems to lie in the fact that it is hardly pssible to obtain a reasonably stable flow of raw material. Further inquiry into this problem will certainly be needed.

FROZEN BONITO

Maintaining a working stock of raw material

The costs of maintaining a working stock naturally depend on how large the stock is required to be. As this depends on locational and environmental circumstances, it is hardly possible to work out a general approximation of the optimum magnitude. However, it could be assumed that the model canning plant is so unfavourably located that it will need enough raw material for six months full production, eg, from April through September. Assuming the stock can be built up in two months, the cost of maintaining it can be expressed as follows:

17.5 (Freezing cost) + 7.5 (Finance cost) + $\frac{1}{2}(8 \times 12.5)$ (Cold storage per month) = US $75/ton.

By adding this amount to his raw material price, the operator can find out if such stocking is worthwhile or if it is better to close down temporarily or switch to another production possibility.

Export of frozen bonito

The export of frozen bonito, headed and gutted in the Greek 'Lakerda' style, was recently tentatively undertaken. This product is in great demand in the Mediterranean markets and it was expected to be a profitable operation. Cost and revenue data of a trial shipment were as follows:

			US $
Cost per ton, FOB			325
Revenue per ton, FOB			
	Sales price	500	
	Certex 15%	75	575
Gross margin			250
Finance costs			25
Net margin			225

These costings were based entirely on gutting and freezing on contract externally. The US $225 margin has only to pay for management activity.

The level of profit in this realistic example seems to be high and again one wonders why this gold mine is not being exploited by more people. It seems that here, too, there are conditions which limit the scope of such an operation:

Availability of proper freezing facilities. The relatively large size of the fish makes blast freezing necessary and these installations are scarce in areas where there is a regular supply of bonito.

Possible limited absorption capacity of the export market.

Availability of raw material: even in times of fairly abundant catches, supply may be difficult because as a result of price regulation on bonito; the fishermen often withhold their catches from regular market outlets.

Selling price will be subject to rapid changes once competitive bidding by suppliers starts.

Comparison of the freezing and canning operations

The freezing operation, under the same circumstances as canning, could possibly be even more profitable,

231

although its future potential seems to be subject to a number of doubts. A fair comparison between the economic aspect of both operations is hardly possible because of the great difference in scale and scope. Canning is already on an industrial scale but freezing for export does not seem to have such a large-scale future. Product outlets are probably limited and the relative simplicity of the process will surely attract many entrants, thus thinning out profits very quickly and making other enterprises more attractive. Both freezing and canning are hampered by the very factor which gives rise to their existence – the raw material. The most serious bottleneck seems to be a lack of a dependable supply despite all evidence of the abundance of the resource. Thus, anyone wishing to enter this field must devote a lot of thinking and energy into overcoming this problem.

An evident possibility is building a buffer stock for the canning plant. Maintaining such a stock would have the additional advantage of reconciling two operations, canning and freezing for export, into one synthesized activity, giving immeasurably more flexibility and scope than in the case of two separate operations. In such a case management would have to show skill in timely accumulation of a frozen stock and in its division for frozen exports and for the actual buffer stock for the canning plant.

DRY-SALTED BONITO

Part of the bonito catch of Peru (fluctuating around 15 per cent) is sold in a dry-salted form. Its present landing price, sold mainly 'per fish' on the beach of Sechura, is around US $120 to $180 /ton. Retail prices in the mountain and jungle areas range from US $0.25 to US $0.38 per kg. A small part of the production is exported to Ecuador. Although dry-salted fish has a lot of potential as a protein rich food for use in remote areas, the utilization possibilities for bonito are too good for the fish to be processed in this relatively unsophisticated form. However, given the ruling conditions around the Sechura area, not much can be done to change the present situation there.

SOME GENERAL ECONOMIC CONSIDERATIONS

Gross production value

What is the importance to the national economy of the yearly catches of bonito? The answer mainly depends on the catch of the particular year. An approximate indication of the gross production value of the 1970 catch (a particularly bad year) may be gleaned from the following figures:

Estimated gross production value from bonito resource in 1970

		million US $
Fresh		3.8
Salted		1.3
Canned – Home market	5.0	
Export market	2.4	7.4
		12.5

Clearly, the utilization for canning, generating 60 per cent of the production value whilst using around 40 per cent of the catch, yields the best value especially as it brings in some US $2.4 million in foreign currency. To find the net foreign currency earnings, about US $0.4 million must be deducted because some 75 per cent of the tin costs represents foreign currency input. Thus, net currency earnings are around US $2 million.

Social effects

Besides providing income for the fishermen, the fresh bonito market has secondary income effects, mostly through wholesaling, transporting and retailing.

The canned bonito market goes further than this. In 1970, the industry must have generated a labour income of around US $1.5 million in the canning stage and about US $0.3 million in the manufacturing of cans.

An adverse social effect may perhaps be caused by the canning industry's practice of maintaining only skeleton staffs and hiring and firing workers according to labour needs. This practice is a direct consequence of the unstable raw material situation combined with the inability of many (especially small-scale) manufacturers to plan their production as a well managed economic activity.

Another comparison between canning and freezing

A comparison has been made between canning and freezing of bonito from the producers' point of view. In this case the aim is to find out what effects the different utilization of bonito have on the national economy, so that the Government can judge the possible effects on any aid or taxation policy it wants to establish.

In Table 9 an attempt has been undertaken to make a rough breakdown of the costs of three different operations and their effects on the economy. The implicit assumption underlying the figures is that raw material is a scarce factor which the Government wants to channel in accordance with its socio-economic goals. For example, if the Government had as a sole policy the acquirement of foreign exchange, it would want to stimulate the export of frozen bonito. However, if its policy was to stimulate labour-intensive industries which also create other work, the canning industry would receive first consideration.

Capacity and potential

The daily capacity of existing fish canning plants in Peru amounts to just under 50,000 cases but as many plants are inefficient it may be more realistic to assume a potential of some 30,000 cases. If only half of this capacity was used for bonito canning during 220 days a year (one shift of 8 h) the demand would be far more than 80,000 tons of raw material per annum. This could not be met by the total annual catch which from 1966 to 1970 has averaged less than 60,000 tons, only enough to provide for 10,000 cases per day or one fifth of the theoretical total capacity. In view of this situation, it is clear that plans to build jumbo-sized factories, with raw material intake capacities of 25,000 tons per annum are unrealistic. The present need is to expand and regulate the raw material supply and to reconstruct, modernize and rationalize the present canning industry.

TABLE 9. HOW 1 TON OF BONITO TRANSFORMED INTO PRODUCTS WILL AFFECT DIFFERENT SECTORS OF THE ECONOMY
(*In US $*)

Sector of the economy affected	Canned	Canned	Frozen
	Solid and grated for export	*Solid:Exp Grated:Home*	*Export*
1. Labour	52.50	52.50	37.50
2. Energy and services	25.00	25.000	15.00
3. Costs generating secondary income in the country	64.00	64.00	51.30
4. Costs to be paid in foreign currency	52.50	52.50	12.50
5. Total of costs (not including bonito as raw material)	194.00	194.00	116.30
6. Revenue	487.50	417.50	553.80
7. Certex	112.50	92.50	72.50
8. Revenue-Certex (6–7)	375.00	325.00	481.30
9. Margin for raw material cost price and profit (8–5)	181.00	131.00	365.00
10. Net foreign exchange earnings (8–4)	322.50	272.50	468.80

CONCLUSIONS AND THEIR CONSEQUENCES ON POLICY

If the model analysis is confirmed by reality, the need is to use as much bonito as possible for canning because it has the following advantages:

(1) it is potentially profitable and has a lot of scope for growth, integration and diversification;
(2) home and export markets are available, needing little development;
(3) capacity and potential capacity and experience in the field are available; and
(4) the industry earns foreign currency, has a high employment rate and creates extra income through secondary industries.

From this conclusion, the following recommendations for industrial development seem logical. They are to:

(a) enlarge the catching effort by a well balanced fleet expansion and modernization programme;
(b) channel raw material into canning by suspending the artificially maintained low price on the fresh market;
(c) ensure that a dependable supply of raw material reaches the industry;
(d) carry out a general reconstruction and rationalization programme of the canning industry by shutting down hopelessly unprofitable plants and providing investment incentives;
(e) give major preference and aid to construction of freezing and cold-storage capacity so that a working stock of raw material can be held;
(f) stimulate diversification and integration plans by identifying new product possibilities and developing home and export markets for such products (an example is canned caballa (tuna style) and horse mackerel for the home market and canned anchoveta sardine and machete for export);
(g) subsidize products which are not profitable but which have a certain social value; and
(h) set up an economic institute for the canning industry to provide professional advice on manufacturing problems.

Such a policy can only succeed if it is well planned and synchronized so as to achieve a maximum synergetic effect. Moreover, it must be clearly formulated so that it will also serve to stimulate the confidence of private enterprise to invest in the industry.

The Potential of the By-Catch from Shrimp Trawlers
W W Meinke

Le potentiel des captures accessories des chalutiers crevettiers

Dans la présente communication on décrit la complexité et les difficultés d'une utilisation rentable des captures accessoires des chalutiers crevettiers, qui sont généralement désignées sous le nom de poissons de rebut ou de 'faux-poisson'. On estime à quelque 6 millions de tonnes le volume de ces poissons qui est capturé et rejeté chaque année. Environ 20 pour cent de cette quantité pourraient peut-être servir pour l'alimentation humaine, et le reste à des fins industrielles. Bien que l'on ait proposé un certain nombre de méthodes pour récupérer ces notables prises accessoires de la pêche à la pêche à la crevette (les principales suggestions faisant l'objet d'un examen critique dans la présente communication), aucun procédé économique viable n'a encore été appliqué.

Posibilidades de la pesca accesoria de arrastreros camaroneros

En ste documento se examina la difícil y compleja situación de la utilización económica de la pesca accesoria de los arrastreros camaroneros que, generalmente, se conoce como morralla. Se estima que cade año se capturan y desechan unos 6 millones de toneladas de morralla. De esta cantidad se calcula que, aproximadamente, un 20 por ciento podría utilizarse para la alimentación humana, y el resto, para fines industriales. Aunque se han propuesto diversos métodos para recuperar gran parte de esta pesca accesoria – las principales sugerencias se examinan críticamente en el documento – aún no se ha aplicado un método económicamente viable.

Trash fish of the shrimper's trawl has often been suggested as one possible means of adding to the world catch. Many words have been written and spoken concerning the waste or loss of potential revenue resulting from the non-utilization of the heterogeneous fish catch of the shrimper and to describe techniques designed to utilize the catch. Why, then, have not some of these collection and processing techniques resulted in the significant utilization of the fish as food for humans and/or animal feed? This paper, based to a large extent on shrimping in the Gulf coast waters, presents some of the problems involved in a combined shrimping/trash fish operation, especially in relation to costs in the United States of America. Although this is a somewhat narrow base, the problems should be the same as in other parts of the world and only economic considerations could be different.

POTENTIAL BY-CATCH

According to Bulllis and Carpenter (1968), some 591,500 t of fish were taken in shrimping operations in the Gulf of Mexico and discarded during 1967. This catch was comprised mainly of croakers, spots and sea trout, and a number of lesser species of bottom fish. Weight ratios of fish/shrimp taken in trawls, in experimental or in actual shrimping operations, also have been used to estimate the potential catches. Commercial shrimpers of the Gulf coast area estimate fish:shrimp (heads-on) ratios from 1:1 to 20:1 and, in other literature, the ratios given are as variable. Such reports often do not specify the basis for comparison. Siebenalar (1952) used deheaded shrimp as a basis for calculation and reported ratios from 2:1 to 6:1 for two different waters of the State of Florida. Baughman (1950) reported a ratio of 6 kg of fish/kg of marketable shrimp produced. Robas (1959) employed a ratio of 10:1 in his evaluation of the economics of operating a small wet reduction fishmeal plant using trash fish. Kristjonsson (1968) estimated the 1965 shrimp catch of the Gulf of Mexico at about 109,200 t. This catch was estimated as 19 per cent of the total world catch of shrimp. Using the 109,200 t of shrimp value and the 591,500 t of trawl fish reported by Bullis and Carpenter (1968), a trash fish:shrimp ratio of around 5:1 is indicated. The data of Kristjonsson also suggest that a total of 574,737 t of shrimp (heads-on) were caught on a world basis for 1965. In 1965 the total world production of crustacean products was estimated at 263,000 t and in 1970 at 415,000 t (FAO 1971). These estimates are for lobster, shrimp and prawn, and crab processed in fresh, frozen, dried or salted products for human consumption. The 1965 data indicate the use of 2.2 kg of shrimp (heads-on) for each kg of crustacean products produced. Applying this ratio to the 1970 weight of crustacean products, assuming a proportion increase in all products, it may be estimated that the 1970 shrimp catch amounted to approximately 913,000 t. The foregoing comments indicate that a trash fish:shrimp ratio of 6:1 may be realistic for the Gulf coast. Assuming such a ratio on a world basis, and a catch of 0.9 to 1.0 million t, it may be estimated that from 5.4 to 6.0 million t of trash fish may be taken in the shrimper's trawl each year. These values represent from 7.7 to 8.7 per cent of the 69.3 million t of all fish taken in 1970 (FAO 1971) or more than 50 per cent of the 1970 Peruvian anchoveta catch of approximately 10.9 million t (Brody 1972).

COMPOSITION AND END USE

Trash fish taken in different shrimping waters, vary in genera and species, physical size and chemical composition and also for given locales with the fishing season. Thompson (1958–60) conducted an evaluation of some trash fish common to the Gulf of Mexico. However, his investi-

TABLE 1. LENGTH AND WEIGHTS[a] OF SOME GULF COAST TRASH FISH

Fish	Length (cm)	Weight (g)
Anchovy – *Anchoa hepsetus*	11	14
Bumper – *Chloroscombrus chrysurus*	13	67
Butterfish – *Protonotus triacanthus*	13	58
Croaker – *Micropogon undulatus*	19	70
Croaker (banded) – *Larimus fasciatus*	16	62
Hardheads – *Galeichthys felis*	18	84
Harvestfish – *Peprilus alepidotus*	13	80
Menhaden – *Brevootia*	16	82
Pigfish – *Orthopristis chvsoptera*	16	70
Porgy – *Stenostomus caprinus*	10	27
Razor bellies – *Harengula pensacolas*	13	38
Silver eels – *Trichiurus lepturus*	48	69
Silver perch – *Bairdiella chrysura*	14	41
Spot – *Leiostomus xanthurus*	18	72
Threadfin – *Polydactylus octonemus*	13	41
Thread herring – *Opisthonema oglinun*	15	57
White trout – *Cynoscion* sp.	21	95
Average	17	60
Range[b]	6–55	8–212

[a] Averages (calculated from winter, autumn, spring and summer averages)
[b] Range taken from data of Thompson (1958–60)

TABLE 2. PROXIMATE ANALYSIS[a] OF SOME GULF COAST TRASH FISH

Fish	Protein (%)	Oil (%)	Ash (%)	Volatile matter (%)	Total solids (%)	Non-oil solids (%)
Anchovy	17.1	2.8	3.3	77.0	23.0	20.2
Bumper	18.3	3.0	4.9	75.5	24.5	21.5
Butterfish	16.8	2.7	3.2	77.8	22.2	19.5
Croaker	16.6	2.7	5.2	75.7	24.3	21.7
Croaker, banded	17.3	3.9	4.3	75.0	25.0	21.1
Hardheads	16.3	5.1	6.4	72.4	27.6	22.5
Harvestfish	16.4	3.8	2.5	77.5	22.5	18.7
Menhaden	15.3	6.4	4.7	72.5	27.5	19.1
Pigfish	16.4	4.8	4.1	75.8	24.2	19.4
Porgy	17.8	2.5	6.2	72.8	27.2	24.7
Razor bellies	18.8	4.5	5.3	71.9	28.1	23.6
Silver eels	17.7	3.9	2.8	76.1	24.0	20.1
Silver perch	17.1	3.8	3.8	75.3	24.7	20.9
Spot	16.6	4.4	2.9	74.8	25.2	20.8
Threadfin	18.3	5.5	3.3	73.3	26.7	21.2
Thread herring	18.3	6.8	3.7	71.7	28.3	21.5
White trout	17.4	4.5	3.0	75.4	24.6	20.1
Average	17.2	4.3	4.1	74.7	25.3	21.0
Range[b] Min.	14.4	1.2	3.2	67.3	18.5	17.3
Max.	20.8	14.5	8.8	81.5	32.7	17.2

[a] Averages (calculated from winter, autumn, spring and summer averages)
[b] Range in values reported by Thompson (1958–60)

gation, although extensive, did not cover the 175 species of 78 families of fish which have been taken from Gulf waters. The data of Tables 1 and 2 are based on Thompson's evaluations. The tabulated values are averages of 4 seasonal (winter, spring, summer and autumn) studies. Table 1 data indicate that the average trash fish would be around 17 cm long and would weigh 60 g. These values are strict arithmetic calculations and in no way consider the quantitative distribution of the fish within a given trawl catch. However, the measurements listed do represent extremes in length and weight of fish caught. The size and weight ranges, as well as species distribution, have definite implications on potential end-use of the product. For example, lengths and weights would have little or no effect on a fishmeal programme using the wet reduction process. However, for human food, the extremes in length and weight could cause problems in evisceration and selection of fish of suitable size. The question then becomes – what can be done with the remaining non-food grade fish? Table 2 data, also derived from the reports of Thompson, suggest that the 'average trash fish' would contain 17.2, 4.3, 4.1 and 74.7 per cent protein (nitrogen $\times$ 6.25), oil, ash and volatile matter (moisture), respectively. These data are valid only for a catch containing equal yearly weights of each of the fish listed by the table. Minimum and maximum seasonal (winter, spring, summer and autumn) variations listed by Table 2 must be evaluated within a given assay – protein, oil, etc. That is, the summation of minimum or maximum values is not valid because these data only suggest that a composite season sample of a given species of fish gave the minimum or maximum assay values. How well the data of Tables 1 and 2 apply to other trash fish is an unknown factor. However, the Gulf coast data do suggest that fish size is a problem in utilization other than for fishmeal or other animal feeds (liquid fish or fish hydrolyzate products) which use the whole fish. The quantity, quality and size of food-grade fish taken from the world shrimping waters are also unknown factors.

SHRIMPING EFFICIENCY AND FISH SALVAGE

In the early fifties an attempt was made to salvage the Gulf trash fish to supply a land-based fishmeal plant. The fish were retained above deck for pick-up by a collector boat or mother ship. This operation failed. According to Bullis and Carpenter (1968), catch handling and transfer problems, and interference during peak shrimp seasons, were the prime reasons. Prices paid for the trash fish ranged from US $17 to 22/t. In 1955–60, some shrimpers were enticed to resort to bottom fish trawling. Small catches per unit of fishing effort, small gross catches because of small boat size, a price of US $17 to 22/t, and the return of the boats to shrimping during peak shrimp runs, doomed this effort to operate a fishmeal plant based on trash fish. How realistic were the shrimper's objections? A calculation based on the 1968 shrimping season for Texas (Cobb 1970) clearly shows the validity of such concern relative to 'cent a pound trash fish'. A total of 1,669 shrimp trawlers harvested 39,350 t of shrimp (heads-on) with a value of US $45,689,585. With a 6:1 fish to shrimp ratio, the fish catch amounted to 236,100 t. At US $22/t, the total estimated value of this catch was US $5,194,200. These data show that the revenue ratio of fish:shrimp was 1:9. On a 'per trawler basis', the shrimp yielded a gross return of US $27,480 and the fish an estimated US $3,000. It is evident from these calculations that a decrease in shrimp harvesting efficiency due to trash fish handling could easily offset the added revenue obtained from saving the fish. Also, the dollar return per ton of raw material handled was US $22 for the fish and US $1,166 for the shrimp. These comparisons indeed support the shrimper's objection to a combined shrimp/trash fish operation. Shrimping alone involves far less work and is possibly more rewarding because efficiency is retained.

LOGISTICS OF HANDLING

Both the shrimp and trawl fish are deposited on deck. The shrimp, whole or headed, are iced below deck and the fish are returned to sea or used as the raw material for ultimate processing in feeds or foods. As suggested, deck storage of fish for later pick-up by a collector boat decreases shrimping efficiency. Also, the shrimpers fear the loss of out-riggers in fish transfers, especially in rough seas. Other methods have been proposed for utilization of the fish catch. Storage of comminuted fish, 'gurry', in refrigerated tanks below deck has been suggested (Baughman 1950). Modifications of this technique are enzymatic procedures involving the addition of pre-formed industrial enzymes to the gurry. High temperatures, preservative and pH extremes, acid or alkaline, afford preservation until the fish gurry is processed into products. Keyes and Meinke (1966) used preservatives and chelating agents in their enzymatic approach to the

TABLE 3. DATA ON SHRIMP LANDINGS AND TRASH-FISH ESTIMATES FOR TEXAS LANDINGS (1968) AND GULF OF MEXICO (1959–63)

		Texas	Gulf of Mexico
Trawlers	number	1,669[a]	2,000[b]
Shrimp value	US $	46,000,000	55,000,000
Shrimp weight:			
tails	tons	28,400	37,300
heads-on	tons	39,400	59,700
Trash fish	tons	236,000	358,000
Trash fish value	US $	5,200,000	7,800,000
Per trawler:			
shrimp value	US $	27,600	27,500
shrimp (heads-on)	tons	23.6	29.9
trash fish	tons	142	179
trash fish value	US $	3,100	3,900

[a] (Cobb 1970)
[b] (Osborn et al. 1966)

TABLE 4. SHRIMP[a] AND ESTIMATED TRASH-FISH LANDING AT TEXAS PORTS, 1968

Shrimp landings	Shrimp[b] (t)	Trash fish[c] (t)	(%)[e]	Potential fishmeal[d] (t)
Brownsville, Port Isabel	13,660	81,960	34.7	20,000
Aransas Pass, Corpus Christi, Fulton	9,860	59,160	25,0	14,440
Port Lavaca, Port O'Connor, Seadrift	1,990	11,940	5.1	2,910
Matagorda, Palacios	1,360	8,160	3.5	1,990
Freeport	6,640	39,840	16.9	9,720
Galveston	3,760	22,560	9.7	5,500
Baytown, Kemah, Port Bolivar, San Leon, Seabrook	1,130	6,780	3.0	1,650
Port Arthur, Sabine Pass	950	5,700	2.1	1,390
Totals	39,350	236,000	100.0	57,600

[a] Based on report of Cobb (1970)
[b] Shrimp with heads
[c] Estimated, 6:1 ratio trash fish:shrimp
[d] Estimated as 0.244 t meal/t of 'Average Trash Fish', Table 2. Fishmeal – 70 per cent protein, 6 per cent oil, 8 per cent moisture and 17 per cent ash
[e] Based on total estimated catch of 236,100 t

harvesting of trash fish. The patent of Hasdenteufel (1968) describes the preservation and hydrolysis of fish with pepsin at pH_3. High temperature tolerant alkaline proteases also have been evaluated for their ability to digest fish protein (Hale 1969). These approaches, as well as many others, are covered in the excellent review by Hale (1972). The waste heat of the boat engine is the basis of the process involving dehydration of comminuted trash fish on board (Meinke 1971, personal communication). This technique provides approximately a 25 per cent yield of full oil fishmeal. As indicated earlier, the oil contents of such meals could be excessive by good fishmeal standards, 4 to 8 per cent oil on an 8 per cent moisture basis. The oil content could vary from locale to locale and season and with the distribution of the species of fish within catches. A chilled brine or chilled seawater system also has merit in retaining the fish in a fresh state aboard for a period of time. However, the safe storage time (days) could be a function of the species of fish comprising the catch. Firm flesh fish have greater storage potential than the soft flesh fish such as Pacific hake (*Merluccius productus*). Salt intrusion in the soft fish, as well as possible autolysis at chilling temperatures of 2 to 4°C, can reduce much of the soft fish flesh into a gel in a matter of 5 to 7 days. Evidence of this was observed in hake supplied to the Experimental and Demonstration FPC Plant in Aberdeen, Washington, USA.

All of the methods mentioned, other than the collector boat concept, have one thing in common – the fish are removed from the deck to the hold for delivery to a land-based processing plant. How much fish would be involved? Around 230 kg of shrimp (heads-on) is a good average catch per 12 h of fishing by a Gulf coast trawler, 18.3 m long and 45.5 gross t (Osborn *et al.* 1966). Assuming a fish:shrimp ratio of 6:1, the daily trash fish catch would be 1.38 t or 248.4 t for 180 days of fishing. The average Gulf shrimper spends 2 to 4 days at sea. The space needed for brine refrigeration or a process tank would be relatively small, 3 and 6 m^1 respectively. The average trawler is large enough to permit such an installation along with auxiliary equipment; grinder, temperature-control heat exchangers, refrigeration equipment, etc. However, the 'below deck' approach to trash fish salvage presents another possible logistics problem. The total Gulf coast trash fish catch, Table 3 (Osborn *et al.* 1966), is indicated as 358,000 t and involves a minimum of 1,440 trawlers. Actually, some 2,000 trawlers were involved. On 2 and 4 days turn-arounds, there could be 1,440 vessels docking for unloading shrimp and 2.76 or 5.52 t of fish for 2 and 4 days schedules, respectively. Obviously, one land-based plant could not cope with the 1,440 vessels in need of rapid unloading in order to return to their shrimping. Fortunately, trawlers have different home ports and thus, the pressure on a given land-based plant is reduced. Then how large should the plant be? Table 4, based on data quoted by Cobb (1970), refers to 8 shrimp-landing sites along the Texas coast and shows that the flow of fish varies from a low figure of approximately 2 to a high figure of nearly 35 per cent of the estimated 236,100 t catch. Based on a 180-day shrimping season, plants would be needed to process from 30 to 460 t of fish per day and would be required to have unloading and storage or process facilities from 2 to 4 times this tonnage. A shrimping operation, subservient to the plant, would permit better sizing and operation of plants because programming of shrimp landings would be easier – at least to a degree. However, as previously indicated, the high economic value of shrimp, as compared with trash fish at US $22/t, makes such a proposal unrealistic.

Deck storage of fish for pick-up by a collector boat has been mentioned earlier as an undesirable approach. The Gulf coast shrimper will trawl from $1\frac{1}{2}$ to 5 h before bringing his catch aboard. Thus, in a 12 h shrimping run, from 3 to 8 trawl catches are deposited on the deck so that a very big number of pick-up boat transfers would be needed to service the shrimpers on a per trawl basis. Below-deck storage in a brine-refrigeration system or in tanks employing enzyme processes could perhaps enable the pick-up to be made while the trawler is at anchor. A 22 to 25 m vessel with a gross tonnage of 90 t could possibly collect the daily fish catch, estimated as 1.38 t per boat, from approximately 40 shrimp boats during their 12 h at anchor. This approach would tend to permit better operation of the land-based installation. Also, only shrimp would be in the hold of the shrimp vessel when it returned to home port after 2 to 4 days at sea.

A factory ship also could serve as a pick-up boat. With multiple transfer lines, more shrimp boats could be unloaded to such a ship than to a smaller pick-up boat. Further, a factory ship involves only one transfer of the catch as compared with two needed for supplying the process plant. The economics of these suggested methods must be determined. At today's prices for fishmeal, around US $440/t, the shrimper's fish could fetch US $4 to 50/t. Complete utilization of the estimated trash fish catch of 1968 for fishmeal at US $440/t would bring in a gross income of about US $25 million – around 50 per cent of the value of the 1968 shrimp landed in Texas. These comparisons, based on high-priced fishmeal, indicate that trash fish could have an effect on the overall fishing economy of a state or country.

FISH FOR FOOD

It is not difficult to envision end-uses for food-grade fish and this is not the main problem. The estimated Gulf coast trash fish catch of 358,000 t with a 20 per cent yield of food fish selling at US $220/t would bring in about US $10,930 per trawler for food fish in 180 days of shrimping. Is the 20 per cent food fish estimate high or low for a shrimping season? Would the food fish revenue have to be twice the US $10,930 estimate in order to pay for added crew, for boat modifications and for loss of shrimp revenue due to decreased shrimping efficiency? Would the residue non-food fish be salvaged or discarded? These are the unknown factors, not how to use the food-grade fish. Finite estimates of the human food potential of trash fish can only be obtained by systematic surveys of catches. The Sea Grant Programme at Texas A & M University is currently engaged in such a survey. Results should provide information as to the economic feasibility of using selected fish for human consumption. Similar surveys in other shrimping waters are needed.

The proximate analyses of Table 2 indicate that the fish could be used to produce Fish Protein Concentrates (FPC) by the solvent extraction or enzymatic processes. Both should be tried at a site other than on the shrimp boat. I do not think that a solvent extraction system is suitable for use on a trawler because of the hazard potential and space required for the equipment. Enzymatic processes, such as covered by Hale (1972), would obviate the objections inherent in the solvent system. However, the quality and process control does not seem compatible to shrimping operations. A point in question is digestion time – a factor which would be difficult to programme on a boat because of variable times at sea and multiple small catches of fish. Fish preserved by chilled brine should be of a quality to permit FPC production by processes in land-based plants or on factory ships. Flavour, fluoride content, presence of possible toxic species of fish and yield, are some factors that must be considered in evaluating the feasibility and economics of such an FPC venture. Also, because of economics, it must be realized that the price per ton paid to the shrimper for the fish would have to be in the range of US $22 to 44/t. At US 22/t for fish, the cost of the FPC in the fish would range from US $132 to 154/t. So, again, the question is: 'Can the shrimper be paid enough to satisfy his needs and still permit the economic production and sale (with profit) of the FPC?' Production of a deboned FPC from eviscerated fish is an unknown factor, in which, the basic question is that of eviscerating fish of variable size and species.

TRASH-FISH FISHERIES

The foregoing comments apply only to trash fish as an auxiliary to a shrimping operation. What about the reverse – shrimp and/or food fish as by-products of industrial trash fish fisheries? According to Bullis and Carpenter (1968), there is a latent sustainable industrial bottom fish catch of some 2.6 million t which could be taken from the Gulf of Mexico as against an actual production of only 44,000 t. How much shrimp and/or food fish would be taken in such trawling by large boats is unknown. However, personnel would be available, with the aid of mechanical fish classifiers, to save both food-grade fish and shrimp. Also, the large boats with 2 to 3 days at sea, would have ample room for icing the food fish and shrimp in separate holds. An industrial firm (Meinke 1972, personal communication) has conducted a fishing pilot run. The data obtained indicated favourable economics and the catches were processed into fishmeal and oil by the conventional wet reduction process. This experimental run did not consider shrimp or food fish as a by-product. Bullis and Carpenter (1968) also demonstrated the increased catch of bottom fish per unit of effort as compared to menhaden. The menhaden seiner, with a capital investment of US $600,000 and an 18-member crew, obtained a catch of 380 t/man. Four trawlers, with the same estimated capital investment and a total of only 8 crew, produced 1,180 t of trash fish per man in the same period of time. Operational costs were estimated to be essentially the same for both. No mention was made by Bullis and Carpenter as to food fish or shrimp as by-products. These reports indicate that a trash fish industrial fishery may indeed be an economic possibility even with shrimp trawlers and food fish and shrimp catches could add to the income. Finally, the success of the concept depends to a large degree upon keeping the food fish and shrimp catches subservient to the main purposes – catching industrial trash fish.

CONCLUSIONS

The shrimp-trawl fish catch represents a significant part, 7.7 to 8.7 per cent of the world fisheries catch of 69.3 t for 1970 (FAO 1970). The variable physical size, length and weight of the trash fish is related to end-use. Size would not be a significant factor for fishmeal production but would be in evisceration of food-grade deboned flesh and in filletting or other such processing procedures. Seasonal and species variations in chemical composition must be considered.

Logistics of handling the raw material rather than supply and chemical composition, are the greatest problems associated with the utilization of the trash fish catch. The variable size of shrimp vessels, variable times at sea, methods of storage and/or processing aboard, transfer of fish catch to collection boats or factory ships, size and location of land-based processing plants, shrimp boat modifications, industrial and/or food fish use of the trash fish and price paid to the shrimper are all involved in the economics of operating such a trawl fish industry. Also, a 10 per cent loss in shrimping efficiency would tend to offset the revenue obtained from saving the trash fish.

Data on the Gulf of Mexico suggest the presence of a latent bottom fish supply capable of supporting a sizable industrial fish operation. Such a fishery would provide some food fish and some shrimp without deterring industrial fish harvesting. This approach seems to be feasible but does not resolve the problems of a shrimping/trash fish combination.

As of today, the discard of trash fish is the most economical method of disposal from the shrimper's viewpoint but, hopefully, future developments will result in the economical salvage and utilization of the fish.

References

BAUGHMAN, J L Utilizing waste fish resulting from the shrimping 1950 industry. *Fish Meal and Oil Industry*, 2(12):9–10.
BRODY, J Fish supplies decline. *Fd Engng*, 44(4):69–71 1972
BULLIS, H R and CARPENTER, J S Latent fishery resources of the 1968 Central West Atlantic region. Seattle, Washington, USA *University of Washington Publications in Fisheries, New Series*, 4:61–64.
COBB, B R Texas marine resources. The fisheries view. *Texas A & 1970 M University–SG–70–115*. August, 1970.
FAO *Yb. Fish. Statist.* 31:4. 1971
HASDENTEUFEL, J B Preservation and hydrolysis of fish. *French 1968 patent, 1,534,769.* 2 August 1968.
HALE, M B Relative activity of commercially available enzymes 1969 in the hydrolysis of fish protein. *Fd Technol.* 23(1):107–110.
HALE, M B Making fish protein concentrates by enzymatic 1972 hydrolysis. *NOAA Technical Report SSRF–657*.
KEYES, C W and MEINKE, W W Method of processing fish. *US 1966 patent, 3,249,442,* 3 May 1966.
KRISTJONSSON, H Techniques of finding and catching shrimp in 1968 commercial fishing. *FAO Fish. Rep.,* (57): 125–191.
OSBORN, K W, MAGHAN, B W and DRUMMOND, S B Gulf of 1966 Mexico shrimp atlas. Bureau of Commercial Fisheries, US Department of the Interior, *Circular 312*.
ROBAS, J S To plan the production of fish meal from trash fish. 1959 *Fish Boat,* 4:37, 39, 41.
SIEBENALAR, J B Studies of 'trash' caught by shrimp trawlers in 1952 Florida. University of Miami, Marine Laboratory, Coral Gables, Florida, USA. *Proceedings of the Gulf and Caribbean Fisheries Institute, Fourth Annual Session,* November 1952: 94–99.
THOMPSON, M H Studies on the proximate composition of some 1958– Gulf of Mexico industrial fish. *Technical Releases,* Wash-1960 ington D.C., USA. Fish and Wildlife Service, US Department of the Interior.

The Abalone Industry in Australia
D G James and J Olley

L'industrie australienne des ormeaux

L'industrie australienne des ormeaux n'a guère plus de dixans, mais elle a maintenant un chiffre d'affaires de dix millions de dollars E-U. Son essor pourrait avoid des répercussions sur les perspectives de développement d'autres secteurs industriels. L'auteur décrit les mesures de contrôle appliquées pour empêcher la surexploitation de la ressource et réglementer la qualité des produits. Des études de marché et des recherches technologiques sur la manutention, le transport et la transformation ont permis d'éliminer diverses contraintes qui handicapaient l'industrie. Les techniques servant à la production d'ormeaux en conserve et séchés sont examinées, de même que les facteurs relatifs au transport des ormeaux vivants et à la fabrication d'ensilage pour l'alimentation animale avec les viscères des ormeaux.

La industria de la oreja de mar (abulon) en Australia

La explotación de la oreja de mar en Australia, con sólo 10 años existencia, ha alcanzado un valor de 10 millones de dólares EE.UU. y su crecimiento puede tener repercusiones en las perspectivas de desarrollo de industrias de este tipo en otras regiones. Se describen las medidas aplicadas a la industria para impedir un exceso de explotación y regular la calidad. Los estudios de mercados y las investigaciones tecnológicas sobre la manipulación, el transporte y la elaboración han eliminado algunos de los bostáculos que impedían el desarrollo de esta industria. Se examinan las técnicas necesarias para la producción de oreja de mar congelada, en conserva y seca y los problemas que plantea el transporte de la viva y la fabricación de ensilaje para piensos con las vísceras de este molusco marino.

The abalone is a snail-like marine mollusc of the genus *Haliotis*, a number of species of which are found around the southern coasts of Australia, from slightly north of Perth in Western Australia to Sydney in New South Wales. The major accessible concentrations being exploited commercially are in Tasmania, Victoria and South Australia. Abalone can be canned, frozen whole or as steaks, dried, or eaten raw in the Japanese style. Before 1963 there was little exploitation of abalone in Australia, although several small drying establishments were set up in the last century by Chinese immigrants. However, the industry did not grow, possibly because there was no local market, and even today Australians do not eat abalone except as a curiosity. With this background, it is interesting that Australia should have become the world's largest producer of abalone. The major reason for the growth has been the sustained demand from Japan and Southeast Asia, where it is considered to be a delicacy with aphrodisiac properties.

CONTROLLING THE INDUSTRY

When the industry started there were no controls but it was soon apparent that a sessile population, relatively easy to catch, could be severely overexploited in accessible areas. Control measures were therefore introduced by the State Government fisheries departments. Inspection and regulation of the quality of Australian exports is the responsibility of the Commonwealth Department of Primary Industry. This Department was able to inspect and register the processing premises from the start to ensure a hygenic standard. However, it was not possible to set quality standards, because Australians had no experience of eating abalone and market requirements varied. The rapid development and growth of the industry since 1965 put a strain on the processing resources. The high returns encouraged companies with no experience in fish processing to set up plants and intense competition resulted in price cutting and a general lowering of the standard of export packs, particularly of canned abalone. By about 1968 the buyers reacted against high prices and low drained weights in canned and frozen abalone and several companies caught with large inventories of low quality product went out of business. The surviving companies set out to regain the Australian reputation as producers of good quality abalone. It is now appreciated that the industry can make the best return to all concerned if the highest possible quality products are exported.

Abalone is a luxury product and therefore the returns for high quality are very good. There is still a market for lower quality products but the price is much reduced. As the processor usually pays the diver at the same rate for all the catch, any loss resulting from off-grade or poor quality is reflected in the processors' profits. There is always a proportion of discoloured or split abalone in the catch, and these can be packed as second or third grade. However, loss of quality between catching and processing can, and should, be avoided by good handling practices. In 1968, when the industry was seriously threatened, a code of practice for handling and processing abalone was drafted based on the general principles of fish technology, rather than being specifically related to the problems of handling abalone. Following consultation with industry and research into the technology of abalone processing, a revised code was adopted in 1972 (Anon. 1972a). From the early days of the industry the Tasmanian Food Research Unit of the CSIRO Division of Food Research had to answer numerous inquiries from processors by conducting *ad hoc* experiments. In 1968 a more systematic programme of research was started to find objective methods of measuring the quality of abalone as a raw material for processing and as a finished product. During the last two years this work has been aided by a grant from the Australian Fisheries Research Trust Account and some of the results are included in this paper. Tasmanian abalone, handled under Tasmanian conditions, were used throughout these experiments, but differences in handling methods between the various States must be taken into account in order to obtain an overall view of the Australian abalone industry.

HANDLING AND TRANSPORT

Tasmania is the only State which requires that abalone be delivered to the processing plants in the shell and alive. Although introduced as a conservation measure, to prevent the taking of undersized abalone, it does, in fact, suit Tasmanian conditions. The fleet is generally composed of heavy displacement boats of up to 80 ft (24 m) which carry up to six divers. They work on isolated areas of a rough coast, with no convenient ports, and stay at sea up to 10 days, keeping their catch alive in steel baskets held in circulating sea water tanks. In some cases the baskets are transported to the processing factories where they are held in ponds with pumped sea water circulation. There are also in Tasmania some small fast planing boats making day trips. These too are required to keep their catch alive, which is normally done by holding it in nets or bags. In most instances the Tasmanian processing factories are close to the point of landing which reduces the problems of transport. In Victoria and South Australia the boats are almost all of the outboard runabout type, which stay out up to 10 h. They may operate from a small fishing port or be trailed to isolated beaches by four-wheel drive vehicles. The catch is often landed more than 300 mi (480 km) from the processing factories and the abalone must be transported by road at ambient temperatures which often exceed 40°C. In these two States the regulations allow abalone to be shucked on the boat. As the recovery of meat is only of the order of 35 per cent it would obviously be uneconomic to transport live abalone such distances and then have to dispose of the shell and viscera. In addition, most of the small boats operating in these states cannot safely carry the full weight of a day's catch of live abalone. The code of practice for export products makes provision for shucking at sea or in registered export premises. Abalone shucked in unregistered premises are not acceptable for export.

Storage of live abalone

Experience has shown that, provided the sea water temperature is not too high, abalone will live for prolonged periods in tanks if the water is changed about four times per hour. However, once they are taken out handling problems start. It is a characteristic of littoral organisms, such as some molluscs and crustacea, that they can remain alive out of water for extended periods. The survival time depends on temperature and, for abalone, there is a point after which the animal will not revive when returned to water although it still appears to be alive (Table 1). It has been found in Japan and Australia (James and Olley 1970) that 6°C is the optimum temperature for keeping abalone alive out of water. Below 6°C the animal appears to suffer a cold shock and contracts and dies. Above 6°C mortality

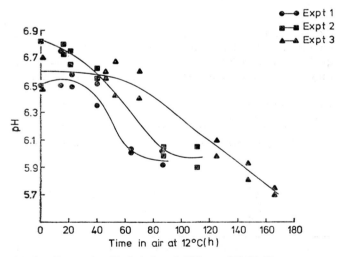

Fig 1 Changes in pH of abalone held live at 12°C (pH was determined on a muscle homogenate in distilled water)

is inversely related to temperature and obeys the Arrhenius equation (Olley 1971, Olley and Ratkowsky 1973) with an apparent activation energy of 17,000 cal/mol. For approximately two days at 12°C the muscle pH remains steady and then falls gradually (Fig. 1). The minimum muscle pH which has been noted is 5.7, and only after an extended period, when the abalone has become completely rotten, does the pH rise again. The delay before this rise

may be due to the suppression of bacterial activity because of the presence of an antibiotic which has been noted by Li (1960) and Prescott and Li (1960). The pH of the muscle can, in fact, be used as a fairly reliable index of quality.

TABLE 1. SURVIVAL RATE OF ABALONE WHEN RETURNED TO WATER AFTER HOLDING IN AIR AT VARIOUS TEMPERATURES (J L SMITH 1971, UNPUBLISHED)

Average size (g)	Holding temperature in air (°C)	Survival rate after returning to water for one week (%)		
		Time out of water		
		20 h	30 h	40 h
700	6	100	83	82
650	12	100	100	50
800	12	100	83	0

When it is necessary to transport live abalone they should be carried as close as possible to 6°C. It is a characteristic of molluscs that they lose fluid when removed from the water and the loss of weight during storage and transport has been a serious cause of disagreement between the fishermen and the processors. Continual inquiries from all sides of the industry led to attempts to quantifty these losses. It was found that abalone in shell will lose about 16 per cent of their weight, as fluid, when held in air, the rate of loss depending on temperature. When the fluid loss rises above 10 per cent the animal is normally dead (James and Olley 1970). The composition of the liquid which drains from abalone has been investigated. Death appears to result from internal bleeding because in the later stages the fluid is almost pure blood, as is shown by its protein and amino acid content and the deep blue colour of oxygenated haemocyanin. However, the first 10 per cent of the fluid is colourless and has a low protein and amino acid content. It does not appear to be blood.

Investigation of the physiology of respiration of abalone, held in an enclosed space, identified some parameters which could become important in the transport of live animals (Fig. 2). Size, carbon dioxide build-up in the surrounding air, time and temperature were shown to have significant effects. The onset of bacterial spoilage after death is shown by the rapid consumption of oxygen in the later stages of storage. Apparently small animals can draw on a readily available energy reserve for anaerobic respiration because, although the oxygen consumption is proportional to size (Fig. 3), the smaller animals produce the same amount of carbon dioxide after fifteen hours.

Storage of shucked abalone

Contrary to experience with most fish, shucked abalone muscle remains metabolically alive for an extended period due to the slow breakdown of adenosine triphosphate (ATP) (Arai and Saito 1961, Arai 1966). At temperatures close to 0°C a cold shock similar to that seen in whole animals occurs, and muscle contraction squeezes fluid from the vessel cut during shucking. Approximate results are shown in Table 2. Such losses of weight during transport have led to argument between fishermen and processors but it is now established that bleeding is unavoidable. Freezing on board or at the point of landing, which has been suggested as a method of overcoming this loss, only passes the loss of weight on from the fisher-

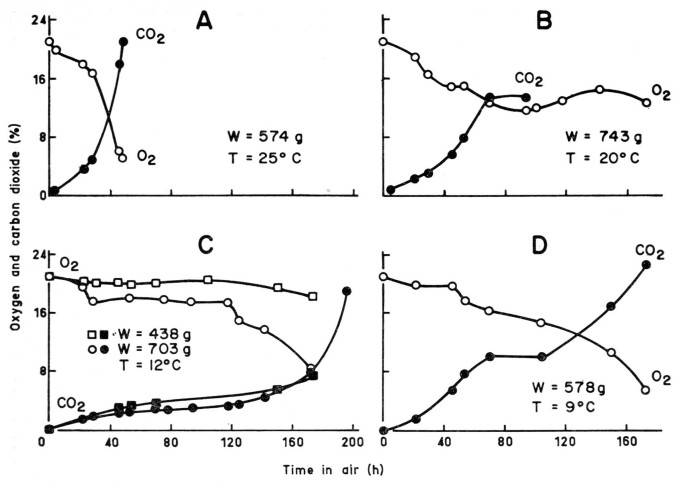

Fig 2   *Consumption of oxygon (O_2) and production of carbon dioxide (CO_2) by abalone of different weight (W) held at different temperatures (T) in an enclosed volume of 2.3 litres. (J L Smith 1971, unpublished)*

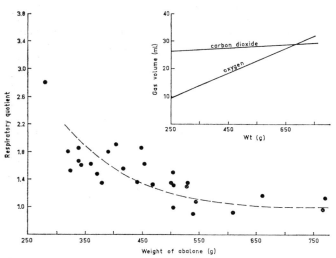

Fig 3   *Relationship of oxygen consumption and carbon dioxide production to size. (Abalone 15 h in air)*

man to the processor as some blood is lost during the cold shock period and the remainder drains from the muscle when it is thawed. Losses are at a minimum at 6°C, but generally no ice or refrigeration is carried on the small boats which shuck at sea. They drain their catch on landing and add some ice or hold it in a chill store to reduce the temperature for transport to the processing factories. For short storage periods abalone retain their quality better at 6°C, but if longer storage is envisaged they are normally held close to 0°C to reduce spoilage.

TABLE 2. APPROXIMATE PERCENTAGE OF FLUID DRAINING FROM ABALONE AFTER SHUCKING[a]

Weight of shucked muscle	*Time after shucking*		
(*g*)	$\frac{1}{2}$ h	2 h	5–24 h
100	11.0%	18.0%	21.0%
200	16.5%	23.5%	26.5%
300	22.0%	29.0%	32.0%
400	27.5%	34.5%	37.5%

[a] The nine data sets examined had a common slope of 0.055 p<.001

PROCESSING

Most of the catch is frozen or canned, but there is some production of steaks and dried abalone. A limited, but potentially lucrative, market for live abalone also exists in Japan. As the market demand fluctuates rapidly from one product to another, particularly between frozen and canned, the processors have to be flexible. Successful companies have been able to develop a range of products and grades of quality. Outlines of production methods and some details of quality considerations for the various products are given below.

Freezing

Shucked abalone frozen for export is usually washed and packed in 20 or 40 lb (9 or 18 kg) blocks wrapped in polyethylene in flat cartons (Anon. 1971). The packs may either be ungraded or graded for size and colour. Ideally, abalone should be frozen rapidly as soon as possible after shucking, stored at the lowest possible temperature (at least −18°C) and not thawed at high temperatures. Although importers have complained about the freshness of abalone used for freezing, most of the disagreements on quality have been about the amount of free fluid draining from the blocks on thawing. Ironically, the freshest abalone have most often been implicated, but it can be seen from Table 2 that if freshly shucked abalone are not drained for 30 minutes before packing, up to 22 per cent of the weight can be frozen blood, which exudes from the block when it is thawed. Free fluid also exudes during the pre-freezing period and collects at the bottom of the block in unsightly pools, suggesting to buyers that packs have been adulterated with water. Weight losses due to bleeding appear to be inevitable but processors are advised to take all possible steps not to include blood with frozen blocks. In addition, poor freezing and thawing practices can increase the overall loss of drip fluid. Experiments have shown that rate and temperature of thawing have a greater effect on quality than speed of freezing. As the water-holding capacity of the muscle on cooking depends on pH, the aim should be to ensure a time-temperature relationship during thawing which causes the minimum amount of *post mortem* glycolysis and drop of pH. *Pre rigor* frozen meat and fish muscle generally show a rapid drop in pH on thawing. Abalone, which should be frozen at a high pH, can easily suffer loss of water-holding capacity during thawing and subsequent cooking if not handled correctly. This is an important marketing consideration for importers who thaw out frozen blocks for retail sale to housewives for home cooking. The relatively large (20 and 40 lb) (9 and 18 kg) blocks will naturally have a higher temperature and faster rate of glycolysis at the outside than at the centre. The smaller blocks are therefore to be preferred. Frozen steaks are also produced from fresh shucked abalone. After the muscle has been allowed to relax, all the pigmented parts and the tough outside surface of the pedal sole are trimmed off. The remaining muscle is cut into horizontal slices about 1 cm thick and pounded with a wooden mallet to break down the tough texture. The steaks thus produced are interleaved with polyethylene or waxed paper and frozen. The main market for steaks is the United States which gives the best return for the largest steaks. However, the process is labour-intensive and recoveries are low due to the amount of trimming involved, although excellent soups, patties and dried powders have been made from the trimmed waste.

Canning

The unsightly black pigment on the epidodium and foot must be cleaned off before canning. In material which has been frozen for storage it can easily be washed off with water at 49°C but in fresh material it is difficult to remove. Brining loosens the pigment and this is a convenient treatment as the addition of some salt is required. Strong brines produce the cleanest product but weight losses are proportional to the strength of the brine (Olley and Young 1972). Initially the brine extracts water from the muscle by ismosis and salt penetration is not rapid in fresh material. Uptake of salt is inversely proportional to size and Young (unpublished 1972) has found that after prolonged storage of raw material (5 days at 6°C) brining produces significant increases in salt and water contents. Normal practice is to rumble in brine or to hold overnight. The use of 1 per cent polyphosphate (MERA 67) in the brine significantly reduces the weight loss during brining (Young unpublished 1972). In some areas when the abalone is destined for canning, salt is added immediately after shucking on the boats and brining takes place during transport.

The processor must give a guarantee as to drained weight, which must be marked on the can or at least agreed with the importer. This is difficult with a product like abalone which loses a great amount of weight between shucking and final equilibration with the can liquor after retorting. Pre-cooking is sometimes used as a measure for stabilizing the drained weight. However, during retorting, which is normally 65 min at 115°C for a 1 lb (0.45 kg) can, further weight losses occur. The two main causes of weight loss, in addition to the inevitable bleeding before cooking, are loss of water and loss of solids. The water-holding capacity after cooking depends on the pH or freshness of the raw material. Solids are lost from the muscle by conversion of collagen, which is present in large quantities, into gelatin which diffuses out into the can brine (James and Olley 1971a). Texture and final yield depend on the extent of hydration of the protein which is correlated with pH and the degree of salt penetraion caused by brining. Texture can be measured with a puncturing device, such as the CSIRO maturometer, which gives a good correlation with taste panel results (James and Olley 1971b). The quality of the can brine is an important market consideration and a milky opalescent appearance is appreciated. The degree of opalescence can be measured with a single turbidity comparator and has been correlated with the glycogen content (James et al. 1971). Hashimoto (1965) claims that glycogen gives body and mouthfeel, therefore its presence, if the can brine is used as a soup, is important. Australian abalone has always been found to contain less glycogen than the Mexican product, which is the main competitor on world markets. During the summer months blue discolorations sometimes occur after retorting. These are apparently caused by complexes of oxidized haemocyanin with protein. Although uncooked abalone can be decolorized with reducing agents, such as ascorbic acid, the change is irreversible after retorting (Olcott and Thrower unpublished 1972).

Drying

In 1963 one small factory on the east coast of Tasmania was producing dried abalone, then the only processed product available in Australia. But the drying side has not shown the same development as the whole industry. Dried abalone is the oldest traditional product used in Asia but the market is small and very selective. The traditional Asian market requires a fully dried, whole, amber-coloured and translucent product with a moisture content of less than 22 per cent. There is also a growing market, in places like Hawaii, for a partly dried product,

241

with a moisture content of about 40 per cent. This is kept under refrigeration and retailed as small packs of thin slices which have a pleasant, though rubbery, consistency and a very delicate flavour (Young *et al.* 1973). Other interesting products can be made by deep oil frying of partly dried abalone. Recently some of the technology of abalone drying has been investigated and a report by Young *et al.* (1973) outlines products, quality and marketing, while Doe *et al.* (1973) describes the drying characteristics. Natural sun drying can be used, but for continuous commercial production hot air drying is preferred. Before drying, abalone is cleaned in strong brine, then brought to the boil in water or weak brine. These processes cause some reduction in the moisture content. Although boiling before drying is at variance with the normal practices of western fish technology, it is widely used in Asia (Tanikawa 1971). Young *et al.* (1973) discuss the desirable qualities produced by limited cooking. Drying at high temperatures causes severe case hardening which effectively stops the centre drying out. This tendency can be reduced, and the most rapid drying effected, by using air with a high relative humidity (Doe *et al.* in press).

Export of live abalone

The Japanese practice of eating abalone raw as 'sushi' or 'sashimi' requires very fresh raw material, preferably alive. Freighting by air appears to be the only way of handling small quantities as transport by ship in circulating tanks would require a larger volume for profitability. The temperature must be kept close to 6°C and insulated boxes and some coolant must be used, which requires that the boxes be closed. Investigations of the physiology of respiration, particularly the production of carbon dioxide as a damaging factor, may have a most important bearing if the animals are to revive when placed back in sea water. The future of this trade depends on rapid handling and immediate marketing on arrival in Japan.

UTILIZATION OF VISCERA AND SHELL

A very high proportion of the live weight of the abalone (about 65 per cent) is viscera and shell in approximately equal proportions. The viscera have quite a high protein and a low fat content (2 per cent) and, if blended with 10 per cent by weight of a carbohydrate source, such as 2 per cent malted barley and 8 per cent other cereal grain, the mixture is self ensiling. Other cheap carbohydrate sources, with free sugar available, can also be used to produce a free flowing viscous sludge with a pH of about 4.5, which keeps well for up to three months. Feeding trials with pigs, where 40 per cent silage was used in the ration, were successful and there was no fishy taint in the meat although the flavour was rather bland (Anon. 1972b). There is also a demand for cleaned and cooked viscera in Japan, but cleaning is time consuming and breakage, which reduces the market value, occurs easily. Some of the shell is used for decorative purposes but most is wasted.

CONCLUSIONS

The Australian abalone industry has become the third most important on the list of marine products exported. The industry is still in the experimental stages but many of the early problems restricting growth have been solved. Technological and market research has removed some of the constraints so that the processor now has a good idea of what to produce by assessment of the quality of his raw material and market demand. Although there is some evidence that production is approaching a maximum, conservation measures should prevent over-exploitation. Demand is expected to increase and with relatively static production economic returns should improve. All abalone exported is identified as a 'Product of Australia' and producers should take advantage of this brand image and ensure that the quality of their product is consistently high.

References

Anon. Survey of the Australian Seafood Processing Industry.
1971 Australian Government Publishing Service, Canberra, Australia, p. 134–146.

Anon. Code for handling and processing abalone. *Australian*
1972a *Fisheries*, 31(5):9–11.

Anon. Treating abalone waste. *Rural Research in CSIRO*, 77,
1972b September, p. 28.

ARAI, K and SAITO, T Changes in adenine nucleotides in the
1961 muscles of some marine invertebrates. *Nature, Lond.*, 192:451–452.

ARAI, K Nucleotides in the muscles of some marine invertebrates.
1966 *Bull. Jap. Soc. scient. Fish.*, 32:174–180.

DOE, P E, JAMES, D G and YOUNG, F Studies on the processing of abalone. V. Dried abalone; techniques and characteristics of drying. *Food Technol. Aust.*, 25 (in press, 1973).

HASHIMOTO, Y Taste-producing substances in marine products.
1965 In R Kreuzer (ed.), *The Technology of Fish Utilization*, London, Fishing News (Books) Ltd., p. 57–60.

James, D G and Olley, J Moisture and pH changes as criteria of
1970 freshness in abalone and their relationship to texture of the canned product. *Food Technol. Aust.*, 22(7):350–357.

James, D G and Olley, J Studies on the processing of abalone. III.
1971a The effect of processing variables on abalone texture with special reference to brining. *Ibid.*, 23(9):444–449.

James, D G and Olley, J Studies on the processing of abalone. II
1971b The maturometer as a guide to canned abalone texture. *Ibid.*, 23(8):394–398.

James, D G, Olley, J and Smith, J L Abalone. Division of Food
1971 Research. Report of research 1970–71, CSIRO, Sydney, Australia, p. 22–24.

Li, C P Antimicrobial Effect of Abalone Juice. *Proc. Soc. Exp.*
1960 *Biol. Med.*, 103:522–524.

Olley, J Handling of abalone. In *Report on Quality in Fish Pro-*
1971 *ducts Seminar No. 3.* Fishing Industry Board, Wellington, New Zealand, p. 89–95.

OLLEY, J and YOUNG, F Abalone, *Notohaliotis ruber*. Size effects
1972 Brining. Division of Food Research. Report of research 1971–72, CSIRO, Sydney, Australia, p. 21.

OLLEY, J and RATKOWSKY, D A Temperature function integration
1973 and its importance in the storage and distribution of flesh foods above the freezing point. *Food Technol. Aust.*, 25(2).

PRESCOTT, B and LI, C P Abalone juice, fractionation and anti-
1960 bacterial spectrum. *Proc. Soc. Exp. Biol. Med.*, 105:498–499.

TANIKAWA, E Boiled-dried abalone ('Hoshi-awabi'). In *Marine*
1971 *Products in Japan*, Tokyo, Koseisha-Koseikaku Company, p. 241–242.

YOUNG, F, JAMES, D G, OLLEY, J and DOE, P E Studies on the
1973 processing of abalone. IV. Dried abalone; products, quality and marketing. *Food Technol. Aust.*, 25 (in press).

The Potential Use of Squid as a Protein Resource
Tung-Ching Lee and C O Chichester

C M Lee,

Utilisation possible des encornets comme sources de proteines

Les auteurs présentent et discutent les études préliminaires faites dans leur laboratoire sur la possibilité de produire des concentrés protéiques d'encornets par hachage et dessiccation en atomiseur. Les résultats montrent que l'on peut facilement transformer les encornets en une poudre de concentré protéique de haute qualité. Cette poudre présente une bonne solubilité et une excellente valeur nutritive. Ses propriétés fonctionnelles – solubilité dans l'eau, pouvoir de fixation des lipides, stabilité des émulsions – sont nettement meilleures que celles des concentrés de protéines de poissons. Aussi les auteurs sont-ils persuadés que l'encornet repré sente une importante source de protéines d'origine marine.

Empleo potencial del calamar como fuente de proteinas

Se examinan y resumen los primeros estudios realizados sobre la posibilidad de producir un concentrado do proteínas de calamar en el laboratoro de los autres mediante trituración y secado por pulverización. Los resultados muestran que es fácil transformar el calamar en un polvo proteínico concentrado de excelente calidad. La solubilidad de este polvo es buena y su valor nutritivo excelente. Sus propiedades funcionales, por lo que se refiere a solubilidad en agua, capacidad de ligar aceites y estabilización de emulsión, son mucho mejores que las de los concentrados de proteínas de pescado. Los autores están convencidos, pues, de que el calamar ofrece una fuente importante de proteínas marinas.

Sprague (1973) points out that whatever rate of consumption one adopts, species at lower trophic levels produce a greater amount of protein than do their predators. As the food fish harvest appears to be at levels approximating maximum sustainable yields, there is a need to turn to underexploited species, such as red herring, sardinella, krill and, possibly, squid, if harvests are to be increased. The common squid is a mollusc and belongs to the class Cephalopoda. In general, it has a thin external epidermis and an internal pen and ink sac. The catch of squid at present totals approximately 880,000 t (FAO, 1971). Although this overall catch has increased during the last ten years, there have been wide fluctuations which appear to run along geographic lines rather than representing an impact on the resource. The total squid resource is unknown although it is estimated to be from two to ten times that which is harvested.

PROPERTIES OF THE RAW MATERIALS

The proportion of edible protein to the whole in squid is very high (80 per cent) and although the traditional dried squid has poor digestibility (de Gouveia and de Gouveia 1951, Tanikawa and Suno 1952) the fresh meat has high digestibility. Squid contains a higher level of water soluble proteins than fin fish (Matsumoto 1958). It is also rich in non-protein nitrogenous compounds (Simidu and Takeda 1952, Endo *et al.* 1954, Velankar and Govidan 1957). Monoamino nitrogen, glycine, proline, trimethylamineoxide, trimethylamine, and betaine are abundant in the water extractable nitrogen compounds. Monoamino nitrogen and trimethylamine are the major constituents of the volatile bases found in the animal (Simidu 1961). Free amino nitrogen levels of 300 mg/100 g of flesh are usual in crustaceans and molluscs compared with only 20 to 40 mg/100 g in fin fish flesh (Velankar and Govidan 1958). Villadelmar (1956–57) studied the amino acid

content of squid and showed that approximately 3.2 per cent of the total protein is methionine. The nutritive value of squid was compared to other molluscs by Varela *et al.* (1962). Octopus has the highest biological value followed by squid, then by shrimp. The meat portion, including the mantle and arm, are obviously best converted to food protein while the viscera may be converted to animal or other feedstuffs and serve as an excellent source of vitamins B2 and B12 (Kawata *et al.* 1955). The liver is a good source of unsaturated fatty acids (Shchenikova and Smirnova 1972). The hardening of squid in drying, without stripping, is thought to be due to the presence of collagen in the skin (Tanaka 1958) aggravated by the interaction of simple nitrogen compounds with other compounds during the drying procedure. The proximate analysis of squid is shown in Table 1 (Lee 1970). It can be seen that the fat content is comparatively low, which would augur well for the possibilities of developing a low fat protein concentrate. Because of the level of the trimethylamine-type compounds, the squid is a highly flavoured mollusc and for those unaccustomed to its flavour, the flesh is relatively unacceptable, and unless the ink sac is removed, the flesh is apt to be dark coloured.

UTILIZATION OF THE SQUID

The beak and other hard portions are removed by comminuting the washed, chopped flesh and passing it through a standard finisher. The resultant slurry is then spray-dried after dilution with water. The dried product could be used directly as a protein concentrate, although it still contains a significant odour and flavour. Extraction by the isopropyl alcohol process almost completely removes both the odour and the flavour. The average overall yield is not high, but could be improved considerably if the soluble material removed by washing were recovered. This would give a total yield of approximately 50 per cent of the solids.

TABLE 1. PROXIMATE ANALYSIS OF RAW SQUID, SPRAY-DRIED SQUID, AND SOLVENT-EXTRACTED SPRAY-DRIED SQUID

Sample	H_2O (%)	Fat (%)	Protein Nx 6.25 (%)	Non-protein nitrogen (%)	Protein corrected for non-protein nitrogen)%(	Ash (%)	Other (%)
Raw, unwashed	78.7	1.38	14.97	—	—	2.03	2.92
Spray-dried	4.4	2.11	81.20	1.83	69.75	4.10	8.91
Solvent-extracted[a]	1.5	1.22	90.37	1.43	81.41	2.02	4.89

[a] Extracted with absolute insopropanel in three stages (Solvent:sold ratio = 2:1; fresh solvent was used in each stage)

The spray-dried product has approximately 83 per cent protein, 2 to 3 per cent fat and 5 per cent moisture. Extraction with alcohol results in a product with a fat content reduced to below 1 per cent and a protein content of approximately 90 per cent. About 1 per cent of the material is non-protein nitrogen. The solvent extracted from squid protein concentrate is highly flavoured and dark in colour when hydrocarbon solvents are used as the extractor. Alcohol extraction does not effectively remove the colour unless a high ratio of solvent to flesh is used. Since the ink is water soluble, water extraction of the flesh after the removal of ink during the washing process produces a light-coloured concentrate. If this is followed by alcohol extraction, using either ethyl or isopropyl alcohol, the resulting product is very light-coloured and has extremely low residual flavour. A process for producing a protein concentrate of this type has been developed in the laboratory (Lee 1970; Lee, C.M., C.O. Chichester and T.-C. Lee unpublished results). It consists of removing the skin of the squid by agitating the body in a container armed with a set of wire projections. These remove the soft, filmy skin effectively and the squid is then chopped into small pieces, loosening the ink sac and the viscera. By the use of an agitating washer, it is possible to remove completely the ink and some of the flavouring components from the pieces of flesh. The protein concentrate derived from the squid by the water isopropanol process was analysed for solubility, oil binding capacity and emulsion stability and tested for the protein quality. Solubility was determined by the ADMI (American Dry Milk Institute) standard method (1962) for milk. The concentrate was soluble to the extent of 92 per cent compared to a spray-dried milk which had a solubility of 97 per cent. Its solubillity is significantly higher than protein concentrates derived from hake via the isopropanol extraction process. Squid protein concentrate also has a considerably higher salt soluble protein content than many animal products—67 per cent (Lee 1970) compared with 45 per cent for pork protein and 41 per cent for beef, as determined by Saffle and Galbreath (1964). The binding capacity of the protein is lower, however, than that of the mammalian proteins, approximating 16 to 17 mm/100 mg of salt soluble protein (Lee 1970). The stability of oil in water emulsions using the protein as an emulsifying agent was measured. Heating at 90°C for 15 min showed no break in the emulsion. Thus, while the emulsifying power and stability of the squid protein concentrate may be considered superior to formal protein concentrates, it was lower than that of some meat products.

The protein efficiency ratio of the squid protein concentrate was compared with casein and fish protein concentrate made from hake, using Sprague-Dawley rats as the test animals. The results showed ratio values, on a net protein basis of 3 to 3.6 compared with 2.5 for casein. It thus appears to the authors that squid provide a significant protein marine resource for which the technology required for the production of protein concentrates, either slightly flavoured or taseless, is available. They could be utilized in a larger number of products than the concentrates which are now available. The potential of the squid resource is very large and the main deterrents to its full exploitation lie in the technology of harvesting.

References

DE GOUVEIA, A J A and DE GOUVEIA, A P   Contribution to the
1951   chemical study of mollusks from the Portuguese coast. 1. Analytical study of the Squid *Loligo vulgaris* Lamarck. *Conservas de Peixe* 6(65):18.

ENDO, K, HUJITA, M and SIMIDU, W   Studies on muscle of aquatic
1954   animals. XXII. On distribution and extractive nitrogen and free glycine content in squids. *Bull. Jap. Soc. Scient. Fish.*, 20:723–725.

FAO   Catches and landings. *Yb. Fishery Statist.*, 30:216.
1971

KAWATA, H, KATAYA, K, TAKAHASHI, T and KURIYAMA, H   Studies
1955   on the complete utilization of whole fish. IV. The chemical composition of some fish viscera and the fish soluble feed made from cuttlefish liver. *Bull. Jap. Soc. Scient. Fish.*, 21(7):503–508.

LEE, C M   *A study of process requirements and properties of protein
1970   concentrate prepared by Spray Dehydration of Squid.* M.S. Thesis, University of Georgia, USA.

MATSUMOTO, J   Some aspects on the water soluble protein of squid
1958   protein. *Bull. Tokai Reg. Fish. Res. Lab.*, (20):65–75.

SAFFLE, R L and GALBREATH, J W   Quantitative determination of
1964   salt soluble protein in various types of meat. *Fd. Technol.* 18:119.

SHCHENIKOVA, N V and SMIRNOVA, G A   Composition of squid
1972   lipids. *Rybnoe Khoz.*, (1):62–63.

SIMIDU, W   Nonprotein nitrogenous compounds. In Borgstrom, G
1961   (ed) *Fish as Food*, New York and London Academic Press, 4:353–375.

SIMIDU, W and TAKEDA, M   Studies on muscle of aquatic animals.
1952   XII. Distribution of extractive nitrogen in muscle of squids. *Bull. Jap. Soc. Scient. Fish.*, 18:234–236.

SPRAGUE, L M   Prospects of the world's fishery resources, with
1973   emphasis on the western hemisphere. In Chichester, C O and H D Graham (ed.) *Microbial Safety of Fishery Products.* New York and London Academic Press, p. 41–51.

TANAKA, T   Histological studies of muscle tissue of squid for
1958   utilization. In Migita, M and E Tanikwa (ed.), *Chemistry of Processing of Squid Meat.* Hokkai, Suisan, Shinbun, Hokkaido, Japan, p. 75–88.

TANIKAWA, E and SUNO, M   Studies on the complete utilization of
1952   squid. V. Nutritive value and digestibility of squid meat. *Bull. Fac. Fisheries*, Hokkaido University, 3:75–80.

VARELA, G, PUJOL, A and MOREIRAS, O   Biological value of the
1962   protein of some fishes consumed in Spain. Influence of some preservation techniques. In Heen, E and R Kreuzer (ed.) *Fish in Nutrition*, London, Fishing News (Books) Ltd., 259–260.

VELANKAR, N K and GOVINDAN, T K   Free amino-acid nitrogen
1957   of the skeletal muscle of some marine fishes and invertebrates. *Curr. Sci.*, 26:285–286.

VELANKAR, N K and GOVINDAN, T K   Preliminary study of the
1958   distribution of nonprotein nitrogen in some marine fishes and invertebrates. *Proc. Indian Acad. Sci.*, 47:202–209.

VILLADELMAR, M   Determination of amino acids in twenty-four
1956–   Mexican foods. *Ciencia*, 16:17–23.
1957

Utilization of Squid as Food   *T Takahashi*

Utilisation des encornets pour la consommation humaine

L'auteur décrit les techniques japonaises de capture des encornets et les multiples façons d'utiliser ces derniers pour l'alimentation humaine au Japon. Il estime que, si 'lutilisation des méthodes japonaises de capture des encornets se généralisait, les prises mondiales pourraient quasiment sextupler, c'est-à-dire passer du niveau actuel de 700,000 tonnes à 4 millions de tonnes par an.

Utilizacion de los calamares para la alimentacion

En este trabajo se describen las técnicas de pesca que utilizan los japoneses para la captura del calamar y la enorme variedad de formas en que se aprovecha este cefalópodo para el consumo humano en el Japón. El autor estima que, si se difundieran los métodos de pesca del calamar utilizados por el Japón, las capturas mundiales podrían sextuplicarse, pasando de 700,000 o más toneladas en la

L'un des problèmes fondamentaux associés à la pleine utilisation des encornets pour l'alimentation humaine consiste à combattre la résistance des consommateurs en particulier dans les pays occidentaux. Pour parvenir à ce résultat, le mieux serait, de l'avis de l'avis de l'auteur, que les spécialistes des sciences et de la technologie alimentaires mettent au point des produits acceptables à base d'encornets.

actualidad a cuatro millones de toneladas al año. Un element básico para aprovechar plenamente el calamar como producto alimenticio es superar la resistencia de los consumidores, especialmente en los países occidentales. La mejor forma de conseguirlo, sugiere el autor, sería que los bromatologos y technólogos de la alimentación prepararan productos aceptables a base de calamares.

Squids are not abundantly utilized for food in all countries but have long been consumed in Japan in various forms where they are an important source of protein. The majority commercially caught are *Todarodes pacificus* (Japanese flying squid), *Loligo* app. (common squid) and species belonging to the Loliginidae and Ommastrephidae families. Most squids are caught in the sea adjacent to Japan. The catch from 1910 to 1970 in Japan is shown in Fig 1, 80 to 90 per cent being *Todarodes pacificus*. The increased catches after 1950 are due to improved fishing gear and techniques. About 50 per cent of the squid catch was frozen in 1970, some being used as bait for tuna

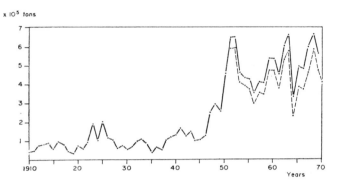

x 10^5 tons

Fig 1   Annual catch of squids in Japan from 1910 to 1970

longline fishing. About 35 per cent was sold to retailers as fresh squid, and about 15 per cent used as raw material for processing. Squid liver extract is used as feed for livestock after evaporation or dehydration while oil of good quality is also produced from the liver. Squid as well as mackerel, horse mackerel, Alaska pollack and others, are regarded in Japan as cheap and abundant fish. However, their price has risen year by year due to a decreasing catch and an increasing demand for fresh food, raw material for processing and bait for tuna fishing. Japanese retailers sold more fresh squid in 1970 than any other marine product – both in quantity and cash.

COMPOSITION AND NUTRITIVE VALUE

There are considerable differences in the histological and chemical natures of fish and squid meats. In squid the percentage of edible protein is about 80 per cent, in the trunk 50 per cent and in the arms 30 per cent. The water content of squid meat is between 77 and 80 per cent. The fat content is about 1 to 1.5 per cent and the protein content about 17 to 20 perc ent. The meat of squid caught in summer contains more water but less crude protein than that caught in autumn. The liver has maximum oil content, minimum water and less nitrogen in October and November. Sarcoplasmic protein (about 14 to 27 per cent), myofibrillar protein (about 68 to 79 per cent)

and stroma protein (about 2 to 5 per cent) are the same as those in the protein of fish meat. The myofibrillar protein in squid meat is soluble in water. About one half of the protein in squid meat may be extracted by prolonged washing in water. Due to abundant extractive nitrogen (0.6 to 0.9 per cent on the nitrogen basis), squid meat has a characteristic sweet taste. The meat includes various amino acids, betaine, taurine, trimethylamine oxide, etc. When the meat shows an alkalin reaction due to decrease in freshness, or if the meat is cooked, the pigment cells break and redden the meat. The inner surface of trunk is also covered with a thin membrane.

Even in Japan where squid meat is widely consumed many people underestimate its nutritive value and regard it as almost indigestible. However, Japanese research has shown that the proteins are highly digestible and that their amino acid pattern is similar to that of fish. Thus, squid may be considered as an excellent source of protein.

PROCESSED PRODUCTS

The total production of squid products for 1966 to 1970 is given in Table 1.

Dried products

Various types of dried products are manufactured. For example, there are skinned, moonfaced and bag-shaped dried squids. Dried squid prepared from *Loligo edulis* is of higher grade than that prepared from *Todarodes pacificus*. Economically, the latter is most important because of the large volume caught. Dried squid has long been used in preserved foodstuffs but is used today mostly as raw material for seasoned foods, especially *Todarodes pacificus*. For making a dried product, the squid is first cut open, and the entrails and eyeballs removed, but not the arms. Thus, the body becomes flat and triangular in shape. After washing, it is generally hung on straw ropes for outdoor drying until the water content drops to 18-22 per cent. In fine summer weather the drying may be completed in three days. During the drying, the meat is shaped into the desired appearance.

Canned squid meat

Squid meat is canned in the USA, Spain, Korea, and Japan. A large amount of seasoned meat is canned in Japan. Canned meat in brine is being produced in smaller quantity. The raw material is from *Todarodes pacificus*. The arms and entrails are removed and the entrails are cut off. After washing, the meat is cooked at about 45°C in a salt solution (10°B) for ten minutes and then stirred to remove the skin in water. The skinned meat is then heated in a boiling salt solution (3°B) for ten minutes. After boiling, the eyeballs are removed from the arms. The trunk and arms are washed, and the latter is put into the former. The meat is packed into C-enamel

TABLE 1. PRODUCTION OF PROCESSED PRODUCTS OF SQUID IN JAPAN (TONS)

	1966	1967	1968	1969	1970
Dried	21,327	25,114	27,041	14,507	11,113
Paste	7,214	8,910	9,136	7,921	9,631
Smoked	504	309	351	577	730
Seasoned			53,056	59,810	58,034
Canned[a]	193,656	452,914	308,530	327,107	274,094
Frozen				245,021	154,721

[a] Number of cases

cans with seasoning, which consists of soypaste, soy bean sauce, sugar, salt and water or brine (4°B) containing small amounts of monosodium glutamate and citric acid. The cans are vacuum sealed and sterilized at 107°–110°C for 60 to 85 minutes. A small amount of minced boiled squid meat is also prepared. In Spain, canned squid meats in oil are produced.

Autolytic digested products of squid meat

Products from squid meat and liver digested by their proteolytic enzymes have been made from ancient times in Japan. They are generally used as a delicacy at 'sake' parties. There are three different preparations: red, white, and black. *Todarodes pacificus* is the principal raw material. The entrails and eyeballs are removed. The arms are treated with salt to remove the horny rings of their suckers. After washing, the trunk and arms are sliced into small pieces and mixed in a barrel with liver slurries, 5 per cent of the sliced meat and some salt (30 per cent in summer, 15 per cent in winter). During the first week of storage, the mixtures are stirred three times a day and the water is removed as required. The barrel is sealed and stored until the mixture is moderately digested. Ageing depends on the amount of liver slurries and salt used and storage temperature. Usually, the products are ready after a month. If the product is stored for two months or more at the ambient temperature, a volatile base may develop, causing the flavour to deteriorate. The 'red' type of product is the main one of the three. The white product is made from skinned meats, and the black is made by adding the squid ink to the red product.

Miscellaneous processed products

Various seasoned products based on squid meat have recently appeared in the market in Japan. These include, for example, boiled and roasted meat, sliced smoked meat, and slender slices of boiled meat. The production of seasoned smoked squid was about 6,000 tons in 1965 but is now only several hundred tons.

Smoked products are made as follows: the trunk, with the entrails and arms removed, is stirred in hot water (50° to 55°C) for about 10 to 20 minutes for skinning. The skinned meat is washed and cooked at 80° to 90°C for a few minutes. The meat is then mixed with seasoning incredients consisting of salt, sugar, monosodium glutamate and sodium 5'-ribonu-cleotide. The seasoned product is smoked for seven to nine hours, the temperature being gradually raised from 30° to 80°C. It is then cut into small pieces, sprinkled with seasoning liquor, and dried by infra-red rays. The slender sliced product is made as follows: after seasoning, the skinned,

dried or boiled trunks are grilled. In order to loosen the meat fibre, the grilled material is then passed through several rollers, after which it is sliced. The annual production of dried squid was about 10,000 tons several years ago, but today more products are being made of boiled squid.

FROZEN SQUID

Squids caught in distant waters are frozen abroad and landed in Japan. Half of the *Todarodes pacificus* caught around Japan have also been frozen in recent years. After washing, the squids are placed in galvanized iron pans which are held in the freezer at −25° to −30°C for 20 hours. The frozen squid cakes are then removed and ice-glazed by immersion in cold water for five to ten seconds. The cakes are usually stored at −15°C. If frozen squids are kept in high or at fluctuating temperatures, the pigment cells in the skin are broken, reddening the meat, which reduces its commercial value.

FUTURE OF SQUID UTILIZATION

Squids are becoming an imporant food. Apart from those caught around Japan, the majority of squids in the world belong to the family of Ommastrephidae, of which there are many species. The scientific names, average sizes and habitats are shown in Table 2.

TABLE 2. SIZE AND HABITAT OF MAJOR SPECIES OF OMMASTREPHIDAE

Scientific name	Average size	Habitat
Todarodes sagittatus	47 cm (length of trunk)	North Sea, eastern Atlantic Ocean, Indian Ocean (coast of Africa), Mediterranean
Ommastrephes caroli	61 cm (length of trunk)	Northeastern Atlantic Ocean, Mediterranean
Illex illecebrosus	25 to 28 cm (length of trunk)	Northwestern Atlantic Ocean
Dosidecus gigas	about 400 cm (total length)	Pacific Ocean (coast of America)
Nototodarus sloani gouldi	about 150 cm (total length)	Around Australia
Nototodarus sloani sloani	20 to 30 cm (length of trunk)	Around New Zealand
Todarodes pacificus	26 cm (length of trunk)	Around Japan

If and when the Japanese angling technique is used generally, the catch of squids could amount to 4 million tons a year – 500,000 tons from the northern, western, southeastern, and southwestern Pacific Ocean respectively, and 2,500,000 tons from the Atlantic Ocean. Nutritious products which do not, however, fit in with the eating habits of the consumers concerned are not usually accepted. And it is especially distasteful for people to eat animals which are different in appearance from those they usually use as food. Thus, the squid, which is called the 'devil fish' because of its appearance, is accepted as food only by some population groups of Europe and North America. Although the appearance of the product can be improved by shaping the meat after cutting, the peculiar sweetish taste of the meat cannot be altered. This is disliked by many people unfamiliar with it. Again, the raw meat of squid has almost no smell, but when cooked it does smell, probably due to the Maillard reaction. While the meat consists mostly of fine muscle fibres with few connective and no fatty tissues, its texture is different from, say, beef or chicken and to many western people it seems very tough. However, despite these drawbacks, squid meat could become a

significant source of protein for people in many countries. This could be achieved if food scientists and technologists developed new types of squid products that had a strong appeal to consumers. Such new products could be made from dried fibrous meat in an easily reconstituted form, dried meat powder with the solubility of fresh meat, and canned products of various types.

Utilization of Krill for Human Consumption

L L Lagunov, M I Kryuchkova, N I Ordukhanyan and L V Sysoeva

Utilisation du Krill pour la consommation humaine

L'une des innovations les plus intéressantes en matière de pêche est représentée par les travaux soviétiques sur le krill. Les auteurs expliquent comment ont été résolus les problèmes relatifs à la capture du krill et à sa transformation en denrée comestible ainsi qu'en aliments pour animaux. S'agissant de la pêche, un chalut pélagique spécial a été mis au point. Pour la transformation, outre la production de farine destinée à l'alimentation animale, produit par lui-même coûteux, on a conçu une installation spéciale qui fonctionne à bord des navires de pêche. Cet équipement, qui comprime le krill et traite à la chaleur le liquide obtenu, coagule les protéines qui sont ensuite congelées et entreposées en attendant leur traitement ultérieur dans des usines de produits alimentaires en Union soviétique. Maintenant, la pâte de krill, nourrissant et de daveur délicate, est très demandée sur le marché inférieur et est incorporée dans de nombreux plats traditionnels. Par ailleurs, de nouveaux produits à base de pâte de krill ont été lancés ou sont en cours de mise au point. Les difficultés et problèmes qu'il a fallu surmonter pour développer la pêche du krill proviennent du fait que le krill est pêché une seule fois par an dans l'Antarctique et doit subir un long entreposage. En outre, le krill est tellement vulnérable qu'il se détériore très rapidement après la capture. Aussi est-il indispensable de le manipuler et de le transformer sans délai à bord. Le mêmes considérations valent pour la pâte de krill. Les auteurs décrivent les techniques qui donnent au produit une conservabilité d'environ un an. L'importance de la pêche du krill est soulignée. Les captures annuelles potentielles de krill sont estimées à 100 millions de tonnes.

Utilizacion de los eufasiaceos (Krill) para el consumo humano

Uno de los progresos más interesantes del sector pesquero es la experiencia soviética con el krill (eufasiáceos). Los autores de este trabajo explican como se han resuelto los problemas que planteaban la captura del krill y su transformación en un alimento apto para el consumo humano y para piensos. Para su captura se preparó una red específica de arrastre pelágico. Para su elaboradión, aparte de producir harina para piensos, producto éste antieconómico, se preparó una instalación especial que habría de funcionar a bordo de los pesqueros. En esta instalación, gracias a un proceso de prensado y al tratamiento térmico del jugo obtenido, se coagulan las proteínas, que luego se congelan y almacenan para elaborarlas ulterioriormente en fábricas de alimentos en la Union soviética Gracias a esto, la pasta de krill nutritiva y de aroma delicado, no sólo encuentra excelente demanda en el mercado interior, sino que, además, se está aqadiendo a muchos platos tradicionales. Al mismo tiempo se han preparado nuevos productos basados en esta pasta y se están preparando aún más. Las dificultades y problemas que hubo que superar para desarrollar esta pesquería pueden apreciarse por el hecho de que el krill se captura sólo una vez al año en el Antártico, y ha de conservarse en almacén por mucho tiempo. Son animales tan delicados que se deterioran rapidísimamente una vez capturados. Por tanto, es esencial tratarlos y elaborarlos a bordo con rapidez y almacenar bien la pasta obtenida. En el trabajo se describen las técnicas utilizadas, que permiten conservar el producto durante un año, aproximadamente. Se hace notar la importancia de la pesquería de krill, indicando que la captura potencial anual de estos animales se calcula en 100 millones de toneladas.

Providing the population with high-grade protein products is one of the main problems of today. As the stocks of planktonic crustaceans are vast, they may serve as one of the potential sources of animal protein for human consumption. The potential annual catch of krill is estimated to be 100 million tons, which is more than the present total world fish catch. During the surveys of FRV AKADEMIK KNIPOVICH (VNIRO) and SRT (medium trawler) MUKSUN (AtlantNIRO) in the Scotia Sea area of the Antarctic (1965 to 1971), the krill there were found in concentrations which can be commercially exploited. Average catches were from 3 to 6 t/h trawling, with some rich areas yielding as much as 9 t/h (Groisman *et al.* 1969). A special pelagic trawl designed at VNIRO was used. Krill are characterized by a high content of trace elements, vitamins, and amino acids indispensable to man. So far, development of the krill fishery has been restricted by the lack of methods of processing the catch into food. The krill provide good raw material for the production of animal feed but that alone is uneconomical. However, the problems involved in processing krill into human food were solved by the VNIRO scientists during the expedition of FRV AKADEMIK KNIPOVICH in 1965 when a method for making a paste for human consumption was developed

(Kryuchkova 1970). The technique is based on the extraction of the liquid protein fraction (juice) with subsequent heat treatment. A special plant (AKP VNIRO) for this processing on board was developed.

CHARACTERISTICS OF KRILL

The Antarctic krill (*Euphausia superba*) are 3 to 6 cm in size and range from pale pink to brick red in colour when caught. This size and weight are variable, depending on age and biological condition. The average weight ranges from 0.3 to 1.2 g, with juveniles weighing about 0.6 to 0.7 g and adults from 0.7 to 1.2 grammes. Fat content varies from 1 to 6 per cent, moisture from 72 to 80 per cent, protein from 11 to 15 per cent and ash from 2 to 3 per cent, depending on the season and the physiological condition of the krill. An analysis of moisture and fat content in males, females and juveniles in the same catch is shown in Table 1 and the percentage of edible and inedible parts and processing losses in Table 2.

Chemical composition varies according to size, area and month of capture. This chemical composition is similar to that of small shrimp. Krill meat has the delicate flavour which is a feature of the meat of all crustaceans.

Krill spoil rapidly because their organs contain highly

TABLE 1. Moisture and fat content in male, female and juvenile krill taken from two catches

	February			March		
	Moisture (%)	Fat (%)	Fat, dry base (%)	Moisture (%)	Fat (%)	Fat, dry base (%)
Males	76.4	1.6	6.8	79.3	1.8	8.7
Females	79.1	2.8	13.4	75.0	4.3	17.2
Juveniles	75.9	4.9	20.4	73.7	7.2	27.4

TABLE 2. Edible and inedible parts of krill and processing losses

	Raw (%)	Cooked (%)
Edible (tail meat)	29.0	35.0
Inedible (cephalothorax and carapace)	61.5	60.0
Processing losses	9.5	5.0

active enzymes, causing quick development of autolysis. Within two hours on deck they turn pale in colour, lose transparency and become soft and flabby, with the cephalothorax turning dark. Quality is assessed organoleptically, and by determination of the volatile base nitrogen. At temperatures of 5° to 7°C the volatile base nitrogen increases from 6 mg% to 17 mg% within 24 h and reaches 66 mg% within 72 hours. Based on these data and other observations, it is considered that krill can be stored at a temperature under 7°C but not for more than 4 hours. For convenience, krill are usually graded into three size groups: less than 35 mm, from 35 to 55 mm, and more than 55 millimetres. Catches off South Georgia usually consist of 60 per cent of krill less than 35 mm long, 28 per cent of 35 to 55 mm and 12 per cent over 55 mm long.

PRODUCTION OF FOOD PROTEIN PASTE

The main features of good paste processing methods are the pressing of the raw krill and the heat treatment of the resulting liquid to coagulate the protein. The following technological scheme has therefore been formulated:

(1) Pressing the raw krill to obtain the liquid protein fraction – the juice.
(2) Collecting the juice (storage time in ambient temperature not over 10 minutes)
(3) Heating the juice to coagulate the protein.
(4) Separating the coagulated protein from the liquid fraction – the broth.
(5) Condensing the coagulated protein and packing it in forms for freezing.
(6) Freezing and storage.

The juice from pressing is a reddish creamy mass. The cake from pressing contains much protein and is therefore a good raw material for making meal for animal feed. The quality of the juice is better when large krill are used, the dry matter content being as high as 25 per cent compared to approximately 17 per cent obtained from small krill. The juice, stirred continuously as it is heated, coagulates at a temperature of 90° to 97°C in large protein flakes. The chemical composition of krill and of the products obtained from it is given in Table 3.

TABLE 3. Chemical composition of krill and krill products

	Moisture (%)	Oil (%)	Total nitrogen (%)	Ash (%)	Nitrogenous substances, N × 6.25	
					Wet base (%)	Dry base (%)
Whole krill	79.0	1.2	2.7	2.3	16.9	80.5
Juice	81.7	2.4	2.0	1.8	12.7	69.4
Coagulated protein	67.6	4.6	4.0	3.0	24.5	75.6
Broth	87.4	0.3	1.5	2.6	9.5	75.4

Experiments have shown that the process of coagulation should be rapid and finish within 10 minutes. Coagulation is one of the most important operations because the heating conditions determine both the yield and the quality of the paste. As already pointed out, treatment in the coagulator yields both the coagulated protein and the broth. These are separated on the screen conveyor. Lumps of coagulated protein are put through a grinder after which the coagulate is packed and frozen. Freezing is done at a temperature not higher than −32°C and the temperature inside the block goes down to −18°C The blocks are removed from the freezer and packed in cardboard boxes, cellulose or other packaging materials. The frozen protein paste is stored at a temperature of −18° to −20°C. As krill is fished only once a year, the product has to be stored for a long time. Studies on the quality of the paste during storage have shown that changes are caused mainly by changes in oil properties. The storage time of the paste at a temperature of not above −18°C is about a year. Krill meal obtained from the press cake has the following characteristics: 6 to 10 per cent moisture, 53 to 55 per cent protein, 10 to 15 per cent oil and 13 to 15 per cent ash. Biological tests have shown that it is highly suitable for animal feed.

Chemical characteristics of krill paste

The final product is known as 'Ocean Paste'. Its chemical composition is as follows: 70 to 78 per cent moisture, 13 to 20 per cent protein, 3 to 10 per cent oil, 1 to 3 per cent ash and 1 to 2 per cent carbohydrates. The paste has a delicate sweetish flavour typical of shrimp meat and is a pink curdled mass. The protein of the paste contains all the essential amino acids with a particular high content of Lysine (Nikolaeva 1967). Table 4 shows the content of some amino acids in krill paste, egg and meat as compared with the FAO/WHO standards (in percentage of the total indispensable amino acid content). Like the meat of invertebrates, krill paste is characterized by a high content of macro- and micro-elements essential for the human organism. The percentage of these elements in the paste (in mg/100 g of dry matter) is phosphorus: 45 to 65; iron: 0.9 to 1.4; copper: 0.7 to 0.9; zinc: 2.3; titanium 0.09; chromium: 0.02; cobalt: 0.02; molibden: 0.002. The paste contains almost the whole complex of B-group vitamins. The oil in it has a high content of phospholipids. The content of unsaturated fatty acids is over 70 per cent, with C-18 and C-20 making up as much as 30 and 16 per cent of the total amount respectively. The amino acid compounds, trace elements and vitamins in the krill paste determine its high nutritive value. This has been proved in a four-year study in the Kiev Research Institute of Food Hygiene conducted through experiments with animals and through clinical observatons. The animals (rats) receiving krill paste as a protein component of their diet showed a higher rate of increase in weight than those receiving beef. Some results of these experiments are shown in Table 5.

TABLE 4. CONTENT OF SOME AMINO ACIDS IN KRILL PASTE, EGG AND MEAT COMPARED WITH THE FAO/WHO STANDARDS, EXPRESSED IN PERCENTAGES OF THE TOTAL ESSENTIAL AMINO ACID CONTENT

Amino acids	FAO/WHO standard	Krill paste	Egg	Beef
Threonine	9.9	7.9 (4.7)	9.9 (5.0)	9.7 (4.3)
Valine	14.1	15.9 (9.4)	14.7 (7.4)	12.6 (5.6)
Sulphur – containing acids Cystine + methionine	10.7	6.4 (3.8)	10.1 (5.1)	9.7 (4.3)
Isoleucine	12.9	12.9 (7.6)	13.1 (6.6)	11.6 (5.2)
Leucine	17.2	16.3 (9.6)	18.4 (9.2)	18.4 (8.2)
Tyrosine + phenylalanine	19.5	16.4 (9.7)	17.5 (8.8)	16.0 (7.1)
Lysine	12.6	21.8 (12.8)	12.9 (6.4)	19.1 (8.5)
Triptophane	3.1	2.4 (1.4)	3.4 (1.7)	2.7 (1.2)
Total	100	100 (59.0)	100 (50.2)	100 (44.4)

Note: Bracketed figures denote the content of essential amino acids as a percentage of protein.

TABLE 5. WEIGHT GAIN OF RATS FED WITH KRILL PASTE, BEEF AND/OR CASEIN

Diet	Weight (g)		Weight gain	
	Initially	At the end of the trials	(g)	(%)
100% casein	198	321	123	64
50% casein and 50% beef	155	280	122	78
50% casein and 50% krill paste	167	305	138	82
100% krill paste	194	365	171	88

Histological analysis of internal organs in the rats did not reveal any pathological change. Blood tests also confirmed the favourable effect of the krill paste: the haemoglobin content and the phagocytic activity were higher in the experimental than in the control animals.

Experimental introduction of the paste in the diet of patients undergoing dietary treatment showed favourable effects with such diseases as hyperacid ulcer of the stomach, atherosclerosis, etc. The healing effect of the paste on patients suffering from ulcer of the stomach, for example, was reflected by a 60 per cent increase in the number of patients cured by therapeutic means without surgical intervention.

THE AKP-VNIRO PROCESSING UNIT

Research carried out at VNIRO (Terentyev and Tsareva 1972) resulted in the development of the AKP-VNIRO plant for the production of protein paste from krill. This processing unit consts of a screw press, a collector, a gear pump, a screw coagulator, a screen conveyor and a grinder.

Specification of the plant
Input: 1,000 kg/h
Output: 250 to 300 kg/h
Consumption of steam: 60 to 80 kg/h
Coagulation temperature: 90° to 97°C
Installed capacity of electric motors: 16 kW

Specification of the coagulator
The coagulator is designed for heat treatment of juice
Input capacity: 500 kg/h
Speed of the screw: 3 to 9 rpm
Consumption of steam: 50 to 60 kg/h
Coagulation temperature: 90° to 97°C

The coagulator is a jacketed drum fitted inside with a rotating screw perforated along its full length. Live steam is supplied to the hollow shaft of the screw. The coagulator is fitted with an opening for juice supply and a discharge port. When the juice is heated up to 95° to 97°C the protein coagulates and falls out as bright pink flakes. The design of the coagulator allows for adjusting the coagulation time within 3 to 7 minutes. This is achieved by varying the speed of the screw. The top of the coagulator is fitted with a fan to remove vapour. All parts of the coagulator in contact with the product are made from stainless steel. The plant is designed for use on fishing vessels.

UTILIZATION OF KRILL PASTE AS FOOD

The utilization of krill paste in the manufacture of fish speciality products and new kinds of food has been studied. The paste adds high-grade proteins, trace elements and vitamins to food. The paste goes well with butter, cheese, various vegetables, mayonnaise, etc. Two broad ways of using this product have been suggested. One is through the network of public eating places. It is easy and simple to use the paste in food such as salads, pâté, krill butter, stuffed eggs and tomatoes, pelmini (Siberian dumplings), pies and zrazy (fish balls), etc. The other way is product development. New food items and recipes have been produced such as 'shrimp butter', 'shrimp with mayonnaise', 'fish sausage with krill', etc, containing from 15 to 60 per cent krill paste. Particularly promising is the incorporation of the paste in melted cheese. While natural krill paste is in great demand, food processing plants have been successfully developing and increasing the variety of products with krill incorporated.

References

Anon. Krill may have potential as human food. *Comml. Fish. Rev.*, 1967   29(6):24.
Anon. Antarctic fish stocks. *Fishg. News int.*, 9(3):11.
1970
BUROKOVSKIY, R N (Ed.) *Antarkticheskii Kril'* (Antarctic Krill), 1967   Kaliningrad, USSR, AtlantNIRO, 92 p. English translation. *Soviet Fishery Research on the Antarctic Krill*, Washington, D.C. 20443, USA, US Department of Commerce, Joint Publications Research Service: 42, 053, TT:67–32683.
GROISMAN, M Ya, KARPENKO, E A and STEPANOV, G N   Opytnyi 1969   lov Krilia b more scotia (Experimental fishing for krill in the Scotia Sea). *Trudy VNIRO*, 66:276–283.
KRYUCHKOVA, M I   Poluchenie pistchevogo belka iz krilia (Obtain-1970   ing food protein from krill). *Rybnoe Khoz.*, 46(11):53–56.
KRYUCHKOVA, M I and LAGUNOV, L L   Kril' istochnic belkovogo 1969   pitania (Krill, the source of protein nutrition). *Rybnoe Khoz.*, 45(5):58–59.

KRYUCHKOVA, M I and MAKAROV, D E Technokhimiskaia
1969   kharacteristica krila (Technochemical characteristics of
        krill). *Turdy VNIRO.*, 66:295–298.
KRYUCHKOVA, M I, LAGUNOV, L L, LESTEV, V, MAKAROV, P P and
1971   TSAREVA, L D Kril' kak pistchevoe syr'e (Krill as a food
        source). *Trudy VNIRO.*, 79:153–157.
LAGUNOV, L L and REKHINA, N I Technologia productov iz
1967   bespozvonotchnykh (Technology of products from inverte-
        brates), Moscow, Pistchepromizdat.
MAKSIMOV, S I Issledovania jira krilia (Study of krill fat). *Rybnoe
1968   Khoz.*, 44(6):68–69.
NIKOLAEVA, N E Aminokislotnii sostav belka-koaguliata krilia
1967   (Amino acid composition of protein coagulates in krill).
        Trudy VNIRO., 63:161–164.

PEQUEGNAT, W E Whales, plankton and man. Shrimplike animals
1958   consumed by whales may help solve the food problem of
        man. *Scient. Amer.*, 198(1):84–86,88,90.
SRINIVASAGAM, R T, RAYMONT, J E G, MOODIE, C F and RAYMONT,
1971   J K B Biochemical studies on marine zooplankton. The
        amino acid composition of *Euphausia superba*, *Meganycti-
        phanes norvegica* and *Neomysis integer*. *J. mar. biol. Ass.
        UK*, 51(4):917–925.
TERENTEV, A B and TSAREVA, L D Agregat AKP-VNIRO dlia
1972   proizprodstva belkovoi pasty iz krilia. *Rybnoe Khoz.*,
        (9):67–68.
YANASE, M Chemical composition of *Euphausia superba* and its
1971   utilization as condensed solubles for human food. *Bull.
        Tokai Reg. Fish Res. Lab.*, 65,59–66.

Aquaculture and Fishery Products Development *T V R Pillay*

Aquiculture et developpement de produits de la peche

L'auteur fait le point de la situation actuelle de l'aquiculture et
signale les principaux produits sur le marché. Il examine les divers
moyens permettant d'accroître la production et d'améliorer la
qualité des produits. Cimpte tenu de ces objectifs, il souligne
l'importance de la sélection génétique, de l'hybridation, de l'amélioration du nourrissage et du contrôle de l'environnement, et insiste
sur l'urgende d'organiser des recherches dans ces domaines si l'on
veut tirer pleinement parti des possibilités offertes – sur le plan
aussi bien quantitatif que qualitatif – par le développement des
produits aquicoles.

La acuicultura y la preparacion de productos pesqueros

En este documento se examina la situación actual de la acuicultura
y se hace referencia a los principales produtos que se obtienen con
ella. Se examinan las diversas maneras en que la producción puede
ser aumentada y mejorada la calidad de los productos. En relación
con este objetivo, en el documento se pone de relieve la importancia
de la slección genética, hibridación, mejoramiento de la alimentación y control del medio ambiente, al mismo tiempo que se
señala la urgente necesidad de organizar investigaciones sobre estos
asuntos, caso de que se quiera obtener las mayores ventajas de las
posibilidades de preparar productos de la acuicultura, tanto en
cantidad como en calidad.

Aquaculture as a means of increasing fish and shellfish
production is receiving special attention in many countries of the world. While all acquaculture involves human
intervention in the life cycle of the cultivated organism,
the techniques adopted differ considerably, consequently
there have been many definitions, ranging from the
propagation of aquatic organisms under complete human
control to the manipulation for the purpose of increasing
their production and yield. Fish and shellfish husbandry,
with complete domestication, as in agriculture or animal
husbandry, cannot be achieved in many areas because
the technology has not advanced sufficiently so the bulk
of current aquacultural production is obtained through
partial control. Since the quality of aquacultural products
is often related to the nature of culture operations, it will
be useful to mention here some of the major types of
aquaculture. Culture may be (a) for food production,
(b) to improve natural stocks through artificial recruitment and transplantation, (c) production of sport fish,
(d) production of bait fish, (e) production of ornamental
fish, (f) for recycling organic wastes, and (g) for industrial
or other purposes (such as raising fish for reduction to
animal feed, fish meal or fertilizer and pearl culture)
(Pillay 1973). Another broad classification based on the
level of operations is (i) subsistence level or 'familial' type
of aquaculture and (ii) commercial aquaculture. Classification of aquaculture according to techniques is much
more complex on account of the many modifications
and combinations adopted. Pond culture of fish and
shrimps is one of the most important types. Culture in
tanks, cages, enclosures, raceways and recirculating
water systems in indoor tanks represent some of the new
developments, many practised only on a small scale.
The culture of oysters, mussels and other molluscs form
a third type of aquaculture, widely practised in a number
of countries in estuaries, sheltered coastal areas or rivers.
Two sub-types of this are the traditional bottom culture,
and the hanging or 'three-dimensional' culture. Seaweed
culture forms a fourth and distinct type. Monoculture
and polyculture form a broad classification based on the
organisms. A similar classification based on the feeding
habits of the organisms is (i) herbivores, (ii) carnivores,
(iii) omnivores, (iv) detritus feeders and (v) sedentary and
sessile organisms.

Few countries have reliable statistics of aquaculture
production. Based on information collected from some
48 countries, the world production for food has recently
been estimated as follows (Pillay 1973):

		Tons
1.	Finfish	3,680,373
2.	Shrimps and prawns	14,298
3.	Oysters	710,500
4.	Mussels	180,000
5.	Clams	56,260
6.	Other molluscs	19,700
7.	Seaweeds	373,200
		5,034,331

This does not include sport and bait fish, production
of which is substantial, or pearl culture.

Because of the many imponderables involved it is
extremely difficult to make realistic estimates of future
production. FAO's Indicative World Plan for Agricultural Development (1969) considered an expansion factor
of five by the year 1985 as feasible. Bardach and Ryther
(1968) estimated a rate of increase of ten times by the
year 2000.

It is clear that, after a period of apathy and neglect,

fishery administrations in both developing and developed countries are devoting a greater attention to aquaculture. Increased production can be expected as a result of the expansion of areas under culture and/or through the intensification of operations. Technology, capable of being transferred after necessary testing under local conditions, exists in respect of many types of aquaculture. In most developing countries, there appears to be no difficulty in finding suitable sites, particularly in coastal and brackish water zones. Preliminary surveys have identified some 11.3 million ha of freshwater swamps and floodlands and some 9.7 million ha of brakish and salt swamps and other tidal lands in 11 countries of the Indo-Pacific region alone (Pillay 1973). This is nearly ten times the present area under culture in that region. In other regions where aquaculture has not yet been developed to great extent, there are many more suitable areas available for cultivation, particularly in estuarine and coastal zones. Kesteven (1972 unpublished) estimates that there are 10 to 20 million ha of lagoons and mangrove swamps in the world and a good percentage of these may be suitable for aquaculture.

Research and development of improved technology can intensify production and the increasing interest in supporting research in this promising field leads to some optimism in this regard. Even the wider application of existing techniques can result in significant increases as recent experience in India shows. Although the techniques of intensive polyculture were known in India and demonstrated on government farms, the average national production was only 800–1,000 kg/ha. Under a coordinated production programme, the average was raised to 4,000–5,000 kg/ha in pilot areas by the adoption of moderately intensive culture techniques. Again, improvement of culture techniques increased the average production from milkfish ponds in the Philippines from 300–400 kg/ha to 1,000 – 1,200 kg/ha in about five years. With the provision of all the necessary inputs, the rate of increase is expected to be doubled in a project planned to be implemented in Indonesia.

AQUACULTURE PRODUCTS

Fresh or live fish and shellfish from culture installations probably form the most popular and high-priced products. In many countries trout and carp are transported alive to markets. Special tanks with aeration and, where possible, air circulation, are used for transport and for holding the fish alive at stalls. Kuruma shrimp (*Penaeus japonicus*) is also often marketed alive in Japan. Oysters and mussels are generally marketed in the live condition, although they may be processed. Oysters are generally exported in the frozen condition. The bulk of production is marketed in the fresh state, sometimes in ice, being preferred by consumers in this form and fetching a higher price. In countries where processing and transport are not well developed, production near consumption centres makes wholesome fish and fish products available there. When production is in areas far from the main markets, or when the consumers demand it, when production is in excess of local market demand, processing methods are employed. For example, the milkfish (*Chanos chanos*) in Indonesia is boiled in brine to preserve it for short periods before sale. In some areas the fish are boiled in earthenware pots in which they are later sold (Schuster 1952). Smoked milkfish is a popular product, particularly in the Philippines. Freezing the products is at present restricted to some countries, such as the United States, where 12 to 15 per cent of the farmed catfish (*Ictalurus* spp.) are skinned, frozen and packaged for marketing Cultivated trout (*Salmo* spp.) is frozen before marketing in many countries. Freezing of shrimps and carps is done on a small scale for export. Some quantities of shrimps from rice fields in India are dried and shelled for export. Cultivated seaweeds are consumed green and fresh or mashed and dried into sheets. Speciality products, such as caviar and the mullet roe, are processed for storage and marketing.

AQUACULTURE AND PRODUCT QUALITY

In the majority of known cases, culture fishery products seem to be preferred to other fishery products and fetch a higher price in the markets. This may primarily be due to their freshness because it is possible not only to plan harvesting according to market demands, but also to hold most of the catches in a live state after capture. A further advantage is that the farmer can decide the size at which the fish or shellfish should be harvested and uniformity of size can be a great advantage in processing and packaging the products. Another advantage of the aquaculture product is that in the majority of cases a year-round supply can be maintained. There is no need to regulate the size of aquaculture products, as the consumer-preferred size can be harvested. An example is the 'pan salmon', raised in saltwater pens in the United States, a new product weighing between 250 and 500 g. This is a size and weight not commercially available through capture fisheries. Similarly the recent development of cage culture or the monosex culture of tilapia, which prevents breeding and consequent overpopulation and stunting, ensures the production of fish of acceptable size. In seaweed culture, particularly that of laver (*Porphyra* spp.) the lustre and other characteristics of the product depend to a large extent on the culture technique. The nutrient salts in the environment also appear to have a direct influence on it, consequently laver is harvested between December and February, when it is of superior quality.

The quality of products can be improved through special techniques. Fish that develop 'off' flavour are held in tanks or ponds in which a flow of clean water is maintained. The fish are starved or fed with special feed to help remove the 'off' flavour. Culture of bottom feeders in floating cages, particularly when special feeds are used, is often effective in avoiding 'off' flavours. Depuration of oysters, mussels and other molluscs grown in areas affected by pollution, using ultra-violet rays or ozone, is a technique now widely employed, and, of course, molluscs from the open water may also be so treated. Aquaculture products do not always have the advantage over other fishery products. Preference for flavour and appearance is subjective and the wild varieties are generally held to be superior in this respect although this may not apply in specially selected cases, such as farmed chicken, strawberries, mushrooms, etc. Some consumers prefer trout from open waters to those grown in ponds due to difference in taste. Plaice (*Pleuronectes platessa*) and sole (*Solea solea*) raised experimentally in the UK are reported to have a pigmentation pattern different from that of wild fish and the flesh has also been observed to be darker in appearance due to excessive amounts of melanin in the walls of the blood vessels. While such darker coloured products are considered acceptable, but not preferred in the UK, the deeper coloured cultivated Kuruma shrimp (*Penaeus japonicus*) and yellowtail (*Seriola quinqueradiata*) are preferred in Japan. It should, however, be possible to modify colouration through the adjustment of the light regime or similar means.

SPECIAL CULTURE TECHNIQUES FOR IMPROVED PRODUCT QUALITY

Feeding

Strict control of the quality of feed must be maintained or the quality of the cultivated fish or shellfish can be adversely affected. For instance the high content of DDT noticed in some samples of cultivated fish, mainly in catfish (*Ictalurus*) produced in the United States, has been traced to feed prepared with grains from heavily sprayed fields. The cage culture of rainbow trout (*Salmo gairdneri*) in sea water is expanding because it is believed that, besides a better growth rate, it results in better colour and flavour of the fish. The addition of 10 to 15 per cent of shrimps or shrimp offal in the feed has been found to give a bright pink colour to the flesh. Oysters produced by raft culture have shown high condition factor, almost double of those grown on the bottom (Quayle 1971) and they are generally held to be superior in colour and in flavour. Culture of oysters in trays helps in achieving uniformity of size and shape, and the flavour of such oysters is considered very attractive. Direct pigmentation of canned salmon has not been very successful but indirect pigmentation of pink salmon (*Oncorhynchus gorbuscha*), rainbow trout (*Salmo gairdneri*) and cutthroat trout (*Salmo clarkii clarkii*) has been achieved by incorporating the carotenoid pigment canthaxanthin with wet feed (Schmidt and Baker 1969). Diets containing 190 and 450 mg of anthaxanthin per kg of feed were fed for periods ranging from 7 to 31 weeks. The rainbow trout, when canned, had the appearance of processed coho salmon (*Oncorhynchus kisutch*) and measurements indicated that induced pigmentation may be more stable to heat processing than natural pigmentation. One of the factors that determines the acceptability of common carp (*Cyprinus carpio*) in many countries is the fat content and this can be greatly reduced or increased as required by the manipulation of feed. While genetic selection and hybridization have been employed to develop leaner varieties of carp and high-density culture has been shown to produce less fatty fish, feeding remains the chief means of regulating fattiness. Some consumers like fat carp but there appears to be a greater demand for leaner fish. Janeček (1972) has shown the relation between feed composition and fat content in carp and the possibility of altering product taste through feed manipulation. By excluding feeds of animal origin for some time before harvesting, the flavour can be considerably improved. High content of unsaturated fats can cause problems in processing and storage. In the case of trout, some producers add anti-oxidants to the feed to improve the keeping quality of the product.

Better utilization of low-quality products

By-catch fish and fish offal can be used as feed in trout and eel (*Anguilla*) culture. In many other types of culture, feeds containing up to 40 per cent fish meal are used. Conversion ratios of up to 1:1 of dry feed to wet fish have been obtained.

Genetic selection and hybridization

Genetic selection and hybridization probably offer the most exciting possibilities of product development in aquaculture. This aspect of the science is still in its early stages but the experience achieved so far gives great hope for the future. Most of the work done has been to develop strains with improved culture qualities, such as growth, food conversion, temperature and disease resistance, yield, etc. But some attention has also been devoted to product quality, the maximum work being done on the common carp. The colouration and scalation have been modified considerably in some strains. By systematic selection, strains with highly developed dorsal musculature have been developed. The high-backed Aischgrund and Galician carps are considered of excellent quality. A relatively smaller size of head and higher dressed weight are important product qualities thus achieved. By crossing Indian carps, *Catla catla* and *Labeo rohita*, a hybrid with the small head of *L. rohita* and the large body of *C. catla* has been produced (Chaudhuri 1959). Hybridization has also made it possible to reduce the fat content of common carp. The numerous fine intramuscular bones in carp are a limiting factor in its consumer acceptance in some countries and genetic selection has been proposed as a means of producing a 'boneless' variety (von Sengbusch 1967, von Sengbusch and Meske 1967). The large rainbow trout and Chinook Salmon (*Oncorhynchus tshaneytscha*) stocks developed by selection in the United States (Donaldson 1970) have desirable product qualities besides favourable biological characteristics. One of the aims of hybridization of sturgeons (*Acipenseridae*) in the USSR has been to increase fecundity. The hybrid of beluga (*Huso huso*) and sterlet (*Acipenser ruthenus*) has a much higher number of ova and therefore yields larger quantities of caviar than the parents, about 1 kg of eggs from fish averaging around 8 kg in weight. The hybrids mature earlier and as the eggs can be removed by the administration of hypophysial injection and subsequent incision of the abdominal wall, without causing mortality of brood fish, caviar production can be considerably increased through hybrid culture. The flavour of the hybrid fish is also reported to be better than that of the parent.

NEEDS AND PROSPECTS

Future aquaculture in developed countries is likely to concentrate on the production of specialty foods in which quality must be a prime consideration. Quality is also important in low priced foods but the volume of production, costs and nutritive values may take precedence. The bulk of present-day aquaculture production is obtained through what may be called 'extensive' methods of culture where the main source of feed is natural food. In order to obtain significant increases in production, therefore, it will be necessary, in a majority of cases, to resort to supplemental or complete feeding with efficient artificial feeds. These could give feed conversion ratios of about 1:2 (one unit of wet fish to two units of dry feed). If, in the next decade or two, a five-fold increase in the world aquaculture production is to be achieved, the quantity of feed needed will be considerable. Formulations of pelleted dry feeds, which are generally more efficient, contain fish meal up to 40 per cent. If they are used the demand for fish meal would exceed the present availability of the material. There is, therefore, an urgent case for scientific research to develop new feeds that can meet the coming needs of aquaculture. Environmental control during the whole period of culture, or for an appropriate period before harvesting can have a decisive effect on the quality of the product, therefore more research is needed to develop suitable techniques for such control.

As already mentioned, genetic manipulation offers the greatest possibilities for product development but, due mainly to the scarcity of trained fish geneticists and the facilities for planned genetic selection and hybridization studies, not much progress has so far been made in this work. A further handicap is that many of the cultivated species have not been fully domesticated. Controlled breeding is a key to genetic manipulation and work on it deserves a high priority in the case of a number of species. Greater support for organized research, particularly on aspects emphasized earlier, appears essential and urgent if full advantage is to be taken of product development possibilities in aquaculture.

References

BARDACH, J E and RYTHER, J H The Status of Potential of
1968   Aquaculture, US Department of Commerce, Vol 2: 225 p.
CHAUDHURI, H Experiments on hybridizaton of Indian carps.
1959   *Proc. Indian Sci. Congr.*, 46(6):20.
DONALDSON, L R Selective breeding of salmonid fishes. In McNeil,
1970   W J (ed.) *Marine Aquiculture*, Oregon State University,
        Corvallis, USA: p. 63–74.
FAO   Provisional Indicative World Plan for Agricultural
1969   Development, Vol 1 and 2, 672 p.
FAO   Seminar/Study Tour in the USSR on Genetic Selection
1971   and Hybridization of Cultivated Fishes. 19 April–29 May
        1968. Lectures. *Rep. FAO/UNDP(TA)*, (*2926*): 360 p.
HUME, A, FARMER, J W and BURT, J R A comparison of the
1972   flavours of farmed and wild plaice. *J. Fd. Technol.*, 7:27–33.
JANEČEK, St V. Effect of intensifying interventions on the quality
1972   of fish flesh. Part II, *Bull. VUR Vodnany*, 1:3–12; 2:3–10.
PILLAY, T V R The role of aquaculture in fishery development and
1973   management. Paper presented at the *Technical Conference
        on Fishery Management and Development*, Vancouver,
        Canada, 1973, Rome, FAO, FI:FMD/73/5-47, 24 p.
QUAYLE, D B Pacific oyster raft culture in British Columbia.
1971   *Bull. Fish. Res. Bd. Can.*, 178: 34 p.
SCHMIDT, P J and Baker, E G Indirect pigmentation of salmon
1969   and trout flesh with canthaxanthin. *J. Fish. Res. Bd. Can.*,
        26:357–360.
SCHUSTER, W H Fish-culture in brackish-water ponds of Java.
1952   *Spec. Publ. Indo-Pac. Fish. Coun.*, 1: 143 p.
SENGBUSCH, R von Eine Schnellbestimmungsmethode der Zwis-
1967   chenmuskelgräten bei Karpfen zur Auslese von 'gräten
        freien' Mutanten (mit Röntgen-Fersekhamera und Bilds-
        chirmgerät), *Der Züchter*, 37(6):275–276.
SENGBUSCH, R von and MESKE, Ch Eine Schnellbestimmungs-
1967   methode der Zwischenmuskelgräten bei Karpfen zur
        Auslese von 'grätenfreien' Mutanten. *Der Züchter*, 37(6):
        271–274.
White Fish Authority Trial of farmed fish at Lowestoft market.
1970a London, White Fish Authority, *Trials Record*, 48: 3 p.
White Fish Authority Preference test on wild and farmed fish.
1970b London, White Fish Authority, *Trials Record*, 49: 15 p.

Studies on the Acceptability of Farmed Fish   *A Hume, J R Burt,*
C S Wardle, C A Bustard and D E P Watson

Etudes sur l'acceptabilite du poisson d'elevage

Les caractéristiques économiques de l'élevage des poissons de mer au Royaume-Uni deviendront sans doute plus intéressants dans un proche avenir, en raison de la diminution des captures de poissons démersaux et de l'augmentation du prix du poisson. Les essais réalisés dans les stations piscicoles de la White Fish Authority ont révélé la possibilité technique d'élever des poissons démersaux, encore que les conditions idéales de cette forme de pisciculture n'aient pas encore été établies. Les études sur le poisson élevé dans ces stations montrent que certains facteurs sensoriels diffèrent de ceux que présente le poisson sauvage. L'auteur décrit les travaux entrepris au sujet de la saveur et de l'aspect de la plie et de la sole d'élevage.

Deux groupes distincts de dégustateurs – l'un composé de fonctionnaires de la Torry Research Station et l'autre de ménagères de la région de Londres – ont eu à se prononcer sur diverses préparations de poissons d'élevage et de poissons sauvages. Une différence de saveur a été mise en évidence entre ces deux types de produits. Les tests réalisés avec des poissons d'élevage ayant reçu des rations différentes ont montré que le régime alimentaire des poissons n'a pas d'influence sur leur saveur.

La chair et la peau n'ont pas la même couleur chez les poissons d'élevage et les poissons sauvages; à ce propos, un jury de ménagères s'est nettement déclaré en faveur du poisson sauvage. Les variations de la teneur en crustacés du régime des poissons et de l'intensité de la lumière incidente sont demeurées sans effet sur la teneur en mélanine des vaisseaux sanguins, facteur qui intervient pour beaucoup dans les différences de l'aspect de la chair. Toutefois, une lumière intense a bien donné lieu à l'appartition d'une nuance argentée dans la couleur de la peau et des vaisseaux sanguins de la plie.

Estudios de la aceptabilidad de los peces procedentes de explotaciones piscicolas

Es probable que en un próximo futuro aumente el interés en el Reino Unido por los aspectos económicos de la piscicultura en aguas marinas, debido a la disminución de las capturas de peces demersales y al aumento de los precios del pescado. Los ensayos realizados en las unidades piscícolas del Organismo para el Pescado Blanco (White Fish Authority) han mostrado que es técnicamente posible producir peces demersales, aunque no se han determinado aún cuales son las condiciones ideales para ello. Los estudios de los peces producidos hasta la fecha en estas unidades indican que algunas de sus características sensoriales no son idénticas a las de los peces en libertad. El estudio describe los trabajos hechos sobre el sabor y la apareiencia de la solla y el lenguado de Dover criados en explotaciones piscícolas.

Se han organizado dos grupos independientes, uno de personal de la estación de investigaciones de Torry y otro de amas de casa de la zona de Londres, ye se han realizado experimentos triangulares de degustación con peces criados en libertad y peces criados en explotaciones piscícolas, demostrándose la existencia de una diferencia de sabor entre ambos. Los ensayos hechos con peces procedentes de explotaciones piscícolas y criados con regímenes diferentes indicaron que los diversos regímenes empleados no influyen en el sabor.

El color de la piel y de la carne de los peces procedentes de explotaciones piscícolas difiere del de los peces criados en libertad y, a este propósito, un grupo de amas de casa mostró clara preferencia por los peces procedentes del océano. Las variaciones en el contenido de crustáceos en la alimentación y en la intensidad de la luz incidente no repercuten en el contenido de melanina de los vasos sanguíneos, al que se debe en buena parte la diferencia de

Les différences de saveur mises en évidence lors de ces tests de dégustation ne semblent pas devoir affecter l'acceptabilité du produit par le consommateur; en revanche, les différences de couleur pourraient jouer en rôle plus important dans la commercialisation.

aspecto de la carne. En cambio, el empleo de luz intensa da un color plateado a la piel y a los vasos sanguíneos de la solla.

No es probable que las diferencias de sabor encontradas influyan en la aceptabilidad de estos peces entre los consumidores, pero las diferencias de color pueden tener más importancia desde el punto de vista de la comercialización.

The responsibilities of the White Fish Authority (WFA) include that of ensuring a continuing supply of good quality fish for the British consumer. As one means of meeting this requirement, the Research and Development Division of the WFA has, for several years past, been engaged in the development of techniques and systems for farming marine fish in Scottish sea-lochs at Ardtoe and elsewhere, and in the warm water outflow from Hunterston Power Station. The programme is not aimed at scientific discovery, nor only at technological innovation, but also at providing potential commercial investors with facts and figures against which to make investment decisions. Attention has been concentrated thus far on the propagation and rearing to marketable size of plaice (*Pleuronectes platessa*). Whilst this is not the most obvious and commercially attractive subject for fish farming because its market value is as yet well below the cost of production by farming, it has a number of scientific and technical advantages for a development programme of this nature at this stage, such as the availability of juvenile wild stock in quantity and the relative ease with which plaice can now be spawned, hatched and reared from the egg. Plaice are therefore being used to gain essential experience of the basic hatchery and rearing techniques and facilities required for commercial marine fish cultivation. It is moreover quite possible that as knowledge increases and production costs fall, and as the market price of traditionally caught fish continues to rise, plaice could well become a commercially viable species for fish farming in the not too distant future.

Experience has also been gained in the cultivation of other marine flatfish and round-fish species some of which, being of greater current market value than plaice, may well prove to be farming subjects of greater and more immediate commercial potential. Dover sole (*Solea solea*) like plaice, have been hatched and reared from the egg to marketable size, and turbot (*Rhombus maximus*), lemon sole (*Pleuronectes microcephalus*), cod (*Cadus callarias*), saithe (*Pollachius virens*) and grey mullet (*Mugil* spp.) have all been reared to marketable size from juvenile stages captured at sea. Turbot and lemon sole have also been spawned and hatched but have not yet been successfully reared through the early larval stages to metamorphosis, and beyond, outside a research laboratory. Trials to this end are however continuing. The team of workers includes veterinarians and pathologists looking into the problems of health maintenance and disease control; nutritionists engaged in the formulation for trials of a variety of wet fish feeds and, more recently, moist and dry pelleted feeds; engineers responsible for the design and development of a variety of fish holding facilities onshore as well as in the sea; and food science/ market development staff who, in conjunction with staff from the Torry Research Station (TRS), are engaged in assessing the quality of the product in comparison with fish caught by traditional methods, and in determining market acceptability. To the potential fish farmer the most important feature of the operation is profitability.

Certain obvious factors determine this, namely, growth rate, availability of a suitable diet, feed conversion ratios, cost of holding facilities and density of stocking, survival rates, disease limitation and selling price. In particular, unless the appearance, texture and flavour of the final product are acceptable to the consumer, the fish farm can never be commercially viable. The work described in this paper examines some aspects of the consumer acceptability of some of the fish so far produced. Some of the experiments were carried out with the collaboration of the Marine Laboratory of the Department of Agriculture and Fisheries for Scotland (DAFS).

INVESTIGATIONS INTO FLAVOUR

The flavour of a single species of fish is known to vary depending on local environmental conditions. Vale *et al.* (1970) reported kerosene-like taints in mullet due to pollution and Mann (1969) has reviewed much of the earlier work on taints in fish due to phenolic and mineral oil contamination. Off-flavours due to feed have been reported by Motohiro (1962) in work with canned salmon and by Ackman and co-workers (Sipos and Ackman 1964; Ackman *et al.* 1966; Ackman *et al.* 1967) in work with cod from the Labrador area. In the review paper by Mann (1969) it was mentioned that farmed carp develop off-flavours when fed a diet of maize or barley and Baeder *et al.* (1945) reported that wild brook trout were preferred to the farmed variety by a group of six judges though all the fish tasted were acceptable. When farmed plaice from the WFA Fish Cultivation Unit at Ardtoe, Argyllshire, were tasted by experienced staff at TRS it was agreed that the fish had a good flavour but that it might not be the same as the flavour of wild plaice. Accordingly a triangular testing scheme was set up to compare the flavours of farmed and wild plaice. A similar scheme was used to examine whether the flavour of farmed fish was affected by controllable pre- and post-slaughter conditions such as starvation, exercise, storage time, etc. The results have been published (Hume *et al.* 1972) and can be summarized as follows:

Out of 28 triangle tests comparing the flavours of farmed and wild plaice only eight proved positive at the 5 per cent significance level. This level of discrimination showed that no great difference existed between the flavours of this batch of farmed and wild plaice. Equally valid is the conclusion that the flavours of the two types were not identical. The positive results obtained did not correlate with the number of days the fish were held in ice before tasting or with any of the features of the panel system used. Insufficient samples were taken to prove whether the flavour difference changes seasonally but, certainly, more positive results were found in the March/ April samples than were found later in the year. If a greater difference does exist at this time it could be due to seasonal flavour changes in the wild fish or to the different maturity states of farmed and wild fish of the same size. It was also noticed that a few tasters were able to discriminate with much greater precision between wild and farmed plaice by flavour than did the majority.

The tasting tests designed to show whether the flavour was affected by the pre- and post-slaughter regime proved negative except in one case. From these results it was concluded that special treatment of the fish is not necessary prior to slaughter but that it would be desirable to eviscerate the fish as soon as possible after harvesting.

As the taste panels used in all the above experiments were relatively small (the average number of members in each panel lies between nine and ten) it was felt desirable to conduct a larger scale exercise. One hundred plaice were obtained from the experimental sites at Hunterston and Ardtoe and a similar number from the TRS research trawler, all the samples being harvested within the same six-hour period. The wild fish were sorted into batches depending on size and the batch most similar in length to farmed fish (250–350 mm) were used in the experiment. The plaice from all three locations were eviscerated on harvesting and stored in ice. The tasting sessions took place 48 hours after harvesting. The skin-on whole fish were prepared and steamed in casseroles for 25 minutes. The cooked flesh from each fish was apportioned into four warm serving dishes and the triangle tests assembled, each test consisting of two portions from the same fish and one portion of a fish from a different location. The samples were allocated a symbol rather than a letter or number and were presented to the tasters on a plate so that there was no definite order of presentation. The composition of the triangles and the order of presentation of the tests were changed at each taste session. The tasters were chosen at random from the staff of TRS, the only criteria used in selection being that they normally ate fish and that they would be available for the taste sessions. In all, 84 tasters were employed at half-hour intervals using six per session, each taster being presented with three triangle tests, one comparing wild plaice with plaice from the warm water farm at Hunterston, a second comparing wild plaice with the plaice from Ardtoe (a repeat of the smaller scale experiments described above) and a third comparing farmed plaice from the two experimental farming sites. The information given to each taster was that the fish were fresh plaice and that there were three tests, each test consisting of three samples, two identical and one different. The tasters were asked to taste and choose the odd one out by flavour. They were also informed that they were obliged to give an answer. The results are shown in Table 1. An examination of the data obtained shows that there was no bias toward any of the three symbols, that there was no correlation between the number of correct responses and the order of presentation of the tests (less correct responses for the third test might have indicated tasting fatigue), and that there was no correlation between the number of correct responses and the odd sample type in each test. For example, it was immaterial to the tasters whether the odd sample was a wild or a Hunterston sample in that test as an approximately equal number of correct responses was given in each case. The tasters in the last six sessions were asked not only to pick out the odd sample by flavour but also to choose whether or not they preferred the odd sample to the other two. The results from those who chose the correct odd sample were examined and it was found that there was a slight preference for the wild fish.

To determine whether housewives could differentiate between farmed and wild plaice and farmed and wild Dover sole, the WFA, in conjunction with a market research agency, conducted a series of tasting tests (WFA 1970b). A panel of 96 housewives from the London area were selected on the basis that they ate fish regularly. The panel was split into two groups of 48 tasters, one group tasting only plaice and the other tasting only sole, each group doing the two trials for that species. The questionnaire was designed to examine whether the housewives noticed a difference between three pieces of cooked fish. If they noticed that one was different from the other two they were asked why they thought it was different, whether they preferred the odd sample or the other two and their reasons for this preference. The information given and questions asked were different from the TRS tasting sessions described above and the difference is of importance in the interpretation of the results. The housewives were not told that it was a triangle test and, therefore, there could be no forced choice as was the case in the TRS experiments. The results from the first part of the questionnaire are given in Table 2. It is difficult to deal with the first two choices given in Table 2 statistically but the number of tasters who discriminated correctly is sufficient guide to the overall response. It appeared that there was only a relatively low percentage of the tasting groups who could consistently discriminate between farmed and wild fish. The preference tests results from those who discriminated correctly in two tests also showed that there was a slight preference for the wild fish. The reasons given for discriminating correctly and for preference showed no trend toward any particular characteristic of flavour or texture. The overall impression from the evidence presented is that differences in flavours exist between farmed and wild fish but that these are comparatively minor. Changes in the farm environment, however, could increase or decrease such differences and it would be desirable to monitor the flavour of farmed fish at least until a commercial farm environment has been established. Two other minor points are worthy of note. The first is that those aspects of the pre-slaughter regime tested do not appear to alter the flavour of the farmed fish. The second is that although the number of tasters used was small and no statistical tests were applied, a slight preference exists for the wild fish in two diverse groups, namely, a panel of London housewives and the staff of Torry Research Station in Aberdeen. It is not proven that the non-experts in either group could have distinguished whether a single sample was wild or farmed.

TABLE 1. RESULTS OF TRIANGLE TESTS COMPARING THE FLAVOURS OF WILD, ARDTOE AND HUNTERSTON PLAICE

Test	Number of Tasters[a]	Correct Responses	Significance Level[b]
Wild/Hunterston	83	57	<0.1%
Wild/Ardtoe	83	43	<0.1%
Ardtoe/Hunterston	83	31	>5%

[a] 84 tasters were used but one return was invalidated
[b] The lower the figure in this column, the less likely it is that the result was due to chance

TABLE 2. RESULTS OF TRIANGLE TESTS COMPARING THE FLAVOURS OF FARMED AND WILD PLAICE AND SOLE

Choice	Response of Tasters			
	Steamed Plaice	Fried Plaice	Steamed Sole	Fried Sole
Thought all the same	4	2	4	8
Thought all different	4	3	7	3
Discriminated incorrectly	18	18	14	13
Discriminated correctly	22	25	23	24

TABLE 3. DESCRIPTIONS OF GILL COLOURS OF FARMED AND WILD PLAICE STORED IN ICE

Description	Frequency of Occurrence of Each Description					
	1 day in ice		3 days in ice		7 days in ice	
	Wild	Farmed	Wild	Farmed	Wild	Farmed
Pinks	10	2	16	2	5	—
Reds/Bright Reds	8	1	3	1	—	—
Dark Reds	2	8	2	7	—	6
Browns/Brown Reds	—	2	—	6	—	—
Purples/Dark Purples[a]	—	2	—	6	—	—
Purples/Dark Purples[a]	—	10	—	5	—	—
Blacks[a]	—	15	1	20	—	4

[a] See text for details

TABLE 4. DESCRIPTIONS OF FLESH COLOUR OF FARMED AND WILD PLAICE STORED ONE DAY IN ICE

Description	Frequency of Occurrence of Each Description	
	Wild	Farmed
Grey	1	—
White	1	—
Pink	1	—
Slight blue	4	1
Bluish	—	2
Blue	2	7
Blue Black	—	8
Black Fibres	—	4

INVESTIGATIONS INTO APPEARANCE

The appearance of farmed fish is likely to be the most important single factor in determining whether it is acceptable to the consumer because of the way fish is normally marketed in the United Kingdom. The factors affecting the visual appeal of the fish are the shape, skin colour and, when displayed as fillets, flesh colour.

As the shape of farmed fish produced so far falls into the spectrum available in nature there is no reason to suppose that the fish would not be acceptable. In fact, the only difference in shape compared with normal wild plaice is that farmed plaice so far have tended to be deeper from top to underside, that is the fish are fatter and in prime biological condition throughout the year. This may be of importance in processing the fish as preliminary trials have shown that farmed plaice can give an average of 5–6 per cent higher filleting yield than wild plaice of the same length.

When farmed plaice were shown at Lowestoft Fish Market (WFA 1970a) to merchants and traders, an encouraging response was obtained but it was noted that the skin pigmentation was slightly unusual though not likely to affect its acceptability. Wild plaice have the top (right) side coloured and the under (left) side white although occasionally the top side colouration is found on the underside. To date, with farmed plaice, a far greater variety than this exists, from no pigmentation on either side to both top and undersides having the usual top side colouration. While an unusual skin pigmentation is unlikely to affect the nutritive value or the flavour its unfamiliarity to the consumer could well affect its acceptability. No definite figures are available for the frequencies of occurrence of such a abnormal pigment distributions but incidences are reckoned to be quite high.

When the housewives were asked to look at whole sole and plaice from the farmed and wild stocks a high percentage saw a difference although there was only a slight preference for the wild fish. For the sole 98 per cent of the housewives could pick out a difference between the farmed and wild stocks, the preference being 50 per cent for wild, 35 per cent for farmed and 13 per cent having none. The most important reason given for preferring the wild was that the farmed sole shown had distinctive orange blotches on the underside. For the plaice 90 per cent of the housewives could discriminated between the farmed and wild fish: the preference being 40 per cent for wild, 33 per cent for farmed and 17 per cent having none. The reason given for preferring wild fish was that they were lighter in colour, and looked younger and fresher. Again, however, it is not proven that anything unusual would have been noticed if a single farmed fish had been presented to them in normal shopping conditions. The figures given above indicate there should be no problem with farmed fish being acceptable to the consumer. However, the farmed fish had been selected for the tests, removing those fish with partial or complete lack of pigmentation. No figures are available for acceptability of very unusually pigmented fish.

Other colour differences became apparent when the trained TRS taste panel was asked to assess the quality of farmed fish. In a normal quality assessment members of the trained panel are asked to observe certain features of individual fish and give a score for each according to a predetermined scoring sheet (Shewan et al. 1953). For this experiment the panel was asked to give scores and descriptions of each feature for some wild and farmed fish after storage for one and three days in ice. There was a considerable difference in the descriptions though no difference in the scores for the colours of the gills and flesh. Merchants use gill colour as one of the means to determine freshness and price on the fish market and the difference in colour could be of importance in this respect. The gill colour descriptions are given in Table 3. The panel consisted of four members and the numbers in Table 3 show how many times a description was given by any of the panel members (each member had a free choice of descriptive terms). The two unusual colour descriptions, 'blacks' and 'purples/dark purples', should not be taken to indicate an overall colour of the type specified. They represent comparative descriptions indicating that a noticeable tinge of this colour is present. It is obvious, however, that the gills of farmed fish so far examined are darker than those from wild fish.

Much more important from the consumer acceptance viewpoint would be the flesh colour. Here again differences were shown and are presented in Table 4. The

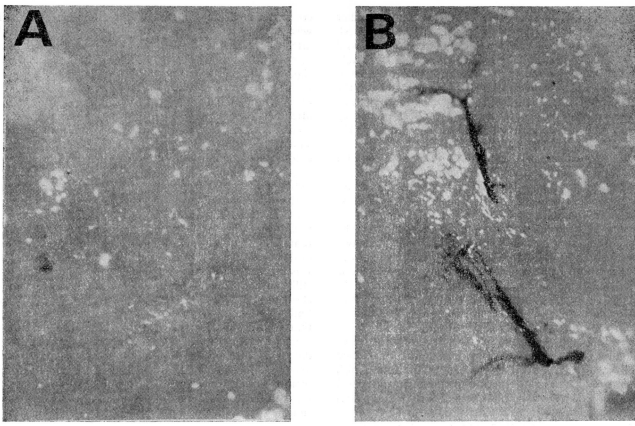

*Fig 1   Photomicrographs of a portion of the cut surface of (A) **wild plaice** and (B) farmed plaice (x47)*

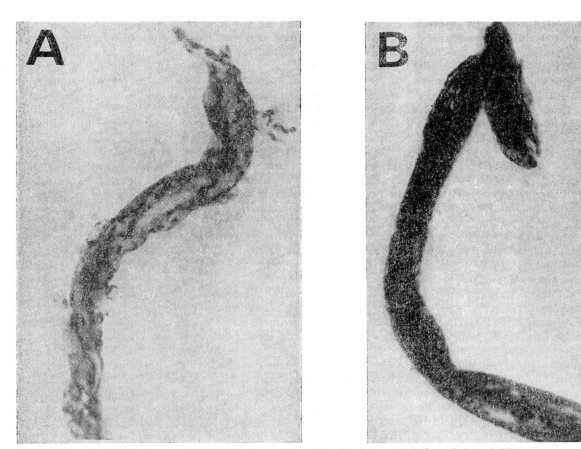

*Fig 2   Photomicrographs of an excised dark blood vessel from (A) **wild plaice** and (B) farmed plaice (x47)*

results given are for one-day-in-ice fish though the other samples tested showed a similar trend. Obviously the flesh of the farmed plaice tested is darker than that of wild plaice. Whether the differences in flesh colour are likely to affect consumer acceptability cannot be judged from these experiments but in the opinion of some of the panel members the darker appearance of the flesh was likely to affect it. This opinion is in part substantiated by the results from the panel of London housewives (WFA 1970b). A triangle test was used to compare the appearance of farmed and wild fish fillets. The panel was not told that a triangle test was being carried out yet 85 per cent could discriminate between farmed and wild plaice and 71 per cent between farmed and wild sole. Of those who could discriminate 73 per cent preferred the wild sole and 61 per cent the wild plaice. Again it should be observed that they had the opportunity of comparing two samples and it is not proven that they would have noticed a darker colour had the farmed fish been presented alone in normal shopping conditions. An examination of the flesh and skeleton of farmed and wild plaice has revealed that the reason for the darker appearance is an excessive amount of melanin associated with the blood vessel walls. Fig 1 shows on the left the flesh of wild plaice and on the right the flesh of farmed plaice both magnified to an equal extent (x 47). In the case of the farmed fish there is no difficulty in observing the blood vessels. Fig 2 shows on the left an empty excised dark blood vessel from the skeleton of a wild plaice and on the right from a farmed plaice. The increased amount of melanin associated with the blood vessel wall in the farmed plaice is obvious. Two reasons for the extra melanin have been suggested: the first is that the crustacean content in the diet might be sufficient to produce excess melanin since it is known that iced shrimps blacken due to enzymic production of melanin from tyrosine; the second is that the intensity of daylight on farmed fish might produce a protective reaction within the fish resulting in excess melanin since farmed plaice are normally kept in shallow water (1–1.5 m deep) as opposed to the much greater depths at which wild fish are found (20–200 m). These two factors have been examined in an experiment at Torry.

Four tanks (1.2 × 1.2 × 1.2 m) containing sea water at 10°C were each stocked with 20 farm plaice (mean weight 30 g, mean length 110 mm). The fish in two tanks were given a crustacean-free fiet and fish in the other two a diet containing 50 per cent scampi waste and 50 per cent of the crustacean-free diet. One tank from each dietary regime was supplied with a low light environment (black painted walls and a 1 W tungsten bulb placed about 25 cm above the water surface) and the other tanks with a high light environment (white painted walls, 2 × 60 W tungsten bulbs) containing an ultraviolet lamp (Philips 300 W type 57265F/28). The lighting systems were controlled by time-clocks with an 8 hour-on, 16 hour-off cycle for the tungsten bulbs and a 1-hour ultraviolet irradiation period in the middle of the 'on' part of the tungsten light cycle. The fish were fed approximately half an hour after the tungsten lights were switched on. The experiment was terminated after six months, the fish having increased in size (mean length 160 mm, mean weight 55 g). The fish (three from each tank) were killed and the top fillet removed and placed skin upward in a covered dish (skin sample). The remainder of the fish was placed skin downward in a second covered dish after the head, tail and all traces of top skin had been removed. (skeleton sample). The skin samples and the skeleton samples were then ranked individually by eight members of staff at TRS. Further samples were ranked on subsequent dates and a final sample was examined after all the remaining fish from the high light environment had been transferred to a low light environment. The results show that there was no difference in the colours of the skin or flesh due to diet. However, there was a marked difference between the fish from the two light regimes. The fish in the high light intensity tanks had taken up a silvery appearance. When a sample of these fish was killed and the top fillets removed it was noted that the blood vessels had silvered walls. The remaining live fish were put into a low light environment tank but even after three weeks when a second sample was taken, the silvering of the skin and blood vessels was still present. This indicates that the process is not a short-term camouflage reaction. However, despite these findings, the flesh of these fish was still different from that of wild plaice and probably unacceptable to the consumer. The fish in the low light regime tanks had very dark skins though the flesh had much the same appearance as that of normal farmed fish. An obvious experiment resulting from this work would be to keep the fish on a white background but supplying only a low level tungsten light source.

CONCLUSIONS

From the evidence presented above it is obvious that the appearance and flavour of farmed and wild fish are not identical. Flavour differences are detectable when the fish are tasted side by side in a laboratory. Normal domestic conditions are such that the fish would not be tasted in this way and it is therefore highly unlikely that the consumer would pick out farmed fish by flavour. Even then, since there is no consistent preference for the wild fish, there seems to be no reason why farmed fish should not be acceptable to the consumer.

It is impossible to predict the consumer's reaction to the appearance of farmed fish whether as fillets or whole fish. The results show that the housewives who did the tests have a dislike for the darker fillets of the farmed fish when compared directly with wild fish and this may well present a difficulty in marketing. Insufficient work has been done with consumers to gauge their reaction to the unusually pigmented whole fish but it seems likely that this is a characteristic of the farmed fish which should be corrected.

Further research is required as it appears that all the differences shown could be altered by changes in the farm environment and it will be important to monitor changes and to experiment with new conditions until a commercial system is finally established. What will determine to a large extent whether farmed fish will be acceptable to the consumer are the method of presentation and the price, both of which could overcome any consumer resistance due to appearance or flavour. What is important is that the farming of flatfish has progressed considerably in the past 10 years and with similar advances over the next 10 years evolved from the basic types already in existence, farms will be producing perfectly acceptable fish on a viable commercial basis and contributing significantly to the demersal fish catch of the United Kingdom. It remains to be said, not for the first time, that the farmed fish of the future may not resemble closely any of the species which are at present available on the market, any more than domesticated cattle resemble wild cattle or deer.

References

ACKMAN, R G, DALE, J and HINGLEY, J Deposition of dimethyl-
1966 ß-propiothetin in Atlantic cod during feeding experiments. *J. Fish. Res. Bd Can.*, 23(4):487–497.

ACKMAN, R G, HINGLEY, J and MAY, A W Dimethyl-ß-propio-
1967 thetin dimethyl sulphide in Labrador cod. *J. Fish. Res. Bd. Can.*, 24(2):457–461.

BAEDER, H A, TACK, P I and HAZZARD, A S A comparison of the
1945 palatability of hatchery-reared and wild brook trout. *Trans. Am. Fish. Soc.*, 75:181–185.

HUME, A, FARMER, J W and BURT, J R A comparison of the
1972 flavours of farmed and wild plaice. *J. Fd. Technol.*, 7:27–33.

MANN, H Factors affecting the taste of fish. *Fette Seifen Anstr-*
1969 *Mittel*, 71(12):1021–1024.

MOTOHIRO, T Studies on the petroleum odour in canned chum
1962 salmon. *Mem. Fac. Fish. Hokkaido Univ.*, 10(1):1–65.

SHEWAN, J M, MACINTOSH, R G, TUCKER, C G and EHRENBERG,
1953 A S C The development of a numerical scoring system for the sensory assessment of the spoilage of wet white fish in ice *J. Sci. Fd. Agric.*, 4:283–298.

SIPOS, J C and ACKMAN, R G Association of dimethyl sulphide
1964 with the 'blackberry' problem in cod from the Labrador area. *J. Fish. Res. Bd. Can.*, 21(2):423–425.

VALE, G L, SIDHU, G S, MONTGOMERY, W A and JOHNSON, A R
1970 Studies on a kerosene-like taint in mullet (*Mugil cephalus*). I-General nature of the taint. *J. Sci. Fd. Agric.*, 21:429–432.

WFA. Trial of farmed fish at Lowestoft market. White Fish
1970a Authority, London, *Trials Record* No. 48, 3 p.

WFA. Preference test on wild and farmed fish. White Fish
1970b Authority, London, *Trials Record* No. 49, 15 p.

Acknowledgement

The authors acknowledge the help of many colleagues who participated in experiments described in this paper and in particular thank the staff of the Fish Cultivation Units at Ardtoe and Hunterston

---

Environment-Related Off-Flavours in Intensively Cultured Fish *T Lovell*

Apparation d'odeurs desagreables en rapport avec l'environnement dans le poisson faisant l'objet d'une culture intensive

L'Auburn University a fait une étude sur les causes d'apparition d'odeurs désagréables dans le poisson-chat. Des méthodes permettant de combattre les organismes responsables de ces odeurs ont été examinées. Le document contient un certain nombre de suggestions pratiques en vue de lutter contre l'apparition de mauvaises odeurs dans la chair de poissonschats élevés en étang.

Perdidas de sabor de los peces cultivados en regimen intensivo determinadas por el medio ambiente

En este trabajo se describen los estudios realizados en la Universidad de Auburn sobre las causas de la pérdida de sabor del bagre. Se estudiaron los métodos que han de utilizarse para determinar cuáles son los organismos responsables de esta pérdida de sabor. El trabajo concluye con algunas sugerencias prácticas para limitar la pérdida de sabor del bagre criado en estanques.

Fish have been aptly described as biological sponges. They can absorb many inorganic and organic materials through their gills as well as from the intestinal tract. Some absorption probably occurs through the skin. Sources of off-flavour compounds may perhaps be industrial or agricultural chemicals and wastes; however, by far the most common types are those synthesized by organisms in the aquatic environment. Considering that there are numerous microorganisms in the pond that synthesize compounds which fish can absorb and store in their bodies, it is understandable that occasionally a few of these may have an adverse effect on the flavour of the fish flesh.

STUDY OF OFF-FLAVOUR CAUSES

A study was conducted at Auburn University (Lovell, 1972) to determine the capability of geosmin-producing blue-green algae to impart the earthy-musty flavour in the flesh of channel catfish. Cultures of geosmin-producing blue-green algae *S. muscorum* and *O. tenuis* were obtained from the Federal Water Quality Control Laboratory in Cincinnati, Ohio. Fifty-gramme channel catfish were held in 150-litre stainless-steel tanks containing dense masses of luxuriantly growing *S. muscorum* or *O. tenuis* to determine the capability of these algae to impart the geosmin flavour in the fish. To measure the rate of off-flavour development in the tanks, four fish were collected from each of two tanks of *S. muscorum* and four from

each of the two tanks of *O. tenuis* at 1, 2, 4, 6, 10 and 14 days after stocking. After each collection the fish were quick-frozen and stored in hermetically-sealed pouches at −23°C for subsequent sensory analysis. To determine time required to purge the fish of any flavour acquired from the algae, catfish were held in two tanks of *S. muscorum* for 14 days, then removed and placed in charcoal-filtered, flowing water. The fish were removed from the flowing water after 0, 3, 6, 10 and 15 days and quick-frozen for subsequent analysis.

To determine the ability of fish to absorb the flavour compounds from the water without having an opportunity to ingest the algae, two 'algae-free' tanks were stocked with fish. Water passed from two *S. muscorum* culture tanks into the two cell-free tanks by gravity through a glass wool filter, and was exchanged between the tanks twice daily. The algae tanks and the algae-free tanks both were enriched with nutrient solution; consequently, exchange of water between the two tanks did not dilute the nutrient concentration in the algae tanks. Fish were removed from the algae-free tanks according to the same schedule as was followed with the fish taken from the algae tanks. After all samples had been collected, the frozen fish were thawed, dressed, and cooked for sensory evaluation for earthy-musty or algae-related flavour by a taste panel composed of four trained, experienced evaluators. They assigned each sample a score of 1 to 10 on the following basis: 10 = no off-flavour; 8 = slight off-flavour;   6 = distinct   off-flavour;   4 = intense   off-flavour; 2 = extreme off-flavour. Sensory scores were analyzed for differences among means by the Duncan Multiple range test (1955). Within one day the fish from the *S. muscorum* tanks had developed a distinct earthy-musty flavour, similar to the odour of the algae, which became stronger at two days and reached maximum intensity at ten days (Table 1). Algae-related flavour was only slight, but significant ($P < 0.05$), in fish from the *O. tenuis* tanks at 2 days and reached a maximum at 14 days, but never equalled the intensity of that in the fish from the *S. muscorum* tanks. Stomach contents of the fish revealed that moderate amounts of both algae were eaten during the first day they were in the culture tanks. The fish which were exposed to the algae-free filtrate from algae culture tanks developed a flavour qualitatively similar to that of the fish held in direct contact with the algae. This indicated that the fish were able to absorb the dissolved geosmin-like compounds from the water, primarily across the gill membrane, into the blood. Absorption of the off-flavour compounds was appreciably slower by fish held in the algae-free filtrate than by those held in the algae culture tanks (Table 1). Evidently acquisition of algae-related off-flavour by channel catfish is greatly facilitated when the fish ingest the algae.

Flavour of the fish held in the *S. muscorum* tanks for 14 days was subsequently improved when the fish were transferred to flowing, charcoal-filtered water (Table 2). After three days in clean water at 25°C, the flavour had improved significantly ($P > 0.05$). At ten days the flavour of fish transferred from the algae tanks was not significantly ($P > 0.05$) different from that of control fish. The quantitative significance of blue-green algae in the flavour problem in fish has yet to be evaluated. No intensive study has been conducted to identify algal species from culture ponds containing off-flavoured fish. An algae identified as *Anabaena sirceneria* was found to be growing intensively and predominantly in ponds with earthy-musty flavoured cat-fish at the Auburn University Fisheries Research Unit in the spring of 1971 and again in 1972 (Lovell, 1972). Because of the variety of algae which produce noxious odours and tastes in natural waters (Palmer, 1962) and the widespread seasonal and geographic distribution of earthy-musty flavour in cultured fish, it is likely that a number of the blue-green algae may be the cause of it. Because of the ubiquity of odoriferous actinomycetes, the same may possibly be said of these organisms, also.

FACTORS AFFECTING GROWTH

Some of the more important factors known to affect the growth of flavour-producing organisms are availability of nutrients, temperature, sunlight, and oxidation-reduction potential in culture ponds. The diagram in Fig 1 illustrates the relationship between nutrients in the pond supplied by unabsorbed feed and off-flavour in fish

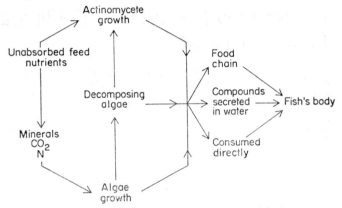

Fig 1   The diagram shows how uneaten or undigested feed may contribute to the development of earthy-musty flavour in pond-cultured catfish

(Lovell, 1971). The blue-green algae are autotrophic in their nutrient requirements and do not need organic matter, hence, their growth is stimulated by CO_2, P, N and inorganic materials released when fish feed and excrement decompose and NH_3 is excreted in the water. Actinomycetes, on the other hand, are hetertrophic and must grow on organic matter; consequently, unconsumed feed, faecal material and dead algae may serve as growth substrate for these organisms. All algae that have been found to produce odorous compounds are generally warm-weather plants. Some may be highly temperate

TABLE 1. AVERAGE SENSORY SCORES FOR CHANNEL CATFISH HELD FOR VARIOUS PERIODS OF TIME

Tank Environment	Holding time (days)						
	0	1	2	4	6	10	14
Algae: *S. muscorum*	9.8	6.8	5.5	5.7	5.7	2.8	3.0
O. tenuis	9.0	8.5	8.0	6.8	6.7	6.6	4.7
Algae-free	9.0	9.1	—	8.8	8.5	6.0	5.3

TABLE 2. AVERAGE SENSORY SCORES FOR CHANNEL CATFISH HELD IN TANKS CONTAINING S. MUSCORUM FOR 14 DAYS AND SUBSEQUENTLY HELD IN FLOWING, CHARCOAL-FILTERED WATER. CONTROL FISH WERE HELD IN FLOWING WATER ONLY

	Holding time in flowing water (days)						
	0	3	6	10	15	Control	fish
Sensory score	3.2	5.7	6.7	8.7	9.0		9.1

TABLE 3. AVERAGE SENSORY SCORES AND WEIGHT LOSSES FOR OFF-FLAVOURED CHANNEL CATFISH HELD IN FLOWING, CHARCOAL FILTERED WATER AT VARIOUS TEMPERATURES

Water temperature (°C)	0 day		3 days		6 days		10 days		15 days	
	Score [a]	Weight (%)	Score	Weight (%)	Score	Weight (%)	Score	Weight (%)	Score	Weight (%)
15	4.7	100	6.1	95.6	7.1	93.2	7.4	92.3	9.1	91.2
22	4.9	100	7.0	90.6	8.7	90.5	9.3	87.8	9.6	85.9
26	5.0	100	7.7	87.6	8.7	85.0	9.6	83.1	9.6	82.5

[a] Score descriptions: 10 = no off-flavour; 8 = slight; 6 = distinct; 4 = intense; 2 = extreme.

species. An anabaena species in ponds at Auburn University bloomed intensively when the water temperature had just reached 21°C, and caused earthy-musty flavour in catfish; however, as the ambient temperature increased the alga was found only sparingly and caused no flavour problems. Actinomycetes are considered to be the causative organisms in off-flavoured catfish ponds in cool weather. Algae need sunlight for growth, consequently by preventing penetration of sunlight below the surface of water their growth may be restricted. Catfish were grown in ponds at Auburn which were kept muddy by releasing compressed air into the ponds near the bottoms. Fish growth was satisfactory in the turbid ponds, very little algae grew, and the flavour of the fish was good. The amount of dissolved oxygen in the water affects the metabolism of algae and actinomycetes. *Oscillatoria chalybea*, a notorious odour-producing alga, grew well in an aquarium that was aerated but produced no odorous compound (Leventer and Eren, 1969). In the same medium under low oxygen conditions the organism produced an earthy-musty odour. Actinomycetes are facultatively aerobic and, reportedly, the oxygen condition of the environment influences the ability of some species to produce odorous compounds (Dickson, 1968).

SUGGESTIONS FOR CONTROLLING OFF-FLAVOUR

Removal of the earthy-musty flavour by holding the fish in flowing water was investigated at Auburn University (Lovell, 1971). Three collections of catfish were brought into the Fishery Research Laboratory and held in flowing, filtered water at a temperature of 15°, 22° or 26°C for 15 days. The fish were weighed and evaluated for flavour at 0. 3, 6, 10, and 15 days. Table 3 showed their changes in flavour and weight. The off-flavour may be purged from fish relatively quickly by clean water and an increase in temperature enhances the process. However, the weight loss, especially at higher temperatures, makes this method economically impractical for the catfish industry. Suggestions for controlling off-flavour are as follows:

(1) Pond wastes should be minimized. The farmer can help this situation by using good feeds and feeding practices. Unconsumed and unabsorbed nutrients stimulate the growth of pond microorganisms. Much attention from experimental stations is being directed toward removing wastes from fish culture systems.

(2) Frequent exchange of pond water can minimize opportunity for the development of off-flavour in fish. This removes nutrients from the pond and also reduces the concentration of a specific population of micro-organisms.

(3) Chemical control of growth of algae in ponds is possible, but it is questionable whether such a practice would be desirable or feasible. Algae are important in the food chain of pond organisms and in producing oxygen through photosynthesis. Also, poisoning algal blooms will increase the biological oxygen demand in the pond and is hazardous unless there is a water reserve or aeration. Another advantage of a plankton bloom is shading the pond bottom to prevent growth of rooted plants in the pond. It should be remembered that algae are not the only causes of off-flavour, and only a few of the blue-green algae are responsible for the production of these compounds. Chemical treatment only kills the algae and does nothing to eliminate the cause of growth. With profuse quantities of nutrients going into the pond daily, it will require continuous infusion of poison to control algae growth. If too much algae die at one time the oxygen demand upon the water may increase too rapidly and cause a fish kill. More research is needed on the feasibility of chemical controls.

(4) Other possible methods for controlling micro-organism growth in ponds involve biological means. Use of viruses or bacteria to control algae have been suggested. The uptake of pond nutrients by higher plants to prevent algae growth has been investigated at Auburn. Water hyacinths effectively suppressed algae growth.

(5) Mechanical agitation of ponds to increase turbidity, or muddiness, of the water may be an effective suppressor of plankton growth. Also, there is a possibility that suspended particles of clay may act as adsorbents for off-flavour compounds in the water.

The earthy-musty flavour always disappears from catfish over variable periods of time even with no pond treatment. A week to several months may be required, depending upon the persistence of the flavour-producing organisms. Catfish farmers who find off-flavour in their fish are urged to continue to feed the fish, because if fish are hungry they may begin feeding on materials on the pond bottom which may accentuate the problem; the pond water should be exchanged if possible. If a dense plankton bloom accompanies the off-flavour, the algae should not be poisoned unless there is an abundant supply of water for replacement: the fish should not be removed from the pond, unless they can continue to feed while the off-flavour is being cleared up because weight loss will be excessive.

References

ASCHNER, M, LAVENTER, C and CHORIN-KIRSCH, I   Off-flavour in
1969   carp from fish ponds in the coastal plain and the Gelid. *Bamidgeh*, 19(1):23-25.
DOUGHERTY, J D, CAMPBELL, R D and MORRIS, R L   Actino-
1966   mycetes: isolation and identification of agent responsible
1966   for musty odours. *Science*, 152:1372.
DUNCAN, D B   Multiple range and multiple F tests. *Biometrics*,
1955   11:1.
DICKSON, K L   Actinomycetes and water quality. *J. Am. Water*
1968   *Works. Ass.*, 60:379.
GERBER, N N and LECHEVALIER, H A   Geosmin, an earthy-
1965   smelling substance isolated from actinomycetes. *App. Microbiol.*, 13:935.
LEVENTER, H and EREN, J   Taste and odour in the reservoirs of the
1969   Israel National Waster System. In *Developments in water quality research*. Proc. Jerusalem International Conf. on Water Quality, p. 19–37.
LOVELL, R T   The earthy-musty flavour in intensively-cultured
1971   catfish. *Proc. Ass. South. Agr. Workers* 67th Annual Meeting, p. 102.
LOVELL, R T   Absorption of earthy-musty flavour by channel catfish
1972   held in monospecies cultures of geosmin-producing blue-green algae. *Trans. Am. Fish. Soc.* (In print).
MALONEY, T E   Research on algae odour. *J. Amer. Water Works*
1966   *Ass.*, 55(4):481–486.
MEDSKER, L L, JENKINS, D and THOMAS, J F   Odorous compound
1968   in natural waters: An earth-smelling compound associated with blue-green algae and actinomycetes. *Environ. Sci. Tech.*, 2:461–464.
PALMER, C M   Odour and taste algae. In *Algae in water supplies*.
1962   Cincinnati, Ohio, USA Division of Water Supply and Pollution Control, Public Health Service, US Dep. Health, Education and Welfare, p. 18–21.

ROSEN, A A   Committee report: research on tastes and odours.
1968   Cleveland, Ohio, USA *Rep. of AWWA, June 6, 1968.*
ROSEN, A A, MASHNI, C I and SAFFERMAN, R S   Recent develop-
1970   ments in the chemistry of odour in water: the cause of earthy-musty odour. *Water Treatment and Examination,* 19:106–119.
SAFFERMAN, R S, ROSEN, A A, MASHNI, C I and MORRIS, M E
1967   Earthy-smelling substance from a blue-green alga. *Environ. Sci. Tech.,* 1:429–430.

SILVEY, J K G   Tastes and odours-effects of organisms. *J. Amer.*
1966   *Water Works Ass.,* 58(6):706–715.
SILVEY, J K G and ROACH, A W   Actinomycetes may cause tastes
1956   and odours in water supplies. *Public Works Magazine,* 87(5).
THAYSEN, A C   The origin of an earthy or muddy taint in fish.
1936   *Ann. Appl. Biol.,* 23:99–109.

Pond-Grown Catfish in the United States: Present Situation and Future Opportunities   *T J Billy*

Elevage du poisson-chat en etang aux etats-unis: situation actuelle et possibilites d'avenir

Ce document donne des renseignements de base sur les principaux facteurs qui interviennent dans le développement de l'élevage du poisson-chat aux Etats-Unis et on y trouve une description de l'organisation de cette industrie. Parmi les considérations générales concernant le poisson-chat, d'élevage, de l'étang au marché en passant par l'usine de traitement et le produit, on examine notamment la situation actuelle de l'industrie, les principaux problémes techniques et économiques et les perspectives futures de développement. Bien que l'élevage du poisson-chat en étang ait atteint aux Etats-Units un niveau de développement qui offre des possibilités d'expansion énormes, il faudra pour que cette croissance se poursuive se concentrer sur la principale production et faire de nouveaux progrès techniques.

El bagre de estangue en estados unidos: situacion actual y oportunidades futuras

En este documento figuran los antecedentes sobre los factores principaes de la creación de la industria de cultivo de bagre en Estados Unidos, y se describe su organización. Se estudian las consideraciones generales relativas al traslado del bagre de criadero desde los estanques hasta las instalaciones de elaboración y se hacen descripoiones del producto y del mercado, con respecto al estado actual de la industria, los problemas principales de tipo técnico y económico y las perspectivas de su expansión futura. Aunque la industria estadounidense del bagre de estanque ha alcanzado un desarrollo cuyas posibilidades de ampliación son enormes, se necesitarán concretos avances importantes en la producción y la tecnología que permitan ese crecimiento.

Warmwater fish farming in the United States achieved new status in the late sixties because of the rapid growth of the pond-grown catfish industry. Production is based upon the intensive culture of several species of catfish under controlled conditions. Those raised in order of importance are the channel catfish (*Ictalurus punctatus*), the blue catfish (*Ictalurus furcatus*), and the white catfish (*Ictalurus catus*) (Bardach and Ryther 1968). They all share the distinguishing characteristic of prominent whisker-like sensory barbels and are highly prized in certain areas of the country as excellent sport and food fish. The channel catfish is the species predominantly used as it is the easiest to culture. Catfish farming is similar in many respects at this stage in its development to that of the high-volume broiler industry in the USA some 20 to 30 years ago, sharing many similar problems. This paper does not take an in-depth look at the culture (production) or processing systems used for pond-grown catfish which have been amply reviewed (Grizzell *et al.* 1969, Anon. 1970a, and Billy 1970). Rather it discusses the present status of the US industry to illustrate many of the factors, both technical and managerial, which will determine the success or failure of many future aquaculture developments.

INDUSTRY DEVELOPMENT

The following factors led to the development of the pond-grown catfish industry in the sixties: (1) an overall levelling-off in the production of wild catfish in the USA; (2) an established and expanding market demand for this high-quality food fish; (3) concerted Federal Government research in the late fifties and the sixties to develop improved production and harvesting techniques; (4) the suitability of catfish for commercial culture due to its adaptability and hearty nature; (5) the abundance

and relatively low cost of fresh water in the south-central part of the USA, and (6) the availability of land surplus to agricultural use which was suitable for pond construction.

The harvesting and marketing of wild catfish had developed a growing regional demand which could not be fulfilled by natural production (Donahue 1968). Also, the wild catfish supply was seasonal in nature, limited primarily to the summer period, which left an unfilled demand. The heart of the catfish market was, and is, the small cities and towns located along the major river systems of the Midwest and southern States. In addition pockets of demand exist in almost all major cities where a strong rural to urban migration has taken place. The catfish market is a specialized one in which, however, previous knowledge of the species appears to be extremely important. The catfish possesses several attributes which makes it highly suitable for culturing. Perhaps its most important feature is its adaptability. It can be spawned easily, using one of several techniques, tolerates a wide range of water temperatures as well as temporarily reduced dissolved oxygen conditions, and adapts well to artificial food and feeding. In addition, the optimum conditions for catfish growth coincide well with the climatic conditions found in the geographic areas in which the interest in commercial culture developed. Another advantage was that many of the techniques developed for raising minnows also worked fairly well with catfish. Finally, Government-sponsored research in the late fifties and early sixties resulted in the solution of several of the key animal husbandry problems and developed the basis for commercial catfish farming (Anon. 1970b). A clean, abundant supply of water is essential for successful fish farming (Schumacher 1969) and the south-central region of the USA has such a supply in ground water. It generally has a pH range between 6.5 and 8.5, a temperature of 18° to 27°C, is devoid of toxic dissolved gases, such as nitrogen, and does not contain excessive amounts of minerals, such as iron. This water is often deficient in oxygen, however, and must be aerated prior to use. Surface water, although frequently considered a somewhat more economical source, is generally much less desirable in this area due to potential problems with silt or mud, contamination with pesticides or herbicides used in agriculture, and the introduction of wild species into the ponds which compete for the food supplied to the catfish. The land most suitable for pond construction is somewhat impervious to water and well graded. It should consist of a mixture of different size particles of sand, silt and clay in proportions which afford proper compaction in the construction of levees (embankments) and pond bottoms and prevent seepage and leaks. Another desirable feature is a flat terrain to minimize the amount of each which must be moved during pond construction. Many farmers in this region had idle land not well suited for crops such as cotton, rice, or soybeans due to poor yields, but ideal for pond construction because of the features mentioned above.

ORGANIZATION OF THE INDUSTRY

Although catfish are native to almost all waters of the United States, the commercial industry development has been concentrated in the river basins of the Gulf Coast and the southern half of the Mississippi River drainage system, where catfish are highly regarded food. In 1970, about 80 per cent of the production of pond-raised

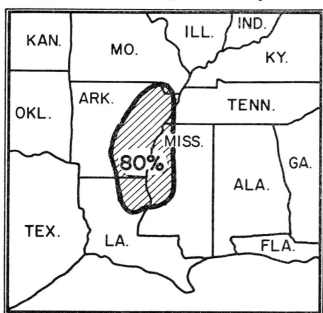

Fig 1   In 1969, about 80% of the total United States production of pond-grown catfish came from the circled area

catfish came from the area embracing parts of Arkansas, Mississippi and Louisiana, as shown in Fig 1 (Greenfield 1969). This area has several characteristics that especially lend themselves to catfish production, as described above. Another feature was the availability of large, well capitalized farm enterprises which could afford the investment required to enter into production. In addition, many of the farmers had already acquired some experience in fish

culture. So, commercial catfish farming expanded from a total production area of 160 ha in 1960 to an estimated 27,000 ha in 1972 (Jones 1969), with the production increasing from 140 to 38,200 t. The harvested area is lower than the total because of two factors: (1) some of the ponds hold brood fish for spawning and others for growing the fry to the desired 10 to 20 cm size (fingerling), and (2) some farmers choose to carry market size fish over till the next season, depending upon the supply-demand picture when the fish are ready for harvesting.

CATFISH PRODUCTION

The practice of commercial catfish culture is continually evolving with new or improved procedures. There is no single approach applicable to all situations. For example, the time required to grow fish to market size varies considerably with the climate, which also has an impact on hatchery operations, the nutritional requirements of the fish and the number of growing days. For these reasons, it is not possible to provide a comprehensive description of catfish production procedures. Rather, a brief presentation of several of the key factors in production is provided, looking at it from the viewpoint of one about to enter the business. The following are key considerations in such farming: (1) site selection; (2) design and construction of ponds and facilities; (3) source of fingerlings; (4) growing procedure; (5) disease and parasite control; (6) harvesting and (7) market alternatives.

MARKETING AND PROCESSING

Several species of fish, both freshwater and saltwater, are marketed in the USA today as catfish. A saltwater species, commonly called wolffish (*Anarhichadidas*) is sold as 'ocean catfish' and imported catfish species native to Brazil and Mexico are available in significant quantities (Donahue 1968). Catfish produced from native waters in 1970 made up about 80 per cent of the total amount of processed product available in the market, about 10 per cent were imported, with pond-grown catfish and other making up the remainder. Until 1968, the entire harvest of the catfish farming industry was marketed alive to restaurants, retailers, fee-fishing lakes, and farm ponds. By 1972, due to processing facilities in the production area, only about 82 per cent of the harvested fish were so disposed, the remainder being processed directly prior to marketing. Fig 2 shows the marketing distribution flow for farm-produced catfish. As the live hauler can pay a premium price to the farmer, this market will continue to receive a major portion of the supply of pond-grown catfish unless production greatly outstrips the demand of this segment of the market. The predominant output of the processing plants is a headed, gutted, and skinned product weighing 0.25 to 0.45 kg (Anon. 1972a). In 1970, just over half the processed product was sold fresh, with the remainder frozen (Anon. 1972b). Fig 3 shows the major steps in processing in the industry today (Billy 1970). The boxes within the broken line include the major plant operations. This example does not show the only sequence of flow possible. It is presented merely to illustrate the typical procedure involved in processing pond-raised catfish. The catfish are shipped alive in specially constructed 'live-haul' tank trucks. There are two reasons for pro-

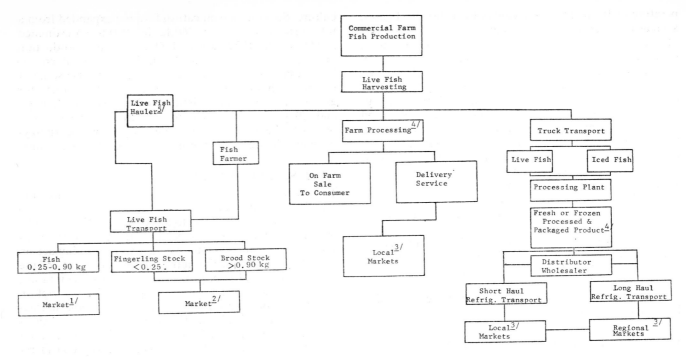

(1) Private fee fishing lakes; state, municipal, & county recreational fishing agencies;
    private fishing clubs; farm ponds; restaurants.
(2) Fish farmers; state, country, & municipal fish agencies.
(3) Local and regional markets presently consist of restaurants, chainstore & other retail outlets;
    church and other social and civic groups.
(4) Catfish food market form is primarily a headed, eviscerated, and skinned product.
(5) Estimated 85 percent of farm catfish are sold through live fish haulers.

Fig 2   Marketing distribution flow chart for farm produced catfish, 1972

cessors handling live fish: (1) the fish can be sold to live haulers from the centrally located processing plant vats at premium prices, and (2) a product of better quality is obtained because spoilage does not start until the fish are slaughtered. Nevertheless, dead fish are transported and held on ice prior to processing in certain situations, particularly during the summer months when problems with live hauling and holding are more acute. Beginning with live holding at the plant site, all the operations through fresh or frozen storage shown in Fig 3 are considered plant operations. The most popular method for holding fish live is in vats which are generally rectangular in design, built above ground in rows, and supplied with running well water. An adverse feature of this system is the need to minimize temperature differences between the water in the vats and the water in which the fish arrive. Frequently, it is necessary to cool or heat the vat water, depending on the time of year. This operation takes time and often requires special equipment. An additional consideration is the loss in weight incurred when the fish are held without being fed for several days. The amount of weight loss is directly related to the temperature of the water, other stress factors, and the initial amount of food in the stomach.

Most processors prefer to skin and dress stunned fish. Several methods are used to stun them. A common one is to fish electrically with a 115-volt alternating current or a high-voltage, low-amperage direct current. This, it is claimed, traps most of the blood in the head area and prevents discoloration of the white flesh. It also facilitates the heading operation because the fish are paralyzed. The skinning operation is considered the most difficult

TABLE 1. VALUE ADDED ANALYSIS FOR PROCESSED CULTURED CATFISH IN 1969 (GREENFIELD 1970)

	US $/kg
Growing expense	0.62
Harvesting expense	0.11
Margin	0.18
Price to processor	0.91
Price of fish	0.91
Transportation	0.02
Dressing loss	0.60
Processing expense	0.42[a]
Margin	0.00
Price to wholesaler	1.95
Price of product	1.95
Margin and expense	0.49
Price to retailer	2.44
Price of product	2.44
Margin and expense	0.73
Price to consumer	3.17

[a] Assuming 15 per cent of plant capacity is utilized over an entire year

part of processing. Catfish have traditionally been skinned. This practice has been due in part to the dark, unattrative colour of the wild catfish skin and to the off-flavours imparted to the cooked fish. Although it has been shown that pond-grown catfish need not be

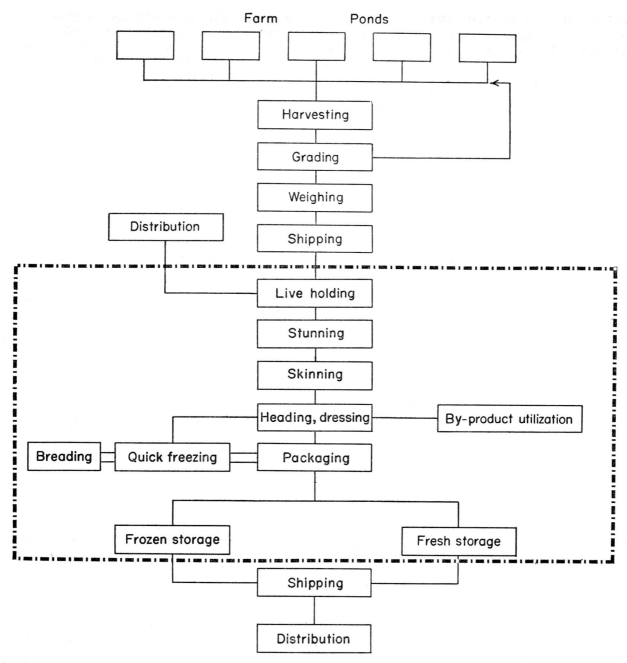

Fig 3 The major steps involved in moving cultured catfish from ponds to and through a processing plant (the broken line encloses the major plant operations) for distribution to market

skinned (Anon. 1970b), this traditional practice has been continued due to consumer preferences. Skinning by hand has always been difficult and time-consuming. Recently, however, machines have been developed to skin the fish. They remove the outer layers, leaving a thin, silvery, inner membrane which has a desirable appearance. Several processors are already using, or plan to use, these machines. Although heading and dressing were listed after skinning in Fig 3, they are not necessarily performed in this order. For example, with the use of skinning machines, the fish are first headed, then gutted and skinned. Many mechanical concepts used in process equipment designed for other species, such as vacuum evisceration, have been applied successfully to processing

cultured catfish. By-products or offal are disposed of by: (1) selling or giving the offal to a local rendering plant or pig farmer; (2) grinding, packaging, and freezing it in bulk for shipment to a pet-food plant; (3) cooking it to produce a source of protein on which a supplemental feeding ration for catfish is based; and (4) making fish meal from it.

Conventional methods are used to freeze and package the product. Studies have shown that commercially processed catfish, fresh or frozen, exhibit the storage stability typical for freshwater fish (Boggess *et al.* 1971). Table 1 gives a value added analysis for processed pond-grown catfish in 1969 (Greenfield 1970). There has been little change in this cost structure until very recently.

PRESENT STATUS OF INDUSTRY

The pond-grown catfish industry appears to have entered a period of levelling-off, with some retrenchment and adjustment needed. In addition to typical difficulties which have been experienced with short-term imbalances in supply and demand, more basic problems remain to be solved before significant new growth can begin. Had catfish farming matured at a slower pace, many of the problems experienced or being faced could probably have been avoided. In the circumstances, it has been predicted that, because of slim margins and significantly rising costs, a production cutback will occur in 1973 (Heffernan 1973). Costs are expected to increase all along the line, the most significant being an estimated 50 per cent rise in the price of feed. This may have an adverse effect on the industry, particularly as pond-grown catfish already face stiff competition from lower-cost imports. And those who continue in operation will have to avoid the problems of diseases, the lowering of quality of products, etc, which can result from trying to cut corners. The reasons for this period of levelling-off appear to fit into the following general categories: (a) too rapid growth, (b) unresolved technical problems (c) foreign competition, and (d) high production and processing costs. A brief discussion of each is provided to demonstrate the breakthroughs required for further industry growth and development.

The very fast growth of the industry resulted in many small size production and processing firms that could not engage in significant market development. Moreover, there is overcapacity in the processing segment due in part to the present seasonal nature of production which requires sufficient capacity to handle gluts during certain period of the year. Another logistics problem is resulting from the gradual southward shift in production operations to take advantage of a longer growing season. This shift is away from the existing live-hauler markets and the processing plants. It is increasing the technical problems associated with handling live fish, particularly during the summer months.

Many technical problems in both production and processing require solution. On the production end, the major problems limiting profitability and increased productivity include: (a) a general lack of knowledge of catfish nutrition resulting in the use of high-cost feeds; (b) a lack of approved chemicals used in treating diseases, infections and viruses, thus restricting the development of higher-density culture systems; (c) improved performance of the species itself through selective breeding, and (d) the varied sizes of the catfish being produced which result in uneven finished products. No firm produces enough of a desired size to permit the supply of a uniform product on a continuous basis. In-pond grading techniques and selective harvesting systems are required. From a processing viewpoint, key technical problems include the need to develop improved, mechanized processing techniques, to eliminate the earthy or musty off-flavour common in the product during certain periods of the year, and to avoid product contamination by pesticide or herbicide residues in the fish from the feeds or from aerial spraying near the production ponds.

If one compares the cost structure shown in Table 1, taking into consideration the expected cost increases, to the present price of 1.10 to 1.32 US $/kg for imported catfish, the serious threat of this competition to the future growth of the pond-grown catfish industry becomes apparent. Fortunately, for the domestic industry, serious supply and quality problems at the present time limit interest in, and use of, these imported products. Assuming these supply and quality problems can be solved without a major increase in price, however, then drastic cost reductions will be required if the domestic pond-grown catfish are going to continue to compete in the same markets.

One of the keys to future development is the introduction of production techniques with fundamentally lower costs. Raceway systems, for example, hold promise of concentrating fish density to give greater production per dollar of fixed investment. The greater concentration, as with all livestock, will intensify disease and other management problems. These can be solved, however, and with improved production systems and the solution of the other production problems mentioned above, one can expect cost reductions in the area of 30 to 40 per cent and a further growth of the industry. Another saving could be made by the use of lower-cost feeds and more effective feeding techniques. As basic research on nutrition permits a better understanding of the requirements of the catfish under given production conditions, modified feed formulas and feeding techniques can be developed to result in better conversion ratios.

PROSPECTS FOR FUTURE DEVELOPMENT

Although many problems and risks confront the pond-grown catfish industry in the USA, there is reason to believe that it will become a healthy, growing industry through hard work, management knowhow, timely research and development, and systematic market expansion. Those farmers and processors with the foresight and resourcefulness to develop or adopt new technology should prosper. Polyculture, the concept of raising more than one type of aquatic crop in a given environment, is now receiving wide attention. This technique offers further possibilities regarding increased yield and efficiency in a given production operation. Market development and expansion, particularly directed toward the gourmet market, appear to offer real potential. If the processor develops the capability to turn out a high quality, portion-controlled product in high volume, then, according to a 1971 study, catfish consumption will multiply by more than tenfold (McDlung 1972). Catfish lends itself to the development of alternative product forms (Anon. 1970b). Studies have shown that smoked catfish has considerable potential. Convenience type TV dinners using catfish also appear to have merit and prototype products have been developed and tested.

References

Anon. *Report to the Fish Farmers.* Resource Publication No. 83.
1970a Washington, D.C., USA, Bureau of Sport Fisheries and Wildlife, Department of Interior, 124 p.

Anon. *A Program of Research for the Catfish Farming Industry.*
1970b Project Report, Washington, D.C., USA, Economic Development Administration, Department of Commerce, 216 p.

Anon. *A Statistical Reporting System for the Catfish Farming*
1972a *Industry, Methodology and 1970 Results.* Project Report, Washington, D.C., USA, Economic Development Administration, Department of Commerce, 233 p.

Anon. *Catfish Processing*. Agricultural Economic Report No. 224.
1972b Washington, DC, USA Economic Research Service, US
Department of Agriculture, 33 p.

BARDACH, J E and RYTHER, J N *The Status and Potential of*
1968 *Aquaculture*. Springfield, Virginia, USA, Clearinghouse,
Part I, p. 135.

BILLY, T J Processing Pond-Raised Catfish *Proceedings: California*
1970 *Catfish Conference*, Sacramento, California, USA,
Agricultural Extension Service, University of California,
p. 71–77.

BOGGESS, T S, HEATON, E K and SHEWFELT, A L *J. Fd. Sci.*
1971 38:969.

DONAHUE, J R *The United States Catfish Market*. Project Report,
1968 Washington, DC, USA, Marketing Research and
Services Division, National Marine Fisheries Service, p. 2.

GREENFIELD, J E Economics of Fish Farming and how it Relates
1969 to Trout and Catfish Industries. *Amer. Fishes and US
Trout News*. 14(4):6.

GREENFIELD, J E Economic and Business Dimensions Dimensions
1970 of the Catfish Farming Industry. *Proceedings: California
Catfish Conference*, Sacramento, California, USA,
Agricultural Extension Service, University of California,
p. 15.

GRIZZELL, R A, DILLON, O W and SULLIVAN, E G Catfish
1969 Farming – A New Farm Crop, *Farmer's Bulletin*, No. 2244,
Washington, DC, USA, Soil Conservation Service,
Department of Commerce, 16 p.

HEFFERNAN, B E Fish Farming in 1973 – Slim Margins Signal
1973 Production Cutback. *Fish Farmg. Ind.* 4(1):4.

JONES, W G Market Prospects for Farm Catfish Production.
1969 *Proceedings of Commercial Fish Farming Conference*,
Athens, Georgia, USA, University of Georgia, p. 54.

McCLUNG, J Catfish Industry Stabilizing after Troubled 1960's.
1972 *Feedstuffs*, 44(50):1.

SCHUMACHER, P Pond Construction, Water Quality, and Quantity
1969 for Catfish Farming. *Proceedings of the Commercial Fish
Farming Conference*, Athens, Georgia, USA, University
of Georgia, p. 4.

Problems in the Utilization of Freshwater Fish   *D G Iredale*

Problemes poses par l'utilisation du poisson d'eau douce

On identifie certains des plus importants problèmes associés à
l'utilisation du poisson d'eau douce, y compris les effets de la
dégradation du milieu à la suite de l'évacuation des déchets industriels et domestiques dans des systèmes hydrographiques oú ils
causent un enrichissement excessif, ainsi que l'accumulation de
substances toxiques. On étudie aussi l'insistance nouvelle mise sur
une utilisation plus efficace de cette ressource: il s'agit par exemple
d'utiliser plus largement la totalité des espèces disponibles grâce à
l'application de nouvelles méthodes de transformation et à la mise à
point de nouveaux produits, aux perfectionnements techniques
visant à maximiser l'efficacité de la production et aux avantages que
l'on peut escompter de la création d'une société de commercialisation du poisson dans le Canada central.

Problemas que plantea el aprovechamiento del pescado de agua dulce

Se señalan algunos de los problemas más importantes asociados
con el aprovechamiento de los peces de agua dulce, entre ellos las
repercusiones de la degradación del medio ambiente debido a la
descarga de desechos industriales y domésticos en los cursos de agua,
con el consiguiente exceso de enriquecimiento y acumulación de
sustancias tóxicas. Se habla también de la insistencia actual en el
aprovechamiento más eficaz de los recursos como, por ejemplo, el
mayor uso de todas las especies disponibles aplicando nuevos
métodos de elaboración y creando nuevos productos, de los
progresos technológicos tendientes a elevar al máximo la eficiencia
de la producción, y de los beneficios que han de esperarse de la
creación de una corporación de mercadeo pesquero en la zona
central de Canadá.

The production of freshwater fish as human food in
Canada represents a significant proportion of the total
Canadian production. Commercial landings amount to
more than 450 thousand kg annually. The production
of this inland fishery could be substantially greater if the
many abundant species of fish that have remained underexploited due to their low commercial value were taken
into account. The continuance of this resource and the
attempt to resolve some of its associated problems has
become a subject of increasing national concern. The
greater emphasis on improving the quality of the environment will help increase the capacity of the inland fishery
to meet the growing demand for fish protein resources
and will at the same time result in improved socio-
economic benefits to the Canadian community.

ENVIRONMENTAL DEGENERATION

By far the most potentially damaging crisis threatening
the utilization of freshwater fish is environmental degradation (Bligh 1971). In relation to the fishery resource
there are two basic contributing factors: eutrophication
and the accumulation of toxic substances. The effects of
eutrophication or nutrient enrichment, a result of high
human population density, are most clearly evidenced in
North America's Great Lakes. This condition has had an
observable effect on the fish fauna of Lake Erie. It is
anticipated that research and strict controls will eventually result in a reversal of environmental degeneration

and a reappearance of many species that are valued highly
as a human food and for their recreational appeal. The
presence of toxic substances, whether resulting from
domestic and industrial waste, agricultural runoff or from
those that occur naturally, has had a profound effect on
the usability of freshwater fish. Another factor contributing to restrictions on the use of some freshwater fish is the
occurrence of off-odours (Bligh 1971). This problem can
be attributed in some instances to direct industrial contamination of water. In the case of earthy odours it is
generally concluded that they originate from certain
types of actinomyces and blue-green algae present in
water environments (Rosen *et al.* 1970). Some success
has been achieved in masking or neutralizing this earthy
taint through various processing techniques (Iredale and
Rigby 1972, Iredale D G and K J Kewich, unpublished
data).

PROBLEMS RELATED TO THE UTILIZATION
OF FRESHWATER FISH

Problems associated with harvesting, processing and
distribution of Canadian freshwater fish differ significantly from those encountered in the marine fishery.
These differences are related largely to such factors as
the nature of the resource environment and apparent
consumer resistance to many species of freshwater fish.
Production conditions and methods vary widely from
one part of the country to another. These disparities are

evidenced when comparing the well developed commercial fisheries of the Great Lakes to the fihserman who may work alone fishing an isolated lake in a more remote area of northern Canada. One of the principal deterrents to exploiting the fishery in some of the northerly areas has been the lack of chilling facilities essential for the fishery which is active during a short but intense late summer season. Conventional methods of storing natural winter ice for summer use, such as the traditional ice house, are impractical in many of these areas due to the lack of a sufficient supply of natural building materials in locations close to, or beyond, the limit of the tree line. This problem has been alleviated in part by the use of such innovations as a portable insulated storage building developed by the Fisheries Research Board for holding and chilling fresh caught fish before transporting them to processing centres (Scott 1970). Such innovations, coupled with educational programmes designed to increase the fisherman's awareness of the necessity of carefully handling his catch at the lake, will ensure a more salable product. There still remains a need to create more interest and understanding on the part of the fisherman and to upgrade lakeside facilities and transportation services.

As a result of the introduction of smelt (*Osmerus mordax*) into the Great Lakes early in this century, the species has become sufficiently well established to sustain a substantial commercial fishery. However, until late in the fifties production was based upon an inshore fishery, which took advantage of annual spawning behaviour when the fish migrated toward shore. As a result of gear development, the fishery is now practically a year-round operation and the production of Great Lakes smelt has superseded the value of the marine smelt catch. Another problem peculiar to this fishery is a reproductive factor affecting the size of smelt in alternating years (Hart and Ferguson 1966). This in turn affects the marketability of the species.

PRODUCT DEVELOPMENT

Many species of freshwater fish previously classified as being of little commercial value are now being recognized as potential human food. An early recognition of this potential by the Fisheries Research Board of Canada resulted in considerable basic research in product innovation and development (Lantz 1966). Because of the low consumer appeal of these species, much of this innovation has been directed toward changing the natural characteristics of some of these fish to more acceptable forms designed to satisfy the growing demand for convenience foods. Advances in processing technology have resulted in the development of equipment which now offers the processors automated systems to reduce hand labour and allow maximum recoveries of the edible part of his raw material. The introduction of the flesh separating or deboning machine allows a high recovery rate of boneless flesh which can be utilized in a variety of products (Anon. 1972). This type of equipment is being used in Canada to produce raw material from many of these previously difficult to market species, which is being transformed into a variety of highly acceptable food products. An obvious outlet for one of these types of products is the growing market for breaded and

battered fish portions, which represents a significant proportion of North American fish consumption. However there are problems of colour and textural dissimilarities between boneless formulated freshwater fish products and their principal competitors, fish sticks and portions made from marine species such as cod and haddock. In addition, consumer education and continuing product innovation are required, not only to gain an entry into this market but also to retain the interest of the consumer.

Parasitic infestation of certain freshwater fish remains another continuing problem. Although it is generally concluded that most fish parasites will not develop in man if eaten raw, and none is harmful if the infested fish is cooked prior to consumption, the presence of intense parasitic infestation is aesthetically unappealing and unacceptable in the North American market (Lawler 1959). At the present time detection of parasitized fillets is usually accomplished using conventional handling methods. However, results of recent studies by the Fisheries Research Board show a potential for the use of pulses of high frequency ultrasound to detect parasites in the tissue of whole fish which would obviate the necessity of filleting before inspection (Freese 1971).

A species which has received much attention in the past decade is the alewife (*Pomolobus pseudoharengus*). Much of this attention is due to massive mortalities of this species at certain times of the year, resulting in large quantities accumulating on the lake shores where rapid decomposition takes place. In some locations the alewife has been harvested for reduction to fish meal; in other areas it has been used in its raw state as a fertilizer. Work by the Fisheries Research Board has shown this species to have greater potential value as a human food source. Processed in a similar manner to the ocean sardine or brisling (Lantz 1966), it yields a canned product of excellent quality.

A freshwater Fish Marketing Corporation was established in 1969 to improve and stabilize the earnings of Canada's inland fishermen, through control over the production, transportation, processing and marketing of the output of the freshwater fisheries of central and northern Canada. This came about because problems of inefficiency and economic disparity had plagued the industry for many years. It has resulted in considerable modernization, including the construction of modern processing facilities and improved marketing techniques: and, for the fisherman, it has provided a greater incentive as his production is now assured of a market at a guaranteed minimum price.

References

BLIGH, E G Environmental factors affecting the utilization of
1971   Great Lakes fish as human food. *Limnos*, 4(1):13–18.
FREESE, M Ultrasonic inspection of parasitized whole fish. In
1971   *Fish Inspection and Quality Control*, (ed.) R Kreuzer, London Fishing News (Books) Ltd., pp 256–262.
HART, J L and FERGUSON, R G The American smelt. *Trade News*,
1966   18(9):22–23.
IREDALE, D G and RIGBY, D Effect of smoke processing on muddy
1972   odour and taste in rainbow trout (*Salmo gairdneri*). *J. Fish. Res. Bd. Can.*, 29(9):1365–1366.
LANTZ, A W Special products from freshwater fish. *Fish. Res. Bd.*
1966   *Can. Bull. 151.*
LAWLER, G H Parasites in fish: Pike-whitefish tapeworm, Part 1,
1959   Life history. *Fishing, A Bulletin for Commercial Fishermen*. Fisheries Branch Prov. of Man. Dept. of Mines and Nat. Res. 1(3):11–14.

Rosen, A A, Mashni, C I and Safferman, R S Recent develop-
1970   ments in the chemistry of odour in water: The cause of
        earthy/musty odour. *Water Treatment and Examination*,
        19(2): 106–114.

Scott, K R Portable refrigerated fish holding unit for remote
1970   freshwater fisheries. *Can. Inst. Food Technol. J.*, 3:139–142.
Anon.   Mechanical fish separators catch on slowly. *Fish Farming*
1972   *Industries*, 3(6):38–41.

Problems in the Utilization of Freshwater Fish in Some Countries of the Asia and Far East Region   *D D Tapiador*

Problemes poses par l'utilisation des poissons d'eau douce dans certains pays de la region de l'asie et de l'extreme-orient

Le présent document passe un revue les problèmes liés à l'utilisation des poissons d'eau douce à Hong Kong, en Inde, en Indonésie, en République khmère, au Laos, en Malaisie, au Pakistan, aux Philippines, à Singapour et en Thailande. Etant donné que la plupart des poissons sont commercialisés vivants ou à l'état frais, les principaux problèmes touchent à leur manutention, à leur transport et à leur distribution. De nombreuses difficultés technologiques se posent aussi, surtout en matière de transformation et de commercialisation.

Problemas que plantea el aprovechamiento de los peces de agua dulce en algunas paises de asia y el lejano oriente

En este trabajo se examinan los problemas que plantea el aprovechamiento de los peces de agua dulce en Hong Kong, India, Indonesia, la República Khmer, Laos, Malasia, Pakistán, Filipinas, Singapur y Tailandia. Dado que la mayoría de los peces se ponen a la venta vivos o frescos, los principales problemas son la manipulación, al transporte y la distribución. Se plantean también muchos problemas technológicos, especialmente en el campo de la elaboración y la comercialización.

Statistics on the production of freshwater fish in the Asia and Far East region are unfortunately lacking but a guess would probably put the figure close to 2 million tons per year. Demand exceeds supply and a major problem in most of the countries is how to increase production. The main difficulties are in handling, transport and distribution as most of the fish are marketed alive or fresh (iced or un-iced). This paper reviews the situation, on a country-by-country basis, using data from the Indo-Pacific Fisheries Council (IPFC) and from correspondents in the region.

HONG KONG

Almost all locally produced and imported freshwater fish are consumed fresh, the production of preserved and processed commodities being negligible. A small part, eg, 4 per cent in 1971, was exported to the USA. As the distance between the production areas (or points of importation) and the wholesale and retail outlets is short, the longest being some 40 km, distribution is rapid. The demand for freshwater fish exceeds supply by more than 60 per cent. The *per caput* consumption of freshwater fish jumped from 3.6 kg in 1961 to 8.0 kg in 1964 to slightly over 8.0 kg (1971). The wholesale marketing of imported freshwater fish in the urban areas has presented problems because of inadequacies in trading space and so on. The Hong Kong Government is planning to provide improved facilities.

INDIA

The main problems in utilizing freshwater fish in most places in India are technical, economic and sociological. As consumers generally prefer fresh fish, the use of ice is required. Insulated and/or refrigerated transport, rapid distribution and efficient marketing organizations are also needed. While the preference is for fresh fish, new products could be developed and made acceptable, such as frozen and canned freshwater fish. Canned fish is most suitable for use in schools and in children's feeding programmes and can be 'tailored' to suit local tastes.

Small-sized fish, which are now used only by the local fishing community, fresh or after crude roasting, could be canned to advantage.

INDONESIA

Shortage of transport facilities constitutes a serious problem for marketing the sometimes large quantities of freshwater fish. Lack of transport sometimes limits the amount of salt available for processing. Dried, salted or smoked fish are generally lower in price than are fresh fish of high quality, such as *Leptobarbus hoeveni* and other Cyprinidae. For technical and marketing reasons, fish such as Ophiocephaloidae, Siluroidae, *Trichogaster* spp. and *Helostoma temincki*, are usually required to be salted and dried. Siluroidae are smoked. Cultured fish, such as *Osphronemus gourami*, *Cyprinus carpio*, *Puntius javanicus*, and other less important species, are sold alive or fresh. *Tilapia mossambica* in dried, salted and spiced form is is occasionally available.

KHMER REPUBLIC

Most of the freshwater fish in the Khmer Republic lend themselves to 'live preservation' in enclosures set up near the bank or in the middle of the shallow water. Some are also held in open containers supported by floats. These containers may hold up to 200 or 300 tons of fish. Small baskets, too, are used to keep a few kilogrammes of live fish. The fish may be transported live in junks with open-work planks through which freshwater constantly flows. When transported over land, the fish are kept alive in containers half-filled with water, while in the markets they are kept in water-filled basins or in transport containers or sometimes in baskets. Problems of preservation, curing and processing are met in dealing with small fish and those species which cannot endure a confined life or high temperatures often found in shallow water, especially in the dry season. Traditional methods of processing are used to preserve these, as well as the fish which die in the enclosures or containers.

The following products are processed in the Khmer Republic:

Fish paste ('prahoc')

This is widely consumed by the rural population. It is whitish in colour and has a strong odour. It is not very different from 'tinned anchovy' in preparation and taste. The small fish, mainly small Cyprinidae, are headed, gutted and scaled. They are then washed in running water, squeezed to defat them, and properly drained before being dried-salted. They are stacked in piles or put in baskets for 2 to 3 days to ferment, after which they are pounded and packed tightly in jars under a layer of prickling brine. Problems have arisen in the traditional processing of 'prahoc'. First, the manpower required cannot be found at the landing place. The farmers have to move families to these places to buy the fish and prepare their year's supply of the product. This is expensive in time and money and is no longer acceptable in the circumstances ruling today. In the second place, the types of packing used, especially the earthen jars, make storage and handling difficult. For this reason distribution and marketing are limited. There is, therefore, a need to find a way to mechanize the manufacture of the product. This would have the advantage of improving and standardizing the quality, as well as making possible a stricter application of the rules of hygiene.

Fish Sauce ('nuoc-mam')

This is a yellowish liquid extracted from the juice produced from fish paste ('prahoc') or specially prepared from small fish. There is usually a glut of small fish in the main fishing season and as these cannot be made into paste, they are used for the manufacture of sauce. The fish are salted as soon as possible after removal from the water and placed in vats with the layers of salt. The proportion is usually 2 kg of fish to 1 kg of salt. The vat is covered with matting and large stones are placed on top to compress the contents and prevent any overflow. After six months of fermentation, the juice is drawn off by a wooden faucet through a filter. It is a clear yellowish liquid, not very odorous but very rich in nitrogen. After exposure to the sun, it is filtered, bottled or put in special jars, and is ready for consumption.

Profit-hungry operators are debasing this traditional method. Fish which have already reached a very advanced degree of decomposition are being used to shorten the autolysis period. The drawing-off of the juice is forced, calling for later cooking, and additives, such as toasted rice, saccharine glutamate, etc, are used to make the product appear to be normal. This has not only damaged the reputation of the product but is a danger to public health.

Use of waste material

Wastes from paste or dried-salted fish preparations were formerly used, along with small fish, for oil extraction but as oil no longer fetches a worthwhile price, they are now used as fertlizer or as feed in fish culture.

The current method for making fertilizer is to spread the wastes on beaten earth in the sun. This method is far from satisfactory as the loss is high and the product is no good for storage or for handling. It also has a very bad odour. Therefore, the use of such wastes and surplus small freshwater fish to make meal for livestock would seem to be a good solution. But there are difficulties because the quantity of raw material available is not sufficient for the establishment of a plant, and the sources of supply are too widely scattered. The small amount of fish meal from freshwater fish now on the market is obtained from thin species which dry quickly.

Salted-dried fish

A large part of the yearly freshwater fish production of the Khmer Republic, until 1950, was made into salted-dried fish for export. However, the market for this product has dwindled. It seems that consumers, both domestic and foreign, are changing their taste and now prefer fresh fish, which are cheaper and lend themselves better to many culinary preparations. Salted-dried fish, however, could retain an important place in the market if new techniques were used to produce a better quality product.

Smoked fish

Species chosen for traditional smoking are those with flat, thin bodies. The fish are skewered through the head to form 'hands' of 4 to 10 fish and glued to one another by their ventral fins. The 'hands', covered with matting, are spread on wicker trays under which a fire produces smoke Such smoking is done in a closed hut for a large-scale production.

As this traditional method consumes too much wood and time, and will cease when fuel wood is no longer available from the forests near the fishing grounds, the need is to introduce modern smoking techniques which will yield an improved product of higher standard quality.

Use of refrigeration

Only a short time ago, one kilogramme of ice cost as much as one kilogramme of ordinary fish so nobody considered using ice to preserve fish. But fish have become very costly while ice can now be produced in abundance and cheaply. Its use, therefore, has become economic and profitable. The use of refrigeration in the fishing industry has been restricted in the past by the limited amount of electricity generated, its high cost, and the heavy taxes on ice (30 per cent on the sale price). In the changed circumstances of today, there is an increasing use of refrigeration in the freshwater fish industry.

LAOS

The Government of Laos has recently begun a fisheries programme in this land-locked country because of the decline of freshwater fish stocks. The decline has resulted in the import of fish from Thailand, amounting to about 65 per cent of the country's yearly consumption. The fish culture industry is, therefore, being developed to increase supplies. So far the lack of ice and cold-storage facilities have resulted in poor preservation, while processed fish is of poor quality and available only in small quantities.

MALAYSIA

The suitability of some freshwater fish for processing was investigated in Malaysia in 1971. In the first trial four species of carp – common, hybrid (common carp × *Puntius gonionotus*), bighead and grass carp, *Puntius gonionotus* and *Tilapia* sp.–were canned in oil, brine, curry and tomato sauce. In the second trial, grass and bighead carp and *Tilapia* sp. were canned in salt, using various techniques. Fish fingers and fish cakes were also made. The first trial showed that the canned fish were not firm in texture and, with the exception of bighead carp, had a muddy taste. The longer the fish were kept in frozen storage before canning, the softer the texture of the finished products. Canned hybrid carp and *Puntius*, which did not undergo the one hour precooking, were also soft in texture. *Tilapia*, held in frozen storage for 11 days, broke up during frying. In the second trial the process was modified and a product of satisfactory appearance and texture was produced, but the grass and silver carp and *Tilapia* had a muddy flavour while bighead carp did not. The muddy flavour could perhaps be removed by transferring the fish to a tub of clean water a week before processing. Carp and other freshwater fish are known to be rich in lipids and during separation of the flesh of the cooked fish large depots of lipids were noticed. In the second trial, fish fillets for storage were quick frozen in a plate freezer, glazed in water and stored in a cool room (−18° to −23°C). Fish sticks could be made from bighead carp but the large number of bones in the fish made such manufacture impractical. Fish cakes made from carp were of poor texture. The limited production of freshwater fish in Malaysia and the lack of any surplus indicates that canning or processing them is uneconomical at this time.

Pond fish are produced in Sabah. Those caught in natural waters are seldom brought to market, being consumed locally.

While the fish are mostly eaten fresh, the following are common methods of preservation: salt-dried, smoke-dried (with or without seasoning); hot smoked (for immediate consumption); and fermented (only small fish are used, such as *Tilapia*, *Trichogaster*, and *Puntius*). A problem is how to get rid of the small bones in the carps. The method of transporting and keeping of live fish for marketing also requires attention.

PAKISTAN

All freshwater fish produced in Pakistan are marketed fresh and consumed locally. Landings for the last five years have ranged from 14,000 to 28,000 tons annually.

PHILIPPINES

The demand for freshwater fish far exceeds production, and utilization is dependent on the habits of the people. In most parts of the country, the fish are preferred almost at 'fresh-from-the-hook' condition or alive. It is generally considered that freshwater fish lose their good taste soon after death, therefore they are not frozen or refrigerated because their taste becomes flat. For instance, there is virtually no market for dead snakehead, *Ophiocephalus striatus*. Catfish (*Clarias batrachus*), *Trichogaster* and *Puntias* are usually fermented with cooked rice. The small freshwater shrimps, *Palaemonidae* and *Atvidae*, are usually sun-dried but if they can be sold alive, they fetch a very good price. The white goby, *Glossogobius giurus*,

and the silvery perch, *Therapon plumbeus*, are also sun-dried during periods of abundance. Normally, small fish are dried while large ones are sold in the local markets. Common carp is not processed at all but is sold whole and fresh. This species is usually very fatty and processing it would pose a problem.

In the utilization of the following species particular problems are encountered:

Catfish (Clarias macrocephalus)

Means are required for effectively removing the black skin, which is unattractive in the canned product; the flesh easily breaks when canned; only flat oval or square cans may be used; the product has a strong grassy odour; and rancidity easily develops in the dried-salted split fish.

Tilapia (Tilapia mossambica)

Problems in the utilization of this species are the development of randicity in the dried-salted split fish; its short shelf-life at room temperature; the relatively dark colour of the flesh even when canned in tomato sauce; the low yield in canning; and the unattractive colour of the fish.

SINGAPORE

All freshwater fish in Singapore are marketed without refrigeration, preferably alive. As most people prefer marine fish, freshwater fish are cheaper.

THAILAND

The annual production of freshwater fish in Thailand is more than 110,000 tons (1970). Of this, some 60 per cent is sold or consumed fresh, over 16 per cent as dried and salted, some 5 per cent as boiled or smoked, more than 12 per cent as fermented fish, less than 0.2 per cent as fishmeal, and a little less than 4 per cent as fish sauce. Some small quantities are also used as fertilizer. A major problem is the seasonal fluctuation in supply. There are no significant problems in utilization, particularly in the north of the country.

Discussion on Part III

Establishing a fish product industry

The discussion concerning problems and trends in the utilization of resources dealt with the various requirements that should be taken into account when establishing a fish product industry. There is the need to take into account the socio-economic problems of the developing countries and to organize training at all levels. This requires government involvement. The importance of research for the future progress of the industry was pointed out and it was emphasized that it is necessary to ensure that joint ventures will serve the best interests of developing countries.

GUIZADO (Peru) said that the requirements for establishing a food fish industry are dependent on the degree of development of the fisheries concerned. Training at all levels is a critical factor and he suggested that FAO should give priority to such training programmes. At the same time the government should ensure a close working arrangement with the private sector.

ALVAREZ (Mexico) and MATTOS (Uruguay) also emphasized this view.

SANCHEZ (Peru) said that in developing countries governments are usually motivated by socio-economic factors in product development and the work of the research laboratories has to conform to this approach. The effort, therefore, is to develop new products which will contribute to the improvement in the diet of the mass of the population.

APPLEYARD (FAO), speaking about the general situation in developing countries where efforts are being made to develop fishery industries, stressed the team nature of an undertaking where international assistance is being provided. The initial need is to define clearly the priority and objectives and to attempt only that which can be achieved. In the context of such aid, he pointed out that FAO could assist in many ways in identifying investment opportunities, setting up joint ventures, attracting foreign funds, providing technical experience and training at various levels, and so on. Not the least of FAO's services, he added, is to be realistically negative to eliminate non-productive activities and projects.

BILLY (USA) stated that the research worker has an important part to play in developing the initial technological data-base for the development of an industry and its products while the technologist has varying and continuing roles to play in bringing an industry to full potential. He gave as an example the American catfish farming industry. Research had assisted the industry to rapid growth which now has levelled out. The role of the research worker is now to resolve the new technological and biological problems to enable the industry to make further progress. The work to be done includes research on nutrition, diseases, high density culture systems, selective breeding, and improved grading and harvesting techniques.

TALABI (Nigeria) explained that in his country the fishing industry has been developed by local and by foreign industries in cooperation with the Government. The latter has financed two fishing companies, one for deep-sea fishing and one to establish a coastal shrimp fishery. Product development was not required because only frozen fish was demanded.

AMANO (Japan) mentioned that the government has not provided much assistance to industry in establishing fish sausage production as its policy is to assist the fishing rather than the processing industry.

MOSS (Canada) made an appropriate conclusion to the discussion on this subject in saying that industry must become more politically conscious in relation to developing countries and take into account their socio-economic problems. These are of concern at all stages and require that the risks involved in the development of fisheries should be shared by the government and industry.

The utilization of fish resources

The question of utilizing the resources to meet the future needs was of primary importance in all Sessions of the Conference. The situation with a number of marine white fish resources, for example, of the merluza family, Alaska pollock, etc., appears essentially similar. Most species are as raw material interchangeable and they can help to fill the expanding demand in the convenience food market. This market offers also possibilities of an increase in the potential utilization of a large number of presently underutilized species. Considerable attention was given to the utilization of small pelagic fish species, especially from tropical waters. In this respect this Conference differed from past conferences which dealt mainly with traditional fish, and, at the same time, the changing patterns of fish supplies became obvious. It was mentioned that economic conditions will, to a great extent, shape the use of small pelagic fish whether used as animal feed or directly for human consumption (see also Discussion in Chapter IV).

STEINBERG (USA) referred to the problems in the utilization of Pacific hake (*Merluccius productus*) for food purposes because of the proteolytic activities associated with the Myxosporidian parasite. Industry has lately begun, with good success, to use this resource for sale as fresh fillets. Pre-frying, storage and oven-cooking have been investigated in laboratory trials to determine influences of enzyme activity on the quality of the product. The flavour of the pre-fried product was not as good as that of one completely fried at 350°F for 3.25 minutes. However, there appeared to be no enzyme induced texture differences between the highly parasitized and the non-parasitized fish due to the different rates of cooking or multiple exposure to heat.

PEROVIC (FAO) reported on the discovery of a resource of snipe fish (*Macrorhamphosus seslopex* and *Macrorhamphosus gracilis*) off Morocco. Laboratory tests show the fish, not so far exploited for human consumption, to have very tasty white meat suitable for making fish hamburgers, fingers, etc.

FLEAR (UK) reported on the changing pattern of landings in the UK and on the need to use increasing quantities of under-priced fish species such as haddock, whiting, etc., as a result of the government's policy to provide grant and loan facilities to build up the inshore fishing fleet. Increasing quantities of small fish are expected to be landed which are difficult to process and market in the accepted manner.

BYKOV (USSR) mentioned that the possibilities to utilize fish of lower market value for human consumption are being investigated in the USSR with the aim to develop both traditional and new types of products. The development of new product forms is being carried out along the following three lines:

(1) Production of frozen minced fish. There is already a small commercial production of frozen minced fish but the marketing of this product is difficult.

(2) Production of protein hydrolysates. Promising results can be expected although the work is still in the experimental stage. The hydrolysate can, for example,

be used as a protein base for the development of such products as caviar. Black grain caviar which is comparable to that derived from the sturgeon has already been produced on a laboratory scale, and it is intended **to** organize its commercial production for domestic consumption.

(3) Production of powdered products. Only research work and laboratory experiments have been carried out in the past. It is, however, intended to organize the production of extracted and non-extracted FPC and of fish soups which are being developed according to Norwegian techniques.

BLIGH (Canada) emphasized the urgent need to develop knowledge and processes for the preparation of products from new or underutilized species, with strong emphasis on quality which today is much more important than heretofore. He added that industry in Canada is sensitive to these factors and needs and will cooperate with the Government in improving the overall use of the fishery resources. There is a general feeling that fish are now too valuable to waste and many more technologists are being employed by industry in the effort to make handling and processing of fish more efficient.

PETERKIN (Guyana) said that shark resources have been developed with UNDP aid in Guyana. Products acceptable to consumers have been developed from dry-salted shark meat. The main difficulty was to overcome the strong traditional resistance to eating shark flesh.

HERBORG (Denmark) mentioned that shark salting programmes failed in other areas of the Caribbean because of the consumer prejudice against shark as food.

TALABI (Nigeria) said, with reference to the experience gained in Guyana, that the shark cake industry there may owe its success to a similarity of this product to stockfish which is well accepted.

CLARKE (Guyana) in reply to Talabi explained that the intention was to use salted shark products as a substitute for cod, rather than an alternative. He added that salted sea trout (*Cynoscion* sp.) closely resembles salted cod but does not influence the demand for salted shark.

BRAEKKAN (Norway) mentioned that investigation of the nutritive value of 10 species of shark has shown that good smoked products can be produced. Salting removes urea; only with blue shark are there some problems concerning texture. Shark is a good source of protein.

Problems in the utilization of shellfish resources

Some specific problems were discussed such as colour changes and yield from shrimp held in refrigerated seawater but a clear picture did not result. Much attention was directed to the utilization of squid.

BALASINGAM (Malaysia) said that in his country the shrimp are cooked and peeled, so that a desirable bright pink colour is imparted to the flesh, then frozen for export. A red dye is often added to brighten the colour of the flesh. The oxidation of astaxanthin to astacin may not be undesirable in all cases.

ACKMAN (Canada) stated that Canadian shrimp are normally marketed dull red in colour. In one case where some imported shrimp were bright red the Canadian authorities confiscated the consignment, suspecting the shrimp had been dyed, but tests showed only astaxanthin.

AAGAARD (Denmark) said that the colour of the meat of the deep sea shrimp marketed in Denmark is bright red. This is the colour looked for by the markets concerned, mainly European. He added that this shrimp is also known as 'pink' shrimp.

STEINBERG (USA) stated that discoloration of the carapace of shrimp can be prevented by the addition of carbon dioxide to the refrigerated sea water in which they are held. This aids in retaining the desirable astaxanthin pigment of the tail meat for longer than is possible when storage in ice is used. Steinberg also expressed the view that the idea of reduced yields as the result of such storage may be illusory because the water picked up during storage is lost during cooking and peeling.

AAGAARD (Denmark) claimed that there is an actual decrease in yield. He and his colleagues have measured the yield in terms of the amount of processed meat obtained from the same weight of raw shrimp. They had weighed the shrimp on board before starting their storage experiments, placing the same amounts in RSW and in boxes with ice and comparing the amount of meat finally obtained from each source.

JAMES (Australia) said that the yield of cooked and peeled shrimp following seawater storage for extended periods is always reduced even if the uptake of salt and water is taken into account. He observed that the addition of CO_2 to seawater results in unacceptable products because of acid flavour and poor texture. Seawater buffered with citrate and phosphate has been shown to be effective in Australia, but whereas CO_2 inhibits the development of black spots, the buffered seawater does not.

BYKOV (USSR) said with regard to the utilization of krill that this is a new, large and complicated problem in the USSR. The results of technical research are encouraging while significant commercial and economic data can only be obtained from long-term experiments. Anyhow, some quantities of krill paste have been marketed under the brand name 'Ocean Paste'. Krill yields 20 to 25 per cent of this paste.

ANDERSON (UK) referring to the under utilized resource of squid and the need to prepare new products from this raw material, pointed out that a squid protein isolate has been obtained. It has functional properties, which suggests that there are now new opportunities for utilizing this large resource.

TAKAHASHI (Japan), in discussing the world's huge squid resources, stated squid could be made available as a food for people in all countries if products were evolved from it to meet the tastes of the consumers concerned. This is how it is processed in Japan where it is very popular in, for example, soft dried sliced form. On the other hand, the Japanese consumer does not like smoked squid products which, he thought, might have a strong appeal in many other countries.

KONOSU (Japan) said that the structure of the amino acid of the squid protein is similar to that of fish meat protein, therefore, the nutritive value of squid is very high.

KARNICKI (Poland) reported that his country produces canned squid in tomato sauce and onion and there is a good market for this product.

MATSUMOTO (Japan) referred to Takahashi's paper. This author mentioned that 'water-soluble myosin' might induce a feeling that protein yield on washing squid meat is poor. Matsumoto, however, pointed out that the water-solubility of squid meat is evoked by a particular condition and the protein is readily precipitated and recovered by adding a small amount of salts such as Na Cl (0.01 M), Ca C12 or Mg C12 (0.001 M). There must be a proper solution for each particular kind of fish if trouble is to be avoided in processing.

Handling and processing tropical fish

The discussion focussed on aspects of chilling, freezing and frozen storage. The production of minces, sauces and dried products was touched on briefly. Among the marine species two groups must be distinguished, those living in the warm surface water and those in the colder, lower currents. There is good evidence that the former keep much longer under chill conditions than the latter. It seems that containerization offers advantages (See Discussion in Chapter II on 'Handling and chilling of fish').

HANSEN (FAO) reminded the meeting that in many tropical waters the warm layer is of limited depth and lies on top of heavy cold waters so that two distinct groups of fish species are found. The fish inhabiting the upper 50 m of water, which has a temperature of around 26°C, are often greyish in colour. The fish living in the cold water, at 10°C or lower, are often reddish in colour. It is necessary to distinguish between these two groups when talking of the storage characteristics of tropical marine fish.

KARNICKI (Poland) replied to a question by Hansen as to whether, in trawling for the cold water species, it is possible to bring the net up so fast that the fish are still cold when deposited on deck. He said that in Polish experience it depended on the size of catch and species of fish. For example, herring and mackerel are easy to discharge but if the catch includes dogfish the operation becomes difficult. Polish vessels fishing in tropical waters have found that discharging such small species as red snapper and jack mackerel from the cod-end is so difficult that it is necessary to cut the net and force the fish out by using high pressure jets of water.

BYKOV (USSR) told the conference that Soviet experience in the Indian Ocean shows that with most species of fish *rigor mortis* sets in within an hour of capture. In order to obtain a high quality product it is necessary, therefore, to store them in chilled sea water immediately after catching. Commercially it is possible to do this with a rather small quantity in about half an hour but difficult with larger catches. For best results the fish should be gutted and the head and fins removed. Other experience with tropical sardine also shows the importance of freezing the fish as soon as possible after catching.

HERBORG (Denmark) reported on icing experiments with sea trout from warm waters. He said there is practically no difference after storage in ice for 2½ weeks between gutted and ungutted fish. The fish used in the experiment were delayed on deck for about four hours in a temperature of 30°C before being iced.

DISNEY (FAO) pointed out that it is often very difficult in tropical countries to ice fish immediately after capture. He described some tests on the effect of timed delays prior to icing conducted in Malawi and Ghana. Tilapia in the former and sea bream in the latter country were held at ambient temperature for six hours, then iced. In each case storage life was reduced only marginally when compared with fish iced immediately after capture.

BREBNER (New Zealand) expressed interest in these results because experience in New Zealand showed that the snapper caught in his country's semi-tropical waters has to be iced immediately – or within half an hour – to prevent rapid deterioration.

HANSEN (FAO) referred to consumer preference in tropical countries for live fish. He said it often reflects a prejudice against iced fish. However, this is not unusual and is known in Europe. As a result there is a thriving trade in 'shelved' cod – that is, cod which rests on ice but shows no sign of icing on the skin. This system might be usefully employed in the tropics. He added that Danish research technologists are developing a new box system which will be ideal for the handling and transport of 'shelved' fish which will rest on layers of ice and be chilled mainy by water dripping from the boxes above.

ILYAS (Indonesia) summarized the problems faced by developing countries in the tropical regions in handling and utilizing fish as follows: (1) the great variety of species which have not yet been studied biologically and biochemically; (2) the lack of knowledge of the fishermen on handling and processing techniques; (3) the lack of experience of research and extension staff; and (4) the lack of infrastructure and facilities, such as ice, clean water, transport and distribution. He suggested that FAO should survey the research and development programmes of developing countries and help advise on future planning. Further, he pointed to the need to establish standards regarding spoilage patterns, etc, and for handling, icing and preserving fish in tropical conditions. Several other speakers discussed this queston.

DISNEY (FAO) added that the apparent quantitative and qualitative differences between tropical and temperate fish during chill storage complicate the task of drawing up international standards.

BURGESS (UK) proposed that FAO should undertake publication of a handbook on handling and processing technology for tropical fisheries.

Factors affecting the utilization of farmed and freshwater fish

The discussion centred on problems of off-flavour which fish can pick up under aquacultural conditions. A muddy flavour can result from the presence of algae but also other types of off-flavour occur. Discoloration of the flesh and of the skin can appear under cultural conditions. In general, although excellent information was presented, it became obvious that additional scientific research and more information with regard to influences on quality of farmed fish and to consumer reaction are required.

LOVELL (USA) said they used the channel catfish culture for the model as the problem is of the greatest importance to the industry. A similar problem exists in the trout and carp industries and in tropical fish culture in the Philippines, Thailand, Central America and elsewhere. Two types of aquatic organisms have been identified in association with cultured catfish off-flavours: species of *Sheptomyces actinomycetes* and certain species of blue-green algae. Fortunately, the off-flavour compounds can be purged by holding the fish in clean, flowing water for 10 to 15 days, depending on flavour intensity and temperature, but unfortunately the fish lose 10 to 15 per cent of their weight in this process.

COLE (UK) mentioned that there appear to be two distinct types of muddy taint in freshwater fish – the evanescent and the more permanent. The former may effect all fish in a lake or pond but the off-flavour may disappear a few months later. Leaching with ice water and cold storage reduces the level of such off-flavour, The second type, the permanent muddy taint, is found, for example, in Lake Chilwa, Malawi. The off-flavour cannot be reduced by leaching or cold storage and persists strongly even in hard-dried, heavily smoked fish. The off-flavour is, however, not considered objectionable by the local consumers.

BIRIBONWOHA (Uganda) said that the muddy flavour is common to both cultured and wild species in Lake Kyoga, such as Nile perch, but can be leached out as described by Cole.

COLE (UK) replied that in their investigations the off-flavour found in Nile perch from Lake Kyoga disappeared naturally before the investigations were completed. As the fish is an active predator it was assumed that the chemical substance responsible for the off-flavour entered via the gills.

TAPIADOR (FAO) stated that the problem of off-flavour in cultivated fish is common to many Asian countries.

HINDS (New Zealand) related that consumers in New Guinea rejected Tilapia reared in sewage ponds because of taste but after the fish had been in fresh water for 7 to 10 days, the people found them quite edible. He said that trout and eel cultivated in sewage ponds in New Zealand are accepted for human consumption.

BALASINGAM (Malaysia) reported that he has used pond farmed grass carp, silver carp, bighead carp, hybrid carp and tilapia for canning in brine and for making fish cakes and fingers. Most of the flesh of the canned fish became soft in texture and all the products had a muddy flavour.

KARNICKI (Poland), referring to his country's long tradition in carp cultivation, said Polish commercial practice is to keep the fish in cold, clean water for 3 or 4 weeks before use. This method removes most of the muddy flavour.

YAMAKAWA (Japan) stated that aquaculture in Japan now produces some 160,000 tons of fresh-water fish and 600,000 tons of marine fish and crustaceans. Fish with off-flavours are treated in several ways, such as by starving or leaving them in clean flowing water or by cooking the flesh in special ways. One method is 'koikoku' in which a paste-like seasoning 'miso', made from soy beans, is used. This absorbs the off-flavour of carp.

KANEDA (Japan) said that they add carotinoid to the feed pellets to produce good meat in farmed trout and feed eels with pollock liver oil to fatten them. He added that oil refineries buy the fish caught near their plants and dispose of them because of their oily flavour which is considered unacceptable by consumers.

DISNEY (FAO), referring to the question of storage, said that investigations of the biochemical and quality characteristics of aquarium reared tilapia in East Africa showed that the treatment of the fish – well fed, starved, exhausted or rested – has a profound influence on their entry into *rigor mortis* and on their textural characteristics in iced storage. Those starved produced a much softer texture overall while the flesh of well fed fish tended to become harder. These results indicate possibilities for manipulating quality of products made from farmed fish.

DOESBURG (Netherlands) referred to the studies being made at the Freshwater Fisheries Institute, Nyegezi, Tanzania, on the keeping quality of iced tilapia. The aim is to develop a grading scheme for iced fish for inland distribution. The determining criteria are the outer appearance and gill odours in relation to flesh quality. Experiments show that the difference between gutted and ungutted fish can be detected after 15 days of storage. After three to four weeks, the outer appearance of stored fish becomes unattractive because of the accumulation of bacterial slime on the skin. This, however, can be easily removed by water spray, leaving the fish with a normal appearance. At this stage fillets from gutted fish remain acceptable while those from ungutted do not.

STEINBERG (USA) said that it now seems practical to raise fish, such as tilapia, in large single-species or poly-culture operations for use as raw material for minced flesh products. The fish could present new problems, he added, because black belly linings are incorporated in the edible flesh in the deboning process unless earlier removed by manual or mechanical processing. Bones in carp, however, now present no problem as effective deboning machines are available. He concluded that the long-range solution to the problem of undesirable characteristics, such as black belly lining, is genetic.

ALLSOPP (IDRC) suggested that the Conference should stress the need to improve systems of distribution and marketing of live or fresh farmed fish because most of the harvest in tropical countries is sold in this form.

Part IV

PRODUCT DEVELOPMENT

The Practice of Product Development   *R Kreuzer and C Day*

PRATIQUE DU DEVELOPPEMENT DES PRODUITS

Le document décrit les diverses mesures appliquées par une entreprise européene moderne de pêche en vue de l'amélioration et du développement de ses produits. Il convient de noter que la manutention soigneuse et le contrôle de la qualité du poisson sont des éléments essentiels de ces mesures. Bien que l'exemple étudié ici soit celui d'une entreprise hautement industrialisée qui fabrique des produits de la pêche destinès à un marché très exigeant, on insiste sur le fait que les principes fondamentaux de l'amélioration et du développement des produits valent pour les industries de produits halieutiques du monde entier quel qu'en soit le stade de développement économique. Le document indique ce que les pêcheries artisanales devraient faire en premier lieu pour développer leurs produits.

Metodos para la creacion de productos

En el documenta se describen las diversas medidas emprendidas por una moderna compañia europea de pesca para mejorar los productos y crear otros nuevos. Es de observar que la manipulación cuidadosa del pescado y el control de calidad forman parte esencial del proceso. Aunque el ejemplo que se estudia en el documento se refiere a una compañia muy industrializada que se dedica a confeccionar productos pesqueros para un mercado muy selectivo, se pone de relieve que los principios fundamentales para mejorar los productos y crear otros nuevos pueden aplicarse a las industrias de productos pesqueros de todos los países y cualquiera que sea su grado de desarrollo técnico. En el documento se determinan los primeros pasos que hay que tomar para la creación de nuevos productos de la pesca artesanal.

Product development has become a matter of increasing concern to the fisheries processing industry for a number of reasons. A principal one for fishery products companies in the western world is the need to meet intense competition, to maintain and, if possible, expand their position in the market. This reason is allied to the need to meet the changing tastes and demands of consumers. Another reason is to make the fullest use of all available raw material and, yet again, to develop products from fish which are unfamiliar or new to the consumer. These reasons apply in varying degrees throughout the world wherever fishery products are distributed and wherever it is hoped to establish markets for them. And as the food habits and the taste demands of people are very deeply ingrained, and as these tastes and likings differ from country to country, product development in harmony with them is essential for establishing any fishery products industry. Thus, whether such industries are located and operate in technically advanced or developing economies, the underlying principles of product development apply. While, therefore, this paper, which has been prepared with the full collaboration of 'Nordsee' Deutsche Hochseefischerei GmbH, Bremerhaven, refers to the policy and practice of product development of a highly sophisticated western processing company, it provides an example of work in this field which can be of practical value to all concerned with fishery products development.

BACKGROUND

'Nordsee' is a 68 per cent subsidiary of the Anglo-Dutch international Unilever concern, although it operates as an entity. It is based in Bremerhaven and in Cuxhaven, Federal Republic of Germany, and is concerned exclusively with all operations based on fish. The company, which was established in 1896, employs 10,000 people, makes some 800 products and has a turnover of about US $ 300 million a year, mostly earned in the European Market. In relation to the number of products, it should be pointed out that, while the company market an extensive list of their own brands – such as 'Norda' and 'Lysell' – they also produce branded products for some companies and a very big range for many other distributors, such as retail chains and supermarkets. The organizational structure of 'Nordsee' is in three divisions – trawling, industry and trade. Each division is run by a director, who has a seat on the overall 'Nordsee'

Board of Directors, which is headed by the Chairman of the Company. The main administration and two factories are located at Bremerhaven. The plants produce a wide variety of frozen, canned, smoked and marinated products, including convenience ready-to-serve products, and handle smoked and fresh fish. Cuxhaven is also the home base of the 'Nordsee' fleet, which consists of some 50 trawlers, including 22 factory ships. An integral part of 'Nordsee' is the trade organization consisting of 39 depots for the wholesale activities to third parties and the distribution of all goods for 300 retail shops and 100 restaurants. These are mainly located in Germany, Austria and the Netherlands.

QUALITY CONTROL

Relative to the large-scale and complicated set-up, and to product development, mention must be made of quality control measures as these have a vital influence on the quality of the end product. Such quality control starts with the careful handling of the catch on board. For example, the new factory ships, which are of 3,500 tons displacement, and can carry 1,000 tons of fish fillets in their holds (plus the fishmeal production from offal), and cost about US $ 7 million each, are each equipped with a laboratory, chiefly to control the oil factor, which is important in processing herrings. But the general design and organization of the machinery and layout for processing the catch, starting as soon as it is hauled on board, ensures that the filleted frozen fish are kept in prime condition. Even when off-loaded in port, they are mechanically put straight into containers and taken into cold storage without exposure or being touched by human hand. Similarly, quality control is exercised all along the line. For instance, all fresh fish handled by 'Nordsee' are under the control of qualified inspectors, while all the frozen, canned, marinated, smoked, etc, products are subject to control by the laboratories. There are two laboratories to cover the factory products and two for the fishmeal plants. The control standards are set and the work coordinated and supervised by a central laboratory. The work of the laboratories has an influence on the quality of the end products at every stage in processing. The laboratories control the physical, chemical and bacteriological standards relative not only to the fish throughout its processing but also those concerning all ingredients used, such as salts, spices, vegetables, liquids, etc. The control is exercised over metals and all materials concerned with canning and other packs, including all the packaging materials. The control is also concerned with weights and accurate descriptions of the products. In particular, it is the responsibility of the laboratories to take into account the requirements of the multitude of rules and regulations of the countries to which the products are being sent. This latter consideration is of the utmost importance because of the wide variations in these requirements and the fact that failure to comply with them could be disastrous to the company's export trade.

As much as possible, all this control work has been systematized and a check list has been established which helps to ensure that the control work is completely and thoroughly carried out at each stage. When special problems arise, such as those requiring research, the central laboratory calls in the assistance of the Unilever laboratories in Great Britain or elsewhere or, if need be, independent laboratories outside the group. In addition to this scientific and technical control, the general objectives of such control are maintained throughout processing by, for example, such simple measures as requiring all processing staff to wash their hands with bactericidal soap on entering the factory. Suitable washing facilities are placed at the entrances to each factory. Another seemingly small but important point is that all fresh fish are prepared and despatched within the day of their arrival. Further, they are sent out, fully iced, in disposable baskets. Perhaps the most critical control factor in producing high-quality fishery products is the time taken in processing frozen fish through its various stages until it emerges in a new shape and a new appearance as a product. For instance, in the process to produce fishsticks or portions or fishcake, the time taken for each stage has a direct bearing on the bacterial count. In order to keep this well within the standards set, it is necessary to design and operate the machinery to perform the required tasks within a limited time. This has often required exceptional engineering and organizational ability, a cost that has to be paid in order to make a product not only acceptable to the consumer but with a keeping quality—that is, a shelf life—to meet the requirements of both the wholesale and retail trade. This means they must have a trade shelf life of at least six months.

PRODUCT DEVELOPMENT

Before enumerating the steps taken in the actual process of product development, it is desirable to consider first the kind of product concerned. In the case of 'Nordsee', their aim is clearly defined: to develop top quality products for a sophisticated market. Other companies in Europe and elsewhere may have different priorities. But the principle remains the same. In 'Nordsee's' view, an essential element in developing the sophisticated market is to provide products in harmony with a new image of fish. The aim is to get away from the traditional image of a good, nourishing food which, unfortunately, smells when being cooked, calls for a lot of work in the kitchen, and may present trouble in eating because of its bones. This latter point is of great significance to mothers when their children are small not only because of the trouble of deboning the fish but because even a small bone may easily stick in a child's throat. The aim, therefore, of companies such as 'Nordsee' is to provide odourless, boneless, easy-to-prepare fish products. This 'easy-to-prepare' concept has grown in importance because many housewives in Europe go out to work and, in any case, because increased incomes and changing habits mean that women are no longer happy to spend the hours in the kitchen as was traditionally the case with housewives. In view of these considerations, 'Nordsee's' development efforts have been directed to the 'ready-to-cook' or 'ready-to-eat' products.

All development work is centralized in a body called the Development Board (Entwicklungsleitung) consisting of the technical director of the industry division and the senior chemist of the control laboratory. The Development Board has four committees, one for problems concerning the fishery, one for canned fish products, one for frozen products and one for trade problems. The Board meets once a year to discuss present and anticipated trends and to determine which ideas should be taken up for improvement or which new products should be created to meet the oncoming situation. As this evaluation process suggests, not all proposals are adapted for further exploration and of those that are pursued no more than 10 in 100 ever come to anything. When required, one or more of the individual committees (which normally consist of one or two technical members, one marking member, one commercial member and the head of company planning) are called together and consulted by the Development Board. Such consultations take place throughout the development of the product.

PRACTICAL DEVELOPMENT WORK

The work is carried out in four phases, each controlled by an appropriate form which marks the beginning and end of each phase. Briefly, the work done in each phase is as follows:

Phase 1—This starts with a 'Development Proposal' which is submitted on a form. This phase is the responsibility of a development committee which reports to the Development Board. The work done at this stage is in the test kitchen and the laboratory. The first calculations of cost are also made. If the proposal is considered suitable for further exploration, a 'Development Request' is prepared, recording the information given and views expressed by the test kitchen and laboratory, and the industry, marketing and sales groups. The 'Request' is then considered by the Board of Directors and, if approved, moves on to the second phase.

Phase 2—This consists of more detailed investigations of the proposal which, if favourable in result, leads to the preparation of a 'Project Proposal' (not on a form) by the marketing group together with the Development Board. This 'Proposal' is considered by the Board of Directors and, if approved, goes forward to the third phase.

Phase 3—This includes market test carried out under contract by a professional concern. The marketing people of 'Nordsee' are responsible for handling this arrangement and for preparing the 'Introduction

Proposal' which is then considered by the Board of Directors. If they approve it, then the project moves into its fourth and final phase.

Phase 4—This phase sees the commercial production of the product and its launching on the market.

These phases of product development are costly and may well involve an expenditure of some US $ 100,000. Actually, as far as 'Nordsee' are concerned, they may spend in total some US $ 900,000 a year – up to about 3 per cent of their turnover—on development but that covers development in their whole field of activity, including their ships and shops and restaurants. Large as this sum is relative to the turnover, their thinking is in terms of a larger amount, as and when the stability and profitability of the industry permits. Further to the four phases, some of the details about the work done provide indications of the care taken throughout the process to ensure the emergence of a readily marketable product. For example, in the first phase, in which tests are carried out in the kitchen and/or in the pilot plant, a 'taste panel' of staff members samples the new preparation and, if they approve it with a substantial majority, the problems associated with its commercial production are analysed. If the various divisions concerned, having examined all factors in their field of interest, approve the product, it goes back to the industry division for them to make a sample lot of the product. At the next stage, the independent consumer research test, 80 to 400 housewives are invited to try the product and give their opinion about it regarding taste, texture, packaging, price and so on. They are given a questionaire to fill in for this purpose. An important element in this test is that the housewives are given, say, seven different products of the same type to test because experience has shown that a range of products—not just one item on its own – is needed if a reasonable impact is to be made on any market. A range of products on a retailer's shelf or in his cold cabinet catches the eye and makes an impact whereas one item might easily be missed. In any case, a range of products is required in order to provide for, say, a selection of flavours in soup or a selection of content in such a product, in order to cater for a greater number of consumers.

At the next phase effort is directed toward designing and making a pack and package with a novelty appeal. Such a development may even call for designing new machinery for the production line but at this stage the product is produced in a handmade pack and given to the consumer research organization to test again. After this, the next step is to make a commercial test of the market on a limited scale – perhaps by putting 5,000 packs of the product in retail shops, supported by point-of-scale advertising matter, such as showcards and posters. Here, too, a questionaire is distributed with the product, seeking consumer reaction. If the result of this trial marketing is also successful, the five most popular items of the range are put into production, the last two of the seven being discarded. At this point the detailed actual costs involved in producing and launching the product are worked out, replacing the tentative earlier estimates. This calls for a firm commitment as to the number of units to be produced in the year ahead, with projected increases of production scheduled in accordance with the marketing plan and all associated costs as well as

those involved in the marketing and distribution effort, including the cost of the advertising campaign. Also pinpointed at this penultimate stage is the profit margin. Production is then started and all arrangements for launching the product are placed in the hands of the marketing division who have to gear the whole operation to that of the production plan.

It will be noted that this whole development process is a closely coordinated and managed effort, carefully checked at each stage by all concerned and such caution in product development is wise as the wellbeing of the company largely depends on correct judgement in this field. The process of such development as described here may take anything from two to five years, depending on many factors. For example, if production machinery has to be designed and fabricated, the latter figure may be on the mark. Even improvement or modification of an existing product may take a year or more. A case in point was the development of a fish salad. Because of a change in the taste trend, the product was modified and it took a year to get it relaunched on the market. But fish salads form only one of many new or improved products put on the market by 'Nordsee' in recent years. Some others are fish soups, ready-to-cook meals, herring snacks in delicate sauces, and a large variety of fish portions. It will be noted that the concentration of 'Nordsee' is on the use of fish as food for human consumption, with fishmeal and fish oil as a fringe benefit. As a consequence, the company is market and consumer oriented, with the strongest emphasis on activities leading to the provision of products demanded by the consumer. This concern with the end product starts with the resource, with the raw material being preserved in the most suitable technical way and, at the same time, in the most economic way for each group of products. Thus, the freezing of fillets in block form at sea is, for example, the most suitable way to preserve the raw material for further processing on shore under prevailing market conditions in Germany. In this respect 'Nordsee' is among the leaders in the fishing industry. This is further demonstrated by their modern freezer trawlers, the prototype of which is the 3,500 tons *Bremen*. The considerable costs involved in this type of operation must be based on a concept which includes restriction of catching operations to trawling, using exclusively only those fish species which can be processed by the filleting machines, producing frozen blocks of fillets, and ensuring that every stage in production contributes to maintaining product quality. The present range of species used consists of white fish of the northern waters, red fish and of herring. If there was a need to exploit resources with new species, it would, unavoidably, require the installation of a different kind of filleting machine to handle fish of a different size and shape from those now processed. Although the operation of a fleet of such freezer trawlers is limited in flexibility, as the catch from the familiar and popular stocks of fish dwindles in the absence of effective regulation and control, the need to make full use of unfamiliar or new species is fully taken into consideration. Such fish are preserved in the round on board for investigation and product development on a trial basis in shore-based laboratories. While the raw material required for all frozen and canned products is frozen at sea, the raw material for the fresh fish market and some traditional products is caught by conventional stern trawlers. In this type of fishery the age-old problem of the preservation of wet fish still exists and a fishy smell cannot always be avoided at the time the housewife buys the produce. This is one of the impediments to the expansion of the wet fish trade in a country such as Germany.

As already emphasized, 'Nordsee' is geared to work in highly sophisticated markets and with products of a high quality where the need is constant to maintain quality control and product improvement, an objective greatly aided by the extensive marketing and sales organization of the company. Of course, all this involves a high level of expenditure from start to finish, including considerable expense for such items as containers and wrapping and for their design in a form appealing to the consumer and ensuring that there can be no contamination during distribution. Neither the elaborateness of their quality control and product development procedures nor the high expense level of these are feasible in starting or in expanding the development of fishery processing industries in developing countries, but the principles underlying such policy and practice are applicable. The degree or level at which they should be applied must depend on the state of the industry concerned, the viability of the stocks in relation to more intensive exploitation, the infrastructure of fisheries in the country, the availability of trained labour at all levels, the market potential, the existing marketing and distribution system and many other factors.

CONCLUSIONS

What can be done by those concerned with developing fisheries and fishery products in making the fullest use of the fish caught, is: to ensure maintenance of quality of the catch during handling and stowage on board fishing vessels, to plan carefully the utilization of the landings in the light of existing markets, both domestic and export, and to follow the example of 'Nordsee' in the careful step-by-step check on the viability of the present product and its profit potential. In any case, this latter practice is an essential in any fishery enterprise in the private sector or in any joint venture involving private industry. The first step is to determine the kind of product needed and to ensure that it is in general harmony with the food habits and taste of the consumers concerned. Again, the care and attention given by 'Nordsee' to packaging is a good example to follow but, in most developing countries, such packaging is not required. Elaborate packaging is a luxury for which a wealthy market is willing to pay. What is needed in many developing countries is a form of processing and wrapping (if necessary) that keeps the price at a level low enough for

the consumers to buy the product. This price factor, it will have been noted, is one kept firmly in mind by 'Nordsee' despite the wealth of the market in which they are dealing. It is, therefore, of even greater importance in the markets in developing economies. 'Nordsee' considers the task of improving existing, as well as developing new products, to be most important, first, to extend the range of existing products to continue to attract the attention of the consumers and, second, to use raw material with improved methods or to use new types of raw material when required or to meet changing tastes and food habits. In this respect the integration of product development with an efficient marketing service is significant; when a product is accepted for production, its launching is made the responsibility of the marketing division. In many countries insufficient attention is paid to marketing and distribution yet this is a key operation. Countries seeking to establish and build up their fishery products industries should ensure the development of a strong marketing and distribution service as an essential step toward achieving their objective. Finally, a word should be said again about handling the catch and quality control to ensure a clean wholesome product. While highly mechanized handling systems and elaborate laboratory control work cannot be introduced into developing economies in the measure described, the principles can certainly be applied in relation to the local circumstances and the situation. Thus, more careful handling of the catch from the time it is hauled on board until it reaches the consumer – whether in fresh, frozen or processed state – can be introduced. Gutting at the earliest moment can be done. The catch can be washed in clean water and, if ice-making facilities are available, a measure of quality control can be initiated by ensuring that the ice is made from clean water and that the fish are adequately iced at the earliest moment and that they are transported in clean baskets or boxes. Such simple measures as these are basic requirements as a first step towards quality control and the production of good quality products. With such practices established, the improvement of products and the development of new ones of equal or better quality become possible. And from there on, with the development and expansion of the fishery products industry, the more sophisticated and rigorous controls can be gradually introduced, growing with the industry, the supporting infrastructure, the trained manpower and all the required inputs already mentioned.

Acknowledgement

The authors are grateful for cooperation by the Chairman and Directors of 'Nordsee' in the preparation of this paper.

Reprocessing Fish into Composite Products *S Ishii and K Amano*

Retransformation du poisson en produits composes

Le document expose les divers facteurs dont il faut tenir compte à propos de la production de produits composés à base de poisson. Pour illustrer les méthodes appliquées, ainsi que les difficultés et problèmes rencontrés et résolus, on cite comme exemples le kamaboko et la saucisse de poisson. Comme l'indique le document, les problèmes qui se posent ne sont pas uniquement d'odre technique:

Reelaboracion del pescado en productos mixtos

El texto examina las diversas consideraciones que han de tenerse en cuenta para la producción de productos mixtos a base de pescado. El kamaboko y los embutidos de pescado se utilizan como ejemplos de los procedimientos que se siguen y de los problemas y dificultades con que se tropieza y que han de superarse. Según indica el texto, tales problemas no son sólo técnicos sino que

il faut également prendre en considération les habitudes et préférences alimentaires traditionnelles, qui risquent de limiter l'adaptabilité de ces produits en vue de leur commercialisation dans d'autres pays.

comprenden la consideración de los hàbitos alimentarios tradicionales y de las preferencias, cosas que pueden limitar la adaptabilidad de tales productos para su venta en otros países.

Composite fish products are those made chiefly from fish meat with other ingredients such as cereals and vegetables and usually with the addition of flavouring and colouring substances. Thus, such products differ greatly from the usual fish products not only in content but also in shape because the ordinary products tend to retain a recognizable fish appearance whereas the composite products can often be shaped as desired. A further distinction between the two is that composite products can be prepared from a wide range of fish because the flesh is comminuted. Generally speaking, composite products are not yet popular except in a few countries, chiefly in southeast Asia in the Orient and Scandinavia in the West. They have become very popular in Japan as the increase in production in the recent years (see Table 1) shows. Total production now exceeds 1.126 million tons, using some 2.5 million tons of raw fish. However, experience with composite products indicates that they cannot be easily introduced into all countries. This being the case, it would appear most useful to discuss in this paper some of the characteristics of such products and the problems and difficulties that have to be overcome if they are to be established in new markets.

COMPOSITE PRODUCTS: MATERIALS, PRESENTATION AND ACCEPTANCE

One big advantage is that such products are based on comminuted fish flesh. This means that there is no need to be concerned about maintaining the fish shape or any size nor is there need to restrict the species except in cases of adverse characteristics, such as flavour and odour. In Japan a number of species have been excluded as raw material because they lack 'Kamaboko–forming quality'. But, in general, Japanese experience indicates that the majority of species can be used so long as the price factor does not rule them out. And there may also be some technological problems to be overcome if the raw material is not adequately prepared for processing. In making composite products, the wet fish flesh is comminuted into a slurry, along with other ingredients. It can therefore be formed into whatever size and shape determined by the processor. This is a distinct advantage as the finished product can be packaged in the most economic and convenient form for handling and distribution as well as for styling, labelling and display. The natural flavours imparted by the species of fish used to make composite products can be modified to meet the preferences of consumers. For example, in making Kamaboko such ingredients as sugars, sweet saké, monosodium glutamate and other flavourings are often added, depending on the taste preferences of the consumers concerned. Where it is desired to retain the specific flavour of the fish flesh used in making the product, a small amount of common salt is added. Further, if it is considered desirable to enrich the product nutritionally, the required nutrients can be easily added.

Any way of cooking may be employed in processing composite products—boiling, steaming, frying, baking, broiling and so on—or any combination of these, such as baking after steaming. By these means the slurries made from the same species of fish can be processed to yield different flavours and to be different in finished appearance. In Japan, for instance, some manufacturers make a variety of products from one lot of 'Surimi'.

TABLE 2. PRODUCTION OF FROZEN "SURIMI" IN JAPAN BY YEAR AND LOCALITY (TONS)

Locality	1968	1969	1970	1971	1972[1]
Hokkaido	56,699	82,445	89,929	112,412	128,000
West area	6,291	4,744	4,534	5,228	5,000
Tohoku area	6,645	5,500	20,506	20,207	26,800
Floating plants	74,933	103,600	134,454	183,535	205,200
Total	144,568	196,319	261,206	321,382	365,000

[1]Figures for 1972 are tentative

As already pointed out, many species of fish can be used in making composite products, including those not normally used by the processing industries. Also, as already stated, other materials may be introduced, especially vegetable and cereal protein. For example, in Japan wet wheat protein and soybean curd are mixed into fish sausage and Kamaboko. This is usually done to reduce manufacturing costs, particularly when the fish used are expensive. Thus, the quantity of added ingredients is usually related to the cost of the fish. It is also related to the flavour of the end product. Care must be taken in this respect because some ingredients, such as soybean, impart a characteristic flavour, therefore the quantity used must be restricted. A high degree of technological skill and control are required in making the best use of such cheap sources of protein. With the upward trend in living standards, especially in industrialized societies, food habits tend to change and diversify. In these circumstances fish faces very strong competition

TABLE 1. PRODUCTION OF KAMABOKO AND FISH SAUSAGE IN JAPAN, 1967 TO 1971 (TONS)

| Year | Total | Baked Chikuwa | | Steamed Kamaboko | Boiled Kamaboko | Fried Kamaboko | Fish Sausage | Fish Ham | Fish Hamburger |
		Fresh	Frozen						
1967	911,887	—	—	—	—	267,549	112,032	52,399	—
1968	999,378	141,079	53,956	283,050	53,314	289,501	108,590	53,163	—
1969	1,077,190	153,039	51,251	306,995	61,021	319,191	113,664	55,124	—
1970	1,081,331	174,171	47,312	303,356	53,041	313,552	115,714	53,824	13,977
1971	1,126,147	192,255	46,283	323,427	56,387	322,161	113,705	50,704	14,839

from other foodstuffs which are easier to prepare and consume. This situation is fully appreciated by producers of fishery products for sophisticated markets who are now concentrating on bland types of fishery products. In particular, the younger generation in such markets do not want to bother with the bones and skin and odours of traditional fish dishes. In this respect, therefore, composite fishery products are in a favourable situation. They have no bones or skin and the odours and flavours can be controlled. Experience has shown that even children who refuse the normal cooked fish, readily consume composite products .

PROBLEMS IN PRODUCTION

While the advantages of composite products, such as those mentioned above, are of considerable practical value, there are also problems to be faced and overcome in the manufacture of such products. It has become compulsory in many countries to list the ingredients used in food products. This is not always easy to do in the case of composite products when the fish flesh use is from several species and when, in addition, other ingredients are used. A suitable and accurate description of the contents of the product must be printed on the label or the container. This is especially needed in the case of composite products because an important ingredient is starch, used because of its binding quality. However, starch could be used in excessive quantities as a substitute for fish flesh and thus become an adulterant. It is essential, therefore, to state the starch content of the product. So, too, it is necessary to state the quantity used of such additives as colouring and flavouring agents, polyphosphates, chemical preservatives, and so on. A serious problem is the short shelf-life of composite products, a problem aggravated under natural temperatures and especially in tropical countries without cold storage systems. This problem has been to some extent overcome in Japan by the use of chemical preservatives.

While this conforms to Japanese requirements, the practice may need adjustment to meet the specifications in some other areas. It seems, therefore, that the objective in the effort to extend the shelf-life of composite products should be to establish cold chains for their distribution and display. There are many ways of pretreating raw material which is to be used for reprocessing. An example in Japan are the various kinds of dried fish – strips of bonito, and dried mackerel, horse mackerel and herring. Such dried products are used in making soups, for which purpose they are cut into thin flakes. This process has been industrialized through the production of 'Kezuri-bushi', which means 'dried fish shavings', the production of which had reached 40,000 tons in 1971. Another example is fermented fish. This product is stored for a year or more to mature. Salt and rice bran are added. While production is small, there is a good demand for it in the area along the Sea of Japan. Dried squid is another product widely used for reprocessing. But the most notable of such products produced in recent years is frozen 'Surimi' (Table 2). This is not only produced on a large scale but has made possible the growth of the Kamaboko and fish sausage industries as 'Surimi' provides the basic material for these products. It is supplied in frozen and non-frozen form.

CONCLUSION

As these various examples show, there is a wide acceptance of composite fishery products in Japan. No doubt the prevalence of fish, shellfish and edible seaweed in the traditional diet of the Japanese people has made such acceptance feasible, which has not proved to be the case in a number of other countries. Efforts, therefore, to establish such products in countries where fish are not part of the traditional diet are not likely to succeed unless preceded by thorough research of the market, test-marketing campaigns and planned marketing and distribution based on the results of the research and consumer tests.

Preparation and Properties of Chemically and Enzymically Modified Protein Isolates for Use as Food Ingredients   *J Spinelli H S Groninger, Jr, and B Koury*

Preparation et proprietes des isolats proteiques modifies par voie chiminique et enzymatique en vue de leur utilisation comme ingredients alimentaires

Les auteurs décrivent comment on a préparé des isolats protéiques functionnels par modification enzymatique ou par succinylation des muscles de poisson.

On a préparé les isolats modifiés par voie enzymatique en hydrolysant partiellement le muscle du poisson au moyen d'une enzyme protéolytique, puis en recueillant la protéine sous forme de complexe phosphato-protéique. On a obtenu un produit stable, fonctionnel et doté de qualités organoleptiques en extrayant le complexe phosphato-protéique humide, tout d'abord par l'iso-propanol, puis par l'eau avant le séchage. Les auteurs examinent les propriétés des isolats protéiques de poisson, par exemple leur aptitude à émulsifier les lipides, et leur utilisation comme succédanés de l'albumine dans les systèmes alimentaires.

Preparacion y propiedades de los aislados proteinicos modificados quimica y enzimaticamente para su empleo como ingredientes alimentarios

Los autores describen cómo los aislados funcionales de proteínas de pescado fueron preparados por modificación enzimática o por succinilación del tejido muscular del pescado.

Los aislados modificados enzimáticamente fueron preparados hidrolizando parcialmente el tejido muscular del pescado con una enzima proteolítica y luego recuperando la proteína como un comple jo proteína-fosfato. Se logró la estabilidad, funcional y organoléptica, extrayendo en primer lugar el complejo húmedo proteína-fosfáto con isopropanol y luego con agua antes del secado. Se examinan las propiedades de los aislados proteínicos del pescado, tales como su capacidad para emulsificar lípidos y su empleo como sustitutos de la albúmina en los sistema alimentarios.

Los aislados succinilados se prepararon haciendo reaccionar el tejido muscular del pescado y el anhídrido succínico en un medio

On a préparé les isolats par succinylation en faisant réagir le muscle de poisson et l'anhydride succinique dan un milieu aqueux alcalin. Les isolats séchés de ce type sont facilesment solubles dans l'eau, formant des solutions de haute viscosité aux faibles concentrations. Les solutions des protéines ne sont pas thermo-coagulables, mais sont précipitables par les acides. Le document examine les études concernant leur utilisation possible dans les systèmes alimentaires et comme liants des aliments pour poisson en aquiculture.

alcalino acuoso. Los aislados succinilados secos se disuelven fácilmente en agua formando una solución muy viscosa a bajas concentraciones. Las soluciones de las proteínas no se coagulan al calor pero se precipitan en ácidos. Son tema de discusión los estudios relativos a su posible empleo en los alimentos y también como aglutinantes de las raciones de peces en la acuicultura.

Many species of fish are difficult to market for such reasons as size, poor palatability characteristics, or simply because they are difficult to harvest, preserve, or process. As a result, a large part of the catch of so-called underutilized fish is processed directly into meal. Until recently, there have been no systematic investigations of methods for converting fish into a bland, flavourless, stable product suitable for direct addition to foods. The seemingly insurmountable problems of flavour and odour associated with fish undoubtedly acted as a major deterrent in efforts of this sort. Research in the area of fish protein concentrate (FPC) during the last 8 years (Finch 1970), however, has shown that fish can be converted into organoleptically acceptable high protein adducts that can be added to a variety of foods (Sidwell 1970). Although the development of FPC represents the first concentrated effort to increase the use and value of underutilized fish by converting it into a more readily acceptable form, this is only one path by which fish may be upgraded in value. It should be kept in mind that FPC was not developed to solve a world food problem but rather to aid in a sector of the problem, ie, the need for protein for people. The diversity of foods throughout the world, particularly in the developed countries, suggests that while FPC represents the cornerstone of the fish-derived proteins, it is by no means the ultimate product for utilizing otherwise poorly used fish. In many countries, the exploitation of fish protein can still be accomplished by conversion into forms that can be used as an essential functional component of a more complex food system. Mattil (1971) points out that proteins in themselves are not foods, but rather food components or food ingredients, and that while they are recognized as being essential dietary nutrients, they owe their widespread appeal to the gastronomic pleasure they afford. Investigations at our laboratory have been directed toward studying processing techniques that could form the basis for the preparation of functional proteins derived from fish. Specifically, our objectives were to (1) evaluate different routes that could be used in preparing functional protein isolates, (2) evaluate those factors that effect the organoleptic and functional stability of the protein isolates, and (3) evaluate the physical and chemical properties of the protein isolates in relation to their inclusion in food systems.

USE OF FISH AS A RAW MATERIAL FOR PREPARATION OF PROTEIN ISOLATES

The most critical factors in preparing protein isolates intended for use in a variety of food systems are those that contribute to functional properties. The term 'functional properties' in a broad sense includes all those properties that are related to organoleptic as well as physical characteristics that may contribute directly to or affect the properties of other components in a food system. Proteins are reactive substances. In nature, they are never found as pure components and their properties are inextricably related to their origin. The preparation of functional isolates always involves separation and purification techniques oriented toward the removal of components that will adversely affect the organoleptic, chemical, and physical properties of the protein during preparation or subsequent storage. The problems associated with the use of fish as a raw material for protein isolates are complex because commercially caught fish differ in species and come in various stages of maturity. Thus, fish muscle constituents not only vary because of these factors, but can also vary depending on when and where the fish are caught. Basically, fish muscle proteins are of two broad categories, ie, the insoluble or myofibrillar fraction that comprises about 70 per cent of the total muscle protein and the remaining soluble or sarcoplasmic proteins. Spinelli et al. (1972), in their investigations on approaches to the utilization of fish as a raw material source for the preparation of fish protein isolates, concluded that the reactive properties of proteins contained in the sarcoplasmic fraction precluded their use in food products. This fraction was irreversibly denatured during processing and contained the major portion of substances that contributed to the development of off-flavours during and after processing. They also found that in order to prepare a functionally and organoleptically stable isolate from the myofibrillar fraction, it was necessary to modify the protein prior to removing residual constituents that could adversely affect the functional characteristics of the isolate.

PREPARATION OF FISH PROTEIN ISOLATES BY ENZYMIC AND CHEMICAL MODIFICATIONS OF THE MYOFIBRILLAR PROTEIN

In its native state, myofibrillar fish protein has many desirable functional properties. Its gel-forming properties have been extensively used in the preparation of kamaboko, and its ability to emulsify lipids in a water-protein-lipid system are also well recognized. When myofibrillar fish protein is dried or exposed to polar organic solvents, these desirable properties are quickly and irreversibly damaged. Considerable attention has already been given to the preparation of functional protein isolates derived from fish proteins (Rutman 1971, Tannenbaum et al. 1970, Hyder and Cobb 1972) but the problem has always remained that, because of their sensitive nature, functionality of the proteins could not be maintained unless they were first modified by either chemical or enzymic treatment. Chemical treatments by alkali and acids have been extensively investigated (Library of Congress 1970). This type of treatment usually produces a complete or partial hydrolysate with organoleptic, physical, and nutritional

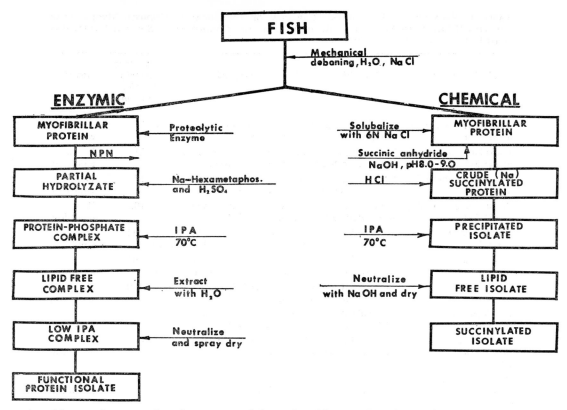

Fig 1   Preparation of functional protein isolates by enzymic and chemical modification of myofibrillar fish proteins.
IPA = isopropanol; NPN = nonprotein nitrogen

characteristics that limit its use. Enzymic modification overcomes some of the problems associated with acid or base treatment, but control of the reaction has been difficult and final products have not been uniform in their characteristics. Cheftel *et al.* (1971) recently described a system for enzymic modification of FPC that appears to overcome these difficulties. However, the economics of methods using a once-processed raw material would have to be weighed against methods using unprocessed fish as a source of raw material. Consideration of the problems associated with the preparation of isolates derived from fish led us to explore two routes that had not previously been investigated. Fig. 1 shows both procedures. One is a modification of fish muscle by enzymic treatment followed by recovery of the isolate as a phosphate complex. The other is a chemical treatment that uses succinic anhydride to form a succinylated isolate. In both routes, the starting material is the myofibrillar fraction of fish muscle protein obtained by washing out the sarcoplasmic fraction from deboned and minced fish tissue with 0.1 M NaCl.

Enzymically modified myofibrillar protein (EMMP)

The preparation of fish protein isolates by enzymic modification outlined in Fig. 1 follows the basic steps described by Spinelli *et al.* (1972). Briefly, myofibrillar protein is partially hydrolyzed (not more that 10 per cent nonprotein nitrogen formed during the hydrolysis) with a proteolytic enzyme. Then the reaction is simultaneously stopped and the proteins precipitated by the addition of sodium hexametaphosphate and an acid. The pre-

cipitated proteins, which are in the form of a phosphate complex, are easily centrifuged from the reaction mixture. While still in the acidic state, the complex is extracted with hot isopropanol (IPA) (50° to 70°C) to remove residual lipids. The IPA remaining on the complex is extracted by water. The complex, which contains about 1.5 per cent IPA, is then neutralized with NaOH and spray dried. Isolates prepared by the above method have several advantages over other proposed methods involving enzymic modification. First, yield is quantitative, ie, phosphate complexing results in the

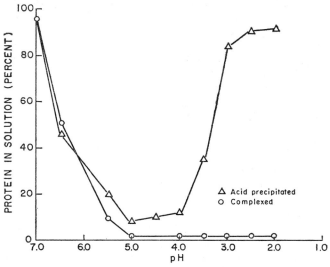

Fig 2   Recovery of enzimically modified myofibrillar protein by phosphate complexing and iso-eletctric precipitation

TABLE 1. RELATION OF EMULSIFYING CAPACITY OF ENZYMICALLY MODIFIED MYOFIBRILLAR PROTEINS (EMMP) TO METHOD OF RECOVERY AND THE CONDITIONS OF SOLVENT EXTRACTION WITH ISOPROPANOL (IPA) AND WATER.

Method of recovery Extraction with IPA and water—conditions		Emulsifying capacity (g oil/g protein)	Remarks
Phosphate complexing at pH 3·0	Extracted the acidic complex at 50°C, washed with H_2O, neutralized to pH 7·0, and dried	268	Excellent emulsion
Phosphate complexing at pH 3·0	Extracted the acidic complex at 70°C, washed with H_2O, neutralized to pH 7·0, and dried	216	Excellent emulsion
Phosphate complexing at pH 3·0	Neutralized the complex to pH 7·0 extracted at 50°C, washed with H_2O, and dried	172	Poor emulsion
Phosphate complexing at pH 3·0	Neutralized the complex to pH 7·0, extracted at 70°C, washed with H_2O, and dried	102	Poor emulsion
Iso-electric at pH 5·0	Extracted the acidic precipitated protein at 70°C, washed with H_2O, neutralized to pH 7·0, and dried	144	Poor emulsion
Iso-electric at pH 5·0	Extracted the acidic precipitated protein at 50°C, washed with H_2O, neutralized at pH 7·0, and dried	162	Fair emulsion
Iso-electric at pH 5·0	Neutralized the protein to pH 7·0, extracted at 50°C, washed with H_2O, and dried	120	Poor emulsion
Iso-electric at pH 5·0	Neutralized the protein to pH 7·0, extracted at 70°C, washed with H_2O, and dried	—	No emulsion
Precipitated the proteins with 50% IPA	Extracted the precipitated proteins at 50°C, washed with H_2O, and dried	—	No emulsion
Precipitated the proteins with 50% IPA	Extracted the precipitated proteins at 70°C, washed with H_2O, and dried	—	No emulsion

final recovery of all the functional protein as contrasted to iso-electric precipitation that can leave at least 10 per cent of the functional protein in solution (Fig. 2). Second, the reaction can be precisely controlled because the pH of the reaction mixture can be dropped to a point well below the activity range of the enzyme (excluding those that are active at acidic pH) without any resolubilization of the proteins. Third, the complexed proteins can be extracted with polar organic solvents with minimal damage to their functional properties. Comparative isolation procedures and their effects on an important functional property, ie, emulsifying capacity (EC), are given in Table 1. It can be seen that phosphate complexing followed by IPA extraction is superior to that of isoelectric precipitation followed by IPA extraction or by direct precipitation with IPA. A further point to be considered in any process utilizing polar organic solvents is the problem of their removal from the finished product. Experience with FPC manufacture showed that IPA residues could not be reduced to less than 250 ppm unless the dried product was steam stripped (Ernst 1971). Our work (Spinelli et al. 1972) showed that even in the freeze-dried isolates, IPA residues averaged about 800 ppm. The use of water to remove the IPA from the isolate followed by spray drying, however, reduced the IPA levels to about 50 ppm. Observations at our laboratory suggest that IPA probably forms a weak complex with the protein. Fig. 3 shows that when the IPA-extracted, protein-phosphate isolate was repeatedly washed with water, free IPA was removed in theoretically calculated amounts. However, when the IPA level reached 500 ppm, the amount of IPA removed from the complex with each successive wash was significantly less than the calculated amount.

Chemical modification by succinylation

Succinylated myofibrillar protein was prepared by blending the myofibrils in 0.6 M Nacl for 30 seconds at 0°C. Connective tissue was removed from the solubilized mixture by centrifugation. The suspension was then reacted (0°C) at pH 7.5 to 8.5 with solid succinic anhydrides at a ratio of 1 part anhydride to 20 parts protein. The pH of the reaction was controlled by the addition of 1 N NaOH and termination of the reaction was indicated by a stabilization of the pH level. The succinylation protein was recovered by adjusting the pH to 4.5 with 1 N HCl followed by centrifugation of the precipitated product. Residual lipids and odour-bearing compounds were extracted with IPA at 78°C. The alcohol-extracted succinylated isolate was washed with water to remove the alcohol and then suspended in water. Sodium hydroxide was added to the suspension to form the soluble sodium salt of the succinylated proteins. The solubilized isolate was dried by either freeze or drum drying. Prepared in the above manner, the isolate has about 30 per cent of its epsilon amino group reacted with the anhydride and has a dry composition (88 per cent protein and 11.4 per cent ash). It is odourless, possessing a slightly salty taste and disperses quickly in water, forming highly viscous solutions at low concentrations.

PROPERTIES OF MODIFIED PROTEIN ISOLATES
Emulsifying capacity (EC)

The ability of proteins to emulsify lipids is of primary importance to the food industry. For this reason, we chose this index as one of our main criteria for determining the functional value of the isolates. The

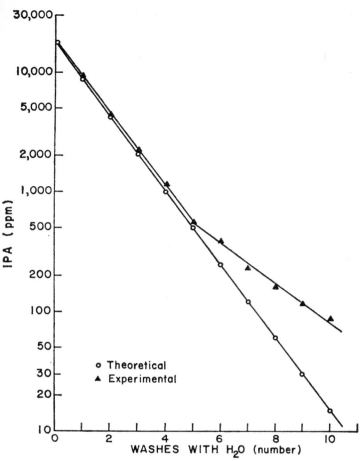

Fig 3 Amounts of IPA (isopropanol) remaining on enzymically modified myofibrillar protein that had been extracted with IPA and then repeatedly extracted with water. The calculated theoretical amounts of IPA remaining on the protein are also shown

comparative emulsifying capacities (measured by a modification of the method of Webb *et al.* 1970) of several proteins were measured and the results are shown in Fig 4. Enzymically modified myofibrillar protein emulsified 30 per cent more oil than native myofibrillar protein, 40 per cent more oil than sodium caseinate, and 5 per cent more oil than a commercial soya isolate (Promine D). The denaturing effects of drying unmodified myofibrillar protein are shown by the reduced EC of the protein dried under vacuum. Succinylated myofibrillar protein was superior to all products shown, emulsifying over 500 g of oil per g of protein.

Solubility and viscosity

EMMP is 20 per cent soluble in both water and 5 per cent salt. Water dispersions are colloidal in nature, forming light sediments on standing. Succinylated proteins are water-white in aqueous solution. The solutions are highly viscous and are stable to heat up to 100°C. The viscosity of aqueous solutions of succinylated protein was compared against a commercial xanthan gum and the results are shown in Fig 5. At equal concentrations (0.5 to 2.0 per cent by weight), the viscosity of the succinylated protein is almost twice that of the gum. The presence of sodium chloride and inorganic phosphate decreases the viscosity of the solution.

Protein efficiency ratio (PER)

The PER of EMMP was found to be 3.1 compared to a value of 3.0 for standard reference casein. For the succinylated protein the PER was 2.8 when compared to casein. The lower value for the succinylated product is attributable to the reaction of succinic anhydride with the epsilon groups of the lysine.

Storage stability

A processing parameter yet to be satisfactorily controlled is that of maintaining functional stability of the EMMP during storage at ambient temperature. Dry preparations of EMMP when stored at ambient temperatures were found to lose a significant portion of their EC after 1 or 2 months. Attempts to prevent this deterioration in EC by co-drying with carbohydrates were only partly successful. Storing at low temperatures had a significant effect in maintaining the EC of EMMP. Fig 6 shows that EMMP stored at refrigerated temperatures (−16°F and 35°F;—27°C and 2°C) loses only a small amount of its EC even after 1 year. The effect of carbohydrate is also shown. The EC of a sample co-dried with 10 per cent corn syrup solid (CCS) is about 30 per cent higher than that of the control after 9 months at 70°F (21°C). More recent work has shown that water activity plays an important role in maintaining functional stability. Samples of EMMP stored at a relative humidity of 23 showed no loss of EC after 2 months (at 20°C), whereas samples stored at relative humidities lower or higher

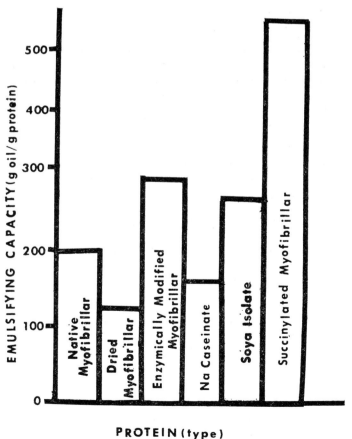

Fig 4 Relative emulsifying capacity of sodium caseinate, soya isolate, myofibrillar fish protein, and enzymically and chemically modified myofibrillar protein

287

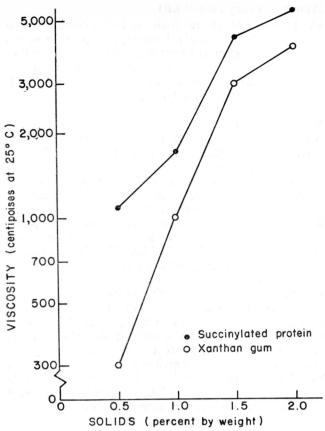

Fig 5 *Relative viscosities of succinylated fish myofibrillar protein and xantham gum*

as an egg albumin replacement in some baked products. In collaborative experiments done at the University of Washington's Home Economics Department, it was shown that 30 per cent of the egg albumin could be replaced in angel food cakes with no loss in cake volume. In taste panel evaluations, no differences were found in either flavour or texture between control cakes and those in which EMMP was substituted for albumin. Other work at our laboratory showed that in the undried form EMMP can serve as an excellent base for the preparation of protein beverages. EMMP was emulsified with coconut oil to give a concentration of 4 per cent protein and 3 per cent oil in the final product. This mixture was pasteurized at 100°C for 15 minutes with no evidence of protein coagulation after 1 week of storage at room temperature. When 10 per cent sucrose was added in the mixture, pasteurization time was increased to 30 minutes with no evidence of protein coagulation.

The succinylated isolates may have their greatest potential as viscosity control agents in liquid systems and as whipping adducts in dessert-type foods. Recent work shows that the effective range over which the succinylated isolates will function can be extended into the acid range by mildly hydrolyzing the isolate with a tryptic enzyme. Very stable acid-type emulsions were prepared with the hydrolyzed succinylated isolate, indicating that it could be used in acid-type foods such as mayonnaise, desserts, and beverages. A novel use of the succinylated isolate as binder for lobster feed is currently being investigated. The feed is made by mixing 3 parts of a lobster diet with 1 part of neutral (in aqueous solution)

than 23 showed significant losses of EC during the same storage period. The functional characteristics of the succinylated proteins show no change during storage.

USE OF FISH PROTEIN ISOLATES IN FOOD SYSTEMS

While the use of EMMP and succinylated isolates in food systems has not been extensively investigated, some experimental work done shows that EMMP can function

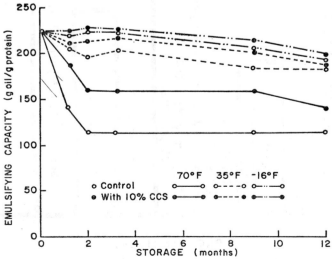

Fig 6 *Functional storage stability (as reflected by emulsifying capacity) of enzymically modified fish protein score at –16°F, 35°F, and 70°F. CCS = corn syrup solids*

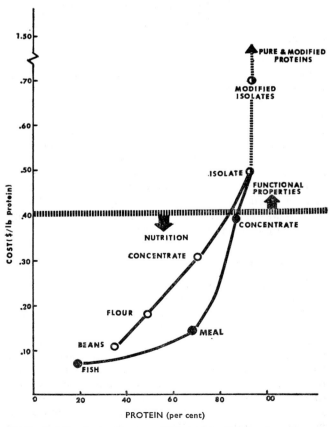

Fig 7 *Relative costs of soya and fish proteins starting from the basic commodity to more refined and modified forms of the proteins*

succinylated isolate. The mixture is then extruded into a weak solution of acetic acid to form a rubbery, spaghetti-like strand. The feed retains its consistency in salt water and experiments at the Massachusetts State Lobster Hatchery show that it is readily acceptable by lobsters.

ECONOMIC CONSIDERATIONS

The economic considerations in developing cost figures for the preparation of functional protein isolates are quite different from those used when the product is considered only for its nutritional attributes. These differences become apparent when one considers the costs involved in preparing proteinaceous components from the raw material source. In Fig. 7, the relative costs of processing soya beans are given. Also shown are the relative and projected costs of using fish for the same purposes. In the use of soya, the cost per pound of protein in the bean is roughly US $ 0.10/lb (US $ 0.22/kg), in the flour it is US $ 0.18/lb (US $ 0'40/kg), and in the concentrate US $ 0.31/lb (US $ 0.68/kg). At US $ 0.50/lb (US $ 1.10/kg) in the isolate, the cost of protein begins to become prohibitively high as a nutrient source; thus, as indicated, soya isolates are sold essentially for their functional properties. If the isolates are further modified, costs increase rapidly and approach the selling price of native or highly purified protein fractions such as egg albumin or sodium caseinate. It is important to note, however, that these latter increased increments of cost no longer bear any relation to the protein content of the product. The cost of fish protein in relation to the form of product follows the same pattern as that of soya. Presently the estimated cost of protein in FPC is about US $ 0.30 to 0.70/lb (US $ 0.07 to 0.15/kg) more than the protein in soya concentrate (Devanney and Mahnken 1970, Crutchfield 1972). Based on current processing techniques, this relation is unlikely to change (Crutchfield 1972). Improved processing techniques based on solvent extraction of meals could substantially reduce FPC costs (Finch 1972) and recent work at our laboratory (Pelroy and Spinelli—unpublished data) shows that FPC costs could be reduced by using stable presscake as a starting material.

At this time it would be impractical to project definitive cost figures for the preparation of protein isolates. However, some reasonable costs can be estimated based on our experience with FPC. First the yield of isolate is about 25 per cent lower than that of FPC prepared from deboned fish. If one assumes similar processing steps, particularly those involving solvent extraction, then the cost of protein in the isolate would be at least US $ 0.50/lb (US $ 1.10/kg) (assuming US $ 0.38/lb or U.S. $ 0.84/kg for the concentrate). The added costs in preparing the isolate would reside mainly in the steps involved in separating the sarcoplasmic proteins from the myofibrillar proteins, and the cost of enzymes, chemicals and drying. Some credits might be received by recovery of the sarcoplasmic proteins (Spinelli and Koury 1970), but these would be minimal. The cost of enzymes and chemicals in preparing enzymically modified isolates has been calculated to be about US $ 0.055/lb (US $ 0.121/kg). If one assumes that the processing costs of preparing a fish isolate (using FPC as a base) are similar to those in preparing soya isolates (using soya concentrate as a base), final costs would be in the range of US $ 0.70 to 0.75/lb (US $ 1.54 to 1.65/kg). To be competitive at these costs, fish protein isolates must possess either unique functions or functions that are similar to native proteins that are used in various food systems. To date, we have demonstrated that fish proteins can be isolated and prepared to perform some of these functions. That there is a need and a market for these proteins is a matter of record. Hammonds and Call (1970) have pointed out that in the United States alone, two thirds of the 1.5 million ton potential for protein ingredients will be for those possessing functional properties. It seems quite possible, therefore, that like so many of our natural products, fish will someday appear as an indistinguishable component in a variety of foods that are blended to cater to people's food sensitivities.

References

CHEFTEL, C, AHERN, M, WANG, D I C and TANNENBAUM, S R, 1971 Enzymatic solubilization of fish protein concentrate: Batch studies applicable to continuous enzyme recycling processes J. Agric. and Fd Chem. 19:155–161.

CRUTCHFIELD, J The economics of fish protein concentrate. 1972 International FPC Conference, Cambridge, Massachusetts, USA.

DEVANNEY, J W and MAHNKEN, G The economics of FPC. National 1970 Technical Information Service, No. PB 195226, Springfield, Virginia, USA, 170p.

ERNST, R C JR FPC: The NMFS experiment and demonstration 1971 plant process. Comm. Fish. Rev. 33:22–28.

FINCH, R Fish proteins for human foods. Critical Reviews on 1970 Food Technology, 1:533–539.

FINCH, R FPC processes. International FPC Conference, Cambridge 1972 Massachusetts, USA.

HAMMONDS, T M and CALL, D L Utilization of protein ingredients 1970 in U.S. food industry. Part 2. The future market for protein ingredients. Dept. Agric. Econ., Cornell Univ. Agric. Expt. Station, Cornell Univ., Ithaca, New York.

HYDER, K and COBB, B F Development of a process for preparing 1972 a fish protein concentrate which can be reconstituted into a meat-like product. Sea Grant Publ. No. TAMU-SG-72-201, Texas A & M University, USA.

LIBRARY OF CONGRESS Fish protein concentrate. A comprehensive 1970 bibliography compiled by Special Bibliography Section, Science and Technology Division, Washington, D.C., Cat. Card No. 79–606672.

MATTIL, K F The functional requirements of protein for foods. J. 1971 Amer. Oil Chem. Soc. 48:477–480.

RUTMAN, M Process for preparing high-energy fish protein con- 1971 centrate. US Patent 3561973, 9 Feb.

SIDWELL, V D, STILLINGS, B R and KNOBL, G M, JR The fish 1970 protein concentrate story. 1.0 US Bureau of Commercial Fisheries FPC's: Nutritional quality and use in foods. Fd Technol. 24:40–46.

SPINELLI, J and KOURY, B Phosphate complexes of soluble fish 1970 proteins. Their formation and possible uses. Agric. and Fd Chem. 18:284–288.

SPINELLI, J, KOURY, B and MILLER, R Approaches to the utilization 1972 of fish for the preparation of protein isolates. Isolation and properties of myofibrillar and sacroplasmic fish proteins. J. Fd Sci. 37:599–603.

SPINELLI, J, KOURY, B and MILLER, R Approaches to the utilization 1972 of fish for the preparation of protein isolates. Enzymic modifications of myofibrillar fish proteins. Ibid. 37:604–608.

TANNENBAUM, S R, AHERN, M and BATES, R P Solubilization of fish 1970 protein concentrate. J. Fd Technol. 24:96–98.

WEBB, N B, IVEY, F J, CRAIG, H B, JONES, V A and MONROE, R J The 1970 measurement of emulsifying capacity by electrical resistance J. Fd Sci. 35:501–505.

Acknowledgement

The authors thank Charlotte Mortensen for her work in evaluating the function of the fish isolates in cake mixes and Larry Lehman for the analysis of residual IPA in the isolates.

Functional and Nutritive Food Proteins from Fish   E G Bligh, W J Dyer, L W Regier, J R Dingle and R Legendre

Obtention de proteines alimentaries fonctionnelles et nutritives a partir du poisson

Le programme canadien de recherche et de développement relatif aux concentrés de protéines de poisson, opérationnel depuis 1955, a conduit à la mise au point du procédé à l'isopropanol ou 'Procédé Halifax' servant à la préparation d'un produit de Type A à partir de nombreuses espèces de poissons. Ce procédé et le produit en question ont fait l'objet d'études approfondies au Canada et aux Etats-Unis et ce produit a été homologué comme denrée alimentaire dans les deux pays. Etant donné que les débouchés potentiels d'un article strictement nutritionnel sont limités en Amérique du Nord, on s'est intéressé surtout à un concentré *fonctionnel* de protéines de poisson susceptible d'être utilisé dans des produits carnés prêts à la consommation. Le laboratoire de Halifax a élaboré une méthode (demande de brevet déposée) pour fabriquer un tel produit avec des poissons maigres ou gras. Les aspects économiques et techniques de l'approvisionnement en matière première et de la commercialisation du produit constituent maintenant les principaux facteurs qui freinent le développement d'une industrie canadienne des concentrés de protéines de poisson.

Proteinas alimentarias funcionales y nutritivas obtenidas del pescado

El programa canadiense de investigación y preparación de concentrados proteínicos de pescado, en curso desde 1955, ha permitido encontrar un proceso denominado isopropanol o 'Halifax', para preparar un producto de excelente calidad a partir de diversas especies de peces. Este proceso y el producto que con él se obtiene se ha estudiado ampliamente en Canadá y en los Estados Unidos, aprobándose en ambos países su empleo para la alimentación del hombre. Debido a las limitadas posibilidades de mercado que tiene en América del Norte un producto de carácter estrictamente nutricional, se ha prestado atención sobre todo a la preparación de un concentrado *funcional* de proteínas de pescado, que pueda utilizarse para la preparación de productos cárnicos. En el Laboratorio de Halifax se ha ideado un proceso (que en breve se patentará) para la preparación de este producto, que puede obtenerse a partir de pescado magro o graso. Los factores más importantes que limitan el desarrollo de una industria canadiense de concentrados de proteínas de pescado son los técnicos y económicos del abastecimiento de materias primas y la comercialización de los productos terminados.

Fisheries technologists throughout the world look upon fish protein concentrate (FPC) differently than they did a few years ago. In Canada we, too, have altered our objectives since initial work on this challenging product began at the Halifax Laboratory around 1955. Dr H Fougère's report (1962) to the FAO International Congress on Fish in Nutrition, Washington, 1961, on fish flour, 'Technological Developments in Canada', stressed the potential of FPC in meeting human requirements for animal protein. At that time fish was low in cost and underutilized. However, we face a contrasting picture today and most countries are much concerned that many ocean food resources are being fished near to commercial extinction. Prices are the highest in history and fish becomes increasingly the gourmet's delight rather than the poor's food (for example, eggs and poultry are generally much cheaper in Canada than fish). In addition, many are convinced that the use of fish in animal feeds cannot continue. In this connexion, Canada has enforced regulations to prevent the use of Pacific herring for reduction. Canadian priorities are no longer founded on the role of FPC as an animal protein supplement for human diets but on the demand for a protein with 'functional' properties. By functional we mean having the capacity to bind water and fat and to gel on cooking. Such a protein concentrate can be utilized in the formulation of products such as luncheon meats and wieners. The market place sets a much higher price on such a product and a demand exists in both developed and developing countries. In the last few years we have devoted our attention, therefore, towards the development of a process for making a 'functional fish protein' (FFP) concentrate. Other countries have been working on specialized FPC products as well and some have been developing soluble products for use in milk-like drinks and as milk replacers in animal rations. Another factor that we must recognize is that more and more fish, including hitherto unutilized species, are being used directly as human food. The scarcity of supply and increasing prices are forcing industry to eliminate waste and to look for more protein from alternate species. This creates acute competition for the large quantities of fish required for economical operation of an FPC plant. We must accept the fact that our concepts regarding FPC must be consistent with a limited world supply of fish.

FUNCTIONAL FISH PROTEIN (FFP)

As noted before, it became apparent that North American markets for FPC were demanding products possessing positive functional characteristics as well as nutrition. The studies on FPC at the Halifax Laboratory were expanded in 1969 to put emphasis on the development of a functional fish protein concentrate (FFP). Instead of trying to resurrect the properties from the hot-IPA-extracted product, effort was put on the retention of the functional properties of the original fish proteins. This resulted in a process yielding a product which retains many of the desirable protein characteristics. The dry product readily rehydrates, taking up adequate water, functions as an effective emulsifier, and coagulates on heating. This process, for which a patent is pending (Dingle *et al.*) uses several aqueous steps followed by several IPA extractions and drying. Deboned fish flesh is washed with water to remove much of the characteristic flavour material as well as electrolytes. This has been done on a batch basis in both the laboratory and the pilot plant and is the most critical part of the process from a yield standpoint. The fish protein tends to form a colloidal suspension in the cool water used for the washing and is difficult to separate even by centrifugation. Control of the pH to slightly below 7.0 with hydrochloric acid or sodium hydroxide has a marked effect. The washed protein is resuspended in cool dilute brine and the pH is adjusted to between 7.5 and 9. This allows the proteins to swell and become sufficiently dissociated to disrupt the fibrous structure of the original muscle. Too low a pH at this stage prevents the swelling, while too high a pH tends to start hydrolysis. After acidification to pH 4–5, the dispersion is heated to 65°C for a few minutes and then cooled. This treatment causes the swollen protein to contract and flocculate sufficiently to allow separation in the centrifuge. The pH is normally raised to about 7 and the mixture allowed to cool before being centrifuged, but these steps are not essential. The heating of the acidified material is important for retention of desired properties. The wet cake from the centrifuge is subjected to countercurrent extraction with IPA. In our laboratory and pilot plant, three or four extractions have been made, with fresh 99 per cent IPA being used for the final extraction. This extraction, which is done at approximately 25°C, removes nearly all of the residual lipids, including the readily oxidizable phospholipids. The centrifuge cake usually contains 40–60 per cent IPA and has been dried in rotating vacuum dryers at 25–70°C without any great loss of functionality. The yields on a laboratory scale have been near the maximum possible (12 per cent for cod flesh). In the pilot plant, the problems of centrifuging in the water-washing steps have caused losses which lower the yield somewhat.

The usefulness of this product depends upon a combination of properties. We have adopted two test methods for evaluating the effects of the variables in the process. In the first, which is based on the sausage test used in the meat industry (Dingle *et al.*), the fish protein, water, salt and lard are combined to make an emulsion with the proportions essentially equal to those in a wiener or beef sausage. The emulsion is cooked and the gel strength is measured on an Instron tester as the force necessary for a cylindrical plunger (0.2 cm²) to penetrate 0.5 cm into a 1.0-cm-thick layer. The other test uses a more dilute emulsion of fish protein, salt, water and soybean oil which is near the oil water ratio of mayonnaise. This emulsion is also heated and cooled and is then subjected to a varied centrifugal force to determine the conditions under which the emulsion will break. It should be noted that both of these methods require the protein to hydrate, to emulsify and to heat coagulate. When the emulsification tests used in the meat industry were tried (these do not involve heating), it was found that all the fish protein samples were good emulsifiers and the test did not discriminate. It is thus apparent that a more crucial test, such as those described above, must be adopted if the food processing industry is to compare functional proteins in a standardized way. Trials with fatty species such as capelin, mackerel and herring have shown that these potential raw materials can also be used for producing FFP. However, pilot plant studies on these species are still underway.

CONCLUSION

It would appear that the future of FPC in Canada and elsewhere is no longer limited by the lack of technology. Many processes have been developed and tested. It has been demonstrated repeatedly that FPC is a highly nutritious protein with excellent potential as a human food supplement. A wide variety of products have been tested and they have the necessary approval of world health authorities. The problem of functionality in these products is also being resolved (FFP), opening the way to their wider use in both human and animal nutrition. Nevertheless, the commercial feasibility of both FPC and FFP has yet to be demonstrated. At the present time it is difficult to be optimistic in view of the cost and limited availability of raw materials, the lack of developed market outlets and competition from other protein sources.

References

DINGLE, J R, KENNEDY, D J and Dyer, W J Improved fish protein
0000   concentrate, Case No. 4752, Canadian Patents and Development Limited, Ottawa 4, Canada, Can. Pat. Appl. No. 113, 942, Filed 26 May 1971.
FOUGÈRE, H Technological Developments in Canada (Fish Flour).
1962   In Heen, E and Kreuzer, R (ed.), *Fish in Nutrition*, London, Fishing News (Books) Ltd., p.413–415.

L'Utilisation du faux-poisson ramène par les crevettiers de l'Atlantique   *R J Eyssalet*

Utilizing by-catch fish from Atlantic shrimp trawlers
A large part of the living resources of the sea is now rejected because it is traditionally considered uneconomical. In view of the increasing needs of animal protein, research workers, shipowners and traditional fish meal manufacturers have joined forces to develop new products for human consumption, based on the use of trash fish. The process of enzymatic hydrolysis was chosen and the paper describes installations, on board and on the shore, for the processing of trash fish.

Metodo para elaborar la morralla capturada por camaroneros del atlantico
Gran parte de los recursos vivos del mar se desechan debido a que tradicionalmente se consideran antieconómicos. Teniendo en cuenta que cada vez es mayor la necesidad de proteínas de origen animal, los investigadores, armadores y productores de harina de pescado han aunado sus fuerzas para elaborar a base de morralla nuevos productos, dedicados al consumo humano. Se ha elegido el método de la hidrólisis enzimática y, en el documento, se describen diversos tipos de instalaciones, a bordo y en tierra, para la elaboración de la morralla.

Une des techniques essentiellement employée est la pêche au chalut. Le navire remorque son filet pendant par exemple trois heures, puis le ramène à bord pour en vider le contenu et le trier. Les espèces nobles sont traitées pour la commercialisation, le reste, le by-catch fish (faux-poisson), est rejeté à la mer. Traumatisé, sans vie, il repart au début du cycle biologique, c'est-à-dire au niveau des déchets organiques. Il est pratiquement perdu pour le milieu marin et pour les hommes. Et pourtant, il représente une part importante des prises, parfois 30, parfois 50 et jusqu'à 80 pour cent. Les grandes unités, par exemple les morutiers-congélateurs dont l'entrepont est équipé pour la transformation de la pêche en filets surgelés, traitent parfois les sous-produits de filetage et fabriquent de la farine et des huiles. Mais il est fréquent de rejeter les sous-produits à la mer et le tonnage ainsi perdu est égal au double du tonnage de filets mis en cales. En effet, 3 kg de poisson brut donnent seulement 1 kg de filets. Il apparaît ainsi que sur l'ensemble de l'activité mondiale des pêches, plusieurs dizaines de millions de tonnes de matières biologiques nobles sont chaque année extraites de la mer, pour y être aussitôt rejetées sans être exploitées.

Les solutions envisagees pour sauver les ressources perdues

C'est en partant de ces constatations et en les rapprochant des grands besoins en protéines animales profondément ressentis par de nombreux pays, que l'Association d'Etude des Problèmes de Nutrition (AEPN) s'est créé en France en 1963 pour rechercher des solutions réalistes et travailler à leur développement industriel. Les chercheurs de l'Université de Nantes, les armateurs à la pêche, les producteurs de farines traditionnelles de poisson, et Nacoma SA Engineering, se sont réunis dans l'AEPN à cette fin. Dès le départ, le but assigné a été la mise au point de produits destinés à l'alimentation de l'homme, par conséquent fabriqués à partir d'une matière première biologiquement intacte, et par un procédé non-dénaturant, excluant toute action chimique traumatisante ou d'incidence toxique même lointaine. La voie de l'hydrolyse enzymatique a été choisie et largement explorée. Le procédé se développe en phase liquide et à température modérée, ce qui conserve leurs qualités naturelles à la masse protéique, aux lipides, et à l'ensemble des éléments nutritifs. En cet état physique, les fractionnements et la séparation des lipides sont également facilités et le produit final se présente après concentration sous vide et séchage au spary drying sous la forme d'une fine poudre blanche ou légèrement teintée, entièrement ou partiellement soluble selon la fraction observée et titrant environ 85 pour cent de valeur protéique. La flaveur de ce produit est pratiquement neutre. Il est étudié pour répondre aux normes appliquées aux industries alimentaires, pour la préparation d'aliments solides ou liquides. Des recherches de caractère plus fondamental sont poursuivies sur le plan de la diététique et dans le domaine médical, et les huiles qui sont d'une exceptionnelle qualité, laissent entrevoir d'autre part, des applications qui concernent la cosmétologie par exemple. Bien entendu, le niveau de ces applications n'exclut pas pour autant l'intérêt qui s'attache aux aliments d'élevage aussi bien pour les animaux terrestres qu'aquatiques. C'est aisni qu'un double objectif a été précisé: d'une part, la valorisation de la totalité des prises de la pêche; d'autre part, la production de facteurs alimentaires nobles susceptibles d'apporter une réponse aux nécessités de notre temps. Des études de développement industriel ont été engagées dans cette optique et certaines réalisations sont en cours. Etant donné qu'il était fondamental de traiter une matière biologiquement intacte, il fallait prévoir ce traitement, ou tout au moins la première phase de stabilsation de la matière travaillée, directement sur les lieux de pêche, ou à proximité immédiate. Il fallait donc que le procédé soit suffisamment simple et souple pour être adaptable au travail à la mer, ou dans une zone proche des pêcheries côtières.

Trois solutions ont été retenues, qui répondent à ces contraintes:

La première solution se situe dans le cadre d'un port de pêche français de la côte de Bretagne, qui pratique la pêche fraîche par des marées de 12 à 15 jours réalisées par 15 chalutiers-arrière de 55 m. Ces navires seront équipés sur 1972 et 1973 des installations de traitement à la mer du by-catch fish ramené dans les chaluts, pour le transformer en hydrolysat liquide stablisé et le ramener au port oú il sera débarqué par pompage sur le centre de traitement final. Le procédé est pratiqué dans ce cas en deux étapes complémentaires, l'une à bord des navires, l'autre à terre (Figures 1 et 2). La pêche est triée dès la sortie du chalut. Le by-catch fish est déposé sur un transporteur qui' l'amène à trémie de stockage (1) d'ou il est extrait par la vis (2) pour tomber dans le broyeur (3) la pompe (4) aspire le broyat et alimente alternativement les cuves d'hydrolyse (5) la digestion enzymatique liquifie le broyat qui s'écoule dans le tamis (6) oú il est filtré. Les squelettes et écailles sont récupérés à part. La pompe (4) reprend l'hydrolysat filtré et le stock dans la cuve (7) d'oú il repart vers les réservoirs en cales après avoir subi une flash-pasteurisation en (8). L'hydrolysat est maintenu à 0°C dans les cales d'oú il sera extrait par pompage au débarquement. L'hydrolysat est alors transporté en citerne autoportante jusqu'à l'usine de traitement où il est stocké dans les cuves A_1 et A_2. Il est additionné d'eau et réchauffé dans les cuves B_1 et B_2 avant son accès à la station de séparation. Les décanteuses, séparatrices et clarificatrices S_1, S_2 et S_3 réalisent les fractionnements et la séparation des huiles qui sont récupérées à part. L'hydrolysat délipidé est concentré sous vide, en Co, puis il est séché au spray drying en At et conditionné en sacs. A bord, dès la sortie du chalut et comme à l'habitude, les poissons sont triés et le by-catch fish écarté, mais au lieu d'être rejeté à la mer, il passe dans la trémie d'accès de la ligne d'hydrolyse. Broyé, hydrolysé, filtré pour écarter les squelettes, flash-pasteurisé, il est stocké à état liquide à 0°C dans les cales aménagées. Chaque navire est équipé pour ramener environ 40 m³ par marée, qui équivalent à près de 50 tonnes de by-catch fish. A terre, le centre de traitement collecte les apports des navires et pratique les fractionnements, séparations, concentration sous vide, et spray drying, pour obtenir le concentré proéique sec.

La seconde solution correspond aux navires de grande taille. Dans le présent cas, il s'agit d'un morutier-congélateur dont la base est située sur la côte sud-ouest de la façade atlantique française. Ce navire pratique des marées longues de trois mois et pêche au droit du Groenland, de l'Islande et de la Norvège. Il est équipé pour produire les filets surgelés, et la quantité de sous-produits qui résultent de ce filetage est en moyenne de 20 tonnes par jour de pêche. Il ne pourrait être question de transformer en hydrolysat 20 tonnes par jour pendent trois mois de mer et de stocker à bord un aussi important volume. Prolonger le procédé jusqu'à la concentration à 50 pour cent de matière sèche ne donnait pas non plus la solution, le volume à stocker étant encore beaucoup trop fort. Il a donc été envisagé d'implanter à bord l'installation complète, y compris le spray drying et cette solution a été retenue. Elle constitue un premier exemple d'équipement de navires-usines susceptibles d'aborder l'exploitation des très importantes réserves d'espèces actuellement d'elaissées et qui sont pourtant disponibles.

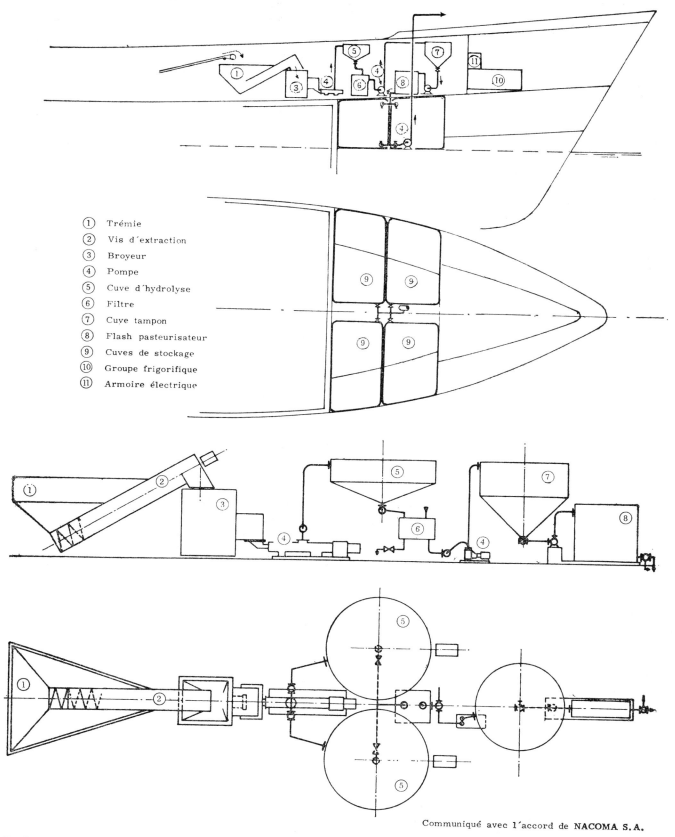

1. Trémie
2. Vis d'extraction
3. Broyeur
4. Pompe
5. Cuve d'hydrolyse
6. Filtre
7. Cuve tampon
8. Flash pasteurisateur
9. Cuves de stockage
10. Groupe frigorifique
11. Armoire électrique

Communiqué avec l'accord de **NACOMA S.A.**

Fig 1 Préparation de concentrés protéiques: 1ère phase–à bord

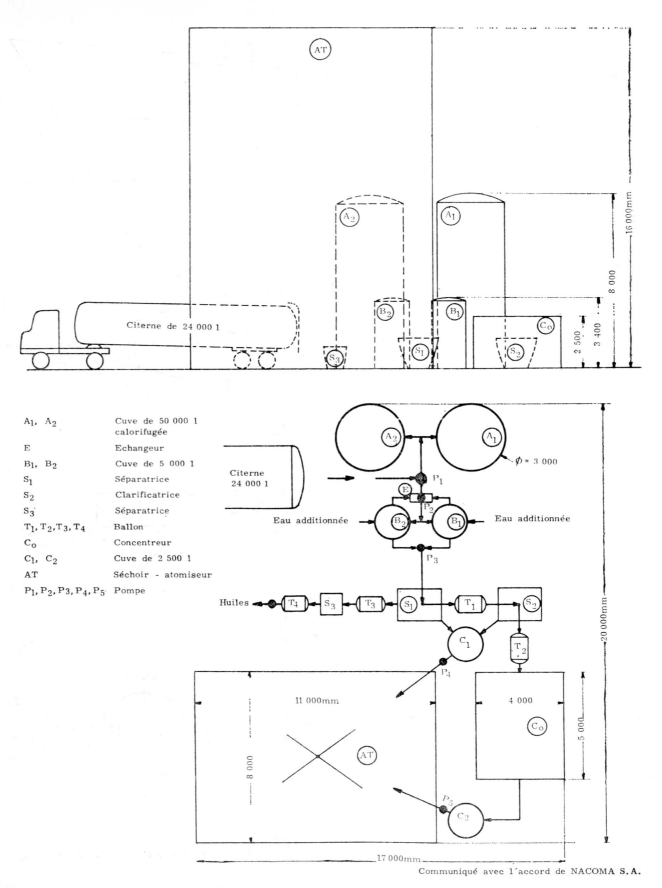

A_1, A_2	Cuve de 50 000 l calorifugée
E	Echangeur
B_1, B_2	Cuve de 5 000 l
S_1	Séparatrice
S_2	Clarificatrice
S_3	Séparatrice
T_1, T_2, T_3, T_4	Ballon
C_0	Concentreur
C_1, C_2	Cuve de 2 500 l
AT	Séchoir - atomiseur
P_1, P_2, P_3, P_4, P_5	Pompe

Communiqué avec l'accord de NACOMA S.A.

Fig 2 Préparation de concentrés protéiques: 2ème phase–à terre

294

La troisième solution découle du morcellement fréquent des flottilles de pêche en unités légrères, travaillant en vue des côtes et rentrant chaque jour au port. Dans ce dernier cas, le problème a été posé à propos d'une zone très poissonneuse de la côte occidentale d'Afrique, dont la flottille est constituée de bateaux de moins de 20 m, mais dont le nombre, joint à la proximité des lieux de pêche et à leur richesse, présente des possibilités potentielles tout à fait remarquables. Dans ces conditions, l'équipement des unités pour le travail à la mer n'était pas du tout envisageable, et le problème a été travaillé sous l'angle d'une installation complète sur la côte, avec un aménagement du centre de stockage des mises à terre particulièrement étudié dans le souci de l'hygiène en tenant compte des contraintes imposées par le climat. L'installation sera capable de traiter 100 tonnes de poisson brut par jour.

REFLEXIONS ET CONCLUSIONS

Le premier type d'exploitation mixte, partie à la mer, partie sur la côte, est adapté aux flottilles moyennes pêchant au large par séquences de 2 à 3 semaines. C'est le cas des grands ports de pêche européens alors que le second type, c'est-à-dire l'installation complète sur le navire est adapté aux flottes de pêche puissantes, à grands rayons d'action (c'est par exemple le cas de l'URSS) et que le troisième type d'installation correspond au contexte général des pays qui ne disposent que d'un outil de pêche très morcelé, à rayon d'action très

faible et travaillant sous des climate sévères. Il est difficile d'établir entre ces trois types d'exploitation une comparison valable sur le terrain économique parce que les critères retenus dans chaque cas sont différents. Il est nécessaire de bien comprendre que la notion de profit immédiat ne constitue pas forcément la motivation essentielle, et qu'elle doit parfois céder le pas à la nécessité de satisfaire les besoins impérieux des populations, et aussi à l'exploitation plus raisonnable des ressources marines. Les pays développés orientent les applications des concentrés protéiques vers les améliorations de qualité et de prix des nourritures dont ils disposent en abondance, ainsi que vers les applications diététiques et médicales. C'est là un objectif important. Les pays en voie de développement très généralement déficitaires en protéines animales, ont besoin de compléter leurs ressources alimentaires habituelles basées le plus souvent sur les farines végétales. C'est là un objectif tout à fait primordial. C'est ainsi qu'après nombre d'années de recherches, et après avoir franchi les étapes expérimentales sur le chalutier océanographique La Thalassa et l'étape pilote sur le chalutier de pêche fraîche Captaine Cook, l'AEPN a pu engager le développement industriel des procédés qu'elle avait mis au point. Mais, son activité de recherche continue, dans le but d'obtenir des produits utiles toujours élaborés, et dans l'étude des formulations pour la création de nouveaux aliments à partir de l'enrichissement équilibré des concentrés protéiques issus de la mer.

The Use of Fish of Lower Market Value for Human Consumption *N I Rekhina*

Utilisation du poisson de faible valeur commerciale pour la consommation humaine

Ce document est consacré ã certains travaux intéressants effectués en URSS sur l'utilisation d'espèces de poisson négligées ou peu communes, notamment la morue du Pacifique occidental, le sprat de la Caspienne, le capelan, le poutassou, les petits sparidés, le trichiure et les déchets du parage d'autres poissons. Ces travaux portent sur trois domaines principaux: le poisson haché congelé, les hydrolyzats protéiques et les protéines de poisson en poudre. L'auteur esquisse l'expérience acquise dans ces trois domaines et décrit le type et l'utilisation des produits fabriqués.

El empleo de pescado de poco valor comercial para la alimentacion del hombre

Se describe en la ponencia parte de los interesantes estudios que se efectùan en la URSS en lo relativo al aprovechamiento de especies descuidadas o poco concocidas, particularmente el abadejo de Alaska, la sardina del Mar Caspio, el capelán, la faneca, pargos pequeños, tahalís y desechos de otros pescados. Se estudian tres posibilidades: pescado picado congelado, hidrolizados de proteína y polvo de proteína de pescado. Se esboza la experiencia adquirida en los tres casos y se describe la clase de productos fabricados y su empleo.

A considerable number of commercial marine species do not appear to be in great demand among consumers. In the USSR these are Alaska pollack (*Theragra chalcogramma*), Caspian kilka (*Clupeonella* spp.), capelin (*Mallotus villosus*), hairtail (*Trichiurus harmela, T. lepturus*) and some others which are in limited demand although their flesh is of fairly high nutritive value. It is important, therefore, to carry out investigations to develop suitable methods of using the flesh (protein) of these species. At present, the utilization of these species of lower market value is developing along three main lines: frozen fish minces (pastes), protein hydrolyzates, and fish protein powder (FPP). Though the direct consumption of these products is fairly limited, they are used in the production of various moulded and structurized

foods resembling food items or made into completely new products.

FROZEN FISH MINCE

Frozen fish mince, which is a product retaining the properties of fish flesh to a greater degree than fish protein powder (FPP) or hydrolyzates, is likely to be used more extensively. The production of minces from many small and medium-sized fish is made possible by the use of separators (neopresses) of various systems which produce meat free of bones. This valuable food amounts to 70 or 90 per cent of the weight of beheaded and gutted fish. In the USSR fish minces are prepared from Alaska pollack, blue whiting (*Micromesistius poutassou*), small porgies (*Gymnocranius griseus*), offal obtained in processing grenadier (*Macrurus berglax*), hairtail and some other species. Since both quality and yield of the mince are higher if it is prepared from the fish at the stage of rigor mortis, or immediately after, it is advisable to prepare this product at sea. Two processes are used in the USSR: production of washed (special) and non-washed minces. Washed minces are obtained on the processing lines in vessels of the type of 'Severodonetsk' and '50 years of the Soviet Union', which have a capacity of 6 and 25 tons/8 h respectively. Non-washed mince is produced on vessels of the NATALIYA KOVSHOVA type.

Production of washed mince involves the following steps: the beheaded and gutted fish, with the black peritoneum thoroughly cleaned off, are sent through the neopress to separate and crush the meat. The coarse mince thus obtained is washed twice with fresh water at the ratio 1 to 3 to remove mobile water-soluble nitrogenous, mineral and other substances. After removal of excess moisture, the mass obtained is finely crushed and common salt, sugar, phosphates and some other substances are introduced to inhibit protein denaturation which is responsible for changes in the technological properties of the product. The mince is then packed into 10-kg polyethylene bags, frozen and stored at −18 to −20°C. The storage life of this product is six to nine months, depending on the species.

The production of non-washed mince is a much simpler process: the fish meat, coarsely crushed in the neopress, is fine minced in the microcutter or a similar apparatus. After the addition of the anti-denaturants, it is packed and frozen. The storage life of this product at −18 to −20°C is three to six months, depending on the species used. The yield of non-washed mince (40 to 45 per cent of the weight of whole fish) is much higher than that of washed mince or fillets.

The storage time of both washed and non washed mince is mainly determined by their water retention capacity and the formation of a cohesive structure. The products made from both minces include fish sticks, sausage, Frankfurt-style sausages (skinned or skinless), puddings, delicatessen pastes, fish dough, croquettes, etc. When frozen mince is used to prepare a culinary mass (semi-product) it should be introduced in a semi-defrosted state (−5 to −4°C).

PROTEIN HYDROLYZATES

A number of studies have been recently undertaken in the USSR to develop the production of enzymic hydrolyzates with different degrees of proteolysis. The material used is small-sized fish, containing active enzymes, such as Caspian kilka, capelin, etc. The hydrolysis is conducted at different temperatures depending on the use of the final product. To obtain the protein mass from Caspian kilka, containing 25 to 30 per cent of dry matter, the fish are hydrolyzed for 18 to 28 h at 0 to 5°C. Bones and excess moisture are removed from the

hydrolyzate and the conserving agent added to the mass. The finished product is used as a neutral protein-enriching ingredient in making bread and in the manufacture of sausages, and in the preparation of dietetic foods. For liquid hydrolyzates from Caspian kilka, with the dry matter content of 8 to 10 per cent, the fish are hydrolyzed for 8 to 10 h at 60 to 65°C. After the removal of unresolved muscle tissue and bones, the hydrolyzate is concentrated by evaporation and can be used as a protein basis in the production of structurized foods, such as black grainy caviar, etc.

FISH PROTEIN POWDER (FPP)

In the USSR, as in many other countries, the problems involved in the manufacture and application of FPP have been given much consideration. Pilot plant experiments have been made to produce FPP from Caspian kilka, Alaska pollack and cod. The three-stage ethanol extraction or successive benzine and ethanol extraction methods have been used. The advisability of treating raw material with a weak acid or alkali prior to solvent extraction has been looked into, and studies have been made of the effect of the fineness of the grind on the swelling ability of finished powder in water. Also investigations have been conducted to find out various uses of FPP, for example, as an additive to bread and macaroni products and as a basic ingredient in the preparation of fish soups. The use of FPP in powdered fish soups is of considerable interest. Much importance is attached to the swelling ability of FPP, which is appreciably effected by the fineness of the grind (the finer, the better). The FPP production method adopted by the VNIRO at present seems to be the most reasonable one. In this method the gutted and beheaded Alaska pollack, for example, are treated in the neopress and the mince obtained is cooked, strained of excess moisture, finely ground and dried in a spray drier. The dry product thus obtained is used as an ingredient in several fish soup recipes.

CONCLUSION

These three lines of development described above make it possible to utilize fish species which are not in demand for direct consumption. But, of course, the extent to which one or another of these methods of processing is adopted by a country depends on a number of factors, such as the requirements of the national economy and the tastes and food habits of the people concerned.

References

LYSOVA A S and CHERNOGORTSEY, A P The use of enzyme prepara-
1968   tions in the production of protein hydrolyzates from kilka.
        Bulletins of Institutions of Higher learning. Food Technology,
        No. 4.
REKHINA, N I Production of frozen fish mince and mince products.
1971   *VNIRO Proceedings*, v.LXXIX, Moscow.
REKHÍNA, N I, POLYAKOVA, L K and BUDINA, V G Frozen fish
1973   mince as raw material for the production of fish sausage.
        Rybnoe Khozyaistvo, No. 4.

Product Development Experiments in Peru   *H Beumer*

Essais de mise au point de produits nouverux au Perou

La présente communication décrit les essais réalisés au Pérou sur cinq espèces choisies de poisson existant en abondance mais sous-utilisées. Les travaux ont été réalisés conjointement par l'Empresa Pública de Servicios Pesqueros (EPSEP) et le Projet PNUD/FAO de commercialisation et d'utilisation du poisson. L'expérience acquise a mis en lumière de nombrèux problèmes liés à ces travaux de mise au point de produits nouveaux, notamment lorsqu'il s'agit d'espèces peu utilisès ou peu appréciées de poisson dans des pays en voie de développement. Les résultats des expériences ont aussi donné une indication des possibilités commerciales de ces produits nouveaux, tant sur les marchés intérieurs qu'à l'exportation.

Experimentos de preparacion de nuevos productos en Peru

En este trabajo se describen los experimentos de preparación de nuevos productos realizados en Perú con cinoc especies seleccionadas de peces abundantes pero subaprovechados. El trabajo fue realizado conjuntamente por la Empresa Pública de Servicios Pesqueros (EPSEP) y el Proyecto PNUD/FAO de Comercialización y Utilización de Pescado. La experiencia lograda pone de relieve muchos de los problemas que se han encontrado en este trabajo de preparación de nuevos productos, especialmente en el caso de especies de peces no familiares o impopulares en los países en desarrollo. Al mismo tiempo, los resultados del trabajo experimental han indicado las posibilidades comerciales de estos nuevos productos en los mercados interiores y de exportación.

The Peruvian Government decided in 1969 to adopt an aggressive policy to increase the utilization of fish in the nation's diet and one of the results of this was the enterprise, which is the counterpart agency of the UNDP/FAO Fish Marketing and Utilization Project. Among the objects of Empresa Pública de Servcios Pesqueros (EPSEP) is to increase foreign exchange earnings by the development and marketing of products suitable for export, and promotional and other activities aimed at increasing the consumption of fish in Peru.

The project operates a pilot plant where the following equipment is installed: a semi-automatic sealing machine for round tins; a semi-automatic sealing machine for 1/4 dingley and 1/4 oblong aluminium tins; a 10–1 pan with steam jacket for the preparation of sauces; a steam-heated continuous exhauster, adopted for precooking; a small over-pressure autoclave; a Torry smoking kiln and a Torry Mini kiln as well as an Altona-type oven; a continuous heat-shrinking tunnel for demonstration of improved presentation of final product; a rotary mincing/ mixing machine; a small Gram contact freezer with 6 stations; a commercial refrigerator/freeze storage cabinet and a number of filleting and packing tables, etc. Further, a hake-filleting line, consisting of a Baader 421 heading machine, a Baader 188 filleting machine and a Baader 47 skinning machine, was installed in the processing plant at Paita belonging to Productos Marinos SA This company has been cooperating closely with EPSEP and the Project in trials aimed at demonstrating the commercial potential of machine processing of Peruvian hake. When selecting the range of products to be included in the programme it was decided to concentrate work on five main species: anchoveta (*Engraulis ringens*); machete (*Ethmidium chilcae*); caballa (*Scomber japonicus peruanus*); sardina (*Sardinops sagax*), and merluza (*Merluccius gayi*). The common factors for these species are abundant landings and a low price due to consumer preference for other species, such as flounder, bonito and dogfish. Further, the fishing for the selected species is not greatly affected by seasons. It was also felt that a variety of products based on these species would have an export as well as a local potential demand because they are similar to some North Atlantic species in great demand and decreasing supply.

ANCHOVETA (*Engraulis ringens*)

Canned anchoveta, Norwegian brisling style

This fish reaches a maximum size of 18 to 20 cm. Considerable efforts were put into trials to make a product similar to the Norwegian brisling pack, partly because experience with this products was availabe within the project. A number of experiments were carried out to starve the anchoveta at sea. This is a basic requirement for the production of brisling sardines as the fish is canned without removing the viscera. One approach was to try to keep the fish alive in floating nets in the sea and another was to try to keep them alive on board in tanks of sea water, filtered to remove plankton. The water was continuously aerated. These experiments were eventually abandoned for various reasons, ie, no plankton free water available near the fishing grounds; attacks on the nets by birds and seals; the non-commercial feasibility of the tank method because of the low fishto-water ratio; the fact that the intestinal string of the anchoveta is black which would detract from the appearance of the final product. Two methods of nobbing anchoveta were employed in experiments. The procedure was: (1) opening the throat and removing the viscera without severing the head. This has the advantage that the fish can be smoked hung on rods so that it does not become marked. It is, however, time consuming, labour intensive and can only be done by hand; (2) severing the head partly and pulling it away with the viscera. This is a fairly quick procedure and could possibly be done by machine. The main disadvantage is that the fish can only be smoked on wire-mesh trays. This marks them and may damage the skin, which would spoil the appearance of the final product. However, with sufficient care during the processing a satisfactory product can be made.

Canned anchoveta, smoked

The anchovetas were nobbed, washed and put in a 15 per cent brine for approximately 5 min, depending upon size and fat content (min. 6 per cent fat is required to obtain a satisfactory texture of the final product). The purpose of the brining was to give a slightly salty flavour to the fish and also to make the flesh firmer. After brining, the headless fish were laid on wire-mesh trays or, in the case of head-on fish, hung on rods piercing the heads. The fish were then smoked in a Torry kiln, gradually increasing the temperature over 1 to $1\frac{1}{2}$ h to approximately 100°C. The aims of the smoking process were to: dry the fish sufficiently (18 to 22 per cent weight loss depending on fat content) in order to avoid getting water in the oil; smoke the fish lightly. The basic reason for this is import duty rates in the USA which are lower for smoked products; and cook the fish sufficiently. After smoking, they were allowed to cool down. The head-on fish were cut with scissors from the rods, leaving the heads which were discarded. The fish were packed in 1/4 rectangular tins, with one or two layers, depending on size. They were carefully cut to a size to fit the tin correctly. The size gradings were: 8 to 10 cm, crosspacked; 10 to 13 cm, length-packed, double layers; and 13 to 16 cm, length-packed, single layers. Soybean oil or tomato or mustard sauce was added hot, and the tins sealed and cleaned. The tins were sterilized for 1 h at 110°C. In the case of aluminium tins it is necessary to sterilize in water, using over-pressure by the help of compressed air. Quick cooling under pressure is necessary to ensure a good quality of the product and to avoid bulging of tins.

Nobbed anchoveta in tomato sauce, precooked

Because of the abundance of the anchoveta it was logical to consider the possible production of a low cost product for mass distribution in less sophisticated markets, as well as more expensive products. By omitting the smoking process, considerable economies can be made in respect of labour costs, etc, and with a higher unit weight the packaging cost will obviously be lower per kilogramme. The product requirements are such that less fish need be discarded. The anchovetas were nobbed, washed and brined and then packed in 1-lb (454-g) tall tins alternately with the tail up and down. They were then steam-precooked at 100°C in the tin for approximately 40 min and subsequently drained. The hot tomato sauce, which should be spiced in accordance with the requirements of the market, was then added and the tins sealed as soon as possible, cleaned and sterilized.

Nobbed anchoveta in aromatized oil

The same procedure as described in the foregoing section was applied but aromatized oil was added instead of tomato sauce to give the product a smoked taste. In summing up, the fresh raw material has a short storage life and will keep for only one day in ice. When producing sardine-type packs the colour of meat and the skin was darker for anchoveta than for brisling and similar species. The taste of the final product, however, was excellent and very favourable comments were received from several overseas buyers who expressed interest in purchasing the product when it was in full production. Certain difficulties were encountered in respect of analyses of fat content because of the pilot-scale production facilities. There were also limitations in the range of types of tins which could be sealed. Problems were encountered in obtaining raw material of suitable quality because of the existing practice of rough handling of anchoveta for fish meal. An important point in the development of canned anchoveta was the required labelling for the US market. It would be highly desirabl, if the product could be labelled as 'sardines' as this term is well established and the marketing effort would, consequently, be considerably less than in the case of introducing an entirely new name. Following discussions with the US Food and Drug Administration, it appears that such products may be labelled 'sardine style', provided that the words 'Peruvian anchoveta' also appear in bold print on the label.

Frozen anchoveta

On several occasions trials have been made to freeze anchoveta in blast tunnels and in plate freezers to: maintain a stock of raw material for the canning experiments; produce samples for foreign pet food manufacturers; supply raw material for gutting/nobbing trials by overseas manufacturers of processing machinery; and to supply samples of potential raw material for overseas anchovy processors. Immediately after catch the fish were put in boxes of expanded polystyrene with crushed ice and brought ashore within 4 to 6 hours. They were frozen as soon as possible, usually within 24 hr of catch, in blocks of about 5 kg, glazed, polybagged and put in master cartons. Anchoveta could have an effective storage life of 4 to 5 months, minimum, if stored at temperatures not exceeding−28°C.

Salted anchoveta

Experiments were made with the salting of anchoveta as a potential low-cost source of protein for the population of the'Peruvian highlands. Nobbed fish were placed in vats with a fish/salt ratio of 2 :1 and could be kept in good condition for several months, provided the temperature did not exceed about 10°C. Further trials, including test marketing, will be made to produce salted anchoveta, mechanically pressed to remove excess water, when the raw material becomes available again.

Dried anchoveta

Whole fresh fish were placed in a 15 per cent brine for 5 to 10 min, partly to make the flesh firmer and partly to remove scales. They were stirred twice in the brine to remove all scales (a rotary washer with brine would probably be more efficient). After this they were dried in a Torry kiln at about 40°C for 40 to 50 hr. Samples were submitted to the UK and Japan and were considered acceptable by potential buyers. But as the main export market appears to be Sri Lanka, where ruling c.i.f. prices are approximately 50 per cent lower than the production cost in Peru, no further production has taken place. The product, however, might find a market in the Peruvian highlands.

MACHETE (*Ethmidium chilcae*)

The machete is a pelagic fish which can reach a maximum size of approximately 30 cm. It appears to be most concentrated in the central part of the Peruvian coast. The machete has traditionally been fished mainly for meal as it is not popular with the consumers as a food fish due to its bone structure, which is similar to that of the Atlantic herring. There is no particular fishing season, and it is possible to catch the fish throughout the year, which makes it a most suitable raw material for canneries. Due to the very poor landings of bonito, previously the most important raw material for the Peruvian canning industry, machete is now becoming quite popular and considerable quantities are being processed on a regular basis. The bulk is being processed in the form of chunks, as a grated pack in ½-lb (225-g) flat tins and as a sardine-type product in 1-lb (454-g) oval tins with tomato sauce.

Smoked machete fillets, skin on

As the canning industry was processing machete commercially, it was felt that experiments with developing smoked products from the fish should be given a higher priority in the pilot plant. Fresh machete were washed, scaled and filleted, yielding approximately 40 per cent fresh fillets. The fillets were put in a 10 per cent brine for 2 to 3 min, drained and placed on wire-mesh trays for smoking in a Torry kiln. They were carefully smoked, gradually increasing the temperature from 40°C (with air vents fully open) up to 100°C (full smoke) until they turned an even golden colour. The weight loss during smoking was approximately 20 per cent so the yield of the final product from raw material is about 30 per cent. The product compares favourably with fresh smoked herring fillets.

Cold smoked machete, kipper style

Fresh machete were washed, scaled and split from the back as is traditional for kippers. The fish were then placed in a 15 per cent brine for 10 min, with added 'kipper-brown' dye. They were then drained and placed on wire-mesh trays in a Torry kiln, where they were allowed to dry at ambient temperature for 30 min before being smoked for 4 hr at 20 to 25°C. Weight loss during drying and smoking amounted to 15 per cent. The product compares favourably with kippered herrings and should be acceptable on markets where the consumers are accustomed to this type of product. In the local market, however, there is a strong bias against the bone structure.

Canned smoked machete

This is basically the same product as smoked fillets but canned. The smoking must be done very carefully as the aim is a light smoked product, sufficiently dry (20 per cent weight loss) and sufficiently cooked. In processing, the basic procedure is, in the first instance, to dry the fillets and, subsequently, to smoke/cook them. It is necessary to start at low temperature with as much fresh air intake as possible. While the temperature is gradually increased and smoke is added, the fresh air inlet is gradually closed. If the temperature is increased too quickly, white droplets will form on the surface, consisting mainly of water and coagulated proteins. These spots do not take the smoke colour while they are wet, resulting in an unpleasant appearance of the final product. Smoked products become much darker during sterilizing, so that a product with a nice colour when freshly smoked, might become almost black in a sterilized tin. The fillets were, therefore, smoked so lightly that they were of the desired colour after sterilizing. After cooling, the fillets were trimmed to fit the tin. Two types of pack were made, either two whole fillets in a 1/4 oblong tin or pieces of fillets cut to a size fitting $\frac{1}{2}$-lb (225-g) round tins or 1-lb (454-g) talls. In the case of the latter, the pieces were packed in such a way as to obtain a type of solid pack. Oil may be added, but it was not found to be essential. Several samples sent abroad elicited favourable comments in respect of taste and presentation. The main problem faced was the quality of the fresh raw material due to it being landed in bulk, without ice, and roughly handled.

Marinated products

Some trial batches of marinated machete were made in the form of rollmops. Fresh fillets without scales were salted in saturated brine for 24 h after which they were placed in a $12\frac{1}{2}$ per cent solution of acetic acid, saturated with salt. After at least five days they were rinsed for 10 to 15 min in clean water, drained, dipped in sugar with white pepper and rolled around a piece of onion, then put in the final sugar/vinegar/water solution and allowed to mature for at least two days. According to Europeans with a knowledge of Scandinavian and German marinated herring products, the samples were acceptable, but no further trials have been made so far as this type of product is not acceptable to traditional Peruvian taste. There does, however, exist a possibility of exports of a semi-product for subsequent reprocessing abroad.

CABALLA (*Scomber japonicus peruanus*)

The caballa (Pacific mackerel) is pelagic and reaches a maximum size of some 35 cm. It is fished along the entire Peruvian coast. This species is similar to the common Atlantic mackerel and suitable material for the same products. Recently, the canning industry has been increasing its utilization for products such as replacement of bonito (solid pack), mackerel in brine (salmon style) and pet foods. As the fish is very suitable for hot-smoking it was decided to concentrate in the pilot plant on smoked products.

Smoked whole caballa

The fish, 300 to 500 g each, were eviscerated, the gills removed and washed to remove all traces of blood and viscera. They were placed in a 10 per cent brine for about 30 min, then hung on rods, piercing the eyes, in the smoking kiln. They were then dried with slowly increasing temperatures: 15 min at 40°C; 15 min at 50°C; 15 min at 60°C and 15 at 70 to 80°C. Smoke was added and smoking continued until the skin became a golden yellow colour and the flesh was completely cooked, usually after $2\frac{1}{2}$ to $3\frac{1}{2}$ hours. The fish were occasionally moved to different parts of the kiln, depending on the type of kiln. The product is virtually identical to smoked mackerel and should have good sales prospects. However, as there is some bias against the product locally, there can be no large-scale marketing at present.

Canned smoked caballa fillets

The process was similar to that used for canned smoked machete and similar care should be taken to smoke the product lightly to achieve the correct colour after sterilization. Problems of shrinkage during sterilizing were encountered with the 1-lb (454-g) tall tins.

SARDINE (*Sardinops sagax*)

The sardine closely resembles the pilchard. Its maximum size is 30 to 35 cm, and weight from 400 to 500 grammes. The size of the annually sustainable yield is not known but substantial quantities are landed at times without any apparent damage to the stock. Sardines are utilized by the canning industry, especially if and when bonito and even machete are in short supply. The fish are usually considered as less suitable due to softness. However, this appears to be mainly due to bad handling. It was decided to experiment with smoking, canning and marinating when fish of suitable quality became available.

Sardine smoked as Buckling

Fresh sardines were eviscerated, washed, brined and smoked at temperatures which were being gradually increased from 40°C to 80°C until they became of even golden colour and the flesh was completely cooked. The final product was of excellent taste and appearance. Experiments will now be made with frozen raw material to investigate its potential as raw material for countries having difficulties in securing supplies of Atlantic herring.

Canned sardines in tomato sauce

The fish were nobbed by removing the head, washed and brined to improve the texture of the flesh. They were cut into lengths suitable for the 1-lb (454-g) tall tin, packed and precooked for about 40 min at 100°C. The tins were drained and hot tomato sauce added, then sealed, washed and sterilized for about 75 min at 115°C. This ensured that the backbone was soft in the final product. Examples have been sent to interested customers abroad.

MERLUZA (*Merluccius gayi*)

The merluza, or Peruvian hake, is potentially one of the most important Peruvian food fish. So far, as it is presently used for this purpose, it is frozen headless, dressed, or, to a smaller degree, processed as individually frozen fillets. There are plans for making frozen fish stick blocks. A number of experiments have been made to produce skinless and boneless fish stick blocks from round, bled and gutted or bled only material. The final product was examined against the specifications of various commercial companies in the UK and USA for the standard 16½-lb (7.5-kg) block. Some difficulties were encountered with regard to bone count and measurements, etc., and were due, partly, to the somewhat primitive processing facilities and, partly, because the small size of fish makes the V-cut for removal of pinbones labour-intensive and slow. The experiments proved that the project filleting line performs very well on Peruvian merluza. The main problem in operating a hake processing plant will be the supply of first-class raw material required, bled and gutted at sea, necessary to achieve an acceptable colour of the frozen block. A number of trials of the Baader 166 gutting machine were made at sea with good results. They will be followed up with a 'Shetland' gutting machine. In view of the small average size of the fish and to reduce costs, it is virtually certain that gutting and bleeding need to be done by machine.

Cold-smoked merluza fillets

Experiments to produce cold-smoked merluza fillets from fillets frozen at sea were made to judge the potential for a commercial production for the Australian market. The blocks were thawed out at about 21°C and put for 20 min in a brine of 60 per cent saturation, coloured deep yellow with a British commercial fish dye. After draining, the fillets were smoked in the Torry Mini kiln at ambient temperature, ie, about 20°C for 1¾ hour. The weight loss was 5 per cent of the defrosted fillets. After smoking, the fillets were packed in cartons with sheets of polyethylene between layers and blast-frozen. The taste and texture were satisfactory but, due to Australian import regula-

tions, further trials will have to be made using a vegetable (anatto) dye, the only one permitted in Australia for fish products.

Canned merluza roes

It was decided to conduct an experiment to see whether merluza roes might be a suitable alternative to the popular cod roes. The raw material, frozen at sea, was carefully thawed out and washed. The membrane covering was removed and the pure roes were mixed with water and salt as follows: water: 15 per cent of the weight roes; salt: 1.5 per cent of the weight of the roes. The mixture was filled into 8-oz (225-g) round tins, sprayed inside with soy oil to avoid the contents sticking to the can. (In a commercial operation, agar should be used for this purpose.) The cans were closed and sterilized for 90 min. The final product was acceptable and with a taste comparable to cod roes but with a more gritty texture. Further experiments therefore need to be made with roes in different stages of development.

Merluza fish cakes

The Co-operative for American Remittance for Everywhere (CARE) is providing low-cost school meals for children in low income areas in Peru and requested assistance in developing a cheap fish cake with a high protein value. A number of different recipes, developed by the project home economists, were tested and the following recipe was accepted: merluza meat: 62.5 per cent; quinua: 8.0 per cent; pork fat: 10.5 per cent; salt: 0.5 per cent and water: 18.5 per cent. The quinua (which is a locally grown seed, rich in protein and starch) was cooked and absorbed the water. All ingredients were minced and mixed. The mixture was frozen in blocks in the plate freezer for sawing into portions and frying in the school kitchens.

MISCELLANEOUS PRODUCTS

In addition to the activities described, some secondary experiments were also made in an effort to diversify the range of products based on traditional food fish species. It was thought that such a diversification could stimulate the interest in fish as a food on the part of some of the consumers who are not regular fish eaters.

Tuna ham from bonito

Fresh bonito were filleted and the fillets cut into pieces of 130 to 150 g each. After washing, they were put in a 12 per cent brine for 5 to 6 min and hot-smoked. After ½ h drying at 40°C, smoke was added and the temperature gradually increased to 80°C over a period of 1½ to 2 hours. The resultant product is attractive and this experiment will be followed up with marketing tests when bonito again become available in quantity.

Hot-smoked fillets of dogfish (Mustelus sp.)

The fresh fish were filleted and the fillets washed and placed in an 18 per cent brine for 15 minutes. In order to make comparisons of the final product, half were brined with UK kipper-brown dye added and the other half were brined without dye. They were drained and placed on trays in the Torry Mini kiln. After drying for 30 min at 40°C, smoke was added and the fillets smoked for

Months	Species / Anchoveta (central zone)	Machete	Caballa	Merluza	Bonito
	Average 1961ᵃ72			1972	1972
January	7.44	8.20 (1972)	2.20 (1968)	0.59	1.54
February	7.33	7.51 (1972)	1.72 (1968)	1.35	—
March	8.07	8.36 (1972)	6.1 (1973)	1.15	3.89
April	8.66	8.48 (1972)	—	0.55	—
May	8.74	—	1.59 (1973)	0.77	3.48
June	8.81	6.81 (1972)	—	0.31	2.23
July	6.94	7.74 (1972)	—	0.46	5.79
August	5.92	6.8 (1973)	—	—	—
September	4.78	6.7 (1973)	—	—	6.23
October	6.06	3.71 (unknown)	9.93 (1972)	—	—
November	8.60	—	11.15 (1972)	0.79	—
December	8.94	3.53 (unknown)	—	—	—

60 min at 60°C, 30 min at 80°C and 15 min at 90°C. It was found that the dyed fillets were of better presentation for Peruvian taste. However, marketing trials have not yet been carried out because of discussion on the advisability of launching an artificially dyed smoked product when the trend in most countries is toward undyed food products.

FAT CONTENT

The fat content of commercially used fish species is of considerable interest to the processing industry. Analytical data for some species from Peruvian waters are given in Table 1 which shows a representative average for anchoveta of the central zone. Full information on fat content of anchoveta, which is normally somewhat higher in the northern zone and lower in the southern zone, is available in the Instituto del Mar, Lima, Peru. Two maxima occur in the course of a year, the one – normally the highest – in April/June, the other in December/January. The data for the other fish species, based on a few analyses, give an incomplete picture. However, even these indicate that seasonal variations occur. The lack of data is mainly due to the fact that interest in industrial utilization of these species, except Bonito, has developed only recently.

SOME COMMERCIAL DEVELOPMENTS

A joint venture between EPSEP and a group of Norwegian interests to can anchoveta as a brisling type product is being planned. In its first stage, the proposed plant would have a capacity of 25,000 cases per annum, which is viewed as production on a semi-commercial scale. Another anchoveta cannery to be set up will be constructed with a Dutch Government loan and technical assistance. Machete fillets are now being smoked on a limited commercial scale and distributed for sale in the Lima area. Finally, samples of canned sardines in tomato sauce, which were submitted to the UK, were favourably received and a private cannery has been put into contact with the potential buyers with a view to producing trial quantities.

The work described was carried out by the author with the assistance of Mr J de Visser (FAO) and Eng S Carrion (EPSEP).

Rapid Salting of Fish   J M Mendelsohn

Salage rapide du posson

Une nouvelle technique a été mise au point pour le salage rapide du merlu américain (*Merluccius bilinearis*) et d'autres espèces de poisson. La durée du salage (de plusieurs jours à plusieurs semaines avec les méthodes classiques) est réduite à un jour. Cette technique est conçue pour permettre de traiter les importantes quantités de poisson débarquées en été. On peut préparer, au moyen d'un exsiccateur à tambour sous vide, du poisson salé, séché et emballé en quelques heures. Le produit fini est non seulement de bonne qualité et stable à la température ambiante (c'est-à-dire sans réfrigération), mais encore il possède un grand nombre des propriétés du posson salé selon les méthodes classiques et peut être aisément reconstitué afin de servir à la fabrication de pâté de poisson. Des essais de dégustation ont démontré qu'après un entreposage de huit mois à la température ambiante, il peut servir d'ingrédient pour la confection de pâtés de poisson tout à fait acceptables.

Salado rapido del pescado

Se ha perfeccionado una nueva técnica para el salado rápido del merlán (*Merluccius bilinearis*) y otras especies de peces. El tiempo que se necesita (de días a semanas) en las técnicas de salado tradicionales queda reducido a un día. La técnica tiene por finalidad manipular grandes cantidades del pescado que se descarga durante el verano. Cuando se emplea un tambor vacuosecador, en cuestión de horas, se sala, seca y envasa el pescado. El producto final es de gran calidad, dura mucho tiempo (sin refrigeración) y conserva muchas de las propiedades del pescado salado tradicional preparándose fácilmente para la preparación de pasteles. Los ensayos sobre el sabor han demostrado que después de ocho meses de almacenamiento a la temperatura sambiente pueden prepararse pasteles de pescado de gran aceptación.

Usually in the summer months there has been an overabundant supply of one species of fish or another in many of the United States fishing ports. These, having a limited market, are sold at a very low price for processing into pet food, fish meal or even fertilizer. The Atlantic Fishery Products Technology Centre of the National

Marine Fisheries Service, formerly the Bureau of Commercial Fisheries, began investigating methods for quickly processing these fish into products for human consumption. New products, as well as substitutes for familiar products with commercial acceptance, were considered. The final product was designed for both domestic use and export. Whiting (*Merluccius bilinearis*), considered an overabundant species prior to 1968, was tried as a substitute for haddock and cod products, such as fish cakes and fried fillets, and new products such as fish casseroles and salads. These were taste tested at this Technology Center. Although the products received satisfactory scores, processing times were too long, and there was no apparent need for additional products of this type, while for the casseroles and salads, new markets would have to be found. A convenience-type product appeared to have the greatest commercial potential. The product needed to be of high quality, shelf-stable (preferably without refrigeration) and be processed in a minimum amount of time so as to handle the large quantities of fish landed during the summer months. Moreover, the product and its processing had to be able to use other fish species such as ocean perch (*Sebastes marinus*), white hake (*Urophycis tenuis*), and red hake (*Urophycis chuss*) that have limited markets. Therefore, a rapidly salt-cured fishery product was considered.

This paper describes a technique for salt-curing fish in less than eight hours (Anderson and Mendelsohn, 1972). The process developed makes use of fish of low market value to produce a suitable substitute for salt cod, for which there is still a strong demand in many parts of the world. For instance, in 1969, only 387,000 tons of salted fish were produced compared with 446,000 tons in 1967. In the United States only 0.2 ton is produced so that most of the 17,000 tons used there in fish cakes has to be imported. The salt-curing processes now in use are too lengthy and costly for handling large quantities. In addition, the product usually needs refrigeration (not easily available in developing countries) and in many cases is of poor quality. A quick salting process has been reported (Del Valle and Nickerson, 1968; Del Valle and Gonzalez-Iñigo, 1968). The technique was designed for use in developing countries and requires little processing equipment.

TECHNIQUE

In the rapid salting process developed in this Technology Center skinless fillets were ground in a Waring blender (3.8 l capacity) in saturated salt solution (fish to brine ratio 1 to 1, weight to volume) to which sufficient excess salt (25 g/100 g fish) had been added to bring about the greatest fluid loss (synersis) when the brine was diluted with the water of the fish (Table 1). Blending for two 15-sec periods with the blender on 'Hi' and a Variac setting of 40, using a plastic baffle placed just under the surface of the salt solution to prevent foaming (Dyer *et al.* 1950), was sufficient to grind the fish to a particle size similar to ground beef (hamburger). Between periods, the mix was stirred by hand to ensure even comminution. The mixture was allowed to stand about 15 min to ensure complete salt penetration (Table 2). The mixture was stirred occasionally during salting. Free fluid was then drained through cheese-cloth. The drained, salted product

Fig 1   A meat-bone separator for maximum recovery of fish flesh

was either (1) spread on trays of plastic screening and dried for five hours in an air-circulating oven set at 37°C or (2) passed two or three times through a laboratory model vacuum-drum drier with steam input set so that, with the short dwell time on the drum, cooking did not occur (about 30 min required for small-scale batch processing). The dried product was packaged in transparent plastic pouches under vacuum and put in cardboard cartons (browning of the product is catalyzed by light).

Fig 2   A batch type ribbon blender

TABLE 1. RELATION OF ADDITIONAL SALT TO FLUID LOSS AND GELLING DURING SALTING OF 800 G OF GROUND WHITING IN SATURATED BRINE FOR 20 MIN

Salt added to brine (g)	Fluid loss on draining (ml)	Amount of gel[a]
0	0	No free fluid; gelled mass
50	510	Drained fish appeared gelled
100	685	Small amount gel in drained fish
200	865	No gel
300	815	No gel

[a] Amount of gel was determined by visual examination.

TABLE 2. SALT CONTENTS OF DRAINED WHITING PREPARED WITH VARIOUS SALTING TIMES[a]

Salting time (min)	Salt content (%)
0	27.0
5	28.5
10	27.9
24	27.3

[a] Salt content was determined in accordance with Section 18.010, AOAC (1965)

The salted product was prepared for use in fish cakes by adding water, bringing the mixture to a boil and discarding the free fluid. The fish cake mix consisted of reconstituted salt fish and potato flakes (fish to potato ratio 1 to 1) with spices and dried onion and parsley flakes as seasonings.

Fish cakes made from salted whiting stored eight months at room temperature were rated very acceptable and comparable to fish cakes made from good quality commercial salt cod (Table 3).

Discussion

The technique described brings together the most advantageous conditions for rapid salt-curing of fish, provided vacuum-drum drying is used:

(1) Grinding the fish greatly increases the surface area exposed for salting and decreases diffusion distance, an advantage shared with the Del Valle-Nickerson technique.

(2) The fish is covered with brine during grinding so that exposure to oxygen is virtually excluded as the whole

TABLE 3. TASTE PANEL SCORES[a] FOR FISH CAKES MADE FROM SALTED WHITING WHICH WAS STORED IN CANS AT ROOM TEMPERATURE AND FROM COMMERCIAL SALT COD[b]

Storage time (months)	Whiting cake	Salt cod cake (control)
0	7.8	7.4
1	7.4	7.7
2	7.7	7.9
3	7.1	7.6
4	7.0	8.6
5	6.7	7.8
6	6.8	7.7
7	7.3	7·8
8	7.4	8.2

[a] Based on the average score for appearance, odour, flavour and texture, a score of 9 = excellent; 8 = very good; 7 = good; 6 = fair; 5 = borderline; 4 = slightly poor; 3 = poor; 2 = very poor; 1 = inedible.

[b] The commercial salt cod was purchased fresh (no storage time) for each taste test.

Fig 3   A mechanical screw press

surface of the fish is brought into contact with brine immediately.

(3) Use of additional salt to maintain saturation when the brine is diluted with the fluid of the fish provides a large salt concentration gradient until salting has taken place throughout the groundfish. Thus salting takes place within 5 min (Table 2).

(4) Syneresis results when the muscle protein is dehydrated in the presence of high concentrations of salt. Its occurrence indicates that the saturated salt solution diffuses so quickly that 'salting-in' of the muscle protein is followed immediately by 'salting-out' with no visible gel formation.

(5) The small particle size of the ground fish is retained throughout processing. This greatly facilitates drying so that drying time is short. In addition, reconstitution of the dried product is accomplished so simply that the product is considered a convenience item.

The experimental laboratory salting process has been scaled up to produce semi-commercial quantities of salted fish. A meat-bone separator used for maximum recovery of fish flesh is shown in Fig 1 and a batch-type ribbon blender used to mix the fish flesh, salt water, salt and antioxidants (butylated hydroxyanisole – BHA and butylated hydroxytoluene – BHT) is shown in Fig 2.

Fig 4   A batch vacuum tumble dryer

(Continuous mixers are available for large-scale processing of salted fish.) A mechanical press used to reduce initially the water content is shown in Fig. 3 and a batch-type vacuum tumble drier used to dry the salted product is shown in Fig. 4. (It seems that a large-scale continuous vacuum-drum drier is needed for maximum efficiency.) Dried salted fish is vacuum packaged in transparent plastic pouches prior to overwrapping in light-impermeable containers. This protection is needed to stop chemical reactions initiated by light. The semi-commercial technique produces salted fish of high quality similar to that produced by the laboratory process. The technique also produces a high quality salted product from other species, such as ocean perch and white hake, and should do so from any species.

References

ANDERSÒN, M L and MENDELSOHN, J M A rapid salt-curing technique. *Fd Sci.* 37:627.
1972

AOAC Official Method of Analysis, Washington, DC, USA, Association of Official Agricultural Chemists, 10th ed.
1965

DEL VALLE, F R and GONZALEZ-INIGO, J L A quick-salting process for fish. 2. Behaviour of different species of fish with respect to the process. *Fd Technol.* 22:1135.
1968

DEL VALLE, F R and NICKERSON, J T R A quick-salting process for fish. 1. Evolution of the process. *Fd Technol.* 22:1036.

DYER, W J, FRENCH, H V and SNOW, J M Proteins in fish muscle. 1. Extraction of protein fractions in fresh fish. *J. Fish. Res. Bd. Can.* 7:585.
1950

Acknowledgement

This work was supported by the USDC, Economic Development Administration under Technical Assistance Project Number 01-6-09131.

A Quick-Salting Process for Fish F R Del Valle

Methode rapide de salage du poisson

Le document décrit la mise au point d'une méthode rapide de salage pour la fabrication de pâtés de poisson. La chair du poisson est broyée et mélangée soigneusement avec du sel jusqu'à obtention d'une pâte homogène, qui est ensuite pressée et séchés. Des essais out démontré que le produit ainsi obtenu se conserve bien quand il est entreposé à la température ambiante, mênme sous u climat tropical. Les pâtés de poisson sont passés à l'eau bouillante avant l'emploi afin d'en extraire le sel. Le produit dessalé est de saveur agréable et peut être accomodé facilement avec d'autres aliments cuisinés. Des essais de sapidité effectués parmi des groupes d'enfants et d'adultes au Mexique ont fait apparaître un niveau élevé d'acceptabilité, atteignant dans le cas des enfants une moyenne de 96 pour cent au petit déjeuner et de 95 pour cent au déjeuner. Ce procédé permet d'employer une température ambiante, bien que les meilleurs résultats soient obtenus avec du poisson maigre. Le document décrit l'expérience acquise à Progreso, au Yucatan (Mexique), avec la mise en service d'une usine-pilote et fournit des estimations sur la rentabilité que l'on peut escompter d'une production commerciale. Ce procédé sera particulièrement utile dans les pays en voie de développement, on il fournira le moyen de produire en abondance un aliment d'une haute valeur protéique pour la consommation humaine.

Proceso rapido para la salazon de pescado

En este trabajo se describe un método sencillo y rápido de salazón para preparar tortas de pescado. Se tritura la carne de pescado, mezclándola uniformemente con sal, prensándola y secándols. Los ensayos realizados han mostrado que la torta que se obtiene se conserva perfectamente a temperatura ambiente, incluso en países tropicales. Antes de utilizarlas, las tortas se hierven en agua para lixiviarlas. El producto, una vez desalado, tiene un sabor suave y se presta a mezclas con otros alimentos cocidos. Los ensayos de sabor realizados con niños y adultos en México han revelado un alto grado de aceptabilidad, que en el caso de los niños ha llegado a un 96 por ciento en el desayuno y un 95 por ciento en la comida. Es posible aprovechar de esta forma peces de tipos muy diversos, pero el producto de mejor calidad se obtiene con pescado magro. Se describe la experiencia de funcionamiento de una fábrica piloto situada en Progreso, Yucatán (México) y se dan estimaciones del posible rendimiento de la producción comercial. Se trata de un método preparado especialmente para los países en desarrollo, con vistas a producir grandes cantidades de alimentos ricos en proteínas para el consumo humano.

In normal salting and drying, fillets or pieces of flesh of a certain thickness are employed. If the ambient temperature is high – which is the usual cases in most developing countries – microbial and enzymatic attacks on the fish occur faster than salting penetration is completed. As a result, the interior of the fillet decomposes. This is one explanation for the relatively low quality of such products. The problem is aggravated by long processing times. These could be decreased by tunnel drying but this would increase the cost of the final product. Yet, because of its simplicity, salting and drying of fish does remain a challenging possibility as a method of preservation and the paper describes a process for producing an inexpensive salted fish product of good quality.

THE PROCESS

A quick-salting process for fish was developed which yielded a stable product of good quality and low cost with good storage stability at ambient temperature. The product could easily be smoked if desired. The fish flesh or muscle is separated by hand filleting or by a deboning machine, ground and mixed with salt. Dehydration takes place simultaneously with the salting. The salt-extracted water is removed from the ground salted flesh by pressing. Fairly high pressures (100 to 150 kg/cm²) are employed to expel the maximum amount of water mechanically and to form compact, coherent cakes. The final step is to dry the cakes, either artificially (in a tunnel) or naturally (in the sun). Quick-salted fish cakes are not attacked by microbes, insects, rodents and birds during salting or dehydration due to their high salt content. Fish muscle so treated as soon as possible after being taken out of the water retains, therefore, most of its freshness and possesses little 'fishy' or other off-flavours or odours. It is possible to smoke wet cakes in order to flavour them. The smoked cakes are then dried.

In preparation for consumption, the cake is desalted by leaching once or twice in boiling water. It does not disintegrate, but rather retains its shape. The desalted product has a bland, practically neutral flavour, and can be cooked as desired. In countries, where use of spices is frequent, their incorporation into the cake is easy. Table 1 shows fish species used and the amount of salt employed. The salt content varies from as low as 22 per cent in the case of shark to as high as 100 per cent of the weight of

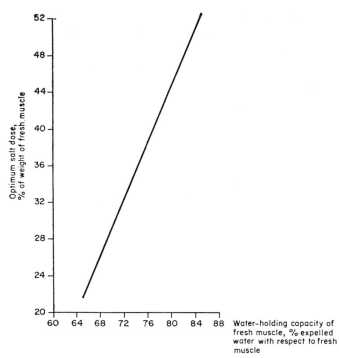

Fig 1 *Optimum quantity of salt for making quick-salted fish cakes versus water-holding capacity of fresh muscle*

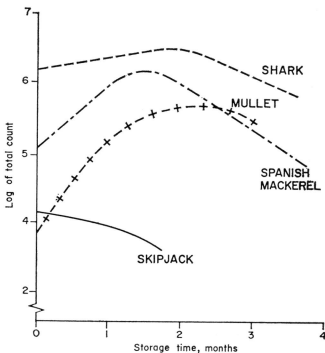

Fig 2 *Variation of total plate count with storage time for fish cakes made from different species*

the wet flesh in the case of sardine. In general, the quantity of salt required appears to correlate well with 'salting-out' of the flesh proteins, as shown in Fig 1 (del Valle and Gonzalez-Iñigo 1968). The process is applicable to most species of fish. Results obtained with shark cakes after three leachings, using a water product ratio of approximately 10:1 (del Valle and Nickerson 1968) show that two leachings gave an edible product, while three leachings resulted in near complete salt removal. Desalting cakes resulted in negligible protein losses, while the product was efficiently desalted (del Valle and Gonzalez-Iñigo 1968).

STORAGE STABILITY

Organoleptic testing showed that quick-salted fish cakes required no refrigeration, even at tropical temperatures. This stability was due to their high salt and low moisture content. It was desirable, however, to obtain a quantita-

tive measure of the stability of the dry cakes. This led to a study of bacterial counts and rancidity estimates of the product. Plate counts were made, using freshly-made cakes as well as those stored without packaging, during different times at an ambient tropical temperature of 35 to 40°C, to determine: (1) the total plate count to measure the general quality of the product as well as detect the presence of micro-organisms which could decompose the cakes; (2) the halophilic count to detect the presence of salt-tolerant micro-organisms which could decompose the cakes; and (3) the staphylococci count as they are potential pathogens capable of growing in fairly high salt concentrations. Nutrient agar was used for the total plate count; nutrient agar with 10 per cent sodium chloride for the halophilic count; and glycine tellurite agar for the staphylococcal count. Incubation temperatures were 25°C for the total count and 37°C for the other counts, while incubation times were 24 hours in all cases. Fish species used in this work were skipjack (*Katsuwonus*

TABLE 1. SPECIES TO WHICH THE QUICK-SALTING PROCESS HAS BEEN APPLIED AND CORRESPONDING QUANTITY OF SALT EMPLOYED

Spanish name	English name	Scientific name	Source	Salt dose	Reference
Tiburón	Shark	*Mustelus mustelus*	Gulf of Mexico	22%	del Valle & Nickerson 1968
Dorado	Dolphin	*Coryphaena hippurus*	Gulf of California	25%	del Valle & Gonzalez-Iñigo 1968
Carpa	Carp	*Cyprinus carpio*	Gulf of California	35%	Idem
Lisa	Mullet	*Mugil cephalus*	Gulf of California	40%	Idem
Sierra	Sp. mackerel	*Scomberomorus sierra*:	Gulf of California	45%	Idem
Barrilete	Skipjack	*Katsuwonus pelamis*	Gulf of California	45%	Idem
Rubia	Red gunard	*Paranthias furcifer*	Gulf of Mexico	75%	del Valle *et al.* 1973a
Mojarra		*Eucinostomus gula*	Gulf of Mexico	75%	Idem
Mero	Grouper	*Epinephelus morio*	Gulf of Mexico	75%	Idem
Huachinsango	Red snapper	*Lutianus gutatus*	Gulf of Mexico	75%	Idem
Chac-chic		*Aemulum espurus*	Gulf of Mexico	75%	Idem
Sardina	Sardine	*Anchoa mychilli*	Gulf of Mexico	100%	Idem

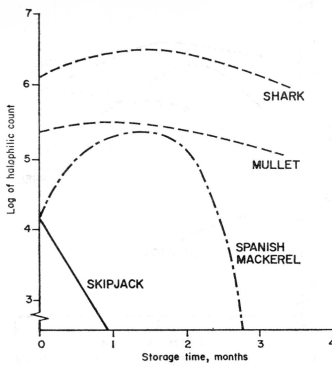

Fig 3 *Variation of halophilic count with storage time for fish cake made from different species*

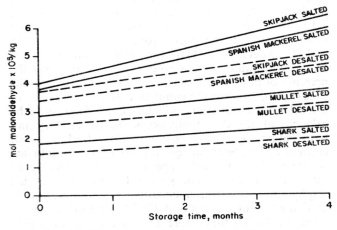

Fig 4 *Rancidity index versus time for sun-dried cakes*

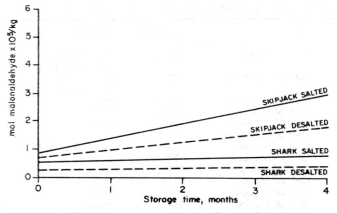

Fig 5 *Rancidity index versus storage time for tunnel-dried cakes*

pelamis), mullet (*Mugil cephalus*), Spanish mackerel (*Scomberomorus sierra*) and shark (*Mustelus mustelus*) from the Gulf of California. The cakes were not dried but were stored wet after being formed in order to simulate the worst possible storage conditions. They dried out during the run (del Valle *et al.* 1973a). Fig 2 shows that the total plate count increased, passed through a maximum, and then decreased in all cases. The increase was probably due to the fact that the cakes were wet, thus permitting growth of halotolerant species. As the cakes became drier there was a decrease in water activity, resulting in suppression of bacterial growth. Fig 3 shows that halophilic counts followed the same general pattern observed as total plate counts. Finally, with respect to staphylococci, no growth of these organisms was in any of the plates at any time, thus eliminating the possibility of intoxication by these potential pathogens.

In rancidity studies, the thiobarbituric acid (TBA) index was determined in sun-dried and tunnel-dried cakes after storage for different times without packaging at an ambient temperature of 35 to 40°C. It was thought that some of the rancid-flavour components, being of low molecular weight and/or water soluble, might be eliminiated by leaching or steam distillation in desalting. This hypothesis was verified by making additional rancidity determinations in desalted cakes which were boiled for 5 minutes in 12.5 parts of water per part of dry cake. Species used in these experiments were the same as those used in bacterial counts (del Valle *et al.* 1973b). Figs 4 and 5 show results of rancidity determinations in sun-dried and tunnel-dried cakes. It may be seen that all cakes tended to become more rancid with time, although there were differences between the species. The order of increasing rancidity was found to depend upon various factors, including oil content of the species and the iodine number of the oil. In the case of skipjack cakes, which were the most rancid, the presence of hematin pigments was undoubtedly another factor in increasing the susceptibility of its oil to rancidity besides the high degree of unsaturation of the oil. Figs 4 and 5 also show that rancid components are indeed, partially removed by the desalting operation, due to leaching or steam distillation or both. Tunnel-dried cakes were less rancid than those sun-dried. This difference was probably due to the shorter drying time required in a tunnel than in the sun, as well as to the presence or absence of sunlight, which is known to catalyze rancidity reactions.

Thus, to sum up: bacterial contamination of the cakes decreases with increasing salt and decreasing moisture content. Contamination is never high and decreases with time, tending to zero after a few months; staphylococci are apparently not present in the cakes if the salt content is high enough; cakes become rancid with time to different degrees. The amount of rancidity depends upon the species used, the drying time, the presence or absence of hematin pigments and the presence or absence of sunlight when drying. Lean species are easier to use than fatty species for making quick-salted fish cakes. However, small fatty fish would in many cases be more readily available and their use may permit the production of lower cost products in many countries. Some of the rancid components in the cakes can be removed in desalting.

PILOT PLANT PRODUCTION

A pilot plant was set up in Progreso, Yucatan, Mexico, financed by a grant from the Government of the State of Yucatan and by private sources. The capacity of the plant was 250 kg of dry salted cakes in 8 hours. Basic equipment included a Hobart-Dayton Model 4612 meat grinder with a $\frac{1}{2}$ hp motor, a specially designed hydraulic press and sun-drying racks. The press was equipped with a 19 l/min, 140 kg/cm² (maximum pressure) hydraulic pump and an 8 hp, 1,750 rpm motor. All parts of the press which came into contact with the material were made of type 316 stainless steel. The piston diameter, which was also equal to the cake diameter, was 15 centimetres. The height of the pressed cakes was about 1.25 centimetres. Each dried cake weighed approximately 450 grammes. All steps in commercial processing of different raw materials were studied including: determination of yields, production rates, pressing times and pressures and sun-drying times. The raw materials studied including trimmings and rejects from filleting plants as well as trash fish (del Valle et al. 1973b).

Table 2 summarizes the most important data obtained during pilot plant production, and the following observations may be added:

(1) Filleting rates were generally good, considering that a skilled person can produce roughly 250 g of fillets per minute. Filleting yields were found to vary with species, depending upon such factors as the weight of heads, bones and viscera relative to flesh. A fillet yield of 40 per cent or over is considered to be very good. Both rates and yields could undoubtedly be improved by use of a deboning machine.

(2) Fairly high quantities of salt were employed in order to obtain rapid and thorough coagulation of flesh proteins. Production rates were found to depend upon ease of grinding the flesh. Generally all were of the same order of magnitude except for sardine, which was ground whole and clogged the grinder with scales and bones.

(3) Total pressing time, about 1 to 5 minutes, was approximately the same for all species. So were production rates of wet cakes for the different species –about 350 g/min.

(4) Roughly 30 per cent of the weight of the ground salted flesh was removed by pressing. Since the press liquor consisted mostly of a saturated salt solution (approximately 26.5 per cent salt), it may be calculated that approximately 52 per cent of the water originally present in the flesh was removed by this operation.

(5) Average sun-drying times for the cakes were of the order of 3 to 4 days under the following ambient conditions: dry bulb temperature, 33 to 37°C; relative humidity, 65 to 75 per cent.

(6) Average weight losses in drying were approximately 15 per cent. If this figure is considered together with that of weight losses in pressing, it may be calculated that 75 per cent of the water originally present in the fresh flesh was removed in converting the fillets to dry cakes.

(7) Final yields of dry cakes to fillets were all approximately 1:1. This shows that salt simply replaced water in the conversion of fillets to dry cakes.

The data obtained from the pilot plant also made it possible to calculate the approximate protein, salt and water contents of wet and dry cakes. These approximate values were calculated on the basis of the quantity of salt used and yields obtained in different phases of processing, combined with the values of raw fish composition found in literature. The calculations have shown that on average wet cakes contain 20 per cent protein, 50 per cent salt and 30 per cent water, and dry cakes 25 per cent protein, 58 per cent salt and 17 per cent water.

Experience showed that it was possible to translate the quick-salting process from the laboratory to a semi-commercial operation without serious problems. In doing this, it was found that the principal unit to consider was the press, and considerable experience was gained in its design and maintenance.

ACCEPTANCE TRIALS

Taste trials were conducted among Mayan adults and children. The cakes were desalted and cooked according to a popular local recipe for fish, described by del Valle et al. (1963b). The resulting product, somewhat resembling chile con carne, was served to tasters in tortillas in

TABLE 2. SUMMARY OF MOST IMPORTANT DATA OBTAINED WITH PILOT PLANT PRODUCTION OF QUICK-SALTED FISH CAKES

Species:	Chac-Chic	Rubia	Small Mero	Mojarra	Sardine	Rejects	Trimmings
FILLETING							
Rate, kg/min person	0.28	0.21	0.21	0.15	—	0.23	—
Yield, fillets/whole fish, %	28.6	41.9	32.6	46.0	100.0	30.3	100.0
SALTING AND GRINDING							
Salt dose, %	75	75	75	100	75	75	75
Rate, kg/min	3.7	5.2	4.4	4.0	0.5	5.8	2.1
Yield, ground salted meat/fillets, %	172	170	172	173	172	175	198
PRESSING							
Pressing time, min	1.3	1.2	1.5	1.7	1.7	1.5	1.5
Pressure applied, kg/cm²	147	147	147	147	147	147	147
Av. weight of wet cake, g	478	470	459	471	419	451	431
Rate, kg/min of wet cakes	0.39	0.38	0.30	0.38	0.25	0.29	0.29
Yield, wet cakes/ground salted meat, %	73.8	72.4	70.8	72.3	64.7	69.4	66.1
SUN-DRYING							
Sun-drying time, days	6	5	3	4	3	3	3
Yield, dry cakes/wet cakes, %	89.6	91.2	80.4	89.4	78.1	89.6	83.7
Yield, dry cakes/fillets, %	114	114	98	112	87	100	107

TABLE 3. PRODUCTION COSTS OF QUICK-SALTED FISH CAKES IN US $/KG OF DRY CAKE

Species	Whole Fish	Salt	Direct Labour	Indirect Labour	Depreciation	Total Cost	Cost of fresh fish/kg
Chac-Chic	0.15	0.01	0.04	0.06	0.03	0.29	0.05
Rubia	0.42	0.01	0.04	0.06	0.03	0.56	0.20
Mojarra	0.20	0.01	0.04	0.06	0.03	0.34	0.10
Small Mero	0.19	0.02	0.04	0.06	0.03	0.34	0.06
Sardine	0.23	0.02	0.02	0.06	0.03	0.36	0.20
Rejects	0.18	0.02	0.04	0.06	0.03	0.33	0.06
Trimmings	0.02	0.01	0.02	0.06	0.03	0.14	0.02

Notes:
1. Cost of salt is US $0.02/kg.
2. Direct labour: pilot plant requires 2 persons per 8-h shift, each paid US $2.50 per 8-h day; production of cakes is 160 k per 8-h shift. Filleting cost is US $0.2/kg of fillets.
3. Indirect labour: one person for management of entire operation at U.S. $240 per month Production of cakes 3,840 kg/month
4. Depreciation of capital investment (US $11,660) in 10 years, equal to US $1.166 per year.
5. Manufacturing costs (electricity) were negligible in all cases.
6. Cost of fresh fish is reported in US $/kg of raw material, be it whole fish or fillets, as in the case of trimmings.

the form of *tacos*. Tests with adults were conducted in five different inland villages. It should be noted that only inland locations were considered because it was desired to test acceptance of the product among people who do not normally eat fish. An average of 65 persons from each village participated in the tests.

Results of these tests, summarized by del Valle *et al.* (1973b), show that acceptance was excellent in all cases. Many persons asked for more samples, and some ate as many as 10 tacos. The observations made during the tests also reveal the great hunger which exists among Mayan Indians. One woman told the author that this was the first time in her life that she had been able to eat to her satisfaction.

Tests with children were conducted within Government-sponsored breakfast and lunch programmes. All test participants were of pre-school age (2 to 5 years). Cakes were desalted and cooked in the manner previously described. The cooked product was served to tasters in the form of sandwiches. Approximately 25 sandwiches were prepared from each 450-g cake. Acceptance was measured by simply noting if a child ate or rejected the sample. Four tests were conducted, consisting of two breakfasts and two lunches. An average of 50 children participated in each test. Cakes used in all of these tests were made from a mixture of 50 per cent trimmings and 50 per cent rejects. Results of these tests reported by del Valle *et al.* (1973b) show that acceptance was as good as that obtained in tests with adults. Data on percentage of tasters who ate more than one serving were also obtained. The percentage of acceptance was higher with breakfasts than with lunches. This is reasonable, since children are normally more hungry in the morning than at noon.

COSTS

Total investment required in the pilot plant, including inventories, building, equipment, and installation and organisation costs amounts to US $11,660. Equipment required consists of a hydraulic press (US $5,000), grinder, table, utensils, sun-dryer and a 1-ton ice-box. Table 3 reports production costs/kg of dry salted cakes. In terms of absolute cost, all cakes seen to be cheaper than either fresh iced or frozen fish, which retails in Mexico at US $1.20 to 2.00/kg. In terms of cost/kg of

protein, the price of the cakes is still quite low when compared to prices of other protein foods in Mexico (del Valle *et al.* 1973b). Another important aspect of the quick-salting process is its profitability. Although the final product is obviously intended for low-income groups and should be as low-priced as possible, a plant should make some profit, or at least be self-sustaining, in order to encourage investment by private sources. Based on a retail selling price of US $0.45/kg of dry cakes, and a monthly production of 6,300 kg of cakes at US $0.30/kg, the net profit before taxes amounted to 7.4 per cent, yielding a net return on investment of 21.6 per cent per year.

TABLE 4. ESTIMATED TOTAL INVESTMENT VERSUS CAPACITY FOR PLANTS OF DIFFERENT SIZES

Capacity in dry cakes/month	Capacity in kg of dry cakes/month	Total Investment in US $
14,000 (Pilot plant)	6,300	11,660
28,000	12,600	17,630
56,000	25,200	26,650

Note: In calculating capacity it has been assumed that the plant works 2 shifts/day and 20 days/month.

Table 4 shows estimated cost versus capacity for plants of different sizes. If the raw materials were available at various places along the coast of a developing country, many small plants would be desirable. If, on the other hand, the raw material was concentrated in a few places along the coast, a small number of large plants would be preferable. Research in the process is now being focused on finding means for using whole fish, including skin and bones but excluding scales and viscera. It has been found necessary to use a higher powered grinder for this purpose

References

DEL VALLE, F R GONZALEZ and IÑIGO, J L A quick-salting process
1968   for fish. 2. Behavior of different species of fish with respect to the process. *Food Technol.*, 22:1135.
DEL VALLE, F R and NICKERSON, J T R A quick-salting process
1968   for fish. 1. Evolution of the process. *Ibid.*, 22:1036.
DEL VALLE, F R, HINOJÒSA, J, BARRERA, D and DE LA MORA, R A
1973a   Bacterial counts and rancidity estimates of quick-salted fish cakes. Paper accepted for publication in *J. Fd Sci.*
DEL VALLE, F R, PADILLA, M, RUZ, A and RODRÍGUEZ, R Pilot
1973b   plant production of and large scale acceptance trials with quick-salted fish cakes. Paper to be published in February 1973 issue of *J. Fd Sci.*

Roller-Dried Fish Protein
L Herborg, F Vilien, A Bruun and B Eggum

Proteines de poisson seches sur cylindres

Les auteurs décrivent diverses expériences relatives à la fabrication de produits à base de poisson séchés sur cylindres et ayant une teneur élevée en protéines; la saveur traditionnelle spécifique de poisson séché a pu être facilement reconstituée. Les expériences ont porté sur la morue, l'églefin, l'orphie, la limande, le lançon, le flétan, le hareng et l'aiguillat. Le produit ,de même valeur nutritive que d'autres concentrés de protéines de poisson, a été utilisé avec succès pour accompagner divers plats de légumes, de riz et d'autres mets. Bien que certains problèmes techniques et économiques ne soient pas encore résolus, les résultats des expériences sont encourageants et l'on envisage maintenant de procéder à de nouveaux essais dans des secteurs commerciaux clés.

Proteina de pescado secado en cilindros

Los autores describen varios experimentos de fabricaciòn de un producto pesquero secado en cilindros, con un elevado contenido de proteínas y en el que es fácil reconstituir el sabor tradicional del pescado seco. Se realizaron experimentos con bacaleo, egelfino, aguja, barbada, lanzón, platija, arenque y mielga. El producto, de igual valor nutritivo que otros concentrados de proteínas de pescado, se ha utilizado con éxito junto con diversos platos de hortalizas, arroz, etc. Aunque perduran aùn algunos problemas técnicos y económicos, los resultados de los experimentos han sido alentadores, y actualmente se tiene intención de realizar nuevos es ensayos orientándolos hacia zonas determinadas.

There are several successful examples of stable fish products suitable for human consumption in unsophisticated markets. These include: smoke-dried, salted and/or dried fish and fermented fish sauces. Our experiments have sought to reproduce and stabilize some of the good characteristics of the best dried products, ie, the high protein content, the specific flavour, and suitability for reconstitution. There is no problem in obtaining a high protein content but it is difficult to avoid protein denaturation during the process, especially when extra time and/or high temperatures are used to accelerate drying. Freeze-drying is in this respect perfect but the equipment is complicated and expensive. In 1956 Cutting *et al.* reported on small and large scale experiments in drying fish, mainly minced, cooked fish including roller-drying. They were mainly carried out with pre-cooked fish,as evidenced by the temperature of the roller (135 to 142°C) and the contact time between roller and product (5 to 10 sec), but it was stated that raw fish can also be used.

EXPERIMENTS

The Technological Laboratory, Ministry of Fisheries, Denmark, started experiments in 1970 in drying minced raw fish meat on a roller-dryer (General Food Package Equipment Corporation, Model 215 GF Dryer Flaker), using skinless cod fillets minced in a cutter and homogenized in a colloidal mill. To get a proper flow through the homogenizer 10 to 30 per cent of water was added. It was just possible to dry this material at the minimum speed (contact time 25 sec, temperature on rollers about 155°C, the rollers interspaced 0.2 mm), and get a coherent protein web from the roller. The capacity of the roller was about 8 kg minced fish meat/h yielding about 1. 6kg dried product/h with a protein content of about 85 per cent. The steam consumption was about 1.70 kg/kg raw meat or 2.10 kg/kg evaporated water (Fig 1). While the product showed fair reconstitution characteristics it was not as good as required and the binding effect was 'spongy'. On the other hand, it mixed in various dishes as well as do solvent extracted fish meal, dried fish proteolysate and fresh fish meat. A similar experiment was carried out with minced herring but the drying was not successful. The fat content was about 8 per cent in the raw fillets and during the process the oil separated between the rollers and boiled. It became as hard as a varnish, making the product similarly hard. Experiments indicate that when the fat content of the raw material is about 1 per cent the product does not adhere well to the rollers, resulting in uneven drying. When the fat content

exceeds 2 per cent there is a tendency for it to separate in the space between the rollers. When the fat content is about 4 per cent the separated oil builds up rapidly and overflows, hence a discrepancy between the fat content in the raw material and that in the dried product. If the oil is not drained off frequently, it boils and hardens as already described. The roller-dried product varies from the yellowish white of cod and haddock to the brownish of garfish and herring. Fat is visible in the product made from dogfish, flounder and sand-eel. Samples of the oil have been analysed for development of peroxide, and in two experiments with cod and antioxidant butylated hydroxyanisole (BHA) was sprayed in alcoholic solution on the product coming from one of the rollers; the product from the other being used as a control. There was no observed effect since the peroxide value was 0 in both sample and control.

The list of fish used so far in the experiments is given in Table 1.

When the product comes off the rollers its temperature is about 80°C but with a proper airflow it is soon cooled. With new machinery it is hoped to pasteurize the product without much denaturation of the protein.

Fig 1 Drying minced raw fish meat on a roller-dryer

TABLE 1. FAT CONTENT OF RAW AND DRIED FISH USED IN DRYING EXPERIMENTS

		Fat content of raw meat (%)	Fat content of dried material (%)
Cod	Gadus callarias	0.3–0.6	1.7–2.2
Haddock	Melanogrammus aeglefinus	0.5	2.1
Garfish	Belone belone	1.2	3.0
Dab	Limanda limanda	1.9	5.0
Sand-eel	Ammodytes lanceolatus and tobianus	4.4	6.2
Flounder	Platichthys flesus	4.0	9.4
Herring	Clupea harengus	8.0	—
Dogfish	Squalus acanthias	13.4	22.6

TABLE 2. NUTRITIVE VALUE OF ROLLER-DRIED COD

	Centre °C	t_{max}	F_{250}	TD	BV	NPU
Raw fish	—		—	96.4	77.7	74.9
Roller-dried fish	75–80		—	97.8	84.6	82.7
Canned product	103		0.2	96.2	88.2	84.9
Canned product	110		3.0	95.2	85.7	81.5
Canned product	105		0.2	96.3	83.7	80.6
Canned product	115		3.5	94.3	82.2	78.1
Canned product commercial with 5 per cent starch	104		3.0	95.4	71.3	68.0

Preliminary experiments in drying pre-salted minced fish meat have been encouraging as far as the eating quality is concerned. However, there are technical difficulties, particularly in getting the meat to adhere to the rollers. A salt crust formation affects it so that the product is unevenly dried, permitting mould to grow in it when stored at room temperature (25°C). The dried cod product was tested for nutritive value in a rat feeding experiment, raw fish meat being used as the control. Canned products of the same raw material, cooked to two different F_{250} values at two temperature levels (110 and 119°C), were also used. The results are given in Table 2.

As the above data show, the nutritive value does not suffer from the drying process. The dried product develops a slight smell soon after production. With time this becomes stronger, resembling what is regarded as good quality dried fish. When tested some two years after production by a panel of experts familiar with the taste of traditional dried cod, the product was preferred to one freshly made. It had been stored at 30°C dry, packed in polyethylene bags.

YIELDS AND ECONOMICS

The dried product from cod and haddock will amount to 10 per cent of the live weight of the fish. With a price of about US $0.05/lb (US $0.10/kg) live weight, the conversion price will be about US $0.50/lb (US $1.10/kg). If labour, running costs, depreciation, transport, etc. are, say, 75 per cent of the conversion price, the sales price will be about US $0.85/lb (US $1.85/kg) compared with the US $0.53/lb (US $1.17/kg) of the soybean product Promine D and US $0.72/lb (US $1.58/kg) for caseinate. The average fob export price of stockfish is about US $0.45/lb (US $1.00/kg), and the retail price about US $0.60/lb (US $1.32/kg). It does not seem therefore that the roller-dried product would be competitive. However, this product might be competitive if unmarket-

able lean fish or minced meat obtained by separator machines from waste of the white fish filleting industry were used as raw material.

EXAMPLES OF UTILIZATION

The product made by the Technological Laboratory, Ministry of Fisheries, Denmark, has been used in various dishes and has shown superior characteristics in palatibility and texture compared to other fish protein concentrates, as earlier mentioned. In a single experiment it showed no difference compared to a sample prepared with fresh minced fish meat.

Following are some results of acceptability tests:

Potato soup with 4.5 per cent protein added.
A strained soup flavoured with onion and tomato and boiled with (1) ground roller-dried cod, (2) powdered proteolysate and (3) fish meal.
Preference: (1) roller-dried fish, (2) proteolysate and (3) fish meal, the latter being unacceptable.

Kroepoek – an Indonesian snack served with rice dishes. Prepared out of potato starch with 15 per cent protein added and deep-fat fried.
Preference: (1) roller-dried fish, (2) proteolysate and (3) fish meal, the latter not being quite acceptable.

Vegetable rolls – a product similar to Chinese spring rolls. Prepared from dried vegetables with 6 per cent protein added, the mix battered and deep-fat fried.
Preference: (1) roller-dried fish, (2) proteolysate and (3) fish meal, the latter not being acceptable.

A Kenyan school dish prepared from semolina, with 6 per cent protein added. The protein consists of (a) roller-dried fish and (b) minced fish meat. There is no difference in acceptability.

Graham bread prepared from $\frac{3}{4}$ Graham flour and $\frac{1}{4}$ bread flour with 5 per cent protein added and the bread flavoured with coriander.
Preference: all acceptable.

Fish soufflé – a common Scandinavian dish prepared from margarine, flour, milk and eggs, with 4 per cent fish protein.

Preference: (1) roller-dried fish, (2) proteolysate and (3) fish meal, the latter not being acceptable.

Rice – Five per cent fish protein added and the dish cooked after the absorption method.

Preference: (1) roller-dried fish, (2) proteolysate and (3) fish meal, the latter not being acceptable.

The roller-dried product has been proved stable in storage for more than two years when packed in poly-ethylene bags and held at 25° to 30°C with low humidity. The next step is to carry out experiments for probable target areas.

References

CUTTING, C L, REAY, G A and SHEWAN, J M Dehydration of Fish, 1956 Dept. Sci., In *Res, Special Report* No. 62.

HERBORG, L Quality Control and Inspection of European Comminuted Products. In R Kreuzer (ed.) *Fish Inspection and Quality Control*, London, Fishing News (Books), Ltd.

Salting, Drying and Smoking *Tilapia galilae* from Volta Lake (Ghana)   *K Watanabe and E M Mensah*

Salage, Sechare et fumage des *Tilapio galilae* captures dans la lac Volta (Chana)

Une méthode associant les procédés de salage, de séchage et de fumage du poisson a été mise au point avec succès pour les conditions climatiques arides de l'Afrique centrale, mais on ignorait si cette méthode conviendrait pour les zones tropicales humides du continent africain. Le présent document décrit comment cette méthode a été introduite et démontrée dans la zone côtière humide du Ghana; les produits halieutiques salés, séchés et fumés ainsi obtenus sont supérieurs en qualité à ceux que donnent les procédés locaux traditionnels. Toutefois, ainsi qu'il est dit en conclusion, l'acceptabilité de ces produits améliorés dépend d'un certain nombre de facteurs autres que la qualité et le prix des denrées.

Salado, secado y ahumado de *Tilapia galilae* del lago Volta (Ghana)

Se había preparado un método combinado de salado, secado y ahumado de pescado que functionaba perfectamente en el clima seco del Africa Central, pero no se sabía si ese método tendría aplicaciòn práctica en las zonas tropicales hùmedas de continente. En este trabajo se describe la introduc tión de ese método en la zona costera hùmeda de Ghana y las demostraciones realizadas, en las que so han obtenido productos pesqueros salados, secos y ahumados de calidad superior a los conseguidos con los métodos locales tradicionales. Pero, como concluye el autor, el afianzamiento de estos productos mejores depende de diverses factores independientes de su calidad y de su precio.

The traditional method of producing salted, dried and smoked fish has been improved in Zambia (Watanabe and Cabrita 1971), which has also been proved suitable generally in the dry climatic conditions of Central Africa where the relative humidity (RH) ranges from 40 to 85 per cent. However, it was not known whether the method would be suitable for use in the coastal area of Ghana which is humid throughout the year, the RH ranging from 65 to 95 per cent. This paper describes the work done to adapt the method successfully for processing *Tilapia galilae* caught in the Volta Lake by the Institute of Food Technology with the assistance of the UNDP/FAO Volta Lake Research Project (VLRP), based at Akosombo.

THE PLANT AND OPERATIONS

The experimental drying plant was established at the Marina in Akosombo, with facilities for gutting and splitting, brining, drying, smoking and storage. Fresh *Tilapia* of commercially available sizes (small 200 g, medium 450 g and large 700 g) were collected from the local fishermen, packed in ice in an insulated box and taken to the drying plant and processed. During processing, changes in the weight of the fish were recorded. After processing, the following analyses were carried out: moisture (Anon. 1965), salt content (Greig and Seagran 1965), total bacterial count (nutrient agar, Difco Manual 1969) and pH (glass electrode). Appearance and smell of non-cooked fish were examined organoleptically, according to Watanabe and Dzekedzeke's scheme (1969), and scored on a ten-point scale (excellent – 10, good – 8, fair – 6, poor – 4, half rotten – 2, rotten – 0). Eating quality of the cooked fish (boiled for 30 min in distilled water) was determined for smell and taste by a panel of 4 members of the laboratory staff.

Effect of dressing and salting on quality

Locally processed *Tilapia* are only gutted and never split, except those landed spoiled. The smaller fish are salted and the larger fish usually smoked. The reason for this is that only smaller fish can absorb a fair amount of salt fast enough to keep the fish unspoiled during pre-drying. As salt penetrates into the meat of the larger fish too slowly to protect it, hot smoking is the only way to preserve them. Splitting fish increases the exposed surface, thus allowing quicker salt penetration and drying. This makes possible better water evaporation and salt absorption than are possible with just a skin surface. The results of an experiment in the dry season on brining times for split or gutted whole fish of various sizes are tabulated in Table 1. Loss in fresh weight after brining was less than 5 per cent in all cases, and even showed in some an increase of 1 per cent. Brining half an hour, small split fish resulted in a product of fair quality. An hour's brining was found to be essential for split or gutted medium size fish. Large split fish need brining for over an hour, and more than that if only gutted. Split fish, especially of medium to large size, seem to be superior in keeping quality as well as being easier and quicker to process.

The taste panel rated split fish significantly better (P <0.01) than gutted, small fish better than that of large, and the longer brined fish better than short brined.

311

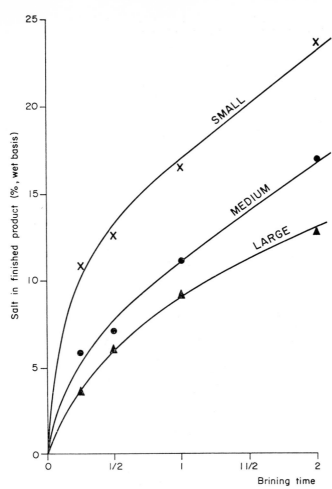

Fig 1 Salt penetration into the flesh of Tilapia galilae *during brining. The small, medium and large fish weighed about 200 g, 450 g and 800 g, respectively. Water content of the finished product ranged from 32 to 45%.*

Generally, the data indicate that fish dried to a level of 45 per cent of their wet weight will keep well if the salt content is over 10 per cent. Additional trials were conducted by dipping the fish in a saturated brine for $\frac{1}{4}$, $\frac{1}{2}$, 1 and 2 h. After being dried and smoked, they were analysed for salt content (Fig. 1). Stirring the fish in the brine helped to make the brining uniform. Table 2 shows the proposed brining time for the commercially available sizes of *T. galilae* from Volta Lake.

Effects of season on drying time

May to July is the rainy season in the Akosombo area, and September and October the minor rainy season. Humidity ranges from 70 per cent at 15.00 h to 100 per cent early in the morning. In the dry months the RH drops to 35 per cent at 15.00 h but is still about 80 per cent early in the morning. While total processing time in the dry season varied from 24 h for small to 36 h for large fish, in the rainy season it varied from 30 to 70 h. The processing of small fish could be completed in 12 h in the dry season. They could, in fact, be overdried down to 60 per cent yield. In such cases the smoke was deposited on the fish more slowly than when they were dried up to 80 per cent yield. Except for small fish in the dry season, few fish are dried at night. Occasionally, in the rainy season, the smoker-dryer (Watanabe 1973) was used as a dryer at night, which shortened the process to such an extent that the drying time required became shorter and similar to that during the dry season but led to a triple consumption of firewood. Fortunately, most of the rain in Ghana takes the form of showers of short duration so that some sun drying can be carried out with good results. Table 3 shows the results of chemical, bacteriological and organoleptic examinations and Table 4 those of the taste panel tests. While the finished products in both seasons were similar in water and salt content, mould grew on the medium fish processed

TABLE 1. CHEMICAL, BACTERIOLOGICAL AND ORGANOLEPTIC ANALYSIS OF SALTED, DRIED, SMOKED *TILAPIA* BY DRESSING, BRINING TIME AND FISH SIZE

Dressing method	Fish size[a]	Brining time (h)	Storage time (days)	Water (%)	Salt (% wet basis)	pH	Total viable count/cm² skin	Cooked fish score[b]	Appearance score	Mould growth[c]	Blow-fly larvae[c]	Off odour[c]
Split	S	$\frac{1}{4}$	70	31.8	10.8	6.8	10	5.3	8	—	—	—
		$\frac{1}{2}$	60	34.1	12.8	6.8	35,000	7.0	8	—	—	—
		1	60	32.7	13.7	6.8	180,000	7.0	8	—	—	—
	M	$\frac{1}{4}$	60	34.3	9.5	7.5	10	0	4	+	—	+
		$\frac{1}{2}$	60	33.0	13.6	6.8	450,000	6.8	8	—	—	—
		1	60	38.1	1.4	6.7	300	7.5	8	—	—	—
	L	$\frac{1}{4}$	60	38.6	7.2	7.6	1,600,000	0	4	+	—	+
		$\frac{1}{2}$	60	37.0	8.4	7.6	48,000	0	4	+	—	+
		1	60	44.1	8.9	7.2	8,200,000	6.8	8	—	—	—
Gutted	S	$\frac{1}{4}$	60	38.0	7.6	7.8	300,000	0	6	—	—	+
		$\frac{1}{2}$	60	25.5	8.5	6.8	2,300,000	6.3	8	—	—	—
		1	70	24.2	10.5	6.9	10	3.3	6	—	—	—
	M	$\frac{1}{4}$	50	36.7	5.9	7.4	550,000	0	4	+	—	+
		$\frac{1}{2}$	50	44.5	10.1	7.0	2,100	4.5	4	—	—	—
		1	50	26.0	9.1	6.8	8,500	7.2	8	+	—	+
	L	$\frac{1}{4}$	10	61.6	2.3	7.9	3,200,000	0	0	+	+	+
		$\frac{1}{2}$	10	44.4	4.5	8.0	—	0	0	+	+	+
		1	10	49.1	5.2	7.4	1,500,000	0	4	+	+	+

[a] S: Small 200 g, M: Medium 450 g, L: Large 700 g   [b] Average of smell and taste for 4 scores.   [c]—none, + some, ∓ slight.

TABLE 2. PROPOSED BRINING TIME FOR DIFFERENT SIZES OF *TILAPIA* FOR A FINISHED PRODUCT CONTAINING 10% SALT ON WET BASIS OF 40–45% WATER

| Fish size (g) | Gutted | Split | | | |
	Very small 200	Small 200	Medium 450	Large 700	Very Large 1,000–1,500
Brining time (h)	½	½	1	1½	2–6

TABLE 3. CHEMICAL BACTERIOLOGICAL AND ORGANOLEPTIC ANALYSIS OF SALTED, DRIED SMOKED *TILAPIA* BY SEASON AND FISH SIZE

Season	Fish size[a]	Storage time (days)	Water (%)	Salt % wet (basis)	pH	Total viable count/cm² skin	Cooked fish score[b]	Appearance score	Mould growth[a] larvae[c]	Blow-fly	Off odour
Dry	S	20	24.6	8.6	6.8	80	6.8	6	—	—	—
	M	30	23.5	9.2	6.6	50	7.0	8	+	—	—
	L	30	40.7	11.7	6.6	80,000	7.0	8	—	—	—
Rainy	S	28	24.3	12.5	6.6	1,200	8.0	8	—	—	—
	M	13	36.7	11.8	6.9	1,400	7.5	6	—	—	—
	L	13	40.5	10.8	6.8	1,000	7.5	8	—	—	—

[a] S: small 200 g; M: medium 450 g; L: large 700 g.
[b] Average of smell and taste for 4 scores.
[c] — none, + some.

TABLE 4. ANALYSIS OF PANEL SCORES ON PALATABILITY OF SMOKED *TILAPIA* BY SEASON AND SIZE

| Source of variation | DF | Smell | | Taste | |
		MS	F	MS	F
Dry vs. rainy season	1	9.83	8.57[a]	6.00	4.43
Sizes	2	4.33	3.69	0.19	0.12
Members of taste panel	3	4.72	4.47	0.67	0.49
Residual	17	1.15		1.365	

[a] Indicates a significant difference at $P0.05$.

TABLE 5. MINIMUM TIME (IN H) NECESSARY FOR OPEN-AIR DRYING TO PREPARE SPLIT, SALTED, SMOKED, DRIED *TILAPIA* AT AKOSOMBO, BY SEASON AND SIZE

| Season | Drying stages | Fish Size | | | | |
		Very small 200 g	Small 200 g	Medium 450 g	Large 700 g	Very large 700 g
Dry	Pre-smoking	5	5	10	15	25
	Post-smoking	0	0	5	10	30
	Total including brining and warm smoking	12	12	25	35	65
Rainy	Pre-smoking	20	20	25	30	50
	Post-smoking	0	0	20	30	55
	Total including brining and warm smoking	30	30	55	70	120

during the rainy season. This was due to surface absorption of moisture and suggests the need to protect dry fish from reabsorbing moisture in the rainy season. The better smell of the products in the rainy season could be due to the different firewood used. The minimum drying time for processing salted, dried, smoked *T. galilae* by the method at Akosombo is summarized in Table 5.

Effect of smoking temperature and storage time on quality

The local products are non-salted and processed at temperatures above 100°C, resulting in a brittle texture but a shelf life of only two days, unless the fish are resmoked every day. The Akosombo improved method, including brining, gives a firm texture. In Ghana, as in Zambia, hot smoked fish are preferred to warm smoked ones

(Watanabe and Dzekedzeke 1971). The main advantages of hot smoking are in shortening the drying time in sterilizing the product. To avoid brittleness, the fish can be smoked in warm temperatures at first, with increased temperatures of 110°C toward the end of the process. This method enabled us to prepare non-brittle products quicker than by warm smoking only, a most useful technique in the rainy season. Smoking with wood of the species *Talbotialla gentii* resulted in fish of the most attractive colour and good flavour. The trees are abundant on the lake.

Comparison in flavour between local and VLRP products

The improved method described calls for the following steps: (1) Scaling; (2) Dressing in split-open form; (3) Cleaning and washing; (4) Soaking in saturated brine for the time shown in Table 2 and quick washing afterwards; (5) Pre-smoking open air drying down to 75 to 80 per cent yield; (6) Warm smoking at 40° to 60°C; and (7) Post-smoking open air drying down to 40 to 45 per cent yield. These steps are basically similar to those developed in Zambia (Watanabe and Cabrita 1971). For comparison, some local products were bought in the Akosombo market and boiled in a 5 per cent brine so that they would have a salt content of approximately 2 per cent, similar to the VLRP products. In all four tests made the products were analysed for chemical, bacteriological and organoleptic quality. The taste panel scores indicate that the locally prepared smoked *Tilapia* were significantly inferior in taste but not in smell. But the former had been in storage only 4 days whereas the VLRP products had been stored for at least 1 week. When packaged in sealed plastic bags, the local products were usually found to be heavily infested within 2 days by blow-fly larvae except when dried to less than 15 per cent water content. Such highly dried fish, however, imply low yield percentage and consequently less profit on a weight basis. In Zambia fish traders adopted within 2 to 3 years the new fish processing method. This was attributed to the steady effort of the Zambian Fisheries Department Development Section to promote the product, especially through conducting training courses and field demonstrations.

References

Anon. Official methods of analysis, 10th ed. Ass. Off. Agric.
1965 Chemist, Washington DC, 419.

Difco Manual 9th ed., Detroit, USA, Difco Laboratories.
1969

EVANS, W A and VANDERPUYE, J Early development of the fish and
1970 fisheries of Volta Lake, Ghana. Internal Report (mimeo.), Volta Lake Research Project, Akosombo, Ghana.

GREIG, R A and SEAGRAN, H L A rapid field method for determin-
1965 ing the salt concentration in fresh and smoked chub. *Comm. Fish. Rev.*, 27(12):18–21.

KAGAN, B and TRANNING, A Reports on visits to traditional pro-
1968 cessing sites in Greater Accra, Food Research and Development Unit, Food Research Institute, Report No. 5, Accra, Ghana.

Volta River Authority, (Meteorological Section) Daily rainfall and
1972 air temperature, year 1972, Job No. VIC/OP/DS/4. Drawing No. 038. Volta River Authority, Akosombo, Ghana.

WATANABE K Experimental Fish Drying plant on Volta Lake,
1973a Ghana; its design, construction and economic considera- tion. Internal Report (mimeo.), Volta Lake Research Project, Akosombo, Ghana.

WATANABE, K and CABRITA, F J Directions for the preparation of
1971 salted and dry-smoked fish. *Fish. Res. Bull. Zambia*, 5:225–233.

WATANABE, K and DZEKEDZEKE, O Recommended Zambian stan-
1969 dards for grades for split, dried, smoked bream (*Tilapia* spp.). Technical Conference on Fish Inspection and Quality Control, Halifax, Canada, 15/25/7/1969, FAO, Rome, FE/FIC/69/0/46, 4 p.

WATANABE, K and DZEKEDZEKE, O Taste preference of Zambians
1971 for various types of dried and smoked fish. *Fish. Res. Bull. Zambia*, 5:199–206.

WATANABE, K and MENSAH, E M Prices and market quality of
1973 salted-dried and smoked-dried *Tilapia* from Volta Lake, Ghana. Internal Report (mimeo.), Volta Lake Research Project, Akosombo, Ghana.

Acknowledgement
Thanks are due to Mr F. Agbenu for his technical assistance in the experimental work.

Discussion on Part IV

Position of government and industry in product development

There was a strong feeling that in developed countries industries should carry out product development using government support in areas where more fundamental research is required. In developing countries the current situation is in most cases quite different due to the small scale of most industries and the lack of expertise and research facilities. This, however, points to an urgent need for high level training of staff in government institutions since advising on research and development means having available and maintaining technical expertise of a high standard.

ELSTON (UK) considered that the prime responsibility for product development lies with the processing industries because they have the appropriate marketing experience, although he recognized that the situation might be very different in developing countries. Large, commercial concerns usually have well-equipped laboratories for product development, with the staff working in co-operation with marketing colleagues. However, the work of governmental research laboratories on fundamental technological and scientific problems provides important information and guidance to industry.

FLEAR (UK) contended that development of fish species unfamiliar to the consumer requires government help in both developed and developing countries. He cited as an example the situation in the UK where more small fish of under-priced species are being landed. It is necessary in the circumstances for the government laboratories, in agreement with industry, to assist in determining how best to process and market the small fish.

JAYARAJ (India) mentioned the assistance given by the Government of Japan to India in fish processing technology and product development. The Japanese Government has established a centre for fish processing at Leanpalon and Japanese experts have developed a fish sausage suitable for Indian taste. Its production on an industrial scale is intended as there appears to be a strong demand for this product.

ALVAREZ (Ecuador) stated that cooperation with international agencies is vital and should mainly cover training. There is a lack of trained technicians in developing countries who are essential to give impetus to the industry.

MATTOS (Uruguay) stated that support from FAO is essential in countries without a long fishing tradition as training of technicians and workers at all levels engaged in fishing and the fish processing industry is required.

BLACKWOOD (Canada) stated that the decision to develop new fish products should be based on market intelligence thus there is reasonable expectation that the product will receive satisfactory consumer acceptance. There is ample evidence of excellent new products developed in government laboratories which have never been marketed. In view of this he posed the question: 'Is it the role of government research laboratories to develop new fishery products or is this the essential responsibility of the fish processing industry with assistance from technological research laboratories to solve problems associated with the development of new products?'

BALASINGAM (Malaysia), speaking about government participation in fish processing research, expressed concisely the view of developing countries. In these countries fish processing industries are often small and lack the facilities and expertise for research. In addition, private industry is often only interested in exporting particular commodities and making money. The lead in development has to come from the government. The government has also to be concerned with the assistance in establishing industries in an attempt to secure through government assisted industries a more equitable distribution of income and wealth. He said that the steps to be taken by the government could include: (1) surveying resources and improving fishing methods; (2) helping to establish fish processing industries; (3) establishing research laboratories and carrying out product development; and (4) assisting the industry to export high quality products. He pointed out that, with regard to product development, the laboratories should identify products requiring upgrading as well as develop new products.

ILYAS (Indonesia) and TALABI (Nigeria) made similar comments about the private sector. The latter said that his government has provided funds to establish two fishing companies over which it will have complete control.

AMANO (Japan) emphasized, as many other speakers did, the need for close cooperation between government and industry in product research. He pointed out the key part played by technologists from research institutes and industry in developing fish sausage and surimi and in making the industrial production of these products a success.

FINCH (USA) mentioned that the Conference itself was a good example of government–industry cooperation.

KARNICKI (Poland) referred also to Blackwood's question and pointed out that this was, indeed, a very important problem in his country. When trying to solve it it was found that the scientists did not understand the problems facing the industry. On the other hand the industry needed assistance. The problem was then tackled in the following way: technologists from the industry were invited to take part in all discussions on new products and on test panel sessions. They were asked to find out where problems, may occur when the product is produced on an industrial

scale. The government laboratory staff by these means learn to understand the problems of production and marketing and obtain guidance in their work. When a new product has reached the commercial production stage, the institute and company concerned sign an agreement for its launching on the commercial market and for the payment of royalties.

BURGESS (UK) concluded the discussion on this subject by saying that part of the problem appears to be a question of definition. What industry might call back-up work might well be regarded as product development by laboratory workers. There is no doubt a need to maintain close relations between government research laboratories and industry.

New products

Key issues that emerged and were stressed by many speakers were the vital need to use underutilized and new fish resources and the elimination of waste. All information related to product development aroused great interest, in particular information on new commodities, such as minced fish products. There was a coming together of interests in developed and developing countries which Burgess, Chairman of the Session, indicated in his closing remarks by saying: 'To an extent never reached at any earlier meeting, we have been made aware of common features in fisheries throughout the world. All fisheries in a sense are nowadays developing fisheries . . . we are now all looking at what we catch to see how . . . we can best make use of it.'

KANEDA (Japan) said that sometimes a simple idea leads to a popular new product. He cited the example of an instant fish noodle which only requires the addition of boiling water to make an excellent soup.

TOMIYAMA (Japan) gave an example of the kind of difficulty which can prevent acceptance of a good product. Just after the second world war Japanese scientists succeeded in preparing a substitute milk for babies but the milk industry, feeling menaced by the new product, succeeded in exerting pressure on the government to withdraw the budget allocated for making it.

ANDERSON (UK) referred to the possibilities of producing new products of consistent flavour, texture and appearance from minced fish flesh and pointed to the example of the margarine industry which, because of problems of raw material supply and price stability, has learned how to make a product of consistent characteristics from raw materials which often vary. The fish processing industries should learn to do the same by acquiring a thorough understanding of the flesh protein and the flavours and textural characteristics of the various fish species used to yield minced raw material.

COLE (UK) explained that the difference in product development in developed and developing countries is largely related to the number of technologists available and the level of education in the industry. He added that product improvement may be a more useful approach than the development of new products, especially in places where people are very conservative in their dietary habits.

BLACKWOOD (Canada) drew the attention of the Conference to the utilization of separated fish flesh. The development of sophisticated machines made possible the utilization of unfamiliar species not suitable for processing in traditional ways: the recovery of fish flesh by means of these machines exceeds substantially the yield from conventional filleting operations. The minced flesh derived from mixed species of similar flesh colour, texture, odour and flavour can be prepared in the form of a wide range of new, high quality fish products. Blackwood said that the demand in Canada for minced fish flesh products exceeded the suplpy. One company's sales had increased by more than 50 per cent in 1972 and sales are still going up. The products in popular demand include fish cakes and fingers, party starters with shrimp and crab added and salmon croquettes, etc. While there is a need for research in the field of minced products and questions of quality standards, nomenclature and labelling are still to be settled, industry will not wait for the final answers. It is important to industry and control agencies alike that no artificial barriers are being placed in the path of utilizing new species of fish and that the marketing of the new products should be orderly.

FINCH (USA) concurred with this view, stating that the Japanese have been in the minced fish flesh business for a number of years. The opportunities offered by minced flesh to mould, colour, texturize, stabilize and otherwise modify the raw material to make a variety of products are so irresistible that industry will go ahead and use them.

BLIGH (Canada), speaking about the problems associated with minced fish flesh, pointed out that the process disrupts the cellular structure of the muscle and that blood, air, micro-organisms and contaminants can be readily incorporated with the raw material, all of which may seriously change spoilage and storage characteristics. The process also lends itself to the incorporation of additives about which there is little information at present on their proper use and effectiveness. There is also a need to acquire technological data on the non-traditional species of fish which may be utilized in minced fish products.

MACKIE (UK) agreed that more research is needed on comminuted products. He mentioned that according to their experience increased protein denaturation has been found in certain species and may in fact be a direct result of mercury and may occur in all species. British investigations have revealed correspondingly high levels of dimethylamine and formaldehyde in other gadoids, such as cod (*Gadus morhua*) and saithe (*Pollachius virens*). This general problem, in his opinion, is associated with comminuted products prepared from most, if not all, species of fish.

KARNICKI (Poland) mentioned that there is a great need for fundamental research on minced fish, for example, regarding changes of texture in minced products during cold storage. There are still bacteriological and technological problems to be solved.

OKADA (Japan) stated that sugar prevents denaturation of muscle proteins during cold storage, and so do some amino acids, such as Na-glutamate. The rate of denaturation during cold storage depends on the species of fish. Proteins of fish meat deteriorate in the following order: whole fish, fillet, minced meat. Protein denaturation of minced fish flesh during cold storage can be retarded by washing the material with cold water, to which should be added 5 to 10 per cent of sugar. It acts as a deterring agent. He added that while Pacific cod deteriorates as quickly as Alaska pollock does in cold storage, Japanese researchers have confirmed the staple properties of the muscle protein of hake from South American waters.

JONES (UK) stated that under some circumstances a measure of denaturation can be desirable in the handling and cold storage of pre-rigor fish.

BLIGH (Canada) said, with regard to the poor quality of frozen stored Alaska pollock, due to protein denaturation by the DMA-HCHO process, Canadian studies have confirmed that the same problem exists in Atlantic hake and pollock.

BLACKWOOD (Canada) stated, regarding the problem of discoloration of the flesh of fish, especially in minced form, that such discoloration can be minimized by removing the blood from the kidneys, air bladders, and gut cavities in general, by vacuum-sucking equipment and then washing thoroughly by high pressure sprays.

DREWS (Germany, Fed. Rep. of) said that all parts which discolour the flesh and adversely affect the keeping qualities of minced products should be removed, including the main bones and black belly skin, therefore a rough filleting operation is required before mincing. In the case of larger fish, both fillets and minced material can be produced at the same time. The meat left after filleting can be used for the mincing process.

BRAEKKAN (Norway) said that the discoloration of fish flesh is most probably tied up with enzymatic processes. This problem recalls a report on the effect of spawning on the flesh of American plaice. The female, in particular, may have difficulty in recovering the loss of muscular protein which had been used to build up the gonads.

JAMES (Australia) also pointed out that the greyish discoloration of Alaska pollock is sensual and follows spawning. It is, therefore, impossible to wash out.

There were a number of interesting interventions in the discussion on various aspects of development of new products.

AMANO (Japan) explained that a liquid fish protein made by dissolving Alaska pollock, mackerel, krill, squid, etc., by means of commercial protease is a kind of protein hydrolyzate. It is spray-dried and contains about 90 per cent of crude protein and 6 to 7 per cent ash, the remainder being water. It has almost no fat. The crude protein is made mainly of low molecular peptide, which dissolves easily in water, and has a balanced amino acid content. The product has a high nutritional value and promotes animal growth faster than casein, but it has a bitter taste and the flavour of dried shrimp. It is being considered for use in diabetes therapy, as a milk replacer and in the cultivation of bacteria.

YOUNG (UK) stated that some large industrial research laboratories are now very active in producing a functional FPC from trash fish. The functionality offers several new possibilities, such as the development of fish structuring materials as, for example, flakes, fibres and chunks. Allied with the binding properties of functional fish protein is the technical capability of producing sophisticated fish analogues, comparable with meat analogues made from vegetable protein where the structuring materials are spun fibres. It is also possible to extend existing fish products with functional FPC, just as meat products are extended with vegetable protein.

LEARSON (USA), in a further comment on Mendelsohn's paper, said that the salted product made by the process is very stable at room temperature and storage tests indicate that, when packed in light impermeable pouches, it keeps without rancidity for more than a year. It can be used as a direct replacement of the traditional salted fish. Several new products have been made from the salted minced flesh, the most acceptable being salt fish and potato cakes, pre-cooked and frozen as a convenience food.

COLE (UK) reported that the Tropical Products Institute, London, had made cakes from shark, using a hamburger press. These had been well received in limited taste trials in a developing country where shark is eaten. The cakes have been made under pressure as low as 2 lb/sq in. The pressure was not as high as that applied in the Del Valle method.

DEL VALLE (Mexico) explained that the technique of quick salting of fish flesh developed in Mexico uses the less common species and 'trash' fish, especially the small ones. The purpose of his process is to produce a high-protein low-cost food for developing countries, and a plant has already been set up in Yucatan, Mexico, and has started commercial production of the cakes.

BLIGH (Canada) wondered if Del Valle incorporated his product in highly spiced Mexican dishes since he does not use antioxidants.

DEL VALLE (Mexico) said, replying to this question, that he uses high pressure in making the product so as to eliminate the maximum amount of water mechanically. This reduces the sun-drying time. About 50 per cent of the water originally present in the flesh is so removed. Further, the application of high pressure also results in compact cakes. With regard to the rancidity question, only lean species of fish have been used because fatty species present a rancidity problem. In any case, some of the rancid components in the products are removed by leaching when it is put into boiling water for desalting. This process improves the flavour of the product.

HERBORG (Denmark), referring to roller-dried fish protein, said that one feature of the product is that the meat structure is recognizable as well as the dry fish smell.

Only raw material with not more than 2 per cent oil can be used. Products containing salt have also been produced. The shelf-life of the unsalted product is more than 3 years at 20°C. Acceptibility tests have not yet been carried out.

PETERKIN (Guyana) stated at the end of the discussion that there was a need to disseminate information on the development of new products through a central agency, such as FAO, and expressed the hope that the Organization will be able to undertake this task.

Acceptance of products

The discussion on acceptability of products brought into focus the differences in the acceptability of traditional and new types of products. Accordingly, the approach to their introduction must vary and must be in harmony with local food habits. It also became apparent that technologists working in research institutions need close collaboration with marketing and promotion experts.

MATSUMOTO (Japan) said there are basically two categories of new products – (a) those similar to traditional foods, the development of which does not differ substantially in developed or developing countries, and (b) completely new products, such as fish protein concentrate. The introduction of new types of products requires great care. Traditional tastes and preferences of the consumers need to be studied and the products be introduced in harmony with their food habits. Flavour can, for example, be adjusted by means of natural additives such as amino acids. We should not rely too much on nutritional value but be guided by what people like and what they will accept when introducing new products.

AMANO (Japan) stressed the time required and difficulties faced in developing and establishing new products. In this connexion he referred to Japanese experience with fish ham and sausage. These were evolved by Prof W Simizu in 1930 but they did not become commercially viable until 1954. This was due in part to socio-economic reasons following the second world war.

BLACKWOOD (Canada) made the point that the decision to develop new fishery products should be based on marketing intelligence of consumer acceptance.

BYKOV (USSR) said Soviet experience showed that it is easier to establish products which follow traditional patterns. This is, however, not always feasible. The utilization of krill, for example, is a new and very complicated question. However, progress has been made toward achieving satisfactory commercial results with the new krill products.

TALABI (Nigeria) said that the product development technologists should try to make new products resembling traditional ones, such as shark cake which resembles stock fish.

KANEDA (Japan) stressed that one particular important aspect is that traditional methods of production of food product are followed in Japan where it is not possible to change the basic consumer preference for certain traditional products. But, of course, those traditional methods are improved by the application of science and modern technology. This policy of following traditional methods and consumer preferences in product development means also that the products conform to the particular taste of Japanese consumers and may, therefore, not suit the taste of consumers in other countries.

KREUZER (FAO) agreed that this is a very important aspect of product development. As a general rule, when seeking to transfer products from one country to another, it is advisable to study the principles of the methods involved, and the properties of the available raw material. Based on the results of such investigations, products which suit local tastes can be developed. Such studies will indicate how the products and the processes have to be modified to meet the requirements of the consumers in the adopting countries. This approach to the transfer of products and methods from one country or region to another appears to be more successful, particularly in non-industrialized societies, than to attempt to adopt specific recipes.

AMANO (Japan) stressed the importance of social factors in product development and mentioned living standards as another significant factor. Fish sausage was readily accepted by the people who could not afford to buy meat sausage.

BALASINGAM (Malaysia) said that canned sardines in tomato sauce have in Malaysia consumer preference over canned tuna in oil or brine. The retail price of a 720 g can of tuna flake is US $0.30 and that of a 1,502 g can of sardines in tomato sauce is US $0.38. It is obvious that the price influences consumer preference.

BYKOV (USSR) said, with regard to acceptance of products and consumer preferences, that in the USSR the preference for freshwater fish and for anadromous fish species was very strong and there was resistance against eating sea fish. Cod, for example, has only recently been accepted. The experience is that small pelagic fish can be introduced best as traditional products. For example, salted mackerel is now replacing salted herring which is in short supply. Minced fish meets with consumer resistance as does krill paste. Consumer education is most important and all news media should be used.

Part V

QUALITY REQUIREMENTS IN PRODUCT DEVELOPMENT AND TRADE

Les exigences de qualitè en matière de produits de la pêche   *F Soudan*

Quality requirements for fishery products

Factors determining the quality grading of fishery products are varied, due to technical, economic, hygienic, climatic and other considerations. The author examines the criteria for quality assessment and concludes that there is a need to set up standards for food commodities to protect the consumer and facilitate the marketing of food products.

Countries manufacturing a given product could establish codes of practice describing the technology used and the standard of hygiene. If such a standard practice proved acceptable to the consumers familiar with the product, other countries could then adopt but would, of course, remain free to manufacture, under a different name, a similar product better suited to their tastes, appropriately describing it.

In practice, the author proposes first that a catalogue should be compiled, listing the characteristics of similar products and, at a second stage, that standards be established for each product on the basis of its characteristics. Such standards would primarily meet a need for information and offer customers a guarantee as to the nutritive value, wholesomeness, organoleptic qualities and appearance of the product. Such descriptive standards would be supplemented by codes of practice, giving the main principles of hygiene and technology for the different species of fish processed.

Exigencias de calidad en los productos pesqueros

Los motivos que determinan la calidad de los productos pesqueros son muy variados y de diversos órdenes: económicos o sanitarios, geográficos o ideológicos. Tras examinar los criterios de los juicios de calidad y concluir que es necesario establecer una codificación ed los productos alimentarios para responder a las necesidades nutricionales del hombre y facilitar su comercio, el autor hace algunas sugerencias para normalizar los productos pesqueros.

Estimando que convendría reelaborar las normas partiendo de la idea de mercado, el autor opina que los países en los que se fabrica de ordinario un producto prodían describir en una norma la especie de pescado utilizado, la técnica de preparación empleada y las características detalladas del producto terminado, según el modo de preparación que ellos utilizan. Si esta norma va bien para la población que mejor conoce ese producto, los demás países podrían adoptarla, quedando libres de fabricar bajo otro nombre otro producto que respondiera mejor a sus gustos y que podría ser objeto de otra norma.

En el plano práctico, el autor propone reunir en una especie de repertorio las diversidades encontradas en una serie de productos análogos, preparando a continuación normas específicas para cada producto teniendo en cuenta los elmentos que lo caracterizan, que corresponden a las costumbres de un mercado determinado. Estas normas tendrían ante todo valor informativo y darían al consumidor ciertas garantías sobre el valor nutritivo e higiénico del producto, así como sobre su calidad gustatoria y estética. Estas normas descriptivas se completarían con códigos de empleo, que mostrarían cómo deben aplicarse los principios generales higiénicos y tecnológicos según las especies y el clima, para tener un producto que reúna las características de que trata la norma.

La qualité est probablement l'un des mots qui revient le plus souvent dans le commerce, peut-être parce qu'il est ambigu et qu'il laisse place aux interprétations qui sont propres à la négociation qu'est toute vente. On parle de 'qualité' par opposition à 'quantité', l'une étant appréciée, donc *a priori* subjective, tandis que l'autre est mesurée et théoriquement indépendante du sujet. Le client veut, à prix égal, la qualité la meilleure, ce qui implique qu'li existe plusieurs qualités pour une marchandise donnée. Dans ce cas, le mot 'qualité' correspond plutôt à 'catégorie'. Le client choisit la qualité qu'il estime convenable pour ce qu'il veut faire, chaque catégorie étant définie par un ensemble de caractéristiques qui sont souhaitables ou indésirables et sont, par conséquent, considérées comme des 'qualités' ou des 'défauts'. Le mot 'qualité' est alors associé à certaines propriétés.

Nous savons aussi que le classement de qualité est une telle nécessité pour le négoce que, depuis toujours, on s'efforce de lui donner une base plus large que le jugement individuel en définissant de mieux en mieux la marchandise par des caractères mesurés. C'est à ce besoin de définition que répond la création de la Commission du *Codex Alimentarius*. Celle-ci a entrepris, comme chacun sait, de décrire dans des normes les principaux produits alimentaires faisant l'objet d'un commerce important soit par le volume des transactions mondiales, soit par le nombre des pays concernés. De plus, il se propose de décrire dans les codes d'usage la manière de procéder pour préparer des produits conformes aux normes.

LES BASES DES JUGEMENTS DE QUALITÉ

Voyons donc quels sont les caractères sur lesquels se base le plus souvent un classement de qualité quand il s'agit de produits de la pêche. Nous admettrons qu'il s'agit de produits consommables par l'homme. Ces caractères sont de quatre ordres: hygiénique, nutritif, gustatif, esthétique. Nous les examinerons en cherchant ceux qui sont susceptibles de fournir une norme acceptée universellement.

Qualitè hygiénique

Toxiques endogènes. La première exigence évidente est que le produit ne soit pas toxique. L'exclusion des poissons toxiques du marché mondial est une nécessité unanimement reconnue, mais comment la réaliser avec la sécurité désirable? On sait que certains posisons sont vénéneux, en particulier dans les eaux tropicales, et que d'autres sont capables d'accumuler dans leurs tissus des substances toxiques. Le tri d'après une liste d'espèces établie au niveau international est insuffisant, car l'espèce n'est pas seule en cause. Telle espèce qui est toxique à l'île de la Réunion et à l'île Maurice est sans danger à Madagascar. En Polynésie, telle espèce devient dangereuse seulement en certaines circonstances (travaux publics touchant le fond de la mer). Aux Antilles, les vivaneaux ou les barracudas, non toxiques à la Martinique ou dans le sud de la Guadeloupe, provoquent la ciguatera lorsqu'ils sont pêchés au nord de la Guadeloupe s'ils dépassent le poids de 1,500 g après vidage. La liste des poissons à exclure pour ichtyotoxisme, qui est liée non seulement à l'espèce mais à l'âge et au lieu de pêche, est donc sensiblement différente d'un pays à l'autre.

Contaminants. S'agissant des contaminants qui s'accumulent au long de la chaîne alimentaire tels que les métaux lourds ou les biocides, les règles à respecter pour garantir la santé humaine devraient, semble-t-il, être universelles. A partir du moment où des études ont déterminé d'une part la dose maximale tolérable par l'homme pendant un temps donné, d'autre part la façon dont le contaminant s'accumule dans la faune aquatique par espèce et par organe, il semblerait raisonnable de fixer la dose maximale qui sera tolérée dans les produits de la pêche mis dans le commerce international. Mais ce faisant, on n'aurait pas tenu compte des habitudes alimentaires du consommatuer: taux de consommation par habitant et par an, qui peut varier de moins de 1 kg à plus de 40 kg (taux norvégien d'après Halvorsen) suivant les pays, fréquence de consommation des espèces ou des organes normalement les plus chargés en produits chimiques rémanents, probabilité d'ingestion d'autres ailments éventuellement contaminés par le même contaminant ou par un produit qui en atténue ou en renforce la nocivité. La limite tolérable de contaminant dans les produits de la pêche ne peut donc être fixée valablement que dans une aire déterminée en relation avec ales habitudes alimentaires de la région.

Micro-organismes pathogènes. Mais ce genre de con-
Micro-organismes pathogenes. Mais ce genre de con-
tamination n'est sans doute pas ce qui vient immédiatement à l'esprit lorsqu'on parle de qualité hygiénique. La notion d'hygiène évoque plutôt un produit microbiologiquement sain, c'est-à-dire qui ne contienne pas de germes pathogènes pour l'homme. A première vue, une exigence limitant le nombre mazimum de germes microbiens de tel ou tel type dans un poids donné de produit est légitime en toute occasion. Cependant, les limites imposées ne sont pas forcément valables universellement. Par exemple, si la règle est donnée pour des coquillages qui sont toujours mangés cuite dans un pays alors qu'ils sont mangés crus dans un autre, la règle pourra être moins exigeante dans le premier pays. De même la norme bactériologique admise pour des huîtres vendues vivantes dans leurs coquilles, selon l'usage français, ne convient pas nécessairement pour des huîtres découquillées destinées à un long transport, comme cela se fait aux Etats-Unis. Par ailleurs, il arrive que certaines populations soient plus sensibles que d'autres à certaines maladies. Elles sont par conséquent amenées à imposer des règles plus strictes à l'égard des maladies en cause. Faute d'exemple dans le domaine de la pêche, nous rappelerons la fragilité des Indiens à la tuberculose qui justifie une protection particulière des aliments qui leur sont destinés.

Substances formées par alteration. Une autre exigence
Substances formees par alteration. Une autre exigence
très générale est la fraîcheur du produit. Chacun répète à l'envi que les produits de la pêche livrés au consommateur doivent être bien frais, que ceux destinés à la transformation (congélation, appertisation) doivent être aussi frais que possible. Mais lorsqu'il s'agit de définir un état de fraîcheur ou de choisir une technique de mesure de la fraîcheur ou un seuil d'acceptabilité, les avis sont moins unanimes. En effet, l'altération ne suit pas les mêmes processus dans les différentes espèces ou aux différentes températures. Par exemple, le modèle classique de l'altération de la morue conservée dans la glace fondante s'applique mal au cas des sardinelles des mers tropicales ou à celui des thons. On sait que chez la morue, l'altération se manifeste d'abord par une production précoce d'hypoxanthine, dont le taux augmente proportionnellement à la durée du séjour en glace, puis par une production de triméthylamine suivant une loi exponentiell.

Chez le thon, la formation d'hypoxanthine est plus faible et plus tardive, celle de triméthylamine reste lente et limitée alors qu'un autre produit du métabolisme bactérien, l'histamine, apparaît dans certaines conditions en quelques dizaines d'heures en quantités qui peuvent être dangereuses pour l'homme. On ne peut donc pas définir la qualité de fraîcheur du thon avec les mêmes indices que celle de la morue. Par conséquent, les pays où l'une ou l'autre de ces espèces est dominante n'auront pas les mêmes normes pour juger de la fraîcheur des produits de la pêche. Les règles varieront d'ailleurs non seulement en raison des différences d'espèces mais aussi en raison de la situation géographique du pays par rapport aux lieux de pêche. Par exemple, St-Pierre et Miquelon peut accepter la mise en criée de gros poissons entiers, non vidés, parce que ceux-ci y parviennent dans les 24 h qui suivent la pêche, alors qu'en France métropolitaine, l'usage est de vendre les mêmes espèces au moins vidées, parfois étêtées. Il est aussi certain que le degré d'altération toléré par les populations maritimes habituées à consommer du poisson sortant de l'eau est plus bas que celui accepté par des populations plus continentales. L'éloignement de la côte du marché de consommation imposera d'ailleurs des précautions qui n'ont pas lieu d'être lorsque les produits sont utilisés près du port de pêche. Par exemple, en France le listao est obligatoirement cuit préalablement à la mise en conserve alors que dans des pays proches des lieux de production (Maroc, Italie), la mise en conserve est faite à partir du poisson cru sans inconvénient. La limite de fraîcheur acceptable varie donc suitant l'espèce et suivant la situation géographique du pays vis-à-vis des lieux de pêche qui conditionne en partie les goûts de la population. Si, donc il est très facile d'écrire dans une réglementation que le poisson doit être frais, il est beaucoup plus malaisé, au moins au niveau international, de préciser ce qu'il faut entendre par là. A cela s'ajoute la difficulté du choix de la référence. Quelle sera-t-elle? Teneur en tel ou tel produit de la dégradation enzymatique ou bactérienne, disparition de tel ou tel constituant, flore bactérienne, caractéristiques organoleptiques? La question n'a pas encore été résolue au niveau international; il faut bien reconnaître que la diversité des goûts des consommateurs aussi bien que celles résultant de techniques de dosage différentes ne facilitent pas un accord éventuel des techniciens sur la définition de la fraîcheur. En définitive, il apparaît que les caractères qui déterminent la qualité hygiénique des produits de la pêche sont beaucoup moins généraux qu'on ne le penserait *a priori*.

Qualité nutritive

Constituants naturels. La qualité nutritive dépend en premier lieu de la composition qui, en matière de produits de la pêche, est encore le plus souvent l'ouevre de la nature puisque l'élevage, qui permettrait d'agir quelque peu sur la composition des produits, est encore peu important par rapport à la pêche proprement dite. Il y a des poissons gras, des poissons maigres, des espèces riches en vitamines ou en acides aminés indispensables, toutes choses qui ne donnent pas matière à réglementer au moins tant qu'il s'agit de produits frais. Mais lorsque le produit est transformé ,sa composition est modifiée, intentionnellement ou non, dans le but de satisfaire une certaine clientèle. Dans un pays dont l'alimentation est à base de céréales, le poisson sera à la fois source de lipides et de protéines. La technique de préparation s'efforcera donc de garder toute la graisse de poisson. Il en sera de même dans les pays où le poisson représente la principale nourriture carnée. Ainsi les Esquimaux recherchent-ils les poissons gras. A l'inverse, une population dont la nourriture est abondante et variée donnera parfois la préférence à un poisson ayant perdu une partie de sa graisse. Les transformateurs seront ainsi conduits à trouver des techniques qui favorisent l'élimination partielle des graisses: cuisson préalable des sardines à la vapeur (sur gril par exemple) de préférence à un emboîtage à cru qui, à moins de précautions spéciales, garde toute l'huile dans la boîte. Dans d'autres cas, considérant que la présence d'un peu de graisse témoigne d'une bonne condition physique, on imposera une teneur minimale à trouver dans la matière première. Ainsi la réglementation norvégienne exige-t-elle que le sprat mis en conserve contienne au moins 5 pour cent de graisse. Ce minimum pourrait être différent dans un autre pays dont les goûts seraient différents.

Additifs correctifs. Parfois, le transformateur s'efforcera d'améliorer la composition du produit par des additions visant à un meilleur équilibre des constituants. Il ajoutera par exemple des vitamines. Mais cette addition n'aura d'intérêt que si le consommateur auquel est destiné l'aliment ne trouve pas cette vitamine en quantité suffisante dans le reste de sa nourriture. L'utilité d'une telle addition dépend donc étroitement des carences nutritionnelles qui peuvent exister dans telle région selon les usages alimentaires. Ainsi pourrait-il êtra opportun de supplémenter en vitamine B_1 les conserves de poisson à l'intention des populations qui se nourrissent de riz décortiqué, ou de préparer pour elles des conserves avec les 'muscles rouges' des thons alors que dans d'autres pays dont le régime est assez riche en aneurine la mise en conserve des muscles rouges du thon est interdite en raison de leur propension à l'altération.

Additifs conservateurs. Le transformateur ajoute parfois des antiseptiques ou des antibiotiques en vue d'améliorer la conservation, ce qui ne va pas sans inconvénient pour le consommateur puisque généralement ces inhibiteurs des micro-organismes sont également des inhibiteurs du métabolisme cellulaire chez l'homme. Il y a là un équilibre à trouver entre le risque microbien et le risque chimique d'intocication. Cet équilibre ne sera pas le même sous tous les climats: là où des températures et une humidité élévees favorisent une croissance très rapide des germes, l'emploi d'antiseptiques et d'antibiotiques peut représenter un moindre mal alors que cet emploi est superflu ou inutile dans des climats froids et secs. La nécessité d'assurer l'approvisionnement d'une population dépourvue d'installation frigorifique suffisante pourra aussi justifier l'emploi de conservateurs chimiques malgré leur nocivité relative, car il faut d'abord satisfaire les besoins quantitatifs. Par contre, cet emploi devra être proscrit là cù on peut conserver les produits de la pêche par d'autres moyens.

Qualité gustative

Des goûts et des couleurs on ne discute pas, dit-on communément dans beaucoup de langues du monde.

Comment ce qui est vrai à l'échelle individuelle ne serait-il pas vrai aussi à celle des groupements humains?

Texture. En matière de texture, certains rechercheront un produit qui se désintègre facilement à la mastication alors que d'autres voudront un produit résistant. Ainsi la chair un peu caoutchouteuse des ormeaux sera-t-elle hautement appréciée aux Etats-Unis alors qu'elle l'est moins en Europe. De même le degré d'autolyse jugé optimum dans l'anchoitage varie selon les consommateurs, ou encore l'addition de polyphosphates visant à maintenir l'hydratation des filets de poisson congelés pourra être utile sur certains marchés alors que d'autres préféreront s'exposer à manger une chair un peu sèche et fibreuse plutôt que d'accroître la dose de phosphate de leur régime qui en est déjà amplement pourvue. Ici, comme dans bien d'autres cas déjà cités, c'est une question de choix: chacun mise sur le risque qui lui paraît moindre, soit intuitivement, soit après une analyse raisonnée où interviennent le tempérament propre, les conditions de milieu et le niveau des connaissances.

Saveur. Prenons un autre exemple, celui des sauces tomate qui sont utilisées dans de très nombreux pays comme couverture de conserves. Les uns y ajoutent de l'huile, d'autres du vinaigre, d'autres du sucre peut-être en vue de corriger les caractéristiques de goût du poisson jugé sec, douceâtre ou amer suivant les cas, mais peut-être aussi pour assortir les caractéristiques du produit aux habitudes culinaires de la population qui sont elles-mêmes fonction de ses conditions de vie. Il est remarquable que l'addition de sucre dans les sauces de poisson soit fréquente dans le nord de l'Europe alors qu'elle est quasi inexistante dans le sud où une abondante consommation de fruits fait rechercher par contraste dans le plat principal de viande ou de poisson des saveurs salées, aromatisées, épicées mais non sucrées. Les normes de qualité pour la sauce tomate employée dans l'industrie de la conserve dans ces différents pays seront donc différentes. En matière d'exhausteurs de goût ou d'édulcorants, nous retrouvons la même différence d'attitudes suivant qua la population destinataire a besoin d'une nourriture stimulante ou adoucissante en relation par exemple avec le climat déprimant ou excitant. L'emploi d'exhausteurs de goût: glutamate, nuoc-mam, épices, est classique, et sans doute utile, dans les pays où une chaleur excessive réduit l'appétit au-dessous des besoins de l'organisme, alors que sous d'autres climats il surmèneraient inutilement l'organisme et sont peu recherchés.

Qualité esthétique

Couleur. Les remarques que nous venons de faire à propos du goût s'appliquent aussi bien à la couleur, à ceci près que les corrections éventuelles de couleur dans les produits ont plus facilement un caractère frauduleux que celles de goût. Mais, admettons que la coloration artificielle n'ait d'autre intention que d'améliorer la présentation du produit, par exemple celle des crevettes qui se décolorent à la cuisson. Il est hors de doute que la couleur fait partie des stimulus qui favorisent l'appétit et l'utilisation digestive des aliments. Cependant certaines populations préféreront un aliment moins attrayant mais naturel, tandis que d'autres attribuent plus d'importance à la présentation. Suivant le cas, la réglementation sera amenée à accepter ou interdire la coloration. De la même manière, les pays connaisseurs de l'anchois salé accepteront la présence des efflorescences blanches de tyrosine qui se forment durant la conservation dans l'huile et y verront même un facteur de qualité alors que d'autres pays chercheront un traitement pour faire disparaître ces moucheteures blanches qui évoquent certaines moisissures.

Parasites. Plus délicate est la question des parasites. On sait que les muscles de certains poissons contiennent naturellement des parasites, enkystés, en nombre parfois très élevés. Bien qu'ils soient rarement pathogènes pour l'homme (on connaît l'exception d'anisakis), ils suscitent une répulsion surtout s'ils sont bien visibles. Cependant l'expérience montre que certains marchés s'en accommodent. Ainsi l'hirondelle de mer *Brama raii* qui est habituellement parasitée dans le golfe de Gascogne est-elle très appréciée en Espagne au moins en conserve à l'huile alors que sa mise en conserve en France est interdite à cause des vers. Notons aussi que le parasitage d'une espèce varie suivant les lieux de pêche et que, par conséquent, les règles à son égard peuvent différer d'un pays à l'autre. Dans d'autres pays, le problème des parasites est réglé en imposant une élimination à la main après inspection. Tel est le cas au Canada où les parasites sout excisés des filets de morue, examinés par mirage avant la congélation. Intervient alors un autre choix: celui du consommateur qui préfère payer des frais de main-d'oeuvre pour éliminer quelque chose d'indésirable alors qu'un autre préférera épargner son argent quitte à céder un peu sur le confort de sa table.

Présentation. Dans le même esprit, certains marchés souhaiteront que le parage soit extrêmement poussé. Ils exigeront par exemple des conserves de sardines sans arêtes ou des filets de poisson sans peau et sans arêtes poiru des motifs de commodité ou d'appétance, mais aussi pour épargner du temps à la maîtresse de maison surmenée, alors que d'autre pays préféreront un produit moins élaboré et moins couteux. La taille du poisson peut être un élément pris en compte soit qu'elle facilite la distribution par portion individuelle, soit qu'elle s'associe à une texture, un goût ou une couleur de la chair différente entre les individus jeunes et les plus âgés. Ainsi la sole portion sera-t-elle plus prisée sur certains marchés alors que d'autres estimeront que les grandes soles charneues sont de qualité supérieure. Le mode de découpage a aussi son importance. Certains marchés acceptent seulement le filet de poisson congelé, d'autres préfèrent les tranches ou le poisson entier, c'est-à-dire une présentation qui soit aussi proche que possible de celle du poisson frais. En maitière de conserves de poisson cuisinées, divers pays africains comme le Sénégal apprécient davantage une préparation où la chair est découpée en des mélanges aux végétaux alors que le consommateur français préfère trouver le poisson dans la boîte en un seul gros morceau. En définitive, nous voyons que les motifs qui interviennent pour déterminer le classement de qualité sont très variés. D'ordre tantôt économique, tantôt sanitaire, tantôt géographique ou philosophique, ils comprennent fatalement des choix très différents suivant les populations. A l'intérieur même d'une nation, des groupes cohabitants ont des préférences différentes qui rejoignent d'ailleurs parfois celles de groupes appartenant à une autre nation. On objectera sans doute que plusieurs des exemples données sont des cas marginaux qui pourraient être négligés sur le plan international. Il n'en reste pas moins que le nombre des facteurs qui interviennent dans un classement de qualité est tel qu'un accord sur l'ensemble, au niveau international, est problématique. Les débats passionnés qui ont lieu dans certains comités du *Codex* en sont la preuve. Comment en effet trouver sur le plan condial les caractères qui définissent la qualité d'un produit quel qu'il soit, alors que chacun se fait une idée différente de cette qualité. Vue sous cet angle, la tâche entreprise par le Codex alimentaire semble vouée à l'échec et on peut s'étonner que de bons esprits s'y soient essayés.

NECESSITE DES NORMES

Mais, par delà les difficultés que nous avons signalées, existe un besoin aigu d'une condification des denrées alimentaires afin de satisfaire les besoins nutritionnels des hommes et de faciliter le commerce des denrées alimentaires. Il est en effet hautement souhaitable que chacun ait à sa disposition une nourriture saine et abondante, ce qui implique des échanges de denrées alimentaires entre pays lointains pour complèter qualitativement et quantitativement les ressources des pays mal pourvus. Il est indispensable que l'acheteur sache ce qu'il achète, qu'il soit informé des propriétés particulieres d'unè marchandise sans l'avoir vue, qu'il soit assuré de retrouver sur le marché, s'il le désire, une marchandise déjà goûtée et qui répondait parfaitement à ce qu'il souhaite. Il est nécessaire que le prix corresponde à une marchandise définie. Tout ceci nécessite une normalisation des denrées alimentaires.

En effet, normaliser c'est d'abord donner une description des produits suffisamment détaillée et fidèle pour qu'en aucun cas une marchandise ne puisse être substituée à une autre à l'insu de l'acheteur. La norme est donc une sorte de carte d'identité qui authentifie la marchandise et qui donne au consommateur certaines garanties du point de vue de l'hygiène alimentaire. La normalisation entraîne une certaine uniformisation de la marchandise car elle impose la constance d'un certain nombre de caractères dans les fabrications successives. De plus, la transcription des caractéristiques dans un texte engage implicitement le producteur à y conformer sa production. Or, la description laisse de côté les contingences pour fixer les caractères majeurs du produit de manière à exclure les produits de même nature présentant des défauts. La normalisation, d'abord limitée à quelques caractères jugés primordiaux pour le produit considéré, s'étend de proche en proche aux caractères secondaires lorsque le risque de confusion augmente du fait de l'arrivée sur le marché de produits qui ressemblent à ceux auxquels l'acheteur est accoutumé. Le besoin de normalisation augmente donc avec l'élargissement du marché. Mais cet élargissement qui a mis des siècles à passer du clan au canton, puis à la nation, est passé brusquement à l'échelle du monde. De ce fait, le besoin d'information de l'acheteur et de loyauté dans les transactions est plus aigu que jamais parce que les échanges commerciaux qui impliquent une sorte de confiance mutuelle entre acheteurs et vendeurs se font maintenant entre personnes qui ne se connaîtront probablement jamais, avec des marchandises qui sont souvent connues seulement après un long transport. La normalisation est aussi une nécessité pour le producteur. En incitant à une réflexion sur les caractéristiques qui ont vraiment un effet sur la qualité du produit, elle conduit à écarter celles qui sont la survivance d'usages liés à une technique périmée ou l'effet du caprice de l'acheteur. La normalisation favorise ainsi la fabrication de série, en quantités correspondant aux besoins pour lequel le produit est adapté; elle réduit les risques de différends commerciaux coûteux par les règlements contentieux, les retours de marchandises ou les destructions. La normalisation aboutit donc à des économies substantielles. Acheteurs et vendeurs y trouvent leur avantage. D'où la multiplication des instances qui se préoccupent de normaliser les produits au niveau d'une province, d'une nation, d'un groupe d'Etats ou du monde. Il semble en effet à première vue qu'une normalisation est d'autant plus efficace qu'elle est appliquée dans une aire géographique plus étendue.

Suggestions en vue de normaliser les produits de la pêche

Mais comment faire puisque nous venons de voir qu'en matière de produits de la pêche tout au moins, les caractéristiques considérées comme des qualités changent suivant les marchés. Il semble qu'il faille repenser les normes en partant de l'idée de marchés. Imaginons une marchandise préparée dans une région déterminée, disons, pour fixer les idées, les filets d'anchois salés à l'huile qui sont préparés communément dans le bassin méditerranéen occidental avec cependant quelques variantes d'un pays à l'autre. Les pays qui fabriquent d'ordinaire ce produit peuvent décrire dans une norme l'espèce de poisson utilisée, la technique de préparation, les caractéristiques détaillées du produit terminé selon le mode de préparation employé. Ils tomberont assez facilement d'accord entre eux sur les facteurs à réunir pour obtenir un produit de qualité parce que dans une aire géographique soumise à un climat déterminé les modes de vie sont assez semblables, les espèces de poissons traitées sont les mêmes. Si cette norme convient à la population méditerranéenne qui connaît le mieux le produit, les autres pays pourraient l'adopter s'agissant d'un produit qu'ils ne savent pas ou ne peuvent pas faire mais qu'ils sont susceptibles de consommer même si les caracteristiqués ne sont pas celles qu'ils préfèrent par goût. Ceci ne les empêcherait pas d'ailleurs de fabriquer dans leur pays, sous un autre nom, un produit un peu différent qui répond mieux à leur goût et pourrait faire l'objet d'une autre norme. Ainsi aurait-on par exemple une norme pour le kipper norvégien en conserve et une pour le hareng-saur à l'huile français, l'une et l'autre concernant des harengs fumés en conserves mais de caractères distincts, les deux normes étant par ailleurs reconnues à la fois par la France et par la Norvège, éventuellement par d'autres pays.

En restreignant son champ à un produit typique, la norme trouve plus facilement les caractéristiques propres au produit considéré, par exemple la morphologie ou le goût spécifique. Etant plus précise, elle répond mieux à son objet. Elle peut aussi plus facilement prévoir plusieurs niveaux de qualité correspondant aux différentes catégories de clientèle. L'expérience montre d'ailleurs que les normes élaborées par la Commission du *Codex Alimentarius*, de champ restreint, telles celles sur les "Saumons du Pacifique, éviscérés, surgelés" sont parvenues rapidement à leur version finale sans grande discussion. Malgré la restriction à un seul produit préparé dans une aire géographique limitée, la norme pourrait être admise mondialement. A ceux qui s'inquièteraient d'une prolifération excessive des normes, nous proposons de réunir tout d'abord dans une sorte de répertoire les n variantes possibles de caractères qui sont rencontrés dans un ensemble de produits similaires (répertoire que nous avons appelé 'norme tribale'), puis un ensemble de produits similaires (répertoire que nous avons appelé 'norme tribale'), puis de faire des normes spécifiques pour chaque produit en reprenant dans la liste des éléments qui le caractérisent et qui correspondent aux habitudes d'un certain marché.

Le *Codex Alimentarius* ainsi conçu se diversifierait pour répondre à la diversité naturelle des produits aussi bien qu'à celle des goûts et des couleurs que nous nous sommes plus à souligner. Il pourrait tenir compte de la variété des situations: espèces de poisson (il y en très peu qui soient universelles), population concernée, degré d'évolution des techniques. Les normes auraient d'abord valeur d'information. Elles seraient pour chaque produit une codification des usages loyaux et constants sur les lieux de production. Elles apporteraient au consommateur des garanties sur la valeur nutritive et hygiénique aussi bien que sur les qualités gustatives et esthétiques. Elles tireraient leur force du fait que ces usages seraient reconnus universellement. En se limitant à un produit préparé dans une aire géographique limitée, elles laisseraient sur le marché une grande variété de produits entre lesquels le consommateur aurait toute latitude de choix au lieu d'être contraint d'accepter une marchandise préparée pour être conforme à un modèle uniformément admis dans le monde, mais qui ne répond pas forcément à ses goûts. Les normes descriptives seraient complétées par les codes d'usage. Ceux-ci auraient à enseigner comment les grands principes d'hygiène et de technologie doivent être appliqués selon les espèces traitées et le climat, pour obtenir les différentes caractéristiques des produits faisant l'objet de normes. De plus, ils seraient un guide pour la préparation des produits ayant un marché trop restreint pour faire l'objet d'une norme internationale. Ils apporteraient ainsi indirectement une partie des garanties que le consommateur peut attendre de la normalisation.

N'oublions pas que le nombre des produits qui ont été sélectionnés pour être normalisés par la Commission du *Codex Alimentarius* est très faible par rapport à ce qui se fabrique dans le monde. Quelle que soit l'importance de ces produits, et la diligence avec laquelle les Comités du *Codex* parviendront à rédiger les normes qui les concernent, il y aura encore, pendant très longtemps des produits en circulation qui seront, au mieux, définis par une norme nationale. Pendant toute cette période, l'engagement d'un pays à fabriquer selon un code d'usage, préparé et admis par les meilleurs experts mondiaux comme ceux qui ont été faits par le Département des Pêches de la FAO, constituera une garantie non négligeable de la qualité des denrées alimentaires mises à la disposition du consommateur. Ceci nous paraît essentiel. Car, si l'on peut discuter de la manière de faire des normes, du champ à leur donner ou même de l'opportunité d'en faire, la masse des consommateurs est pratiquement unanime à demander des garanties de qualité pour sa nourriture, plus particulièrement en matière de produits de la pèche. En effet, en dehors des populations vivant au bord de la mer, des lacs ou des grands fleuves, les connaisseurs dans ce domaine où les ressources sont extrêmement variées sont peu nombreux. L'acheteur moyen, connaissant mal la denrée, est toujours un peiu inquiet de savoir s'il obtenir le mets délicieux dont on lui a vanté les mérites, car tout en sachant que les produits de la pêche s'attèrent facilement à l'état frais et que les caractères gustatifs varient beaucoup d'une espèce à l'autre, il craint de ne distinguer ni l'état de fraîcheur, ni l'espèce. Fraîcheur au moment de la préparation et identité d'espèce sont bien en effet selon nous, les exigences majeures de qualité aussi bien pour les profanes que pour les initiés. Pour le reste, les choix varient comme nous l'avons vu. Bien qu'ils soient inspirés par les mèmes préoccupations, ils aboutissent à des classements de valeur différents suivant les marchés. Nous devrions nous réjouir de cet état de fait, puisque, moyennant des échanges appropriés, cela permet une utilisation plus large des ressources aquatiques.

Utilization of Mechanically Separated Fish Flesh— Canadian Experience   *C M Blackwood*

Utilisation de la chair de poisson separee mecaniquement— experience canadienne

Dans le présent document, on décrit les résultats obtenus su Canada dans la séparation mécanique de la chair du poisson et la mise au point de produits de consommation à partir de cette denrée. On étudie l'utilisation des espèces sous-exploitées et des déchets de parage des produits classqiues, susceptibles de servir de matière première pour l'obtention de chair hachée, et on analyse les besoins de normalisation, de description et d'établissement de spécifications d'identité des produits, ainsi que la nécessité de procéder à des contrôles de qualité pour garantir la salubrité des produits de consommation ainsi préparés. On présente des données sur les procédés de transformation, ainsi que sur la qualité des produits du point de vue bactériologique.

Utilizacion de la carne de pescado separada mecanicamente—la experiencia canadiense

Se describe en este trabajo la experiencia canadiense con la separación mecánica de carne del pescado y la preparación de productos a partir de la misma. Se estudian el empleo de especies subexplotadas y desechos de los productos tradicionales como materia prima para la preparación de carne picada, las normas de calidad del producto, su descripción e identificación y la necesidad de controlar la calidad para que el consumidor esté seguro de que obtiene un producto sano. Se presentan datos sobre los métodos de elaboración y la calidad bacteriológica.

In recent years the increased worldwide demand for animal protein, and the overexploitation of certain traditional species of fish, have led to rapid developments in techniques for higher recovery of fish flesh for human consumption and pressure to increase sources of raw materials. Specialized equipment has been developed to attain a greater yield for species commonly utilized for human food and to permit utilization of species which do not readily lend themselves to such use by conventional processing methods. It is only in very recent years that mechanical fish flesh separators, such as Bibun, Baader, Paoli, and Iwema, have been introduced into Canada for the preparation of minced or comminuted fish flesh. Approximately forty plants were using such equipment in 1972 and there has been an appreciable increase in 1973. As this rapid expansion takes place, special consideration is being given to quality control, product standardization, and product description and identity. The raw material for minced flesh must be of a quality suitable for marketing as fresh fish. In order to ensure high market acceptability, this process must not become a salvage operation for fish otherwise unacceptable due to spoilage, abnormal physiological conditions and parasitic infestation. The mechanical separation of fish flesh in Canada has been used for marine fish, crustacea and freshwater fish.

MARINE FISH

The mechanical separation of fish flesh began as a more profitable utilization of V-cuts and other trimmings from fillets. In most of the larger filleting and freezing plants, this has now become an established practice. Fish frames are also used in some instances. At the present time some, plants are also utilizing headless dressed fish for this process. Minced flesh is packed in blocks of 6.13 and 7.50 kg for export. However, a growing number of plants are further processing the flesh into consumer products. Problems with organoleptic and microbiological quality occurred early in the development of this process. There were instances where V-cuts and other trimmings were held at room temperature up to 12 h prior to processing. In some instances all types of trimmings, including those with heavy bruises and blood spots, were used. In addition, the importance of frequent and thorough cleaning of the equipment was not recognized by some in the industry. Although this process lends itself to many abuses and difficulties, it is possible to produce products of very high organoleptic and microbiological quality. A comparison was made of the microbiological data from two plants using similar facilities and raw materials. Plant A used only first quality trimmings which were processed, packaged and placed in the freezer within 2 h. The equipment was washed at hourly intervals and, in addition, was dismantled, cleaned and disinfected at least once each 8 h work shift. In Plant B, trimmings often contained bruises and blood clots and were held up to 4 h before separation. An additional 3 h elapsed prior to packaging and placing in the freezer. The equipment was not hosed down frequently and was not as carefully cleaned. Of 56 samples analysed at Plant A, the average Standard Plate Count (SPC)/g at 25°C was 67,000. One sample only was positive for faecal coliforms and had a Most Probable Number (MPN) of 20/100 g. From Plant B, 13 samples were analysed and the corresponding SPC result was 1.5 million/g.

On the 13 samples, 8 were positive for faecal coliforms. The average MPN of the positives was 41/110 g. This example illustrates the effectiveness of proper quality control in the production of this type of product. The accumulated results of over 500 analyses of products from 28 plants showed that 60 per cent had an SPC at 25°C of less than 1 million/g, and 80 per cent less than 2 million/g. The faecal coliform results showed that 84 per cent of the samples had an MPN of less than 100/100 g and 93 per cent less than 360/100 g. Coagulase positive staphylococci have not presented problems in minced blocks or in final consumer products. Experience gained in the use of the various types of equipment has eliminated problems arising from the presence of bones and scales in separated flesh. A common defect found in products from all types of recovery equipment was brown discolouration. The degree of discolouration varied from very slight to very pronounced, depending upon the number of blood clots and bruises present in the raw material. Pigmentation from black nape also affected appearance unless it was removed from the raw material. The organoleptic quality of the product was directly related to that of the raw material used and may be adversely affected by delays in processing and failure to maintain suitable temperatures.

CRUSTACEANS

In the crustacean industry (particularly lobster) it was long recognized that a satisfactory recovery of meat was not possible by using traditional manual shucking procedures. Now that mechanical separators have become available, a significant increase in yield has been attained, recovered from those segments of lobster which were previously discarded. Traditionally lobster paste has been prepared from "clean, sound roe, green liver and lobster meat free from inedible parts". The material recovered from parts of the lobster body previously discarded is suitable for incorporation into paste. However, the presence of residues, such as gill fragments and cartilage and shell particles, can be a problem. It is essential that, for paste containing such recovered flesh, standards be developed to maintain the high reputation of this product. Laboratory procedures are being developed for the detection of particles of gills, cartilage, and shell in the product. The small amount of production which has thus far taken place in Canada has demonstrated that a microbiologically satisfactory product can be produced if good quality control is exercised. As in the case of marine fish, a comparison of processing plants indicates that microbiological quality can be associated with plant sanitation and operation. In general, the end product is of a puree consistency with an odour and flavour characteristic of the species. In addition to its use in paste, this material lends itself to inclusion in such products as chowders, soups and bisques. The production of mechanically separated flesh of crab is still in its infancy in Canada. However, there is evidence of problems with shell particles and discolouration. Standards for this product will also have to be developed in the near future.

FRESHWATER FISH

Mechanical recovery of fish flesh from freshwater species not previously entering into commercial trade promises to be a very significant development in Canada. Historically, species such as whitefish, pickerel and lake trout have been the mainstay of the freshwater fishing industry. Species which abound in Canadian lakes, such as mullet, maria and sheeps-head, have been greatly underutilized. In the last two years mechanical recovery equipment has been used for processing them. There does not appear to be any significant difference between the proximate composition of fillets and minced flesh prepared from the same fish, as may be seen in Table 1. The process involves the prompt beheading and dressing of the fish and thorough cleaning of the belly cavity to remove all traces of kidney, air bladder and blood. This necessitates manual scraping along the backbone or the use of equipment which has been designed to do this operation. The fish are then split longitudinally, either manually or mechanically, and thoroughly washed in a rotary or high pressure washer. The fish halves are next put through equipment which separates the flesh from the skin and bones. The processing of whole fish instead of trimmings has the advantage of being the primary usage for the raw material and, therefore, lends itself to more effective quality control. The flesh, often referred to as comminuted or minced, is expeditiously and continuously formed into blocks and frozen without delay. As in the case of marine products, the chief defect was found to be discolouration. This problem can be minimized if the kidney, air bladder, and any excess blood are carefully removed. As in the instance cited for marine species, it could be demonstrated that where effective quality control was exercised, it was practicable to process a product of very high bacteriological quality. Of 24 samples tested from one plant which had a good quality control programme, 19 had an SPC of less than 50,000/g, and of the five exceeding this number the highest was 77,000/g. Only one sample was positive for faecal coliforms. The results from over 400 bacteriological analyses showed that 42 per cent had an SPC at 25°C of less than 100 thousand/g and 61 per cent less than 250 thousand/g.

TABLE 1. PROXIMATE COMPOSITION OF FILLETS AND MINCED FLESH (FRESHWATER SPECIES)

Proximate Composition	Whitefish (Coregonus clupeaformis)		Mullet (Catostomus sp.)		Northern Pike (Esox lucius)	
	Fillets	Minced Flesh	Fillets	Minced Flesh	Fillets	Minced Flesh
Moisture	79,.0	77.8	79.7	81.3	78.9	80.2
Protein (NX6.25)	17.2	15.7	16.6	14.7	19.4	17.2
Ash	1.2	1.0	1.6	0.9	1.2	1.0
Fat	2.3	2.9	3.1	2.9	1.9	1.8

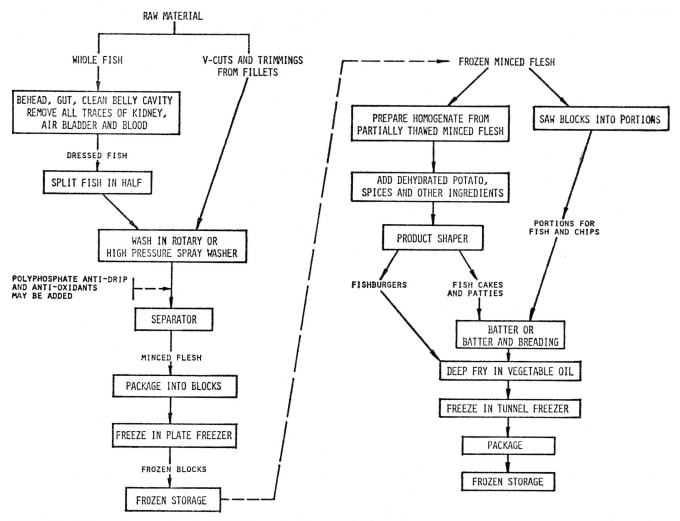

Fig 1. Flow diagram for processing of minced flesh

The faecal coliform results showed that 62 per cent had less than 20/100 g and 92 per cent had less than 230/100 g.

PRODUCTS PREPARED FROM MINCED FLESH

Minced flesh is generally frozen into blocks for further processing into convenience consumer products. The raw material utilized to date includes headless dressed ocean perch, gray cod, pink salmon; trimmings from halibut, various species of salmon, cod, haddock, pollock and flat fish. The increased yield from V-cuts and trimmings from such species as cod and haddock averages 8 to 10 per cent. To date, the greatest development in the processing of minced flesh from headless dressed fish has occurred in the freshwater fishery. Species being used include mullet, carp, sheepshead, tullibee, maria, whitefish, northern pike and bass. Certain of these species are utilized only to a very limited extent for processing into conventional products. Yields from dressed freshwater species range from 64 to 78 per cent. Minced flesh offers great opportunity for the preparation of new, imaginative, high quality fishery products tailored to the requirements of a wide range of consumers. Examples of products being produced in Canada include hors d'oeuvres, such as 'Party Starters', with shrimp, crab, oyster and onion flavours. Other more traditional type products are fish cakes and patties, fishburgers, fish and chips, and fish portions. Ingredients added to the minced flesh include cereal products, dehydrated potato, spices, skim milk powder, and egg powder. The fish content of the final product is about 60 per cent by weight. The important steps in the preparation of minced flesh and its further processing into typical products for the Canadian consumer are shown in Figure 1. This processing should be carried out as an integral part of the overall plant operation and not as some type of makeshift arrangement. In view of the importance of minced flesh in international trade, consideration is being given by the Codex Committee on Fish and Fishery Products to the elaboration of a standard for blocks of minced flesh. In addition, the Fishery Industries Division of FAO's Department of Fisheries is considering the development of a Code of Practice for their processing. The products prepared from minced flesh appear to be receiving good consumer acceptance in Canada. For example, sales of such products from one plant increased by 52 per cent in 1972 and have shown an additional 48 per cent increase so far in 1973. Supply generally has not kept up with demand.

PRODUCT DESCRIPTION AND IDENTITY

Separated material for further processing

Up to the present time the tendency has been to use trimmings, V-cuts or dressed fish of a single species to produce the intermediate product, which is frozen in plastic bags or conventional rectangular blocks. In this case, there is no identity problem in terms of naming the fish component. The terms now in use to describe and distinguish separated flesh blocks from fillet blocks include 'comminuted', 'grated', 'minced', 'pureed' and 'pressed'. From a control agency's view point it can be said that all but the last imply a product of small particle size and, when combined with the common name for the species, accurately describes the products. However, the type of equipment used and varying processing treatments can result in a separate product that ranges from semi-fluid to reasonably dry, discerned muscle fibres. Because of the small particle size the product is susceptible to water absorption during processing or the intentional addition of water. For this reason, composition standards may be required to limit moisture and provide for a minimum protein content.

In order to take full advantage of the opportunities offered by flesh separators, consideration has been given to the possibility of permitting blocks to be produced from two or more species of fish that are similar in terms of flesh colour, texture, odour and flavour. Experience has shown that in similar species of fish, the factors, both real and fancied, that result in consumer product identification by species largely disappear in mechanically separated flesh and are further masked in final products. Flesh separators will undoubtedly encourage increased harvesting of a number of underutilized species that are not individually available in quantities sufficient for conventional utilization. For example, the group of rockfish off Canada's West Coast has some 15 to 20 subspecies but because of the mixed catches taken, it is not economical to process, package and label them on an individual basis. However, as they are similar in terms of flesh colour, texture, odour and flavour, blocks prepared from mixed species are very little different from those prepared from any of the individual species in the group. 'Minced rockfish blocks' is considered an adequate description for this product. Similarly, it makes economic sense to permit industry to mix in blocks material recovered from V-cuts, trimmings, etc., from fish of different species, but again only if the flesh being used is similar in respect to texture, odour and flavour. An example of such species might be a combination of cod, haddock, cusk, hake, and perhaps one or more of the flounders.

The problem is, how could or should this type of product be controlled and be identified in a manner that can be carried through in a meaningful way to consumers? There are at present two schools of thought on this subject, with the first favouring standardization by regulation. This would involve introducing requirements which would specify the combinations of fish that could be used in a single block and acceptable common names that could be used for such combinations. For example, either of the terms 'groundfish' or 'white fish' might be considered acceptable for a block containing any one or all of cod, haddock, hake, cusk, or flounder. The other

approach would regulate the species that may be combined in a block, but would require all of the species that might be included in a particular type of block to be listed on the container either as 'Cod and/or haddock and/or hake, etc.', or in descending order of proportion. The group name approach through regulatory standards appears most practical in terms of providing the flexibility needed by the industry and would become meaningful to consumers. This type of regulatory standard could also cover food additives, such as protein extenders, flavours, drip inhibitors, preservatives and colours which may become desirable or necessary as the range of products develops.

Consumer products

Traditionally, an appropriate name for the species of fish used has been shown on consumer packages, usually as part of the common name, eg, 'cod fish sticks'. In a few instances where the fish component loses its identity through mixing with other ingredients, eg, 'fish cakes', the species identification appears only in the ingredients list, with the product name appearing as 'fish cakes'. With the introduction of new products, prepared from separated fish flesh having attractive but non-descriptive names, such as 'Fischimo' and 'Party Starters', control agencies are faced with the problem of establishing labelling requirements that would be factual and meaningful to the consumer. In addition, separated flesh blocks can be used to produce conventional products, such as fish sticks and breaded portions which had previously been prepared from fillet blocks. Canada has not yet regulated the labelling of these products except for a provision passed some years ago prohibiting the preparation of fish sticks from comminuted fish flesh. The labelling problem for products prepared from minced flesh blocks of a single species is relatively straightforward. Using 'Fischimo' as an example, the product name would be Fishimo with the term 'prepared from minced fish' shown immediately adjacent to the name. The list of ingredients would contain all in the product in descending order of proportion and show 'minced mullet flesh' in the appropriate place in the listing. For a product such as fish cakes, or fish croquettes, where the name itself clearly indicates the nature of the product, it would be quite acceptable to indicate only in the ingredients list that the product was made from minced fish flesh of the appropriate species.

The question of meaningful consumer labelling for products prepared from minced flesh of several species is more difficult. Control agencies could adopt the attitude that the consumer is entitled to know precisely what the fish content comprises and require that each species be shown in descending order of its proportion. This would result in industry adopting practices which are harmful to quality and not in the best interest of the consumer. The new generation of convenience foods being developed from minced fish flesh requires a departure from tradition by industry and control agencies. The supply and demand situation points to the need for maximum utilization of available fish supplies, and products derived from minced flesh, should occupy the same relative position with respect to fillets as hamburger does to a fillet steak. However, the consumer will have to be 'sold' on these products on the basis that they are innovative, wholesome, high quality, convenient-to-use fishery products. The emphasis should be on the development of new products rather than the imitation of existing ones; presentations to the consumer should feature fish as a nutritious, interesting, high quality food. Estimates of world fish stocks show a potential for increased catches of some 40 million t. Much of this potential, however, is made up of little known species that are either not suited for the production of traditional products or cannot be processed in traditional ways. Fish flesh separators offer an answer to their utilization, and make possible the production of high quality fish protein

material for further processing. The challenge facing industry is to develop wholesome, superior quality, tasty, attractive, convenient-to-use fishery products from this starting material.

Acknowledgements

Appreciation is expressed to various members of the Inspection Branch, Fisheries and Marine Service, Department of the Environment—specifically to G G Anderson, R M Bond, O M Linton and Z A Navratil for their contribution to this paper. The assistance of Canadian fish processors is also gratefully acknowledged.

Considerations in the Use of Tropical Fish Species
J G Disney, R C Cole and N R Jones

Considerations sur l'utilisation des poissons tropicaux

Les auteurs passent en revue les problèmes particuliers que pose l'utilisation des poissons tropicaux et attirent l'attention sur certaines différences qui distinguent ces derniers des espèces d'eau froide, notamment beaucoup plus longue durée de conservation et nombre total de bactéries relativement moins élevé à la température de la glace. Etant donné que la réfrigération des poissons tropicaux a davantage fait l'objet de recherches récentes, que d'autres techniques, les auteurs traitent essentiellement de cette méthode. La congélation, le séchage, le salage, le fumage et d'autres techniques de transformation ne sont qu'effleurées. La pénurie de renseignements sur l'application de la technologie moderne aux poissons tropicaux est soulignée. Divers thèmes sont proposés pour la recherche appliquée.

Consideraciones sobre el aprovechamiento de peces tropicales

Se examinan los problemas especiales que plantea el aprovechamiento de peces tropicales y se señalan algunas de las diferencias existentes entre los peces tropicales y las especies de aguas frías, entre ellas su duración mucho mayor en almacén y el número total relativamente menor de bacterias a la temperatura del hielo. Dado que recientemente se han hecho más investigaciones sobre enfriado de peces tropicales que sobre cualquier otra tecnología, los autores se han concentrado en torno a este aspecto. Se examinan brevísimamente la congelación, secado, salazón, ahumado y otras técnicas de elaboración y se pone de relieve la escasez de información sobre aplicación de tecnologías modernas a especies de peces tropicales. Se sugieren diversas vías para la investigación aplicada.

The consumption of fish is relatively high in the Far East and very low in the Near East, India and in many landlocked countries. It is a popular food in West Africa, the Caribbean, the Pacific Islands and the maritime South American countries. Several tropical countries are involved in the increasing international trade in processed fish, and the economic value of this trade is important. Within a country there can be a balance of priorities between protein deficiency problems and the demand for foreign exchange. Another important consideration in fisheries development is the desire of countries to make greater use of, and exert more control over, their fish resources. There is a growing awareness of the possibilities of modern industrial fishing and the need to improve the technology of fish capture, processing, distribution, etc. Thus problems in the development of fish processing and preservation fall into two broad categories.

(a) There is the need to meet the nutritional requirements of the producer country. This can involve the improvement of traditional techniques, and the introduction of other techniques, such as the use of ice, freezing, canning, etc.,

(b) There is a desire to export. This can present problems, such as differing patterns of consumer acceptance or the need to meet quality standards despite a lack of technical background.

These problems can be exacerbated when consumer countries introduce quality and public health controls applicable at the point of production. In both categories, production can be hampered by the lack of application of established technology or by a lack of relevant in-

formation. Much of the technology of developed fisheries is applicable to developing tropical fisheries, but some attempts to apply the results of work on temperate or cold water species to tropical species may well fail for lack of basic understanding of spoilage parameters. The development of fish preservation in some tropical countries has followed very closely that in cold water fisheries. There has been very little research, however, on the evaluation of control parameters in the preservation, handling and processing of tropical species or to relate these to acceptability and the economics of production and marketing. The dearth of information on the preservation of tropical fish is reflected in the recent literature. For instance, in the three conferences organized by FAO in recent years (Husum 1965, Madrid 1967, and Halifax 1969), over 200 papers were presented of which only 10 related specifically to tropical species (other than the tunas). This paper considers various techniques of fish preservation available to tropical countries in the light of existing information and attempts to identify situations differing significantly from those of cold and temperate fisheries. Since the use of ice in the tropics has been studied more than other forms of fish preservation, more space is devoted to this aspect than to others. Recent research on tropical fish preservation, offering possibilities for improving commercial practice, is also discussed.

ICING

Kreuzer (1971) and Jones (1969) referred to the lack of knowledge on the bacteriology and biochemistry of

TABLE 1. SHELF LIFE OF FISH STORED IN ICE

Fish (Common Name)	Length of Acceptable Storage (days)	Reference	Notes
TEMPERATURE AND COLD WATER			
Marine			
Cod	12–15	⎫	
Haddock	12–15	⎪	Most flat fish keep
Whiting	9–12	⎬FAO, 1968b	better than round fish
Hake	8–10	⎪	
Redfish	13–15	⎭	
Herring	5–6	Stroud (1972)	Fatty fish spoil more
Mackerel	7–9	Fraser *et al.* (1968)	quickly than lean
Freshwater			
Yellow Walleye (Canadian)	20	Dugal (1967)	Fatty fish spoil
Whitefish	18	Bligh (1969)	more quickly than
Trout (Europe)	10	Hansen (1972)	lean
TROPICAL			
Marine			
Snapper (Brazil)	11–16	Watanabe (1961)	N.B. Subtropical water temperature 20°C
Tuna (USA)	29	Crawford and Finch (1968)	
Pomfret ⎫			
Mackerel ⎪			Acceptable quality
Horse mackerel ⎬(India)	7–45	Velankar and Kamasastri (1956)	based upon trimethyl-amine values
Seer fish ⎪			
Perch ⎭			
Synagris japonicus (India)	27	Govindan (1971)	
Bonga ⎫	290		
Sea bream ⎬(West Africa)	26	Amu and Disney (1973)	
Bumper ⎪			
Burrito ⎭			
Mixed species (West Africa)	17–20	Aldrin *et al.* (1970)	Acceptable quality based upon total volatile base estimation
Freshwater			
Mrigal carp (India)	35	Balakrishnan Nair *et al.* (1970)	
Tilapia (East Africa)	28	Disney *et al.* (1969)	
Nile perch ⎫			
Bagrus ⎬(East Africa)	20–28	Hoffman *et al.* (1973)	
Lung fish ⎭			

chilled tropical fish and this was illustrated by a recent FAO publication 'Ice in Fisheries' (prepared at the request of the Indo-Pacific Fisheries Council) in which the authors indicated that it was written without any relevant information on tropical fisheries. It is desirable that tropical countries with an interest in the use of chilling techniques should arrange for iced storage trials to be carried out on potentially important species at the outset of development programmes. The limited amount of evidence which is available suggests that many tropical species have much longer keeping times in ice than do temperate or cold water species and thus the choice of preservation technique in relation to time scale may differ also.

The storage life in melting ice of temperate and cold water marine fish is well documented, rarely extending beyond 15 days for round fish, and frequently far less (Table 1). The spoilage of freshwater fish from cold waters is less well documented but as a general rule they tend to have a longer storage life in ice than do marine fish. For some time it has been considered that fish from tropical waters might benefit from storage in ice more than fish from colder waters. Spoilage bacteria in tropical fish would presumably not be adapted to low tem-

peratures so well as those from colder waters. The results of the limited number of investigations carried out on tropical fish support this view. Investigations on marine fish in the tropics have been restricted largely to India, Sri Lanka and West Africa whilst the work on freshwater fish relates mainly to India and East Africa. As with temperate and cold water species, the keeping time in ice varies considerably between different species, depending largely on the fat content and the degree to which fat oxidation is a problem. From the limited information available, it would appear that tropical fish have a much longer shelf life in ice than temperate or cold water species. At ambient temperatures, by comparison, tropical fish spoil very rapidly, often within 24 hours – for example, Disney *et al.* (1969, 1973) have reported that 1 hour at ambient temperatures for East African freshwater fish is roughly equivalent to 1 day's storage in ice.

The effect of gutting

It is generally accepted that temperature or cold water fish, with the exception of fatty fish, keep better in ice when they are gutted (Bramsnaes 1965). Little work has been reported on tropical species other than tuna but

Lantz and Gunasekara (1965) concluded that the quality of 8 species of fish from Sri Lanka was improved as a result of gutting. Watanabe (1965–66) investigating Kariba bream (*Tilapia*) found that gutting did improve quality during ice storage, but pointed out that gutting and good washing would be very difficult in an artisanal type of fishery. This agrees with our own findings on East African freshwater fish (Disney *et al.* 1969) that gutting marginally extends the shelf life of iced *Tilapia* but the improvement does not justify commercial gutting, particularly as it would be difficult to implement and local custom demands whole fish. Further work is needed on any benefits to be derived from the gutting of tropical fish but it would appear that the species and local consumer demand will be a major factor. The difficulties in an artisanal fishery argue against it unless the benefits can be shown to be very substantial.

Bacteriological considerations

The quantitative and qualitative changes occurring during the iced storage of temperate and cold water fish, such as cod, have been studied widely. In a recent review, Shewan (1971) indicated that in cod there is a lag period of 2 to 3 days followed by a logarithmic increase in bacterial numbers until the tenth day when there is a total count of 10^8 organisms per square centimetre of skin or per gramme of muscle. Other quantitative studies on temperate and cold water species, eg, trout (*Salmo trutta*) and herring (*Clupea harengus*) (Hansen 1972), plaice (*Pleuronectes platessa*) and haddock (*Melanogramus aeglefinus*) (Huss 1972) confirm this general pattern, although counts as high as 10^9 per gram of flesh have been reported. Freshwater fish appear to follow a different pattern; surface slime seems to promote bacterial growth up to 10^{10} organisms per gramme after 6 days at $3°C$ (Bligh 1969, Gillespie and Ostavar 1971) whereas flesh counts remain relatively low. These findings would seem to support the view that freshwater fish have a different type of spoilage microflora (Bramstedt and Auerbach 1961). By comparison few quantitative bacteriological studies have been carried out on iced tropical fish but total viable counts appear to be considerably lower than in cold water species. This is probably related to the extended shelf life of tropical fish. Also the pattern of microbial growth in freshwater fish does not seem to be much different from that of marine species. Velankar and Kamasastri (1956) found that microbiological deterioration was slower and less pronounced in several species of Indian marine fish than that reported for cod. Watanabe (1961) reported bacterial counts of 10^8 per square centimetre of skin in Brazilian fish after 19 days storage in ice, although these fish may be regarded as sub-tropical rather than tropical. Subsequently the same author investigated the spoilage of Zambian freshwater fish (Watanabe 1965–66) and found that the growth rates of bacteria at $0°C$ on Kariba bream (*Tilapia*) were considerably slower than those on Brazilian marine fish. An Indian study on freshwater carp (Balakrishnan Nair *et al.* 1971) reported total viable counts of 10^6 or 10^7 organisms per square centimetre of skin and 10^3 organisms per gramme of flesh after 21 days storage in ice (Tropical Products Institute, unpublished). A study of West African marine fish mentioned earlier

(Amu and Disney 1973) found total viable counts of 10^5 to 10^6 organisms per gramme of muscle at the limit of acceptable storage (20 to 26 days). Although relatively few detailed studies have been reported, it would appear that the extended shelf life of tropical fish is due at least in part to greater effect of ice temperatures on tropical microflora than those attacking temperate and cold water species. Deterioration of fish during iced storage arises primarily from the activities of bacterial and autolytic enzymes. The smaller bacterial population observed in tropical fish could indicate either that the smaller population produces very active proteolytic enzymes, the bacteria actually responsible for spoilage being present at the limit of acceptability in similar numbers to those of cold water species, or that autolytic spoilage plays a more significant role in tropical fish. The spoilage of tropical fish without temperature control is very rapid, for example, *Tilapia* becomes inedible some 15 to 20 hours after death when the total viable counts is in the order of 10^3 to 10^5 organisms per gramme of tissue. Only detailed investigations on the qualitative bacterial changes during storage and an investigation of the autolytic enzymes involved can resolve this problem, but the possibility of such a fundamental difference between cold water and tropical fish certainly warrants some further investigation.

Qualitative bacteriological changes during iced storage have been studied in both tropical and cold water species of fish, and the groups of organisms involved in spoilage appear to be similar. The methods of identification and general taxonomic situation are not generally regarded as entirely satisfactory (Shewan 1971, Liston 1960, Da Silva and Mendez 1963, Karthiayani and Mahadeva 1963, Velankar and Kamasastri 1956, Watanabe 1965–66). In spoiling cod, the pseudomonads constitute 90 per cent of the total flora after 12 days storage in ice (Shewan 1971). From the inoculation of sterile pieces of muscle from freshly killed fish, it has been established that only a small percentage of these are actually involved in spoilage. The active spoilage organisms occur in very small numbers in the slime of newly caught fish and are absent from the flesh. The microbial spoilage of fish muscle may not necessarily be related to the skin flora since the ability to penetrate the skin has been found to be restricted to a few species. Qualitative studies carried out on West African sea bream (Tropical Products Institute, unpublished) have shown that the predominant organisms on the skin are pseudomonad species but the dominant species in the flesh throughout storage were of the *Moraxella* genus (gramme-negative coccobacilli). Similar studies on *Tilapia* have found that the early predominance of micrococci and staphylococci is replaced by pseudomonads. Valenkar and Kamasastri (1956), after investigating bacterial spoilage in several Indian marine fish, found that the generic succession during the course of spoilage, referred to above, only occurred in one of their experiments. This was attributed to the influence of environmental factors on the bacterial flora of the fresh material. However, a generic succession of the type found in cod has been reported by Da Silva and Mendez (1963) and Wood (1949), although the latter found that the dominant species during spoilage of elasmobranchs were gramme-positive organisms of the type which are only present in significant numbers in teleost fish during the early stages of spoilage. Further qualitative studies on tropical fish are required.

Inspection and quality control

Most of the publications referring to tropical fish which which have been mentioned in this paper have included work on the microbiological or chemical assessment of fish quality storage in ice. Estimations of pH, trimethylamine, total volatile bases, hypoxanthine and others have been carried out on tropical fish, but there appears to be no general difference from temperate or cold water species. All of the tests examined to date have serious defects as quality control techniques, and no really effective objective test has yet been developed. Although continuing to develop satisfactory chemical tests for quality is fully justified, particularly in countries with important export industries, this is not the shorter term need in tropical countries. Of more immediate importance is the need to determine precisely the physical and organoleptic changes that can form the basis of a fish inspection system. It is apparent that standards of microbiological control (other than those of public health significance) may well require to be different from those for non-tropical fisheries (see also below).

Commercial implications

The differences between tropical and temperate or cold water fish species, illustrated above, have many commercial implications. It is perhaps unfortunate that the lines of research and development of fish preservation in some tropical countries have so closely followed those of developed countries with an interest primarily in cold water fisheries (Jones 1969). This has retarded the rational improvement of traditional processing and preservation techniques for, although many of the principles of modern fish technology may be applicable to tropical fisheries, all techniques must be considered in the light of local climatic and socio-economic conditions, and the innate properties of the species available.

The extended shelf life in ice of tropical fish could have a significant effect upon the pattern of fish distribution. An acceptable storage life of 3–4 weeks should be sufficient to permit extended periods of fishing, distribution over considerable distances or the provision of short-term buffer stocks in cases of shortage due to bad weather, etc. In certain situations the long shelf life may favour the establishment of a distribution network of iced fish rather than the development of a central freezing facility and frozen distribution network (but see also below). Unfortunately the benefits of iced storage may be severely reduced in practice by the methods of fish capture. Delays prior to the application of ice can occur during high catching rates or as a result of the fishing techniques. For example, the use of fixed gillnets in many African lake fisheries results in dead fish hanging in the net for many hours and a fair proportion of the fish are partially spoiled before they are landed. A modification of the fishing technique, such as the more regular removal of fish from the net, could solve this problem, although fishermen are reluctant to change their traditional mode of fishing.

Most of the work on iced storage of tropical fish refers to the application of ice immediately after capture, which is rarely possible under practical commercial situations, particularly in artisanal fisheries. In tropical countries, the application of ice after a limited period of spoilage at ambient temperature is a more likely commercial possibility but there have been few investigations on this. Antunnes *et al.* (1971) found that the bacterial population increased during several hours on deck prior to icing and recommended a maximum period of 1 hour, but fish held for 6 hours prior to icing had only 10^6 organisms per gramme of flesh after 10 days' storage in ice. Work carried out in India (CFTRI Annual Report 1969) on 2 species of freshwater fish has shown that fish kept at ambient temperatures for 6–8 hours prior to icing remain acceptable for 4 weeks. Similar work carried out by the present authors on *Tilapia* in Uganda has shown that a lapse of 6 hours prior to icing does not significantly reduce the length of acceptable storage in ice. If this is true for other species there would be no need to ice the fish immediately after capture in some fisheries; this could be done on loading. This could have enormous advantages in artisanal fisheries.

In tropical fisheries as others, the improvement in storage life and quality which may result from processes such as the use of ice, gutting, bleeding, hygienic handling, etc, must be balanced against the economic return in such changes. The question of consumer acceptance must also be considered since different peoples may have different preferences. The quality required for export can well be significantly different to that demanded by the local consumer and technological changes within the fishing industry have to be geared accordingly. The development of codes of practice and quality standards in tropical countries are all too frequently based upon those of more developed countries. This may be correct where fish exports are important but need not necessarily be best for the domestic fishery. Similarly, international codes of practice and quality standards, such as those being developed by Codex Alimentarius, are based almost entirely upon procedures used in developed countries, usually with cold water fisheries. This is understandable since the information relevant to tropical countries is just not available but some of the data presented in this paper, eg, the extended shelf life of tropical fish in ice and the relatively low bacterial counts, make the drawing-up of international standards much more difficult.

Methods of fish handling developed elsewhere will often be relevant to tropical conditions, but this should not be taken for granted. As indicated above, more information on the spoilage of tropical species at chill temperatures is needed, and where the development of a modern fishing industry in the tropics is planned, this information should be obtained for commercially important species before embarking upon major improvement schemes. Multilateral and national fisheries development projects in the tropics could well be employed to collect additional information on the processing and preservation of tropical fish.

SUPERCHILLING

There have been various approaches to the superchilling of fish in which the flesh temperature has been reduced to $-1°C$ and $-3°C$, (Carlson 1969 and Scarlatti 1965).

One of the earlier procedures involved the hermetic sealing of whole fish in galvanized iron boxes which were then cooled in a continuous stream of brine maintained at −2°C to −3°C. More recently, fish have been stored in ice initially and the temperature has been reduced subsequently. A consensus of opinion appears to be that temperatures of the order of −2°C can give a considerable extension of keeping time over fish maintained at 0°C in ice and that fish so prepared may be suitable for smoking. The economics of such preservation are debatable and present evidence would appear to indicate that any advantage in the introduction of such operations in developing countries is likely to be marginal. If the retarding effect on the microflora is primarily or partly related to temperature differential from ambient, one would expect the benefit in a tropical fishery to be small relative to that in a cold or temperate fishery.

FREEZING

Fish which has been properly frozen and stored with adequate precautions to prevent dehydration, oxidation and denaturation can remain in an edible condition for considerable periods. The storage life and the quality depend on the species, its physiological state and chemical composition at time of capture, treatment before freezing and the freezing and storing regimes to which it is subjected. A considerable body of experience has been built up in the last 40 years, largely concerned with the handling of cold water species destined for consumption in sophisticated markets. Two important exceptions to this general observation are the tunas and crustacea which are caught in the tropics or sub-tropics and frozen for subsequent sale in the markets of the developed world.

Little information is available for the majority of the edible species caught in tropical waters but the introduction of freezing and cold storage technology based on the methods employed in the developed countries has often not been considered to be a practical economic proposition for developing countries. Alternative methods of conserving fish, such as salting, drying and smoking, require little capital equipment, and the products are popular with consumers in many countries. Equipment for freezing and cold storage require considerable outlay of capital, and the maintenance of equipment and advanced technology may not be available. During the last decade a number of nations, often in conjunction with an international fishing company which possesses the required capital and technology, have developed an interest in exploiting tropical fishing grounds. Ranken (1969) and Kordyl and Karnicki (1969) have outlined some of the problems encountered in these fisheries, particularly perhaps when the catch is to be exported to developed countries. These usually involve the effect of higher ambient temperature upon fish spoilage. Some of the species taken in these fisheries are valued in the countries where the vessels engaged are owned, others are more popular in the countries bordering the fishing areas. This has resulted in an important marketing development in West Africa which is well described by Krone (1970). Ungutted fish, frozen by contact plate freezer, is landed in West African ports in blocks weighing 20 or 30 kg. Distribution is through a chain of cold stores from which the fish mammies, who are the tradi-

tional fishmongers, purchase their supplies. Transport is mainly in insulated but unrefrigerated trucks. The fish are sold whole, or partially thawed, and are thus a direct substitute for fresh fish. Considerable quantities are hot smoked before retail sale. The impact of this development on the West African countries can be judged from the fact that in 1967, about 120,000 t of frozen fish was landed in West African countries, mainly from foreign vessels. In Ghana, for example, these landings represented 27 per cent of the total marine fish production (Krone 1970). The success of these operations results from a concept in the marketing of sea-frozen fish differing from present markets in the West but reminiscent of earlier developments in, for instance, the United Kingdom. In the markets of Europe and North America, the demand is primarily for convenience foods, such as fillets and fish fingers, which are sold from refrigerated cabinets to buyers who possess domestic refrigerators. The African buyer seldom possesses a domestic refrigerator and prefers to buy intact fish. This is also the case in much of Asia and South America; the expectation of quality is thus very different in certain tropical and non-tropical markets. The availability of cold storage facilities in West Africa has encouraged some freezing of locally caught fish during the peak season for later sale in times of shortage. Subba Rao (1969) has reported that in urban areas of Sri Lanka, fish frozen and marketed in a few days is competitive in price with iced fish and is preferred by the consumers. Disney (1968) reports similar marketing methods for *Tilapia* in Uganda. According to Krone (1970), the costs of distributing fish in ice and freezing and then distributing frozen fish, are likely to prove little different. He points out that freezing and subsequent cold storage has the advantage of greater flexibility and suggests that a choice between the two systems will depend on consumer acceptability, available capital and managerial expertise, and structural factors rather than on direct cost comparisons. Fish handling systems which combine chilling in ice and subsequent storage in a refrigerated chamber are also possible but no information is as yet available.

Tuna

Most tuna is frozen at sea and the two main fishing methods (longline and purse seine) each impose peculiar handling problems. The purse seiner takes its catch at unpredictable intervals, in quantities of 20 tons or more, and this must be considered when designing the freezing plant (Ranken 1969). According to Ranken (1969), the conventional method of handling tuna is to cool it to as near the −1° as possible in chilled sea water. Salt is then added to the sea water at a rate of about 50 kg salt per ton of fish to produce a brine with freezing point of 13.5°C. The brine and fish are cooled until the fish reaches −7.8°C or lower. The brine is then drained out and the fish is stored dry at a temperature not higher than 12°C. Each operation takes about 24 hours on normal sizes of tuna. In more modern vessels, lower brine temperatures are used and the fish may be cooled to −15°C before draining the brine. Tuna often weigh over 100 lb (45 kg) and consequently they freeze slowly. There is also some salt uptake from the brine but since the fish are used almost exclusively for canning, this is not too objectionable. Crawford *et al.* (1969) reported that there are definite, but not vast, quality advantages to be gained by rapidly freezing tuna in refrigerant 12 (dichlorodifluoromethane) rather than by good brine freezing. Improved quality and the apparently high yield gained by refrigerant 12 freezing would be a very favourable economic consideration, but there were apparently some problems with blood streaks and scorch. Tuna longliners catch fish singly and may expect to catch 10 to 12 tons over a period of 18 hours. Individual fish may weigh several hundred pounds. The fish may have been dead in water at 30°C for some hours before landing, or they may be freshly dead. The slower catching rate permits gutting, gilling and washing the fish before they are frozen. Since some of the frozen tuna sold in Japan is eaten as fresh or raw fish, salt uptake and discolouration would be objectionable. The Japanese thus freeze in air blast tunnels operated at temperatures down to −50°C and storage temperatures of −35°C are recommended (Bito, 1964). Two major problems have arisen in canning frozen tuna. Honeycombing, a condition in which the flakes of canned fish are perforated by small holes, is caused by fish which were partially spoiled (Nagaoka *et al.* 1971). The serious problem of 'green tuna', which is associated with the chemical modification of the haem pigment, is less easily solved. The green discolouration appears only after cooking and cannot be predicted from visual examination of the raw fish. In practice, processors commonly test small portions of the flesh before canning the main bulk. The development of the green colour is closely correlated with the trimethylamine oxide (TMAO) content of the raw fish and Nagaoka *et al.* (1971) reported a method for predicting the greening of tuna before cooking, based on the assay of TMAO.

Crustacea

The export of frozen prawns, shrimps and crawfish earns much needed foreign exchange for many developing countries in the tropics. Since the products are sold in Europe, North America and Japan, high quality standards must be maintained. Inspection and grading before shipment are essential if that quality is to be achieved. The standards for frozen prawns set by the Indian Standards Institution are reviewed by Govindan (1972). Since shrimp trawlers rarely catch more than 2 tons per day, it should be possible to regulate fishing activity so that only material in prime condition arrives on deck. Since most methods used in developing fisheries are based upon those developed in the Gulf of Mexico, the account by Thompson and Farragut (1970) is of particular interest. These authors stress the importance of early and rapid chilling prior to freezing and suggest that icing may produce better results than the use of refrigerated seawater. The proper use of the ice is important and, with headed shrimp, the problem of black spot (so named from the darking of the flesh surface due to the oxidation of tyrosine to melanin, an enzyme-controlled process) can be much reduced or avoided entirely (Love and Thompson 1966). Additives such as sodium bisulphite and nitrofurans may be effective but are unnecessary if the shrimp are iced properly (Thompson and Farragut 1970). A product of excellent quality is obtained if the shrimp are frozen at sea within 2 or 3 hours

of leaving the water, and preferably before *rigor mortis* sets in. Air blast, contact plate freezers, and immersion freezers using a solution of salt and sugar are all employed in American vessels. Freezing at sea avoids black spot and is replacing the use of ice in the Gulf of Mexico fisheries (Thompson and Farragut 1970). Many accounts stress the importance of freezing only the freshest possible material, with due regard to adequate washing and hygiene generally (Govindan 1970, Anon 1968, Savoie 1971). It has been claimed that a superior product results if prawns are individually quick frozen in liquid nitrogen sprays, plate or blast freezers (Savoie 1971). The same author comments that frozen shrimp should be stored at a temperature of −26°C or lower and that temperature fluctuations are harmful to the product.

Other species

Ranken (1969) has evaluated modern techniques and equipment for freezing whole fish at sea in the tropics from the design/engineer's standpoint, taking into consideration biochemical parameters. He points out that the best methods for freezing whole fish at sea depend, as in non-tropical areas, upon the type of vessel, port and shore processing facilities, distribution methods and consumer preferences. On the basis of experience in commercial fisheries elsewhere, the major difficulties to be expected are likely to arise as a result of handling and utilization of species not hitherto preserved by freezing. Having noted this, it should be recognized that certain general principles have emerged which are of potential value to freezing operations already in production in tropical countries and in the avoidance of difficulty in new projects. Many of the papers already quoted provide useful background information. Jones (1969) discussed many of the problems involved in freezing and storing fish at sea and ashore and their possible solution. Heen (1969) reviews specific problems in shore-based fish freezing industries and Govindan (1972) reviews research on freezing preservation of fish in India.

Kordyl and Karnicki (1969) have described fishing operations by Polish vessels in West African waters where ambient deck temperatures can reach 30°C. They refer to the use of pre-chilling in refrigerated sea water and to the use of flake ice for handling larger fish and they stress the necessity to control *rigor* and autolytic activity. Reference is also made in agreement with other workers to the necessity for controlling catching rates.

There is some evidence (Tropical Products Institute, unpublished) which suggests that if the tropical freshwater fish *Tilapia* is handled in accordance with the best practices devised for cold water marine fish, products of good eating quality result. Storage times of 6 months or more have been achieved at a temperature of −30°C. This is in excess of the time likely to be required in commercial practice. Perhaps what is most needed here is work to determine whether cheaper practices would also provide acceptable quality and adequate storage life. Recently, in our laboratory, we have been examining the possibilities of eliminating off-flavours found in freshly cooked *Tilapia* and other freshwater fishes from the tropics. This is variously described as 'muddy' or 'manurial' according to intensity. In some situations the off-flavour, which appears to derive from the presence of an unidentified thio-ether, has been removed by leaching from wet fillets. We have also had some success in eliminating the compound by storage at sub-zero temperatures. In other situations, an apparently rather similar taint is due to a so-far unidentified compound of quite different structure which is unaffected by either leaching or storage at sub-zero temperatures.

DRYING, SALTING AND SMOKING

Primitive drying to preserve fish has been practised for centuries and quite sophisticated attempts to dehydrate fish go back for almost a century as Jason (1965) has pointed out in his excellent review. The theoretical aspects of this drying have largely been carried out on cod and herring, which are biochemically different in many respects from fish of tropical waters. For example, tropical fish remain whole at temperatures at which cold water species would cook and break up.

Salting

Dry salting may be regarded as a development of simple drying. Jarvis (1950) has described methods of preparing dry salted fish in warm climates. Where humidities are low, the approach is relatively simple, but in high humidity areas artificial heat may be required to lower the moisture content to acceptable levels. In the latter case, for instance in much of Africa, the fish may be dried on grills over open fires, and hence it is often broiled in the process. There has been some concern about this form of drying as a possible contributor to the high incidence of primary carcinoma of the liver commonly occurring in parts of the tropical world. Nitrosamines can be formed, and the flesh can be contaminated with polycyclic compounds from open fires. No firm evidence on cause or relationships appears to be available. This is a field that the chemist and epidomiologist should obviously investigate, by comparison, for instance, with the current interest in the contamination of staple tropical foods, such as groundnuts, with mycotoxins.

Developments of such drying at the simple technological level commonly involve salting together with smoking. Indeed, the three approaches are often used in combination. In the more humid areas dry salting reduces the water content of the final product to 36–65 per cent. In drier areas the moisture content may range from 33 to 39 per cent. At the higher end of the moisture range, South-east Asian products may have a life of only a few weeks whereas fish sold through Aden may be marketed in Sri Lanka and East Africa 3 months or more after processing (Cole and Greenwood-Barton 1965).

Most salt used for curing in the tropics is prepared by the direct evaporation of sea water and small quantities of calcium and magnesium salts are invariably present in commercial salt. These whiten and stiffen the flesh, imparting a bitterness that most salt fish consumers like. At the same time fish of very bad colour may be produced from material cured with some crude commercial solar salts. The presence of copper and iron salts in trace amounts is pratically conducive to carbonyl-amino reactions that, in addition to precursing excessive quantities of brown pigment and the production of off-flavours, are also a potential hazard to nutritional quality.

One hazard in dry salting is the presence of salt-adapted microflora that causes 'pinking' in fish of high moisture content. The bacterial count of salt can be reduced by long-term storage under tropical conditions. The microflora are relatively inactive when the fish is held under concentrated brine or in fish of very low moisture content. Consequently, where 'pinking' difficulties arise, a salt pickle technique should be used together with rapid drying, possibly accompanied by hot drying.

Acceptability of salt fish products in some tropical countries follows a pattern quite different from others. Fish that a European would consider of good quality is not necessarily preferred in the tropics to fish affected by the flavours of rancidity, and pink or partial decomposition. It will be seen, therefore, that there are possibilities of tailoring products, with the help of chemists and bacteriologists, to market requirements. The scientist can also play a major part in the development of new products. Watanabe and Cabrita (1971) have developed a brined, smoked, sun-dried product which has apparently been accepted in Zambia, where it had long been thought that salted fish would be disliked by the average consumer. The more traditional approach, if it is to be carried out satisfactorily, involves immersion of the fish in brine. In practice, in the tropics, this is best achieved by dry salting in layers in a vat or tub so that the brine builds up and covers the fish. Tanks should be shaded to reduce the temperature. Prior to salting, large fish, especially tuna and mackerel, should be bled at sea (to reduce subsequent browning discolouration), and the fish should be as fresh as possible. Dried fish, smoked fish, and quite heavily salted dry fish are all likely to be attacked in the dry stage by dermestid beetles. While these attacks can be reduced by good housekeeping, including the careful disposal of waste from the cutting operations, in many situations the use of an insecticide has proved necessary (Green 1967, McLellan 1964).

Drying

Exposure to direct sunlight should be avoided where possible with fat and semi-fat species, since light accelerates lipid oxidation. The situation is aggravated by the known catalysis of lipid oxidation by high salt concentrations. In some situations, particularly where the humidity is low, more rapid drying may be achieved in the shade rather than in the open.

Smoking

A major problem in many parts of Africa is the shortage of suitable fuel for fish smoking. A number of designs is now available for fish smoking kilns which use minimal quantities of fuel (FAO 1970, FAO 1971a).

FERMENTED PRODUCTS

A wide range of fermented fish products, as sauces or pastes, are prepared throughout South-east Asia and in parts of China. They are less well known in Indonesia and practically unknown in India (Subba Rao 1961). These products are used mainly as flavour additives in diets dominated by rice and they are produced in countries where sun drying presents some difficulty. Van Veen (1965) and FAO (1971b) have produced reviews of this subject. There is considerable interest currently in speeding up processing techniques. Some difficulties have been encountered in the development of desired flavours, which demand the production of lower fatty acid rather than carbonyls (Tropical Products Institute, unpublished). Products of this type may well have potential for development in other tropical countries where questions of economics may limit the adoption of the more expensive drying techniques or refrigeration. Recent attempts have been made to introduce such products in West Africa (Faubeau 1972).

COOKED PRODUCTS

Cooking is used to provide cheap, short-term preservation in many parts of the tropics. The methods include hot smoking and grilling in Africa (FAO 1971) and boiling in salted water in the Far East (Subba Rao 1961). The products are pasteurized rather than made bacteriologically sterile. There have been very few investigations into the microbiological aspects of these processes.

CANNING

The technology of fish canning and some of the problems that arise have been reviewed in the volumes edited by Vorgstrom (1965) and it is not intended to repeat these reviews here. The canning of fish is only an economic proposition where large quantities of suitable fish are available cheaply over long periods. This type of situation is comparatively rare and is likely to become less common in both tropical and colder areas of the world. Where canning is established or contemplated in the tropics, certain aspects must be given special consideration. Heat processing is regulated in order to destroy pathogenic bacteria but since excessive heat treatment affects the organoleptic qualities of the product, contamination prior to canning must be reduced to a minimum, particularly handling which could result in contamination with thermophilic organisms. Obviously this is more difficult under the environmental conditions found in many tropical developing countries than elsewhere. The maintenance of canned produce in an acceptable condition in a tropical environment is also more difficult than in developed countries where the ambient temperature is lower. Keeping times tend to be much shorter and there is a far greater tendency for cans to 'blow' or corrode.

FISH PROTEIN CONCENTRATE (FPC)

Much has been written on the production of FPC and its role in bridging the 'protein gap' in developing countries. A recent review (Halliday and Disney 1971) has pointed out the economic and acceptability problems associated with the production of FPC. In terms of conditions in many developing countries, the most promising means of utilizing supplies of trash fish is as fish meal, particularly if this can be upgraded and used as human food. Recently the UN Protein Advisory Group has published a statement (PAG 1972) summarizing its views which are somewhat critical of the more expensive products in their application to developing country situations.

CONCLUSIONS

This paper sets out some of the problems associated with the processing of tropical fish species and indicates some of the areas where the problems differ from those encountered in temperate and cold water fisheries. The tropical countries include most of the developing countries and the problems discussed here demand solution if development is to proceed at the pace desired by those living in the developing world. The information available is far from sufficient. From the work done so far, as for instance in the use of ice to chill fish, it appears that the differences between tropical and cold water fisheries can be quite marked. Similar differences may be expected in other areas of fish preservation and processing and the authors emphasize that an increase in the effort devoted to research and experiment on fish handling in tropical countries is urgently needed. Many of the investigations which should be made require neither sophisticated technology nor expensive equipment. Much essential information could be obtained by workers in the developing countries at little cost. A number of areas where investigation could yield information of immediate practical value have been cited. The iced shelf life should be investigated for all commercially important species. The alternative of using refrigerated sea water (RSW) or fresh water rather than ice for chilling should be considered as should such combinations as initial chilling in ice or RSW followed by the use of chill stores. Whenever possible such investigations should be accompanied by quantitative and qualitative bacteriological studies. It is also important to discover whether ice must be applied at death or whether a delay of some hours would give acceptable storage times. Further work on the desirability or otherwise of gutting or bleeding is needed. The possibility of freezing whole fish and marketing these as an alternative to chilled fish needs further study. Treatment before freezing, and freezing and cold storage regimes have not been studied at all for many of the commercially important tropical species. All such technological investigations should of course be made in parallel with studies of the economic considerations involved.

References

ALDRIN, J F, AMBROGGI, C and PONY ASSEMIEN, F Le test de l'azote
1970   basique volatil appliqué à quelques espèces de poissons tropicaux. *Recl. Méd. vét.*, 146(7):677-688.

AMU, L and DISNEY, J G *Trop. Sci.*, in press.
1973

Anon. Handling and processing prawns. *Australian Fisheries*
1968   *Newsletter*, October.

ANTUNNES, S A, BRITTO DE CASTRO, L A and NOVAK, A F Investiga-
1971   tions on handling fish and shellfish on board vessels in Brazil. *FAO Fish. Rep.*, (115):102 p.

BALAKRISHNAN-NAIR, R., THORAMANI, P K and LAHIRY, N L
1970   Studies on chilled storage of freshwater fish. I. Changes occurring during iced storage. *J. Fd. Sci. Technol.*, 8:53.

BITO, M *Bull. Jap. Soc. scient. Fish.*, 30:347.
1964

BLIGH, E G Specific problems in the quality assessment of fresh-
1971   water fish. In R. Kreuzer (ed.), *Fish Inspection and Quality Control*, London, Fishing News (Books) Ltd., p.81.

BOSE, A N Freezing of tropical fish. In R. Kreuzer (ed.), *Freezing*
1969   *and Irradiation of Fish*, London, Fishing News (Books) Ltd., p.179.

BRAMSNAES, F Handling of fresh fish. In G. Borgstrom (ed.), *Fish*
1965   *as Food*, New York and London, Academic Press, 4:1.

BRAMSTEDT, F and AUERBACH, M The spoilage of freshwater fish.
1965   In G. Borgstrom (ed.), *Fish as Food*, New York and London, Academic Press, 1:613.

BURGESS, G H O, CUTTING, C L , LOVERN, J A and WATERMAN,
1965   J J (ed.), *Fish Handling and Processing*, Edinburgh, HMSO, 390 p.

CARLSON, C J Superchilling fish—A review. In R. Kreuzer (ed.),
1969   *Freezing and Irradiation of Fish*, London, Fishing News (Books) Ltd., 101 p.

Central Food Technology Research Institute (CFTRI) Mysore and
1969   India Annual Report.

COLE, R C and GREENWOOD-BARTON, L H Problems associated
1965 with the development of tropical fisheries: The preservation
of the catch by simple processes. *Trop. Sci.*, 7(4).

CRAWFORD, L and FINCH, R Quality changes in albacore tuna
1968 during storage on ice and in refrigerated sea water. *Fd.
Technol.*, 22:1289.

CRAWFORD, L, FINCH, R and DALY, J J Rapid freezing of tuna by
1969 immersion in dichlorodifluoromethane. *Fd. Technol. Bull.*,
3(4):1451.

DISNEY, J G *Fish Handling and Preservation in Uganda*, London,
1968 Tropical Products Institute.

DISNEY, J G, CAMERON, J D, HOFFMAN, A and JONES, N R Quality
assessment in *Tilapia* species. In R. Kreuzer (ed.), *Fish
1969 Inspection and Quality Control*, London, Fishing News
(Books) Ltd., p. 71.

DUGAL, L C Hypoxanthine in iced freshwater fish. *J. Fish. Res. Bd.*
1967 *Can.*, 24(1):2229.

FAUBEAU, A The production and use of *nuoc mam* in the Ivory
1972 Coast. Production of fish-protein concentrate. *Report and
proceedings of the Joint UNIDO/FAO Expert Group Meeting
Rabat, Morocco, 8–12 December 1969, Part II*, New York,
United Nations, 151 p.

FAO Fisheries in the food economy. *FAO Basic Study*, (19),
1968a 1968.

FAO Ice in fisheries. *FAO Fish. Rep.*, (59):68 p.
1968b

FAO Smoke curing of fish. *FAO Fish. Rep.*, (88):43 p.
1970

FAO Equipment and methods for improved smoking kilns in
1971a the tropics. *FAO Fish. tech. pap.*, (104):27 p.

FAO Fermented fish products. *FAO Fish. Rep.*, (100):54 p.
1971b

FRASER, D I, PITTS, D P and DYER, W J Nucleotide degradation
1968 and organoleptic quality in fresh and thawed mackerel
held at and above ice temperature. *J. Fish. Res. Bd. Can.*,
25(2):239–253.

GILLESPIE, D C and OSTOVAR, K Effects of washing freshwater
1971 fish on keeping quality. *J. Fish. Res. Bd. Can.*, 28(5):783–
785.

GOVINDAN, T K Grading of frozen prawns, according to Indian
1970 standards. *Indian Fd. Packer*, January-February, p. 25.

GOVINDAN, T K The problem on leaching in iced fish. *Indian Fd.*
1971 *Packer*, January-February, p. 27.

GOVINDAN, T K Research on freezing preservation of fish in
1972 India—A review. *Indian Food*, 26(1):52.

GREEN, A A The protection of dried sea-fish from infestation by
1967 *Dermestes frischii*, Kug. *Pyrethrum Post*, 9(2):24-33.

HALLIDAY, D and DISNEY, J G Fish protein concentrate—A
1971 review. *Tropical Products Institute Report*, G58, 18 p.

HANSEN, P Storage life of prepacked wet fish at 0°C. II. Trout and
1972 herring. *J. Fd. Technol.*, (1):21–26.

HEEN, E Specific problems and techno-economic considerations in
1969 the shore-based fish freezing industry. In R. Kreuzer (ed.),
Freezing and Irradiation of Fish, London, Fishing News
(Books) Ltd., p. 225.

HUSS, H H Storage life of prepacked wet fish at 0°C. I. Plaice and
1972 Haddock. *J. Fd. Technol.*, (7):13–19.

JARVIS, N D *US Fish and Wildlife Service Report*, 18. US Govt.
1960 Printing Office.

JASON, A C Drying and dehydration. In G Borgstrom (ed.), *Fish
1965 as Food*, New York and London, Academic Press, 3:1.

JONES, N R Fish as a raw material for freezing: factors influencing
1967 the quality of products frozen at sea. In R. Kreuzer (ed.),
Freezing and Irradiation of Fish, London Fishing News
(Books) Ltd., p. 31.

JONES, N R Fish preservation. UNIDO Expert Group Meeting on
1969 the Scientific Approaches to the Problems of Preservation
and Refrigeration of Food in Developing Countries,
Vienna, UNIDO (*ID/WG.28/7*) (mimeo).

KARTHIAYANI, T C and MAHADEVA FYER, K Quantitative and
1963 qualitative studies on the bacterial flora of fresh sardines.
Fish, Technol., Cochin, 4(2):89.

KORDYL, E and KARNICKI, Z Factors influencing quality of frozen
1969 fish at sea in sub-tropical and tropical areas. In R. Kreuzer
(ed.), *Freezing and Irradiation of Fish*, London, Fishing
News (Books) Ltd., p. 189.

KREUZER, R Codes of practice for fish and fishery products. In
1971 R. Kreuzer (ed.), *Fish Inspection and Quality Control*,
London, Fishing News (Books) Ltd., p. 287.

KRONE, W Frozen fish marketing in West African countries.
1970 *FAO Fish. Rep.*, (96):59 p.

LANTZ, A W and GUNASEKARA, L D An investigation into the
1965 keeping qualities of ungutted fish from trawlers. *Progress
Report No. 1*, Dept. of Fisheries, Sri Lanka.

LASSEN, S Tuna canning and the preservation of the raw material
1965 through brine refrigeration. In G. Borgstrom (ed.), *Fish
as Food*, New York and London, Academic Press: 4:207.

LISTON, J The bacterial flora of fish caught in the Pacific. *J. appl.*
1960 *Bact.*, 23(3):469–470 p.

LOVE, T D and THOMPSON, M H Annual Report, Bureau of Com-
1966 mercial Fisheries, US Fish and Wildlife Service *Circular
No. 251.*

McLELLAN, R H A pyrethrum-dipping treatment to protect dried
1964 fish from beetle infestation. *Pyrethrum Post*, 7(3):30–33, 40.

NAGAOKA, C, YAMAGATA, M and HORIMOTO, K A method for
1971 predicting 'greening' of tuna before cooking. In R.
Kreuzer (ed.), *Fish Inspection and Quality Control*, London.
Fishing News (Books) Ltd., London, p. 96.

PAG The Potential of Fish Protein Concentrate for Developing
1972 Countries. *PAG Bull.*, 11(2) and (3).

PETERSEN, E and WEERAKOON, A H Experiments on the keeping
1951 quality of fresh iced Ceylon fish. *Ceylon Sessional papers*,
VI, April 1951 (Ceylon Govt. Press).

RANKEN, M B F Evaluation of modern techniques and equipment
1969 for freezing whole fish at sea. In R. Kreuzer (ed.), *Freezing
and Irradiation of Fish*, London, Fishing News (Books) Ltd.,
p. 1.

SAVOIE, R J B Shrimp packaging and shipping methods. Proceed-
1971 ings, Conference on the Canadian Shrimp Fishery, St.
John, New Brusnwick, Oct. 27–29, 1970, *Can. Fish. Rep.*,
(17):213.

SCARLATTI, E System for preserving fresh fish on board deep-water
1965 vessels. *Fish Handling and Preservation*, Proceedings at
Meeting on Fish Technology—Scheveningen, 1964. Paris,
OECD, p. 57.

SHEWAN, J M The microbiology of fish and fishery products. A
1971 progress report. *J. appl. Bact.*, 34(2):299–315.

DA SILVA, N N and MENDEZ, A H W Bacteriology of chilled water
1963 during the preservation of fish. *Bull. Fish. Res. Stn. Ceylon*,
16(1):1–8.

STROUD, G D The herring. *Torry advis. Note*, 57, Torry Research
1972 Station, Aberdeen, Scotland.

SUBBA RAO, G N Fisheries Products Manual; Indo-Pacific Fisheries
1961 Council (draft), p. 61.

SUBBA RAO, G N Discussion of factors influencing quality of
1969 frozen fish at sea in sub-tropical and tropical areas. In
R. Kreuzer (ed.), *Freezing and Irradiation of Fish*, London,
Fishing News (Books) Ltd., p. 194.

THOMPSON, M H and FARRAGUT, R N Shrimp freezing and refrigera-
1970 tion in the USA Proceedings, Conference on the Canadian
Shrimp Fishery, St. John, New Brunswick, Oct. 27–29,
1970, *Can. Fish. Rep.*, (17):185.

VAN VEEN, A G Fermented and dried seafood products in South
1965 east Asia. In G. Borgstrom 1965 (ed.), *Fish as Food*, New
York and London, Academic Press, 3:227.

VELANKAR, N K and KAMASASTRI, P V The Bacterial flora trimethyl-
1956 amine and total volatile nitrogen of fish muscle at 0°C (in
ice). *Indian J. Fish.*, 3:269–289.

WATANBAE, K Spoilage in iced 'pescada-foguette' from South
1961 Brazilian fishing grounds. *Inst. oceanogr. Univ. S. Paulo,
Contr.*, (163).

WATANABE, K Handling and keeping quality of iced kariba bream,
1965– *Tilapia mossambica. Fish. Res. Bull.*, Zambia 4:59–70.
66

WATANABE, K and CABRITA, F J Directions for the Preparation of
1971 salted and dry-smoked fish. *Fish. Res. Bull.*, Zambia,
5:225–233.

Bacteriological Aspects of Tropical Shrimp   D C Cann

Bacteriologie de la crevette tropicale

Des études bactériologiques approfondies ont été faites sur certains genres de crevettes du golfe du Siam et de l'océan Indien. Selon les résultats de recherches effectuées dans différentes conditions d'entreposage réfrigéré, ces crevettes demeurent comestibles pendant1 6 jours au plus à condition d'être correctement manipulées; la détérioration bactérienne est moins importante que dans le cas des crevettes européennes. L'auteur fournit des chiffres sur la charge bactérienne de crevettes congelées dans des établissements commerciaux et discute de divers aspects du contrôle de la qualité bactériologique intéressant en particulier la transformation des poissons tropicaux.

Bacteriologia de los crustaceos tropicales

Trata este trabajo de los estudios bacteriológicos de ciertos generos de camarones de las aguas del Golfo de Tailandia y del Océano Indico. Los estudios efectuados en diversas condiciones de almacenamiento en frigrorífico muestran que cuando los camerones se tratan correctamente se mantienen comestibles hasta 16 días, siendo la deterioración bacteriológica menos importante que en el caso del camarón europeo. Se dan cifras correspondientes a la carga bacteriológica de los camarones congelados comercialmente y se tratan diversos aspectos del control de la calidad bacteriológica característico de la elaboración de crustáceos tropicales.

The increasing world demand for fish products has stimulated exploitation, in particular, of the relatively undeveloped fisheries of tropical countries. Modernization of fishing methods along with the increased use of ice and refrigeration has created a greater internal demand for fishery products and opened up export markets which have become important sources of foreign exchange (Whitaker 1970). To maintain the value of such exports it is essential that they are able to compete in quality, wholesomeness and price with similar products on the international market. They must also meet any bacteriological and chemical standards required by foreign importers. Consequently, it is necessary that the handling and processing industry should establish quality control procedures with the eventual introduction of preshipment quality grading schemes. Before such a scheme can be developed a thorough investigation of the existing industry and its methods must be carried out so that improvements can be made and, from the background data acquired, practical specifications, limits and standards established. The bacteriology of temperate and cold water fish has been extensively studied and was reviewed by Shewan and Hobbs (1967). Work on tropical fishery products has mainly been done in India on fish by Venkatamaran and Sreenivasan (1952); Velankar (1956); Velankar and Kamasastri (1956); Jadhav and Magar (1970) and Balakrishnan Nair et al. (1971); and on shrimp by Sreenivasan (1959); Velankar and Govindan (1959); Pillai et al. (1961); Velankar et al. (1961); Jacob et al. (1962) and Lekshmy et al. (1962). Watanabe (1962, 1965) examined marine fish in Southern Brazil whilst more recent studies have been made on African freshwater and marine fish by Watanabe (1965–66), Disney et al. (1971); Amu and Disney (in press) and Hoffman et al. (in press). Most of these authors, however, concentrated their studies on chemical examination and estimation of total bacterial loads of the iced and uniced material. Little systematic investigation of the bacterial flora has been made. It is desirable, therefore, for more detailed qualitative and quantitative studies to be made of the bacterial flora of freshly caught fish and of the changes taking place during storage and processing. The work on penaeid shrimp described in this report was largely carried out in Thailand at the Fishery Technology Laboratory, Bangkok, in a technical assistance project of the Food and Agriculture Organization of the United Nations.

ANALYSES

Materials

For spoilage studies, freshly caught penaeid shrimp were collected in 3–6 kg quantities, depending on the state of fishing and availability at the ports of landing. For comparison of whole and beheaded shrimp, half of each batch was either beheaded at sea (Kantang and Cholburi shrimp) or on collection at the port of landing. A sample of mud was collected from the sea bed at the time of catching of the Cholburi shrimp. During the return journey to the laboratory the samples were chilled and maintained at 0°C with ice. Samples of shellfish from commercial processors were collected on receipt into the factory and again as the final frozen product. In addition, two samples of frozen, whole raw shrimp imported from Malaysia and Mozambique were examined at Torry Research Station.

Methods

Whole shrimp were first beheaded and the 'tails' of both sets were washed in running tap water before analysis. This procedure was adopted to give uniformity of presentation and particularly to avoid taste panel bias as the head portion rapidly blackens during storage in ice (Cann 1971).

Bacteriological analysis

Fifty grammes of shrimp were aseptically homogenized and analysed by the methods described by Cann et al. (1971) with the exception that total viable counts were made using the Standard Plate Count (SPC) method. This was considered preferable since most existing standards applied to frozen shrimp products specify this method; such a standard is shown in Table 1. In addition, an enrichment culture was made for the presence of Vibrio parahaemolyticus by pipetting 2.0 ml of homogenate into 3 per cent salt nutrient broth and incubating for 24 h at 37°C; this was then subcultured on to Oxoid TCBS agar and incubated for 24 h at 37°C. Colonies with the typical appearance of V. parahaemolyticus were purified and identified by standard physiological and biochemical tests for this species.

TABLE 1. A TYYPICAL STANDARD APPLIED TO TROPICAL SHELLFISH

Standard plate count at 35/C	$<10^5$/g
Escherichia coli (MPN)	Nil/100 g
Enterococci	Nil/g
Vibrio cholera	Nil/g
Total volatile base (Conway method)	<30 mgN/100 g

Total volatile bases (TVB)

The total volatile base (TVB) content of the shrimp was estimated by the Conway diffusion method.

TABLE 2. TOTAL VIABLE COUNTS INCUBATED AT 20°C OF SHRIMP STORED IN ICE (ORGANISMS/G)

Fishing area (Port of landing)	Genus	Days storage								
		2	4	5–6	8–9	10	12	14	16	18
Gulf of Thailand (Songkhla)	Penaeus whole	7.9×10^4		4.2×10^6	5.6×10^6		3.1×10^8	1.5×10^8	1.7×10^8	
	beheaded	5.7×10^5		4.3×10^5	4.2×10^6		3.0×10^8	3.0×10^8	2.1×10^8	
Indian Ocean (Kantang)	Penaeus whole			2.8×10^7	5.3×10^7		5.4×10^7		1.1×10^8	2.4×10^8
	beheaded	1.1×10^7					4.0×10^8	7.0×10^8	1.0×10^9	7.2×10^8
	Penaeus whole	5.3×10^4		3.1×10^5		1.7×10^7		6.0×10^7		
	whole	5.3×10^4		3.1×10^5		9.6×10^6		3.0×10^7		
Gulf of Thailand (Cholburi)	Metapenaeus whole	6.7×10^4	3.4×10^4	9.0×10^5	1.5×10^6		6.5×10^7			
	beheaded	5.8×10^4	6.6×10^4	8.2×10^5	2.2×10^5		2.2×10^5			
Gulf of Thailand (Samudh Sakorn)	Penaeus whole	3.0×10^4	4.3×10^4	7.7×10^4	4.0×10^4		9.9×10^6	2.5×10^7		
	beheaded	3.7×10^4	7.2×10^4	7.9×10^4	1.9×10^6		5.6×10^6	1.5×10^8		
Mozambique	Penaeus whole	5.1×10^4					1.6×10^7 1.9×10^7 1.6×10^7			
Malaysia	Penaeus beheaded	8.3×10^6					2.0×10^8 2.0×10^8 1.8×10^8			

TABLE 3. TOTAL VIABLE COUNTS INCUBATED AT 35°C OF SHRIMP STORED IN ICE (ORGANISMS/G)

Fishing area (Port of landing)	Genus	Days storage								
		2	4	5–6	8–9	10	12	14	16	18
Gulf of Thailand (Songkhla)	Penaeus whole	$>10^8$		1.3×10^5	1.9×10^4		4.5×10^4	4.4×10^5	7.0×10^5	
	beheaded	2.3×10^8		1.5×10^5	1.4×10^4		2.9×10^4	1.7×10^6	3.0×10^5	
Indian Ocean (Kantang)	Penaeus whole			3.4×10^6	4.0×10^6		1.1×10^7		2.9×10^5	5.4×10^5
	beheaded	9.6×10^6			2.5×10^5		2.6×10^5	5.6×10^5	3.5×10^5	1.4×10^5
	Penaeus whole	3.2×10^8		1.1×10^4		1.9×10^4		4.6×10^4		
	whole	2.1×10^8		1.1×10^4		7.9×10^3		2.3×10^4		
Gulf of Thailand (Cholburi)	Penaeus whole	5.7×10^4	1.4×10^6	3.8×10^4	2.0×10^4		9.3×10^5			
	beheaded	3.6×10^4	2.6×10^4	3.6×10^4	2.1×10^4		3.1×10^4			
Gulf of Thailand (Samudh Sakorn)	Metapenaeus whole	2.4×10^4	2.5×10^4	1.7×10^5	6.8×10^4		1.2×10^5	4.9×10^6		
	beheaded	2.2×10^4	4.3×10^4	2.4×10^4	4.1×10^4		3.1×10^4	7.8×10^5		
Mozambique	Penaeus whole	6.3×10^4					2.7×10^5			
Malaysia	Penaeus beheaded	3.0×10^6					2.9×10^7			

Sensory examination

Shrimp were examined by a taste panel using a modified score sheet developed for shrimp at Torry Research Station. The shrimp were examined in the shell-on state for Raw Appearance (RA) and, after shelling and steaming, for Cooked Flavour (CF). The panel comprised members of the scientific staff of the Fishery Technology Laboratory and scores are reported as the average of a minimum of five individual assessments.

RESULTS

Iced storage of shrimp

The results of the total viable counts are presented in Tables 2 and 3. At earliest examination – two days in

TABLE 4. BACTERIAL FLORA OF SHRIMP INCUBATED AT 20°C (%)

Port of landing	Fishing area	Days storage[3] sample	Cornyeform	Micrococcus	Flavobacteria-Cytophaga	Achromobacter	Streptococcus	Pseudomonas II	III	IV	Aeromonas	Enterobacteriaceae	Bacillus	Streptomycetes	No growth[a]	Growth at 37°C
Songkhla	Gulf of Thailand	2 iced	13	38	20	15							8		6	62
		16 iced				4		87	3	1	1				4	4
Cholburi	Gulf of Thailand	2 iced	55	24		5			1	1	1	3		9	2	58
		11 iced	14	11		8		50	6	1		2	5		3	1
		sea mud	46	32	8	7						1	4	1	1	61
	Mozambique	frozen	29	61	7	2									1	44
		12 iced	19		8	67			1	4			1			Nil
	Malaysia	frozen	38	49		3	4							1	5	51
		12 iced	41	1		48		3	4	1		1		1		1

a Randomly selected primary isolates nonviable on subculture.

ice – total counts at 20°C ranged from 3.0×10^4 to 1.1×10^7. There was little change during the early part of storage but after six days counts began to rise; in one case increasing by as much as four orders of magnitude after about 12 days. Counts at 35°C ranged from 2.1×10^3 to 9.6×10^6 and generally fluctuated through one order of magnitude during the storage period. Both 20°C and 35°C counts were similar in comparable whole and beheaded samples. Organisms of public health significance – coliforms, faecal coli and faecal streptococci – were detected only in low numbers. Coliforms, which were always present, ranged from 1.8 to 124/g. Faecal coli and faecal streptococci were usually absent; the highest numbers found were 4/g and 3.1/g respectively. Of the food poisoning bacteria, *Salmonella* spp. *Vibrio parahaemolyticus* type I and *Staphylococcus aureus* were not found. *Clostridium welchii* was detected by enrichment in one sample only. Studies of the bacterial flora (Table 4) showed that initially Gramme-positive organisms predominated. Over 50 per cent of the flora comprised coryneforms and *Micrococcus* spp. Also present in significant numbers were members of the *Cytophaga-Flavobacteria* group, and the genera *Achromobacter Bacillus* and *Streptomyces*. No members of the genus, *Pseudomonas*, were found. After spoilage in ice either *Pseudomonas* or *Achromobacter* species predominated. Where *Pseudomonas* spoilage occurred, over 50 per cent of the strains present belonged to type II (Shewan *et al*. 1960a).

Total volatile bases (TVB)

Table 5 shows that initially the values of TVB ranged from 19 to 27.2 mgN/100 g. Early in storage there is little change but after storage for eight days values begin to rise, reaching as high as 82 mgN/100 g after 18 days.

Sensory assessment

Table 6 shows that shrimp start to lose their flavour as early in storage as 2–4 days. By 6–8 days there is incipient discolouration of the shell by 'black spot formation' which

TABLE 5. TOTAL VOLATILE BASES OF WHOLE AND BEHEADED SHRIMP STORED IN ICE (MGN[3]100 G)   N

Fishing area (Port of landing)	Gennus	Days storage 2	4	5–6	8–9	10	12	14	16	18
Gulf of Thailand (Songkhla)	*Penaeus* whole	27.2		20.4	28.8		31.6	27.2	49.6	
	beheaded	25.6		20.0	24.0		27.2	34.8	40.0	
Indian Ocean (Kantang)	*Penaeus* whole			19.2	20.8		32.0		64.8	73.0
	beheaded	22.0		20.0	36.0		52.0	56.0	69.6	82.0
Gulf of Thailand (Kantang)	*Penaeus* whole	25.8		22.8		25.5		31.5		
	whole	19.0		24.3		23.9		29.6		
Gulf of Thailand (Cholburi)	*Metapenaeus* whole	20.0	16.0	19.4	20.0		28.6			
	beheaded	19.2	20.0	16.8	17.2		21.6	22.4		
Gulf of Thailand (Samudh Sakorn)	*Penaeus* whole	20.8	22.0	19.6	20.8		22.8			
	beheaded	20.4	16.4	19.2	20.0		17.6			

TABLE 6. ORGANOLEPTIC EXAMINATION OF WHOLE AND BEHEADED SHRIMP STORED IN ICE

Fishing area (Port of landing)	Genus	2 RA	2 CF	4 RA	4 CF	5–6 RA	5–6 CF	8–9 RA	8–9 CF	10 RA	10 CF	12 RA	12 CF	14 RA	14 CF	16 RA	16 CF	18 RA	18 CF
Gulf of Thailand (Songkhla)	Penaues whole	3.9	4.8			3.6	4.0	2.3	3.2			2.6	2.9	2.1	2.6	2.0	2.2		
	beheaded	3.9	4.7			3.9	3.9	3.3	2.9			2.5	3.1	2.2	2.7	2.3	2.5		
Indian Ocean (Kantang)	Penaeus whole					3.1	4.3	3.2	3.8			2.6	2.6			2.0	2.3	1.4	1.2
	beheaded					3.1	4.3	3.2	3.8			2.6	2.6			2.0	1.9	1.4	1.2
Gulf of Thailand (Kantang)	Penaeus whole	3.8	4.7			3.3	4.2			1.8	3.1			1.0	1.8				
	whole	3.8	4.7			3.4	4.2			2.3	3.2			1.7	2.4				
Gulf of Thailand (Cholburi)	Metapenaeus whole	4.0	4.6	3.2	4.7	2.7	3.1	2.5	3.0	1.9	2.5	1.4	2.5	1.4	2.0				
	beheaded	4.0	4.6	3.4	3.9	2.7	3.4	3.0	3.0	2.7	2.7	2.0	2.6						
Gulf of Thailand (Samudh Sakorn)	Penaeus whole	3.5	3.5	3.0	3.2	3.0	3.0	2.5	2.8			2.3	2.7	2.0	2.0				
	beheaded	3.8	3.9	3.4	3.3	3.6	3.5	3.5	2.9			3.0	2.8	2.7	2.0				

RA = Raw appearance, score 4–0.
CF = Cooked flavour, score 5–0.

TABLE 7. BACTERIOLOGICAL, CHEMICAL AND ORGANOLEPTIC EXAMINATION OF FACTORY PROCESSED SHELLFISH

Processor	Type	TVB mgN°100 g	Organoleptic assessment RA	CF	Coliforms	Faecal coli	Faecal streptococci	Bacterial count Org/g at 20°C a	Org/g at 35°C
					Most probable numbers/g				
A	Flower shrimp								
	before processing	22.8	2.2	3.0	72	2	6.4	5.1×10^6	6.6×10^5
	frozen packaged	21.2	2.1	3.3	168	168	149.3	8.2×10^6	3.9×10^7
	White shrimp								
	before processing	21.6	2.5	3.3	144	0.9	44	1.0×10^6	2.5×10^6
	frozen packaged	24.4	2.6	2.9	152	152	46.4	5.5×10^6	1.5×10^7
B	White shrimp								
	before processing	23.2	—	—	40.4	2.8	9.7	4.7×10^5	9.8×10^5
	frozen packaged	24.0	—	—	>123	29	30.7	—	1.2×10^6
	Pink shrimp								
	before processing	20.8	—	—	12.9	1.1	34.9	—	2.4×10^5
	frozen packaged	38.4	—	—	122.4	122.4	61.2	—	1.3×10^6
C	Flower shrimp								
	before processing	23.2	3.6	3.8	96	0.8	0.8	4.7×10^6	1.4×10^5
	frozen packaged	27.2	3.8	3.9	27	0.6	113	3.9×10^6	6.7×10^5
	White shrimp								
	before processing	32.8	3.4	4.0	114	96	101	6.5×10^6	4.6×10^6
	frozen packaged	26.0	3.6	4.0	31.2	2.5	19.1	3.3×10^6	4.0×10^5
	Cuttlefish								
	before processing	20.0	—	—	12.8	0.4	0.7	1.6×10^5	4.4×10^4
	frozen packaged	15.2	—	—	5.7	0.6	88	1.0×10^6	3.0×10^3
D	White shrimp								
	before processing	23.6	3.6	4.1	33	4.8	108	1.1×10^6	3.9×10^5
	frozen packaged	24.0	3.1	3.0	15	4.2	0.5	—	7.6×10^5
	Pink shrimp								
	before processing	24.0	3.1	3.5	84	0.12	1.5	1.1×10^6	2.3×10^5
	frozen packaged	29.2	3.4	3.5	21	3.0	33	—	3.1×10^5
	Cuttlefish								
	before processing	20.4	—	—	>108	>105	>108	3.8×10^6	4.0×10^5
	frozen packaged	16.0	—	—	>108	>108	>108	—	3.4×10^6
E	Flower shrimp								
	before processing	23.6	2.3	3.0	130	50.8	116	1.7×10^7	5.0×10^6
	frozen packaged	36.8	2.2	2.2	144	128	128	3.8×10^7	5.9×10^6
	Pink shrimp								
	before processing	25.2	2.3	3.0	144	3.6	72	1.8×10^6	8.6×10^5
	frozen packaged	32.4	2.8	3.0	142	43	23.6	8.3×10^6	1.3×10^6

341

is reflected in raw appearance scores below 3. However, as judged by cooked flavour, shrimp generally remain edible for up to 12 days storage and on one occasion up to 16 days. Comparison of whole and beheaded shrimp showed a slightly longer storage life for the latter.

Handling and processing

The effect of handling and processing is shown in Table 7. Total viable bacterial counts at 35°C were commonly greater than 10^5/g both before and after processing. Organisms of public health significance were always present, frequently in increased numbers as a result of processing. Processing had little effect on the quality of shrimp as judged by chemical and sensory values. *Salmonella*, *Clostridium welchii* and *Staphylococcus aureus* were not detected; *Vibrio parahaemolyticus* biotype II was found in one sample of packaged frozen shrimp. Swabs taken of fish boxes, fish and shellfish at various ports of landing also yielded seven positive isolates for *V. parahaemolyticus* biotype II out of 41 samples tested.

DISCUSSION

Comparison of data from five storage experiments showed that beheading of shrimp did not improve the storage life to the extent that has been found in European and North American shrimp (Lantz 1951; Early 1965; Love and Thompson 1966; Thompson and Farragut 1970). Initial bacteriological quality varied considerably. In one case the shrimp carried total viable bacterial counts in excess of 10^7/g at 20°C and 10^6/g at 35°C – figures which, in other cases, were reached only after gross spoilage had taken place. It is probable, therefore, that these initial figures reflected heavy contamination during catching and landing. The results showed that, at best, shrimp have a storage life of about 16 days in ice and, at worst, of about nine days, using their cooked flavour as the critical test. From this, it appears that tropical shrimp may be expected to have a longer shelf life than certain other shrimp caught in colder waters. This is, of course, conditional on adequate icing of fish during storage. In practice, inadequate icing is the rule (Cann 1971 and Howgate 1971) allowing additional spoilage by mesophilic bacteria which should not be active at the temperature of melting ice. An extended storage life in ice has been reported for a variety of tropical fish (Watanabe 1962, 1965–66; Disney *et al.* 1971; Balakrishnan Nair *et al.* 1971; Hoffman *et al.* in press; Awu and Disney in press). Acceptable storage times of 3–6 weeks are reported in contrast to 15–17 days for nontropical fish (Shewan and Hobbs 1967). Similarly, the present results along with those of earlier workers (Iyengar *et al.* 1960 and Velankar *et al.* 1961) show that tropical shrimp remain in acceptable condition for 12–16 days whilst non tropical shrimp of *Pandalus* and *Nephrops* species are totally spoiled after 8–10 days (Walker *et al.* 1970 and Torry Research Station, unpublished results). Such marked differences in keeping times may be explained by examination of their relative bacterial flora. Because of higher ambient temperatures, the flora of freshly caught tropical fish can be expected to consist mainly of mesophiles which will not be active at the

temperature of melting ice. Consequently, little bacterial spoilage will take place until a psychrophilic flora develops. Moreover, *Pseudomonas* and *Achromobacter* strains, which are generally considered to be the main active spoilage agents of ice-stored fish, are not found to the same extent as in fresh temperate fish and shellfish (Campbell and Williams 1952; Shewan *et al.* 1960b; Shewan and Hobbs 1967; Harrison and Lee 1969 and Hobbs *et al.* 1971).

In the present study the flora of the shrimp after spoilage consisted mainly of *Pseudomonas* or *Achromobacter* strains. Shrimp examined in Thailand yielded a flora of *Pseudomonas* type II whilst shrimp examined in the United Kingdom carried a flora predominated by *Achromobacter* spp. In the light of these and other findings (Campbell and Williams 1952; Walker *et al.* 1970; and Hobbs *et al.* 1971) it is tempting to speculate that the degree of spoilage may be governed by the bacterial quality of the ice used in storage, most of the *Pseudomonas* and *Achromobacter* strains being introduced with the ice.

Bacterial quality control

The subject of microbiological quality control was discussed in detail by Hobbs (1970). The value of total bacterial counts as a measure of spoilage is doubtful. Whilst there is always a rise in the total viable count at 20°C during spoilage, the actual numbers vary considerably between different samples. Counts at 35–37°C do not vary systematically during ice storage, presumably because the bacteria counted at this temperature do not generally grow at 0°C. These counts are therefore more indicative of contamination during handling and processing and do not reflect spoilage changes. The data presented here show that there is little change in the early part of storage followed by a steady rise in the 20°C counts after about four days. As previously mentioned, spoiled shrimp can carry lower bacterial loads than contaminated shrimp of good quality as judged by chemical and organoleptic analysis. If total counts are to be used as a measure of spoilage they should be made at a temperature of incubation of 20°C or less. Much of the previous work on iced tropical fish has been carried out at temperatures of incubation at which spoilage bacteria would grow poorly, if it all. The value of total bacterial counts at 35°C lies, therefore, in the realm of prevention of health hazards and demonstration of insanitary handling and processing. As a measure of this hazard, total viable counts at 35–37°C are incorporated into many of the existing standards for fish, although some authorities attempt to assess both the quality and safety of a given product by the use of counts at 25°C or 30°C (Elliot and Michener 1965: Neufeld 1971).

More specific indicators of potential health hazards are coliforms, faecal coli and faecal streptococci. Standard methods estimating the Most Probable Numbers of these organisms present were found to be satisfactory when used in this study. There was nothing in the bacterial flora capable of giving erroneous results as reported when methyl red violet agar was used for coliform counts (Rosen and Levin 1970).

Quality control procedures are aimed largely at preventing contamination of fish products with food poisoning bacteria. *Salmonella* spp., *C. welchii* and *S.*

aureus are not normally present in fish caught in open areas of the seas although they may be present in fish and shellfish taken from estuarine and penned-off coastal waters.

Two food poisoning organisms are, however, found in free-living fish. The first, *Clostridium botulinum* is found in many species of fish (Dolman *et al.* 1950; Nakamura *et al.* 1963; Johannsen 1965 and Cann *et al.* 1966a) but has not been reported to any extent in tropical fish. This probably reflects lack of research effort more than scarcity of the organism. One worker (Tanasugarn 1970) has demonstrated *Cl. botulinum* types E and D in squid landed on the west coast of the Gulf of Thailand. The second, *Vibrio parahaemolyticus*, is a common cause of food poisoning in the Far East and has been incriminated in one authenticated outbreak of food poisoning in Britain involving tropical shellfish (Peffers *et al.* 1973). Quality control measures for tropical fish products must, therefore, take these bacteria into account. This is particularly so where changes in the pattern of utilization of fish by development of lightly cured and smoked western-type products are made (Howgate 1971). Both grow rapidly at temperatures frequently reported for fish in the tropics so their control must be effected by adequate icing and chilling of fish below 4°C (Cann *et al.* 1965, 1966b and Shewan and Cann 1965).

Bacteriological standards

Although legal bacteriological standards are not yet common, commercial standards are. These are applied to both the internal and imported products of some countries. Any development of an export market for tropical fish products may have to meet existing standards. Requirements vary from a mere certificate of wholesomeness to compliance with a detailed number of bacteriological standards. Dick (1970) reviewed the arguments for and against the application of microbial standards for foods and Shewan (1970) reviewed the situation for fish products. It has been shown that the imposition of a bacterial standard to imported tropical shellfish products has led to the elimination of a food poisoning hazard (Semple 1960). There are, however, disadvantages in the application of too severe and rigid limits which may lead to undesirable practices. Prolonged cold storage, for instance, could lower total and *E. coli* counts in an unacceptable product to a satisfactory level but the accompanying loss of eating quality would, to a large extent, defeat the original object of setting the standard. Examination of the data presented here shows that two of these figures are not being met. Neither are they being met in similar products in the United Kingdom (Hobbs *et al.* 1971). It is suggested, therefore, that such a standard is too severe and is not realistic for raw fish products. In the absence of known food poisoning organisms in a product, who is to say that the presence of perhaps up to ten *E. coli*/g constitutes a health hazard? Standards should be based on the findings of what can be achieved by good hygienic practice. In this context it is apparent, from the data presented, that standards requiring absence of *Salmonella* spp., *S. aureus*, *Cl. welchii* and *V. parahaemolyticus* can be met. To meet existing standards for total viable and *E. coli* counts significant improvements are required. Most important is a supply of potable water for processing of fish. The use of raw river or harbour waters for processing is common (Watanabe 1965 and Cann 1971) and should be either abolished or the water rendered safe by in-plant chlorination of the supply.

References

AMU, L and DISNEY, J G Quality changes in West African marine fish during storage, (in press, 1973).

BALAKRISHNAN NAIR, R, THARAMANI, P K and LAHIRY, W L Studies
1971 on chilled storage of freshwater fish. (1) Changes occurring during iced storage. *J. Fed. Sci. Technol.*, 8(2):53.

CAMPBELL, L L and WILLIAMS, O B The bacteriology of Gulf coast
1952 shrimp. IV. Bacteriological, chemical and organoleptic changes with ice storage. *Fd. Technol. Chicago*, 6:125.

CANN, D C Report to the Government of Thailand on fish handling
1971 processing. *Rep. FAO/UNDP(TA)*, (3021):17p.

CANN, D C, WILSON, B B, HOBBS, G and SHEWAN, J M The growth
1965 and toxin production of *Clostridium botulinum* type E in certain vacuum packed fish. *J. appl. Bact.*, 28:431.

CANN, D C, WILSON, B B, HOBBS, G and SHEWAN, J M Toxin
1966a production by *Clostriduim botulinum* type E in vacuum packed fish. Botulism 1966, 5th International Symposium on food microbiology, Moscow 1966. London, Chapman and Hall.

CANN, D C, WILSON, B B, SHEWAN, J M and HOBBS, G Incidence
1966b of *Clostridium botulinum* type E in fish products in the United Kingdom. *Nature*, 211, (5405):205.

CANN, D C, HOBBS, G, WILSON, B B and HORSLEY, R W The bac-
1971 teriology of scampi (*Nephrops norvegicus*). II. Detailed investigation of the bacterial flora of freshly caught samples. *J. Fd Technol.*, 6:153–161.

DICK, M I B Microbial standards for foods. *Fd Technol. Australia*,
1970 22(9):508.

DISNEY, J C, CAMERON, J D, HOFFMAN, A and JONES, N R Quality
1971 assessment in *Tilapia* species. In R Kreuzer (ed.), *Fish Inspection and Quality Control*. London, Fishing News (Books), Ltd., p. 71.

DOLMAN, C E, CHANG, H, KERR, D V and SHEARER, A R Fish
1960 borne and type E botulism. *Can. J. Publ. Hlth.*, 16:135.

EARLY, J Processing Norway lobsters. *Torry advis. Note*, 29,,
1965 Torry Research Station, Aberdeen, Scotland.

ELLIOT, R P and MICHENER, H D Factors affecting the growth of
1965 psychrophilic microorganisms in foods. *Tech. Bull.*, No. 1320, Agriculture, Research Service, US Dept. of Agric.

HARRISON, J M and LEE, J S Microbial evaluation of Pacific shrimp
1969 processing. *Appl. microbiol.*, 18(2):188.

HOBBS, G Microbial quality control. Proceedings, Conference on
1970 Canadian shrimp fishery, St. John, New Brunswick, October 27–29, 1970. *Can. Fish. Rep.*, (17).

HOBBS, G, CANN, D C, WILSON, B B and HORSLEY, R W The
1971 bacteriology of scampi (*Nephrops norgevicus*). III. Effects of processing. *J. Fd Technol.*, 6:233–251.

HOFFMAN, A, DISNEY, J, PINEGAR, A and CAMERON, J D The
preservation of some East African freshwater fish (in press, 1973).

HOWGATE, P F Report to the Government of Thailand on fish
1971 handling and processing. *Rep. FAO/UNDP(TA)*, (2950):12p.

IYENGAR, J R, VISWESWARIAH, K, MOORJANI, M N and BHATIA
1960 D S Assessment of the progressive spoilage of ice-stored shrimp. *J. Fish. Res. Bd. Can.*, 17(4):475.

JADHAV, M G and MAGAR, N G Preservation of fish by freezing
1970 and glazing: Bacteriology of fresh, frozen and glazed fish. *Fish. Technol. Cochin*, 7(1):89–90.

JACOB, S S, IYER, K M, NAIR, M R and PILLAI, V K Quality studies
1962 on round, headless and peeled and deveined prawns held in ice storage. *Indian J. Fish.*, 9:2, 97.

JOHANNSEN, A *Clostridium botulinum* type E in foods and the
1965 environment generally. *J. appl. Bact.*, 28:90.

LANTZ, A W Shrimp processing. *Fish. Res. Bd Can. Prog. Rep. Pac.*
1951 *Coast Sta.*, 89:82–83.

LEKSHMY, A, GOVINDAN, T K and PILLAI, V K Storage charac-
1962 teristics of frozen prawns in relation to quality assessment. *Indian J. Fish.*, Section B, 9(1):97.

LOVE, T D and THOMPSON, M H Annual Report, Bureau of Com-
1966 mercial Fisheries Technological Laboratory, Pascagoula, Miss., USA, *US Fish. Wildl. Ser. Circ. 251*, IV 25p.

NAKAMURA, Y, IIDA, H, SAEKI, S, KANZAWA, K and KARASHIMADA, T
1963 Type E botulism in Hokkaido, Japan. *J. Med. Sci. Biol.*, 9:293.

NEUFELD, N Influence of bacteriological standards on the quality
1971 of inspected fisheries products. In R Kreuzer (ed.), *Fish Inspection and Quality Control*, London, Fishing News (Books) Ltd., p. 234.

PILLAI, V K, SASTRI, P V K and NAYAR, M R Observations on some
1961 aspects of spoilage in fresh and frozen prawns. *Indian J. Fish.*, 8(2):430.

PEFFERS, A S R, BAILEY, J, BARROW, G I and HOBBS, B C *Vibrio*
1973 *parahaemolyticus* gastro-enteristic and international air travel. *Lancet* 7795 (1):143.

ROSEN, A and LEVIN, R E Detection and incidence of *Escherichia*
1970 *coli* on storage pen surfaces of fishing trawlers. *Appl. Microbiol.*, 20(1):103.

SEMPLE, A B Some recent problems of imported food. *Med. Offr.*,
1960 104:101.

SHEWAN, J M Bacteriological standards for fish and fishery pro-
1970 ducts. *Chem. Ind.*, (6):193–199.

SHEWAN, J M and CANN, D C Botulism and Fishery Products.
1965 *Torry advis. Note*, 22, Torry Research Station, Aberdeen, Scotland.

SHEWAN, J M and HOBBS, G Microbiology of fish spoilage and
1967 preservation. In Hochenhull D J (ed.), *Progress in Industrial Microbiology*, London, Iliffe Books Ltd., (6):169.

SHEWAN, J M, HOBBS, G and HODGKISS A determinative scheme
1960a for the identification of certain genera of Gram-negative bacteria with special reference to the *Pseudomonadaceae*. *J. appl. Bact.*, 23:379.

SHEWAN, J M, HOBBS, G and HODGKISS, W The *Pseudomonas* and
1960b *Achromobacter* groups of bacteria in the spoilage of marine white fish. *Ibid.*, 23:463.

SREENIVASAN, A A note on the bacteriology of prawns and their
1959 preservation by freezing. *J. Sci. and Indust. Res.*, 18C:119.

TANSAUGARN, L The ecology of *Clostridium botulinum* type E in
1970 relation to the radiation pasteurization of fish in Thailand. Report to the International Atomic Energy Agency, Vienna. Research contract No. 549/R2/RB.

THOMPSON, M H and FARRAGUT, R N Shrimp freezing and refri-
1970 geration in the USA Proceedings, Conference on the Canadian shrimp fishery, St. John, New Brunswick, October 27-29, 1970. *Can. Fish. Rep.*, (17):185.

VELANKAR, N K The bacterial flora, trimethylamine and total
1956 volatile nitrogen of fish muscle at 3°C. *Indian J. Fish.*, 3:261.

VELANKAR, N K and GOVINDAN, T K Preservation of prawns in
1959 ice and assessment of their quality by objective standards. *Indian J. Fish.*, 6(2):306.

VELANKAR, N K, GOVINDAN, T K, APPUKUTAN, P N and IYER, K M
1961 Spoilage of prawns at 0°C and its assessment by chemical and bacteriological tests. *Ibid.*, 8(1):241.

VELANKAR, N K and KAMASASTRI, P V The bacterial flora, tri-
1956 methylamine and total volatile nitrogen of fish muscle at 0°C (in ice). *Ibid.*, 3:269.

VENKATAMARAN, R and SREENIVASAN, A Bacterial flora of mackerels.
1952 *Ind. Jour. Med. Res.*, 40(4):529.

WALKER, P, CANN, D and SHEWAN, J M The bacteriology of 'Scam
WALKER, P, CANN, D and SHEWAN, J M The bacteriology of
1970 'Scampi'. I. Preliminary bacteriological, chemical and sensory studies. *J. Fd Technol.*, 5:375.

WATANABE, K Spoilage in iced 'Pescada-Foguete' (*Macrudon*
1962 *ancylodon*) from South Brazilian Fishing Grounds. *Inst. oceanogr. Univ. S. Paulo, Contr.* (163), p. 65.

WATANABE, K Technological problems of handling and distribu-
1965 tion of fresh fish in Southern Brazil. In R Kreuzer (ed.), *The Technology of Fish Utilization*, London, Fishing News (Books) Ltd., p. 44.

WATANABE, K Handling and keeping quality of iced Kariba Bream,
1965 *Tilapia mortimeri* Trewavus (syn. *T. mossambica* Peters).
–66 *Fish. Res. Bull. Zambia*, 4:59.

WHITAKER, D R Trends in world shrimp demand and production.
1970 Proceedings, Conference on the Canadian shrimp fishery, St. John, New Brunswick, October 27-29, 1970, *Can. Fish. Rep.*, (17).

Acknowledgment

The author thanks the staff of the Fishery Technology Laboratory, Bangkok, for their cooperation during this study, in particular Miss Bung-orn Kasensarn, Mr Arun Rattagool and Miss Krisana Tipchong who carried out the chemical analyses.

Discussions on Part V

Quality requirements and standardization

These topics attracted much attention as they are related to both product development and marketing. A topic of current interest is legislation with regard to minced fish and products derived from it (see also chapter IV 'New products').

SOUDAN (France) contended that a definition of 'quality' rests on four criteria—hygiene, nutritive value, taste and aesthetics. While the basis of such evaluation may be the same in all countries, the conclusions are different because the situations are different. For example, permittable toxic levels vary according to species and locations, and acceptable levels of contamination vary according to dietary habits and the degree of general contamination, while levels of bacteriology differ according to the variability of the population, and the state of freshness of the product, depending on local tastes and conditions. Flavour and aesthetic characteristics, too, vary from country to country and from group to group within a country. It is, therefore, impossible to draw up quality standards which could be applied throughout the world. Nevertheless, standardization is necessary in view of the expansion of the markets. Standardization should be undertaken by restricting the coverage of each standard in such a way that it covers a well-defined product. This standard should be applied throughout the world. In cases where a series of similar products exist, a group standard would list the various characteristics. Moreover, the codes of practice indicate the handling and processing practices to be followed and they serve as a guide for the numerous products which are in international trade but will not be standardized for a long time.

NAKAMURA (Japan) explained that inspection of fishery products for export is organized in Japan in two ways: compulsory and voluntary. The compulsory inspection is conducted through the Ministry of Agriculture and Forestry and covers such items as canned fish and shellfish, frozen products, fish meal, oils, etc. Canned and frozen products are inspected by institutes nominated by the Government, while all other items are inspected by one of five Government institutes. The voluntary inspection covers such items as dried squid and other salted or dried fishery products. Such inspection is the responsibility of the export organizations concerned, with the Government keeping a watching brief through random sample checks and through the reports on inspection results made by the organizations. All items passed for export are licensed and export certificates for them are issued. The quality inspection of the products by organoleptic assessment and chemical and physical analysis covers colour, texture, flavour and odour. External damages are checked and so are such items as packing.

BLACKWOOD (Canada) also stressed the importance of quality control in export trade and the need for countries to understand each others quality requirements and standards.

BALASINGAM (Malaysia) said that his country has a Standards Institute but it is not compulsory for an exporter to obtain an export certificate for his products. Mostly, the exporters do not believe that such a certificate guarantees entry of the products into the markets.

HEEN (Norway) mentioned that minced products, which are already popular in some countries, will soon find a wider world market and stressed the need to look into the problems of quality control and standards as a matter of some urgency. He proposed that the Conference should set up an *ad hoc* working group under the chairmanship of Blackwood to exchange information on this whole question and draw up a list of headings under which experience and technical data might be assembled by FAO. Many speakers supported this idea and such a group was established. It submitted the report which is summarized below.

BRAEKKAN (Norway) and several other speakers referred to the need for a code of practice for minced fish to be prepared by Codex Alimentarius. Braekkan said that analytical information of all kinds is required before a code can be drawn up. FAO has been requested to collect background material.

KREUZER (FAO) informed the meeting that FAO, had in fact, been requested to look into this question in 1974 and will compile all the available information on the technology of minced fish processing to produce a background paper for the preparation of a Code of Practice.

YOUNG (U.K.) referred to the new possibilities for FPC products with functional properties, as for example, the production of sophisticated fish analogues or the extension of existing fish products through the incorporation of FPC with functional properties. In view of this emerging situation there is an urgent need to consider the legal implications of the new technology, particularly the labelling of the products. He urged that the Conference should support the framing of such legislation so long as it is not inhibitory to the introduction of new fish products for human consumption.

Report of the Ad Hoc Working Group on Comminuted (Minced) Fish

The terms of reference of the group were:

To discuss the gathering of technical data for consideration by FAO of a code of practice for fish blocks made wholly or in part from comminuted (minced) flesh of fish and shellfish.

The discussion on the processing of fish raised the question of whether a standard should be developed for blocks made from minced fish. It was recognized that this was a very complex matter, in view of the great variety of fish and parts of fish used, and because of the many ways in which this material is extracted. While the technology of comminuted fish is still largely in the development stage, many countries are now making consumer products with this material and are selling it internationally. It was felt therefore that this experience should be gathered and conveyed to FAO for coordination and for the possible development of a code of practice.

A group, chaired by Dr C M Blackwood, met to identify the subject headings under which present experience and technological data might be assembled and suggested the following divisions: Raw Material, Method of Manufacture, Product Composition, Quality Criteria, Microbiology, Additives, and Product Labelling.

Part VI

MARKETS

347

Planning to Expand Markets in Developed Countries   *A H Coburn*

Planification de L'expansion des marches dans les pays developpes

L'auteur expose les problèmes que les ressources limitées et de plus en plus restreintes de matière première posent à l'industrie en général et à son entreprise (Findus) en particulier. Il est persuadé que ces difficultés peuvent être surmontées grâce à un renforcement de la collaboration internationale pour réglementer les captures et il indique à titre d'exemple comment son entreprise a adapté l'offre à la demande et comment elle essaie de modifier les goûts nationaux traditionnels.

Planificacion para ampliar los mercados en los paises desarrollados

El autor esboza los problemas que tiene planteados la industria en general y su compañía (Findus) en particular para abastecerse de materias primas, limitadas y en disminución, a causa de la competencia. Opina que el problema podría resolverse mediante una colaboración internacional más eficaz para limitar las capturas y da ejemplos de cómo su compañía ha conseguido equiparar el abastecimiento a las necesidades y de cómo se esfuerza por modificar los gustos nacionales tradicionales.

The vast majority of fishing operations throughout the world are not coordinated to satisfy a market or markets, so we need to organize a grand strategy to rid ourselves of the underlying defects in the present system which, to my mind, makes planning a nightmare. In other words, we urgently need what the Japanese call "kei ka ku", which we call "planning". If there is a world fishing crisis then, like most others, it is man-made, and is within man's ability to resolve. We should look at what planning can achieve and at examples of where it has worked in practice. In this connexion my own company provides an example of implementing programmes based on planning. And what we have gained from our experiences may hopefully be utilized in other countries.

CASE OF CRISIS

For centuries man has cultivated vegetables and animals for food and high degrees of efficiency have been achieved. The basis for this activity rests on the fact that the land is either owned or let to an individual, group or nation. However, this convenient situation does not exist with the oceans. Extracting protein from them, usually in the form of fish, (apart from those certain limits agreed by international law) is an occupation open to anybody who happens to have a rod and line, a rowing boat and net, or a vast floating factory ship. As a result, it is a free-for-all with everybody trying to catch as much fish as possible. International chaos is the order of the day. While marine biology holds greater available treasures than space, the use of science in the race to extract more protein (fish) has so far aggravated, not improved, the situation as it has in the case of agriculture. I am of course talking about the use of trawling equipment which sweeps the oceans, with the danger of fishing species into extinction. Certain types of whales, for example, are victims of man's efficiency and, more recently, there is the case of the decreasing herring. This catch-as-much-as-we-can attitude is a fairly normal human reaction. I have yet to meet a trawler skipper who really thinks 'I will leave some fish for the next time—or year'. For as he and all of us know, anything left will be hauled up by the next trawler that finds the shoal. So there are few effective methods—and less understanding of the need—as yet of limiting the rate of catch from a particular area. This situation is further complicated by the fact that there are certain countries, such as Norway and Iceland, with economies greatly dependent on fish and fishing, which consider they need special protection. But we must do something about over-fishing. There is no doubt that some fisheries are being over-exploited. In the Northeast Atlantic, for example, most herring fisheries have disappeared under the pressure of heavy fishing and the most marketable fish are already well exploited in the North Atlantic. Aberdeen was a major herring port only four years ago. Today, herring are landed there only during a brief summer season.

One problem as I see it is that the unpredictable nature of our industry encourages trawler owners to ignore their responsibilities for their catch once the fish is landed on the quayside. Too much of today's fish is sold by auction where *theoretically* the product is left to reach its real market value. In my experience the auction does not work for the benefit of the industry. It encourages overfishing and in times of glut produces unsatisfactory prices for both owners and crew and, in the long term, holds no benefits for the consumer for it cannot establish realistic price levels because its very nature tends to force prices down. For example, prices in the United Kingdom are still 'controlled' by the auction and, at present, 3·5 per cent of UK expenditure on food is accounted for by fish – the same figure as a decade ago. In terms of volume, fish consumption fell by 5 per cent between 1961 and 1971, largely attributable to rising prices. However, over the same period the consumption of frozen fish has continued to expand, from which we must conclude that convenience in preparation and shopping habit motivates the purchaser as much as price and it is important to note that the quick frozen fish product was developed very largely *by people unaffiliated with the trawling industry*.

Although a source of first-class protein, fish accounts for no more than 5 to 10 per cent of the protein intake of the average Briton. Why? Well, research reveals that negative attitudes still exist toward fish. A study in 1964 showed that fresh fish was even then a somewhat neglected food. It was bought often on impulse and eaten 'for a change'. People had little real enthusiasm for it and cooked it unimaginatively. Even so, it was thought nourishing and a good light meal, especially suitable for invalids. Other relevant points were that it was considered expensive, inconvenient to prepare and eat, mothers did not like the idea of their children swallowing bones, and it was smelly and unappetizing to look at. Whilst the wider acceptance of frozen fish and fish products in the United Kingdom has helped overcome some of these attitudes, I do not doubt that many are still widely and strongly held. These findings could probably represent the attitudes of many countries and unless we are prepared to change them fish consumption will *not* expand. There are four main markets for fish in the United Kingdom: domestic fresh fish consumption and fish and chip shops; frozen fish in retail packs; catering; and pet foods. Of these, the market for frozen fish is known to be growing as are those of the fish and chip shops and pet foods. Over the past four years, the *per caput* consumption of wet fish has declined by 27 per cent while frozen fish has increased by 18 per cent. With the decline of wet fish, the number of fishmongers has also declined – from 6,330 in 1961 to 5,466 in 1966 and 4,838 in 1971. So where a fishing industry has only concerned itself in the catching of fish, its product has gone into decline – while the sales of 'convenience' fish products have been expanded. Therefore, I am convinced that only by gearing a product to market needs can there be any guarantee of the right sort of profitability.

WHAT PLANNING CAN ACHIEVE

The United Kingdom argicultural industry, unlike its trawling counterpart, has accepted a fundamental planning philosophy and today there are countless farmers who are certainly wealthier for their recognition of the need for long-term planning. One argument put forward by the trawlermen why this approach would not work as far as fishing is concerned, is that they are essentially hunters whose livelihood is controlled by the elements. To a degree this is correct. But agriculture, too, it dependent on the elements. What market planning does is to bring stability through various controls to the see-saw curve of glut and famine. The present-day harmony between farmer and frozen food processor has taken a long time to establish. For its origins we must go back to the beginning of the industry's development, a history which might perhaps be helpful to countries where frozen food industries are not so highly developed because what has happened in Europe can – given time – happen in the developing countries. Frozen foods were very much a novelty in the United Kingdom during the immediate post-war period. Rationing was still in force and Government control and restrictions left manufacturers little room for manoeuvre. British housewives, deprived of the wide range of food which had been readily available prior to the war, clamoured for variety in their families' diet. Imports of convenience food from the United States during the war had helped introduce the new ideas of preservation and presentation. Additionally, an economic revival had begun which eventually allowed a far greater number of households to afford a fuller and more varied diet. The war period had also demonstrated to many housewives that it was possible to have a job and also raise a family successfully, which in turn meant they had less time for domestic chores and, therefore, began to seek quick and convenient meals for serving at home.

As with any successful marketing operation, we had to undertake a long search for information. We had to find out more about the market before we were in a position to plan to satisfy it. It soon became clear that not only answers to some of the more obvious questions required confirmation but an equal amount of fundamental research was necessary on the technical side in order to develop the products and production techniques which would meet consumers' demands. This two-pronged research plan provided the basis on which our present industry is founded. Consumer research showed that

convenience was of prime importance and we publicized the advantages that frozen food has over traditional and other preserved foods. For instance, by using frozen food, housewives can have vegetables all-year-round at prices which rarely fluctuate. Due to the nature and sophistication of freezing techniques, frozen food can claim the quality of freshness which is sometimes missing from 'market' vegetables, fruit and fish. Then there is the time-saving factor – with frozen food there are no peas to shell, no beans to trim and slice, no fish to gut and fillet. And in the case of certain products, frozen food manufacturers have removed the many preparation chores associated with even the simplest of meals. Neither is there any waste with frozen foods. A pound of peas means exactly that – not a pound of peas, pods and vine. Having found answers to our questions, we were able to gear our promotional plans accordingly. In the early days it was an educational job as much as anything. The industry's advertising campaigns clearly stated the advantages which we knew to be true. We set out to get as many people as possible to sample frozen foods, knowing that once they had tasted them we would have achieved a major objective – to overcome any doubts as to the products' quality and value for money. Today the average Briton eats about 16lb (7 kg) of frozen food each year but this is low compared with the 66lb (30 kg) per head in the United States and the 29lb (13 kg) per head in Sweden. Despite the fact that sales last year reached a record £174 million, we still have a long way to go, and I can forecast with confidence that sales will reach £300 million (US$ 700 million) by the mid seventies. In its early stages the industry's attention turned to those food commodities which were in plentiful supply from United Kingdom sources – fish and vegetables. It was necessary to establish guaranteed supplies and this in turn meant the beginning of a long standing relationship between manufacturers and farmers. The suppliers had to be prepared to adhere to high standards of quality and had these standards not been established at the start, the industry could never have expanded to its present size at the rate it has. British farmers had been used to supplying certain vegetables in bulk to the canning industry and the fresh markets but the quality requirements of the frozen foods market was new to them. And while we had discovered what people were demanding, we were also aware of the problems associated with processing seasonal crops on a large scale.

Quick freezing is a natural way of preserving food, with the end products being only as good as the raw materials that are frozen. It was, therefore, essential that processors had absolute control over the growing of crops. So, for the first time, they invaded those areas of activity which were traditionally considered to be the province of farmers and market gardeners. In order to obtain planned quantities of raw materials with characteristics which we knew, through our consumer research, would sell, it became necessary to not only check soil and atmospheric conditions of a particular farmer's land, but also to supply the seed and indicate when it should be planted and harvested. It also meant that a regular watch on crop growth was necessary, along with the use of disease, insect and weed controls. In return for this cooperation the industry was able to offer guaranteed prices depending on yield. This was a rather difficult pill for some traditionally-minded farmers to swallow and change came slowly. But as the industry expanded and was forced to employ more accurate and sophisticated production planning techniques, so greater cooperation was sought and achieved from the farmers in England and in many other European countries. Our earlier experience in southern Sweden provides a good example. There, contract farming has enabled yields to be increased dramatically over the past two decades. When Findus started in Sweden in 1941, fruit and vegetables were purchased from local market-gardens and markets in much the same way that the majority of fish is obtained today. This produce was not fully suited to the requirements of the canning and freezing industry because the fruit and vegetables were intended for immediate consumption as fresh produce, and it soon became evident that it was not possible to build up an effective industry with such raw materials. We had to regulate the supply through contracts with local farmers and market gardeners to grow special crops for us. But what species should be grown? And how should they be grown? To answer these questions experimental comparative species were planted and in 1943 a permanent organization came into existence to deal solely with development work on raw materials. Later research work brought improved harvesting techniques and disease-free crops.

From the beginning the company sought to establish good relations with its growers. This cooperation includes among its aims correct and fair standards of payment, through which growers are given an added incentive in that quality and yield are taken into consideration when fixing prices. As a result, different varieties fetch different prices according to their specific yield and, further, the kilogramme price paid is often related to quality and degree of maturation. It has also been possible to renew the agreements automatically if no special circumstances have arisen. For example, if we wanted to grow a variety of special quality which gave a lower yield we would arrange a new agreement to compensate the growers for the smaller quantity. Most of the time, however, the trend has been toward greater yields. When Findus started to grow peas on a large scale, the average yield was about 1,750 lb/ac (1,960 kg/ha). In recent years the average yield has been around 4,200 lb/ac (4,700 kg/ha). This increase has been made possible by improved varieties, superior growing methods and more efficient harvesting. Greater interest and proficiency on the part of the growers has also helped in solving the problem. Many interested farmers have been able to carry out a crop proposal from Findus that has later been recommended to all growers. This close cooperation has over a number of years proved to be very rewarding for both farmers, processors and consumers so it was not unnatural for us to consider how a similar system might be established with fishermen.

IMPLEMENTATION OF PLANNING

Our first effort was an attempt to stabilize the purchase price of fish and to guarantee regular supplies at a predetermined price. For this purpose we signed a contract several years ago with a Hull trawler owner who agreed to supply frozen-at-sea fish. Such a contract made sense because the freezer trawler, unlike a normal trawler, is able to stay at sea without danger of the fish in the holds deteriorating. Our next step was more revolutionary. The middle and long-distance trawlers in Britain mainly use the ports of Grimsby and Hull. There is also a thriving fishing industry in Scotland where the trawlers concentrate on the fish found off the continental shelf and around the coastline. The fish is of high quality because of the relatively short time taken for catches to be returned to port. So, four years ago Findus decided to build a processing factory at Aberdeen to take advantage of this supply of herring, cod and haddock. Although important, quality is, however, only part of a successful marketing mix. Continuity of supply is also important for the efficient running of a production plant and to satisfy those customers who want to buy a particular product on a regular basis. With this in mind and because we could not rely on the fish auctions for supply, we made history when we agreed with a Scottish trawler owner to take the total catch of a vessel on contract. This agreement caused a stir in Aberdeen and led to the temporary boycott of a catch by another vessel owned by the same company. Fortunately this was only a temporary action by local fish merchants and they soon realized that it was the right of every fisherman to dispose of his catch as he pleased. The situation also led to the Press airing the defects of the auction system. One correspondent wrote:

'Auctioning is a method of disposal that makes costing a nightmare. Crews can return from a 15-day trip, hit a tight market, and take home 'jackpot' earnings. More frequently they find the market sluggish and returns disappointing. So many factors can upset the balance. A spell of warm weather, an abundance of small haddock and whiting, a strike by railwaymen or market porters – any one of these hazards can tip the scales against the fishermen. Only in winter, when gales hold up fishing operations and confine the smaller boats to port, does the auction guarantee glamour prices. There is the further disadvantage that the system creates acute berthing problems at the Aberdeen market as trawlers queue up for the chance to have their fish unloaded by the porters from 04·00 hours onward in time for the sales starting at 07·30 hours. With seine net boats and foreign trawlers also using the market it is often a chaotic scene and one causing some vessels to miss the market altogether. This means a wait of another 24 hours – a costly delay and one which does not help the quality of fish that may already have been on ice for 10 or 12 days. Findus believes the whole set-up to be outdated. It argues that contract buying would sweep away a host of problems. It wants to see boats returning to port and off-loading at any time of the day or night, and getting their fish away to the processors with minimum delay and at prices agreed on a long-term basis.'

Our contract for the whole catch is on a very simple basis. We jointly estimate the cost of running the vessel (in which we include return on capital), we agree the catch rate for the various species over the year, divide one into the other and arrive at an annual price. If the costs are higher or the catch is lower, or viceversa, the difference is shared on an equitable basis. The benefits of the contract system soon became apparent. For example, the skipper and crew of one contract trawler grossed over £100,000 (US$ 233,000) during its first year afloat. But record amounts of cash are not the only benefits. Contracting brings price stability which in turn allows the trawler owner to plan ahead to reinvest. It also means that the crews, for the first time, can rely upon a degree of financial and social security. Most of us here today can plan our working and social lives and contract fishing means that trawlermen and their families can plan theirs too. We have not made as much progress as we would have liked. However, it is still early days as it was with the farmer 20 years ago but I am convinced that in the long term this is the only sane method of procurement. We still have to buy substantial quantities of fish in the open market which makes it difficult to plan ahead when the quality of auctioned fish is often doubtful, when the size of fish could be too small, and when the handling leaves so much to be desired. Recent record market prices have sent several contract vessels scuttling back to the auction but we are determined to make our scheme succeed. It provides a prime example of how planning works and, as I have already stressed, in the long term it is the only solution.

PLANNING IN PRACTICE

World opinion appears to indicate that there are areas of our seas that are overfished. Yet because we know so little about marine life I am sure that it could easily be proved that there are still vast reserves of natural resources contained in the oceans. Dr. John Gulland of FAO, for instance, estimates that the present world catch could be doubled. If 80 per cent of such a catch were economically available, the potential would be about 100 million tons. If the present annual rate of increase continues such a quantity may be reached by the mid eighties. The loss of catches in the north and northeast Atlantic will probably be more than offset by the gains in new fishing elsewhere. There are still valuable resources to be exploited off California, South Africa, Southern Arabia and India.

So there does appear to be enough fish. The question is to determine:

(a) How much fish each nation *can or may* consume.
(b) Where the fish is located and how it can be caught most efficiently.

Despite the shortage of the traditional cod and haddock, there is an abundance of seafood of various species which the housewife is not yet prepared to buy – for reasons mainly traditional. Many species therefore find their way into fish meal for animal feedstuffs, which is an inefficient way of using seafood at current prices. For too long, countries have relied on an established national taste which is directly related to supplies of local national resources. Any attempt to change this situation is usually viewed with suspicion. Imagine the indignation of the average British family if they were served chop suey for Sunday lunch instead of roast beef or, even worse, could only have coley (pollack) instead of haddock for their fish and chips. Such attitudes toward food need to be changed. If we study the problem closely, it looks as though such changes could be brought about. Look, for example, at the opportunist growth of Alaskan pollack in the US market. As the seventies develop, it

seems likely that housewives will more and more want food which can be bought easily, stored easily for longer periods of time, and then prepared quickly, without too much skill or effort. Of all convenience foods, frozen foods have to date shown the fastest growth rates – which provides a wonderful opportunity for expanding the sales of fish as fish, not necessarily species by species. General interest in fish in the United Kingdom stems from the consumer's habitual preference for the three basic fish, and their ignorance of the food qualities of other species. The substantial market for canned salmon shows that tastes are more flexible than this, but to develop a taste for new fresh varieties would require a guaranteed sufficiency of supply and a specific promotional operation. This would involve a degree of preprocessing, so that what was marketed was, for example, 'hake steaks', or 'coley pie'. Ideally at least, some of these should be cheaper fish – such as coley – to overcome the public view that fish is expensive. We are all aware that coley is a dark fleshed fish and most people prefer fish with white flesh, but I am sure there must be some ways in which it can be presented and sold in the quantities in which this unwanted fish is landed. In Germany, for example, seelachs – which is nothing more than cured coley sliced and presented in the same manner as smoked salmon – is sold in substantial quantities. Then there are species of good, edible fish which are still regarded in my country as pet food. Yet, in the United States and Germany, for instance, bream or ocean perch (an unwanted fish in England) is regarded in the same light as we regard cod and haddock. So, if a market could be found for all the unwanted but still edible fish which is normallly processed into fish meal or used as pet food, then a major contribution to profitability as well as a more economic utilization of resources would have been found.

Twenty years ago the first real convenience fish food burst into the market – the fish finger (or, as is known in the United Kingdom, the fish stick). In a way, this is a wrong statement because the first was, undoubtedly, the fried fish from a fish and chip shop. The sale of this product is still expanding in England and could easily expand fish consumption in many other countries of the world. Today the fish finger or stick is the second best selling frozen food item in the United Kingdom after peas and accounts for 15 per cent of the total market currently worth £174 million. It is probably the biggest international breakthrough the industry will ever experience. The fish finger was an overnight success and mothers immediately began to get demands from their children to buy fish in the form of fish fingers. Earlier I referred to negatives as far as fish is concerned. Mothers did not buy fish for fear that their children would swallow the bones and they considered that fish was inconvenient to prepare, smelly and expensive. Fish fingers overcame all these basic objections. There is also the point that if you can start children eating fish – especially fish they like—at an early age the chances are you will have a life-long customer for fish. If fish fingers were served once a week to every school child in the world, think of the planning that would be needed! We supply every school in the Greater London area every week and not one fish finger ever finds its way into the waste bin.

We continue to try to develop new fish products. My company, on an international basis, has already made a start in building a new market by introducing products such as fish in sauces, fish pancakes and fish pie and results are encouraging. We are selling to a new generation of fish eaters who have been brought up on fish fingers and who accept frozen food as part of their daily diet. Over the years researchers have built up a fascinatingly accurate picture of our present and future customers. We predict that our prime target group, ie, the 20 to 39 year olds, will have increased by a fifth by the end of the seventies. We believe they will be better educated, marry younger and become more affluent and, therefore, be more receptive to new ideas and tastes because they will have travelled wider and will have had a chance to try foreign foods not only abroad but at home in the increasing number of Indian, Chinese, French, Italian and other restaurants now opening. Our research shows that domestic appliances will increase in importance for them, including – to the delight of the frozen food industry – sales of refrigerators and home freezers. Put these elements together and you immediately spot market opportunities. But finding these opportunities is not the end of the story. To make sure that new lines stand a chance of surviving, we embark upon exhaustive tests before considering launching a product nationally. These may take several forms – interviewing housewives individually, group discussions, or getting housewives to test the produce in their own homes Promotional activity backing new products is essential. Today it is possible, using sophisticated techniques such as measuring pre- and post-showing shifts in attitude, to estimate the impact of a particular television commercial or press advertisement. A new product may be in the pipeline for many months before we can be satisfied that it is ready to be introduced to the public and during this time practically all departments of the organization are involved. In the case of our pancakes filled with smoked haddock, for instance, our concept research tests showed overwhelming enthusiasm for a savoury filled pancake. But British housewives preferred the more familiar taste of smoked haddock rather than some of the existing continental fillings so we adapted the filling to British taste. Alongside the consumer research, we have organized the technical job of producing the pancakes on a mass scale which, because of the nature of the product, is a highly complicated operation and relies on the technological expertise found only in an organization of our size.

A great deal of money is required to advertise the claims one makes for whatever products one sells but to compete in a highly competitive market such as ours *is* expensive. But more importantly, the company must have a total commitment to its objectives, starting with the agricultural and fisheries aspects, and including consumer research, marketing, new product development, production planning, production, quality control, packaging, storage and distribution, advertising and sales. The company has to be a highly sophisticated machine because it operates in a complex market and it is successful only because everyone understands what the company is trying to achieve and *plans* to achieve it. Finally, as an example of a marketing approach, my company, whose reputation has long been established as producers of high quality fish, decided two years ago to exploit this to the full. Before embarking upon a full scale programme, we learnt from consumer research that British housewives – at least – had already established in their minds that if they considered a company's fish items to be of high quality, then the rest of its products were considered to be the same. So we went to work on creating TV commercials, posters and womens' press advertisements stressing that we were the fish products experts and that all the products we produced had an inbuilt culinary expertise, whether they be specially prepared vegetables, meat dishes or desserts, such as mousse. Our continuous monitoring of consumer attitudes leaves no doubt that our strategy is a success.

Analysis and Characteristics of United States Demand for Fishery Products *R Whitaker*

Analyse et caracteristiques de la demande de produits de la peche aux etats-unis

Les interactions offre-demande dans la détermination des prix jouent un rôle économique essentiel. Toutefois, les responsables des décisions dans l'industrie de la pêche commerciale n'ont pendant longtemps pas beaucoup recouru à l'analyse formelle de la demande sur les marchés. Les gouvernements peuvent faire grandement appel à l'analyse de la demande dans divers domaines: aménagement des pêches, activités d'education et de promotion, tarifs douaniers et contingents d'importation, programmes de subventions, programmes de pêche exploratoire, etc. En analysant les tendances des ventes des produits de la mer, ainsi que les variables qui exercent une forte incidence sur ces ventes, il est bon d'examiner en premier lieu les éléments fondamentaux de la théorie de la demande des consommateurs. Le présent document étudie les principaux facteurs qui déterminent la demande, de même que l'élasticité-revenu des prix. Ces facteurs englobent des paramètres tels que la distribution par âge, la répartition géographique de la population, le niveau d'instruction, le type de profession et le degré d'urbanisation.

Analisis y caracteristicas de la demanda de productos pesqueros en los estados unidos

Las interacciones de la oferta y la demanda a la hora de determinar los precios son elementos clave de la economía. A pesar de ello, los responsables de tomar decisiones en la industria pesquera no han solido recurrir mucho a análisis formales de la demanda comercial. Para los gobiernos pueden ser muy útiles los análisis de la demanda para todo lo relativo a regulación de la pesca, actividades de enseñanza y promoción, aranceles y cupos de importación, programas de subvención, programas de pesca exploratoria, etc. Al analizar las tendencias de las ventas de productos del mar y las variables que influyen de modo importante en ellas, es útil tener en cuenta ante todo los elementos básicos de la teoría de la demanda de consumo. Se examinan los principales elementos que determinan la demanda y la elasticidad de la misma en función de los precios y los ingresos. Entre dichos elementos figuran variables como la distribución por edades, la distribución geográfica de la población, el grado de instrucción, el tipo de trabajo y el grado de urbanización.

Why study demand and prices of sea food products? Who uses the results and how? What value are such studies to to the general public? The fisherman, the cooperative association, the processor, and the sea food distributor need accurate forecasts of consumption and prices for making intelligent adjustments in production and marketing. The administrator and the legislator must have sound theories and accurate measurements of demand as a guide to programmes, policies, and legislation.

Demand and price-making are key elements of economics. It is curious that agriculture and fisheries, though closely related in the market, have been at opposite ends of the spectrum with respect to the amount of price and demand analysis applied. A vast inventory of research on the prices of, and demands for, agricultural commodities has been built since 1920. USA agricultural policies of production, trade, reserve stocks, consumption, and prices lean heavily upon statistical research in demand (Waugh and Norton 1969). In comparison, research on prices of fishery products has been meagre. A programme on demand analysis of sea food should be mainly concerned with such subjects as the analyses of trends in sea food consumption; the identification and assessment of the effects of major economic, social, institutional and technological changes on these trends; the appraisal of income-consumption relationships and of the effects of supply and price factors; the study of the effects of differences in urbanization and region, family background and education, etc. The main emphasis should be on the development of a general framework of knowledge of sea food consumption for both national and regional markets, within which more detailed research can be fitted by local governments, educational institutions and private enterprise. The ultimate purpose of the programme is to expedite production-consumption adjustments in the fishing industry. It can be used by business firms, and, in some cases, government agencies, as the starting point for developing research and market expansion.

USES OF DEMAND ANALYSIS

When considering the framework for fishery management, the true impact of changes in landings of a given species on its price should not be neglected. Governments may also be involved in educational and promotional activities for fishery products. In order to develop efficient programmes, some knowledge of the relative substitutability among fish products and between them and meat is necessary. This can be determined only through the application of results of demand studies. Foreign trade is another area calling for demand analysis, such as in developing a method for predicting price changes to domestic producers and consumers as a result of possible tariff or quota changes. A government agency must continually evaluate its programme in order to assure that the maximum payoff to society is gained from these expenditures. This too requires demand analysis. Another case would be a large unexploited stock. Should the government expend a sizable amount of funds to assist the industry in developing the stock or in promoting its marketing? Would the introduction of a substantial amount from this resource depress the price of the product or related products to such a point that cost of

harvesting, processing and distribution cannot be covered? If so, then the governments' funds may be spent in other areas where the potential payoff to society is greater. Important areas of decision-making exist with individual fishery firms. It is up to each entrepreneur to decide how his firm's activities best fit into the economic situation. Each firm will wish to adjust its activities in order to increase its net profit. To do this intelligently, the firm must have some understanding of demand. Processing and marketing firms likewise require information on expected price movements in order to make reliable production, inventory, and pricing decisions.

CONSUMER DEMAND THEORY

In analysing the trends in sales of sea foods and the variables which influence them, it is useful first to consider the basic elements of consumer demand theory. Demand is generally defined as the various quantities of goods which will be taken off the market by consumers at all possible prices, other things being equal (Hicks 1946). Modern economic theory assumes that the consumer derives a certain amount of satisfaction or 'utility' from the goods purchases (Leftwich 1966). One is ordinarily confronted with a wide range of alternatives from which to choose. The problem is, therefore, one of choice among the vast number of possibilities so that the income spent will yield the maximum attainable total utility. There are numerous factors which bear upon the decision, including a number of variables called determinants of demand.

Determinants of demand

There are several major determinants, one of which is population. As the population increases, we would expect demand to increase. And as individuals become wealthier, they are able to purchase more goods and are able to upgrade their purchases to higher quality and more luxurious items without lowering consumption of other goods. Thus, purchasing power is very important. Another determinant is substitute goods. As the price of substitute goods change, this in turn influences the consumption of a particular item. For example, as the price of haddock (*Melanogrammus aeglefinus*) increases, we might expect consumers to buy more cod (*Gadus morhua*). Likewise, as the price of turbot (*Pleuronectidae*) decreases, we might expect people to consume more turbot and less flounder (*Pleuronectidae*). The reason it is necessary to have a clear understanding of these relationships is because in demand analysis we need to determine how much of a change in a dependent variable (say, quantity purchased) is due to each of the independent variables, such as price, consumer income, price of competing goods, size and characteristics of the population, inflation, etc. The price of any sea food may be affected by hundreds of variables. The reverse is also true. The consumption of any sea food may be affected by hundreds of factors, including the prices of all other foods. In view of this, it may seem presumptuous to try to explain prices by considering only a few variables. True, it is impossible to measure the effect of every factor that may have influenced price. Good statistical analyses of time series never result in perfect correlations. In practice, there are always unexplained 'errors'. Thus, we can never get the 'true' demand curve from statistics, but equations can give estimates of expected price or consumption.

Meaning of elasticities

In expressing the relationship of prices to consumption or the effects of population, income, and prices of other goods on the price-quantity relationships, we use the term elasticity. Price elasticity is consumer responsiveness to price changes. It is important from an industry standpoint to know something about the price elasticity of all items because it indicates what will happen to total revenue when price and/or quantity changes. The key question concerns total revenue. As price goes up, does quantity decrease enough to offset this? If the decrease more than offsets the increase in price, total revenue will go down and demand is said to be elastic with respect to price. If the decrease in quantity is less, total revenue will go up and demand is price inelastic. Thus, we are very interested in knowing whether an item is price elastic or inelastic. Income elasticity is also important. If incomes and quantity purchased of a particular sea food move up and down together, the income elasticity is positive. The larger the income elasticity, the greater will be the change in quantity purchased. The purchase of most goods, for example, lobster (*Homarus* spp., *Panulirus* spp.) increases with a rise in income. However, for some products, like whiting (*Merluccius bilinearis*), less is purchased in the United States when incomes increase. The expression of the relationship between the changes in the price of one item and the resulting change in consumption of another is called cross elasticity. The cross elasticity tells us the per cent by which the consumption of shrimp (*Penaeus spp.*), for example, is expected to change relative to the price of scallops (*Pectinidae*). All of these elasticities are important because a sea food industry needs to know the expected change in consumption of its products as prices, incomes, or prices of competing goods, change.

TREND ANALYSIS

Detailed research on market demand can be time consuming and expensive. It is beyond the reach of many individual firms and often the only available data are those compiled by government agencies which can give revealing trends in sea food demand for most countries. Figs 1 to 4 illustrate several trends that can usually be obtained from government statistics. We study trends for three main reasons: First, to describe past growth or decline; second, to project the future; and third, to discover underlying relationships. Past trends usually cover special years as we need alternative projections corresponding to possible alternative public policies. An obvious way to start is to project past trends into the future. This should tell us something about where our subject would stand 1, 2, 5, or 10 years from now, assuming no basic changes. Then we should adjust these projections to estimate what might happen if we should change our policies. As any such projection is

subject to error, the degree of error increases rapidly with the length of projection.

Sea food in general

There has been a relatively steady increase in US sea food consumption in the past 15 years by 1·6 per cent per year (Fig 1). Since this rate of growth is only fractionally higher than the rate of population increase, *per caput* consumption of sea food has been in the relatively narrow range of 10 to 12 lb (4·5 to 5·4 kg) *per caput*. Such trends, of course, do not reveal the causes for shifts in consumption, such as the declines in 1967 (primarily because of the Papal Decree of November 1966) and 1971 (primarily because of a lack of supplies). Once the general trend has been established, then it is necessary to try to ferret out more detail. The rise in US sea food consumption has come about almost entirely because of a rise in imports. The domestic industry has not been able to supply the growing demand for sea food. Such trends can be extremely important to countries with surpluses and the United States has become the largest export market for sea food in the world. Having established the sea food consumption *per caput*, it is of value to see if there have been any significant shifts among products. Consumers have tended to purchase a little more fresh and frozen sea food, about the same amount of canned products, but slightly fewer cured products, as the following table shows.

Year	Fresh and Frozen	Canned	Cured
	percentage of total		
1950	53	42	5
1955	56	37	7
1960	55	39	6
1965	55	40	5
1970	58	38	3

Fig 2 illustrates the trends in consumption and prices. It would be a fallacy to state that US demand for sea food has remained stable over the years because there has been no upward trend in *per caput* consumption. One definition of an increase in demand is that the same quantity is purchased at a higher price (Watson 1963). Demand is in constant flux because behind the price-quantity relation, such as shown in Fig 2, are always the preferences and tastes of consumers, their incomes, and the prices of substitute and complementary commodities. When they change, demand changes. Other useful data to examine are the trends in consumption of meat and poultry, for these are the principal competitors of sea food in most developed countries. Fig 3 reveals the long-run trends in competing animal protein foods in the United States and indicates that sea food has fared reasonably well. Sea food has retained a favourable national image despite the steady rise in red meat consumption and the spectacular increase in poultry consumption.

Individual commodities

In studying consumption trends for individual sea foods one may draw information from time series of *per caput*

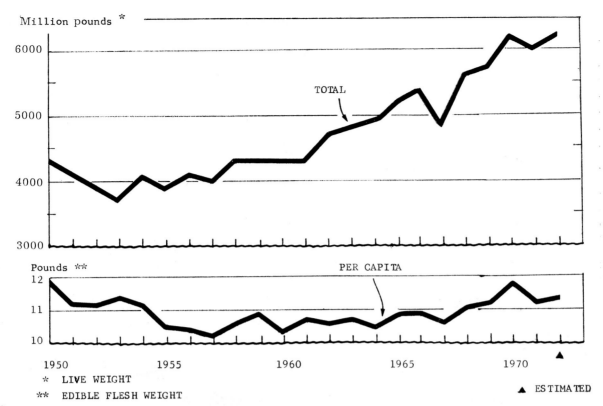

Fig 1 US Seafood consumption

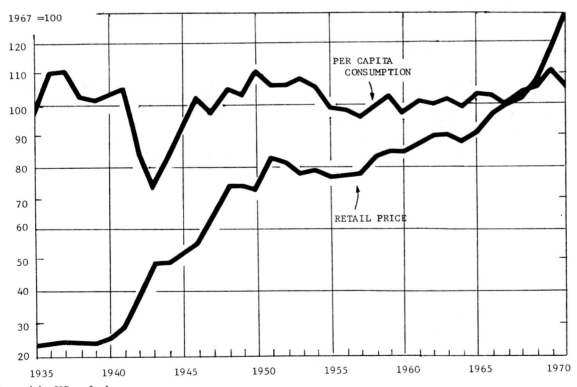

Fig 2 Demand for US seafood

consumption. This information should be related to all available economic data with the objective of observing and explaining past consumption levels, patterns and trends, and forecasting likely future changes. In planning, it is usually necessary to make projections of future prices, production, income, and other economic variables. This can generally be done by studying their past movements, isolating certain important relationships and using these relationships for projection purposes. Fig 4 shows a typical time series chart which illustrates trends for individual commodities. The curve for tuna consumption is the typical 'S' shape of many 'growth

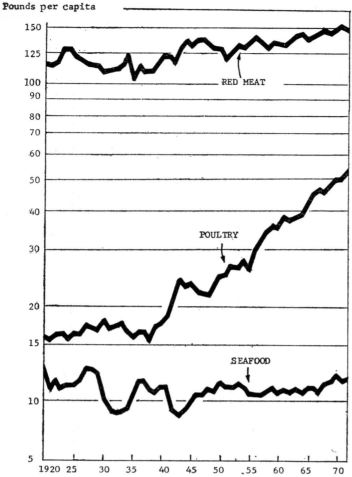

Fig 3 US Consumption of competing animal protein foods

drops at a gradually increasing rate until it reaches an inflexion point, then falls at a gradually decreasing rate, and approaches zero as a limit.

SOCIO-ECONOMIC SURVEYS

There are additional variables to consider which include age distribution, geographical population distribution, educational levels, levels of unemployment, distribution by types of employment, and extent of urbanization. All of these must necessarily be taken into consideration in any study that attempts to explain the nature of the relationships between sales and the factors that significantly influence them.

Regional patterns

The purchase patterns show that some sea food products have achieved the status of a national food while the consumption of many others is strictly regional. Groundfish are rather well known nationwide. Cod seems to be the most evenly dispersed, followed by ocean perch. New Englanders retain a large portion of the haddock for themselves, while marketing ocean perch in other regions of the United States (Fig 5).

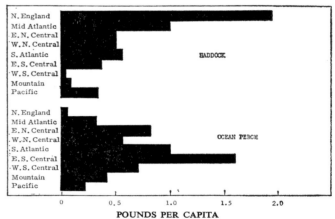

Fig 5 US Purchases by region

curves'. They start small, grow at an increasing rate until they reach a point of inflexion. Then grow at a decreasing rate and approach a maximum. The curve for salmon consumption is a sort of reverse S. It starts high,

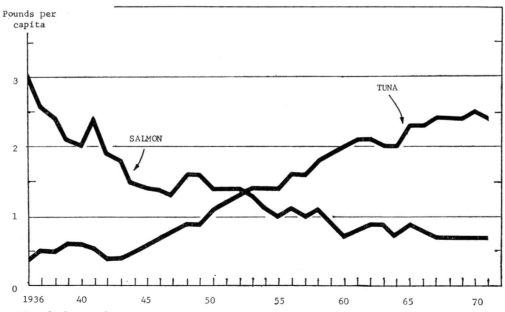

Fig 4 US Consumption of salmon and tuna

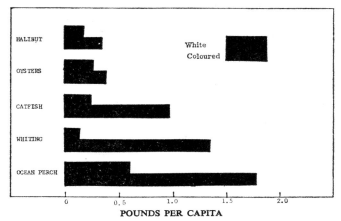

Fig 6 US Purchase patterns by race

Ethnic factors

Ethnic factors are important in determining consumption habits as shown in Fig 6. Coloured people purchased much more oysters, ocean perch (redfish), catfish (freshwater), and whiting, while others consumed more lobsters. Purchasers were about even for fresh and

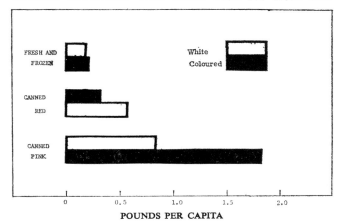

Fig 7 US Salmon purchases by race

frozen salmon, but showed considerable variation for red and pink canned salmon (Fig 7).

Religion

The three major religions in the United States provide a second measure of the ethnic variation in sea food con-

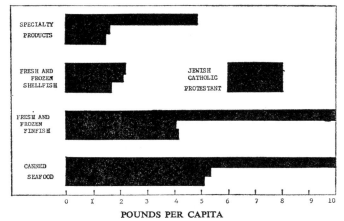

Fig 8 US Purchase patterns by religion

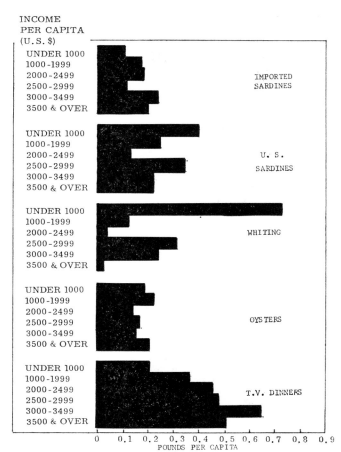

Fig 9 US Purchases by income levels

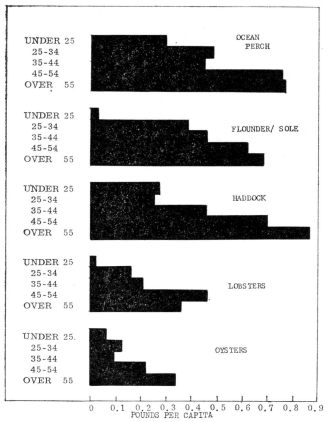

Fig 10 US Purchases by age of household head

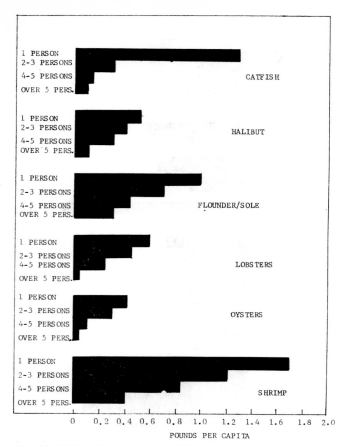

Fig 11   US Purchases by household size

size of the household can also be seen as a significant factor (Fig 11). The smaller households are the highest users. In nearly every product there is a decline as household size increases.

SOME LIMITATIONS OF DEMAND RESEARCH

Any discussion of the nature and functions of demand analysis would be incomplete without full recognition of the chief limitations. The interval between the inception of the analysis and its completion is very important. The results of demand analysis may not become apparent for some time – possibly months or even years – after a study has been completed. The data tend to be very difficult to obtain and the end results may prove inconclusive or negative. It is difficult to appraise the value of the results. In most instances, it is impossible to translate the value received from demand analysis into dollars and cents. Thus, there is a tendency to hesitate to make expenditures when the results are so intangible. Demand analysis is concerned with factors which are dynamic, a condition which precludes absolute exactness or reliability in the interpretation of the data. The time-series approach suffers from a difficulty in disentangling the 'time factor' from the data. Furthermore, it is not very suitable for deriving the elasticities of demand for classes of commodities and services, such as all food or all sea food (Schultz 1938). The family-budget approach also has severe limitations. It does not enable one to derive the elasticities of demand of intermediate goods, or goods that are not consumed directly by human beings, such as fish blocks, etc. It also does not yield a measure of the rate of shift of the demand curve, since the data relate to a single moment in time. It is not adapted for the analysis of the effects of substitutes (Schultz 1938). Despite such limitations, however, it should be stressed again that the analysis of market demand is an essential tool for the rational operation of the modern fishery industry. It provides a guide to all concerned with the processing, marketing and distribution of fish and fishery products and is also, as earlier stated, of value to all those legislators, administrators and controllers who are, in their own spheres, concerned with legislation, policies and programmes affecting fisheries.

sumption. Jewish households are the unquestioned leaders in sea food consumption. They rank highest in every major category of sea foods (Fig 8). There is little difference in the quantities consumed by Catholics and Protestants.

Income levels

Income does not appear to be as strong a factor in explaining purchases as is sometimes ascribed to it. When individual products are compared with incomes, there are significant differences, as Fig 9 shows. As income increases, purchases of imported sardines tend to increase while purchases of domestic sardines tend to fall. Whiting purchases are highly significant among lower income people. Oyster consumption seems to be fairly evenly distributed among all income levels. Convenience items, such as sea food TV-dinners, tend to be purchased more as income increases.

Characteristics of the household

Fig 10 shows an unmistakable pattern of higher consumption associated with higher ages of the household head, which may be an important long-run factor. The

References

HICKS, J R *Value and Capital*. Oxford, England, The Clarendon
1946   Press.
LEFTWICH, R H *The Price System and Resource Allocation*. New
1966   York, Holt, Rinehart and Winston, p. 47–65.
SCHULTZ, H *The Theory and Measurement of Demand*. Chicago,
1938   University of Chicago Press, USA, 817 p.
WATSON, D S *Price Theory and Its Uses*. Boston, USA, Houghton
1963   Mifflin Company, p. 15–27.
WAUGH, F V and NORTON, V J *Some Analyses of Fish Prices*.
1969   Working Paper No. 22, Division of Economic Research,
         Bureau of Commercial Fisheries, 199 p.

Development of Institutional Catering and Other Outlets for Fish in the United Kingdom   *J J Soulsby*

Developpement de l'alimentation collective et d'autres debouches du poisson au royaume-uni

L'auteur traite essentiellement des activitès et expériences de la White Fish Authority visant à développer le marché de l'alimentation collective pour le poisson au Royaume-Uni. Il décrit le cas précis de l'enquête faite par cet organisme sur le marché des repas scolaires, soulignant la nécessité de connaître à fond le système de l'alimentation collective et les caractéristiques des diverses collectivités en cause. L'enquête a comporté des essais d'acceptabilité à grande échelle. Les essais comparés faits avec des plats à base de viande ont abondamment démontré qu'il conviendrait de servir plus souvent du poisson. Les rapas distribués dans les écoles britanniques comprennent maintenant plus de poisson, mais il est difficile de chiffrer les quantités services. L'anteur fait état de l'extension de ces activités au domaine de l'alimentation dans les hôpitaux et mentionne les études sur le système des aliments précuits congelés qui se généralise actuellement au Royaume-Uni. Enfin, les questions suivantes sont brièvement évoquées: vente de poisson préemballé dans les supermarchés, vente par l'intermédiaire de marchands ambulants et mise au point de produits à base de mollusques, autant d'exemples de la façon dont est abordé le développement des marchés.

Promocion del consumo en comedores de instituciones. Y otras salidas comerciales para el pescado en el reino unido

El autor se ocupa ante todo de cuanto ha hecho el Organismo para el Pescado Blanco (White Fish Authority) para fomentar el consumo de pescado en comedores de instituciones del Reino Unido. Presenta el estudio realizado por el Organismo en el mercado de las comidas escolares, mostrando así la necesidad de conocer a fondo el funcionamiento del sistema de comedores y las características concretas de determinadas instituciones. Durante la investigación se realizaron ensayos de aceptabilidad a gran escala. Los ensayos comparativos hechos con platos de carne han permitido descubrir buenas razones para servir pescado con más frecuencia. Se sabe que en la actualidad se sirve más pescado en las escuelas del Reino Unido, aunque es difícil determinar la cantidad. Se menciona también lo que se ha hecho a este respecto en los comedores de hospitales y los trabajos realizados sobre el sistema de cocido/congelado, que en la actualidad emplean muchas instituciones del Reino Unido en sus comedores. Se alude también brevemente a la venta de pescado preenvasado en los mercados, a la venta en puestos móviles al por menor y la a preparación de productos a base de moluscos, dando así nuevos ejemplos de la forma como se ha abordado el problema de crear nuevos mercados.

Outside commerce the main agency for market development in the United Kingdom is the White Fish Authority (WFA) which, in conducting its research and development programme, works closely with the Torry Research Station (Ministry of Agriculture, Fisheries and Food). Approximately 31 per cent of the fish sold in Britain is still retailed by the fishmonger, although the number of fishmongers has decreased and probably will continue to decline. Sales of fish through supermarket and self-service outlets are growing, although this still only amounts to some 10 per cent of the total market. The fish frier (fish and chip shops) accounts for 39 per cent and it is believed that this trade will continue to do well, in line with the trend to convenience meals and 'fast food' consumption. The institutional market (schools, hospitals and other canteens) takes about 13 per cent and the hotel, restaurant and snack bar trade the remaining 7 per cent of the market. The aim of the White Fish Authority's market development programme is to improve the quality, presentation and availability of fish and to increase consumption. The programme involves new methods of presentation, improved methods of distribution and the development of new fish-based products. It is also concerned with improving long-term economic prospects for the fishing industry by increasing acceptability of fish and fish products, especially among the younger consumers. New products and new methods of presenting existing products, are tested under commercial conditions and the results are made available to the trade. The trials are carried out on a scale sufficient to provide practical experience of how the new or improved methods of marketing should be applied commercially. To avoid dissipating effort, the Authority has concentrated staff and resources on a limited number of projects.

INSTITUTIONAL CATERING

A major project in recent years is developing the institutional market. 'Institutional catering' covers a broad field of 'captive consumer' type establishments, including schools, hospitals, factories and old people's homes. The size of this market sector is considerable. For instance, the hospital service in the United Kingdom spends something like £45 million per annum on foodstuffs and the school meals service £85 million. Yet the frequency with which these institutions serve fish is low, when compared with competitive commodities. The Authority felt that, if more fish was to be sold to this market, the quality would have to be improved and that the caterers themselves must be persuaded to look after the fish and present it attractively to these consumers.

Fish in school meals

The School Meals Service is the single largest catering institution in the United Kingdom serving mid-day meals to approximately four million school children each day. The meals are prepared in 16,000 kitchens and served in nearly 30,000 dining rooms. To do this the School Meals Service employs more than 170,000 workers. The Authority involved itself first with school meals because of the size and accessibility of the market and because of the possible long-term influence on the young consumers. An adverse factor in this market was the policy of procurement by acceptance of the lowest tenders offered, which had resulted in the serving of poor quality fish. Much of the initial investigation was to educate WFA market-development staff and to assist the School Meals Service.

Acceptability trials in schools. Cod (*Gadus morhua* L.) is traditionally the most common species of fish served in British schools. At the time the Authority first involved itself in school meals catering (1967) the British fishing industry was becoming increasingly concerned at the depletion of cod and haddock (*Melanogrammus aeglefinus* L.) stocks. Although certain underutilized species were not considered as acceptable as cod when presented in fillet form, it was felt that they might be equally – or even more – acceptable if served in stick or portion form. Accordingly, the first trials were to determine the

359

acceptability of various species of fish presented in a variety of forms. Fillets, portions and fish sticks were prepared from good quality fish of the species *Pollachius virens* L. (coley); *Sebastes* spp. (redfish); *Merluccius capensis* (South Atlantic hake) and cod. The three forms were served, on a 'blindfold' basis, in schools in the three English towns. Eight schools were chosen in each town to cover all ages of school children and, as far as possible, a spread of socio-economic groups. Each trial extended over a complete school term. At each serving, kitchen supervisors were asked to rate their reactions on a scale and the returned waste (fish only) was weighed as a measure of acceptability. Cod was confirmed as the most popular species, with waste varying between 2 per cent and 5 per cent of the amount of fish served. Overall, however, acceptability of all species and forms seemed reasonably good with waste varying between 2 per cent and 11 per cent over the whole range. The Authority was encouraged by the apparent low plate waste and particularly wanted to know how fish measured up in terms of other protein dishes – particularly meat.

Comparisons with meat. Accordingly, the scope of the trials was extended to include comparisons with commonly served meat dishes. Arrangements were made with a city education authority for a total of 16 different meat and fish meals to be served in eight schools to 3,000 children on a number of different occasions. As with previous trials, measurements were made of waste portions and supervisors were questioned regarding their opinions and attitudes to each meal under test. In addition, measurements were made of the cost, convenience in preparation, losses during preparation and methods of preparation of the various dishes. The trial extended over a complete school term (13 weeks). A study of the results showed clearly that from a cost point of view, weight for weight, fish is a considerably better proposition than meat. The delivered cost of meat was more expensive. Trimming losses from meat were greater and the losses in cooking – particularly in some of the roast meat dishes – were very high. Finally, it was found that, on average, a higher percentage of the meat was rejected. In some cases, the level of waste exceeded 50 per cent. The findings of this trial provided the Authority with strong arguments for the more frequent serving of fish in schools.

Frequency of serving fish in schools. The United Kingdom Department of Education and Science (1965) had, in a Working Party Report, recommended that out of every 20 meals served in schools, two should be fish and twelve meat. This recommendation was based on what was considered to be a desirable and nutritionally balanced intake for school children. The Authority had, however, by this stage accumulated sufficient experience of school meals to call into question the justification for this recommendation. A study (White Fish Authority 1971a) revealed that fish was in no sense nutritionally inferior to beef, pork or mutton and in terms of supplying high protein/low calorific food it was vastly superior. The low calorie aspect is considered important in view of the growing incidence of obesity in United Kingdom school children (British Medical Association). The White Fish Authority (1970) argued that if the purpose of school meals is to provide, at reasonable cost, nutritious food

acceptable and palatable to the children and to those who prepare and serve it, then quite clearly a greater utilization of fish is called for both on grounds of cost and cost effectiveness. The Authority pressed for the inclusion of more fish meals at the expense of some of the more costly, or less popular, meat dishes. The value to the British fishing industry of increasing the number of fish meals, from two to four per month in all schools, was calculated to be of the order of £2 million (1969). The Department of Education and Science maintained that the local education authorities were at liberty to use their discretion in interpreting what was, after all, only a recommendation and that it was up to the White Fish Authority to persuade individual school meals organizers to incorporate more fish in the menu. A school meals campaign was subsequently mounted by the Authority.

Quality of fish in schools. In pressing the case for serving fish more frequently, it is vitally important to insist on good quality. All too often the institutional, or large-scale caterer, is likely to be supplied with poor quality fish by the merchant who reserves prime quality for the retail market. In fairly wide-ranging surveys of the quality of fish supplied to schools, Torry Research Station staff revealed that fish is occasionally served in schools in what can only be described as an inedible condition. The Torry Research Station surveys tied in with further large-scale acceptability trials by the Authority to examine the relationships between consumer acceptability and fish quality or, more precisely, the degree of freshness of the fish. Cod, covering a range of qualities from approximately three days to sixteen days in ice (aged and measured in terms of Torry taste panel scores) were served in schools, on a 'blindfold' basis, over a period of two years. Plate waste was once more used as the main measure of acceptability. These trials indicated clearly that both school children and catering staff react adversely to poor quality. The reaction is not pronounced up to, and including, fish 10–11 days in ice after catching. Thereafter, plate waste increases markedly until the 15–16 day-old stage is reached, at which point the increase is dramatic and, indeed, it is extremely difficult to get the fish accepted at the kitchen door. Work in this field confirmed that one of the main obstacles to increased utilization of fish in schools was the problem of quality. School catering staff were apprehensive about ordering fish and, understandably, many were unable to specify their requirements exactly or to judge the suitability of the product delivered. Accordingly, the White Fish Authority and Torry Research Station, between them, drew up purchase specifications for a wide range of fish products and forms of presentation, specially for the guidance of school catering authorities (White Fish Authority, 1971a).

Purchase specifications and advisory/inspection services. The purchase specifications are 'tailored' to the requirements of the School Meals Service, having regard to their particular system of contracting for supplies and to their requirement for precise portion sizes (laid down at 3 ounces (85 g) per child). The specifications provide an objective means of measuring the quality of products delivered, not only by such criteria as skin content, bone content, method of packaging, temperature at delivery, etc, but also in terms of spoilage or eating quality. In emphasis on spoilage and eating quality, these specifications are more advanced than many that have been published and applied elsewhere. Judging the quality of fish is not easy and it was recognized it would be necessary to back the purchase specifications up with technical advice. Accordingly, the Authority established a small Advisory/Inspection Service and made this available to education authorities who use the specifications. There is no doubt that this has been a key factor in imparting confidence to those in the School Meals Service who were dubious about fish supplies. In addition to inspecting deliveries and providing advice on all aspects of fish procurement, the service is also responsible for advising suppliers and merchants in the fish trade how they can best meet the set standards.

Handling and presentation of fish in schools. The fact that good quality fish is delivered to schools does not, in itself, guarantee that the same good quality will be enjoyed by the children. In the quality surveys conducted by Torry Research Station it was observed that fish is often badly stored and mishandled in the kitchen. A campaign was therefore organized by the Authority, to ensure that appropriate advice was given to school cooks in such matters as handling, storage, thawing and preparation of fish (Early and Malton 1970). Most fish served in schools in the United Kingdom is deep fried and, indeed, this is perhaps the most popular form of presentation. Nevertheless, fish can be prepared conveniently and attractively in a variety of other ways and further large-scale trials by the Authority established the suitability (and popularity) of a number of alternative recipes for institutional catering. In many of these dishes it is possible to incorporate the so called underprized species of fish without loss of acceptability and considerable emphasis is laid on the use of such species in cookery demonstrations provided by the Authority as part of its school meals campaign.

School meals campaign. In 1970, the Authority embarked on a campaign aimed at establishing contact and permanent links with each local education authority – there are 215 in the United Kingdom. The fact that the White Fish Authority had conducted trials in schools involving more than 15,000 children and had gained a wealth of experience in all practical aspects of school catering, enabled the staff to speak from a position of strength. The objectives of the campaign were twofold. First, the services available to school caterers were made known, the purchase specifications were introduced, the advisory/inspection services were explained and cookery demonstrations were arranged. Then, second, the information gained in the course of trials and other work was used to persuade school authorities to serve fish more frequently. Five main arguments or selling points were used: cost; cost effectiveness; nutritional merits; popularity and high level of acceptability with children; convenience in preparation. The purchase specifications and back-up services have been particularly welcomed and (at the time of writing) it is estimated that 40 per cent of all school purchasing authorities are now using the specifications in ordering their requirements. It is extremely difficult to quantify the extent to which schools are serving more fish, but many are known to be doing so and undoubtedly the School Meals Service has more confidence in fish as a result if this work.

Hospitals meals

The White Fish Authority has extended its interest in the institutional market to hospitals. Although there are less than 3,000 hospitals, the size of the market is considerable since patients and staff receive all meals in hospital, rather than one a day as do the school children. The Authority conducted surveys in several hospitals to ensure that the WFA staff became fully conversant with the problems of hospital catering before attempting to approach the specialist caterers. The problems do not differ overmuch from those in schools. The type of food required is similar and special dietary requirements feature only insignificantly. Torry Research Station also carried out comprehensive surveys, over a number of years, on the quality of fish delivered and handling practices within hospital kitchens. Following these, purchase specifications for hospital caterers were drawn up (White Fish Authority 1971b) and the Authority recently initiated a campaign, similar to that implemented in schools. The purchase specifications do not differ from those prepared for schools in terms of quality limits and tolerances. They do, however, differ in the advice given relative to the hospital system of contracting for supplies. The structure of the Hospital Catering Service differs considerably from the School Meals Service. The regions are larger – there are 21 in the United Kingdom – and the campaign is being conducted by holding a series of 'teach-ins' in these various hospital regions. In this case, too, the purchase specifications and follow-up services have been particularly welcomed, the specifications having been adopted as standard ordering procedure by the Hospitals Supplies Board.

Other institutions

It is intended to extend this approach to other institutions, notably industrial or factory canteens although it is vitally important to maintain pressure and contact with the institutional and individual caterers already covered. Unfortunately (or fortunately, depending on the view taken) the pressure of work grows geometrically, as the net is spread wider and the field that can be covered is limited by staff commitments. In the event of such limitations, it may be wiser to hold the ground already taken than extend the sphere of operations.

Cook/freeze catering

The institutional catering market in the United Kingdom is undergoing considerable change with the introduction of the cook/freeze system of catering. The system involves the preparation and cooking of meals in central kitchens, their freezing and storage, their distribution in frozen form and their subsequent reconstitution in convection ovens close to the dinning area. The system offers several adavantages. Firstly, food can be purchased in bulk, often at seasons of plenty and frequently at advantageous prices. Secondly, the ability to prepare food in central kitchens means that fewer kitchens are necessary and this can reduce the level of capital investment in buildings. Finally, the recruitment of catering staff is less of a problem since fewer cooks are needed to serve the same number of consumers. To ensure that fish does not get forgotten or ignored by the developers of this system, inadvertently or because it presents peculiar problems,

Fig 1   White Fish Authority test retail van

and to ensure that it is processed in the most acceptable way, one of the White Fish Authority's Food Technologists is conducting work to improve the presentation of fish dishes currently being served and to test additional recipes suitable for the system. There is a danger that conventional recipes normally used by institutional caterers may be discarded if they do not lend themselves to the system or if they create problems. Fish, coated in batter and fried, did not at first turn out well when frozen and subsequently thawed, but considerable success has been achieved by the Authority in improving the acceptability of this very popular dish for the cook/freeze process. The work is being conducted in a city production unit and some Authority procedures have been adopted as standard in the preparation of fish meals. The ultimate aim is to prepare process sheets for both new and improved fish dishes to persuade caterers to use fish more frequently. Incidentally, this system of catering is also coming into use on commercial fishing vessels in the United Kingdom.

OTHER OUTLETS AND PROJECTS

Prepackaged fish

Another project is the sale of prepackaged fish through supermarket and self-service outlets. The term prepackaged fish, as it is used here, means 'catch-weight',

flexible and transparent sealed film packs as opposed to the standard weight, cardboard cartoned consumer packs. It was recognized that wet fish must command counter space in the supermarket, as well as in the fishmonger's shop. Early commercial attempts failed because of the difficulty of maintaining product quality. With Torry Research Station, the WFA developed a system which guaranteed a minimum standard of quality to the consumer, and codes of practice for the preparation, distribution and retailing of chilled prepackaged fish were tested on a large scale and made available to the trade. Following the trials, most large supermarket groups in the country engaged in the sale of prepacks and the size of the trade is now considerable. However, because of the relatively low volume of sales of fish and the short shelf life problem associated with wet fish, many of the retail groups have been undecided whether to sell chilled or frozen prepacks. An experiment therefore was set up to measure consumer preference and to compare the costs of processing, distributing and retailing. Unfortunately, there was no clear-cut answer. The sales figures indicated a marginal preference for the frozen form. Consumer attitude research conducted in the stores, however, revealed that the majority of customers either could not, or did not, distinguish between the chilled and frozen forms. The costs of processing were not found to differ significantly but the shorter shelf life of the chilled product entails more frequent deliveries to the retail outlets, reflected in higher distribution costs. In addition, the relatively short in-store shelf life and consequent higher wastage of chilled prepacks means they are less profitable to retail. Such wastage could probably be reduced, or even eliminated, given a higher level of sales and close in-store supervision. But in the present market climate, where fish does not enjoy such high turnover as other basic food commodities, retailers are more likely to sell frozen, rather than chilled prepackaged fish. Indeed, this is the way the market in UK supermarkets is currently developing.

Improving distribution through motor van sales

A further project is the sale of fish from motor vans. It is believed that motor van retailing could be one of the most effective ways of improving distribution and expanding the market for fish, particularly in areas of high density population, such as new housing estates, where the residents are often far from fish shops but are not accustomed to, or equipped for, once-a-week supermarket shopping. The Authority is using a test vehicle, the object of the project being to indicate the most profitable selling situations and methods of operation, to produce codes of practice for the handling of fish in motor van retailing and to prepare vehicle specifications which incorporate desirable design features (Fig 1).

Development of products based on cockles and mussels

Recently, the importance of developing the mollusc resources of the United Kingdom has been recognized and the Authority believes that diversification of presentation is probably the most effective way of expanding the market. The need to involve industry is also recognized and a contract has been placed for the development of products based on cockles (*Cardium* spp.) and mussels (*Mytilus* spp.), with a company already engaged in shellfish marketing. Several promising products have been prepared and one or two are now undergoing preliminary market tests.

Pacific oysters

The White Fish Authority fish cultivation unit has developed a viable technique for hatching and rearing Pacific oysters (*Crassostrea gigas*). If this animal is to be grown commercially, then a wider market than exists at present for oysters must be found. A programme is in hand to identify potential outlets, relating these to appropriate forms of presentation. A limited number of oyster products has been developed, including breaded oysters, oysters in batter flavoured with Guinness, a dark sweet beer traditionally consumed with oysters, also pastry flans and dishes 'on the half-shell'. Some of these seem particularly appropriate for the bar trade and a test is underway in London to verify this.

CONCLUSIONS

As the examples given in this paper show, there are certain general conclusions which relate to the method of approach to market development projects. Briefly, these are:

(1) It is vitally important to acquire a thorough understanding of the market sector concerned. Knowledge of the practical, everyday problems which arise in the commercial situation will lend credibility to the case presented.

(2) Market tests, acceptability tests or market research should be conducted objectively (eg, plate waste or sales figures are more convincing than opinions) and be carried out on a sufficiently large scale to convince commercial interests.

(3) Research and development projects should be conducted in the commercial environment or in conjunction with commercial companies. This improves the chance of the results being applied commercially.

(4) In a commercial situation where the potential users may not be interested, or are only mildly interested, cost or profit arguments are especially needed to support the case being made.

(5) Fish inspection can be a very real aid in developing markets where the consumer is apprehensive and where quality is a prime cause of the apprehension.

References

British Medical Association *Overweight children*, London.
EARLY, J C and MALTON, R Fish For Caterers and Friers. *Torry* 1970 *advis. Note*, (42):11 p.
United Kingdom. Department of Education and Science *The* 1965 *nutritional standard of the school dinner*. London, HMSO.
White Fish Authority *Fish in schools meals*. London. 1970
White Fish Authority The nutritional value of fish. *WFA Fish* 1971 *Industry Review*., 1(4).
White Fish Authority, Herring Industry Board and Torry Research 1971a Station. *Purchase specifications for Education Authorities*. London, White Fish Authority.
White Fish Authority, Herring Industry Board and Torry Research 1971b Station *Purchase specifications for Hospital Caterers*. London, White Fish Authority.

The Manager's Approach to Evaluating the Feasibility of Food Protein Ventures   *J R Champagne*

Criteres d'evaluation de la rentabilite de la production de proteines comestibles

Avant d'engager des resources financières et humaines importantes dans la fabrication de produits, il importe au plus haut point d'évaluer plusieurs facteurs critiques. Dans le présent document sont brièvement examinés un certain nombre de ces facteurs intéressant la production de protéines de poisson. S'il est techniquement possible de fabriquer pour ainsi dire n'importe quel type de

Evaluacion de la viabilidad de la fabricacion de proteinas alimenticias (punto de vista de un director)

Antes de dedicar grandes sumas de dinero y abundantes recursos humanos a la preparación de un producto, es necesario evaluar diversos factores críticos. En este trabajo se examinan brevemente algunos de estos factores en el caso de una empresa de preparación de proteínas de pescado. Aunque desde el punto de vista técnico es prácticamente factible preparar cualquier tipo de proteínas de

protéine de poisson, il n'en existe pas moins divers problèmes. L'un d'eux est dû au fait que l'approvisionnement en matière première est très limité au voisinage de nombreuses zones peuplées. D'autre part, les meilleures possibilités d'approvisionnement semblent se trouver à proximité des régions où existe un besoin nutritionnel et où l'acceptation des protéines de poisson par les consommateurs est souvent satisfaisante. Dans l'ensemble, la rentabilité économique de la production de protéines de poisson est déterminée par la situation des disponibilités en matière première et par le pouvoir d'achat du consommateur. Lorsqu'il existe une crise nutritionnelle, les problèmes de rentabilité peuvent être surmontés à l'aide de subventions gouvernementales. Mais, si l'on veut intéresser l'industrie privée à la production de protéines de poisson dans une région où aucun besoin nutritionnel ne se fait sentir, il faut aussi tenir compte du rendement des investissements. L'auteur étudie un cas concret de commercialisation des protéines de poisson.

pescado, hay siempre dificultades que afrontar. Una es que el suministro de materias primas en las proximidades de muchas zonas populosas es muy escaso. Por otro lado, las mejores posibilidades de abastecimiento se encuentran cerca de zonas necesitadas desde el punto de vista nutritivo y en las que con frecuencia la aceptabilidad de las proteínas de pescado por parte del consumidor es satisfactoria. En general, la viabilidad económica de la producción de proteínas de pescado se ve afectada por la situación del suministro de materias primas y el poder adquisitivo de los consumidores. Allí donde existen crisis de nutrición, las dificultades de viabilidad económica pueden superarse con la ayuda de subvenciones estatales. Pero si se quiere que las industrias privadas se interesen por una empresa de fabricación de proteínas de pescado en mercados donde no existen crisis nutricionales, es preciso tener en cuenta también los beneficios de las inversiones. En el trabajo se presenta un estudio casuístico sobre comercialización de proteínas de pescado.

Over the past ten years, a good deal of time has been expended in research on means to produce fish protein. Progress has been encouraging from the technical view, and we can be assured that technologists have the tools to utilize this major resource for the common good, if necessary. The term 'if necessary' implies a conditional situation relating, of course, to a *need*. It may also refer to the existence of a *market*. As with all new products under evaluation by potential producers, a need or a market must exist to justify investment by the producer. Whereas the technical and nutritional aspects of producing fish proteins (FP) are well documented, there are few references to the marketing or business aspects. In the USA a comprehensive market survey for proteins was recently made (Hammonds and Call 1970).

There are two distinct markets which must be characterized at the start:

- Industrialized areas
- Developing areas

The industrialized area markets are those which do not exhibit major protein malnutrition, and where the protein ingredients on the market are relatively sophisticated, possessing highly functional and specific properties valuable to the food processor. Purchasing power in these markets is high. The developing area markets are those where protein malnutrition is common. And since purchasing power is low, extensive technical production is not generally feasible. Both areas are concerned with one aspect of FP acceptability – the fish flavour. It is obvious that in the industrialized areas we may search for a *market;* in the developing areas we see a *need*. The question now is: can we tailor a product which will 'fit in' the standard food supply at a profit, or perhaps at a loss, regardless of which market area we decide to enter? Also, will the consumer wholeheartedly and repeatedly accept the product containing FP? These questions form the crux of the manager's problem. Thus, the following factors must be completely evaluated before the commitment of funds:

- Technical feasibility
- Economic feasibility
- Consumer acceptability

RAW MATERIAL AVAILABILITY

Prior to considering any other factor, analysts must review the availability of raw material. Calculations should be made to estimate the supply of such materials well ahead, ie, at least 15 years. All such projections are extremely tentative for many reasons, such as political activities, international economic conditions, raw material stock levels in other areas of the world, and the demand for fish meal, etc.

The industrialized countries of North America and Western Europe which traditionally harvest the North Atlantic have fully exploited the conventional fish resources of those waters and even with improved management of existing North Atlantic stocks it is unlikely that the fish supply in these areas will ever become sufficiently elastic to compete with the soybean as a source of protein for industrialized markets. Excellent stocks of both traditional and non-traditional fish exist in the waters off many developing countries. On the surface, the analysts would find this to be an ideal supply situation, but there are complications. In many of the developing areas, fishing is still done by relatively primitive means. While fishing fleets and fish meal plants exist in many industrialized areas, there is often none in developing countries. This means they must be built and financed, controls must be developed by the government involved, labour trained, and the impact on the overall economy evaluated. Another interesting point was recently brought up in an FAO study which illustrates an additional matter of concern for those wishing to set up an FP enterprise even in a well stocked developing area. Since the oceans are open for use by all, vessels from industrialized nations may some day find it necessary to switch from their overexploited areas to new ones being pioneered by developing countries for local FP production. Distance will not deter such fishing vessels any more than depleted stocks prevent their overfishing in the North Atlantic. A small developing country which invests time and limited funds for the build-up of an expensive fleet and facilities to process fish protein may find such competition unbearable. This aspect must be included in the assessment of raw material availability.

In summary, the analysis must include a review of:
- The overall availability of pertinent species at present and for at least 15 years.
- The effect of external influences on supplies, ie, overfishing in adjacent areas.
- The ability of the area to provide facilities for shipping and processing industries.
- International controls and agreements on the stock management in the area.
- Local requirements for fish meal *vis-à-vis* the value of fish for use as a protein source.

TECHNICAL FEASIBILITY

Technical review papers on this subject may omit an important aspect – the value of the fish protein product. Indeed, the relative *value* of the product, in view of its properties, is one of the most neglected topics in the literature on fish protein. First, let us define value. It is the price at which the product can be sold. A product has marketable value if its properties meet the needs of the market. So there is a trinary relationship: price affordable properties (flavour, solubility, water binding, etc); market needs. When the three are in balance, we have a successful product. If any one is better than average, the product will capture the market.

Industrialized area markets

These markets are in the areas of Europe, North America, Oceania and the River Plate (Pirie 1970). As a whole, this area exhibits certain market characteristics which exert influences on the properties required in protein ingredients. Some of these are: a generally low *per caput* consumption of fish relative to other protein sources, thus less familiarity with its flavour; no widespread major protein malnutrition; high consumption of sophisticated, convenience foods; consumer activism directed against 'empty calories' in soft drinks, cereals, snacks, etc; strong competition among food companies for innovative products; government intervention on nutritional labelling and fortification; generally good purchasing power. A market 'need' for protein fortification has been created by consumer activists, government intervention and industry reaction and, in general, the public seems willing to pay an undefined amount of money for a protein fortified diet. Consumers, however, will not accept fortified products which are 'different' from those they are used to eating. That is, they do not want a protein fortified drink with sediment, or a breakfast cereal with an off-flavour, or a bread which has half the loaf volume and is grey in colour. So they do not want the proteins in their foods to have a deleterious effect on the aesthetic quality of their food supply. A protein venture, fish or otherwise, in an industrialized country must take into account this important consideration.

Table 1 illustrates some of the types of functionality offered to food manufacturers by soy and whey protein producers in the United States and their approximate selling prices.

The protein manufacturers in the United States, for example, are striving for the ideal in their protein ingredients; for instance, in the development of a protein ingredient for use in soft drinks. They aim for as high a protein content as possible, varying degrees of clarity in solution, as much solubility in beverages as possible with a pH below 3·2 with stability to six months, stability of the protein to carbonation to six months, low buffering properties, minimal off-flavour, as high a PER (protein efficiency ratio) as possible (considering the protein source) and a selling price of generally no more than US$ 0·01–0·15 per pound of protein (ie, a 70 per cent protein product should sell at no more than US$ 0·70–1·05 per pound). Such functionality costs both money and talent to develop and produce. The result is an expensive product which significantly affects the selling price and profit derived from the final product. One must therefore be aware of the requirements of the industrialized markets relative to such functional proteins. While the technical feasibility of developing sophisticated protein ingredients from fish is established, one major technical difficulty is the removal of the 'fishy' flavour for use in the industrialized markets.

Developing area markets

These areas include South America, Africa, the Far East and the Near East (Pirie 1970). The market can be characterized, in general, as follows: fish constitutes a major protein source relative to other animal proteins available (Pirie 1970); protein malnutrition; simple, traditional foods based on pulses and cereals are consumed; no consumer activism and minimal government intervention with local food companies; low purchasing power. The market need is based strictly on nutritional requirements and not on nutritional overkill inspired by faddists as is often found in industrialized markets. One factor is common between the two markets – the need for a product to be suited to the consumer's eating habits. Whereas extensive research has been conducted on this subject in the industrialized markets, very little has been done in the developing areas. Before 'tailor-making' protein ingredients for developing areas to ensure good consumer acceptability, the governments, organizations and industries concerned must establish the maximum tolerable cost of fish protein with the function required for the product in question. When the products to be fortified are identified, it must be decided which of the ingredients will be partially or wholly replaced by fish protein, and the functionalities the latter must possess. Such simple questions as the following can be asked: does the product to be partially or wholly replaced contribute flavour important to the consumer; lend texture through thickening, gelling, etc;

TABLE 1. SOY AND WHEY PROTEIN FUNCTIONALITY, PRICE AND USE

General Type of Functionality	% Protein	Approx. Price (US$/lb)	End Usage in Food Products
1. Nitrogen solubility Water absorption	50	0·07–0·14	Baked goods, pasta.
2. Water and fat absorption, thermocoagulability	70	0·18–0·20	Meat products, cereal products, snacks.
3. Water and fat absorption, texture	50	0·25–0·30	Meat products (extruded soy flour), snacks, convenience foods.
4. Varying degrees of water solubility under a variety of conditions	35– 70	0·50–1·00	Beverages, soups, confections, other.

cause desirable colour; exhibit solubility, at what pH; expand on cooking? Can additives be used with fish protein to replace the properties of the supplemented staple? Are they inexpensive enough and available? Thus far, we have pointed out the important factors to consider in evaluating raw material supply and that the development and processing of functional fish proteins is technically feasible, including replacements for low-protein foods eaten by malnourished peoples, with or without additives.

ECONOMIC FEASIBILITY

Economic feasibility refers to the simple question of whether a venture such as fish protein can operate without a loss, at a minimum, and at a profit under certain conditions. For sake of simplicity, we can generalize further by developing the following relationships:

Venturer	Market	Economic Goal
Private industry	Industrialized areas	Minimum 10% profit after taxes
Government or international organization	Developing areas	Non-profit, or minimum subsidized loss

While the critical cost involves the raw material, regardless of the market, there are some differences in types of cost between the two markets. The list below indicates the expenses to be met by the private industry investor in an industrialized market. Such expenses do not necessarily occur in ventures undertaken by governments, for instance, in developing areas.

Costs Incurred by Private Industry in Industrialized Area Markets

Source	Approximate % of Selling Price
Advertising and promotion	2–5
Sales force labour and expense	5–15
Corporate overhead (includes technical service)	15–20
Profit (before taxes)	20
	42–60

This means that the cost of processed raw materials, or cost of goods, would be no less than half the total costs. Such additional costs as distribution, warehousing, packaging, quality control and others are incurred by both private industry and government (or organizational) enterprises. A governmental or international organization venture does not, or should not, expect profits, or spend significant funds for advertising, sales force and corporate overhead (some expenditure, of course, but certainly not as high as 20 per cent). Keeping in mind the added expense incurred by private industry in marketing fish protein products, one must also remember the shortage of raw material (whole and filleted fish) in the North Atlantic, and its effect on the cost of goods in that part of the world. The first important point the analyst

must remember is that the present cost for whole or filleted fish wastes is no indication of what that cost will be in five years' time. Good cost projections should be made at least five years ahead, preferably estimates should cover up to 15 years. These must be based on the supply situation, the effect of international rulings on fishing ground regulations, anticipated political changes, etc. An excellent review of the economics of fish protein concentrate was published by researchers of Massachusetts Institute of Technology (MIT) (Devanney and Mahnken 1970). It clearly illustrated the influence of raw material costs on cost of goods in the USA and Canada. For instance, 6·6 pounds of whole fish (hake, cod or haddock) are necessary for the production of one pound of fish protein concentrate (70 per cent protein). The effect of yield on the cost of raw material is shown in Table 2.

Where a 90 per cent or more protein product is desired, the yield factor is, of course, less and the cost contribution of the raw material to total cost increases dramatically.

Going back to the illustration presented earlier to show the costs incurred by private industry in industrialized market areas, we can quickly determine a necessary selling price for a 70 per cent fish protein product with or without some minimal functionality. If we assume that filleting waste at US$ 0·01 per pound would be used to manufacture this product, and that typical processing costs would be incurred as well as the costs listed earlier, the *profitable* selling price for the concentrate would have to be about US$ 0·52 per pound. As pointed out in the MIT study, the Viobin Corporation in the eastern USA could not survive financially with a selling price of US$ 0·42 per pound. The point to be learned here is that selling protein ingredients in industrialized markets costs money because of the highly competitive nature of the market itself. Should more sophisticated products than fish protein concentrate be desired, the manufacturing costs would increase by at least 30 per cent and, most likely, there would be additional yield costs. The costs of raw material in developing market areas is most difficult to cover completely, but the MIT study reported that the true cost to Chile for hake would be about US$ 0·013 per pound. The cost contribution would be 6·6 times that figure or US$ 0·086 per pound of fish protein concentrate. Adding to that the costs normally incurred by governmental administration, transportation, warehousing and distribution, we arrive at a rough total cost or theoretical minimum selling price for FP in a developed country.

CONSUMER ACCEPTABILITY

The ultimate test of a new product concept is its acceptance by the consumer. The same attention to this detail must be paid to fish proteins as is paid to exotic convenience foods developed for sophisticated markets.

TABLE 2. RAW MATERIAL EQUIVALENT OF PROCESSED FISH PROTEIN AT THE FOLLOWING RAW MATERIAL COSTS (US$/lb)

Raw Material	Yield	0·01	0·02	0·04	0·06	0·08
Whole fish	6·6:1	0·07[a]	0·13	0·26	0·40	0·53
Filleting waste	10:1	0·10	0·20	—	—	—

[a] Unlikely price for whole fish

For that matter, manufacturers of soy protein products are also influenced by this consideration. One can divide the world market into two simple categories: *Fish-loving:* characterized by a high *per caput* consumption of fish in various forms; *Occasional fish consumers:* characterized by a low contribution by fish to total protein consumed. To generalize further, in the industrialized market only a few segments consume large quantities of fish and, therefore, may tolerate and even like fish flavour. Some of these are: the Maritime Provinces of Canada and northeastern states of the USA and the Scandinavian countries. The people in these fish-loving areas, however, are not generally protein-deficient because other sources of protein are more readily available at lower cost. The remaining industrialized area market is not particularly fond of fish or fishy flavour and the more traditional sources of protein are dairy, meat or vegetables.

For most applications in industrialized markets, the producer of fish proteins must strive to develop a bland product. The consumer is particularly demanding and will not easily accept gross changes in the 'quality' of his food even for the sake of nutrition.

Many of the countries in the developing area market are fish-loving. In many coastal or island nations, fish provides a major part of the protein consumed by the population. The removal of the fishy flavour from the protein may not be necessary in the fortification of diets in these areas. This is very important because cost is a particularly sensitive factor in developing areas and the removal of the fishy flavour generally is an expensive process.

Finally, in determing the kind of protein resource to be used for any area in the world, one must screen each candidate protein with an eye to the acceptability of the protein's flavour, consumer appeal (image) relative to the habits, traditions and consumption profile of the population.

This consideration may seem obvious but is often overlooked by analysts. The best examples of where it was ignored in fish protein are those ventures that were started and failed in eastern Canada and the north-eastern USA. The companies concerned failed on several different points but all of them failed to place enough emphasis on consumer acceptability.

SUMMARY

The inputs leading to the question of economic feasibility may be summarized as follows:

Area Market: Region

Input 1: Compare indigenous sources of protein against tastes and customs of the region to determine relative *consumer acceptability* of various raw materials (fish, soy, nut, etc.)

Input 2: Evaluate *raw material supply* (projected a number of years) of each protein source under evaluation.

Input 3: Determine the *technical feasibility* of developing the 'type' of protein the market will require. (Functionality best suited to the intended end use.)

Input 4: Considering all other inputs, include the consumer's purchasing power, or projected value of the protein products in question, against the costs of the venture, and determine the *economic feasibility*.

Using this technique, one can determine if fish protein is best suited to the specific market chosen. If it is not, one can determine which other protein source would be best to use. If the study reveals that all inputs are favourable except one, attempts should be made to overcome the deficiency. In such a case, government subsidies may be applied for to overcome the problems.

References

DEVANNEY, J W and MAHNKEN, G *The economics of fish protein concentrate.* Cambridge, Mass. USA, Massachusetts Institute of Technology, 195 p.
1970

GULLAND, J A (comp. and ed.) *The Fish Resources of the Ocean* (Rev. ed.) Surrey, England, Fishing News (Books), for FAO 255 p.
1971

HAMMONDS, T M and CALL, D L *Utilization of protein ingredients in the US food industry.* Parts I and II. Ithaca, NT, USA, Cornell University Agricultural Experiment Station, 65 p.
1970

PIRIE, N W Complementary ways of meeting the world's protein needs. In R A Lawrie (ed.) *The Proteins as Human Food,* Westport, Conn., USA, The AVI Publ. Co., Inc., p. 46–61.
1970

Expansion of Domestic Markets in Developing Countries *A M Anderson*

Expansion des marches interieurs dans les pays en voie de developpement

Le document examine les raisons pour lesquelles nombre de pays en voie de développement ne parviennent pas à élargir leur marché intérieur du poisson et des produits de la pêche. Ces raisons sont les suivantes: orientation délibérée de la production vers les exportations, notamment par des exonérations de taxes at d'autres stimulants de caractère financier; insuffisance des installations de débarquement de transformation, de distribution et de commercialisation du poisson et des produits de la pêche; insuffisance des crédits alloués pour le développement; manque d'initiative et pénurie de personnel qualifié en matière de commercialisation au sein des services gouvernementaux des pêches et insuffisance de l'infrastructure. L'auteur indique les différentes mesures qu'il

Expansion de los mercados interiores en los paises en desarrollo

En este estudio se examinan las razones por las cuales muchos países en desarrollo no incrementan sus mercados interiores de pescado y productos pesqueros. Las razones son las siguientes: excesiva insistencia en las exportaciones, especialmente mediante facilitaciones fiscales e incentivos económicos; falta de instalaciones de descarga, elaboración, distribución y comercialización de pescado y productos pesqueros; falta de asignación de fondos suficientes para el desarrollo; falta de iniciativa y de personal de comercialización bien preparado en los organismos pesqueros del gobierno; y falta de infraestrictura. El autor senala las fiversas medidas que es preciso tomar, comenzando por que el gobierno reconozca la importancia económica y nutritiva que tiene el fomento del mercado interior y la responsabilidad que le incumbe

serait nécessaire de prendre, à commencer par la reconnaissance officielle de l'importance économique et nutritionnelle que revêt l'expansion du marché intérieur et le lancement, par le gouvernement, de programmes de développement du marché. Il cite en exemple certains pays d'Afrique et d'autres pays où le marché intérieur a été développé avec succès, afin de montrer les résultats que l'on peut obtenir même avec des ressources limitées. Ainsi que le souligne l'auteur, l'adoption d'une politique favorable à l'expansion du marché intérieur non seulement se justifie du point de vue nutritionnel et social, mais pourrait également permettre aux pays en voie de développement d'économiser une grande quantité de devises, car nombre d'entre eux doivent importer du poisson pour une valeur double de celle à laquelle ils exportent leur poisson et leurs produits de la pêche.

en la iniciación de programas de promoción de mercados. Se citan diversos ejemplos de creación de mercados interiores en países africanos y de otros continentes, para ilustrar lo que es posible hacer aunque los recursos sean limitados. Como indica el autor, la necesidad de modificar las políticas en favor de la expansión del mercado interior no sólo está justificada desde el punto de vista nutritivo y social, sino que, además, puede ahorrar a los países en desarrollo abundantes divisas, ya que muchos de ellos tienen que importar pescado por un valor doble del que representan sus exportaciones de pescado y productos pesaueros.

There is no standard strategy for developing markets for fishery products—what is successful for the sophisticated consumer markets of, say, USA, would be quite unworkable in other less developed markets. As it is not possible to cover all situations and, in view of the acute problems they are facing, it seems best to suggest some possible approaches for application in the developing countries. As indicated, many of them do not have the facilities which will allow them to handle and process large volumes of fish. We might therefore give some thought as to why this situation has arisen and what can be done to remedy it – as it seems pointless to suggest new strategies for the development of domestic markets unless the facilities exist to implement them.

CONSTRAINTS TO THE DEVELOPMENT OF DOMESTIC MARKETS

One major reason why the development of domestic markets has been neglected in developing countries has been the over-emphasis given to the expansion of export markets. Admittedly, the build-up of exchange-earning export industries is a logical planning objective for the countries which have the appropriate resources. However, it seems relevant to point out that while the developing countries in Africa and the Americas have, for example, developed an export trade in fish and fish products valued at around US$ 500 million a year, the same countries are importing fish products at a cost over US$ 1,000 million annually. Even after making allowances for the fact that certain of their export products, such as shrimp, have very limited local sales, it is also apparent that many of these countries have access to substantial fish resources which, in the race for export markets, have been neglected. If in these countries there is a substantial deficit in domestic fish supplies then the over-emphasis on export markets must be regarded as a questionable policy. It is not difficult to see how the situation has arisen. Even in cases where it may be a desirable and declared policy of a government to develop its domestic markets, the means to do it do not exist. The fish resources may be available and the catching capacity may be there but, in the absence of adequate facilities for landing, processing, distributing and marketing fish and fish products, development just cannot take place on a scale which will make any real impact.

In contrast, engaging in the export trade is much easier and more enticing to producers and processors alike. Export industries are often set up on a joint venture basis, or at least allow for the employment of expatriate expertise during their early stages. The shorebased processing companies invariably provide the vessel operators with an efficient and exclusive service which includes a reliable and profitable outlet for their catches and efficient facilities for the discharge and servicing of their vessels; the vessel operators thus achieve quick turn-round time and maximum profitability. The processor, in turn, who is usually also the exporter, is often provided with financial incentives on a generous scale by way of tax-free holidays, export bonuses, etc, and, additionally, does not have to operate under the price control systems which are practised in many developing countries. In these circumstances it is no wonder that the development of domestic markets has slipped so far behind.

THE REMEDIES

It is the governments, through their fisheries agencies, who must give the lead. They have to provide the landing, distribution and marketing facilities and the staff to operate them. They will probably also have to plan the entire marketing development programmes, and bring them into operation, at least until such time as the private sector can take over. The question arises, why are they not initiated more frequently? One of the reasons, and this is probably the root of the problem, is that, before embarking on any such projects, the governments concerned have to be convinced of their need and viability. The responsibility of convincing them and for initiating the preliminary planning activities should be with the fisheries agencies concerned and they will have to put up a strong case if they are to get an adequate share of the invariably limited development budget. But, in many cases, the fisheries agencies in the developing countries are very small departments of government, with extremely limited staff and rarely include industry planners, marketing officers, processing technologists or, indeed, any technical staff. Those they have are unfamiliar with the criteria and methods for planning such developments and are, therefore, understandably hesitant to initiate action. Consequently, in the absence of any motivating force, little or nothing is done. Apart from consideration of cost, higher government authorities often take the view that fish marketing is best left in the hands of the existing private sector. As noted earlier, however, the larger private sector interests may be reluctant to enagage in domestic marketing until convinced that it offers profitable opportunities. The other branch of the private sector, often composed of many hundreds or thousands of small traders, may on first sight appear to be an effective force for marketing development but, while they are certainly often enterprising within their own restricted spheres of activity, they are not the instrument for effecting initial radical changes. They control what collection and distribution facilities there are and, being linked together in vertical and horizontal combinations, they are not subject to the full forces of competition, neither in their purchase of fish from small and unorganized producers nor when they sell it through small retailers. This leads to a long tortuous chain of traders, dealers and co-agents between the fishermen and the consumer, all of whom add considerably to the costs of distribution.

It might also be relevant to mention at this point that various capital financing sources, such as development banks, seem to be just as wary as governments in supporting the type of marketing development programmes being considered here. Many of them prefer to restrict their assistance and support to financing the establishment of such ventures as shrimp processing industries where markets are guaranteed, returns can be accurately assessed and profitability assured, but which contribute little or nothing to developing domestic markets. A reconsideration of their present policies in this respect would provide a much needed stimulus to marketing programmes in all developing countries. Governments therefore must accept the fact that it is they who will have to initiate marketing development programmes and that to do so effectively they must strengthen the establishment of their fisheries agencies with planners and technologists. There is no effective alternative; international agencies can assist in conducting surveys, planning and feasibility studies, and possibly in bringing such facilities into initial operation, but it is the country itself which will have to maintain and expand the operations. The consideration of this problem may seem to have led to some digression from the specific topic of this paper, but is so crucial to the whole exercise of developing domestic markets that it deserves attention. Assuming that the problems mentioned are overcome and that the facilities, infrastructure and trained staff exist to implement a marketing development programme, what should be the pattern for development?

PATTERNS FOR DEVELOPMENT

It has been stated earlier that there is no standard strategy, but there is, perhaps, one common denominator which would apply to the developing countries, at least in the initial stages of any such development programme – that is to concentrate on improving and adapting existing products rather than introducing radically new ones. But even this advice should not be followed too rigidly for consumers are not always so conservative as we think and it is not always they who require persuasion to be more adventurous in trying new forms or species of fish or fish products but rather the industry which should display more initiative in introducing them. The first logical step might be to expand the distribution and sales of fresh iced fish. There are limitations to the degree to which this trade can be expanded, but they are not such constraints as are generally supposed, for with proper care, handling and storage, iced fish can be held over a period of many days, transported over hundreds of miles and delivered to markets as a good quality product, even without refrigerated transport. In some areas there is prejudice against iced fish, often

occurring, with some justification, because it is held to be synonymous with bad fish – the consumer having had unfortunate experience with those small-scale vendors who use ice sparingly and operate in the belief that it will turn bad fish into good fish. By perseverance such prejudice can be overcome. As fishing industries expand and operate in more distant grounds the chances are that unfamiliar or low grade species will feature more and more in the landings. They, too, encounter prejudice. This also occurs with some of the fish landed by the artisanal fishermen and it is estimated that something like 30 per cent of their catch (which on a world basis probably works out at 20 million tons a year) is made up of low grade fish scorned by all except the low income consumers. A problem in marketing such fish – and this is often the case with fish from tropical reef areas – is their awkward body structure which the housewife wants no part of. Some enterprising marketing authorities have overcome this by heading, skinning or filleting the fish and selling them successfully as ready-to-cook products in attractive but inexpensive packaging. By these means demand has increased, the fishermen have received a higher price and, since the costs of preparation are relatively small, the price of the product has still been kept well within the reach of the lower income groups. The same could be done with many of the so-called 'trash' fish caught and discarded by shrimp trawlers. Perhaps the fishing industries in the developing countries have more scope and freedom to engage in this area of enhancing low grade species. In many developed countries food regulation laws demand that fish or fish products offered for sale be accurately described with regard to species and, in certain cases, this in itself would be sufficient to create prejudices and kill all sales, with disastrous results. The situation can also exist where legislation prohibits even the landing of certain species, eg, shark, for subsequent use as food fish. Of course, such laws may be well meaning and introduced for the protection of the consumer but there appears to be more scope for flexibility in framing them and more discretion in applying them and they should, perhaps, not be enforced to a degree which will completely foil the equally good intentions of industry, nutritional planners and development authorities to bring about more efficient utilization of wasted fish resources.

In any consideration of ways and means to expand markets for fishery products there is a lesson to be learned from the events which led to the development of the West African markets for frozen fish. This trade, which now approaches 150,000 tons a year, relies on the landing of 20 to 30 kg blocks of frozen fish. These are transported for considerable distances inland, often in unrefrigerated transport, and sold in the thawed or semi-frozen condition as 'fresh fish'. Those quantities unsold are often used for proccessing as smoked fish. When the trade was started sea fish had hardly been seen in the inland areas and frozen fish in itself was undoubtedly viewed with some suspicion but initial prejudice was quickly broken down and this commodity now contributes as much as 50 per cent of the fish supplies in some inland areas of West Africa. The use of frozen fish in this way could be usefully tried in other countries, particularly in the East where the maintenance of adequate fish supplies to distant heavily populated inland areas has always been a major problem. It might be mentioned that in certain countries where ice is sold at an excessive price, as much as US$ 60 per ton and more, there is, indeed, often a very good case for short-circuiting the development of the iced fish trade altogether and moving straight into frozen fish. Conversely, it would seem that in Africa where, in many countries, it is customary to flavour the basic carbohydrate diet with meat and smoked or dried fish, greater attention should be given to developing and marketing a range of fish sauces, soups and relishes such as exist throughout the Far East. One product that might serve this purpose would be a fine grade fish meal of sufficiently good quality for human consumption. In certain African countries such a product has been developed and marketed on a small scale and has sold successfully for it gives the consumer the strong rich fish flavour which he wants. The process is cheap and packaging presents no real problems. This leads us to question why such a product has not been developed on a large scale. Perhaps too much attention has been given to producing hygienic, high quality, solvent extracted powdered products for human consumption. As stated earlier, if existing and acceptable products can be improved and still retain the characteristics the people are accustomed to and demand, why incur the unnecessary expense and trouble of producing a brand new product, the acceptance of which will be uncertain? Other products which require no elaborate preparation or sophisticated equipment and which could be usefully tried might include fish and chips, 'fishburgers', fish cakes and possibly other 'ready-to-cook' products suited to local tastes. There is plenty of evidence to indicate that the lower income consumer in the developing countries appreciates convenience foods just as much as anyone else.

Who is to carry out the exercise of developing products and marketing them? In the developed countries it is usually done by the food processing companies and the accepted procedure is to engage in extended market research and consumer surveys with a view to determining the market demand and to developing products which will meet it. This process of research and development may be very prolonged and is certainly expensive since any new product channelled into the market is usually supported by heavy advertising and other promotional activities. In short, the process is usually to identify the market gap and develop the product. But in many developing countries it is often the other way round. In the situations being considered here, it is assumed there are no large processing companies to initiate product and marketing development. The responsibility is, once again, that of the government fisheries agency. Its mandate may be, quite simply, to expand the distribution and sales of fish and fish products in accordance with national nutritional policies. With limited financial resources and shortage of staff and equipment to engage in extensive market research and product development work, such an agency probably will, as suggested, have to restrict its activity to developing one or two simple products, which may be adaptations or improvements of existing acceptable products, and concentrate its main effort on forcing them into the market by every means possible. There is

nothing basically wrong in this approach. Indeed, something along the same lines was used in developing the West African frozen fish trade referred to earlier. In that case the foreign vessels operating in the area had a surplus of frozen fish which had no market in their own countries so they channelled in into the local West African markets; it came at the right time, the price was right, and the trade quickly established itself. It was essentially a question of 'nothing ventured, nothing gained'. It is interesting to note that in developing that trade the market research aspect was, possibly, minimal and may well have been restricted to the approach that 'these people like fish – we have it in surplus – admittedly it is frozen and unfamiliar – but let us give it a try'. If there was any additional research it would have been mainly concerned with surveying the facilities for handling, storing and distributing the fish. Another one or two interesting points emerge from a study of the development of the trade. Firstly, it was only made possible through the existence of adequate facilities for handling and distributing the frozen commodities at all points in the chain; secondly, the initiative in starting it did not come from the local fish trading community, but they were very quick to see the profitable opportunities it offered and expanded it to everyone's advantage.

This is not to say that market survey and research, and consumer education and promotional activities are not necessary or effective; indeed, they are often vital to the successful expansion of markets, but they can be expensive – US$ 10,000 may not produce very much and some national programmes in these fields have cost US$ 1 million or more. The type of fisheries development agency being considered in the context of this paper will not have this amount of funds, but this should not deter it from embarking on a development programme for often much can be achieved through initiative and enterprise. But it should, at least, employ such promotional means as exist or it can afford in its programme to develop markets; the radio and television which, by and large, have a considerable influence on the community. Even when a fisheries agency has been successful in establishing basic facilities and infrastructure there may still be a doubting fish trading community who have to be convinced of the need to improve the marketing and distribution of fish and fish products and to join in the drive to expand the domestic market. It must be, therefore, one of the major objectives of the fisheries agency to persuade and stimulate the private sector to ensure that they, too, become involved in the development planned. On balance, it is unwise for such an authority to engage in retail operations, for this tends to antagonize the existing traders whose cooperation it is trying to enlist. But, since it has to stimulate sales and expand markets for the products which it intends to promote, it must, initially at least, have the authority and means to carry out retailing operations if it considers such intervention necessary, until such times as the market has been developed the way it wants. One way of achieving this is for the authority to operate its own retail stalls within existing markets so that it can sell and promote its own products vigorously and demonstrate to adjacent traders that they are profitable lines. But first it has to attract the consumers and create a demand for its products. One essential task which it should discharge in its capacity as a development agency is to improve conditions in the markets and lay down minimum standards of cleanliness and hygiene and introduce and enforce the use of improved practices for handling and selling fish. It is a surprising feature of many developing countries that, whereas the meat trade is subject to strict control with regard to inspection, quality and hygiene at all stages from slaughter to sales, the fish trade rarely is. Fish markets are invariably located in the most inaccessible parts of towns; they are often old, without adequate facilities for ensuring even basic standards of cleanliness and sanitation, and the municipal councils or similar authorities, who are usually responsible for operating them, are not familiar with the procedures for handling fish, take little interest in improving them, and merely regard these markets as sources of minor revenue. In such circumstances many consumers prefer to patronize the modern supermarkets where, although they may have to pay for their fish purchases, they can at least shop in comfort in clean and agreeable surroundings. There is really no need for such a situation and the development agency must introduce and enforce measures to bring about improvements. Only then can it use these markets effectively as a vehicle to display and promote its products.

Opportunities for enlisting the participation of other marketing boards and corporations should also be explored. Such para-statal organizations exist in many developing countries. They are usually established to handle agriculture produce and often offer the advantage of having substantial, often underutilized, chill room and cold storage capacity, as well as countrywide distribution, collection and sales outlets. One example of such cooperation which occurred in a developing country could be followed elsewhere. A fisheries development agency, anxious to promote development of the domestic market but not having the facilities to do so itself, persuaded a marketing organization, which had previously only handled agriculture produce, to cooporate in a joint pilot programme. The fisheries agency provided regular 15-ton landings of iced fish from its own vessel – in itself a novel commodity, and more so since it was of a species completely unfamiliar to the local consumer. It also provided the services of one technical officer with experience in handling iced and frozen fish and in simple processing and preparation. The marketing organization made available the underutilized chill room and cold storage capacity, transport, labour, and the facility of its sales outlets. Under guidance and instruction, the marketing organization engaged in both wholesaling

and retailing these new species of iced fish. Later, when the success of sales was apparent to the local fish trading community, who started requesting supplies for themselves, the organization restricted itself to wholesaling but reserved the right to select vendors to ensure that its fish was properly handled and displayed by these vendors. The marketing organization made substantial profits; indeed, fish quickly emerged as its most profitable commodity. It then expanded its operations to include frozen fish for more distant markets and, with assistance from the fisheries technologists, started on the production of packaged fillets and simple 'ready to cook' products. Sales expanded to the point where additional supplies were necessary. A cost feasibility study of the operations identified the justification for additional fleet capacity, credit financing, improved landing facilities, additional plant and equipment. The authorities, impressed with the success of the programme, responded and from relatively small beginnings a significant and successful project for the development of the domestic market materialized.

In planning the above and any marketing development programmes, the opportunity should also be taken to use the outlets provided by institutions such as schools, hospitals, prisons, and so on. Fish requirements in such institutions are usually provided for by purchases arranged by tender months in advance. This offers the advantage of a continuing guaranteed sales outlet for any fishery agency concerned with improving fishery products and expanding domestic markets. Attempts should also be made to enlist the assistance of supermarkets. It has been suggested that in the developing countries they will never replace the colourful town markets. This may be doubted as there is a noticeable increase in the number of supermarkets in these countries and in the numbers of low income consumers patronizing them daily to purchase standard everyday requirements. The management of these establishments are often very cooperative in conducting joint cooking demonstration and promotion activities for good, local products. Vigorously conducted, this whole range of activities and others will, sooner or later, assist toward promoting and expanding the sales of new products and stimulating the interest of responsive elements in the fish trading community and fish processing industries. But it does not happen overnight and the point must be once more emphasized that it will not be achieved unless the facilities, infrastructure and trained personnel are available to bring it about.

Export Markets for Fishery Products from Developing Countries   *W Krone and E Ruckes*

Marches d'exportation pour les produits de la pêche des pays en voie de developpement

Analyse des principales tendances du commerce d'exportation des produits de la pêche, ainsi que des possibilités offertes aux pays en développement de participer à ce commerce. Examen de certains importants problèmes concernant les politiques de promotion des produits halieutiques dans les pays en voie d'expansion.

Mercados de exportacion para productos pesqueros de paises en desarrollo

Se estudian las principales tendencias de las exportaciones de productos pesqueros y se indican las posibilidades que tienen los países en desarrollo de participar en este comercio. Se examinan algunos problemas importantes de políticas relacionados con la promoción de los productos pesqueros en los países en desarrollo.

Among the objectives of economic development the earning of foreign exchange has a prominent place and some countries have looked at the fishery sector to make a significant contribution to this end. There are several economies that rely almost exclusively on fishery products for this purpose, such as, Faero Islands, French Guiana, Iceland and Greenland while, in other countries, such as Peru, St. Pierre et Miquelon, Norway, Panama, Mauritania, Mali and Morocco, exports of fishery products account for an important share of total exports (FAO 1973). The potentials and problems of developing countries engaging in expanding their export trade will be discussed in this paper.

INTERNATIONAL TRADE IN FISHERY PRODUCTS

This trade experienced a tremendous growth during the sixties, accounting for 44 per cent of world catches in 1968, up from 29 per cent in 1958 (Table 1). Since 1969, a reduction in trade volume has been evidenced, due largely to a decline in world fishmeal and oil trade but export values continued to rise reaching US$ 3,200 million in 1971. With the exception of fishmeal and oil and frozen shrimp, the participation of developing countries in world fish trade is still limited (Table 2). As can be noted from Table 3, all principal importers and exporters (with the exception of Peru) are to be found in the developed world, although some developing countries make an important contribution to some commodity markets (eg, Morocco in canned sardine, Korea in frozen tuna). A noteworthy recent development is the emergence of Japan as the second largest importer of fishery products (after the United States of America), the import value having multiplied by thirty.

MAJOR TRENDS IN WORLD FISH TRADE

Table 4 summarizes trade developments between 1958 and 1971 according to international fishery commodity groupings. Although the divergencies in import and export figures, which can be only partly explained by differences in c.i.f. and f.o.b. values of imports and exports respectively, suggest a cautious interpretation of these data, the following principal developments are indicated:

– largest increases in both volume and value have been in fishmeal and shellfish;

TABLE 1. ESTIMATED INTERNATIONAL TRADE IN FISHERY PRODUCTS 1958/71 (1,000 t LIVE WEIGHT)

	1958	1961	1965	1968	1969	1970	1971
Total world catch	33,300	43,000	53,700	63,900	62,600	69,600	69,400
Catch of 151 countries	28,430	36,680	46,800	57,400	55,960	62,240	61,420
International trade of 151 countries (live weight)	8,110	12,330	19,160	25,380	22,700	23,040	23,210
International trade of 151 countries as per cent of their catch	29	34	41	44	41	37	38
International trade (exports) of 151 countries (product weight)	3,400	4,452	6,290	7,690	7,100	7,310	7,440
Total trade value (export) (Million US$)	1,123	1,280	1,943	2,225	2,443	2,885	3,247

Source: FAO 1966, 1971 and 1972

TABLE 2. PARTICIPATION OF DEVELOPING COUNTRIES IN WORLD FISH EXPORTS BY COMMODITY GROUPS

	1958 million US$	%	1961 million US$	%	1971 million US$	%
Fresh, chilled, frozen						
World	283	100·0	341	100·0	994	100·0
Developing countries	22	7·7	30	8·8	107	10·8
Fish processed for human consumption						
World	486	100·0	498	100·0	807	100·0
Developing countries	69	14·2	84	16·9	116	14·4
Crustaceans and molluscs (fresh or processed)						
World	164	100·0	216	100·0	794	100·0
Developing countries	69	42·1	91	42·1	391	49·3
Industrial products						
World	188	100·0	224	100·0	652	100·0
Developing countries	41	21·8	81	36·2	407	62·4
Total all products						
World	1,121	100·0	1,279	100·0	3,247	100·0
Developing countries	201	17·9	286	22·4	1,021	31·4

Source: FAO 1967 and 1972

TABLE 3. PRINCIPAL COUNTRIES EXPORTING AND IMPORTING FISHERY PRODUCTS 1961/71

Exporters	Exports of fish US$1 million		Fish exports as per cent of total exports	Importers	Imports of fish US$1 million	
	1961	1971	1971		1961	1971
Japan	188	367	1·5	USA	361	913
Peru	72	337	37·8	Japan	14	405
Norway	140	300	11·7	UK	175	312
Canada	137	282	1·5	Germany FR of	115	293
Denmark	67	197	5·3	France	81	239
USA	29	136	0·3	Italy	69	189
The Netherlands	49	129	0·9	Sweden	34	104
Iceland	64	125	83·0	The Netherlands	46	103
Spain	22	114	3·9	Belg. Luxemb.	42	100
Total 9 countries	768	1,987	1·8	Total 10 countries	937	2,658
Total world	1,280	3,247		Total world	1,404	3,696

Source: FAO 1966 and 1973

TABLE 4. IMPORTS AND EXPORTS OF FISHERY PRODUCTS BY COMMODITY GROUPS

Commodity group	Imports			Exports			No. of countries
	1958	1968	1971	1958	1968	1971	
(i) Quantity (1,000 t product weight)							
Fresh, chilled or frozen fish	1,000	1,816	2,005	955	1,815	2,037	148
Cured fish	616	488	512	605	485	489	146
Shellfish, fresh, frozen, cured	195	404	575	182	343	510	134
Canned fish	467	601	583	473	608	602	149
Canned shellfish	36	95	98	38	66	71	120
Fish oil and fats	563	878	743	476	825	708	115
Fishmeal	693	3,577	2,845	673	3,550	3,023	92
(ii) Value (US$1 million)							
Fresh, chilled or frozen fish	303	712	1,134	283	629	994	148
Cured fish	198	246	333	179	221	306	146
Shellfish, frozen, fresh, cured	127	487	839	123	386	661	134
Canned fish	307	442	524	306	429	501	149
Canned shellfish	43	129	179	43	98	133	120
Fish oil and fats	123	97	172	99	77	149	115
Fishmeal	103	458	515	90	385	503	92

Source: FAO 1966, 1971 and 1972

- fresh and frozen fish exports have increased more than average;
- fish preparations (in airtight containers or not), which mainly consist of canned fish, increased less than average and even declined slightly in recent years;
- cured fish trade declined, with some recovery during recent years.

Since these groups are mostly composed of a variety of rather different products, some brief comments are necessary.

Fresh, chilled, frozen

Exports of fresh and chilled fish (excluding frozen products) have remained significant in some regional trade, notably between Canada and the United States of America and in Western Europe. However, it should be noted that some countries do not separate trade statistics for frozen fish, so that trade increases in this commodity are partly disguised. Exports of reported frozen fish have gone up from 0·41 million t in 1958 to 1·07 million t in 1971. Behind this rise were, in the main, two distinct developments:

- The first is the rising demand in North America and Europe for frozen fillets (including blocks to be further processed into convenience products, such as, fish sticks and portions). Exports of frozen fillets increased from 0·17 (1958) to 0·40 million t in 1971, with Canada and Norway each exporting more than 100,000 t in the latter year. About half of this trade is made of cod fillets and blocks but since 1970 it has been dwindling due to reduced catch rates in the North Atlantic. The wholesale price for cod blocks on the United States market has multiplied, reaching US$ 0·80/lb (US$ 1·76/kg) in October 1973 from its all-time low of US$ 0·21/lb (US$ 0·46/kg) in 1968/69. This has led to increasing substitution of blocks from flounder (and other flatfish), pollock and hake, particularly on the United States market. While total United States imports of blocks and fillets have increased from 245,000 t in 1971 to 300,000 t in 1972, sales of Alaska pollock blocks rose from 1,600 to 18,700 t during this period.

– The second remarkable trend is the rising trade of Japan, Poland and the USSR in sea frozen fish destined largely for developing countries and the COMECON. The USSR have increased their exports of frozen fish from virtually nothing in 1958 to 260,000 t in 1971, the principal markets being Japan, Cuba, Egypt, West Africa and COMECON countries (Table 5). A large part of this is due to direct landings of Soviet factory vessels operating under charter or other agreements with these countries. In the same period Japan has expanded frozen fish exports (other than tuna, whitefish fillets, etc.) from 20,000 to 90,000 t, a large part going to West Africa. Poland multiplied exports of this commodity from 2,500 (1958) to 37,000 t in 1971, again most of it being sold in West Africa. The evolution of a large market for frozen fish in West Africa is one of the most significant features in both domestic market and trade development during the last decade. The present market volume, to which other countries, such as, Bulgaria, Israel, Romania and Spain, also contribute, can be estimated at more than 200,000 t, of which Nigeria absorbs about half. The product delivered in bulk packs of 20 and 30 kg is relatively unsophisticated, but well accepted in the market. There is considerable potential for greater participation of developing countries in this trade, including some countries within the region (eg, Senegal and Mauritania).

Brief reference must also be made to the important trade in frozen tuna. United States imports have continued to increase and reached 0·28 million t in 1972 (compared with 0·18 million t in 1969). The main additional suppliers are Korea, Taiwan and West African countries.

Cured

This is the only category in which trade decreased significantly between 1958 and 1971, particularly influenced by two products: stockfish, which declined from 43,000 t in 1958 to 15,000 t in 1971 due principally to special circumstances prevailing in the Nigerian market; and salted herring, which dropped from 155,000 t in 1958 to 60,000 t in 1969 with a recovery to 84,000 t in 1971. In this latter case both production and marketing forces influenced this development. On the other hand, exports of salt-dried whitefish in 1971 were slightly higher (217,000 t) than in 1958 (207,000 t) although the intervening years saw considerable fluctuations due chiefly to raw material being channelled into relatively more remunerative outlets, such as freezing. It is conceivable that this factor will grow in importance,

opening possibilities for developing countries to fill the supply gap. This commodity class also includes a miscellaneous group which – apart from speciality items, such as dried shark fins, fishmaws, etc. – mainly covers trade in dried or smoked-dried products from and between developing countries. Although year-to-year fluctuations are in evidence, there is no particular trend. The trade continues to amount to about 100,000 t annually.

TABLE 5. USSR EXPORTS OF FROZEN FISH (1,000 s)

	1958	1965	1970	1971
Bulgaria	—	1·1	2·3	3·2
Czechoslovakia	—	6·4	6·6	8·9
Cuba	—	12·5	27·9	28·2
Egypt, Arab Rep. of	—	10·4	10·0	12·0
German Democratic Rep.	—	10·4	25·4	25·0
Ghana	—	19·9	5·2	11·7
Japan	—	43·0	54·2	47·7
Rumania	—	4·7	22·6	31·1
Togo	—	5·0	7·0	7·6
Other	Φ	38·5	61·0	85·7
Total	Φ	151·9	222·2	261·1

Source: FAO 1966, 1971 and 1972

Canned

This group is composed of the traditional canned products (salmon, sardines/herring and tuna/bonito) and 'miscellaneous' products. While exports of canned Pacific salmon have shown a declining trend (with some recovery in 1971) due partly to production influences and partly to increasing demand in the producing countries, canned tuna/bonito increased by about 50 per cent between 1958 and 1970 (with some diminution in 1971). However, taken together, exports have shrunk from about 0·14 million t in 1958 to 0·11 million t in 1971. Exports of canned sardines and herring show variations between 0·18 and 0·21 million t, the year-to-year changes apparently due to production and raw material influences rather than market trends. It is, however, notable that 1972 imports by the United States of America were about 30 per cent above the 1967/75 annual average, with wholesale prices increased to US$ 16·50/17.00 per standard case (100–125 g) and with a number of new suppliers gaining entry, eg, Peru, Poland and Venezuela. The continuing upward trend of canned fish exports is chiefly due to the increase in the 'miscellaneous' group in which canned mackerel plays a dominating role. Its exports have increased from about 6,000 t in 1958 to 186,000 t in 1971, largely from Japan (from 2,300 to 177,300 t between 1958 and 1971). Also participating in this trade are Morocco, the Netherlands and Norway. The expansion of the Japanese exports was facilitated by a change in import policy in the Philippines which led to a replacement of canned pilchard from South Africa by canned mackerel. Table 6 shows the production and destination of canned mackerel in Japan. This trend continued in 1972, with prices moving up from about US$ 5·75 to US$ 6·50 per standard case between 1971 and 1972.

The export surge in canned mackerel must be regarded as the most significant trade development in this commodity group and should provide potential

TABLE 6. JAPANESE PRODUCTION AND EXPORTS OF CANNED MACKEREL (1,000 t)

	1958	1962	1965	1968	1969	1970	1971
Production:							
in brine	8·0	22·2	36·2	94·1	65·2	—	96·3
flakes or chunks	6·2	17·1	26·6	71·4	74·6	—	119·9
Total	14·2	39·3	62·8	165·5	139·8	—	216·2
Exports:							
Philippines	0·2	3·8	14·7	55·8	50·0	49·6	52·3
Singapore	0·1	0·4	0·4	4·3	0·9	6·5	12·6
New Guinea	—	—	—	5·2	8·0	12·1	13·1
Malaysia	Φ	0·5	1·1	2·5	5·0	4·2	4·8
Ghana	Φ	0·7	0·5	1·3	3·17	13·7	10·4
Zaire	—	—	—	—	—	1·4	6·3
Cuba	—	—	—	—	—	0·6	4·8
Germany, FR of	—	—	—	—	1·3	3·5	3·9
UK	—	—	—	—	0·5	1·4	5·5
USA	Φ	Φ	0·1	6·8	8·4	22·5	8·9
Total	2·3	11·1	26·2	109·4	129·3	161·2	177·3

Source: FAO 1966, 1971 and 1972

opportunities for developing countries, firstly, because mackerel resources are abundant in a number of regions and, secondly, because the product is relatively unsophisticated. It offers also scope for trade expansion between developing countries.

Shellfish

It is not necessary here to elaborate on the well known expansion of frozen shrimp trade, which has been a veritable bonanza for a great number of developing countries. Where resources have offered prospects, investment in vessels and plants has been forthcoming rapidly because of the ready and almost unsatiable market demand. Future developments will depend upon resources availability, while an upgrading of handling practices and product quality will be demanded by increasingly stringent trade and food regulations.

Fishmeal and oil

International trade in these commodities has been governed over the last decade by the unique position of Peru. Similar to the case of shrimp, the availability of abundant, untapped resources and a ready and rapidly expanding market were responsible for this development. At present, the international market for fishmeal is in a state of disequilibrium due to the temporary disappearance of the Peruvian supplies. However, demand continues to be strong and prices have reached exorbitant levels, partly also in response to soaring prices for soya meal. The substitution of fishmeal by soya meal, which has happened on several occasions in the past during periods of excessively high fishmeal prices, is, therefore, at the moment, of less importance. However, in the long run, the greatest danger to the position of fishmeal in the market may come from microbial proteins and from synthetics, although a limited-size market for fishmeal seems certain to continue even at high price levels because of special nutritive properties attributed to it.

Other

From international trade statistics it is generally possible to deduct only trends for the principal commodity groups and large volume items. It should, however, not be forgotten that there exists an interesting trade in a variety of products which has shown expansion over recent years and which can be quite important for some countries. Thus, for example, Japanese imports of frozen squid increased from 15,000 t in 1970 to 28,000 t in 1972 and Italian imports of squid and cuttlefish rose from 11,000 t (1969) to 23,000 t in 1971. There is an increasing market for headed and gutted frozen fish in the United States of America which has led to the initiation of an interesting trade in headed and gutted hake (merluza) from some South American countries. Furthermore, there is a wide range of speciality items, usually extremely high valued, which, albeit in small quantities, offer developing countries potential export trade. A few examples are: frozen or canned clams, roe of fish and sea urchins, algae, dried shark fins, frozen flatfish and other fin fish, eel, trout, carp and other freshwater species, and aquarium fishes.

TRADE POTENTIALS OF DEVELOPING COUNTRIES

The extent to which developing countries can expand their participation in these various markets depends firstly on the fish resources – by quantity and species – at their disposal. While no overall inventory is possible in this paper, some evident areas of emphasis should be mentioned: A number of groundfish species provide potential opportunity in the frozen fillet (and block) market, notably South American hake and Alaska pollack (Korea). Both have already gained some importance in the United States and European markets. There are some other groundfish resources, eg, flatfish which, if not too highly priced in domestic markets, could also be channelled into the international market for fillets and blocks. Other groundfish could enter international trade in headed and gutted form.

There are many possibilities for utilizing pelagic species for export purposes. The market for frozen bulk packs that has developed in West Africa and some other countries is likely to continue to expand, while the market for canned mackerel and pilchard/sardine type products offers possibilities. Although the increase in the canned mackerel trade has been partly at the expense of the canned pilchard, the overall trade in these products, which in many markets are substitutable, has expanded. Supplies of sardine type products have suffered in a number of countries because of irregular supplies of raw material (eg, Portugal, Norway and the United States of America). At the same time, the demand for the less sophisticated type of sardine/pilchard packs is increasing rapidly in many developing countries. There is, therefore, room for pelagic species from tropical and sub-tropical waters, which are similar to sardines, pilchard and herring, to enter the canned fish market. It can also be expected that bonito, mackerel and other scombridae species will play an increasing role in canned tuna-style products (chunk, flake, or even solid packs). Furthermore, the market for salted anchovy, packed in barrels or larger cans, appears to offer increasing prospects for developing countries because of dwindling anchovy catches in the major producing and consuming industrialized countries.

Although trade in salt-dried or dried whitefish has been stagnating over the last decade, important markets exist where consumers continue to have a need for and appreciate these traditional products (eg, Caribbean, Brazil, India and some countries in Africa and the Far East). The situation in Nigeria, where stockfish imports have almost disappeared during recent years, is not indicative of general market trends because special influences have limited this trade. Moreover, the declining groundfish catches in the traditional producer countries of salt-dried whitefish and the trend towards the use of this raw material for higher paying frozen fish products are likely to create increasing supply gaps. These can be filled by salt-dried fish produced from species such as hake.

EXPORT PRODUCT POLICIES

Degree of processing

Setting up an export-oriented industry in developing countries usually does not necessitate the creation of novel products. Product development in these cases would normally aim at utilizing known technology and processes and adapting them to the types of species with characteristics similar to those used for readily acceptable international commodities. This requires intensive technological investigation. It also requires early attention to be given to problems such as product denomination, packaging, labelling, legal provisions in potential importing markets. etc. This approach reduces the time and money that have to be spent in promoting a new product in a foreign market, the sort of cost and effort that a developing industry can seldom afford. The examples mentioned earlier provide possibilities for products from developing countries to be intro- duced into existing markets. However, in such cases, there is often a choice between more or less elaborated products. For example, there is a choice between exporting tuna and bonito in frozen form or as a

canned product. In the case of hake, the alternatives may range from fishmeal to salt-dried bacalao to a frozen-dressed product, to fillet blocks, to individual fillets in different size packages, to ready-to-cook fish sticks or portions. The decision, therefore, is not as obvious as it may seem at first glance. No doubt, there is a genuine desire by developing countries to move from the position as exporters of raw material to that of a producer of final products and long-term strategies should be directed toward this goal. But short-term implications must be taken into account. As explained by Birkeland (1973), establishing a product on the retail market will ultimately have the advantage of greater strategic strength, while emphasis on commodity markets gives greater marketing flexibility. Both have, therefore, their merits and problems. While it may be very desirable to achieve a high strategic strength in the foreign market, this will imply relatively high marketing costs. Moreover, the expected benefits will only occur if a sufficiently high market share can be attained. A developing industry, which still is struggling with problems of production, quality, packaging material, untrained labour, irregular shipping opportunities, etc, will reach this position only over some considerable time and it will, therefore, often be preferable, except for either limited size markets or less sophisticated pro- cessed products, to concentrate on commodities' markets. While production and sales of these products are being developed, a gradual move into retail packs, initially perhaps under an arrangement with a customer using his established label, can be contemplated. From an individual company's point of view, concentration on commodity markets (such as fish fillet blocks) has evident short-term advantages. However, governments, when orientating export policies, will have to consider the implications for the national economy. The more intense processing of the one and the same species, the higher the product value, which results in more foreign exchange earnings for the country. Moreover, processed products require more labour input so contributing to employment. There should also be incentives to utilize plant capacities to the maximum. There may indeed often be a conflict between the interests of the individual firm and those of the country and all aspects should be considered in the proper context. It is necessary, for instance, to analyse not only the foreign exchange receipts but also the foreign exchange costs involved in production (eg, packaging material, depreciation of imported machinery, etc). The quality requirements of the foreign market may also involve greater cost and problems in making the more elaborate product.

Quality

The importance of establishing the highest quality standard from the start in exports cannot be over- emphasized. No compromises should be permitted. While it may be tempting to reap quick short-term benefits from a new marketing opportunity, if a product is once downgraded it will not only damage the reputation of an individual firm but a whole country's industry because ventures in developing countries are generally identified with the nations and sometimes even with a whole region. Governments have, therefore, to take a leading role in product inspection and should intervene forcefully to prevent secondary grade products leaving the country. This involves not only the wholesomeness of the product, but also compliance with exacting international specifications regarding texture, colour, weight, labelling, bacteriological count, mercury, etc. The Codex Alimentarius is elaborating product quality standards, some of which are at the final stage of international acceptance. Fishery industries, in general, particularly those in developing countries, should observe these standards. Further, developing countries should participate more fully in the elaboration of these standards. The more important buyers usually base their product requirements nowadays on such standards, although they may wish to specify some packing and grading details in addition. In order to assist industry in complying with the quality requirements in the importing countries and, incidentally, to improve the quality of products marketed domestically, FAO and Codex Alimentarius have elaborated a series of codes of good technological and hygienic practices.

Exporting or domestic market development

In some developing countries there is a growing pressure to utilize fishery resources to cover urgent food supply needs at home rather than for export. There can be no doubt that for social and humanitarian reasons domestic fish marketing development must receive highest priority. But this should not lead to an 'either/or' approach. It is obvious that, for example, the annual 150,000 t harvest of shrimp in India could not make a measurable contribution to improving protein food supplies in the country, but it adds approximately US$ 70 million to the foreign exchange earnings. Similarly, the Peruvian anchoveta would have remained food for the guano birds, had not an expanding international fishmeal market given an incentive to develop one of the most important industries in that country. There are, of course, examples which appear less extreme. For instance, in Peru there is the alternative of promoting hake consumption on the domestic market (where it was hardly accepted until a few years ago) and sell it at the equivalent of about US$ 0·10/kg or developing an export industry where this fish could earn about US$ 0·40/kg foreign exchange (calculated on an equivalent weight basis). This need not mean depriving the local population of valuable protein:

if there are other species available, with less foreign trade attraction, the effort to promote their consumption on the home market should obviously be spent on them. Under such conditions, it may also be economically sound to export, say, frozen trout rather than to sell it domestically even if wholesale/f.o.b. prices would not be very different in either case because the trout would earn foreign exchange without reducing the availability of fish locally. On the other hand, there may often be circumstances where a bouyant export demand diminishes fish supplies at home or drives prices up to levels beyond the purchasing power of the majority of the population. In such cases the Government may find it necessary to intervene. Some countries have, in fact, introduced legislation which allows fishery products to be exported only after domestic requirements have been satisfied. But it is not always easy to establish internal demand for specific products which will be dependent on price levels, consumer preferences, etc. The problem, therefore, has to be handled in a flexible manner to avoid any undue interference in the export business, which would jeopardize customer confidence.

In conclusion, it has to be stressed that the relative needs of the domestic market have to be valued against the potential earnings of foreign exchange, which, after all, can be used for important national priorities, including the import of protein food. It must also be borne in mind that the domestic market can often be more easily developed on the back of a well established export trade because many problems of product handling, quality control and training of personnel will already have been tackled.

References

BIRKELAND, C Expansion of export markets in developed
1973 countries. *Technical Conference on Fishery Products*, Tokyo, December 1973, Rome, FAO, FII:FP/73/R–11:11p.
FAO *Yk Fish. Statist.* Vol. 21, Fishery Commodities 1965.
1966
FAO The export trade in fishery products from developing countries
1967 to developed countries: Present situation and future prospects. *FAO Fish. Circ.*, (107): 47 p.
FAO *Yk Fish. Statist.*, Vol. 31, Fishery Commodities 1970.
1971
FAO *Yk Fish. Statis.*, Vol. 33, Fishery Commodities 1971
1972
FAO The economic and social effects of the fishery industry—a
1973 comparative study. *FAO Fish. Circ.*, (314):17 p.

Expansion of Export Markets in Developed Countries *L Birkeland*

Expansion des marches d'exporation dans les pays developpes

L'auteur décrit l'organisation de l'industrie norvégienne des produits de la pêche surgelés et son programme d'exportation coordonné par l'intermédiaire de la Coopérative Frionor. La Frionor fixe les normes de qualité pour les 120 sociétés qui font partie de la coopérative et possède son propre service d'inspection du poisson chargé de garantir l'application de ces normes. Elle se charge également de l'exportation des produits. Les programmes de production prévus pour les usines permettent de surmonter l'une des principales difficultés auxquelles se heurtent les industries de transformation du poisson de tous les pays – le caractère saisonnier de l'approvisionnement en matière première et la fluctuation de l'offre. L'auteur analyse les principales conditions nécessaires à la création et à l'expansion des marchés d'exportation de produits de la pêche. Il fait largement appel à l'experience acquise par la Frionor et par sa propre entreprise, qui ont développé avec succès leur commerce d'exportation.

Expansion de los mercados de exportacion de los paises desarrollados

En este documento se describe la organización de la industria noruega de productos pesqueros congelados y su plan coordinado para el comercio de exportación a través de la Cooperativa Frionor. La Frionor establece normas de calidad para sus 120 compañías asociadas y tiene su propio servicio de inspección del pescado para la observancia de estas normas. También se ocupa del comercio de exportación de los productos. Los programas de producción planificada de las fábricas contribuyen a superar una de las principales dificultades de las industrias de elaboración de pescado en todos los países – la naturaleza estacional del suministro de materias primas y sus fluctuaciones. El autor analiza las principales necesidades existentes para establecer y ampliar los mercados exteriores de los productos pesqueros, y pone de manifiesto la experiencia de la Frionor y la de su propia compañía, en la ampliación positiva del comercio exterior.

In developing and expanding export markets for fish products each exporter must find out by himself how he can best succeed. He must then formulate his own policy, tailor-made to succeed in that market. Despite this need for a tailor-made effort, we can learn from one another. So I shall tell about our own experience – about what we do and do not do and why – in the hope that our experience will be useful to others. We catch fish the year round in Norway and ship our products at any time to all parts of the world. Traditionally, Norway can count on certain advantages such as:

(1) an established image for quality, supported by the fact that water and air are cool and clean where our fish are caught and processed;

(2) the rich fishing grounds, only a few hours sailing from the processing plants, where each species of fish tends to move separately, so that our vessels come in with fresh and uniform catches;

(3) the fact that the species fished, such as Atlantic cod, haddock, pollack, halibut, etc, are popular in many markets in Europe and North America, so that there is an established consumer acceptance;

(4) the highly organized Norwegian fishermen who negotiate raw material prices so that they rarely fail to take advantage of a favourable development in the markets. This also means that there is a degree of stability in raw material prices and that fish prices can be discussed with the fishermen in an intelligent way;

(5) and last, but not least, we can avail ourselves of an organized money market to finance our business.

Frionor, the company I work for, has a comfortable share of a sophisticated home market and a stable basis at home is an advantage to any company that ventures into the often unpredictable world of exporting. However, the population of Norway is so small and our production so large, relatively speaking, that we rely on export markets for 95 per cent of our sales. The products are sold in some 30 countries. About one-third of the sales are to the United States market, one-third to the former EFTA markets (which included the UK, Scandinavia, Switzerland and Austria), and the last third to the Federal Republic of Germany, France, the Netherlands, Belgium, the East European countries (COMECON) and Australia. 70,000 to 90,000 tons of frozen fish are sold, mostly as fillets or products made from fillets, including sophisticated consumer items such as fish in sauce, pre-cooked fish and so on. One very important factor is uniformity of quality. Frionor inspectors continually check the plants for quality of production. This inspection is in addition to that of the Government. Frionor is a cooperative of the frozen fish industry in Norway. Any plant able to meet the strict technical standards established may join this cooperative – and leave it if they find this to be in their interest. The Frionor organization has 120 members, all of them run freezing plants along the Norwegian coast. Frionor takes care of marketing, shipping, production planning and quality control, and acts as technical advisers. It also buys packing material and other items. The cost of all this – not including advertising and promotion – amounts to no more than about 1·5 per cent of turnover. In the

export markets we partly rely on our own organizations. Our company has subsidiary companies in the USA, the UK, the Federal Republic of Germany and Sweden. In other markets we operate through agents and importers, mostly on an exclusive basis. Some types of fish processing are better done in centrally located plants. The marketing organization itself, therefore, owns and operates three processing plants, two in Norway and one in Massachusetts, USA The traditional trade in fish is for the first time becoming really international, made possible by freezing techniques, mass markets and modern marketing methods. The United States frozen fish market is an example of what is now happening. As the consumption of frozen fish there increased, and the country's own fishing industry declined, supplies increased from other countries. Production increased with increasing demand and prices remained mostly low, which again encouraged demand. But in 1969 supplies became tight and prices increased. There had been periods of short supply before but this time many things indicated that the position was going to be more or less permanent.

Now, if expansion is being checked in one direction, a businessman looks in another direction for continued growth. As one of our customers in the United States put it: 'We want to expand, preferably by 20 per cent annually, and we prefer to expand on the basis of fish. If enough fish are not available, we shall base our expansion on meat, on frozen pies and desserts or other products or activities.' The big importers of frozen fish in the USA are largely the people who process the fish and, facing a short supply, it was not practical for them immediately to branch into meat and other frozen food. They would tend to search for substitutes, which they did by travelling in Europe, South America, South Africa and the Far East. The results are to be read in the United States import statistics – non-traditional suppliers sending in not only traditional species of fish but, on an even larger scale, non-traditional species. This development, which has become worldwide during the last three or four years, is encouraging newcomers to the international marketing of fish products. It shows that the world is looking for new sources of supply and that the trade is willing to re-think and to listen and work with those who have suitable products to offer.

INTERNATIONAL MARKETING

International marketing of fish products is a bit different from marketing other products and is certainly never monotonous. The main difference between our industry and most others is that we are subject to the ups and downs of the catch. Thus, the industry must always be prepared to adapt to what actually happens in production. This is fundamental and to a great extent decides how we organize our marketing. Similarly, it is difficult to ascertain what is likely to happen in the production of competitors, which makes it hard to estimate the total quantity likely to be put on the market at any time. So it is necessary for people in the industry to keep a cool head and to maintain a large number of contacts internationally, including competitors, in order to appraise the situation as fully as possible. Such uncertainty means that lack of harmony between supply and

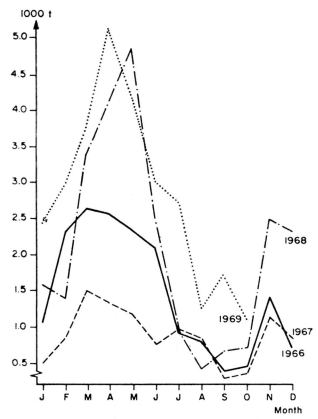

Fig 1 Monthly production of cod fillets by a cooperative of the frozen fish industry in Norway

demand is normal and that an equilibrium is a sort of an accident, at best of short duration. Of course, the degree of instability not only varies from one market to another but from one sector to another and from one product to another. Further, in several important fishing countries there is only a limited degree of vertical integration within the industry, consequently there is only a limited control of activities, production costs, etc, from raw material to consumer. Not everybody is aware of how great these variations are. Some idea of them is illustrated in Figs 1, 2 and 3. The diagrams show the variation month by month in the Frionor production of cod, haddock and saithe during four years. All diagrams indicate three characteristics in our production pattern: the extreme difference between in-season and out-of-season production volume; the concentration in production during spring and summer in the northern hemisphere,. ie, at a time of the year when consumption of frozen fish is lower in this area; and the variation in the seasonal pattern from one year to another. Even if a 'typical' pattern could be constructed, there is no guarantee that, for instance, the next season would behave according to this pattern. We have to market our production throughout the year to meet consumer demand. This means that we have to work on a sales plan which we must coordinate with a production plan, which again is dictated by the seasonal pattern. This is a short-term budget for 12 months. In addition to this we try, of course, to work out a coordinated sales and production budget for a number of years. In a sense, it is this kind of planning which makes the difference between 'selling' and 'marketing' fish. One can sell a product without knowing much about it or caring about where it comes from or where it goes. The marketing

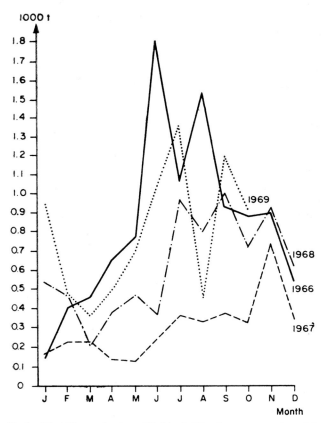

Fig 2 Monthly production of haddock fillets by a cooperative of the frozen fish industry in Norway

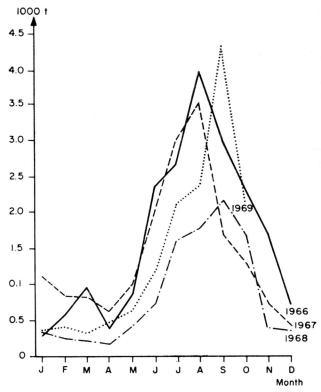

Fig 3 Monthly production of saithe fillets by a cooperative of the frozen fish industry in Norway

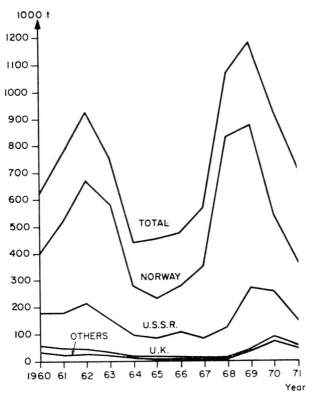

Fig 4   Yearly catches of the cod in the North Cape, Barents Sea area during the 1960–71 period

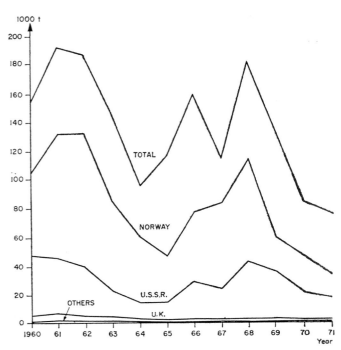

Fig 5   Yearly catches of haddock in the North Cape, Barents Sea area during the 1960–71 period

man is less concerned with the order that comes today, which is the result of his efforts in the past, than he is with the order that should come in tomorrow or in a year's time or in five years. If exports are to be developed and expanded on a healthy basis, we must try to do a marketing job. There is the uncertainty about the availability of raw material. We must also, when we work out our production plan for each member plant, take into consideration its individual interests. This means that a member plant must be given a production programme providing for capacity output during the peak season, at the same time making it possible for the plant to employ its working force and its machinery throughout the year. In practice, the plant must concentrate during the peak fishing season on product varieties that demand less labour and put a maximum tonnage of fish through the freezers, while during the quiet season the raw material must be used on products that demand much labour and give the highest possible production value per kilogramme of raw material.

Determining marketing strategy

Let us revert for a minute to the more or less cyclical variations in catch and production. Figs 4 and 5 show the sharp variations in the catch of cod and haddock in the East Atlantic. It can be noted that maximum cod production in this area has reached 1·1 million tons and that the minimum has been as low as 0·4 million tons. Haddock has had a maximum of around 200,000 tons and a minimum of 100,000 tons. With this kind of short and medium cycle variations in supply, the first and foremost task of the marketing experts is to establish a system or a strategy which is flexible enough to absorb

the variations in production and obtain as high and stable profitability as possible. It is proposed now to take a brief look at various types of markets where Frionor can sell their fish products, and what sort of products are relevant in these different markets. Any geographical market consists of segments with very different characteristics. For practical purposes we have here (Table 1) divided the total market into five segments and by way of illustration have marked down some products (frozen fish) that are typical in these segments. Any exporter of fish must decide whether he wants to move his products into all of the different segments or whether he prefers to specialize in one or two. Whatever the decision, the situation in each segment is different (Table 2). The main advantages that we as fish exporters look for in a market are: high flexibility, low marketing costs, the possibility of achieving a high strategic strength and a high and preferably stable profitability. These factors need closer examination. By flexibility we mean how swiftly we are able in a given situation to increase sales or to reduce sales in a particular market. In other words, we are concerned about the possibility of reducing our volume without seriously reducing at the same time our chances to return later with an increased volume. And we are also concerned about the extent to which we can reduce our volume without losing our investment. The two extremes we have to consider are, of course, the 'commodity market' with a very high degree of flexibility and the 'Frionor label retail market', where flexibility is generally very low and the consequences of failure to supply very serious indeed. By marketing costs we mean payment for the 'entrance ticket' to a market and the 'subscription fee' for staying in. The cost varies from the minimum in the commodity market to a very high level in the retail market. In the latter case it is necessary not only to invest a lot of money to gain a foothold, but we also

TABLE 1. MARKET SEGMENTS AND TYPE OF PRODUCTS SUPPLIED BY FRIONOR

Market segment	Type of products
Commodity market (Semi-manufactured products)	Unsophisticated products, according to given standards, low degree of processing: – Industrial blocks – Slabs – IQF fillets in bulk – Round frozen fish for smoking, etc.
Bulk products Ready to consume ('catering')	Usually unsophisticated products, often according to international trade standards or buyer's specification, low degree of processing: – Fillets in bulk – IQF portions, etc.
Private label	Retail packs under buyer's label according to specifications set by the buyer; high and sometimes very high degree of processing.
Frionor label Ready to consume ('Frionor catering')	Products and packs designed for various types of catering on the basis of own product development and specifications, unsophisticated products with low degree of processing as well as highly developed products including ready-to-serve meals.
Frionor label Retail packs	Retail packs often in a large number of varieties, sometimes even including non-fish products, often including quite complex products, production according to own development and own standards.

TABLE 2. CHARACTERISTICS OF DIFFERENT MARKET SEGMENTS

Market segment	Advantages				Profitability			
	Flexibility in volume	Marketing costs	Strategic strength	Short-term	Long-term	Market up	Market down	
Commodity market (semi-manufactured products)	++	++	––	++	–	++	––	
Bulk products ready to consume ('Catering')	+	+	–	+	–	+	–	
Private label retail packs	+	0	–	0	–	0	0	
Frionor label ready to consume ('Frionor catering')	–	–	+	–	+	–	+	
Frionor label retail packs	––	––	++	––	++	––	++	

++ very high   + high   –– very low   – low

have to spend considerable sums of money each year to keep this foothold. Strategic strength is the strength of our position as a producer relative to our buyers and our competitors. It affects, therefore, the extent to which we are left at the mercy of changing market prices and are forced to price competition and indicates also our position in the distribution system. Usually we can only attain a very low strategic strength in the commodity market, particularly if our share of the market is modest. The Frionor label in the retail market, on the other hand (provided we have a sufficient share of the market and are, therefore, in a well established position) usually means that we enjoy the benefit of a high degree of strategic strength.

On a short-term basis the commodity market tends to show the highest profitability because it requires little investment and very low expenditure in marketing. On a long-term basis, the situation tends to be the other way round. This is because the benefit of the higher marketing costs takes some time to show up, thus only in the longer-term basis are we able to take advantage of a higher strategic strength in the market. The profitability pattern in these different segments also varies, depending on whether the market is heading up or down. In a tight supply situation, higher prices are first in evidence in the commodity market. Higher prices in the retail market may, in some countries, take months to appear. In a situation where there is a prolonged trend toward increased fish prices, such as we have seen since 1969, the more complex market segments may constantly

lag. When the market turns down, there is, of course, a similar lag, but this time in favour of the exporter who operates in the more complex markets. Even temporary over-supplies tend to affect a commodity market immediately, but has usually very little effect on price in the retail market.

It is the marketing manager's job to decide what segment or segments he should concentrate on. No doubt the technical standard in his plant, the total production volume and the extent he can invest in the market will be important factors in reaching his decision. Often, however, he may find that his need for a flexible set-up in the market will make him forgo the advantages of higher strategic strength and the prospect of achieving higher profitability on a long-term basis. Let us, therefore, again have a look at the various market segments regarding strategic strength and flexibility. As Table 2 shows, it is impossible for any segment of the market to have high strategic strength and high flexibility at the same time. The price of high flexibility is low strategic strength. And the price of high strategic strength is, of necessity, low flexibility. Usually, maximum flexibility is achieved in the industrial and catering markets which are the largest segments in the international fish market. The greater part of the international trade in frozen fish is in semi-manufactured and bulk products. This applies to all the major importing countries, with the USA and the UK in the lead. As a consequence, these international markets can absorb very large additional quantities from us, and we can obtain these additional quantities at low marketing cost by using the price as our instrument. In the industrial segment, therefore, it is possible for an exporter to increase his trade by 50 per cent or even by 100 or 200 per cent in a short period of time. The structure and the psychology of the market are such that the exporter can, if need be, also reduce his trade very considerably without too much loss of goodwill, future potential and marketing investments. In a segment like 'retail packs under own label', on the other hand, there may be considerable strategic strength, but also a lack of flexibility. We can, of course, increase our sales of any one item by heavy promotion and price cuts. Such increases, however, will usually be of short duration. If we continue our sales drive for longer periods, our competitors take counter measures. A healthy increase in volume and share of the market can only be obtained by consistent effort, perhaps over several years. It is evident that our investment in the retail market can be profitable only if our goods are available in the freezing cabinets in the shops at all times. If we cannot supply the goods, even for a short time, a greater part of our investment will be lost, and 'our share' of the retail cabinets will be filled up by our competitors. Such non-availability of products may create a worse position than that of entering the market for the first time when the handicap is lack of goodwill. In re-entering a market after a failure to supply, it is not lack of goodwill but the presence of illwill that has to be overcome.

I cannot tell you what priority you should attach to the various segments in developing export markets. I can only describe what our thinking is. Frionor puts the lowest priority on the commodity market and the highest on the Frionor label retail market. This may seem to indicate that we are going in simply for strategic strength. Our motives are, however, a bit more complex:

We need an element of stability in our marketing that the retail market is able to provide.

We believe that in the long run it is more profitable to make finished products instead of selling raw material.

We face a more or less permanent limitation in our raw material supply and can only expand by a higher degree of processing. Consequently, we must concentrate our efforts on geographical areas and market segments where we can sell such products.

But once it is said that we give our retail packs under the Frionor label first priority, the following must be added:

We need a balanced system that comprises all market segments in order to secure the necessary flexibility.

We can concentrate on the retail market only if we have near-certainty that we shall maintain a steady and uninterrupted flow of products into it.

We must accept the fact that there are markets so large that we do not have the quantities of fish or the money to achieve sufficient penetration. So, we have to concentrate our efforts on smaller geographical areas, where we have sufficient resources to obtain a reasonably high share of the total market. A considerable share of such markets is essential since we specialize in fish and base our profile in the market

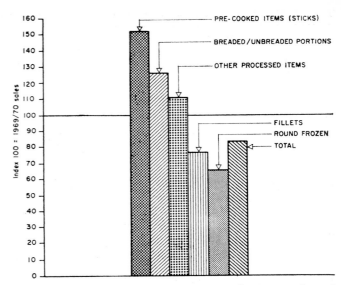

Fig 6   Relative change in the 1970–71 sales of various products of a cooperative of the frozen fish industry in Norway compared to the 1969–70 sales

on fish. We have, therefore, only the sales of fish products on which to charge our marketing costs. This means that if our volume of sales is too low, our distribution costs become high, perhaps prohibitive.

The fish industry, due to its insecurity on the production end, needs a marketing machinery which is flexible enough to cope when production suddenly expands and when it suddenly contracts. Let me give you an example of an actual case. In Fig 6 one can see what happened to Frionor sales from 1969/70 to 1970/71, when there was considerable loss of volume because we did not have enough raw material. It can be seen that, despite the reduced total volume, the enterprise was able to meet the increasing demand for retail packs and even increase deliveries to the catering sector. In order to achieve this the production of round-frozen fish (which goes to the industrial sector as raw material for smoking) and the sales of industrial blocks were cut down. Indeed, we halved the latter. Once we have decided to move into a certain geographical area and have decided what segments of the market we are going to concentrate on, the question of how to organize sales is more or less answered. It takes a very different set-up to move our products into the retail market under our own label than to limit our efforts, for instance, to industrial customers. Subsequently, in Sweden, as an example, we maintain our own fully fledged marketing organization, including the staff for servicing the freezing cabinets in the shops and a substantial advertising budget. But the industrial market in the UK, as a contrast, is limited to a few large customers and we can easily handle our business with them from Oslo by telephone and telex, and a few visits every year.

THE NORWEGIAN SYSTEM

I outlined briefly at the beginning the organization of Frionor. We have found that the system works quite well compared with the usual arrangements in the industry. It has, in my opinion, been the curse of the fishing industry in many countries that there has been more instability than necessary on the production side. There has been little vertical integration, perhaps none, therefore little coordination of the efforts of the fishermen, the processing plants, and the exporter and between the exporter and the importer and distributor in the importing market. As a result of this, the exporter – however capable he might be – is often nothing more than a fishmonger who happens to work across national boundaries, who buys and sells 'according to the market' on a day-to-day basis. We have tried to do this a little bit differently in Norway. Our system starts with the strong organizational pattern that exists among the fishermen. The freezing industry (and this also applies to other sectors of the fish processing industry) negotiates as a group with the fishermen's organization, ie, with the sales board, which consists of fishermen assisted by a well qualified staff, and an understanding has developed over the years of the mutual dependency of every link in the chain from the sea to the consumer's table. Our raw material prices are normally high, but not unreasonably so, and are stable through a period of not less than 3 to 4 months. Such stability is a prerequisite for any planned marketing of fish abroad because, without it, there can be no regularity in prices. There are, of course, large markets like the USA where export/import contracts are made on the basis of price at time of delivery. Although this does not eliminate the risk that the exporter may find himself in an impossible squeeze between production cost and selling price, it does tend to reduce it. In other areas, however, the contract price is firm and there is no honest way that the exporter can escape a squeeze.

A big advantage of a set-up such as Frionor is that all plants are able to produce a uniform quality which is guaranteed and sold by Frionor. As far as the foreign importer is concerned, there is only one product and one producer. The fact that the same product is being produced in a number of plants increases stability in production and safety in planning. With the total production pooled, discrepancies between planned and actual production at each plant tend to be equalled out. As a sort of by-product, it is easier for the plants to specialize in certain products for improved efficiency. The joint marketing organization enables each plant to concentrate on efficient production. Such a marketing organization can operate with flexibility and work in a number of geographical markets. It has access to marketing information from many parts of the world, and can employ qualified personnel and finance the whole process of marketing on a larger scale. Further, it is able to develop markets for highly processed products under its own label and spread the risk in a number of markets. A high degree of concentration through the export of a group of fish products from a country has important advantages over a decentralized system with many independent operations. Under such a system competition among exporters of the same country usually occurs and where one exporter succeeds, others tend to follow his lead, using a lower price to compete. The 1972 landslide in the United States in the price of blue halibut from Japan may serve as illustration of this.

To sum up, the main marketing points we have made are: Fastest expansion of sales is achieved in the semi-manufacture and bulk market, where marketing investments are low. In spite of this, the exporter should strive for a higher strategic strength in the market by concentrating on a limited geographical area or on a particular segment of the market. He should take a realistic view of his strong and weak points in international competition and work from realistic budgets. He should build up confidence as a reliable source of supply of good quality products. If he exports on behalf of several production plants, he should establish one quality standard. He should ensure that he has the volume, flexibility and financial means to make an impact in the market and be able to cope with the ups and downs in production. And, finally, in the interests of efficient operation he should work for the coordination of the marketing effort for all fish exports from his country.

The Japanese Experience in Developing Export Markets for Fishery Products   *M Morisawa*

L'experience Japonaise dans le developpement de marches d'exportation pour les produits de la pêche

Le Japon export depuis 1880 des produits de la pêche salés et séchés vers les pays voisons. Aujourd'hui, par suite du développement des activités de pêche dans le monde entier, de l'utilisation de méthodes de transformation modernes et de la création de nouveaux marchés, le Japon est l'un des plus grands exportateurs de produits de la mer, essentiellement de conserves et d'articles congelés.

Les principaux produits de la pêche se répartissent en trois catégories: ceux qui sont destinés principalement à l'exportation, notament les conserves et l'huile de baleine; ceux qui sont tributaires à la fois du marché d'exportation et du marché intéreuri et ceux qui sont uniquement destinés au marché intérieur.

Dans ce document, on étudie les moyens de développer les marchés d'outre mer. Certains des éléments les plus importants de ce développement sont: l'étude des tendances des marchés étrangers, la promotion des ventes, le maintien de prix de vente

Experiencia Japonesa en la apertura de mercados exteriores de productos pesqueros

Japón exporta productos pesqueros salados y secos a países vacinos desde 1880. En la actualidad, gracias a la expansión mundial de sus actividades pesqueras, la introducción de métodos modernos de elaboración y la apertura de nuevos mercados, Japón es uno de los principales exportadores de productos pesqueros, especialmente en conserva y congelados.

Los principales productos pesqueros se agrupan en tres categorías: los destinados especialmente a los mercados exteriores, en particular los congelados y el aceite de ballena; los orientados tanto hacia la exportación como hacia los mercados interiores; y los destinados exclusivamente al mercado interior.

El presente estudio trata de la forma de abrir mercados en el extranjero. El examen de las tendencias de los mercados extranjeros, la promoción de ventas, el establecimiento de precios estables de venta, el mantenimiento de la calidad de los productos, son algunos de los factores màs importantes para abrir tales mercados. Se

stable et d'une qualité élevée et constante des produits; les efforts japonais en la matière sont décrits en détail. Les succès rencontrés par ce pays dans l'exportation des produits de la pêche sont imputables aux efforts combinés des entreprises privées, de l'industrie et du Gouvernement, ainsi qu'au fait que le Japon possédait des ressources halieutiques abondantes et a déployé de grand efforts pour mettre au point des techniques de transformation du poisson. Entre autres éléments qui ont favorisé l'expansion, on peut citer l'existence d'un important marché intérieur pour les produits de la pêche de toutes sortes, qui existe traditionnellement au Japon depuis une époque très ancienne et a fourni une base solide au développement du commerce d'exportation.

Major markets for fishery products are the United States, Japan and Europe, including Britain. Major exporters are Peru, Japan, Norway and Canada. The share of the developing countries in fishery exports increased from 18 per cent to 29 per cent in the 10 years from 1958 to 1968, while the advanced countries are estimated to have taken 80 per cent of imports in 1968.

JAPANESE STATUS IN WORLD FISH TRADE

Japanese exports of fishery products in 1970 were worth US$ 333 million* accounting for 11.7 per cent of the world total (Table 1). These figures compare with US$ 199 million and 16·2 per cent of the trade in 1958. Thus, the value of Japanese exports had increased 1·7 times but the Japanese share of the world total has been declining gradually. Of the world fishery exports in 1970, the Japanese share in fish products was about 40 per cent, followed by 24 per cent for crustaceans and mollusc products. However, exports of fish (fresh, chilled or frozen) and oils and fats of aquatic animal origin, mainly whale and fish oil, were less than 10 per cent and those of other categories were negligible.

Japanese exports of fishery products go mostly to the industrialized countries. For instance, two-thirds of the exports (in value) go to the United States, Canada and Europe, 17 per cent to Asia, a few per cent to Africa and Oceania and a very few to South America. Japan is also one of the biggest fish importing countries† with about 50 per cent of the imports (in value) coming from Asia and only 14 per cent from North America and

describen detalladamente las actividades de Japón en estos sectores. Su éxito en la exportación de productos pesqueros se ha debido a las actividades conjuntas de las empresas privadas, la industria y el Gobierno, a lo que hay que sumar los abundantes recursos pesqueros del Japón y la ingente labor efectuada para perfeccionar la tecnología de elaboración de pescado. Un factor que ha fomentado este expansión ha sido el enorme mercado interior de productos pesqueros de todo tipo, tradicional en Japón desde la antigüedad, que ha ofrecido una sólida base para crear el comercio de exportación.

Europe. Characteristics of the Japanese fisheries trade may therefore be summarized as follows: Among varied fishery items exported, canned and frozen products are of first importance. While other big fishing countries normally only export products, Japan is both an exporter and importer on a large scale.

JAPANESE EXPORTS OF FISHERY PRODUCTS – PRESENT AND PAST

Present proportion of fishery products for export

The value of Japanese exports of fishery products has shown an upward trend in recent years and, as stated, totalled US$333 million in 1970. Of this, fish products and preparations earned US$185 million or 56 per cent, fresh, chilled or frozen fish US$76 million or 23 per cent, crustacean and mollusc products and preparations US$29 million, and fresh, chilled, frozen, dried, salted, etc, crustaceans and molluscs US$22 million. Of fresh, chilled or frozen fish, the major item was frozen tuna, with yellowfin at 21,755 metric tons valued at US$12,054,000, albacore at 17,219 metric tons worth US$11,745,000 and skipjack at 20,563 metric tons worth US$6,753,000. They went to the United States (US$14,083,000), Puerto Rico (US$8,613,000) and Italy (US$6,201,000) and to Fiji, American Samoa and Spain. Italy purchased mainly yellowfin tuna but the United States and Puerto Rico bought albacore and skipjack as well as yellowfin. There are two types of Japanese exports of frozen tuna: direct from Japan or by transfer of the catch at foreign ports to carriers. Frozen fish

TABLE 1. VALUE OF GLOBAL AND JAPANESE EXPORTS OF FISHERY PRODUCTS BY CATEGORY (US$ MILLION)

Category		1958	1966	1967	1968	1969	1970
Grand total	Global	1,123	2,124	2,114	2,227	2,449	2,847
	Japan	199	284	254	286	282	333
Fish, fresh, chilled, frozen	Global	283	635	580	628	716	846
	Japan	39	106	71	71	63	76
Fish, dried, salted, smoked	Global	179	228	236	223	239	271
	Japan	2	3	3	4	5	5
Crustacean and mollusc, fresh, frozen, dried, etc.	Global	123	293	333	386	474	521
	Japan	6	4	9	16	20	22
Fish products and preparations	Global	306	391	405	429	431	468
	Japan	107	123	134	160	151	185
Crustacean and mollusc products and preparations	Global	43	94	96	98	112	122
	Japan	17	26	25	30	35	29
Oils and fats of aquatic animal origin	Global	99	124	104	77	86	129
	Japan	25	13	9	4	5	11
Meals, solubles and similar animal feeding stuffs of aquatic animal origin	Global	90	359	360	385	391	490
	Japan	3	3	2	1	3	5

Source: *FAO Yearbook of Fishery Statistics*, Vol. 31, Fishery Commodities, 1970.

* Excludes cultured pearls and seaweed products such as agar-agar.

† The value of these imports more than doubled over the past five years to US$427 million in 1971 and exceeded the value of exports (418 million) that year. The value in 1971 was second only to that of the United States.

other than tuna were rainbow trout (3,074 metric tons, US$1,533,000) mostly to the United States and Canada, sauries (16,790 metric tons, US$3,638,000) as bait fish for tuna longlining at overseas fishing bases, sharks (3,897 metric tons, US$1,701,000) and Alaska pollack and sea bream to Europe. Canned tuna, salmon and mackerel were major export items. Canned sardine, horse mackerel and sauries, at one time exported in large quantity, are no longer so marketed. Canned crab meat, oyster and clam were the major export item in crustaceans and molluscs. Canned shrimp and cuttlefish exports were small.

Exports of canned tuna in 1970 totalled 3,041,000 cases (standard case net weight 21.6 kg (47.52 lb)) valued at US$80,172,000. The chief buyers were the United States (US$47,822,000), Canada (US$6,621,000), Britain (US$4,359,000) and the Netherlands, Belgium and Switzerland. Tuna in oil are sold to Canada and Europe, in brine to the United States and in sauce to the Federal Republic of Germany. Canned salmon exports in 1970 were 1,112,000 cases valued at US$44,946,000: Britain took 73 per cent (US$32,796,000) followed by Australia the Netherlands, Belgium and France. Japan exports both red and pink salmon, with the pink variety increasing gradually due to catches. Canned mackerel exports have increased rapidly in recent years, totalling 7,463,000 cases (US$54,346,000) in 1970 and becoming top in value of canned products in 1971. Export markets cover broadly Southeast Asia, the Middle and Near East, Europe, the United States and Ghana. Most of the mackerels are canned in brine and tomato sauce and are sold mainly in Southeast Asia. Canned crab meat exports totalled 83,000 cases valued at US$8,137,000. They are sold mainly to the United States and Europe, centred on France. Due to the strong domestic demand and falling supplies to packers, exports of canned crab meat show a decline. Exports of canned oyster (in brine and smoked in oil) totalled 196,000 cases valued at US$6,320,000, sold mainly to the United States and Canada. Canned clam exports were 271,000 cases valued at US$4,593,000, sold mainly to the United States, Canada, Spain and Italy.

Some US$688,000 worth of frozen oysters were exported, mainly to the United States, US$4,270,000 worth of shrimp to the United States, Britain and northern South America, and US$10,830,000 worth of cuttlefish to Italy, Spain, Greece, etc. However, the actual export value of shrimp and cuttlefish would be far less than indicated above because the catch shipped to Japan after unloading at foreign ports is often listed as Japanese exports. Japan is exporting dried shark fin, abalone, scallop and kelp, mainly to Hong Kong and Singapore. Agar-agar exports were worth US$3,324,000, centred on Europe. However, Japanese imports of agar-agar have been increasing in recent years. Fish and whale oil in 1970 totalled 15,000 metric tons (US$3,125,000) and 34,000 metric tons (US$33,766,000) respectively, centred on Europe. Most of the fish meal produced is for domestic use, but 25,000 metric tons (US$5,101,000) were exported in 1970.

Review of Japanese fisheries trade

In 1870–1900, Japanese fisheries and processing were immature in terms of technology and management. The total catch was about one million metric tons, confined to coastal and adjacent water species and processing was simple drying and salting. Exports were mainly dried shark fin, abalone, sea cucumber and kelp, etc, to neighbouring countries, and dependence on such overseas trade was high. With the introduction of such new items as canned products, whale oil and frozen fish, a rapid increase started in exports. The Japanese fishing industry entered into this developing stage in the nineteen hundreds with the emergence of the high seas fisheries, modern whaling, and canning and freezing, supported by capital accumulation at home and the introduction of foreign technology in fishing and processing. Simultaneously, the export trade began expanding: canned salmon, mainly to Britain, and canned crab meat, mainly to the United States, since 1910. Then in the twenties, came frozen and canned tuna, canned sardine, oyster, fish oil and whale oil. Exports of these increased rapidly and in the thirties exceeded exports of the traditional dried or salted products. While present exports are different and those of dried or salted products have declined considerably, it can be said that the basis for Japanese exports was established in those days.

REVIEW OF DEPENDENCE ON DOMESTIC AND OVERSEAS MARKETS

Of the Japanese catch in 1970 of 8,787,000 metric tons (excluding seaweeds and whales), only 10.4 per cent, or 908,000 metric tons were for export. In other words, many of the products are for the domestic market and Japanese fishing and processing industries have, as a whole, been mainly based on that market. But, of course, this is not necessarily the case with every product. The products can be classified into those that depend (1) mostly on foreign markets, (2) equally on domestic and foreign markets, and (3) mostly on the domestic market. For products in category (1) it is essential to have an assured supply of raw material and a superior production technology so as to meet the demands of the markets at all times and, by obtaining the necessary data, to anticipate foreign needs. Category (2) includes products for both the domestic and export markets. Such trade in exports exists when the diet and consumption patterns of Japan and other countries correspond. While differences between domestic and export prices play a part, stability in both markets is a most important factor. Category (3) products are for the domestic market with incidental exports.

Based on these categories, the products for export can be generally classified as follows:

1. Products dependent mostly on foreign markets (Category 1)

Canned tuna in brine and in vegetable sauce depend mostly on foreign markets. Although canned tuna in oil have a big export sale, this product is now being widely consumed by the domestic market due to changes in the Japanese diet.

Canned salmon of the red variety has been traditionally exported to Britain. Canned pink salmon has also relied heavily on export but canned chum salmon has been mostly for domestic consumption. While domestic consumption of red and pink salmon is increasing, these two items are still for export.

Other canned fishery products. Canned oysters are mostly for export with some domestic consumption, and so is canned clam. About 80 per cent of canned mackerel, now the biggest production of Japanese canned fishery and farm products, is for export; the rest for domestic consumption. There are also some other types of canned mackerel for the domestic market.

Whale oil. The bulk of whale oil is exported to Europe.

2. Products dependent both on domestic and foreign markets (Category 2)

Frozen tuna. While there is competition between the domestic and export market demands for albacore, the demand for canned albacore is heavier for export than for the domestic market.

Others. Rainbow trout, which was heavily dependent on foreign markets in the past, is now in strong demand on the domestic market. Canned crab meat, which was also packed for export, is increasingly in demand on the domestic market due to a decline in the catch and the increase in domestic consumption. Agar-agar, too, is in increasing demand on the domestic market.

3. Products dependent on the domestic market (Category 3)

Dried or salted products. Dried abalone, shark fin, scallop, kelp and cuttlefish, which were dependent on export in the past, are mainly for domestic market now, with only limited exports to Southeast Asia. Domestic demand for these now includes the fresh, frozen or boiled form, depending on species.

Other products. Although exports of frozen cuttlefish, sauries and sea bream are big, their main sale is in the domestic market. As the grounds for cuttlefish and sea breams are distant from Japan, the catch is sometimes sold to nearby countries. Fish meal is mainly for cattle-food and fish culture in Japan, with little for export.

As is well known, fish and fish products are consumed in large quantities and in a vast variety of products in Japan so there is a constant pressure to meet this demand. It is not surprising, therefore, that canned goods are the only Japanese fishery products dependent on overseas markets, two-thirds of them being exported. This, however, does not mean that overseas markets are unimportant for the Japanese fishing and processing industries. Indeed, there are several cases, even in recent years, in which development of an export market played an important role in expanding the Japanese fishing and processing industries. An example is that of the European market for frozen tuna. This was developed when Japanese tuna longline vessels extended their fishing to the Indian and the Atlantic Oceans (in the fifties and sixties). This made possible the direct supply from the fishing ground, or through foreign ports, of the catch to Europe. Although the Japanese tuna industry depends on the domestic market, the importance of overseas markets remains unchanged, particularly for Japanese fishermen operating in the Atlantic Ocean. Some 30 to 40 per cent of the catch of cuttlefish, sea bream, etc, in the Atlantic was first exported to Europe and Africa, but since then the domestic demand has increased and more is brought back to Japan. Exports

of canned sardine, horse mackerel and sauries, which were large in the past, have declined due to changes in the stocks. Instead, canned mackerel has become the main export. This is a result of two factors – increased production and new markets. The catch of mackerel has increased rapidly so that packers can buy raw fish cheap and continuously, enabling them to establish a system of mass production. At the same time new overseas markets have been developed in addition to the traditional outlets.

WAYS AND MEANS FOR DEVELOPMENT OF OVERSEAS MARKETS

In the development of overseas markets and promotion of exports, there are important factors, such as recognition of market trends, active sales promotion and public relations, continuous supply at stable price, improvement in quality, and so forth. For studying market trends, collection and analysis of the following data are of special importance: consumer income, level of consumption, diet or acceptable taste, local distribution route, price and quality of competing items, if any, tariffs and trade policy, and sanitary inspection and hygienic control. Japanese agencies and trading firms with offices in the major countries of the world collect such information. This information, after study and analysis, assists the manufacturers in deciding standards, kinds, price, etc, of products for export.

JETRO (Japan External Trade Organization), established in 1958 by the Japanese Government, plays a significant role in this process. It collects information and data on trade of various countries of the world, surveys market trends, functions in the public relations field, organizes trade fairs and exhibits abroad, and so on. It also organizes exhibits in Japan of products made in developing countries and conducts feasibility surveys for Japanese imports of foreign products. An example of market research by JETRO is that which it conducted in Europe for canned tuna. The following aspects were checked: (i) consumption and production of canned fish by species in each European country together with basic data on their foreign trade; (ii) distribution route, wholesale price, marketing status, such as regional and seasonal characteristics, kinds of brand and retail price; and (iii) European retailer views on Japanese canned tuna, such as size of can, quality, retail price, outer packaging and labelling. In some countries, JETRO surveyed the fishing and processing industries, covering production, species caught, number and scale, fishing vessels and local and export distribution of their catches or processed products.

Japanese trading firms, specializing in foreign trade, have these major functions: handling the business in existing markets; developing new ones; providing the finance for marketing operations and collecting data. The manufacturers assign the selling rights to the trading firms. Such firms handle the marketing of many different products made by many different manufacturers. In order to prevent excessive competition and lowering of quality, etc., the Japanese manufacturers have an association, under the relevant domestic laws and regulations, to enforce their voluntary agreement on quantity, quality, sales price, method of marketing, etc. While quality control or improvement can be achieved by manufacturers themselves through selection of better raw material, optimum production control and improvement in labour skill, a role is played by the Japanese Government. Under Japanese law, all manufacturers of fishery products for export must register with the Government. The Government has established certain criteria on plants and buildings, etc, and requirements of educational background and experience for the senior engineer in charge of quality control. Only those plants which meet the criteria are allowed to manufacture products for export. This system controls frozen tuna, a major portion of canned fishery products, whale oil, pearls, kanten (agar-agar product), etc. Another Government enforcement is quality inspection of export products. Japanese export inspection arrangements have a long history: dried cuttlefish, scallop, abalone and kelp have been so inspected since the 1900s, canned fishery products since the 1910s and frozen fishery products since the 1930s.

The present practice is based on compulsory inspection, established in 1958.

The Government's earlier policy for export promotion should also be mentioned. The Government once encouraged export enterprise by granting the following special tax and financial preferential measures: deduction from corporate income accrued from export, reserves for development of overseas markets and special depreciation under the tax preferences; and rediscount of export trade bills by the Central Bank. These preferences lured enterprises to export. However, almost all such preferences have now been abolished.

Summed up, it can be said that, allied with the strenuous efforts made by all concerned in Japan with fisheries, the huge demand for fishery products at home made possible the remarkable development of the Japanese fishing and processing industries and was the firm base on which the big expansion of export trade was achieved.

Developing Export Markets for New Zealand Fishery Products   *W T Allen*

Developpement des marches d'exportation pour les produits halieutiques de la Nouvelle-Zelande

L'auteur donne un compte rendu précis de la façon dont les exportateurs néo-zélandais de poissons et de produits de la pêche sont parvenus à consolider leur commerce en dépit de séreiux handicaps: distance qui les sépare des principaux marchés mondiaux, situés dans l'hemisphère nord, irrégularité des services de transport et caractère inusité des espèces de poissons et de leurs appellations. Ils ont surmonté ces difficultés avec succès, ainsi que le démontre la croissance des échanges – dont la valeur est passée de 4 millions de dollars néo-zélandais en 1964 à 20 millions en 1971. L'auteur conclut en lançant un avertissement pour dénoncer le risque d'épuisement des ressources, à moins que ne soient adoptées des mesures rationnelles de conservation.

Nuevos mercados de exportacion para los productos pesqueros de Nueva Zelandia

El autor explica como los exportadores de pescado y productos pesqueros de Nueva Zelandia han logrado intensificar su comercio a pesar de las desventajas que supone la gran distancia de los principales mercados mundiales que se encuentran en el hemisferio norte y los servicios de transporte irregulares y especies ícticas poco conocidas incluso por sus nombres. El éxito que han tenido en vencer estas dificultades lo demuestra el aumento de su comercio – de cuatro millones de dólares neocelandeses en 1964 a 20 millones en 1971. El documento termina advirtiendo que a menos de que se adopten medidas adecuadas de conservación puede que los recursos lleguen a agotarse.

The worldwide growth in the export trade of fish and fishery products in recent years has been shared by New Zealand. For example, in 1964 the total fish exports of the country amounted in value to NZ$4 million but by 1971 this trade had increased in value to some NZ$20 million. This increase is a substantial achievement in view of the disadvantages faced by the New Zealand exporter. These include the different species and names of fish in the southern hemisphere, the cost of shipment of exports to the main markets in the world, which are in the northern hemisphere, and the infrequency of transport services. There is also the added problem of the irregularity of fish supplies in New Zealand. Despite these disadvantages, the exports of fish and fishery products have been developed.

SUPPLY AND PROCESSING CAPACITY

There are sharp seasonal fluctuations in the availability of fish in New Zealand. In recent years, in particular, it has been noticeable that the habits, migration and behaviour patterns of fish have become irregular. This, combined with occasional long periods of rough weather which keep New Zealand boats in port, leaves large gaps in supply to overseas customers. As continuity of supply is a big factor in the orderly marketing of a product, this has proved most frustrating to the producer and customer alike when a well designed plan of marketing is badly affected or, in some cases, completely wrecked through the temporary lack of raw material. From the above it will be seen that it would be imprudent for a New Zealand exporter to contract for a set amount of supply to any market. Great strides have been made over the last decade in fish processing in New Zealand, mainly through delicensing, application of stringent hygiene regulations (supervised by the Ministry of Agriculture and Fisheries) and the big expansion of the industry. While the industry experiences few labour shortage problems, there are some difficulties from November until about April, chiefly because the knife hands take employment in the more lucrative meat and wool industry during this period. In the past many processing companies made use of outside storage facilities but this system has now changed and all the larger companies operate their own freezer and ice-making plants as an integral part of the factory. This cuts down handling, transport and freezing delays, helping to produce a better quality product. In most of the New Zealand processing plants mechanization is used wherever possible, such as conveyors, overhead tracks, and filleting and skinning machines. Three New Zealand companies were engaged in the production of fish meal but two closed down. However, the high price being paid for this commodity has created fresh interest in it and two plants are now in production, while a new one is to be set up to use the waste from the pelagic fishery operated out of Gisborne.

THE EXPORT SITUATION

New Zealand has exported fish since 1920, perhaps before this time. Fish was exported whole or headed, gutted and frozen, in wooden cases to Australia. As the demand grew and the competition increased many variants of sizes, types, and quality of packaging appeared. For instance, small packets of fully processed 'ready-for-the-pan' fish were produced for the rapidly growing supermarket trade, convenient, easy-to-thaw 5-lb (2.25-kg) packs were produced for the small hotel and institutional trade, whilst the 20-lb (9-kg) bulk pack was taken by fish and chip shops and larger hotels.

As Fig. 1 indicates that the demand for fish from New Zealand is now coming from many countries. It far exceeds the supply and calls for various types of processing, different types of fish to satisfy different tastes, and, of course, a range of standards.

Marketing factors

There is a growing opportunity for fish exports. Prices of other protein foods are high and people are beginning to discover that fish is an economical food, especially when sold in skinless, boneless fillet form. Many consumers are also preoccupied with the dangers of high cholesterol levels caused by eating fatty foods and prefer to include more fish in their diets.

The following factors are important in developing markets for fishery products:

Products should conform to the highest quality standards.

Top quality packaging and presentation are needed.

There should be strict conformity with the customer's specifications and the import requirements in the country of destination.

Regularity of supply, competitive pricing, coordinated and orderly marketing are required.

Efficient and regular transport services at reasonable costs are needed.

Many suggestions have been made to the New Zealand Fishing Industry Board from within the industry and from the Government that there ought to be more orderly export marketing of New Zealand fish and fish products. The Board is therefore making a comprehensive study of marketing methods employed by other countries which have found it necessary to develop a more orderly approach to export marketing. The two main approaches to market research are personal assessment and contact by executives of the exporting company. The usual practice is for a representative of the company to have 'on-the-spot' discussions on processing, packaging, documentation, short-term or long-

DESTINATION OF EXPORTS BY REGION

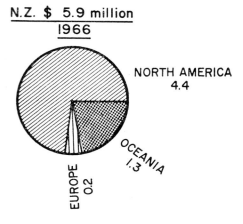

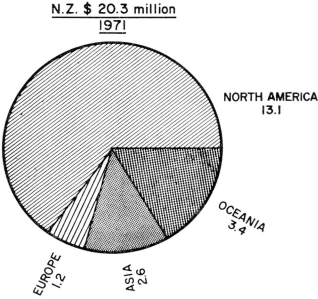

VALUE OF EXPORTS

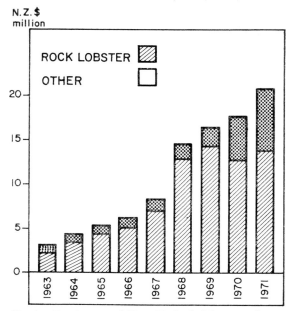

Fig 1   Destination of New Zealand fishery product exports by region and values in the period 1963–71

388

term policies, and so on. The follow-up is usually in the form of a small trial shipment to test the market, followed by, perhaps, some minor adjustments before regular trading commences. Some New Zealand exporters appoint a master agent in a country who imports in bulk, distributes the product, and takes care of invoicing and payment. This system is widely used between Australia and New Zealand and has the advantage that a number of buyers are dealt with by the distributor. Research and test marketing are also often approached through correspondence and samples. This is more difficult and not so successful as the personal contact. Usually there have to be many exchanges of letters before the requirements are made clear. An added difficulty is a language difference and bad translations can cause trouble. The high cost of preparation of sample packages and the need, perhaps, of having to use air freight to speed up decisions can make this type of operation very expensive, particularly if a number of customers are being dealt with in one period. Constant market research is done by the Department of Trade and Industry and inquiries from their Trade Commissioners are channelled to the packers through publications and by circular to members of the New Zealand Wholesale Fish Merchants Association. Trade missions from New Zealand visit importing countries and occasionally a representative of the fishing industry is a member of such a mission. A mission is invaluable for introduction to interested parties, for publicity and availability of 'on-the-spot' credit ratings of inquirers but not for obtaining sales. It generally takes another visit or two to establish regular trading. Promotional activities have been very lightly entered into by New Zealand industry. Some promotion has been carried out at trade fairs by the display of empty packets, although the frozen product has actually been featured in Australian fairs. Possibly the best promotion so far was organized by the New Zealand Industry Board at Expo 70 where New Zealand fish was cooked and featured in the restaurant of the New Zealand Pavilion.

PACKAGING FOR EXPORT

From the early wooden boxes the industry has progressed through the use of ordinary cardboard to very durable highly-protective board in the bulk packs and very attractive multi-coloured waxed sulphite containers for other packs. Insulated packs made of polyurethane and polystyrene are used by some companies for air freighting chilled fillets to Australia. Small plastic trays of ready-to-cook fish, covered with protective see-through film, and the complete frozen meal ready to heat in an aluminium foil dish, are also used. All board used for fish packages is waxed on both sides, heavily or lightly according to the customer's request. Besides the wax of the carton, the fish is also protected by polythene sheeting or liners, the gauge of which is varied with the size of the pack, susceptibility of the product to dehydration, and the degree of quality the packer is striving to obtain within the limits of the profit margin. Chemical glazing is also now used in place of polythene wrapping. Packaging costs are continually increasing but at present we operate at a cost of NZ$0.02/kg on bulk packs and up to NZ$0.04/kg on the more sophisticated consumer packs.

Stringent specifications are laid down by carriers of air freight fish to ensure that no moisture escapes. Leak-proof cartons are used with double polythene internal liners and then the whole carton is heat-sealed inside a heavy-duty polythene outer bag. Leakage in an aircraft can cost thousands of dollars because of the highly corrosive effect of the fish juice, added to which is the nauseating air pollution.

SHIPPING OF EXPORTS

Most exports from New Zealand are made by ship although in recent years more use has been made of air transport, particularly to Australia where fish can be delivered as quickly as it can be to the more remote areas of New Zealand. Consignments must be accompanied by a National Airways Waybill with a certified customs invoice to enable prompt clearance through customs in Australia. As most of this fish is only chilled, not frozen, any delay could be disastrous to the quality. Export of frozen fish is normally by ship in refrigerated bulk lockers or in container vessels. Two container vessels run weekly between Auckland and Wellington and Sydney and Melbourne. Cargo for these vessels from smaller ports has to be containerized and railed to Auckland or Wellington or put into refrigerated freight liners for loading into containers prior to shipment. It is essential that the documents, which include bills of lading and certified customs invoices, are sent by airmail to the consignee immediately after lodgement or sent with the container to ensure no delay in clearing Australian customs. Bills of lading must be accompanied by three copies of an export entry (for the Reserve Bank, the Exporter's Trading Bank and the customs) and a declaration that the seller is a regular fish exporter with a general export licence and has satisfied the local market demand before exporting. A 'Standard Aligned Export Documentation' has now been introduced and has proved itself an efficient and cost-saving method of preparing export paper work. While the traditional export market for wet fish has been Australia, new markets are now opening up, including the USA, the UK, Europe, the Pacific islands and Southeast Asia. As each island supply is loaded separately and the quantities are relatively small, exporters outside Auckland have to put their bulk shipment into a freezer at the port. Each package is loaded as required. This operation increases fob charges considerably. The Government are looking into the possibility of a direct link from the South Island of New Zealand to the Pacific islands to obviate this disadvantage. There is a similar situation with air-freighting fish where the aircraft depart only from Auckland, Wellington and Christchurch. Those who are far from these airports incur a heavy cost in freight on the domestic airline to connect with overseas flights.

FINANCING EXPORTS

The three main methods of financing New Zealand fish exports are:
  (a) the banking system;
  (b) finance by the purchasers;
  (c) the packer using his own funds.

Unlimited finance is made available to New Zealand fish exporters through the banking system. There are variations in the method of this financing, with some traders using an extension of their trading overdraft, but the most favoured method is for the exporter to operate a separate export account through which all purchases and sales are financed. Method (b) is favoured where a packer is regularly shipping to a buyer on a long-term arrangement, particularly where there is a long period between shipments. The buyer makes an advance of 75 per cent, the balance being paid less charges and commission, when the goods are sold. Or an open letter of credit may be lodged with the packer's bank on which he way draw when the shipment is put into store. In both these cases, a warrant or declaration is made by the packer that the product has been put in store and is the property of the purchaser. A packer using his own funds ((c) method) can please himself to whom and when he sells to his greatest financial gain, which is an advantage so long as the market is strong. But when it becomes weak, this method can be a financial disaster to smaller operators.

TAXATION INCENTIVES

Under section 129A of the Land and Income Tax Act a tax-payer may claim a special deduction in respect of export market development expenditure. This deduction is an additional 50 per cent of the 'prescribed outgoings' (as defined in the Act) over and above the 100 per cent deduction ordinarily available. It means that for each NZ$1.00 spent on approved export promotion, a tax-payer is entitled to a deduction of NZ$1.50 from his assessable income. The maximum tax saving accruing from the total deduction of 150 per cent is limited to NZ$0.75 for each NZ$1.00 of approved expenditure. This limitation will have no practical effect provided maximum tax rates do not exceed NZ$0.50 in the NZ$1.00. To qualify for the special deduction, the expenditure must conform to an extensive list of conditions all aimed to ensure that it has been incurred in a genuine export effort. There are also prescribed outgoings and rates governing the allowance of travel expenses. Costs of maintaining permanent overseas sales representatives are allowable. The functions of the permanent overseas representatives must be confined to those which are primarily sales promotion. The claiming of the special deduction is not dependent on the amount of export sales that result from the promotion expenditure. The scheme is operative up to 31st March 1976 and may be extended by further Act of Parliament. There is provision for the Commissioner to disallow any part of expenditure which, in his opinion, exceeds the amount that 'would reasonably be expected to be payable in the ordinary course of business'. There is no special form for claiming the special deduction. Each company has to substantiate its annual income tax return with supporting schedules in appropriate form. There is no compulsion for a company to keep separate accounts of export market development expenditure. However, it would probably be in the company's interest to institute a simple accounting arrangement under which expenditure to be claimed

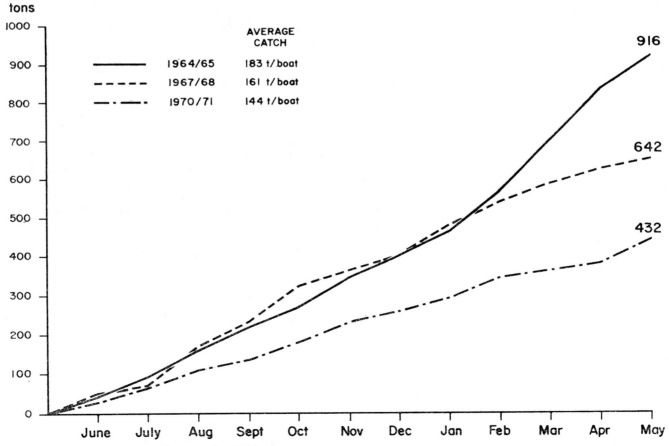

Fig 2 Decline in catch of a small New Zealand fishing company

for the special deduction is recorded separately and properly documented with explanations made at the time the expenditure is incurred. Self-employed professional persons may claim the additional 50 per cent deduction for time spent on promoting their services for overseas projects.

OBSTACLES TO EXPORTS

The New Zealand exporter is faced with a number of obstacles, the greatest of which is geographic isolation, which increases transport time and freight rates. The costs and overheads are constantly varying although in recent years the trend has only been upward. The exporter who contracts on a free-into-store, or cif, or even a c & f basis, is also liable to come up against increased costs. The highly perishable nature of the product and the necessity of critical temperatures being maintained means that any delay vitally affects the product and could result in condemnation of the consignment in the purchasing country. Many countries are not serviced by a direct shipping line from New Zealand and trans-shipment has proved so hazardous and costly that this type of operation is not popular with New Zealand operators. Changes in hygiene laws, nomenclature, unit weights and carton sizes are also expensive when they occur. Payment for goods is normally done by a letter of credit or term drafts. The New Zealand exporter is fortunate that he can reduce his credit risk by enlisting the aid of the Export Guarantee Office, which is Government-backed. It provides insurance against all manner of hazards, both commercial and political.

OUTLOOK

While New Zealand exporters can look forward to an increasing business, they are faced with the problem of supply. Fisheries and resource management have been minimal in New Zealand. Fishery density has never been assessed and resource regeneration levels ignored. Commenting in 1949 to a senior fisheries official that I was perturbed about the fishing for 'terakihi' at the East Cape spawning ground in February and March, I said that the area should be closed at this time. The reply was that the Department's scientists would tell us fishermen when to stop – which was the approach we feared. We needed guidance on long-term fishing that would avoid depleting the resource. So while the overall catch of New Zealand is increasing, the catch per unit of effort is declining rapidly, as is shown in Fig 2. Unless we are able to introduce the measures necessary to conserve and maintain our stocks at a viable level, the long-term outlook will remain doubtful.

Marketing Aspects of Powdered Products in the Future   *P Jaubert*

Perspectives futures de la commercialisation des produits en poudre
Le document traite succinctement des perspectives commerciales de la farine de poisson pour l'alimentation animale, de la fabrication de concentrés de protéines de poisson (CPP), de produits de remplacement du lait et de produits destinés à la consommation humaine. Il analyse la situation (sur la base de données d'expérience, de faits connus, de plans, etc.) pour les périodes 1971–75 et 1976–80. Voici les principales conclusions de l'étude: l'emploi de la farine de poisson pour l'alimentation des animaux, et en particulier pour le nourrissage des poissons, ira en augmentant bien que l'on observe dans les pays en développement une tendance à l'utilisation de substituts dans les produits de l'alimentation animale. En ce qui concerne le commerce d'importation de la farine de poisson, il est vraissemblable que l'on assistera à une baisse dans les pays avancés et à une hausse dans les pays en développement. La production de succédanés du lait s'accroîtra sans doute, passant d'environ 1,760,000 tonnes en 1971 à quelque 4,500,000 tonnes en 1980. Aucune prévision n'est faite au sujet des CPP destinés à la consommation humaine. Initialement fabriqués pour les pays en voie de développement, les CPP n'ont pas encore trouvé de marché stable.

Marketing aspects of the following powdered products will be dealt with:

Fish meal for animal nutrition (poultry, pig, fish farming);
FPC soluble or insoluble products for milk replacers;
FPC for human nutrition.

In order to approach the problem as clearly as possible, we have divided the 1971 to 1980 period into two parts: 1971 to 1975 and 1976 to 1980. Forecasts during the first period can be deducted from the 1971 experience and governmental plans up to 1975 in various countries for developing fish meal and mixed feed production. We

Aspectos de la comercializacion de los productos en polvo en el futuro
En este estudio se examinan brevemente las perspectivas del mercado de harina de pescado para nutrición de animales, de los concentrados de proteínas de pescado, de los sucedáneos de la leche y de los concentrados de proteínas de pescado para el consumo humano. Se analiza la situación (basándose en experiencias, hechos conocidos, planes, etc) durante el período 1971 a 1975 y 1976 a 1980. La principal conclusión a que se llega es que se utilizará cada vez más la harina de pescado para la nutrición de animales, incluidos peces, aunque en los países desarrollados se tiende a utilizar sucedáneos para estos usos. En el comercio de importación de harina de pescado problablemente se producirá una disminución en los países desarrollados y un aumento en los países en desarrollo. Se espera que la producción de sucedáneos de la leche aumente de 1,760,000 toneladas en 1971 a cerca de 4,500,000 toneladas en 1980. No se hace ningún pronóstico sobre las tendencias de la producción de concentrados de proteínas de pescado para el consumo humano. Se producían ante todo para los países en desarrollo, pero hasta la fecha no se ha encontrado mercado para este producto en dichos países.

shall assume that during this period Peruvian production of fish meal will recover and that the 1972 disaster will not occur again. We shall not take into account, even for 1976 to 1980, developments in other sources of protein such as yeast from oil; fluctuations in production of soya and other cakes (sunflower, groundnuts, etc) nor, in particular, the arrival on the world market of soya production from new countries such as Brazil, USSR, etc; protein from leaves, algae, rapeseed, cereals with a high content of lysine, krill meal, and synthetic amino acids other than methionine at cheap prices, etc. These products will arrive on the market sooner or later, but as none of them is at present beyond the experimental stage, it will take a long time before they are produced industrially. Tonnages which could be produced between 1976 and 1980 are unforeseeable. However, even when these new sources of protein become available in large tonnages they will not be used at the expense of fish meal, but in addition to it. The reason is that fish meal will continue to be used for a long time, in developing countries in particular, for its special properties and not as a mere source of amino acids.

FISH MEAL FOR ANIMAL NUTRITION
Trends in fish meal production
Fish meal production is not likely to increase as it did in Peru between 1958 and 1968 (by 1,800,000 tons in 10 years). We forecast a slight increase in some countries, mainly due to the operation of new factory ships owned by the USSR, Poland, Japan, Argentina, Senegal, Mauritania, etc. The introduction of strict measures for the conservation of fish stocks means that the traditional big producers (Peru, Norway, etc.) should level off output. In these and in some others, such as France and the Federal Republic of Germany, it is expected that the production of FPC for milk replacers will increase, most probably at the expense of ordinary fish meal because only limited tonnages are available. As a

consequence, fish meal production, which was about 5,200,000 tons in 1971, should not amount to more than about 5,335,000 tons in 1975 and about 5,625,000 tons in 1980. The main increases will be in the developing countries (Table 1).

Trends in fish meal available for export
As fish meal available for export is directly influenced by mixed feed production we shall examine this point first. We know from the development plans in socialist countries and some others that production, which was about 50 million tons in 1971, should increase to 75 million tons in 1975. Assuming that this trend will continue up to 1980, production at that time should reach about 105 million tons. During the same period the production of mixed feed in developed countries should increase from some 101 million tons in 1971 to about 110 in 1975 and about 126 in 1980. This will be mainly due to increased production in such countries as Spain, Italy, etc.

Pig and poultry feed. The reasons for the increasing use of fish meal for animal feed is the high price of cereals and rising costs of meat production in developed countries, mainly in the EEC and the USA. As there will be an increasing demand for beef and pork meat all over

TABLE 1. STATISTICS OF COMPOUNDS AND FISH MEAL (IN THOUSAND TONS)

	Developed countries[a]			Developing countries		
	1971 (actual)	1975 (estim.)	1980 (estim.)	1971 (actual)	1975 (estim.)	1980 (estim.)
Production of compounds[b]	101,130	110,600	126,600	49,200	75,600	105,700
Production of fish meal	2,389	2,414	2,473	2,816	2,922	3,153
Imports of fish meal	2,080	1,595	1,385	895	1,287	1,532
Exports of fish meal	890	860	925	2,090	2,023	1,993
Consumption of fish meal	3,531	3,149	2,933	1,474	2,186	2,692

Total of fish meal used in developed and developing countries:
$\pm$ 5,000,000 tons in 1971, because there was an increase of stocks $\pm$ 200,000 tons
$\pm$ 5,335,000 tons in 1975
$\pm$ 5,625,000 tons in 1980

[a] Developed countries are countries well advanced in animal nutrition and where feedingstuffs for substitution are available: EEC, others in western and northern Europe, USA, Canada, Mexico, South Africa, Israel, Japan, Singapore, the Republic of China, the Republic of Korea, Australia and New Zealand. Some of these countries are not listed as 'developed' in FAO statistics. In this study they are, considered as 'developed in animal nutrition'.

[b] Only compounds in which fish meal can be used are taken into account (poultry, pigs, fish, mink). As far as USA production is concerned, pig feed is not taken into account because it does not include fish meal.

TABLE 2. STATISTICS ON 1971 PRODUCTION AND TRADE OF FISH MEAL AND COMPOUNDS (IN THOUSAND TONS)

	Production and known stocks	Imports/Exports	Home consump. and stocks	Compounds (pigs and poultry)
EEC (9 countries)	449 + 30	1,247/ 289	1,407 + 30	34,700
Other European countries (western and northern Europe)	517 + 110	363/ 421	442 + 125	9,300
Socialist countries and USSR (eastern Europe)	416	673/ 12	1,177	39,800
USA	260	261	521	33,800
Canada	91	62	29	4,500
Latin America (including Cuba)	2,257 + 696	198/1,953	369 + 829	6,800
Middle East	2	38	40	
Africa	355 + 22	3/ 177	140 + 63	1,500
Far East (including People's Dem. Rep. of China)	806	169/ 22	953	16,500
Oceania	2	23	25	1,700
Various (Panama, Bermuda, Pakistan, factory-ships, etc.)	50	50		100
TOTAL (in round figures)	5,200 + 860	2,980/2,980	5,000 + 1,050	150,000

TABLE 3. FORECAST FOR 1975 PRODUCTION AND TRADE OF FISH MEAL AND COMPOUNDS (IN THOUSAND TONS)

	Production and known stocks	Imports/Exports	Home consump. and stocks	Compounds (pigs and poultry)
EEC (9 countries)	431 + 20	1,000/ 210	1,221 + 20	38,400
Other European countries	513 + 108	360/ 395	478 + 108	11,100
Socialist countries and USSR (eastern Europe)	262	830	1,392	60,900
USA	250	50	300	34,000
Canada	100	70	30	5,000
Latin America (including Cuba)	2,140 + 520	300/1,830	610 + 520	9,000
Middle East	6	65	71	2,400
Africa	403 + 62	11/ 238	176 + 62	2,200
Far East (including People's Dem. Rep. of China)	850	256/ 70	1,036	21,000
Oceania	5	10	15	2,000
Various (Pakistan, Bermuda, factory-ships, etc.)	76	70	6	200
TOTAL (in round figures)	5,335 + 710	2,880/2,880	5,335 + 710	186,000

the world, it is thought by French experts that developed countries should keep their production of meat at the 1971/72 level and buy the extra tonnages needed from developing countries, socialist countries and China. This should encourage those countries to develop their meat production and consequently their production of mixed feed, which contains large amounts of fish meal for pigs. Similarly, developed countries should not increase poultry and egg production which is already in surplus, but developing countries should. This would encourage them to meet the potential demand at home and abroad. These countries include those in the Middle East, Latin America and Africa.

Fish feed. In view of the spectacular development in fish farming throughout the world and increases in production foreseen by plans, fish feed should become a very important factor in the near future. As fish feed requires a high percentage of fish meal more and more of the meal will be needed for this purpose.

Influence of scientific knowledge. In developed countries knowledge in animal nutrition is well advanced and some compounders are already manufacturing rations without fish meal (layers, allmash rations for broilers and pigs.) But in other feeds fish meal is still used (pig-starter, turkey, fish feed, mink). Progress in this field in the future could possibly result in a decrease in the percentage of fish meal used in such feed in the 1976 to 1980 period. Substitution in feedstuffs is not so easy in developing countries because of lack of scientific knowledge and the shortage of ingredients that could be used as substitutes.

As a consequence, developing countries should require more fish meal and developed countries less. Fish meal available for export should decrease in Peru and Chile, where there is a strong increase of home consumption. Even taking into account a slight increase in production in Senegal, Mauritania and some of the developing countries, a levelling of exports is foreseen at about 2,900,000 tons. A slight increase of exports from developed countries from 890,000 tons in 1971 to 925,000 tons in 1980 can be expected.

Trends in fish meal imports

Taking into account these factors we can deduct that there will be a decrease of imports by developed countries and an increase by developing countries. This may be from about 2 million tons in 1971 to about 1.385 million tons in 1980 and from about 895,000 ton sin 1971 to some 1,532,000 in 1980, respectively.

Trends in the use of fish meal

The last line of Table 1 sums up the possible trend: in developed countries a decrease from 3,531,000 tons to 2,933,000 tons in 1980; in developing countries an increase from about 1,474,000 tons to some 2,692,000 tons in 1980. Production of compounds should be about

TABLE 4. FORECAST FOR 1980 PRODUCTION AND TRADE OF FISH MEAL AND COMPOUNDS (IN THOUSAND TONS)

	Production and known stocks	Imports/Exports	Home consump. and stocks	Compounds (pigs and poultry)
EEC (9 countries)	405 + 20	850/ 220	1,035 + 20	43,600
Other European countries	548 + 90	355/ 425	478 + 90	15,500
Socialist countries and USSR (eastern Europe)	685	960	1,645	83,200
USA	250	30	280	35,000
Canada	110	80	30	5,500
Latin America	2,170 + 475	315/1,755	730 + 475	12,500
Middle East	12	90	102	3,800
Africa	410 + 42	22/ 233	199 + 42	3,300
Far East (including People's Dem. Rep. of China)	931	285/ 115	1,101	26,000
Oceania	5	10	15	2,500
Various (Pakistan, muda, factory-ships, etc)	100	90	10	400
TOTAL (in round figures)	5,625 + 625	2,920/2,920	5,625 + 625	231,000

126 million tons in developed countries, with a high percentage of fish feed, and about 106 million tons in developing countries, with a large percentage of poultry and pig feed. Statistics on 1971 and forecasts for 1975 and 1980 production and trade of fish meal and compounds by groups of countries are given in Tables 2, 3 and 4, respectively.

SOLUBLE AND INSOLUBLE PRODUCTS FOR MILK REPLACERS

A shortage in milk products of around 19 million tons (milk equivalent) is foreseen by FAO in 1980. It is felt by experts in milk replacers that such products should no longer use skimmed milk as sole source of protein. Substitutes will have to be used in larger and larger

TABLE 5. PRODUCTION OF MILK REPLACERS (COMPOUNDS) (IN THOUSAND TONS)

	1971	1975	1980
France	678	800	900
Netherlands	362	500	600
Italy	268	450	700
Fed. Rep. of Germany	195	300	400
Belgium	45	100	120
UK	34	60	100
Eire	53	100	200
Denmark	50	100	150
Total EEC	1,685	2,410	3,170
Spain	40	250	500
Norway	5	20	40
Sweden	10	15	25
Switzerland	22	30	35
Austria	6	10	20
Israel	5	10	20
Subtotal	78	335	640
Socialist countries	—	250	500
Latin America	—	50	200
GRAND TOTAL	1,763	3,045	4,470
In round figures	1,760	3,000	4,500

tonnages. Two such substitutes are already used in milk replacers: soluble FPC (French and Chilean patents) and insoluble FPC (Swedish, Moroccan and Norwegian patents). For various technical reasons, such as solubility, iron and mineral content, soluble products can

TABLE 6. POTENTIAL CONSUMPTION OF FPC IN MILK REPLACERS (IN TONS)

	1971 (actual)	1975 (estim.)	1980 (e stim.)
Total EEC	4,000	30,000	40,000
Others (Europe)	5,000	10,000	20,000
Socialist countries	—	5,000	20,000/ 50,000
Latin America	n.a.	5,000	10,000/ 50,000
TOTAL	7,000	50,000	90,000/160,000

TABLE 7. PRODUCTION OF FPC (IN TONS)

	1971 (actual)	1975 (estim.)	1980 (estim.)
France	2,000	10,000	10,000
Sweden	7,000	10,000	10,000
Norway	1,000	10,000	20,000
Fed. Rep. of Germany	—	10,000	20,000
Peru	—	10,000	50,000/100,000
Chile	n.a.	5,000	10,000/ 20,000
TOTAL	10,000	55,000	130,000/200,000

be used in larger tonnages than insoluble ones. Table 5 shows the production of milk replacers and Table 6 the potential consumption of FPC in milk replacers in 1975 and 1980. The 1975 production of FPC is estimated from actual production in 1972 and from plans for new production plants. It seems that production cannot be increased in countries such as France and Sweden due to a shortage of raw materials. Production for 1980 is unforeseeable. It mainly depends on progress in the promotion of the soluble product in socialist countries and in Latin America. Figures given in Table 7 are questionable.

FPC FOR HUMAN NUTRITION

We cannot foresee any developments in this field. Primarily, FPC was produced for developing countries, but the market is still to be found there. A possible use in developed countries could be envisaged if scientists were able to produce isolates or texturized protein from fish as is done in the case of soya protein. The meat industry could absorb large tonnages of such protein to replace meat in sausages, hamburgers, etc. Up to now the problem of production remains unsolved. Most probably it will take up to 10 years before it is solved and industrial production can start.

Technical Note

Important Aspects of Marketing Peruvian Merluza   *P Andersen, W P Appleyard, P W de Haan, G H Hordijk, E C A van Noort and J A R Souness*

RAW MATERIALS

It is axiomatic that the quality of the raw material in fisheries largely determines the quality of the end product. And, as the main export markets for such products demand that they conform to certain standards of quality, this factor is of critical importance, especially in developing countries where such standards are

difficult to attain and maintain. The problem is very well illustrated by the merluza fishery in Peru. The merluza has been traditionally regarded by Peruvian fishermen as a trash fish. This unfortunate fact makes the introduction of a new approach in the catching and handling of the fish to preserve its quality very difficult. Indeed, of the many problems met in establishing the merluza industry, the attitude of the fishermen causes most concern. Thus, while the catching and handling of the fish, and bleeding, gutting and icing on board are essential to maintain the quality of the raw material, the fishermen, despite the efforts to change their attitude, still look on merluza as a trash fish. One requirement to induce a change of attitude is a better price for merluza which will make it well worthwhile for the fishermen to take the extra trouble required, and which will compensate for the lower catch rates. Perhaps the way to this new attitude will be through plant-operated vessels designed for merluza fishing and sailing to a fishing and delivery pattern. In such circumstances, there will perhaps emerge a new breed of fishermen, dedicated to merluza fishing and enjoying the financial rewards and social benefits in a new kind of community. Be that as it may, it is imperative to develop in Peru, as in so many other developing countries, a completely new approach to quality standards before the industry can realize its full potential as an exporter of frozen fish and other fishery products. And such quality standards must be based on the proper handling of the raw material from the time it is caught until it reaches the consumer in product form.

PROCESSING

While good yields from mechanized processing of merluza have long been attained in technically advanced countries, the establishment of, say, filleting lines is still a new experience in some developing countries. In Peru, for example, the FAO/UNDP Fisheries Project has conducted trials with a Baader 421–188–47 filleting line to demonstrate that the processing yields of Peruvian merluza can be comparable to those obtained with hake in other countries. So it was shown that the yield from live fish in using the Baader 166 gutting machine was from 91 to 92 per cent from merluza measuring 38 to 40 cm, the size which has been most abundant during 1973. Frozen skinless fillets with pinbones yielded on average 36 to 37 per cent while skinless, boneless and skin-on fillets yielded 31 to 32 and 42 to 45 per cent respectively, all expressed as packed weight against head-on gutted fish. Processing lines such as the one described above will form the basis of mechanization in the Peru merluza industry. As the trials showed, good yields can be obtained from machine processing even with the soft texture of the fish. The numerous attempts to introduce hand-gutting at sea have failed because of the fishermen's attitude that merluza is a 'trash fish' and the inadequate financial rewards for the extra work. In view of the successful use of a gutting machine, such mechanized operation will be introduced on board. A modified version of the Baader 166 gutting machine to head and gut fish on board will be used in the production of dressed merluza.

MARKET CONSIDERATIONS

The qualitative aspects (segmentation, buyer behaviour, etc) and the quantitative aspects (total demand, growth, etc) of the market are factors which must be taken into account in assessing the market possibilities for a new fishery product. In the case of Peruvian merluza the assessment of the qualitative aspects has been based on the opinion of experts and potential buyers who have sampled the various trial products that have been made. It appears that merluza from the coastal waters of Peru falls into the category of 'cod substitute' products because the flesh is more or less of the same taste and colour and has the same fat content of 0.5 to 1.0 per cent in the whole fish as cod. Its inferiority in comparison to cod is probably attributable to its softer texture (water content of the flesh: 80 to 82 per cent) and to its smaller size. A search for market possibilities for merluza products yielded the following information: Blocks – boneless, with bones, minced; Fillets – fillet block, IQF, smoked; Dressed – large size, small size, skin-off; Salted – wet, dry; Whole – fresh, frozen. While there are market possibilities for all these various products, they are not equal and a practical approach for estimating the quantitative element is to seek out the largest segments.

Blocks

The most important single market for merluza products is for fillet blocks and is based on the consumption of fish sticks and portions. In this respect, the US market seems to offer the best opportunity for exporters as there is a large growth in consumption of these types of products in the USA and the market is more heavily dependent on imports of raw material than is that of any other country. Table 1 shows the size of the market for fish sticks and portions and its estimated growth.

TABLE 1. US CONSUMPTION OF FISH STICKS AND PORTIONS IN THE USA ('000 TONS)

1960	51.0
1965	98.4
1970	160.6
1975	199.0[a]
1980	250.0[a]

[a] Estimated: $r^2 = 0.9113$.

Source: US Department of Commerce. *Food Fish Situation and Outlook, Annual Review 1971.*

TABLE 2. PRODUCTION, IMPORTS AND APPARENT CONSUMPTION OF FROZEN FISH BLOCKS IN THE USA ('000 TONS)

	Consumption	*Production*	*Imports*
1960	40.2	0.3	40.6
1965	90.8	1.3	97.4
1970	131.4	2.3	123.7
1975	143.0[a]	3.6[b]	139.4
1980	163.0[a]	4.6[b]	158.4

[a] Estimated: $r^2 = 0.9769$.
[b] Estimated: $r^2 = 0.7273$.

Source: US Department of Commerce.

The extent to which the US market depends on the import of frozen blocks is shown in Table 2. As catch figures indicate, cod and haddock landings have not changed much in recent years, which is a factor favourably influencing the increased use of 'cod substitutes'. The US market indicates increasing sales for merluza blocks, providing the right quality standards are maintained. Other markets for merluza blocks are to be found in Europe and Australia because demand for fish blocks is growing there. For example, the Australian market for merluza fillets and fillet blocks is estimated at 15,000 tons a year. At the present time the market is already taking more than 2,000 tons of merluza blocks and frozen fillets from South Africa. While the European market seems less dependent on such imports, the enlarged Common Market and its trade-inducing measures will increase demand. As its quality requirements are not usually as inflexible as those of the US market, the European market is becoming more attractive to exporters of such products even though the price paid is US$0.02 to 0.04/kg lower and the cost of shipping somewhat higher.

Frozen fillets

The most receptive markets for frozen fillets at present are probably the USA and Australia. The import of fresh and frozen fillets increased by almost threefold from 1960 to 1970. The growing demand is indicated in Table 3. The demand for frozen fillets is quite strong

TABLE 3. IMPORT DEMAND FOR FROZEN FILLETS IN THE USA ('000 TONS)

1960	38.4
1965	47.3
1970	111.3
1975	111.0[a]
1980	131.0[a]

[a] Estimated: $r^2 = 0.7073$.

Source: US Department of Commerce.

in Australia and the import of them is increasing. A great part of this trade consists of merluza fillets from South Africa and Japan.

Dressed merluza

While the markets for dressed merluza in the USA and Europe is limited compared with those for fish blocks and frozen fillets, they are expanding. Both the domestic and the industrial markets in the USA consume dressed merluza. Domestic consumption is by the lower income classes and by institutions. Industrial consumption is through the use of the fish as raw material for a smoked product. It seems that merluza is replacing haddock (now becoming very expensive) for this purpose and should, therefore, find an increasing demand from this market. With a decreasing production and consumption, it appeared by mid-1973 that the US market for dressed merluza was saturated and stocks were building up. As the price for fish blocks continued to rise, it seemed that producers of dressed merluza would have to pay for their failure to diversify. The US market for dressed merluza has been mainly for smaller sized fish (4–12 oz or 120–360 g), while the European market is for larger fish (1,500 g or more).

Salted merluza

As there is no commercial production yet of salted merluza, the market potential has not been investigated. However, as there is a world market of an estimated 30,000 tons a year for the 'Klippfish' type of product, this is the market into which salted merluza must make

inroads in order to win a share of it. There is also a domestic market possibility for the product in Peru – as a protein-rich food for sale in remote areas, such as the southern Sierras. There is a possible market for wet-salted merluza in the Mediterranean countries although the size of the Peruvian merluza is too small for present market requirements.

Whole merluza

This product can be sold only in the domestic market at a comparatively low price. The market can be considered as a temporary outlet until a more profitable export trade is developed.

Packaging

In any consideration of markets, packaging must loom large. One problem in developing countries is the availability of suitable packaging materials and their cost – especially if they have to be imported; for example, the merluza industry in Peru has had to import such items as waxed wrappers for blocks. Corrugated cartons are made locally but contain a considerable element of imported material. Some idea of the cost and time factor involved is to be seen in the case of waxed cartons for such products as fillets and headless, gutted fish. A locally made lid bottom waxed carton for 5 lb (2.25 kg) head and gutted merluza costs about US$2.75 per 100 kg of product, and delivery time is 3 to 4 months.

Diversification

Another market consideration must be diversification of products to meet changing tastes and changing demands. Some of the private fishery companies in Peru have diversified to the extent of producing small quantities of individually frozen fillets for the US market. The FAO/UNDP project has shown that there are other products to be made from merluza. The project has, for example, produced cold-smoked merluza for the Australian and UK markets, and salted and dried split merluza and wet-salted merluza for the traditional salt fish markets as well as for the domestic market. However, a limiting factor to the diversification of products made from Peruvian merluza is the small size of the fish (38–42 cm and 450–500 g gutted weight). This presents a considerable challenge because the vast bulk of the catch (80 to 90 per cent) is composed of these small-sized fish.

Shipping

As in other countries far distant from lucrative markets (New Zealand, for example), shipping the products presents problems. The choice of shipping arrangements is limited for Peruvian producers and the rates are high – from US$75 to US$100 per ton for refrigerated cargo to North America and European ports. However, as and when the quantities of fishery products for export increase substantially, other shipping possibilities arise, such as the use of charter vessels and containers. Trans-shipment problems and costs will diminish when vessels can be induced to use the smaller ports in the production areas. As shipping is an important factor in such circumstances, it must be taken into account in planning the development and export trade of such a new enterprise as the Peruvian merluza industry.

Launching the Export of Fishery Products in Israel   *M Bar-Ilan*

The country's marine fisheries provided export opportunities as increasing quantities of first-class lagoon fish became available, along with shrimps and squids, which are better marketed abroad because of religious constraints in Israel.

VARIOUS TYPES OF EXPORT

There is a demand for Israeli carps in several European countries throughout the year but particularly during the Christmas season. To meet this demand, live carp are transported in tanks at night to a centre close to the airport, where they are packed in dry ice in plastic foam containers and immediately loaded into aircraft. This is a carefully timed operation and they reach their destination in Europe within 3 to 3½ hr. They are then marketed immediately. The whole operation lasts only 6 to 7 hr so that the fish reach the consumer in an excellent state of freshness. Although this trade started only in late 1972 sales in the first year will amount to several hundred tons.

Live carp by sea transport

A trial shipment of live carp in tanks in a cargo vessel was made in southern Europe in 1972. It was unsuccessful, most of the fish dying *en route*. New efforts are now being made to find a safe and practicable way to keep the carp alive on a journey of several days.

Frozen freshwater fish

Two ways of preparing deep-frozen carp have been introduced:

(1) Cleaning, slicing and freezing the carp, with the slices packed in plastic trays and wrapped in transparent foil or packed in cartons.
(2) Cleaning and freezing the whole carp and packing it in cartons.

The tray-packed slices sell mostly in the USA and the cartons in Europe. The size of the fish varies between 500 to 800 g.

Silver carp (*Hypophthalmichthys molitrix*)

Silver carp are now being grown in nearly all Israeli fish ponds. The fish has a rapid growth rate and is inexpensive to raise but there are certain problems in marketing it. An experimental shipment of minced and frozen silver carp has, therefore, been sent to the USA. In one form it is packed in small plastic trays for retail sale. The other form is frozen blocks for use in making fish balls.

St. Peter's Fish (*Tilapia aurea*)

This fish was first shipped in 1970 in a cleaned and deep-frozen condition and packed in plastic bags. The consignment of about 50 t was sent to the American market. While the fish is pond-grown, it originates in the Lake of Genezareth, a fact of unique marketing value.

Canned carp

A shipment of canned carp to the USA and Europe was the first Israeli freshwater fishery product. The recipe of the product is based on folklore and was originally known as 'Gefilte Fish'. Slices of carp are filled with a mixture of minced fish, bread, egg and spices, in natural sauce. In another form, flat fish balls are made from the mixture. They are packed in cans of 250 to 1,000 g. The product in both forms has already gained a constant market.

Marine products

While the incentive to export freshwater fish was the potential domestic suplus, with marine fish, it was chiefly the high prices fetched, a trend which seems likely to continue. The first exports of deep-frozen fish to Europe were made in 1969, the species being gilthead bream (*Sparus auratus*), later followed by bass (*Dicentrarchus labrax*). These are lagoon-fishes and are available at certain seasons in large quantities. The fish were transported to the nearest marketing centre, rinsed, deep-frozen and packed in nylon bags in cartons and shipped by cargo vessels. The quality of those first shipments was low and efforts were made to improve the techniques of transport before deep-freezing. Then the next step was to export chilled, not frozen, fish by air. By 1972 between 60 and 70 per cent of this trade was handled in this second way which proved more efficient in maintaining the freshness and high quality of the fish. The practice now is to pack fish in plastic foam containers with dry ice and dispatch them by air, about 300 tons a year so far.

Shrimps and squids

Two factors lead to the renewed export of shrimps:

(1) The introduction of special nets and gear, enabling trawlers to fish for shrimps.
(2) The rising price of shrimps in Europe and America.

The shrimps are sorted, cleaned, deep-frozen and packed in cartons of 2 kg each and dispatched by sea. In Europe they fetch from US$1.10 to 1.80/kg, according to the size. Squids are similarly handled in packages of 12 kg each. The volume of this export trade in 1972 was 50 to 60 tons.

Frozen hake

The Distant Fishing Branch, which supplies one-third of the Israeli fish production, sells part of its catch in foreign markets, mostly those close to the fishing grounds. The main species is South Atlantic hake, gutted, beheaded and deep-frozen – and similar species caught on the same grounds. This trade in 1972 amounted to some 1,500 tons.

CONCLUSION

While the volume of exports is at present small, there are reasonable chances for developing the trade. This applies particularly to freshwater fishery products because the already large potential production can be increased by intensive breeding practices, which are now being introduced.

Discussion on Part VI

Markets and trade information

The discussion emphasized that marketing must be the first consideration in making any fishery investment. The need was stressed for taking individual circumstances into account when the question is raised whether to pursue a policy of earning foreign money through exports or to meet domestic needs for fish protein. Developing countries require information on such subjects as market dimension, price levels, packaging and suppliers, and it was stressed that increased input in the field of analysis and forecast would be necessary.

MORISAWA (Japan) stressed the integrated effort of the industry, the Government and commercial enterprise in the careful study, investigation and analysis of each market to determine consumer demands, regulations and controls, quality standards, product forms, presentation and price, etc, which led to success.

APPLEYARD (FAO) emphasized the need to plan production against present and future consumption in order to meet market demands and opportunities. Referring to the theme of the paper by Coburn on planning to expand export markets, he expressed the view that fishery planning could learn from agricultural experience. He agreed with Coburn that indiscriminate development of catching capacity without considering marketing and other related problems led to serious adverse consequences for all concerned.

JOHN (Canada) stated, it is essential to realize the difference between 'markets', 'market opportunities' and 'marketing'. While it is important to know where the markets are and their potentials, it is equally important to develop adequate marketing organization and channels of distribution. Marketing organization has a great bearing on the level of market returns. The structure and organization of marketing are weak and fragmented in many countries and require specific studies which FAO should undertake. Referring to the question of developing a home market base to strengthen the export effort, John pointed out that products are not necessarily acceptable for both domestic and foreign markets. There has to be diversification and, preferably, the achievement of a balance between the two markets.

Moss (Canada) emphasized the need to meet the demands of the consumer. These are known by the buyers in the markets concerned and these are people who should be closely consulted by the industry.

KRONE (FAO) raised the question of whether or not developing countries should export protein-rich products when a large number of their population is suffering from protein deficiency. He contended that while the domestic market should be given priority consideration, there are cases where it is economically more advantageous to concentrate on export trade, or even the only way to develop a fishery. Exports contribute to economic development, the lack of which is the most significant reason for poverty and malnutrition.

HOPPER (UK) replying to Constantinides (USA), who argued that developing countries should use their fishery resources primarily for direct human consumption, agreed but pointed out that fish surplus to local needs can usefully be exported to earn valuable foreign exchange, thus contributing to the country's economy.

BALASINGAM (Malaysia), in support of this view, said that exports of canned tuna and frozen shrimp, smoked bonito fillets and dried jellyfish have not only earned valuable foreign exchange, but have given great impetus to the Malaysian fish processing industry, with the resultant benefit to the national economy and more and better paid employment.

JAYARAJ (India) related a similar report of development through exports: the shrimp export industry earned US$70 million in 1972 and expects soon to earn more than US$100 million a year. He pointed out that even if it was considered desirable to divert the product to the domestic market, it would not be possible because there is no infrastructure for marketing and distribution. In addition, the cost of the product is far too high for the mass market. In the circumstances the immensely rich shrimp resources would be largely unexploited if it were not for the export trade which, in addition to earning a large amount of valuable foreign exchange, has also contributed to economic development and more employment at higher wages. He added that India is making an effort to develop a cold chain for the distribution of low-cost fish. The first cold chain, spanning 900 km and linking four industrial cities, has just been commissioned. It is hoped that the cold chain system will be built up in the next decade or so to make possible the distribution of some 1.5 million tons of cheaply priced fish per year.

BALASINGAM (Malaysia) stated that developing countries can build up a profitable export trade with species of fish of limited acceptability locally. He cited the example of tuna in Malaysia, which is not very popular there but is canned and exported to Western markets.

BREBNER and HINDS (New Zealand) spoke of their experience in exporting fish by air to Japan. The fish are shocked to death in ice and flown overnight from Auckland to Tokyo.

APPLEYARD (FAO) stressed that information on markets and related items is a complex subject covering the need for background information, such as matters of packing, buying and selling countries, etc, as well as prompt current price information. In view of the complexity, the best approach might be on a limited basis, dealing, say, with eight main products and ten main markets.

HJUL (UK) pointed out that while a regular, up-to-date report on fish marketing is most desirable, it would be almost impossible to compile in any comprehensive form. The problem is difficult enough in any one country and if other countries are to be involved the problems multiply.

SLAVIN (USA) said that the US national marine service is conducting a study on obtaining information on market opportunities, prices and products in foreign countries and would be pleased to make the results of the study available to FAO and interested countries as soon as they are published. He added that an international market intelligence system would be most useful and hoped that FAO would look into the feasibility of establishing one, in which case the USA would be pleased to work with FAO in this matter.

JOHN (Canada) said that it is necessary to differentiate between gathering information and the interpretation and analysis of it and making forecasts based on the data. Canada is already making such forecasts up to 12 months ahead. In reply to Jones (UK) he said that the forecasts are largely based on judgement, influenced by continuing contacts with the markets and buyers and sellers, and have attained a high degree of accuracy.

MAGNUSSON (FAO) reported that the Indonesian Director-General of Fisheries and the Ministry of Trade are preparing a directory in which the country's fishery products, raw materials and marketing possibilities, will be described. Information on prices, marketing trends and production is to be sent to the Indonesian fishery industries and to foreign Chambers of Commerce.

JAYARAJ (India) suggested that FAO should set up a market intelligence cell in the Fishery Industries Division to organize the international exchange of information about the products available for export and the demands prevalent in importing countries.

KRONE (FAO) said that the knowledge and experience of trade associations, export promotion boards and so on, which operate in most industrialized countries, could provide a valuable source of information for the developing countries. This could be of considerable significance because access to markets in industrialized countries is often hindered not only by duties and trade restrictions, but also by lack of information on product specifications, market volumes and prices. Therefore, there is a need to ensure a regular flow of market information. The organization of such a service would require appropriate international arrangements.

JOHN (Canada) said that FAO should seriously consider the value of organizing marketing conferences at periodic intervals as a means of stressing the importance of marketing and the market place and of gathering and disseminating the much-needed information on all aspects of markets and marketing.

Part VII

TRAINING IN FISH PROCESSING TECHNOLOGY

Manpower Requirements and Training for Fishery Product Industries   *J Liston*

Besoins en main-d'oeuvre et formation pour l'industrie des produits de la pêche

Les industries de la pêche ont desoin de technologues et d'activités de formation technique à divers niveaux aussi bien durant les premiers stades de leur implantation qu'une fois bien établies. Il convient d'organiser la formation à au moins trois niveaux de technicité: travailleurs affectés à la production; cadres techniques moyens; recherche, développement et enseignement. Les investissements dans les programmes de formation devraient tenir compte des besoins effectifs et de l'importance relative des industries dans l'ensemble de l'économie nationale. Pour entreprendre de tels programmes, le mieux est de faire appel à l'assistance d'un pays étranger techniquement développé; il faudreit cependant les concevoir de manière qu'ils puissent devenir indépendants et autonomes en peu de temps. Ces programmes devraient être intégrés dans le système d'enseignement national pour assurer la continuité de la formation et l'application de concepts appropriés du point de vue professionnel, et devraient faire intervenir l'industrie et le gouvernement. Il y a de grands avantages—dépenses moindres, gain de temps et efficacité accrue—à élaborer et exécuter un programme composite dans le cadre d'un accord de coopération conclu directement entre l'administration nationale chargée de l'enseignement et une institution étrangère expérimentée ou un consortium de telles institutions.

Necesidades de mano de obra y de capacitacion para las industrias de productos pesqueros

En las fases de creación de las industrias pesqueras y luego de quedar éstas constituidas, es necesario contar con técnicos y capacitación técnica. La capacitación debe impartirse por lo menos en tres órdenes de experiencia técnica que corresponden a la producción, ejecución técnica intermedia y actividades de investigación, utilización y capacitación. Las inversiones en un programa de capacitación deberán estar en consonancia con las necesidades reales y la importancia relativa que tengan las industrias en el conjunto económico del país. Los programas de capacitación es mejor iniciarios con ayuda extranjera procedente de un país avanzado técnicamente, pero deberán tener como objetivo la autarquía en un corto período de tiempo. Los programas deberán ser parte del sistema educativo del país, para lograr la continuidad y una buena base profesional, con participación industrial y estatal. Con ello se logra un considerable ahorro, se gana tiempo y se consigue ser eficaz al proyectar y poner en ejecución un programa mixto mediante un acuerdo cooperativo directo entre el sistema educativo del país y una institución o consorcio de instituciones del extranjero que cuenten con experiencia.

In subsistence economies or situations where production is small-scale, processing is simple and distribution is limited to a small area, and the need for technically trained people is minimal. However, it should be noted that even here the supply, quality, and safety of seafood products can be greatly enhanced by the injection of simple technology related to handling methods and sanitation. The development of fisheries industries in most countries has been directed towards an expansion in total production, with wider distribution of a good quality product to satisfy domestic protein needs and/or to the production of seafood items for an export market which normally requires even higher standards of quality and a sufficient and consistent supply of products. Indeed, in some developing countries, the export industry may preempt or at least greatly overshadow an existing domestic fish industry, to the detriment of the latter and of the domestic supply of protein.

THE NEED FOR TECHNOLOGISTS

Though the need for technologists is most acute in the export industries because of the competitiveness of world markets and the conditions imposed by many importing countries, it is clear that such trained individuals are necessary in both the domestic and export industries. It is rare that the needs of an expanding domestic market can be met using the simple technology of the village, since the processes and products of such an industry are usually unsuitable for wide distribution or unacceptable to more sophisticated town dwellers or do not meet the taste preferences of inland consumers. As a result, processes must be changed during development, gearing them to larger production of more sophisticated products with good quality and stability. Technology must replace traditional lore. The new technology may be minimal, involving, for example, proper use of ice, good storage facilities, and good hygiene, or it may be – and this is the more common situation—quite complex, involving, for example, freezing or canning processes where only raw product handling was practised before. Thus, in many cases, the technology jump is too great to permit on-the-job training of operatives as a means of satisfying working technology requirements. In such situations, particularly where export industries are concerned, an immediate short-term solution has been the employment of foreign experts but this is often an inadequate solution to the problem. Modern food processing operations require some understanding of hygiene and processing principles by all employees, and it is rare that a foreign expert can transfer this understanding to poorly educated floor workers. Moreover, the foreign expert is a transient, consequently his expertise may be here today and gone (somewhere else) tomorrow. Of course, another obvious and serious problem of the short-term foreign expert is cultural and technological shock, which sometimes makes it difficult for him to relate his technical knowledge to conditions in the country and to find solutions to technical or personnel problems. All of this points to the need for training technicians and technologists who are natives of the country or even of the area within a country in which the fish processing industry is situated. Knowledge and experience of local conditions and local people are of great value to a technologist, much of whose work actually involves people rather than machinery.

In considering the manpower and training requirements for processing industries, it is necessary to assume that the training of fishermen in catching and handling fish at sea is a precondition for effective operation of land-based processing operations. The technology of proper fish handling, storage, and preservation on board the vessel should be a major component of fisherman training. Even the best land-based technology is hard pressed to produce good quality edible human food from spoiled or badly damaged fish. Within the processing industry, there are three levels of technical skill. Least demanding is the technical capability of the plant operatives or, at least, of some of them. This includes some understanding of the sensitivity of the raw material, of the importance of personal hygiene, and of any equipment or facilities which they may use in their work. The second level encompasses process supervisors, technical management, and quality control. These positions call for a sound understanding of the principles of food processing, equipment requirements and sanitation, and also of handling personnel, costing, and government regulatory problems. This is the key group, representing middle management in its most active role. The third level, which is most demanding so far as technical expertise is concerned, overlaps the second level. It includes product development and analysis and related personnel in industry, government, and university research and development laboratories. Personnel at this level require qualifications equivalent to the MS or PhD degree, with specific training in food or fish technology or with industry experience in these areas. This group is essential for the continuing development of the industry, the maintenance of its competitive position in export and domestic markets, and the supply of trained personnel at the second level. Progression through these three levels is a common and desirable process as training proceeds, eg, skilled operatives becoming production superintendents. Moreover, there are subsets of skills within each level, and in some training programmes these are separately recognized. They may even be recognized legally, as witness the recent United States Food and Drug Administration regulation requiring certification of supervisors of retort operations in industries canning low-acid foods.

Numbers needed

It is next necessary to determine the numbers of technologists required, which depends on conditions of the industry in each country. While the need is most urgent in the beginning of development, it is greatest in terms of numbers when the industry is extensive and well developed. In general, each industry with a major processing operation, such as freezing or canning, will need at least one technologist of the second category. Where a plant operates two processes, such as canning and fish meal manufacture, it is probably desirable to have one technologist for each process. In addition, it can be projected that 20 to 25 per cent of trained technologists will move up each year to management or to better paying jobs in other industries or will retire or die, etc. So, as a simple rule of thumb, the needs of a processing industry might be calculated by multiplying actual or projected unit processing capacity by 1·25. In addition, there is the need for technologists in the primary processing industries – filleting, boat operation management, salting, smoking (small-scale), etc. However, where such operations are limited in size, first-level operatives could probably fit this need. If the scale of operations is large or high-value products are produced, then probably second-level technologists should be employed. These will also be required by government organizations or trade associations concerned with control and regulations. The extent of this need depends, again, on the country and its conditions. Government regulation is necessary to guard the (mostly domestic) consumer against fraud and food products which are dangerous to health. This involves some kind of inspectorate and back-up laboratory capabilities. Moreover, in some countries government-sponsored research is the major source of new

technical knowledge for fish processing industries. Though this activity is inevitably mainly under control of technologists trained at the higher level, it requires participation by the second-level technologists. Where a major export industry based on processed seafoods is involved, it is advisable to have some system of monitoring product quality which is independent of the actual industry itself. This may be done through a trade association or a private group (commercial or university) contracted by the industry. Alternatively, where the government of a country feels the exports are of sufficient importance to the country's economy, monitoring may be done by a government agency. In either case, this operation also needs both second and third-level technologists.

In assessing the number of second-level technologists needed for such control-related operations consideration should be given to the present and anticipated future scale of industry operations and the relative importance of this industry in the national scheme. Obviously, in countries where fishery products constitute the major animal protein source or where they are significant foreign currency earners, a high priority will be given to government technical services, while in countries where fishing is a minor component government activity might be restricted simply to health control. Where fish are important, most of the technical capability may lie at the start of industry development in government departments working closely with the industry. But once industry is effectively established and operating profitably, the ratio of technologists in government to those in industry should not exceed 50 per cent and should, ideally, be much lower. Personnel needs at the highest technological level are restricted to government and universities or other institutions of higher learning and research in the early stages of industry development. However, as industry's product lines become more sophisticated, they need technologists trained at this level. In most cases the most useful level of advanced training for industry appears to be the MS degree. Again, the exact numbers of such people needed are very difficult to arrive at. A government probably needs one for every three or four second level people employed in research and development, but fewer in inspection or control. The greatest need for such people is in the institutions which are responsible for training technologists.

THE TRAINING PROCESS

As soon as possible after the initial stages of industry development are completed – ie, a functioning industry established, with visible products – the country or other regional economic unit should seek to become self-sufficient in training its own technologists. I do not mean to imply that such training should be narrowly national or provincial because, of course, technology and technology development are world-wide phenomena and require a broader view. In any case, the costs of mounting an adequate (or complete) programme may be disproportionately large for a small or impoverished country. But to be effective in its application, technology must be related, or even adapted, to the conditions in a country and should be developed, in part at least, in response to the needs of a country. The task of supplying technologists and developing technology for a fish industry is neither a one-time thing nor a part-time task. It is a mistake to assume that the training of a cadre of individuals at prestige foreign institutions will itself solve the problem. It is equally illusory to try to attach technical training on a long-term continuing basis to a research development operation. Training systems should be firmly embedded in the educational system of the country. Only in this way can continuity be assured. Of course, the teachers must themselves be trained, and therein lies the principal need for MS and PhD degree trainees.

How can training at the various levels be achieved? There are obviously a number of possible mechanisms, depending again principally on conditions in a country and the relative importance of fish industries to its economy. In the unusal situation where a country has a good national educational programme, a high literacy rate, and a strong government interest in fisheries, the situation is straight-forward. Schools keyed to different levels of technical capability are set up as part of the total educational system; and these may span the range from the simplest vocational schooling to university-level education, as in Japan and, to some extent, in Norway. However, in virtually all developing countries, a high degree of literacy does not exist, school programmes are neither comprehensive nor technically oriented and, unfortunately, there is often little incentive to follow a technological career since high salary and social position are often associated with non-technical accomplishments. Fortunately, industry, responding to its real needs, often does much to reverse this latter situation. Surprisingly, perhaps, it is not uncommon to find some technological capability in most countries at institutions of higher learning and research, even when it is almost completely lacking at the industry level. It is frequently possible, therefore, to develop a training programme out of the universities and technical schools as a first step. This has the dual advantage of committing one component of the total school programme to technological training and bringing an important section of the academic community into direct contact with industry and its problems. If government, too, can be pulled into such a programme by lending its facilities and trained personnel, then a near ideal situation is created. An active 'extension' or 'advisory' service will almost always develop out of such an arrangement, which serves both educational and information transfer objectives. Such a service will usually work with industry in helping to train workers in simple hygiene and some elementary technology and will work with the universities and technical schools to provide short training programmes at the higher (professional) technological levels.

Middle management persons

The missing element in the initial phases is likely to be that most important category, the technical middle management people. These are the working technologists and managers who make the wheels turn. Ideally, they should be BS-level graduates in food technology, engineering, or a related science, who have knowledge of and, even better, experience of conditions in industry. Such people have to be specifically trained – usually overseas – in the first stages of development. Their training should be not limited to the academic area but should include industry and, if possible, regulatory experience. However, it is probably useful to locate such trainees in an academic institution since this ensures that their programme is comprehensive and integrated. The academic institution should be aware that the primary objective of the student is not necessarily the acquisition of a degree, and the appropriate department must be sufficiently technologically oriented to have close working relationships with industry and government agencies to facilitate this practical aspect of the student's training. The objective of overseas training of the technical middle management group is to fit them for work in their own country. Unfortunately, such training has often been so closely related to conditions in the host country that the trainee is not really prepared for work conditions in his home country. An adjustment is required by the training institution of its normal practices, which it may not be willing to make for the occasional student. A more general problem of the overseas training process, where individuals are being sent on an *ad hoc* basis, is that it does not *per se* produce training programmes and therefore does not really provide for the future. Another procedure is to develop *ad hoc* training programmes within the country with the help of foreign experts. This has had mixed success, depending on the quality of the foreign help and the degree of rapport between advisers and students. Unfortunately, such programmes have often been linked with newly established research and development centres, rather than with teaching institutions. Research people are not necessarily interested in (or experienced in) teaching as such and have a rather narrow view of their field of expertise. As a consequence, training tends to be strong in sophisticated science areas and weak in the more practical 'journeyman' procedures. Again, continuity of training programmes is difficult to maintain in an institution where this is a secondary activity.

Training and cooperative programmes

The most successful programmes have been developed at teaching institutions which are linked with research institutes and which have strong government and industry backing. Moreover, it appears that the healthiest programmes have been developed out of essentially cooperative agreements between training institutes in the countries concerned. Such an arrangement provides the most effective, and probably the least expensive, procedure for:

a) immediate technical assistance during an interim training period;
b) rapid short-term training of semi-professionals;
c) effective long-term training of more highly qualified professionals, and
d) the establishment of a self-sustaining training programme at all levels of required expertise.

In the cooperative type of programme there is an exchange of personnel and an immediate technology transfer to the developing country. Since the activities are actually an extension of the normal activity of both institutions, there is a minimal problem of recruitment of appropriately qualified people and, in fact, a wealth of experience is immediately available. Of course, to be effective, the scope of such a cooperative agreement should extend in the developing country to include industry and government. United States universities are familiar with the concept of the 'extension' or 'advisory' service which serves both as an information transfer system and as a training device for reaching individuals in industry and government. Something like this should be established in the developing country to provide for training needs at all levels.

The cooperative training sytem

Let us see how such a system might work in a hypothetical situation. Country X has a developing fishing industry. Typically, this includes a large inshore artisanal fishery supplying the local market, some foreign and domestically owned processing plants preparing frozen and canned (eg, shrimp and tuna) products mainly for export, but also some products for the domestic market, and a small fish meal industry. The literacy rate is low but there is heavy government investment in education. There exists a school for fishermen which teaches mainly elementary navigation and seamanship and net and gear handling. A vocational school exists but is mainly oriented toward engineering and agriculture. The national university has departments concerned with engineering and oceanography but no specific programmes in fishery or food science. The government is concerned about malnutrition in the country and sees fishery products as a major source of protein. Industry is concerned about difficulties in the export market, and there is a large, unsatisfied demand for good fish products at low price. The present technology personnel in industry consist of a few foreign trained experts and a number of young chemical engineers who are 'learning the business'. Government personnel concerned with fish products include some classical fisheries biologists, some veterinarians, and a few engineers with some food experience. What are the training needs of such a country and how can they be met? Clearly, the potentially effective units are the vocational school and the university. However, most of the actual technical expertise lies with the few industry technologists. Industry and government are likely to exert pressure on the schools to provide training programmes. Assuming that funding is available, the schools are then faced with the problem of simultaneously training staff and students, while at the same time organizing facilities and developing curricula. If, now, an agreement is established with a foreign institution already running such a programme, many of these problems are at least partly solved.

Basic curricula are already available, as is also expertise in facilities planning and construction and equipment needs. Not infrequently short-term instruction can be offered to fill the time gap between initiation of the programme and completion of preliminary training of domestic instructors. Moreover, short-term training programmes for industry can be developed very quickly in the country. The resources of a large university in a technologically developed country are extensive and cover most fields of scientific knowledge. Moreover, a recent development has been the formation of consortia of universities for this type of overseas activity, and this provides an even broader spectrum of available resources. One example of this is the Consortium for the Development of Technology (CODOT), made up of Food Science and Technology Departments of the universities of California, Michigan State, Rhode Island, Washington, and Wisconsin which operates overseas programmes in Central America and in Brazil.

Thus, problems of training at all levels can be tackled and simultaneous programmes can be maintained. In this type of arrangement it is usual for the foreign institution to undertake technical research on the actual problems, which provides a realistic training experience for the developing country trainees. It is customary to direct domestic students in the university to do research work in some of these areas and then to live and work in the developing country for a few months. This procedure greatly strengthens the training activity there, provides ready exchange of technology by contemporaries, and solidifies the programme. Of course, the primary objective of such cooperative programmes should be to develop self-sufficiency for the training system within the developing country. Economic considerations might preclude complete self-sufficiency because of the cost of higher education at the more advanced level. However, under no circumstances should the foreign institution be indefinitely involved in the actual training operation. A timetable should be established leading to major disengagement within five to ten years. A continuing sister institution relationship beyond this period may be useful but should not be exclusive. Snce the training system is estsblished and functioning, new ideas should be sought from whatever country or institution seems best able to provide them.

Procedures and subject areas

The actual procedure for training and the curricula to be followed will vary according to circumstances.

Plant operative instruction in personal hygiene, sanitary processing procedures, etc, can be done by the plant technologist or a visiting expert or, more methodically, by regular training at a vocational school. It is in the interests of plant management to see that all food plant operatives obtain some instruction in hygiene, and usually it is worth providing an incentive (extra pay, release time, etc) to junior supervisory workers to attend courses at a vocational school. Efficient and clean production depends to a large measure on worker attitudes and activity, and one individual with poor personal hygiene habits can make useless the most elaborate system of plant sanitation. So far as technological training is concerned, it is possible to distinguish two sublevels of the earlier defined second-level training. One is essentially technician training, equivalent to a two-year programme. This can be provided either at the vocational school or the university, depending on facilities. It is essential that industrial technologists be drawn into this activity as teachers but control of the programme should lie in the education sector. This type of training can be effectively carried out where the trainee works part-time in the fish industry during his training period. It is appropriate to concentrate instruction in such programmes on the major processing operations used by local industry; for example, canning freezing, etc. The cooperating foreign institution can usually provide outline curricula and will usually also provide lecturers from school or industry to help the local instructors to get the programme started. Government departments concerned with inspection and regulation will usually find these shorter programmes useful for training inspectors and similar personnel.

The second sub-group is BS-level training, usually involving a four- or five-year programme. This clearly belongs to the university or polytechnic institute. In fisheries technology, it requires a programme solidly based on chemistry, physics, mathematics, and microbiology, with some engineering, including specific instruction in general fisheries biology, fishing technology food technology, food analysis, food engineering, nutrition, quality control and food laws, and other specialized subject areas relating to fish industries (eg, meal and oil manufacture). Some instruction in accounting, production, and personnel management is useful if these topics can be accommodated. The graduate should be capable of entering any branch of the fish industry to operate in production as well as in technology. Some provision should be made in the training for shipboard and industry experience. This can frequently be arranged through employment during university vacation periods. In the ideal situation, a requirement for specified industrial experience should be part of the degree programme. Foreign institutional support for this activity can be provided in curriculum development, short-term lectureships, etc. In the last named situation, one process which was found effective is for a foreign professor, with some knowledge of the local language, to develop a specific course, working with a local faculty member, and then to present it through one term or semester jointly with the local man. In subsequent years, the local person takes complete responsibility for the course but now has a ready-made lecture note series (for annual revision and updating), complete laboratory outlines, and experience of the presentation techniques. The total curriculum and individual course contents should be developed jointly by professors from both institutions and should be offered for critical comment to knowledgeable local industry people and government scientists. Courses should consider general principles but should apply them to local conditions and local products. Associated with the BS programmes, usually in vacation periods, it is desirable to develop and offer short courses designed to update professional knowledge. These are very useful to professionally qualified people working in industry and government. The best instructors in such courses may be industry people. Here again the foreign institute can help to get things started by providing technical information, assisting in preparation of course syllabuses and, in the early stages, by providing expert lecturers.

Advanced training programmes are somewhat more difficult to organize in many developing countries since they are dependent on availability of highly qualified instructors and rather sophisticated facilities and equipment. It is here that the independent research institutions are most useful. Some research activity is essential to provide a vehicle for advanced instruction and experience. It is frequently possible to arrange joint research and training programmes between research institutes and university departments. The cooperating foreign institution can be very helpful in facilitating this type of liaison and providing people with the necessary qualifications to begin a graduate level programme. Even at this level it is helpful to maintain active liaison with industry. Research projects should be concerned with local problems, and even PhDs should be required to experience actual industry conditions. Where the initial training at the higher level occurs overseas, it is helpful if much of the actual research is done in the home country. This provides an immediate relevancy to the training and speeds the actual application of the acquired skills to problems of the country without detracting from the total training programme. It is obvious that one by-product of such training is a rather early infusion of new technology into both the industrial and the educational sectors. Moreover, because the cooperating institution is actively engaged in research and development, there is a continuous updating of technical knowledge during the period of cooperation. The technology of food processing is changing so rapidly nowadays that continuous updating is a requirement, both for education and for industrial development. Obsolescence can be costly, and institutional obsolescence can be disastrous.

CONCLUSION

The main theses of this discussion are that training programmes for the fish industry should be geared to the actual needs of a country and designed to operate within the country as part of the educational process so that continuity is assured. The author suggests that the most efficient mechanism for development is to bring together industry, government and an appropriate institution (university in most cases) within the country and develop a programme with the assistance and cooperation of an institution (or organized group of institutions) in a technologically developed country. The outline for development of such a programme given above follows a system which is familiar to him by experience and which appears to work. He believes that it is not the only method which will work, and it may not apply in all cases, but commends it as one possible approach to the problem of providing trained personnel for the fish industry.

Training for Fishery Product Industries   *B Meyboom*

Formation aux industries des produits de la pêche
Le document examine les difficultés qu'éprouvent les industries de traitement du poisson dans les pays en voie de développement à recruter et à conserver une main-d'oeuvre techniquement qualifiée. L'auteur précise les besoins en matière de formation à des emplois dans les cadres directorial et technique et insiste sur la nécessité de mettre sur pied des cours continus dans ces domaines.

Preparacion de personal para las industrias de productos pesqueros
El autor hace un breve resumen de las dificultades de encontrar y retener técnicos en las industrias elaboradoras de pescado de los países en desarrollo. Menciona los requerimientos para preparar administradores y técnicos y las necesidades de organizar cursos continuos en las disciplinas correspondientes.

The situation in the developing countries with regard to staffing industrial plants with specialized personnel gives rise to the question: 'What sort of specialized personnel do we need to train for the processing industry and what sort of education do they require?'

MANAGEMENT

The technical manager in charge of production could be a veterinarian, a chemist or a biologist but preference should be given to a food technologist or a mechanical engineer. If he lacks technical training, he should be given a course on the basic principles of mechanical and electrical engineering. The fish processing plant concerned may be an integrated one with its own fleet to catch the raw material. A fleet presents its own specific problems with regard to maintenance of vessels, fishing equipment and fishing gear. There is, therefore, clearly a need for a separate fleet manager, perhaps an experienced masterfisherman. A fish processing plant, like any industrial undertaking, needs administrative management. This responsibility should not be shouldered by the technical management, who would then become tied up in adminstrative matters. But if, in a very small plant, the technical manager has to be in sole charge of the whole operation, he should have some training in business administration. Production staff could be organized in the following departments: (a) production, (b) quality control.

Production

As loss of production through mechanical or electrical failure should be as small as possible, the production department staff must include mechanics, electricians and refrigeration engineers. The chief mechanical engineer should be a formally qualified engineer. It is a post often satisfactorily filled by an experienced marine engineer. The diversity of problems such an engineer encounters during his career makes him conversant with most of the machinery he is likely to find in a fish processing plant. But, of course, such people are hard to find in most developing countries. The mechanics, electricians and refrigeration engineers should be well trained in their respective skills. They are responsible for the maintenance and adjustment of such diverse equipment as filleting, washing, and packaging machines, refrigeration and canning equipment, diesel engines, generators, steam plant, etc. Training for this work should include a fair amount of skills such as the production of close tolerance parts, welding and turning, and knowledge of materials. Usually, a refrigeration engineer can also be made responsible for the electrical maintenance. He should, therefore, have a good deal of knowledge of automatically operating switches, relays, time clocks, valves, safety devices, and so on.

Quality control

The chief chemist or chief analyst in charge of this department should keep a check on the quality of incoming raw materials, auxiliary materials and outgoing products, and supervise the work of the chemical analyst(s) and the microbiological analyst(s). Experience shows that a person of a sub-university training and possessing the necessary motivation is required in the position of chief of quality control. He should be given, say, a year in which to familiarize himself with the equipment and routine, and then, in the following year, some specialized training on analysis of fish and fishery products. Such training should be intense and given on an individual basis or in very small groups. As analysis of fishery products is usually limited to the determination of protein, fat, moisture, ash and a range of biochemical compounds to establish freshness, such training need not be limited to a fisheries research institute. It could also take place in university laboratories or in quality control laboratories of food processing plants. The training should also include some instruction in water pollution and pollution control.

TRAINING

Such training as described above is not available on an organized basis in the majority of the world's developing countries and certainly not with emphasis on the fish processing industry. Indeed, there are only a few countries with special training at university level for fisheries and the fish processing industry, such as Japan, Spain, USA and Canada. But other countries have non-specific food technology courses at college or university level to which students could be sent as the courses seem to be adequate. As the foregoing observations indicate, there is a need for specific courses to train staff of fish processing plants. In this respect, the Danish Fishery Research Institute has led the way with a three-month course on fish handling and quality control of fishery products, but other courses are needed, such as for fish technologists and plant mechanics. These courses should cover a wide range of subjects, with plenty of practical instruction to train a man to run a factory single-handed if required. Such training should be given on a regular basis as is done, for example, in The Netherlands and Belgium where a six-month course in food science and nutrition is organized each year for a limited number of participants. This is a much better way of training students than sending them abroad on individual fellowships. Such students require far too much attention relative to the resulting trained manpower. FAO seems to be the most appropriate authority to promote and coordinate such courses, dependent on the facilities that can be made available, either in an industrial country or on a regional basis in one or more of the developing countries.

Management Training in Fisheries   *W P Appleyard*

Whilst the development of management material in the fishery industries of the developed countries is still a problem, I will confine my comments to management problems in the developing countries. These brief notes will deal with two categories: (a) the development of local management, (b) the development of foreign management having an ability to work in developing countries.

THE DEVELOPING OF LOCAL MANAGEMENT

Whilst more countries are producing graduate fishery engineers, it must not be assumed that all are management material. Managementwise, a degree in fishery engineering or a related subject might represent a useful background. However, management in the fishing industry requires a lot more for it is a demanding and, at times, an unrewarding industry in relation to the effort expended. What are we looking for? Above all, leadership and ability to handle a variety of people who are often working in difficult and unpleasant conditions for long hours. Without an ability to communicate and inspire confidence, a manager can jeopardise any operation. Whilst some formal training can be given in developing leadership qualities, the best training is on the site. By allowing management material to develop initiatives in small matters or in small projects, his capacity can be examined or his ability to benefit by experience can be established. An ability to see a job through to a conclusion is all important and not to have his concentration diverted to minor objectives. A sound administrative ability coupled with an appreciation of basic accounting and budgeting is essential. A penchant for clear, lucid and short report writing is most useful. Such experience can be imparted by formal teaching followed by practical immersion in the subject. In the initial years of a manager's development, I am much in favour of the potential manager physically working in as many departments as possible and doing a day-to-day job with some specific responsibilities, however small. He cannot be expected to master all activities but, by such participation, he can appreciate the tasks of others and develop a practical awareness of their subjects and their problems. Also by tackling the question of management this way, it should be possible to identify his strengths and weaknessess so that his strengths can be exploited to the full and his weaknessess reinforced. An academic training, as already said, is not sufficient and during the period of physical training the trainee should be given responsibilities and some, albeit minor, decision-taking role. As the next step, consideration should be given to periods of working in companies overseas in related fields or participating in study tours giving maximum exposure to problems likely to be encountered. In both cases, a detailed and tightly controlled programme needs to be organized otherwise the potential manager is simply a sightseer or a paid tourist. He should be made to prepare regular reports to his home office during such trips – not only for the benefit of himself and his employer

but so that his observations may benefit subsequent fellows. In putting together such programmes, it is essential that there is a clear objective and that the opportunity to visit overseas is not just a reward for good service or because the participant has the correct language ability. It should never be assumed that a person with a good professional ability is a good manager – often the reverse. The professional often resents utilizing his time and talent on management matters whilst the potential manager might have little inclination to apply himself to the specialities of the professional. Furthermore, there is no point in developing a person to a managerial level unless there is a reasonable prospect of a managerial position.

THE DEVELOPMENT OF FOREIGN MANAGEMENT

More and more international fish companies are realizing that a manager who performs well at his home base does not necessarily react in the same manner when removed from his customary environment although the same technical problems apply and he may be working within the same company system. Equally so, some managers who are successful in one overseas area are not necessarily successful in another. A company developing an overseas operation can usually take two management routes: move an existing manager, bearing in mind his ability to perhaps master another language, his attitude to local people and conditions, his ability to work thousands of miles from headquarters, the reaction of himself and his family to a new set of living conditions and customs, and the degree of flexibility which he may bring to his work; or, alternatively, a company may recruit a person from outside who appears to fill the bill. The former course can be somewhat risky whilst the latter course can be very expensive. An interesting case study of an approach to such a problem was that of a major British food company setting up four shrimping operations in the Arabian Gulf in the early sixties. Initially, American management was recruited because of the overall US experience in shrimping; because the vessels were to be built in the USA; because most specialist shrimp equipment is manufactured in the USA; because some of the captains were to be recruited from the USA; and because the main market for the product was to be the USA – all in all, a very logical decision but a highly expensive one. Such people command very high salaries, expensive living quarters and generous fringe benefits. Hence, action was taken to establish a middle management corps who could be developed and eased into senior managerial positions. The first step was to advertise for young men (23–28 years old), preferably graduates, having a spirit of adventure, a wish to work overseas and a willingness to undergo management training in the fishery industry. Several hundreds applied and this number was reduced by professional methods to eighty who were given interviews by the Company's Personnel Department, twenty survived for interview by the Managing Director of the Company's International Division who was, in fact, looking for three or four trainees.

Such was the high quality of the candidates that he selected twelve. All single; all graduates (except for two-ex-servicemen – neither commissioned); all had done something interesting, eg, a pony trek across Iceland, a year in the Atlantic on a German trawler, a walk from India to UK; all showed enthusiasm. Their salary was to be £100 per month and all found. They was offered one year of training in the Arabian Gulf after a one-month briefing at the Company's UK headquarters. This involved talks on Company organization and policy; intensive lectures on fish handling and processing followed by practical work in the factories; a course on quality control; visits to trawlers and a short fishing trip in the North Sea; discussions on marketing; and a major immersion in the atmosphere of the Company; drinks with the Chairman, involvement in the Company Sports Club, meals in the canteen with workers, executives and directors. The Company devoted a lot of executive time to these twelve trainees, and, even after the month, it was possible to detect some of their strengths and weaknesses. Once in the Arabian Gulf, they were either posted in pairs or singly to work on the processing deck of the factory vessel; to work on the shrimp trawlers; to work in the processing factories; to work in the net stores; to work in the victualling department; to work in the sales and shipping office. All these jobs were rotated so that all served in all activities. They worked hard and they worked long hours in difficult and strange conditions. They learned a tremendous amount. It should be noted that the local management collaborated to the full. Without their enthusiasm and cooperation, the scheme would have been dead. What happened? Two dropped out and were shipped home by mutual agreement; one got into trouble for some illicit private trading; one decided he would rather work for an Arab company for more salary and possibly better prospects (as it turned out, it was a good decision); and others stuck it out. Of those eight, four are still with the Company in senior positions and the other four are doing well with other fishing companies around the world. All in all, a most worthwhile experience with lessons to be learnt by everyone. Of course, there can be less ambitious schemes than that just outlined but, in this case, it was a special circumstance needing special action. Had not the demand been such, the same idea would have worked with one or two trainees although some of the spirit of both competition and friendship would have been lost.

SUMMARY

These notes are not intended to be an educational paper. However, it is hoped that they succeed in establishing that once an intelligent and enthusiastic man, preferably with some related experience, has been selected that there is no real substitute for physical involvement and complete immersion in the industry.

Training for Fisheries Products Industries in Developing Countries: Requirements and Possibilities   *R C Cole*

Activites de formation professionnelle pour l'industrie des produits de la pêche dans les pays en developpement – besoins et possibilites

L'auteur examine la nécessité de former des fonctionnaires gouvernementaux et diverses catégories de personnel de l'industrie des produits de la pêche dans les pays en développement. Il propose certains moyens à mettre en oeuvre pour assurer la formation du personnel à différents niveaux. Considérant le grand nombre de personnes qui travaillent dans les pêcheries de subsistance et les pêcheries artisanales, il estime que ces pêcheurs ne peuvent être touchés qus par des services de vulgarisation; l'organisation de ces derniers est brièvement examinée.

Capacitacion de personal para las industrias pesqueras en los países en desarrollo necesidades y posibilidades

El autor examina las necesidades de capacitación de personal para las industrias elaboradoras de pescado de los países en desarrollo, de funcionarios del gobierno y de personal industrial de diversos grados. Se proponen diversas soluciones para capacitar a personal de diversas categorías. Dado que el número de personas que se dedican a la pesca de subsistencia y artesanal es tan grande, se sugiere que la única forma de llegar a estas personas es mediante servicios de extensión y se examinan brevemente estos servicios.

One of the difficulties in writing about training in developing countries is that the stage of development they have reached is so varied, and often a country which has some industries in an advanced stage of development will have a backward fishing industry. The reverse is also true. One important difference between the developing and the developed countries is the part played by government where the economy is not centrally planned. An industry which is well developed and modernized can often take care of most of its needs with little government intervention. Where the fishing industry is in a more primitive state, government must often take the lead at every point if any progress is to be achieved at all. It seems to be generally agreed that governments should be responsible for the training of fishermen, even where the industry is well developed. There are many advantages in this, not the least being that fishermen's training can then be easily integrated into the general educational system of the country concerned. Governments must also usually accept responsibility for the training of fisheries department staff and, in the less industrialized fisheries, for training operatives on the processing side of the industry. Where operations such as freezing and canning are introduced the industrialists concerned may arrange for much of the necessary training, but even here governments may have to play a part in the training of the more senior and highly qualified staff. Where there is a need for inspection and quality control, governments must usually provide the training which is needed. If governments are to provide training to operatives in the fisheries products industries, then governments must employ teachers, who will themselves have to be trained. Obviously the training needs in a developing country may be many and varied, and this paper attempts to indicate what some of these needs may be and how they may best be met.

WHO NEEDS TRAINING

The simple answer to the question 'who needs training' may well be 'everyone who handles fish from the time it is caught until it is consumed'. Those who are to teach also need training and it is obvious that they must be trained first. The levels of training needed will of course be very different for jobs at different levels. The fisherman who is using ice for the first time may need only a few minutes' initial instruction with a follow-up to ensure that the technique is being used to proper advantage. The technical manager of a cannery will need training extending over several years, and the educational basis from which he starts must also be of a high level while the fisherman may have received little formal education. While it is difficult to calculate with any accuracy how many fishermen there are in the world, estimates vary between 8 and 10 million men (Hall 1968). All of these should have received some training in the handling of the fish they catch, for the treatment meted out to the catch during the first few hours can affect irreversibly the final eating quality and storage life of the fish. Many of these millions of fishermen are illiterate, or nearly so, and live in countries where the population increase is of the order of 3 per cent per annum. In fishing villages the actual figure may well be higher because the families of fishermen are better fed than most. If we accept a figure of 3 per cent for the population increase per annum, and this continued unchecked for about 23 years, the world's fishing population would double if there were no migration. Many of these fishermen perform some handling and processing operations, while others are carried out by their families. The number of people engaged on the handling and processing side of the industry seems not to have been estimated, but it must run into millions. This vast number of subsistence and artisanal fishermen and those who handle their catches cannot be reached by any form of training other than that which can be provided by extension or development services – that is, by the fisheries departments. At all stages of development the staff of the fisheries departments will include a number of university graduates employed as fisheries officers, and higher grades, and a much larger number of nongraduates employed as fisheries assistants, fisheries development officers, inspectors, etc. In the early stages of development all these people must be given a very generalized training so that they can undertake or oversee a variety of executive and administrative functions, including licensing and statistics collection as well as the training functions of a development service type. Even in these early stages there are strong arguments for keeping the administrative and executive functions quite separate from the training ones. Wherever possible the extension or development service should be a separate branch or division of the fisheries department. Its officers could well wear a uniform distinguished from that worn by licensing and

enforcement officers. In the more advanced stages, increased specialization becomes necessary, and the graduate staff should include officers responsible for fish inspection, quality control and product development, while the more junior staff should include officers trained to execute these functions. Thus in the early stages, fisheries assistants employed in the fisheries service may be given training in fish catching methods as well as in simple processing such as smoking, salting and drying. Later, with an increase in specialization, such people would be given more advanced training in fish processing. Graduate staff who intend to specialize in fish processing or catching, etc, should receive a general training, which would fit them for higher posts later on, before they undergo specialized training.

Relatively few developing countries have so far opted for an educational system which includes fisheries training at the high school or more junior levels. This system of vocational training is well developed in Japan (Fujinami 1966) and Korea and is also used in the Philippines. All these countries also have nonvocational high schools where only academic subjects are taught. If a vocational school is to be fully effective, it must have trained teachers, must operate one or more sea-going vessels and possess a certain amount of processing equipment. All these are expensive and for most developing countries it would seem to be better to concentrate on giving children a well rounded academic education and to start vocational training at the school-leaving stage. The list of people needing some form of training in fish processing in a developing country may include:

1 General service fisheries officers and other senior fisheries department staff.
2 Specialist fisheries department staff engaged in research, product development and quality control operations.
3 Teachers and instructors for fisheries schools.
4 Extension or development service staff.
5 Processing technologists for industry.
6 Processing plant operatives.
7 Refrigeration engineers and mechanics.
8 Fishmongers and market operatives.
9 Fish curers.
10 Fishermen.

This list could of course be contracted or expanded where certain functions are amalgamated or separated. One of the principal difficulties experienced by the developing countries in providing training is that the numbers needing training are either very small or inconveniently large. Most countries would need only a handful of personnel in categories 1–7, while the numbers in categories 8–10 may run into tens of thousands in a small country and hundreds of thousands in a large one. It would be impractical and indeed unduly expensive to attempt to operate a training class for less than about ten people. Where practical subjects must be taught, it is also impractical to have a class of more than about 25 or 30 people. The thousands of people who need training as fishmongers, market operatives, fish curers and fishermen can only be reached through an extension or development service. Men trained for the public service at public expense often find more lucrative employment in private industry. Binding officers so trained to serve the government for a minimum period may provide a partial answer. Experience has shown that arrangements of this kind are usually not enforceable because no one can make a man do a day's work if he decides not to do so. Repayment of the cost of training would be a powerful deterent, but what government needs is, of course, a trained officer, not repayment of the cost of his training. One solution to this problem would seem to allow for such wastage and to train more men than governments can immediately employ. This could only be done if a sufficient number of adequately educated people were available. It is also an expensive solution. It is usually better to avoid too high a degree of specialization so that there is some mobility of trained labour, and highly specialized training should be given to officers who have a proven record of service.

METHODS OF PROVIDING TRAINING

Training senior fisheries department staff for general service

Senior fisheries department staff are normally graduate level and most will probably be biologists, but the subject for the first degree is not too important. It is generally thought that a one-year course in fisheries technology provides the necessary technical background. For most developing countries, the numbers required are small so this training cannot be provided at the national level. India is an exception to this. Suitable courses exist in India, Japan and in the United Kingdom (FAO 1970). During the one-year course students should spend about 60–75 h studying the theoretical aspects of fish handling, processing and preservation and they should also spend about 75 h practising the technologies involved. The remaining time on the course would be occupied in studying other subjects.

Training specialist fisheries department senior staff and specialists for industry

Obviously specialists need a more thorough background training than the generalists. This may be provided in one of several ways:

1 By following the fisheries officers' course with six months to one year of practical training in a research and development or quality control laboratory. For most developing countries, this training would at present have to be undertaken overseas. A master's degree in food science and technology following a bachelor's degree in general scientific subjects followed by specialization in fish processing technologies is an alternative method of training which has also proved successful.
2 By taking a first degree in food science and technology, and following this with a period of training in a research and development or quality control laboratory.

Where the fisheries department operates one or more training schools, at least one staff member of each should qualify as a specialist and, like all other teachers, follow this with teacher training. The technologist who is to work in an industrial processing plant needs academic and practical training to much the same level as his government counterpart. A degree-level course in food processing or food science and technology is the best starting point, followed by in-plant experience.

Refrigeration enginers and mechanics

Responsibility for the training of refrigeration engineers and mechanics would not normally fall on the fisheries department. The fisheries industries are however among the major employers of these people and thus the fisheries department should take an interest in seeing that a sufficient number is trained. It may be necessary to send the relatively small number of refrigeration engineers needed overseas for training, while mechanics should be trained in national or regional technical colleges.

Extension or development service staff

The vast majority of the fishermen, fishmongers, market operatives and fish curers in a developing country can be reached only through an extension or development service. For many countries, the establishment of such a service and the training of the staff to operate it must be given the highest possible priority. Because the number of operatives involved is so huge, and the area of country to be covered so vast, it is, for many developing countries, impossible to train extension workers solely for fish handling and processing work. Most of them therefore must also be prepared to advise on such things as fish catching, boat repair and engine maintenance. Often the fisheries extension worker will be the only representative of government who meets the people of a fishing village so he should be of high calibre. The training of extension workers should, where possible, be undertaken in a permanent fisheries school with boarding facilities. Recruits to the service should, if this can be arranged, spend a year in the field under supervision before they join the fisheries school. Officers who work in the extension service must expect to find their work takes them into isolated areas and that the work is arduous and demanding. It is far better that people who are unsuited to work in such conditions should discover this for themselves before time and money is spent on their training. Recruits to the service should be fit young men who have completed about 13 years of primary and secondary schooling, with preference given to those who have concentrated on scientific subjects. The course of training should last for two full academic years and during the vacations the students should carry out field projects under the guidance of fisheries department staff. The course must essentially be a practical one. More than half the time spent in residence at the school should be devoted to practical work in fishing boats, laboratories engineering and netmaking workshops and in fish processing workshops. The training should be devised so as to give the students an awareness of the existing status of the fishing industry which they will serve and of the plans made for its development. A typical course would include instruction in seamanship, boat construction and boat handling, fishing gear construction and fishing methods, the handling, processing and preservation of fish, elementary microbiology, hygiene, first aid, nutrition, fish cookery, and the design and operation of fish markets and shops. The food technology and fish handling elements require about 150 h of theory and 200 h of practical teaching. Such a course, lasting two years, normally leads to the award of a certificate of proficiency.

It will be seen that the typical course for an extension worker should produce a man with a widely based knowledge of fisheries subjects. While there would be considerable advantages in training people to a higher degree of specialization, for many developing countries this is at present unduly expensive. It is, of course, desirable that the fisheries extension service should provide a full career structure to those joining it. The officers at the higher levels in the service will inevitably find that they have to control the activities of people who are specialized in very different subjects. It is thus desirable that all entrants should achieve a broadly based knowledge. For some countries, only extension workers with this broad based training will be needed in the immediate future, since they will be dealing with fisheries at the artisanal and subsistence levels. Where the fishery has reached a more advanced stage, and more expert advice is needed, specialists must be trained. The most useful way to do this is to institute a third year of training at the fisheries school, leading to a diploma qualification. Since most trainees attending the diploma course would have spent some time in the field following their initial training, the course should commence with a review of the subject matter taught during the two-year certificate course. This should be followed by more intensive and advanced training in microbiology, hygiene, in-plant sanitation, quality control and fish inspection services and such processing methods as may be appropriate to the country concerned. All trainees for an extension service should receive training in instructional methods, including the use of audio-visual aids.

Processing plant operatives

This is one of the areas in which it is very difficult to generalize about training requirements because the tasks are so many and so varied. When a freezing operation is started, for instance, people must be taught to prepare the fish, package it and operate the freezers and cold stores; when a cannery operation starts, people must be taught fish preparation, can filling, and the operation of can seamers and retorts. Some of these operations, such as, for example, can filling, are quite simple but it may nonetheless take some time before an operative works up to the required speed and accuracy. In other operations as, for example, fish filleting, a high degree of skill is needed. One college in the United Kingdom offers a course lasting three months during which time a student is expected to acquire sufficient skill and speed to take a place on a commercial filleting line. Incorrect operation of can seaming machinery, retorts, freezers or cold storage plant could result in a spoiled product with consequent loss of profits if the fault is detected and danger to the consumer if it is not. All of the operations for which a reasonably high degree of skill is needed could best be taught in a fisheries school rather than on the job. Such courses could be relatively short, lasting for only a few weeks or months. They have the advantage that the trainee can be given some technical background and can acquire the necessary technical skills without being subjected to commercial pressures. This is an ideal which may often be unattainable if only because the numbers requiring training at any one time are likely to be so

small. In such circumstances the only answer is for the operative to be trained on the job. The teachers in such cases must usually be the plant manager and his technically qualified senior staff. Where these people have to be recruited from overseas, counterparts should be provided as quickly as possible, and, as necessary, training overseas arranged for them.

THE EXTENSION SERVICE

There is need for an extension service, as an arm of the fisheries department, to extend the knowledge available to the fishermen and other personnel engaged at the artisanal and subsistence levels. Yasueda (1972) defines the functions of a fisheries extension service thus: 'The function of a fisheries extension service is to spread knowledge and techniques among fishermen with a view to modernizing the management of fishing enterprises, improving productivity and advancing the fisherman's standard of living. In the broadest sense, the service is an educational project.' The officers who work in the extension service must obviously be in very close contact with the people they serve, and this requires that the junior officers, at least, must live in the fishing villages. It is equally obvious that they must gain the confidence of everyone in the village where they are working if they are to be effective. Wherever possible, the extension service should be recognizably separate from other branches of the fisheries service, and its officers should not carry out such duties as statistics collection, licensing or control. Where a uniform is worn, it should distinguish those wearing it from other branches. Many countries, while recognizing the advisability of operating the extension service as a separate branch, cannot do so for financial reasons. In these circumstances the best that can be done may be to arrange that at least the licensing and control functions are not conducted by officers who are expected to carry out extension duties.

In Japan, one extension worker is provided for every 500 fishing families (Yasueda 1972) and this seems to be a reasonable basis for calculating the numbers of workers needed. In most developing countries the number of extension workers employed will be limited by financial considerations. The field extension workers who are living in the villages will have received a general training to fit them for their work. They need expert assistance with such matters as improving fish landing facilities or methods of fish curing. In a developing country, such advice would normally be provided by officers who have spent a third year in a fisheries school attending a diploma course specializing in one topic only. These specialists should interpret the results of research into practical methods which can be used at the village level, and assist the extension workers in teaching these to the village people. It is important that the extension worker should recognize that he is the point of liaison between the people in the villages and government, and it is his duty to inform government through his superiors of the needs, ambitions, and desires of the village people, as well as teaching them the things the fisheries department officers think they should know.

Provision should be made for a reasonable career

structure within the extension service itself or in other branches of the fisheries department. In many countries living conditions are somewhat difficult in the more isolated of the fishing villages and for a young man the prospect of spending his entire working life living under such conditions would be unattractive. There should thus be opportunities for retraining for other duties, for promotion within the service, and for transfer to less exacting duties for older men. An extension worker should not live too long in one village, and a move every few years is valuable for all concerned. The workers benefit because they are able to see a different set of conditions so that their interest is kept alive, and the industry benefits because a new worker, with new outlook and different abilities, replaces the old. Such transfers also enable an extension worker to obtain the broad knowledge of the industry that he will need for promotion. The extension service may carry out its functions in a number of different ways. These may include contact with individual workers and their families, group discussions, lectures and demonstrations by specialists, provision of literature (textbooks, manuals, leaflets) radio and television programmes, and films. Of these, the use of demonstrations of proven practical techniques always proves the most useful in the developing countries. Such demonstrations may be given in

residential schools and this has the advantages that excellent facilities and the best teachers can be made available and also that the trainees from then on feel a sense of possession and pride in the school. The major disadvantage (apart from expense) is that the trainees may feel that what they have learned is useless to them because their own facilities cannot match those available in the school. For this reason, the most effective demonstrations are those given on a work site in a fishing village. The work of the extension service needs careful planning. Each worker should plan his programme well in advance, discuss them with his superiors and with community leaders, and have them approved after appropriate modification. A system of monthly and annual reporting enables both the worker and his superiors to assess the effects of his efforts.

References

FAO   Provisional Directory of Fishery Training Institutions,
1970   COFI: FET/2/70/Inf. 5, FAO Rome.
FUJINAMI, N Fisheries Education in Japan, IPFC/C66/SYN 15,
1968   FAO, Rome.
HALL, D N F Synopsis of Manual on Fisheries Education and
1969   Training, COFI: FET/1/69/Inf. 2, FAO Rome.
YASUEDA, T Fisheries Extension Service, FIE: FET/72/BP3, FAO
1972   Rome.

Establishment of a Fish Technology Laboratory and Training Centre   *P Hansen and E Ruckes*

Creation d'un laboratoire technologique et d'un centre de formation
Le document expose brièvement les répercussions de la recherche technologique appliquée dans le domaine des pêches et cite des exemples emprintés au Danemark afin de démontrer la nécessité de ce type de soutien pour le développement des pêches. En raison de l'expansion prévue des pêches de Sri Lanka, il est proposé de créer dans ce pays un centre pour le développement et la commercialisation des produits à base de poisson. Le centre serait essentiellement chargé d'effectuer des recherches appliquées sur la technologie et la commercialisation du poisson, de fournir des avis et d'assurer une formation à toutes les catégories intéressées, des pêcheurs aux détaillants. Une description est donnée des opérations pour lesquelles du matériel est demandé, ainsi que des besoins du laboratoire. L'importance régionale de ce projet de développement est soulignée.

Creacion de un laboratorio de tecnologia pesquera y centro de comercializacion
Se presentan brevemente las repercusiones de las investigaciones sobre tecnología pesquera aplicada, citando como ejemplo la experiencia danesa, para mostrar la necesidad de sostener el desarrollo del sector pesquero con actividades de este tipo. En vista de los progresos que se espera realice el sector en Sri Lanka, se propone crear un centro para preparar y vender productos pesqueros en el país, cuyo principal objetivo será realizar investigaciones aplicadas sobre tecnología y venta del pescado y facilitar asesoramiento y capacitación a todo el personal que trabaja en este sector, desda los pescadores hasta los pescaderos. Se indican los procesos para los que habrá que facilitar equipo y los aparatos de laboratorio necesarios, y se pone de relieve la importancia regional de estos trabajos de desarrollo.

The impact of technology on fisheries in the technically advanced countries is in evidence at every stage of the industry – from the search for and capture of fish, in the handling of the catch aboard and ashore and processing it, to the marketing and distribution of the end product. While the use of technology is not in itself a guarantee of successful development of fisheries, experience suggests that it should be introduced in accordance with the situation and requirements in developing fisheries. An effective way of doing this is to establish a fisheries technological laboratory of the kind which has helped the world's leading fishing nations develop their industries. Such laboratories are relatively new to the fisheries scene. An example is that of the Danish Fisheries Technological Laboratory which was established in 1931 to carry out investigations and research into the handling,

storage, preservation and processing of fish. The results of its work have been made available to the fishery industries of Denmark and have helped to increase the Danish catch from about 100,000 tons to 1·4 million tons (1968). It has also helped the fishery industries to expand and diversify on a large scale so that today they are exporting products to more than 60 countries. The establishment of such a laboratory in a developing country should be governed by the situation and requirements of its fisheries. The authors feel that such a laboratory should be established, together with a training scheme, when new fishing methods are being introduced, using new and more powerful vessels, gear and equipment; when catches exceed the capacity of the local fresh fish market and the traditional curing industry, calling for chilling, freezing and more sophisticated processing of the fish;

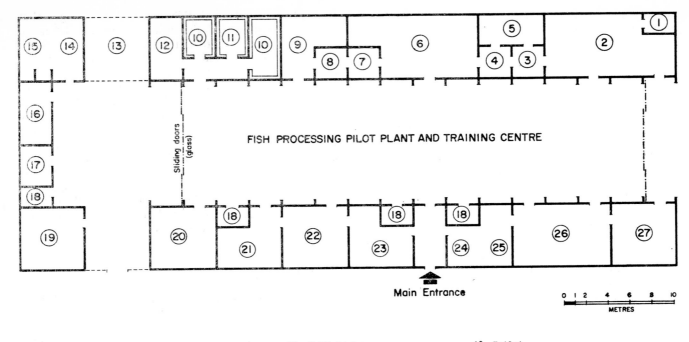

1 Thermostat
2 Microbiology laboratory
3 Culture media kitchen
4 Glassware cleaning
5 Glassware store
6 Chemistry and physics laboratory
7 Weighing room
8 Measuring equipment
9 Food technology laboratory

10 Chilled store
11 Frozen store
12 Compressors and Workshop store
13 Sun-drying yard
14 Salting
15 Drying and smoking
16 Fish meal
17 Steam generator

18 Toilet
19 Canteen
20 Mechanical and electrical workshop
21 Experimental cookery
22 Test panel room
23 Marketing office
24 Secretary – Reception
25 Information centre
26 Library, lecturing and meeting room
27 Directors office

Fig 1 Suggested lay-out of the Centre for the Development and Marketing of Fish Products in Sri Lanka

when ice plants, cold storage and other shore installations are needed in fish harbour development; and when control over the quality and hygiene of fish and fish products should be introduced and made effective. An example of a developing country where such a situation exists is Sri Lanka.

WORK PROGRAMME

A considerable effort has been made in Sri Lanka to modernize its fishing methods and operations, and as a result, the catch has increased by about 50 per cent – from 94,300 tons in 1965 to 141,200 tons in 1969 (the last comparable year since when a new system of recording the catch has been introduced). Even so, the country still has to import about half the fish it consumes. However, the Government's policy is to continue mechanizing the fishing industry and to develop the inland fisheries to make the country self supporting in fish and, indeed, to develop an export trade in fishery products. This is a situation favourable to the establishment of a fisheries technological laboratory and training centre. Accordingly, the Swedish International Development Authority (SIDA) has decided to finance a project in Sri Lanka for this purpose, with the technical guidance and help of the Food and Agriculture Organization of the United Nations (FAO). It should be mentioned that the fishery sector is important to the economy of Sri Lanka. For instance, in 1969 it contributed 175 million rupees (US$27·5 million)[1] to the Gross National Product (GNP)

of US$326 million. It provided work for 74,000 people out of a total labour force of 3·6 million. It also made a major contribution to the diet of the people, providing 5·5 g of the 8·5 g of protein of animal origin in the *per caput* diet of 46·2 g of protein (1968).

Characteristics of the Sri Lanka fisheries are surpluses in certain fisheries during certain times of the year; considerable losses due to inefficient handling, preservation and marketing practices; and a limited use of inland water resources, mainly because of consumer resistance toward the fish produced. The Ceylon Fisheries Corporation operates a canning plant, which it is considering relocating at a site with regular supplies. A fishing complex, mainly for tuna operations, has been developed in Galle. The losses and extra work incurred because of deficient handling and preservation practices must be reduced and the imported fishery products (mainly dried and canned) replaced by domestic produce. These, as well as the increased utilization of inland fishery resources, require considerable development work. The standard of marketing operations needs improvement and market development work must include the determination of potential demand for acceptable new products for the domestic and export markets, and the planning and implementation of a suitable distribution system for these. As this brief outline of the situation indicates, marketing plays a more important role than in the case of the Danish fish technology institute. In addition, the transfer of knowledge to all parties concerned from catch to retailing calls for special attention. As a

---

[1] Official exchange rate U.S.$ 1.00 = Rs 6.00 (as of November 1972)

result of these considerations the Centre for the Development and Marketing of Fish Products in Sri Lanka will be established to increase the supplies available to consumers from domestic catches by improving the utilization of Sri Lanka's resources through improved handling, preservation, processing and marketing. In particular the Centre will aim:

(i) to reduce spoilage at all levels, starting from preserving the catch on board to retailing;

(ii) to find uses for unutilized, or not fully utilized, species through product development and market research;

(iii) to disseminate knowledge on improved handling, preservation, processing and marketing among all concerned.

This will call for demonstration of improved practices in preservation, handling and marketing techniques, and the collection and evaluation of technical and marketing information for use by Government authorities, cooperatives and the fishing industry. This information will cover, in particular, advances in methods of preservation and processing, newly developed equipment for handling and processing, product development, domestic and export markets, consumer acceptability, purchasing power and cost studies of the processing and distribution of fish and fishery products. The Centre will also deal with the utilization of fish species not yet fully used or in surplus and the improvement of existing processing methods as well as to advise on processing techniques not yet used in the country. Pilot processing of small fish species will be undertaken and local labour trained in the operation of this industry. Training of counterpart staff, extension workers, technical staff working in cooperatives and industry, and staff engaged in the promotion and marketing of fish and fishery products, will be important functions. So will be market assessment studies, in particular the acceptability of new products developed by the Centre, and the preparation of material to be used for consumer education and promotion of fish. It is essential that the work done at the Centre is directly related to problems of the industry. As far as research is necessary, it should always be applied research, seeking to solve selected problems. When the initial work of the Centre has demonstrated its practical value, it is hoped that the industry will request the Centre to undertake specific tasks. Eventually the Centre's research work should be based almost entirely on industry requests. For this to come about, the Centre must have good relations with the industry. In such work the Centre must restrict itself to the advisory function and not take over control functions. Quality control of fishery products, for instance, should be the responsibility of Government employees, although the training of the inspectors should, of course, be a very useful function of the Centre. The organizational set-up of the Centre will ensure its independence from the biological research institute, even though some services, such as the library, may be used jointly.

SUGGESTED LAYOUT

It is suggested that the main part of the Centre should be located in a one-floor building containing a large pilot plant for fish handling and processing on a semi-industrial scale (Figure 1). The facilities and equipment of the pilot plant should enable the technical staff and guest workers from industry and abroad to study, improve and develop fish processing technology. Equipment should include plants for freezing and cold storage, gutting, peeling, skinning and filleting machines and the necessary installations for mincing, mixing, paste and sausage production, brining, marinating, blanching, cooking, fermentation and proteolysis, filtration, pumping and centrifuging, canning and vacuum-packaging, heat-pasteurization and -sterilization, and storage at controlled temperatures and humidity. A separate, adjacent building will be used for processes involving pollution problems, such as cooking, drying and milling protein products, and hot and cold smoking. A fenced-in area between the buildings will be used for sun-drying and other drying in the open air. The pilot plant for training of groups of Ceylonese students in fish technology will serve as a model of high standards of hygiene. It will therefore be designed for easy and efficient cleaning and to prevent the entry of insects and animals. The Centre will also have laboratories for:

(a) physical measurements, such as weight, temperature, humidity, acidity, redox potential and air pressure, and chemical analysis for contents of water, salt, fat and protein and for fat and protein quality and breakdown products;

(b) microbiological investigations related to hygiene, fish spoilage and health hazards;

(c) experimental cooking and organoleptic quality assessment, and

(d) food technology.

Rooms will be provided for cleaning, dry sterilization and autoclaving of glassware, agar, etc., equipment and chemical storage, etc. A mechanical and electrical workshop will be associated with the pilot plant, particularly with the refrigeration equipment, the steam generator and the canning and autoclaving equipment. The Centre will also have the necessary offices, and a library with space for holding lectures and meetings, and an information unit and secretariat. The Centre will, of course, have all the usual public services and be located in an area free from noise and dust.

CONCLUDING REMARKS

The benefits derived by the Danish fisheries industries from the work of their fish technology organization were referred to earlier as an example of aid to development. It is expected that the applied research to be carried out at the Centre in Sri Lanka, along with the intensive training and extension activities, will likewise assist in the development of the fisheries industries in that country. There is no doubt that with such assistance developing fisheries can gain great benefits. It is hoped, therefore, that efforts to create similar establishments in other areas where the need exists will succeed. Finally, it should be pointed out that such institutions in developing areas can also be of benefit to neighbouring countries which are exploiting similar resources. The Centre in Sri Lanka, therefore, can be expected to obtain results which can also be applied beneficially in other Indian Ocean countries in that area. Regional training courses and seminars could provide a means for making the results widely known.

Discussion on Part VII

Education and training in technology and marketing

The discussion was an adequate demonstration of the special attention given to training in developing fishery industries in the fields covered by this Conference. The widespread need for training at all levels, including that of managing directors, was emphasized, and it seemed to be widely agreed that training for those responsible for improving fish products and selling fish for domestic consumption requires priority. The need for greater involvement of industry in training, both at home and within processing establishments of developed countries, was stressed. The lack of infrastructure in developing countries makes it difficult to provide practical training. In many developing countries there is a lack or inadequacy of an extension service.

THOMAS (USA) welcomed the emphasis now being placed on the extension function in the broadest sense. He warned that to teach for the sake of teaching and to do research for the sake of research are activities without practical value. The overwhelming problem is to transfer knowledge and skills by all available means – personal contact, mass media, short courses, conferences, etc. Countries such as Japan, Norway and USA, to name only three, have developed effective extension services, although on different lines, and these need to be more fully used in the developing world.

TAPIADOR (FAO) said that only 4 per cent of fishery graduates from 43 vocational schools in the Philippines enter fisheries work. He asked about the effectiveness of the large vocational school programme in Japan.

TOMIYAMA (Japan) said there are eight universities which have a faculty of fisheries and graduate about 800 students a year. There are a further seven universities with a Department of Fisheries and 53 fishery high schools. These latter provide a three-year course in vocational training for about 5,000 students a year. In addition, education in fisheries is also provided through seminars for extension workers. Some 20 per cent of Japanese fisheries students enter the industry and another 20 per cent go into the food industry. The rest go into such work as sales services, transporation (including the mercanile marine) and other industrties.

AMANO (Japan) said that Japanese fishery research laboratories are providing training for participants from developing countries, the funds being provided by the Overseas Fisheries Cooperation Agency (OFCA).

GUIZADO (Peru) stated that lack of infrastructure in developing countries makes it difficult to provide practical training. Practical work for students in Peru is provided by putting them on vessels or in land-based plants. There are also problems in the training of middle management personnel, but these are easier to solve.

KARNICKI (Poland) said that the new Polish research vessel 'Professor Siedlech' offers a good possibility for training of fellows from developing countries. The vessel is now operating in the Atlantic and has on board seven FAO fellows from developing countries. Training in oceanography and biology as well as technology is given on board. There are a processing plant, cold storage and freezing facilities, a small fish meal plant and biochemical and microbiology laboratories. The only problem is the limited space for trainees.

PETERKIN (Guyana) mentioned that industrial fishing in the developing countries is facing a number of difficulties from the point of view of competition and profitability. One serious difficulty is the lack of skilled operating and management personnel. Specialized training applicable to a particular industry is, therefore, the most beneficial assistance which can be given. In the past, the methods used have been to take the trainees to a developed country where he is trained and works on equipment and in an environment which are not similar in any way to his own situation. By far the more useful approach to the problem is the introduction of training vessels and training centres in the developing areas. Such training facilities would be of benefit to the industries. He added that at the present time there is a Japanese training vessel in the Caribbean Sea area which is accepting local trainees.

SÁNCHEZ (Peru) said that the present training system in Peru starts with basic courses for fishermen which cover fishing methods, navigation, elements of biology, technology, organization and cooperatives. The middle management training is for students with a secondary education. A school of fisheries issues diplomas after three years study on catching technology, fish processing and manufacturing technology. For higher level students there are seven universities with departments or faculties of fisheries where fishery biology, fishery engineering and fish culture may be studied. There are also post-graduate courses. He agreed with Peterkin that training in advanced countries should be restricted to high level research workers and university teachers.

LAYACHI (Morocco) stated that there is a need to undertake training and development concomitantly, recognizing that development precedes training. Advanced specialized training only should be provided, if necessary, outside the country.

DEL VALLE (Mexico) said that two institutions in Mexico offer training in fish processing. One at Veracruz provides vocational training. The other, at Guayamas, provides professional level training covering engineering, production, marketing, economics and accounting in addition to processing. So far, some 200 students have graduated and now occupy influential posts in government, industry and universities. About 85 per cent of the students are Mexican, the remaining 15 per cent coming from other Latin American countries.

ARATA (Chile) stated that the School of Fisheries and Food Technology, attached to the Catholic University of Valparaiso, provides training for middle level personnel.

It produces specialists in fisheries and in food technology. The School has received international assistance during its 16 years of existence. It is now offering post-graduate degrees for Latin American students. Its Research Centre is engaged in the development of marine resources, including work in association with bilateral and multilateral organizations on such projects as the marketing and distribution of fresh fish, the mechanization of artisanal fishery vessels, and activities in marine research.

DIAZ-GONZALEZ (Mexico) expressed the view that developing countries need to find ways of attracting boys into fisheries at an early age to ensure sufficient recruitment of personnel at the various levels.

TALABI (Nigeria) discussed the difficulty in developing countries getting leaders in research and training with the required broad knowledge. He suggested that government and international agencies should give more emphasis to training of heads of sections who would have a knowledge broad enough to guide and assess work and to introduce new students to the various subjects related to their work.

BYKOV (USSR) stated that training in the USSR is provided for industry, for science and for developing countries. Specialists for industry and science are trained in one of three institutes in engineering and fish processing, after secondary school education. Workers who handle and process fish are trained in a technical school. Scientists are also given post-graduate courses. Specialists from developing countries are trained in various technical and scientific schools and other institutions, as well as on board a vessel.

VAGNEUX (Canada) illustrated the value of training in a well established industry. He reported on a training programme for the New Brunswick fish processing industry which employs 3,000 factory workers, involving indirectly over 40,000 people in the province. It used only one processing method and all its production was for export. Productivity was low and the process traditional and out-of-date. A five-year programme was started in 1969 through the joint effort of the Government, the industry and the Council for Research and Productivity, to improve the performance of the industry. Training embraced all in the industry, from the managing director and all executive personnel down to the most junior workers. Training was provided in the classroom and in the field, with maximum use of audio-visual materials, study of methods and discussion. As a result of this programme, productivity has increased by Can. $1 million a year for an expenditure of Can. $40,000 a year by the Government, while the workers are better paid and the fishermen are earning about 40 per cent more. Technical competence, too, has greatly improved and a new interest in product diversification and marketing has arisen. Vagneux advised those who might consider taking up similar programmes to bear in mind the need to define clearly the objectives of a programme, ensure the participation of all concerned from the highest management level to the factory worker, arrange follow-up action in the plant to help put into effect the new techniques learned in training, provide for a repetition of such a programme, and introduce a continuous system of recycling and improvement as an institutionalized practice.

MUBANGA (Zambia) laid great stress on the need for 'practical' training. Experts should work hand-in-hand with local people and demonstrate the practical importance of the training they are imparting. He cited as a good example of this approach the work of four volunteers from Japan who are training Zambians in processing technology by working closely with them and demonstrating the practical benefits derived from improved techniques.

YOUSSOUF ALI (Bangladesh) expressed a similar view, saying that the prime need in developing countries is to create technicians and skilled workers by on-the-job training in their own country. Once they have become practical operators they may, if necessary, receive advanced training abroad. In the case of scientists being trained abroad, they, too, should be given on-the-job training in processing plants so that they gain some practical experience and knowledge of the industry.

MATHOTHO (Malawi) declared that much of the resources of developing countries is wasted due to lack of knowledge and means to process the fish for human consumption. Emphasis should be put on training people to process fish into products accepted by local consumers rather than try to produce new ones. Processors, therefore, should be given practical training to do this, taking into account local food behaviour and requirements. He added that in Malawi they are training extension workers to advise the processors in the best methods of attaining these objectives with the further aim of achieving improved and more hygienic products.

DE BRUIN (Sri Lanka) stated that in his country improvement of handling, distribution and presentation of existing products is a social problem because most of the fishing operatives are extremely poor and work under very difficult conditions. The centre for developing and marketing fishery products, which will be established with the aid of SIDA, may look further into this matter, but it will probably not achieve very much. It should be mainly a research centre for the development of new products from unutilized resources and a school for training.

HANSEN (FAO) said that the Sri Lanka Centre can only start work on the elementary technology used in the present fresh and cured fish industries unless additional funds are provided to allow more elaborate fish processing.

KOMBOT-NAGUEMON (Central African Republic) proposed that FAO and other sources of aid should assist in training technicians through regional and sub-regional arrangements.

TOGNETTI (Argentina) said that an evaluation of the training needs region by region is required and that FAO and other such organizations should assist in arranging meetings for this purpose.

ENCISO (Paraguay) proposed that FAO and other sources of bilateral and multilateral aid could help organize seminars and courses regarding training in artisanal fisheries and aquaculture.

KASEMSARN (Thailand) stressed the need to give technologists practical training in industrial plants and laboratories and urged that FAO and other aid agencies should ensure that this is done when providing fellowship training for technologists.

KREUZER (FAO) said that the Indo Pacific Fisheries Council (IPFC) has established a Cooperative Research Programme on Fish Product Development which also covers marketing, training and extension. It aims at initiating technical research programmes and pilot projects oriented toward the needs of the fish processing industries in developing countries in Asia and the Far East and at coordinating such research within the region. IPFC is also preparing, with assistance from FAO, a 'Classified Directory of Fisheries Technological Research Institutes and Programmes' in this region, giving information on staff, facilities and work programmes. Technological problems facing the fish product industry are also being investigated and listed in concise form. An FAO/DANIDA Seminar/Workshop to be convened in the IPFC region is under preparation and similar activities have been commenced or are planned for other regions—for example, a seminar on fish handling and quality control and a seminar on fish technology for Latin America.

LOUSHIN (Brazil) asserted that there is a serious lack of trained fishery workers at all levels, but especially at the university and intermediate technical levels, and mentioned the various ways in which training has been undertaken in Brazil. He pointed out that some South American countries now have rapidly developing fishery programmes with competent scientists working on them. The problem, therefore, seems to be chiefly one of communication and of exchange of the skills available within South America. He suggested that the long-range answer to upgrading fishery science and training in the region rests mainly with the countries themselves because of similarities in language, climate and socio-economic problems. In this connexion, FAO could assist in establishing training centres in the region and give aid in coordination of all such activities through provision of information in this field.

JAMES (Australia) raised the question of priorities in training in developing countries. Which has priority—training in export inspection or for the production of fish products for local consumption? He considered the latter more difficult to carry out but probably more necessary.

PETERKIN (Guyana) said that experience in his country indicates that first priority should go to training boat crews and fishermen, and the second should go to training process plant supervisors and engineers. He contended that any effort to improve the quality of products must start on the fishing boat. The technologist should also start his training on the boat. The next step is to improve processing in the plant.

BIRIBONWOHA (Uganda) mentioned that this is the general line of approach in Uganda where the priority in training is accorded, first, to the artisanal fishermen and, second, to managers, technologists, specialists, etc. Training policy and programming is controlled by the Government through the Fisheries Department. The training itself is best conducted through the extension service with assistance from foreign sources. He suggested that one of the most practical and useful forms of such assistance is the provision of manuals, visual aids, training boats and equipment, as well as the provision of skilled instructors.

BOSHELL (USA) and MEYBOOM (Netherlands) both spoke on the problems of how best to organize training. They stated that it should be broad and not produce only specialists. Further, such training should not only be practical but should include such related subjects as refrigeration, electrical engineering, maintenance of equipment and so on. The personnel earmarked for management should attend such courses, as this would give them some grasp of the work and difficulties of their staff. Meyboom concluded by suggesting that fishery industries should be brought into such training and proposed that FAO should investigate the situation to find out which industries in the various member countries would be willing to receive such trainees and give them further practical on-the-job training.

Part VIII

INTERNATIONAL COOPERATION

The Role of Joint Ventures in Establishing Fishery Industries   *R Hamlisch*

Le role des entreprises communes dans l'etablissement d'industries de la pêche

Les entreprises halieutiques communes offrent de considérables possibilités d'expansion vu le nombre élevé de pays en voie de développement qui ont besoin de capitaux et de connaissances techniques pour mettre en valeur de riches ressources en poissons, encore largement inexploitées et relativement proches de leurs côtes. En contrepartie de leur collaboration au développement, les partenaires d'outre-mer ont l'occasion d'accroître leurs ventres de produits de la pêche qui, par ailleurs, peuvent être obtenus à meilleur marché grâce à l'utilisation des installations et de la main d'oeuvre locales. Bien qu'il existe une complémentarité fondamentale d'intérêts entre les partenaires, des problèmes peuvent se poser – lors de l'élaboration et de l'application de l'accord concernant l'entreprise commune – en ce qui concerne le financement, la gestion, des questions techniques et autres. Le document examine les clauses essentielles relatives aux inputs matériels, à la technologie, à la main d'oeuvre, etc. dans les contrats halieutiques types, et propose des principes à suivre lors des négociations. Les buts visés consistent à minimiser les possibilités de différends et à faciliter la conclusion de compromis. Des avis sont adressés aux gouvernements et aux entreprises de pêche quant aux mesures propres à encourager la constitution d'entreprises communes. Des renseignements détaillés sont fournis sur les activités et projets d'organisations régionales et internationales, dont la FAO, visant à apporter des informations et une assistance en liaison avec la négociation et la mise en oeuvre d'arrangements relatifs à des entreprises communes.

El papel de las empresas conjuntas en el establecimiento de industrias pesqueras

Hay un amplio campo para la expansión de empresas conjuntas pesqueras debido al gran número de países en desarrollo que necesitan la aportación de capital y de técnicas para la explotación de los valiosos recursos pesqueros, aun en gran parte inexplotados, y relativamente próximos a sus costas. A cambio de su colaboración en el desarrollo, las empresas ultramarinas tienen la posibilidad de aumentar sus ventas de productos pesqueros que, por añadidura, pueden producirse con menos costo merced a la utilización de las instalaciones y de la mano de obra locales. Pese al fundamental carácter complementario de intereses entre los consocios, es probable que surjan problemas, al redactar y llevar a la práctica el acuerdo de la empresa conjunta, en lo que se refiere a financiación, administración, aspectos técnicos y de otra índole. El texto examina las clausulas esenciales acerca de insumos materiales, tecnología, mano de obra, etc., en los contratos pesqueros típicos y propone normas para las negociaciones. Los objetivos que se persiguen son: reducir la posibilidad de conflictos y facilitar los compromisos. Se señalan orientaciones a los gobiernos y a las empresas pesqueras sobre la manera de concertar empresas conjuntas. Se dan detalles acerca de las actividades y proyectos de organizaciones nacionales e internacionales, incluso la FAO, con la finalidad de suministrar información y asistencia para la negociación y ejecución de acuerdos sobre empresas conjuntas.

The FAO International Conference on Fishery Management and Development, held in Vancouver in February 1973, noted that, of a potential global increase in fish supplies from the seas of some 56 million tons, as much as 60 per cent, or 35 million tons, might be derived from tropical waters, a fact of particular significance to the developing countries of the tropical zone. Substantial savings can also be made through the reduction of spoilage losses through improved processing. This opportunity for fisheries development can, in general, only be seized by the adoption, in the developing countries, of modern fisheries technologies on an industrial scale, requiring very substantial inputs of both capital and technical and managerial expertise, presently only available in the more advanced fishing nations. A high degree of international cooperation will be needed to effect this transfer, and at the present time, most of the FAO, UNDP and international bank programmes in fisheries are directed to this end. However, a very substantial part of the progress made in recent years has come through direct, operational collaboration between experienced firms from the developed nations and governments or private companies in the developing countries, as partners in joint fishery ventures. This paper discusses the general features of such ventures in the light of recent experience.

INTEREST CONFLICTS IN JOINT VENTURES

There are two main types of joint venture, one, 'contractual joint ventures', where the partners agree to pursue a joint objective without the creation of a mutually-owned enterprise, and the other 'equity joint ventures', where a jointly-owned common enterprise is formed. The former is commonly more limited in scope, usually providing for technical expertise from the developed partners rather than scarce capital inputs, and is sometimes used as a preliminary step toward the formation of a joint equity enterprise, which is by far the most common form of joint venture. Not all governments are desirous or willing to foster the creation of joint fisheries ventures, either because of their political philosophies, or on general fiscal grounds, or, on more specifically fishery considerations, to preserve their natural resources for exploitation by nationals exclusively. In such cases they seek to obtain necessary inputs through multilateral agencies and international banks, or by bilateral intergovernmental arrangements. The development of overseas markets often necessitates the participation of foreign partners. But foreign partners are rarely interested in forming joint ventures from purely altruistic motives, though these may play a part. In general, specific commercial benefits are sought from the arrangement. It is therefore of primary importance that there should be a sufficient complementarity of interest between the partners, whether government or private company, and also that the basic motivation of each should be understood by the other so that areas of divergent or conflicting interest are well understood beforehand.

If the foreign enterprise, for instance, is primarily interested in gaining access to valuable resources, such as shrimp, for delivery to its processing establishments overseas or to supply a foreign market, and to a lesser extent in maximizing the return on the capital invested in the fishery, it may prefer a venture based on vessel rather than shore operations and may be inclined to use vessels designed for other areas and fisheries rather than create a local fleet specifically adapted to local conditions. This desire to maintain 'mobility' and to economize on capital expenditures can be explained by its evaluation of the risks associated with the uncertainty of future resources conditions and political developments. Even where all partners in the joint venture are private enterprises, the government is often heavily involved by providing – or guaranteeing – loan finance which permits a high gearing to the equity participation and tends to raise rates of return on the equity capital, both foreign and local, invested. 'In view of the general shortage of investment funds in relation to the needs of development . . . government must have regard to the efficiency of the investment as a whole, ie the return on total capital invested, particularly as most of it involves a substantial foreign exchange cost. For this reason, it is important that . . . (it) ensures, not only that the project is sound in the financial sense, but also that it represents an optimal solution in the sector concerned' (Campleman, G., personal communication).

COMPARATIVE STANDPOINTS OF LOCAL AND FOREIGN INTERESTS IN JOINT VENTURES

Factors influencing the foreign partners' decision

Several inquiries have been made into the factors which motivate the partners in joint fishery ventures. A sample of multinational companies recently responded to an FAO inquiry, and the following were the more important considerations affecting a decision to participate:

(1) Opportunities to participate in fishing operations from which they would otherwise have been barred.

(2) Opportunities for exploiting attractive foreign – expanding domestic – markets.

(3) Creating a base for the establishment, locally, of related industrial activities ('multiplier' effect of fisheries operations).

(4) Acquisition of skills useful for running other types of operations in the foreign country, through observation of the way the local partner deals with business problems ('cross-fertilization' of experience).

(5) A partner's knowledge of local business practices and ease of communication with him, because of common ethnic background.

(6) Existence of good infrastructure facilities or of a pool of labour that can easily adapt itself or be trained for the fishery operations to be undertaken.

(7) Flexibility of meeting staffing requirements, because reliance on local partner's employees made it easier to deal with problems of redundancy in case of a change of business fortunes for the worse.

(8) Promotional assistance offered by input industries conscious of opportunities for opening up new markets.

(9) Host government incentives affecting foreign investments and joint ventures in particular.

(10) The possibility of securing better 'political treatment' for one's foreign operations.

(11) Special concessions or monopoly rights obtained from the host government.

(12) Support from the government of the country in which the multinational company is domiciled and from regional and international financial and development assistance agencies.

Conversely, lack of the above opportunities and official restrictions on foreign investment, capital and profits repatriation, and joint ventures, were principal factors inhibiting the development of such arrangements. The Japanese experience, as described in publications (Anon, 1971a), and the 1969 FAO International Conference on Investment in Fisheries (FAO, 1970a), suggests the following principal problem areas to be considered:

(1) Political and economic instability.

(2) Risks of nationalization and foreign exchange restrictions.

(3) Lack of social capital and infrastructure.

(4) Difference of institutions and customs.

(5) Inadequate pre-investment information on social and economic conditions in the developing country (both sides appear to be at fault, the capital-importing country for withholding necessary information, and the foreign investors for failing to brief themselves adequately).

(6) Initiation of projects on the basis of inadequate or over-optimistic appraisals of the resources potential.

(7) Over-ambitious scope – or excessive speed in implementation – of projects (due to the developing country's desire for a rapid bridging of gaps).

(8) Lack of effective communications in joint ventures between the foreign and the local partner (often due to differences in mentality and outlook rather than lack of good intentions).

(9) Excessive competition between projects of similar aims and character (failure on the part of foreign investors to take into account initiation of similar activities by other companies, and failure on the part of the developing country to establish controls on the number of ventures authorized to exploit specific resources).

(10) Unforeseen or unforeseeable changes in the general economic and social structure of a developing country.

Other sources have referred to:

(1) The carving up of ocean areas for which government fishing licences are granted into zones too small for successful operations.

(2) The high cost of the preliminary survey to establish feasibility of operations.

(3) Difficulties connected with attracting expatriate staff to take employment in remote areas.

(4) High turnover rates among local crews and excessive costs of hiring and training crews in the implementation of projects.

(5) Difficulties in local procurement of equipment essential for fishery operations.

(6) Food consumption habits increasing difficulties in developing local markets for fishery products.

(7) Assumption by the host government of responsibilities for certain activities which would be of direct commercial interest to the joint venture.

(8) Bureaucratic procedures and excessive costs associated with import of equipment, the obtaining of permits and licences, and the compliance with local regulations.

In spite of these problems, there are strong indications that the trend toward the formation of fishery ventures will continue. The 1971 edition of the Japanese Fisheries Yearbook gives the following explanations:

(1) Increased Japanese demand for fish, particularly for quality fish.

(2) Stagnant Japanese coastal fisheries.

(3) Shortage of fishing labour in Japan.

(4) Rise of production cost in Japanese fisheries.

(5) Expansion of territorial waters and fishing zones by many foreign countries.

(6) Intensified international regulations and control and, at the same time, an increase in requests for Japanese

cooperation, as developing countries seek to develop fisheries to increase animal protein supplies and employment opportunities.

Factors influencing the local partners' decision

In general, the benefits of close association with experienced foreign partners are well appreciated in most of the developing countries, despite an attitude of caution induced by some past experiences.

At the 1969 FAO International Conference on Investment in Fisheries representatives from the developing countries suggested the following principal objections to many proposals for joint ventures:

(1) Failure to adhere to the terms of the joint venture agreement.

(2) Failure to include elements essential for effective operations, eg provisions for the procurement of spare parts.

(3) Stringent repayment terms of loan agreements.

(4) Contractual oblications for high wage payments in foreign exchange to expatriate crews and fee payments on management contracts of a fixed amount rather than made dependent on economic results of operations.

(5) Reluctance on the part of foreign crews to train local men.

(6) Provision of equipment unsuitable for local operations, eg vessels which cannot be accommodated in existing port facilities or vessels equipped with unserviceable engines.

(7) Readiness to enter into agreements with corrupt local officials (although such 'deals' may have advantages in the short run, they are likely to jeopardize operations in the longer run).

(8) Unfair exploitation of the lack of business acumen of local partners.

(9) Failure to make clear to local interests what were the implications on costs of operations of the following: procurement of spare parts abroad, repairs which cannot be carried out in the country, fluctuations in market prices of requisites which must be imported, etc.

(10) Excessive length of the surveys carried out by the foreign partner prior to start of commercial exploitation and/or conduct of commercial operations under the guise of a 'survey', to escape sharing benefits with the local partner.

(11) Interference of joint venture operations with a local, traditional fishery.

(12) Provision of services or incorporation of operations in the joint venture which compete with an already established local business.

(13) Excessive charges for services rendered or unrealistic costing of equipment provided, and other practices engaged in by foreign partners to run down profits and obtain excessive benefits during the life of the venture.

CONFLICT RESOLUTION IN JOINT VENTURE NEGOTIATIONS

There are substantial areas for differences of interest in the negotiation of joint fishery ventures as in other business activities. The primary requirement is that the partners' essential objectives are not mutually exclusive over the period of the joint venture. Given this, the secondary issues of whether the expected benefits are worth the necessary concessions can be established through the bargaining process in the negotiation stage. It is therefore of the greatest importance that the objective facts of the case, eg the extent of the resource, the size of the proposed market, the technical options available, are established and agreed between the interested partners at the beginning. Equally, as mentioned earlier, each partner should understand, through frank discussions and private analysis, the basic motivation and objectives of the other. If these considerations indicate the desirability and feasibility of a joint venture, attention may be given to the practical details of an agreement. Some of the major problem areas in the organization and operation of joint ventures are discussed in detail in the following section.

Companies which have had occasion to participate in international fishery ventures stress that the choice of a partner is of crucial importance for success. This view is shared also by developing countries which have come to recognize that a more judicious selection of partners could have avoided unfortunate experiences. Where private initiative has not yet been sufficiently developed in such countries to allow effective participation in joint ventures, or where development plans are shaped in accord with political considerations, the government itself or a parastatal development corporation may invest in joint-venture equity, provide loan financing, exercise some management or supervisory control or a combination of these. On the capital-exporting side, too, government influence may in some instances, be quite far-reaching, and may include controls over private enterprise participation and the finances and equipment inputs to be made available to joint ventures, as in Japan where government is virtually a 'silent' partner. Centrally-planned countries, exporting capital and skills which have formed special state-financed and controlled entities empowered to make arrangements for international collaboration in development activities, may go as far as to become active partners. On the whole, one source (Friedmann and Kalmanoff, 1961) concludes, direct participation of governments or government-controlled institutions is of far less impact on joint venture development than policy-directing action which 'may find many expressions, through allocation of raw materials, import quotas, currency regulations, negotiations on the purchase of land for factory sites, remission of earnings for foreign personnel to their home country, labour permits and a multitude of other legal and administrative measures'. Silent o ractive government partnership often has the tendency to produce competitive advantages, in respect to material allocations, tax treatment, privileges granted, etc, vis-à-vis enterprises which are exclusively financed and operated by private capital. On the negative side of the ledger, one could mention the conflicts which are likely to arise between public and private partners because of different philosophies of management, different policies on the reinvestment of profit, and different social attitudes. These types of problems are encountered in any kind of joint venture, although they are perhaps more common in a venture in which both the public and private enterprise are represented. The pros and cons of public participation can be assessed only in relation to a particular case and, in a general way, not much more can be said than that the private partner(s) in a 'mixed' joint venture usually have little or no discretion over choosing or rejecting a public partner. Where private enterprises are involved, the problem of choosing the right partner is probably easier to solve for the partner in the capital-importing country, since many of the potential overseas partners are multinational enterprises with an internationally known history and reputation. Even if the overseas partner is relatively unknown, there are, in the major capital-exporting countries, numerous published business reference sources, not to speak of chambers of commerce, better business bureaus, and the like, which can be consulted to fill gaps in information.

In a study summarizing joint venture experience, Business International (Anon), concludes that in searching out potential partners, it is very useful 'to examine what *other* things the potential partner (especially if it is a major corporation) does, beyond the specific area of possible collaboration. By looking at the entire range of others' activities, and stacking them up against the entire range of one's own businesses, both sides can obtain a clearer understanding of the other, what their goals and operations are. It helps either sharpen the basic mutuality of interests or bring to light potential areas of conflict. Further, it can open up from the outset the possibility of later expanded cooperation into new product lines.' A growing number of international joint ventures in fisheries – a review of agreements concluded in recent years shows – is constituted by more than two partners. The meshing of divergent interests becomes more complicated when several rather than two enterprises only are associated. The problem, however, may be solved by conferring the management responsibility on one of the parties. Distinct advantages can be gained, in individual instances, from a larger number of participants, for the following reasons: through the provision of specialized skills and services (fishery ventures with Japanese enterprises, for instance, often benefit from the participation of both widely experienced fishing companies and trading firms), the spreading of the financial burdens and business risks connected with operating the overseas venture among additional partners, and the strengthening – by the aggregation of larger resources – of the competitive position of the joint venture versus other enterprises. The advantages that can be derived from the establishment of international consortia for certain types of fishery operations were emphasized by one of the respondents to the joint venture inquiry of the Department of Fisheries previously mentioned. There is a technical advantage in terms of the opportunity to procure different types of equipment from the countries with specialized production facilities and there are financial benefits too: 'In view of the high cost of a complete project which may range from the construction of a complete fishing port to that of a fishmeal plant – the total cost on credit can only be met by bringing together . . . (several) lines of finance on offer. Quite apart from spreading the risk – in some cases (only) the totalling up of a number of credit limits permits the scheme to get off the ground at all.' From a political standpoint, too, there is much to be gained: 'In the developing world, any enterprise concerned with the production of major food supplies is necessarily highly charged with politics. For this reason, it is political dynamite to permit a situation in which foreign interests have absolute or majority control of a good part of the nation's protein . . . adverse reaction does not arise when the industrialization or development is seen to be divided between various foreign suppliers whose governments cannot by any stretch of the imagination be thought to be in collusion for sinister political motives . . .'.

MAJOR PROBLEM AREAS IN THE ORGANIZATION AND OPERATION OF JOINT FISHERY VENTURES

The negotiation of a basic understanding

Having satisfied themselves on the feasibility of the project, its desirability in terms of overall plans for growth and the partner(s) 'eligibility' for collaboration in its execution, the parties contemplating a joint venture will try to come to a preliminary understanding. A 'memorandum of understanding' might cover, in general terms, nature, scope, and location of activities to be carried out, duration of the partnership, financing, facilities to be utilized and management. Initially, each partner may envisage a range of activities wider than what is ultimately agreed. The foreign company, for instance, may want to take advantage of the off-season in the fishery which is to be developed by the venture to engage in other fishing or, in a tuna baitboat fishery, may want to use its boats to fish for bait to have control over bait supplies. The host government, on the other hand, may be unwilling to permit a branching out into other fisheries, since this might jeopardize the livelihood of fishermen engaged in these fisheries. Host governments may want to promote joint ventures with a view toward fully integrated operations (for the development of specialized operations, eg involving development of a new fishery, they might prefer to engage consultant services, rather than form a special partnership). The foreign company, however, may not want to agree on the establishment of local facilities which compete for supplies with facilities it already owns elsewhere or because it feels that local handling and processing would cancel out economic advantages it expects from participation in the venture. A special problem arises where an alternative exists of carrying out operations at sea or on land. A determination of what is preferable on techno-economic grounds requires, for each case, a careful analysis of resources aspects, capital investment and expected operational costs. Many times, however, the host country's long-run interests are (because of important social benefits) served best if shore facilities are established, even if – under alternative arrangements – the production and deliveries abroad, from factory- and mothership operations, were to be strictly controlled so as to ensure that the local partners received their share of the profits. Agreements envisaging a start of operations with motherships, therefore, usually contain clauses for their phased withdrawal and replacement by shore operations.

The selection of areas and locations for the establishment of facilities and operations is one of the important facets of preliminary survey work. Modern management tends to evaluate the benefits and drawbacks of various sites in broad terms, using manpower, government and finance, 'livability' (amenities for foreign staff, climate etc), and communications and facilities considerations as yardsticks. Some international companies have gone as far as to establish a weighted value index for these factors which they use for decision-making. Where nature or government limits the areas in which joint ventures are allowed to operate, the location of facilities may be more or less predetermined. There may be, for instance, only one or two sites suitable for harbour use or construction. The stipulation in the joint venture contract of a concession area may be of benefit to the project as long as it is accompanied by certain privileges related, for instance, to exclusive operations. Where the area limitation impedes mobility, however, it may result in a net disadvantage. In one country where international joint fishery ventures have been tied to 'concession areas', national companies engaged in similar operations are reported to enjoy greater freedom of action, since they have the possibility of shifting their fishing seasonally from one part of the country to another (Kristjonsson, H., personal communication).

Exclusive or monopoly privileges may relate to other aspects of joint venture operations besides geography, such as rights to engage in specific activities, allocation of materials, fiscal concessions, product marketing, product distribution areas, etc. There is no categorical answer on whether or not these privileges are necessary for successful operations, justified or objectionable on 'moral grounds'. The classical objections to monopoly, that it leads to neglect of cost savings and to abuses of power, raises prices to the public, and prevents entry of potential – more efficient, more cost-conscious – competitors, do not always apply. To induce an enterprise to assume the risks associated with the development of a new fishery, the same protection may have to be offered as for other 'infant industries'. As far as developing countries, in particular, are concerned, there is good ground for supporting the infant industry argument as long as net social benefits are deemed greater than those which could be attained by techno-economically feasible alternative investments. Additional reasons for justifying privileges on the fishing side are connected with the common property character of marine fishery resources. Limitation of entry is today more or less generally acknowledged as one of the essential measures for rational resources management. In the absence of restrictions, vessel productivity may sink to a point where the enterprise cannot break even. This is the main reason why potential foreign partners for joint venture operations demand protection from 'excessive competition'. There is, of course, a difference between placing a ceiling on the total number of ventures authorized and the granting of monopoly status. Clauses on fishing privileges in joint venture agreements, it is suggested, should take into account: (a) the degree of incentive required for a pioneer venture; (b) if sufficient knowledge of stock is available, the potential for economic expansion of the fishing effort; and (c) the time period for which inducements or protection need to be provided. If the duration of the venture is likely to extend from the infant to the maturity stage of the fishery, the contract may stipulate a point of time at which the matter of exclusive privileges is to be reviewed. In general, to forestall potential conflicts, all privileges with respect to operational monopolies, areas, taxes, etc, should be spelled out, and duration as well as conditions under which they become invalid carefully specified. As far as fiscal incentives are concerned, these are usually set down in the host country's investment legislation. Nevertheless, it will be desirable – or necessary, if the conditions applicable to the venture depart in some way from statutory provisions – to detail them in the contract.

In many joint ventures, the complementarity of interests between partners, which motivates the original decision to collaborate, is expected to be of temporary rather than permanent nature. With the passage of time, the host country partner is expected to acquire sufficient financial and skill resources to assume full responsibility for the enterprise, while the foreign partner will have achieved his business objective and will be ready to withdraw. As a rule, therefore, the joint venture contract stipulates the number of years for which the partners agree to engage and do business, sometimes adding a proviso that the contract, subject to host government approval, may be continued by mutual agreement of the partners. Often, a gradual withdrawal of the foreign partner is envisaged, with agreed dates for the transfer of parts of the equity, physical assets and management control until complete 'naturalization' of the enterprise is achieved. Setting an appropriate term for the contract is not always an easy matter, since the partners most probably have different time spans in mind in appraising requirements for satisfying their objectives. The local partner may tend to be optimistic with respect to the time it will take him to be able to stand on his own feet. Local pressure for a term that appears too short for accomplishing what the joint venture has set out to attain may make the foreign partner want to limit his commitment, insofar as it may discourage him from helping in the establishment of permanent shore facilities, or – in the extreme case – make him decide to withdraw from the venture. Setting a period that may be excessively long, on the other hand, also has its drawbacks, unless provisions for periodic review of the terms of the contract are incorporated. Without such provisions, the incentive to achieve the goals within the established terms of the business plan might be lessened. Difficulties may be avoided if the other provisions of the contract (relating to capitalization, material inputs, manpower, etc) are specific on the time periods within which 'naturalization' (transfer of ownership or responsibilities) is to take place. Sometimes, the term of the joint venture agreement is more or less 'predetermined' by the duration of privileges or concessions accorded to the venture by the government, since continuation of the business without them may be unprofitable. Difficulties in reaching agreement on the nature of operations to be carried out, on financing, management, etc, are at times so insurmountable that negotiations have to be cut off before a memorandum of understanding is signed.

Drafting the contract terms

Where a basic understanding has been reached, the document is usually subject to approval by higher authority (top management of the foreign company and the government of the host country before a detailed contract for the joint venture is drawn up). Success in matching the interests of the partners in the writing of the contract depends very much on the thoroughness of preparatory work. Often, however, the extent to which the contract meets the individual partner's aims is a reflection of relative bargaining power. Bargaining is a natural feature of any business transaction involving the transfer of goods and services (know-how and skills, fishing concessions, etc) for which no fixed prices are established. What both sides must not forget in the bargaining process is that there are limits beyond which demands for concessions become unreasonable, when the other party will be inclined – or even forced – to break off negotiations. The art of business negotiating really is not much more than a guessing game concerning these limits. Beyond that, what is required for bargaining is flexibility, a willingness to modify one's position when terms appear clearly unacceptable to the other party, and good legal assistance to eliminate possibilities of ambiguous interpretation once agreement has been reached.

There are two schools on the subject of legal assistance in joint venture negotiations. In the view of one expert, who has had considerable experience in negotiating and establishing joint ventures, 'the very best legal advice is the cheapest' (Appleyard, W. P., personal communication), and both developing and developed countries are well advised to consult only the most experienced international lawyers, since the ordinary company or family lawyer is lost in this field. According to another view, expressed by one of the companies contacted in connexion with the Department of Fisheries' inquiry on joint venture operations, attempts to draw up 'fully comprehensive legal agreements between partners in different countries can lead to endless delays and frustrations. In the end, mutual trust, and a willingness to take some risks are needed, and no amount of legal activity will alter this.' The two statements are not necessarily contradictory. The degree to which reliance can be placed on 'mutual trust' depends on success in the choice of a partner. In some instances, the field of condidates (fulfilling qualifications with respect to capital, know-how or other support they can provide) from whom to choose may be quite limited. On the other hand, the number of experienced international law firms available for negotiating a joint venture may not be large or the cost of employing them may be out of proportion to the marginal benefits that might be gained from concluding a somewhat more favourable contract. As a general rule, the importance of clear and precise phraseology and the precision of time elements as well as of stating, in unambiguous terms, all special conditions, exceptions relevant for the interpretation of the contract clauses cannot be enough emphasized. Although not always unavoidable, certain phrases, eg, 'as soon as practicable', 'will depend on results', 'at the market price' (as long as no explanation is given on how this price is to be determined), etc, are likely to be interpreted differently by the partners and constitute, in some ways 'built-in germs' of conflict.

Contract clauses on material inputs

Joint fisheries ventures have experienced problems, or have failed in some instances, because the contracts did not define in sufficiently precise terms the type of equip-ment to be employed in the conduct of operations, the time schedule for its creation, provisions for the procurement of spare parts, etc. In some instances, contracts have failed to spell out arrangements for ensuring that equipment acquired by the joint venture corresponds to what has been stipulated. Local partners and host governments often insist on playing a role in drawing up specifications for the physical inputs of the joint venture, as foreign partners sometimes have been blamed for providing equipment of the wrong type or of unsatisfactory quality. Where local staff with the requisite skills for the technical and financial appraisal of needs is available, this participation would seem not only appropriate but desirable; where not, the economic health of the venture may be in jeopardy from the start if a local partner's unrealistic ideas on serviceability and costs were to prevail. Lack of expertise can be made up by reliance on consultant services, which might be procured, among other means, by requesting technical assistance by international agencies. While such agencies might not be in a position to arbitrate in cases where the suitability of equipment is under dispute, they should be able, at least, to provide expert counsel. Complaints by local interests with regard to facilities and machinery provided by overseas partners quite frequently relate to 'age' or 'suitability for employment in the local setting' (including the possibility of it being properly operated and maintained by local staff). Sometimes the motivation of foreign partners in providing 'secondhand' equipment – or in other cases, providing overly expensive or unnecessarily advanced or difficult-to-operate equipment – is questioned, and they are suspected of wanting to profit at the expense of local partners. There is no standard answer to the question whether, for instance, 'secondhand' or 'modern' fishing vessels or fish-processing equipment should be employed, since a feasibility study is required to decide what is better suited to achieve the economic and social objectives of the venture. If the products are to be competitive in the export market, and if, in the processes to be employed, opportunities for substitution of labour for material inputs are limited, circumstances may dictate the use of technically up-to-date facilities and methods. Secondhand equipment, on the other hand, often can be made available much more speedily and is likely to be much less costly. Under some circumstances, furthermore, acquisition of new equipment might be precluded by the impossibility of obtaining an allocation or by onerous customs duties. Under normal circumstances, if the value of the assets to be contributed to the joint venture are realistically determined, and if the foreign company is sure that it can maintain a significant equity interest and stable returns from its investment over a longer period of time, there should be no problem about the equipment. There is a need to agree on provisions ensuring that the assets contributed to the joint venture are valued in accordance with commonly accepted accounting standards. It also seems desirable to have the foreign partner acquire more than a token part of joint venture shares entitled to dividends to make sure he has a genuine interest in increasing profits.

Procedures for establishing the value of assets have to take into account the fashion in which they are being created. Where facilities are being constructed, the valuation procedure should include indications on how adherence to technical specifications and costs are to be checked. For already created assets that are to be transferred to the venture, the services of professional inspection and appraisal companies might be engaged. Special care has to be taken in capitalizing contributions of intangible assets, such as goodwill, because of substantial pre-emptive claims on future profits that can be established this way by the partner contributing such assets. Where assets are placed at the disposition of the joint venture on a loan basis or where, for example, fishing vessels are chartered for a given period, excessive charges against income might arise, through inflation of the loan value represented by the assets, stipulation of interest rates that are higher than those that would normally be applicable on loans of this type, and the charging of charter fees above prevailing levels. Unless commonly acknowledged standards for fixing the value of the assets or charges exist (eg, published information in equipment prices, charter fees, etc), advice may have to be obtained from experts or, alternatively, the partners may want to agree on the selection of a professional appraisal service. Attention must also be paid to the time factor in drafting the equipment clauses of the agreement. Many contracts foresee a phased installation of facilities, with the original fishing vessel input, for example, to be increased by specified numbers of additional vessels after a certain number of years until the fleet reaches the size agreed in the investment plan. Achievement of specified results by a given point of time or fulfilment of certain conditions may be prerequisites for the completion of the investment plan, eg, where the contract stipulates that construction of shore facilities is predicated on the results of a fishing survey that extends for an agreed time period. If the initial fishing operations are carried out with chartered vessels, the contract may indicate a time schedule for replacing them with vessels to be contributed by the foreign partner or with vessels bought with the earnings of the venture. Time schedules may be agreed also for the withdrawal of motherships and their substitution with shore facilities. Specific indications of time are desirable with respect to commencement of operations or utilization of the facilities and equipment of the joint venture and the dates of transfer of ownership if a venture is to be gradually 'naturalized'. Some contracts provide for penalties if facilities to be contributed by one of the partners are not put into operation in accordance with the agreed time schedule, in an attempt to forestall delays in delivery detrimental to the achievement of business objectives. Additional contract clauses may detail conditions applying to the expansion of facilities created on formation of the joint venture. While some agreements may say no more on that score than that the venture is entitled to expand its physical plant to a certain size, other agreements may actually obligate the foreign partner to increase, for instance, his fishing fleet investment if and when the catch per vessel reaches a certain level. This is to prevent a venture with exclusive fishing rights from not taking full advantage of opportunities to exploit an, as yet, underfished resource.

Some agreements place restrictions on the source of supply of assets to be originally contributed to, or in the course of operations to be acquired by, the joint venture.

Host countries often have serious misgivings about contracts which obligate the venture to acquire physical inputs from one exclusive source, usually one owned or controlled by the foreign partner. If the transfer prices are high in relation to generally prevailing prices, and if the supplier's stake in joint venture profits is comparatively small, they tend to suspect the foreign company of being interested mainly in selling equipment rather than in collaborating in development activities. In a similar fashion, foreign companies may object to clauses obligating the venture to rely on local sources of supply, eg, local shipbuilders, if there is substantial danger that the venture might not be able to absorb the additional burdens of high cost local operations and unreliable delivery. Sometimes equipment provisions of joint venture contracts include restrictive clauses on utilization. Host governments, for instance, may want to make sure that certain objectives of development policy will not be neglected, by having the partners agree that a part of the fleet that is to be operated will be engaged exclusively in fishing for home market supplies. In some instances, they may make the approval of export operations with prospects of high profits, conditional on acceptance of this clause. For joint ventures that are heavily dependent on foreign-supplied equipment, provisions for the supply of spare parts and foreign assistance in maintenance are essential. Contract clauses should be as specific on this point as for the equipment itself, detailing type, quality, size of inventory, nature and location of storage of parts as well as staff availability for maintenance operations. Whenever one of the partners has a financial interest in material considered as important items of running costs (eg, fuel, freight, ice), the contract should prescribe a procedure for determining quantitative needs and prices, to make sure the supplier cannot bilk the joint venture through overstocking it or through charging excessively high prices.

Another subject that should be covered is the role of government in ownership, procurement, control, fiscal operations, etc. If the government has a direct or indirect (through provisions of loan funds) interest in the assets, it may want to take part in the choice of equipment or as a minimum, in the verification of its technical suitability for the operations contemplated. How to go about exercising this techno-economic control in fishery projects has been described in an FAO study published in 1962 (FAO, 1962). Where new facilities are being constructed for the venture, the government may reserve its right to insist on changes in specifications and to carry out inspections during the building period, and may want to make the granting of credits and other facilites for the venture conditional on certification by inspectors that the standards have been met. The government can be expected to have a role in insurance and guarantee schemes affecting assets owned by – or made available through credit to – the joint venture. The agreement should identify the assets protected in this manner and describe the character, magnitude, amounts insured or guaranteed, duration, cost (insurance premiums) and collateral or surety arrangements associated with the extension of such facilities. Wherever applicable, the contract should be explicit also on special facilities offered by the government in respect to importation of equipment and materials required by the venture, indicating their character, quantities to which applicable, concessionary tariffs or exemptions, and duration of privileges. Details should be provided also in the contract, where government controls exist, on allocations of foreign exchange or of scarce materials to the joint venture.

Considerations on production technology

The type of technology used by a joint venture is, to a large extent, predetermined by the material and man-power inputs at the disposition of the enterprise. Host governments, may want to influence decisions on the employment of these inputs in various ways, by reserving for themselves, for example, contractual rights to approve the selection of fishing rquipment and tech-niques, establishing criteria for their selection, or actually taking on responsibilities for their choice, and by assuming various degrees of initiative also in the man-power field. In contrast, there are joint venture agree-ments involving transfer of equipment and technology from foreign countries where the host country has no choice but to accept a given type of technology. This situation has been examined in a monograph published by the United Nations in 1972. Elsewhere (UN, 1972b), the same study suggests policies host governments may pursue to remedy this situation:

Joint fishery ventures have contributed their share to situations where the wrong type of equipment – or of unnecessarily complicated or costly equipment – has been introduced because of a lack of knowledge of what was suitable for local conditions or because of a foreign company's preference for making profits on equipment sales rather than on the transactions of the joint venture. Yet, frequently the other side also has a legitimate complaint concerning problems related to the transfer of technology. One of the respondents to the FAO Department of Fisheries' joint venture inquiry points out that local partners tend to underestimate the value, from an operational standpoint, of the technology intro-duced and, as a consequence, are unwilling to pay the proper price (in the form of royalties on patents, per-mission to capitalize know-how, contribution to the financing of training programmes, etc) and to think that it is unreasonable to pay for technology made available by the overseas partner. Nor are governments always free from blame, since some countries continue to neglect protection of industrial property rights. The foreign partner can find ways and means of protecting his interests relative to the introduction of new technology. Joint venture contracts, as Business International (Anon.) points out, can be supplemented with licensing and management agreements that are written in such a way that the technology may be pulled back in case of serious disagreement. Licensing agreements giving one party an option to cancel at any time, on the other hand, would seem to be justified only where the abuse of rights to the utilization of technology threatens to cause serious damage to the partner who has introduced it. The number of cases in the fishery industry requiring special protec-tion for processes introduced is probably small. Still, there are situations where the safeguarding of industrial secrets may be a major, perhaps even the principal, concern in the working-out of an agreement. A report on an international joint venture in an Australian fishery

trade publication (Anon, 1971b) some time ago described the 'top-secret atmosphere' which surrounded the operations of the venture's pilot fish-processing factory which was trying to develop gourmet dishes for markets in the Far East: 'Much of the development work', it reported, 'is considered highly confidential because of the financial gains to be reaped from entering the export market on a large scale with such commodities as frozen squid, abalone and surimi . . .'.

Contract provisions relating to manpower

Joint venture contract provisions on manpower have to detail agreed plans for recruitment, utilization, training and, in due time, 'naturalization' of the work force. These plans will be influenced by provisions relating to the staff of joint ventures in investment codes and by labour legislation as well as, in general, institutional factors such as trade union policies in the host countries. Estimates of manpower to be recruited or assigned from the existing work force of the partners should be as specific as possible in regard to occupational and skill levels and numbers required. Time schedules for recruit-ment should take into account the desirability of avoiding operational bottlenecks due to non-availability of staff and, on the other hand, possible idleness because pre-parations for the launching of some operations have not been completed. In addition, they should pay regard to the availability of essential amenities for the staff, especially housing facilities and transportation to the work place, and to educational, recreational, and shopping facilities. Where such facilities are to be specifically created for the joint venture, the contract should provide the relevant detail.

Foreign and local partners may hold divergent views on manpower recruitment, especially where one or the other might stand to gain from assigning from his work force a larger number of staff or staff of higher rank or salary levels. A partner will not engage in a 'dumping' operation and will not burden operations with excessive labour costs if he has confidence in deriving profits over the long term from the venture. Sometimes the pressures to hire staff (especially at high levels of respon-sibility or salary), whose employment cannot be justified on operational grounds, originate with the host govern-ment. While the partners may, for political reasons, find it impossibile to resist such pressures, host governments must realize that the extra burdens they are imposing on the venture will run counter to any efforts of theirs to promote viable joint venture arrangements. Political influence on staffing, and government intervention in labour-management relations in general, are among the major obstacles to expansion of joint venture operations in developing countries. Statutory provisions may stipu-late that local employees must constitute a specified minimum percentage of the work force or that the employment of expatriates – sometimes classified by occupational and skill level – must be limited to certain percentages, that local staff must, for equal work, receive equal pay, and that the entire work force must be 'naturalized' within given periods of time, etc. While such limitations are generally justified, among other reasons, on grounds of a need to increase jobs for local staff or to reduce the drain on foreign exchange paid to expatriates, to avoid antagonisms from unequal treatment between co-workers, to accelerate transfer to local control, etc, they may lead to a loss of flexibility in operations serious enough to deter some foreign companies from entering into joint venture agreements. Such statutory provisions may disregard technical requirements, while 'equal pay' provisions may make it difficult, if not impossible, to induce qualified expatriate staff to accept employment if local scales are to be adopted. Again, if foreign scales are to prevail, it may make the entire venture uneconomic or create an élite of local employees who are overcompensated in relation to others performing similar work in other local enterprises. Provisions reflecting either government or labour organization policies which may be 'unpalatable', in some cases, for foreign partners, are restrictions on hours of work and on the dismissal of staff. Countries which have had no experience in fishing operations on an industrial scale should recognize that the peculiar nature of these operations precludes the adoption of fixed daily working hours such as followed in land-based enterprises. Curbs on – or extremely cumbersome administrative procedures connected with – the dismissal of workers also will involve sacrifices of efficiency which a joint venture cannot afford to make. Quite often, friction between local and expatriate employees arises from other causes such as food habits, standards of cleanliness, attitudes toward work, and through aspirations for economic improvement. These are likely to become major problems, particularly where people of various nationalities and of radically different backgrounds must work in constant close contact as, for example, on a fishing boat. These conflicts cannot be warded off by contractual provisions. Yet, the planners of joint ventures would be unwise if they failed to consider ways and means of preventing clashes, possibly by instituting internal arrangements on board ship or in plants, by staggering shore leaves for foreign crews, and by sponsorship of activities that will encourage people of different backgrounds to get to know each other and create a team spirit. Qualms about the suitability or efficiency of local labour may induce expatriate management to press for the institution of capital-intensive techniques. The latter in turn may be so complicated that opportunities for 'naturalization' of the work force become more remote than they were originally.

Many multinational companies welcome a local organization that can provide staff with a knowledge of local customs and business practices. Staff redundancy problems, among others, can be dealt with more easily, they feel, than in the case of expatriate staff that may have to be reabsorbed in the parent company after repatriation. Where advisable, and where acceptable to both partners, the expert knowledge the expatriate staff is to contribute can be made available by other means. Some joint fishery ventures, for instance, with French interests, include separate technical assistance agreements, under which overseas crew members are assigned to the ventures. In these cases, special arrangements may have to be made to continue the crews' social security protection, especially for French nationals, because of the particular character of the French system. In general, social security provisions and other conditions applying to recruitment, wages, working conditions, separation,

etc, of labour, are of such importance for the running of joint ventures, and often are so complicated, that they merit detailing in a subsidiary agreement or agreements where it is necessary to differentiate between conditions applying to local and to expatriate staff or between different categories of employees. Subsidiary agreements covering the employment of expatriate staff should detail, where applicable, the privileges and immunities granted under the host country legislation, home leave entitlements, transfer of funds and personal possessions between home and duty station, arrangements for housing, medical services, schooling facilities, etc, in order to provide a complete picture of working conditions for the benefit of the staff and, at the same time, indicate the limits of financial and other responsibilities of the employer.

The subject of training has an essential place in any discussion of manpower problems. For developing countries seeking to expand their fishery industries, training opportunities for local staff are a major objective. To accomplish their purpose, the contract provisions on training should be specific on the types of training to be carried out in the joint venture operations and on the additional training facilities available locally, the number of employees (by category and skill level) to be trained, length and content of training courses, allocation of the cost of training, and responsibilities to be assumed by employees who have successfully completed their training courses. Many host governments will be prepared to lend support to training programmes by making government facilities available on a cost-free basis, by providing subsistence for trainees, and in other ways. The joint venture's aim is to provide the best and most practical training at the lowest cost. On-the-job training on board ship or in processing plants is usually less expensive and produces faster results than any other form, especially for staff at levels of skill not requiring much academic instruction. Foreign companies, however, often complain that the training of unskilled cadres on the job has an adverse effect on the efficiency of, and consequently economic returns from, commercial operations. Even where they have agreed to provide on-the-job training, they often find ways and means of evading their obligations. Since the cost of providing special facilities, such as training vessels, is generally too high to be considered in a commercial venture, the partners should agree on some form of on-the-job training. The developing country will do well, in this connexion, to insist of specifying in the contract the arrangements keeping a check on the fulfilment of the obligations. Multinational companies and the governments of the countries in which they are domiciled sometimes find it worthwhile to extend the scope of training offered, so as to include instruction in matters not directly related to operational duties. Some even arrange visits abroad for the more promising trainees. One large Japanese fishery company, for example, has found that, to facilitate verbal communication, local crews should be encouraged to acquire some knowledge of the Japanese language. Crew members with good performance records are, therefore, given an opportunity to visit Japan whenever joint venture vessels are sent back there. Another Japanese company complains that the impact of training programmes is often lost because of shifts to other employment by workers who have completed training courses. This attitude is compared to that of Japanese labour who possess a strong sense of loyalty to their employers. One way of reducing such turnover is by emphasizing, in the description and in the follow-up of the programme, the promotion opportunities and increased salaries that may be available for successful graduates.

Decision on management control

Both host countries and multinational companies tend to overemphasize the importance of ownership in relation to management control. Some of the executives of multinational companies interviewed by Business International expressed the view that a minority partner has 'myriad ways' of frustrating the policies pursued by the majority partner if intent on so doing. The study concludes that, if at all possible, it is better to have both partners participating in management. While the type of joint venture involved, the availability of management talents, and the size of individual capital commitments largely determine whether or not this is feasible, the sharing of management responsibilities, and the 'becoming acquainted with each other's problems' that this entails, enhances the likelihood of overall common interest being served more adequately. To have local executives who are owners and not just professional managers, in the opinion of Business International, is often a definite advantage. 'Involved here', the monograph states, 'is the entire relationship of an individual to his own business as opposed to someone esle's: the local part owner will look at *all* aspects of the business as an entrepreneur, not merely as a functional speciality. In fact . . . one of the major reasons why developing countries frequently promote joint ventures is to develop a class of local entrepreneurs to help speed up industrialization and achieve greater political stability . . .' '. . . international companies . . . (in turn) . . . must make sure that responsibility for them (joint ventures) does not fall between chairs, and that joint ventures receive the kind of management support companies give their wholly owned subsidiaries.'

Multinational companies with experience in joint fishery ventures, the FAO inquiry shows, feel strongly about the need to obtain effective local management support. One company thought a local partner should accept management responsibilities in proportion to his equity ratio and complained about lack of a feeling of such responsibility by local partners who tend to insist on a majority shareholding, while leaving such responsibilities as locating sources of finance, sales promotion, and other entrepreneurial and management functions, to the overseas partner. Another problem faced by this company is the great shortage of local staff at the middle management level. Another respondent, in contrast, credits a major part of the success of its joint fishery ventures to the assistance of local partners in management. Wherever a partner can claim superiority of experience or is providing equipment and technology unfamiliar to his colleague, he will want to retain, at least for an initial period, essential management controls. This can be done by spelling out in the contract specific responsibilities assigned to him, as, for example, in design and construction facilities (vessel and plant), technical management of (fishing and processing) operations, and selection of key personnel. Some degree of management control may be retained even after a majority interest has gone, by amending the bylaws of the joint venture to give the minority holder certain rights, eg, the right to name the managing director. Other techniques applied to help the minority holder keep an influence on management decisions, referred to in the Business International study, include a stipulation on the bylaws themselves that they cannot be changed without a unanimous vote of the board of directors; and the issuance of two kinds of stock, both with equal dividend entitlements but one being non-voting, or issuance of stock with multiple voting rights for the minority holder, while the majority holder receives shares with single voting rights (and, possibly, preferential dividend rights). The problem of loss of management control may not even arise, of course, where the majority ownership is dispersed among a large number of shareholders who have little influence at the board level.

While there is a broad consensus that maximum advantage should be taken of a local partner's special knowledge of the local environment, opinions seem to be divided on the wisdom of fixing geographical boundaries in all managerial decision-making. One respondent to the FAO inquiry argues that the local partner 'should be charged with the responsibility for obtaining the fishing licence and all other necessary negotiations with the government . . . (he should also handle) the hiring of local employees, all matters pertaining to their wages, status, etc . . . so as to avoid any occurrence of racial problems'. Clearly, the local partner is best qualified to assume responsibility in these fields, although close political connexions, which may be useful at the time of the negotiation of the agreement, may have drawbacks in the long run, especially in countries with a marked degree of political instability. Another respondent, in contrast, reports on a joint fishery venture in which the local partner looked after all problems involving local contracts, local labour, and local purchases of fishery requisites while the foreign manager looked after all operating and technical problems (eg, the hiring of skippers, fitting-out of vessels, product packaging, and shipping and sales operations). This, in his view, was not a satisfactory arrangement. In particular, the circumstance that the local partner had no influence on sales operations, which were covered by a separate agreement, was a 'source of constant suspicion'. Where a strict division of responsibilities is agreed, friction can only be avoided, it seems, if the advice of another respondent is heeded that efforts should be made to avail oneself of 'every opportunity to keep . . . partners thoroughly informed on the state of operations in order to enjoy their fullest cooperation'.

Provisions relating to business operations

The contract should, as far as possible, outline particulars on how the joint venture intends to achieve its operational objectives and be specific also on relations with the host government, the foreign company, and non-affiliated private interests. Details of operational plans should be based on feasibility study information. Where such information is not yet available – as, for instance, with surveys for what are to be vertically integrated operations which have been limited so far only to the fishing sector – the contract might stipulate that plans for processing and distribution are to be incorporated at a later stage, upon completion of the necessary feasibility work. In similar fashion, expansion of operations in any one sector might be made contingent on a satisfactory assessment of results by stipulated control dates. In some instances, certain phases of operations, eg, purchasing, marketing, certain payments to government, are covered in detail in special agreements or are otherwise fixed, and projections do not present any difficulties as long as a good base for estimating catch volume exists. Catch, of course, is always the most difficult variable to take into account, especially if the venture does not have exclusive exploitation rights in a given zone and for a given period. Sometimes governments find it necessary, for resources protection, to impose ceilings on the annual total catch the joint venture is permitted to take. The number of fishing vessels allowed, too, may be fixed, based on assuming their average catching capacity. Controls of this sort should be reviewed periodically so as to ensure that ceilings do not constitute, if too low, unwarranted limitations on profit-making opportunities or, if too high, do not provide adequate safeguards for the resource. In a contractual venture, the relations between the partners are usually more complicated than in an equity venture. As a consequence, specific responsibilities assumed by each partner have to be spelled out in great detail and substantial additional record-keeping may be involved to determine the share in benefits and in cost burdens of each partner. The equity joint venture contract also must contain clauses to ensure that transactions between the joint venture and the parent company of the foreign partner are strictly commercial. Such transactions would include sales of services that may not be essential or excessive charges for them. For example, the chartering of vessels may be continued, although substitution by local vessels (with commensurate benefits to the host country economy outweighing eventual sacrifices in efficiency at the enterprise level) has become possible or charter fees may be charged which are significantly above world market levels. Other types of transaction are those where facilities owned by the joint venture are made available to the foreign company without – or without adequate – compensation. These situations, such as where ice, fuel, provisions, etc, are taken on locally by vessels belonging to the foreign company's home fleet, must be distinguished from those in which the joint venture or home country secures specific services (eg, reports on fish prospecting by the foreign fleet) or, in general, benefits from the business the home fleet gives it (eg, expenditures of the crews in the local ports). Prices charged to the foreign company on sales of products produced by the joint venture also need watching for unduly high discounts, although allowances should be made for transport, handling, and marketing services rendered by the foreign company as well as for volume business. Contractual commitments by the foreign company to purchase the entire production should be examined in the light of market conditions likely to prevail over the period covered by the agreement. Having an assured outlet for total output may not be preferable to having a choice of markets, especially in a period of rising demand and prices.

Once an equity joint venture has acquired its separate identity as a business enterprise, its transactions with the host government should be characterized by the same arm's length relationship that should apply to its relations with the parent company of the foreign partner, as long as the joint venture is in direct local competition with other enterprises. (A company with exclusive rights, on the other hand, is from its very beginning in a privileged position and may have additional benefits conferred upon it as far as its transactions with government are concerned, that is, as long as such preferment is considered in the economic and social interest of the country.) Just as, upon formation of the joint venture, the foreign partner is expected to compensate the host government, through his contribution of capital, skills and know-how, for privileges granted, the joint venture should normally be expected to pay at established prices for purchases from government stores and for special government services provided. Similarly, sales of products to the government should be made at prevailing market prices, with due regard to government services utilized in this connexion and to volume transactions, as in the case of sales to the parent company of the foreign partner. One of the most important services government can – but, alas, does not always – render to promote the smooth conduct of business of joint ventures, viz efficient administrative procedures, is provided without charge. In some developing countries, agreements concluded with central government authorities have at times failed to fulfil the promoters' expectations because of inadequate or complicated and time-consuming liaison and communications with local authorities which have immediate supervisory responsibilities where the operations are located. Reduction of red tape and improved coordination of action between government agencies is probably of greater importance for fishery joint ventures than for other business enterprises, since such a business is likely to be of concern to a larger number of administrative units.

Contract provisions covering relations with other enterprises than the parent companies of the partners and the government relate, for the most part, to suppliers and customers and actual or potential competitors. Such contracts, thus, may specify whether or not, and if yes, under what conditions: (a) the venture is permitted to buy fish from non-affiliated vessels, (b) partners' parent companies and the local government have priority rights with respect to others in the acquisition of joint venture products, (c) fixed assets of the venture can be disposed of to others than the partners or the government, etc. Restrictions that are too many or too tight may place management in a virtual straitjacket in decision-making and seriously crimp profit-making opportunities. Yet, frequently limitations of this sort can be defended on sound business or political grounds. A policy of buying from non-affiliated vessels (and, conversely, neglect of affiliated vessels), to take advantage of price fluctuations, for instance, may alienate the crews of the latter because of the effect on earnings under the share system and cause serious labour difficulties. Many foreign companies consider the prospect of increasing their fish supplies as the primary incentive for entering a joint venture, and depriving them of a preferential status as buyers might lead to a loss of interest in the venture (this does not mean that parent companies should be permitted to pay less than prevailing market prices). Similarly, in the disposal of assets, as in that of equity, promoters of the joint venture may legitimately claim rights of 'first refusal'. Host governments tend to intervene in the relations between the joint venture and 'third parties' either to protect the rights of competitors or of small-scale fisheries for which they feel a social responsibility. They try to protect the business of established local interests from interference by the operations of the joint venture and, where the venture has exclusive privileges limited in time, to protect fishery resources which at a future time may be exploited by nationals of the country. A government, for these purposes, may insist on the insertion of a clause in the contract obligating the venture to respect the rights and privileges of local fishermen and pledging it not to compete within the zone where the local fishermen exercise their profession, except if the national authorities find that limited participation of the joint venture is unlikely to harm the local fishery. In other instances, the joint venture may be persuaded by government insistence – or may actually spontaneously come to recognize the propaganda value of such action – to offer direct assistance to local fisheries by, for instance, supplementing its catches by purchases from local canoes or buying bait from the fishermen. Where government restricts bait fishing to local fishermen, the venture may actually find it in its own interest to give material and technical assistance to the bait fishery. In one such instance, a venture is providing nets and other equipment and is training volunteer fishermen to engage in bait fishing.

ACTION TO PROMOTE JOINT FISHERY VENTURES

Contributions by partners and interested governments to expansion of international partnership arrangements

Private enterprises which consider the joint venture as an appropriate arrangement for international collaboration can do nothing better for its promotion than to encourage the spirit of 'live and let live' that must be at the basis of any partnership. For the sake of maintaining the goodwill and wholehearted cooperation of their partners they must be prepared to make sacrifices, involving some surrender of management control and, not infrequently, some part of the potential profit from the business. Further, to ensure fruitful collaboration, partners must become acquainted with each other objectives and ways of doing business and must make an effort to stay in constant and close contact throughout the period of their association. Host governments which try to promote joint ventures should, with a high degree of priority, review statutes and regulations relating to foreign investment, partnership arrangements, and matters of specific concern to fisheries as well as administrative procedures, in general, to identify factors which might hold back such enterprises. Sometimes, the mere removal of restrictions, instituted originally for reasons that have long become obsolete, on the importation of equipment or on the employment of foreigners, will eliminate major problem areas and encourage foreign companies to invest. In other cases, removal of set limits on the percentage of equity which foreign companies are allowed to hold, of discriminatory taxation, restrictions on certain foreign exchange transactions, etc, will have beneficial results. Where removal of obstacles does not appear sufficient, incentive measures may have to be instituted. Options available in this connexion have been discussed in a study FAO published a few years ago on legislative and other measures taken by developing countries to attract and regulate foreign private investment, with special reference to agriculture (including forestry, fisheries and related industries) (FAO, 1970c).

Beyond action on legislative and other measures, there is a variety of ways host governments can give direct support to specific ventures. In particular, financial and technical assistance can be provided which the joint venture cannot procure from other sources. Even before the venture becomes operational, the host government can assist the local partner, by helping to check on overseas companies interested in forming joint ventures, by inspecting the equipment to be contributed, and by rendering other advisory and auditing types of services. Afterwards, the government can exercise supervisory and control functions to ensure the business is conducted along sound lines and that the interests of the local partner, as well as the broader social interest, are not slighted. Governments of the countries in which capital and skill-exporting companies are domiciled tend to be less deeply involved than host governments in such venture agreements, although they may place overall limits by restrictions on exports of capital and skill. On the promotional side, they have often given valuable help through facilitating the training of nationals from developing countries and making available financial assistance and advisory services for companies interested in investing abroad, etc. A high degree of governmental control over fisheries ventures abroad is maintained by Japan, which seeks to ensure that operations conform with the economic and political objectives of the country. Plans for future collaboration in fisheries with coastal countries have been discussed in some detail in the 1971 edition of the Japanese Fisheries Yearbook which outlines official Government policy in the following terms: (1) to promote, through economic and technical cooperation, development of the fishery resources of the developing countries and ensure importation of a part of the production to Japan; (2) to this effect, to conclude mutually advantageous fisheries agreements; and (3) to continue technical assistance under Government auspices and to prepare the ground for private economic collaboration and investment.

Among specific measures that might be taken in support of such a programme, the Yearbook mentions the following:

(1) appointment of fisheries attachés in embassies abroad to facilitate contacts and cooperation;
(2) establishment of a fisheries division in the Overseas Technical Cooperation Agency (OCTA);
(3) establishment of an investment insurance system; and
(4) assistance in the development of infrastructure facilities in developing countries, in the form of Government investments and loans, to facilitate operations of Japanese foreign ventures.

To promote a further expansion of fisheries

operations abroad, the Planning Committee of the Fisheries Association of Japan, after study of recommendations submitted by the Japanese Deep Sea Trawlers Association and the Japanese Tuna Associations, drew up a comprehensive plan in 1972. It envisaged, *ie*, the setting-up of a special corporation – to be established jointly by government and industry – to negotiate bilateral agreements and joint ventures that would secure new fishing areas for Japanese fishermen and would manage, finance, and provide technical assistance and research in support of the projects. In the meantime, the Government has decided to meet the demands of the Association by setting up a body that is to assist in financing foreign fishery ventures.

Efforts by international and regional bodies to promote joint ventures

International and regional bodies lending development support focus primarily on providing financial and/or technical assistance to developing countries. Some of these agencies, however, have taken an increasing interest in promoting international collaboration through joint ventures. The International Finance Corporation (IFC) and some of the regional development banks have even gone as far as to interpret one of their constitutional mandates, that of encouraging the growth of productive private enterprise, to allow them to include the making of direct investments. The IFC subscribes to shares and makes long-term loans to a variety of established private enterprises, and gives assistance in the financing of new ventures and in the expansion, modification or diversification of operations.* Where IFC or a regional development bank participates in the equity of a joint venture, the impact quite often transcends in importance the capital contribution as such. Their involvement tends to enhance the general credit-worthiness of the venture. In a more general way, five of the leading economic organizations of Japan announced in June 1973 that they were issuing 'joint guidelines' for regulating investments in developing countries by private Japanese enterprises. On the basis of these guidelines, the Ministry of International Trade and Industry was to provide advice to Japanese corporations planning to enter business ventures in foreign countries (Anon, 1973). Aside from these public agencies, the role of consortia of private enterprises also must be mentioned. PICA and ADELA are prominent among such consorita which provide finance through equity participation and, in general, offer encouragement to joint-venture formation, the former in the Asia and Far East region, the latter in Latin America.

Services of a different nature are performed by the International Centre for the Settlement of Investment Disputes (ICSID), affiliated like the IFC with the World Bank Group, which makes available facilities for the legal settlement of investment disputes. Consideration has been given for years to the establishment of a multilateral investment insurance (guarantee) scheme and the World Bank (IBRD) has drawn up a draft of Articles of Agreement for an International Investment Insurance Agency which would be loosely affiliated with it. Efforts have also been initiated under international auspices to assist prospective partners in the negotiation of joint ventures. It was recognized that it was impossible to write agreements that could serve as prototypes for other agreements. As has been emphasized (UNIDO, 1971b): '. . . it is the almost infinite number of combinations of possible terms and conditions within the context of a joint venture arrangement that has led to their utility and popularity.'

The panel of experts on foreign investment in developing countries, set up with UN sponsorship a few years ago, agreed that a flexible and pragmatic approach to the establishment of joint ventures should be favoured, with due regard, however, to a few basic considerations such as eventual transfer of ownership and control to local interests, training opportunities, security of the investment, etc. The above-cited UNIDO Manual on the Establishment of Industrial Joint Venture Agreements in Developing Countries attempts to accomplish this by suggesting some alternative provisions that may assist partners in writing relevant contract clauses. For general reference purposes, valuable assistance also is provided by the Guidelines for International Investment, developed in draft form and adopted by a meeting, in October 1972, of the Commission on International Investments and Economic Development. These guidelines, which were submitted to the 96th Session of the Executive Committee of the International Chamber of Commerce, include suggestions for matters to be considered by the foreign investor, the government of the investor's country, and the government of the host country, in connexion with investment policies, ownership and management, finance, fiscal policies, the legal framework, labour policies, technology (including inventions, know-how and skills), and commercial policies.

In response to requests from a growing number of developing countries, FAO has initiated projects to provide assistance in negotiating joint fishery ventures. Under the UNDP/FAO International Indian Ocean Fishery Survey and Development Programme, model clauses for consideration in the formulation of agreements relating to ventures involving countries in the area are at present being drawn up. Similar work has been projected in connexion with another regional fishery survey and development projects covering the Eastern Central Atlantic Area and the South China Sea. In addition, a draft of guidelines for use in negotiating joint ventures is in an advanced stage of preparation. FAO is also engaged in giving on-the-spot advice and assistance. In one instance, a UNDP/FAO project has advised the host government agency, the partner in a joint venture, by participating in the techno-economic feasibility study, providing information on types of equipment needed and processing methods, sources of supply of equipment and purchase price policies, etc. Further assistance was given in the negotiation of the contract and in the operating phase of the venture, when FAO staff advised on the establishment of accounting and administrative procedures, provided information on potential markets and buyers, marketing strategies, production, processing and quality control problems,

---

*See General Policies, IFC, Washington, DC, 1972. The brochure outlines IFC investment criteria, investment limits, terms of financing and other conditions of assistance to private enterprises, and details the procedure for submitting applications for IFC financing.

and – on occasions – acted as mediators in disputes that arose between the partners. As part of its Regular Programme responsibilities, FAO's Department of Fisheries provides assistance to governments and the fishery industry in identifying and planning fishery investment projects. Demands for this type of assistance have become so heavy that under the new structure which is to become effective as of 1st January 1974 a specialized Fishery Industries Development Service has been provided to concentrate on the planning and analysis of development projects. The success of this ambitious new endeavour, which should make it possible to provide direct and comprehensive assistance in this field, will depend in large measure on the degree of support and cooperation it is able to obtain from Member Governments and representatives of the fishing industry.

References

Anon. Overseas Investment and joint ventures by the Japanese
1971a fishing industry in *Japanese Fisheries Yearbook*, Chapter V.
Anon. Top-secret atmosphere surrounds fish processing factory.
1971b *Comml. Fishg.*, 10(9):16.

Anon. Businessmen and officials at working meeting on foreign
1972 investment. Report on Panel on foreign investment in developing countries, Tokyo, November 29–December 2, 1971, *Far East Trade and Development*, 27(1):20.
Anon. Guide for investments in developing countries. *The Oriental*
1973 *Economist*, 41(752):3.
Anon. Recent experience in establishing joint ventures, *Business International*.
FAO Financial assistance policies and administration for fishery
1962 industries by Holliman, E S, *FAO Fish. Stud.* (11), Rome, FAO, particularly 7; Administration of Aid Schemes, p. 75–112.
FAO Report of the International Conference on Investment in
1970a Fisheries, Rome 18–24 September 1969, Hamlisch, R (ed.), Rome, FAO, *FAO Fish. Rep.* (83), Vol. 1:25.
FAO *Ibid.*, p. 26.
1970b
FAO Foreign investment laws and agriculture, Rome, FAO, by
1970c Henderson, J, Rome, FAO, *Legislative Series* (9):224p.
FRIEDMANN, W G and KALMANOFF G Joint International Business
1961 Ventures in Developing Countries, New York and London, Columbia University Press, p.9.
UN *Manual on the Establishment of Industrial Joint Venture*
1971a *Agreements in Developing Countries*, New York, United Nations, p.3–4.
UN *Ibid.*, p.1.
1971b
UN *Appropriate Technology and Research for Industrial Develop-*
1972a *ment*, New York, United Nations, Department of Economic and Social Affairs, p.10–11.
UN *Ibid.*, p.22.
1972b

Some Aspects of the Role of External Aid Relative to Development of Fishery Industries   C Day

Quelques aspects du role de l'aide exterieure en matiere de developpement du secteur halieutique

L'auteur passe brièvement en revue les principales sources de fonds d'assistance au développement, en particulier celles avec lesquelles la FAO est en rapport, par exemple le PNUD, les banques internationales, la CMCF et certaines organisations multi- et bilatérales. Etant donné que le document porte moins sur l'utilisation accrue de l'assistance au développement que sur l'emploi des fonds relativement peu importants servant à faciliter le développement des pêches, les exemples cités pour illustrer cette assistance concernent essentiellement le secteur halieutique. L'auteur souligne que l'amélioration de l'exécution des programmes et projets d'assistance dépend davantage de la planification, de la répartition des ressources et de la fourniture d'un appui par les gouvernements que des activités déployées par ceux qui procurent une aide extérieure, encore qu'une étroite collaboration entre tous les intéressés soit indispensable à l'obtention de bons résultats.

Algunos aspectos de la funcion de la ayuda exterior en el desarrollo de las industrias pesqueras

En este trabajo se resumen brevemente las principales fuentes de fondos de asistencia para el desarrollo, especialmente aquellas con las que la FAO està asociada, como el PNUD, los bancos internacionales, la CMCH y algunas organizaciones multilaterales y bilaterales. Como el ámbito del documento, por lo que se refiere al uso de la ayuda para el desarrollo, es limitado, y se ocupa principalmente de los fondos, relativamente reducidos, que se canalizan hacia la ayuda al desarrollo pesquero, los ejemplos citados de asistencia tratan sólo del sector pesquero. Se subraya que la mejora del rendimiento de los programas y proyectos de asistencia depende más de la planificación estatal, de la asignación de recursos y del apoyo que reciban que de las actividades de quienes facilitan ayuda exterior, aunque una estrecha colaboración entre todos cuantos participan en la asistencia es esencial para lograr resultados óptimos.

Assistance in development is not a new concept because it has been practised in various forms and various ways throughout human history. What is new is the present widespread interest in such assistance and the way it is organized at both governmental and nongovernmental levels. All organizations involved at both levels have policies and objectives in assistance which largely determined their role. And, of course, an understanding of these policies and objectives is required if the maximum assistance is to be gained. In view of this, the most useful purpose for this paper is to try to indicate the range and scope of the assistance available for fisheries development, with particular reference to those sources of aid with which FAO is associated.

INVESTMENT

While it is not possible in a contribution of this nature to give the facts and figures about all the funds directed to development assistance, a reference to the principal sources available will indicate their magnitude. And, while particular attention will be paid to the relatively small total of funds provided for assistance in fishery development, the point should be made that, in many countries, fisheries represent only a fractional part of the national economy which tends to be reflected in the allocation of resources for their development. As always, the decision as to the relative importance of fisheries, as of any other sector, is that of the government concerned.

The United Nations Development Programme (UNDP) is, of course, a main source of multilateral technical assistance. Its Special Fund sector has increased from US$105 million in 1962 to US$293 million in 1973 of which FAO's share is just under one third – about US$97 million in 1973. Of this, the fisheries component is upward of US$11.5 million. The fishery projects and technical assistance assignments cover work on resource surveys, exploratory fishing, gear and equipment improvement, vessel design and construction, development of fish products, marketing and distribution and training of various kinds, as well as the investment stage of development projects. The most important consideration relative to UNDP funds today is that they are allocated under the Country Programming scheme which was introduced in 1972. This means that the allocation of the funds available for a given country is made at the request of, and in accordance with, the economic development plan or the stated priorities of the government concerned. Thus, the choice of use of the funds rests with the government concerned in consultation with the UNDP Resident Representative and the representatives of the various UN technical agencies. Of course, consideration is also given to the availability of funds from other sources so that, overall, the most efficient and coordinated use can be made of the total funds available to the government. While those responsible for such development need to present the strongest case possible for investment in all sectors of fishery, it should be pointed out that the products sector is often neglected and is in urgent need of strengthening if it is to play effectively its full role in fishery development.

The international banks are another main source of development funds but, unfortunately, only a very small percentage of such funds has been invested in food and agriculture, including fisheries and forestry. Of a total of US$19,409 million given in loans and credits up to June 1971 by the International Bank for Reconstruction and Development (IBRD) and the International Development Association (IDA), only US$2,348 million have been invested in the field of agriculture. Of this, only US$46 million have gone to fisheries and forestry. The loans and credits for fisheries have been the following:

Country	IBRD	IDA	Purpose
Taiwan	14,400,000		Longlining
Ecuador	5,300,000		Vessels and port studies
Ghana		1,300,000	Vessels and port studies
Indonesia		3,500,000	Skipjack fishing
Panama	3,400,000		Vessels and port studies
Tunisia		2,000,000	
	23,100,000	6,800,000	Total 29,900,000

This modest amount of investment does not indicate lack of endeavour to obtain more funds. The FAO/IBRD Cooperative Programme has participated in more than 50 fishery missions concerned with identification, project preparation, appraisal, review and supervision. Some reasons why so few fishery projects have been approved are: the failure of the ministries and departments concerned with fisheries to obtain sufficient support from their finance ministries, the scarcity of technical staff at all levels in the fishery departments in most developing countries, and therefore their difficulty in providing their governments with the advice and guidance needed to cope with the problems arising in development programmes, and the high risks involved in many investments in the sector. Another contributing factor to the modest

level of investment by the international banks in this field is that, in most countries with free enterprise economies, considerable capital investment in fisheries comes from the private sector. An essential requirement, if funds are to be obtained from the IBRD or the IDA, is full preparation by the government concerned of a project proposal, including collection of all relevant data, a detailed analysis of the fishery situation and a clear concept of the need for the proposed investment, with a practical projection of step-by-step progress toward the stated objectives. Such a preparation for a mission not only promotes success in negotiations, but does much to cut down the time taken for the Bank to reach a decision on whether or not to invest and to what extent.

The Asian Development Bank (ADB) situation is similar to that of the IBRD and the negotiating requirements are the same. Of the members of the Bank, 22 are governments in the region and 14 from outside, so that there is a complementary approach to development problems. However, this has not, so far, resulted in a higher rate of investment in fisheries. Of the total loans in the 1968–71 period of about US$638.5 million, only US$31.7 million went into fisheries. The projects were: deep-sea fishing in Taiwan; cold storage in Korea; fisheries development in Pakistan and Vietnam and fishing port development in the Philippines. The methods adopted for negotiating ADB loans in the fishery sector are somewhat similar to those of the IBRD. The Inter-American Development Bank so far has advanced only US$75.3 million for fishery projects, which is only a fraction of its total loans, but during the past two years a number of very large projects have been prepared by the FAO/IDB Liaison Office in Washington. The projects or proposals cover industrial and fishing enterprises in Chile, processing in Brazil and fishery industrial development in Venezuela, Colombia, Peru, Mexico, Argentina, Barbados, etc.

One of the most interesting developments in providing funds for assistance is multi- or bilateral aid handled in FAO by the FAO/Government Cooperative Programme. This type of aid amounts to enormous sums even country by country – such as the funds devoted to this purpose by the USA, Japan, France, the Federal Republic of Germany, China, the USSR, the UK, Canada and many others. According to the Society for International Development (SID), the total of such aid in 1971 was US$18 billion. Of this, the chief components were US$3.6 billion from governments, US$8.3 billion from private sources, US$2.8 billion in the form of favourable loans and US$1.3 billion through international sources, such as the UN system. The range, extent and magnitude of this aid would require a substantial paper on its own if it was to be examined in any detail. In 1972 the total of such funds put into projects through FAO amounted to US$22.75 million. In addition, US$5.4 million went into paying for associate technical assistance personnel.

For the purpose of obtaining a closer view of this type of assistance perhaps it might be useful to look at the contribution of the Scandinavian countries in this context. While their contribution is, of course, small relative to the total of such aid, it is large relative to their size and provides a good example of independent work as well as operations in collaboration with international technical assistance agencies such as FAO. The organizations concerned are the Danish International Development Association (DANIDA), the Norwegian Agency for International Development (NORAD) and the Swedish International Development Authority (SIDA). All three are active in the support of fisheries projects. Under the Cooperative Programme, DANIDA has provided funds amounting to US$266,000 for seven fishery projects completed and will provide US$603,000 for two more approved and perhaps US$75,000 for another project which is under consideration. NORAD has provided more than US$300,000 for five projects and is commited to financing the construction of a research vessel for some US$2 million plus its yearly operating costs. SIDA has sponsored five projects now completed (costing US$226,000) and has agreed to fund two others at a cost of US$96,000. It is also considering two more which will cost an estimated US$618,000. The Scandinavian aid agencies tend to favour certain kinds of projects. DANIDA has supported seven training and three development-with-training component projects, while SIDA has sponsored six educational and training projects and is interested in supporting new projects based on integrated development in fisheries. NORAD, too, has favoured the training type of project. It should be made clear that the reference here to the projects supported by the Scandinavian group relates only to those conducted in association with the FAO/Government Cooperative Programme and does not take into account the many other projects in which they have cooperated with FAO nor the projects which they have undertaken directly with the countries concerned. The reference to favourable consideration of integrated fishery development projects indicates a trend in thinking that there should be a supplementary and complementary role to be played even by small projects in the general plan for development. Thus, programmes and projects supported by large funds and resources of the government of the country concerned and by large-scale donors should be strengthened by 'linked-in' small-scale projects, resulting in an overall benefit. All the technically advanced countries provide scientific and technical assistance in one form or another and many provide substantial funds for development investment. Most of the European governments, for example, provide such assistance. Those which formerly had colonies provide special assistance to the now independent countries but also support projects in other developing countries. Other sources of assistance are certain foundations in the USA and Europe, including the UK, such as the Carnegie and Rockefeller foundations which have, for example, contributed significantly to the work on improved varieties of grain.

For the past 12 years, the Freedom from Hunger Campaign (FFHC) has provided funds for many hundreds of projects in FAO's fields of interest. Some of these have been operated through FAO but a large number have been handled directly between the national FFHC Committees and the recipient countries concerned. As at the present time, there are 16 FFHC fishery projects in operation involving contributions totalling almost US$1 million. Further, four more such projects costing US$450,000 are being brought into

action and another four, which will cost US$375,000, have been submitted to prospective donor countries. FFHC fishery projects have covered a wide range, as is indicated by some of the recent ones which are concerned with aquaculture, fishing-boat mechanization, fish preservation and processing, marketing of fish and fish products and training. In general, FFHC donors prefer projects which are linked with the development plan of a country, as in the case of other sources of funds already mentioned. Indeed, the title of the campaign today – The FFHC/Action for Development Programme – reflects this project requirement.

Another source of funds for fisheries development is the United Nations Children's Fund (UNICEF), in relation to its support of Applied Nutrition Programmes (ANP) in various countries. The biggest of these is the ANP in India toward which UNICEF has allocated a total of US$14,615,000 to date. Assistance has been given by UNICEF to a variety of marine and inland fishery projects, the end objective of which is to provide more animal protein in the diet of the people, especially the 'vulnerable' groups, children and expectant and nursing mothers.

EXAMPLES OF PROJECTS

All who have been associated with technical assistance at any level are aware of the frustrations and difficulties of such work for both the recipient countries and the donors. But these are, in a large measure, inescapable because of the complexities of the conditions and circumstances in which most projects have to operate and often a lack of realism in respect of the timescale and other factors. There is also the variety of background, upbringing, training and cultural indoctrination of those persons engaged in the conduct of the projects which may complicate operations. Nevertheless, the achievements in such assistance present an economic gain and social benefits far outweighing the cost of the failures, as the following few selected examples of successful projects show.

A Special Fund project

Of the many interesting FAO/UNDP Special Fund projects in fisheries, one of the most comprehensive undertakings has been in Peru. It has, in fact, comprised two projects which have assisted the Government of Peru to (a) establish and operate an Institute (Instituto del Mar) for research and investigation of marine resources, including the exploitation and management of the fishery and (b) set up and develop a food fish industry. The first project started in 1960 and the second in 1970.

The second project, entitled 'Fish Marketing and Utilization', which is integrated with the work of the Ministry of Fisheries, has made rapid progress in converting anchoveta purse seiners to food fish vessels, in establishing processing facilities and in organizing the wholesale and retail marketing and distribution of fish. This work has included the construction of a number of coastal fish terminals and inland distribution centres, seven of them up in the Andes. By the beginning of 1974 it is expected that nine terminals and 11 depots will be in operation.

The project is also assisting the Empresa Pública de

Servicios Pesqueros (EPSEP) (Public Fishery Service Enterprise) in establishing and operating about 180 retail outlets and introducing the sale of fish in numerous supermarkets. At the same time, a products development programme is being conducted on a pilot basis in a plant at Callao and modern fish processing has been introduced through demonstration of mechanized gutting and fish filleting.

An indication of the complexity of the project is given by the list of areas in which work is being done: economics, technology, civil engineering, fish inspection service, naval architecture, fish processing, marketing and distribution, home economics, fishery cooperatives and training in various aspects of all these.

A special feature of this Peruvian programme to develop the food fish industry is the extent to which it has attracted bilateral assistance. For example, Norway, the Netherlands, Sweden, Finland and Denmark have provided associate experts and the Canada Plus One Committee have donated a fully equipped mobile laboratory and training unit, with a towing vehicle. In addition to this kind of assistance, joint ventures in the Peruvian fisheries are developing, such as a Peruvian/Japanese company for the nerluza fishery, catching and freezing and manufacturing fish sausages and other comminuted products. Also, a joint fishing venture has been established with Poland. Various other countries are also interested in joint ventures of one kind or another, all of which will contribute toward the development of the food fish industry to the benefit of both the domestic and export markets. As an example of using FAO/UNDP and all other kinds of assistance, the Peruvian experience provides a case study of interest and value to all countries seeking to develop their food fish industries. It is also a model of full governmental support at all levels, which in itself is a key to the efficient and effective operation of all such projects and programmes.

Bilateral assistance

A great number of countries are now involved in aid programmes and projects and the selection of one as an example must, because of the number and variety, be arbitrary. With this reservation, a project sponsored by the Federal Government of Germany in collaboration with the Kingdom of Thailand provides a good example of one which has led to the development of a substantial new kind of fishery.

The object of this project, which was conducted in two phases – the first from May to September in 1961 and the second from July 1962 to October 1964 – was to promote the development of the Thai marine fisheries in the Gulf of Thailand through the introduction of trawl fishing and to advise the Government of Thailand on the scientific management of the bottom fish resources in the area. In view of the subsequent success of the project, this management aspect has assumed additional importance. The success of this bilateral project has, as a spin-off benefit, pointed to the possibility of achieving comparable results in the waters of a number of other countries in the region through the introduction of similar trawl fishing techniques. In this connexion, mention should be made of the joint Thai–Malaysian–German trawling survey off the east coast of the Malay

Peninsula (1967). As trawling had already been taken up by Malaysian fishermen, the objective of the joint survey was to establish the extent of the fish stocks. The exploratory fishing showed that some of the coastal waters of the area are rich in demersal fish and catch rates proved even better than those obtained in the Gulf of Thailand. But, as the report on the project points out, much needs to be done to promote fisheries development in the area, such as the expansion of harbour and shore facilities suited to the demands of modern fishing vessels and improvement in the marketing and distribution services. The report also recommended a continuous programme of research to enable the necessary regulatory measures to be taken in good time to ensure that the fisheries of the area are maintained at the maximum productive level.

A further development in this bilateral effort is to be in the form of assistance to the Government of Indonesia with regard to the future of trawl fishing in their waters.

Bank loans

An essential step toward obtaining a loan from any of the development banks is that the request must come from the government of the country concerned. After that, if the bank involved feels that the project presents a good investment possibility, it will send a technical mission. The government concerned needs to make full preparation to meet the searching investigation of all matters relevant to the project. Investment largely depends on the previous technical assistance work done and the extent to which progress in such work has created an investment opportunity. There are also, of course, many other factors concerned, such as the country's priorities in development, social, population and environmental considerations, the timing of the project and the estimated impact on the national economy as well as the economic viability of the project itself. There are a number of good examples of preinvestment operations leading to Bank investment. Two of the most recent, the details of which are still under discussion, are in Indonesia, both of them concerned with skipjack fishing. A similar type of FAO Technical Assistance project was operated in 1970–72, based on Ambon Island. This was on a more modest scale, FAO providing the services of an expert in skipjack fishing and the Government of Indonesia the boat and crew. The aim of the project was to conduct exploratory fishing for bait and skipjack. The result has been so favourable that the IBRD have expressed their willingness to provide a loan for an Indonesian fishing company to be set up to exploit the resource. The company will operate a fleet of 20 fishing vessels, supported by the necessary shore-based processing plant.

FFHC projects

The aim of FFHC projects is to stimulate self-sustaining growth and while there have been many fishery projects with this element, one of the outstanding successes is in a different field but is worth referring to, even though this is a fisheries conference, because it is such a good example of the growth factor. The project is the cattle feed mixing plant set up at Anand in Gujarat State, India, in 1964. The plant, donated by the British FFHC Committee at a cost of £108,000, has not only been a success itself but has generated widespread growth in the establishment of cattle feed mixing plants in India. As a result, not only has this development improved the condition of the beasts concerned and increased milk output but has brought more money to the cattle owners, mostly poor villagers, thus making a contribution toward improving their standard of living.

The cost of a project is not necessarily an indicator of its usefulness and the extent of its impact. An example of the possible impact of a small project is that of providing assistance in fish preservation in Indonesia. This project, financed by the Australian FFHC Committee at the cost of US$24,000, was based on Madura Island.

While the improvements were introduced mainly on Madura Island, they can be equally successfully introduced in all artisanal fisheries where similar conditions exist. Such projects would result in fuller utilization of the catch and in an increase of the earnings of the fishermen, leading to an improvement of their standard of living. At the same time, the consumer would benefit from the regular supply of fish in better condition and, perhaps, at more stable prices.

FUTURE ASSISTANCE

Experience over the years has shown the desirability of aid projects being an integral part of the development plan and programme of a country, whether the projects are in themselves big or little. This means that more effective coordination of aid programmes and projects will be required in the future – which is a prime objective of country programming.

It should be stressed that country programming, if it is to be worked effectively, must be planned and prepared far in advance of the period to be covered by the programme. Much depends, of course, on the planning rhythm of the country concerned, whether it is short-term or medium-term or, as may be likely, segmented within a longer-term economic development plan. Whatever the arrangement, the need is early preparation of the programme so that the priorities and magnitude of the assistance can be known to those who will be called upon to provide it. This is essential if they, in their turn, are to organize the assistance required to meet the timing of the programme which, in itself, is geared to the timing of the national economic development plan. Preparation of the country programme is essentially the responsibility of the government concerned. The part played by the UNDP and the Specialized Agencies and other donors is consultative to the extent required by the government. Similarly, the responsibility for coordinating all assistance is that of the government. In some countries governments have found it useful for the aid organizations to form consortiums as a help toward coordination of foreign assistance, sometimes under the leadership of one of the banks. Arrangements of this kind seem likely to commend themselves to more governments of developing countries as the complexity of the aid situation increases.

FAO's coordinating role

The need for coordination applies to all projects and programmes, whatever their size. In this respect FAO has a useful role to play in its Technical Assistance activities, perhaps particularly in relation to the large number of smaller bilateral and multilateral projects, such as those sponsored through the FAO Cooperative Programme, the Trust Funds, the FFHC and the various bilateral agencies, many of which seek FAO's advice and guidance and, in a number of cases, technical participation. In the case of such projects, FAO can help in tailoring them to meet the requirements and priorities of the governments and in using such schemes as constructive supplements to major programmes and projects. In fisheries, for example, this has been done with a wide variety of Trust Fund and FFHC projects, such as in training schemes concerned with fisheries infrastructure, boatbuilding, processing and marketing and research, etc, linking them with long-term aims for further development. Looking to the future of such aid, FAO has found a growing interest by both donors and recipient countries in the development of harbours and landing facilities, the construction of mechanized small boats and the establishment and expansion of fish processing industries and marketing. Such projects fit well into the pattern of integrated development by supplementing the major schemes in operation.

Plan priority essential

A general requirement in respect of all assistance is that the projected programmes or projects are in the sector accorded a high priority in the national economic plan. In relation to assistance from UN sources, which is only a fraction of that from other sources, the particular need is to identify development opportunities in the sectors concerned, such as fisheries, where such contributions and effort can be most effective in promoting the development process. There has been, over the years, much criticism of the slowness in negotiating programmes and in their implementation. The validity of such criticism is widely recognized by, for example, the UNDP and U.N. Specialized Agencies but they alone cannot change the pace of progress. This requires the combined effort of all concerned, with a major contribution to be made by the governments of the developing countries, which is inevitable because the physical location of any project must be in a country or region and must be largely dependent on the arrangements, personnel, services, facilities and resources made available to it by the concerned government or governments.

Cooperation and support

The integrated development approach to assistance should go a long way toward ensuring that the necessary supporting elements are provided promptly. For example, a national economic development plan and established priorities call for provision of adequate resources in terms of funds, personnel, administrative and supporting services, physical resources, etc, including the spirit of cooperation and support at all levels of the governmental organizations involved. Thus, assistance keyed to such a plan should be assured of the required inputs and support. This latter, which is often an impalpable element – the sense of cooperation, understanding and support – is just as important as, for instance, making available the necessary land, buildings, machinery and other physical inputs and can only be achieved if all involved in the programme or project are fully informed of its nature and purpose. This is an aspect of preparation which has, in the main, been overlooked and has led to as much misunderstanding and delay as has failure to acquire necessary land or appoint project personnel or supply the required machinery and equipment, although the adverse effect is not so obvious as in these cases. The action needed here is development support communication, an activity which aims at keeping all concerned informed about the objectives and progress of a project or programme. FAO has introduced such activity recently as an integral and, indeed, essential part of the development process.

Objectives, targets and time-scale

Another element in project preparation which needs revision is the determination of objectives and a more realistic time-scale for attainment of targets. Experience has shown that the announced objectives and targets have often been little more than pious hopes, sometimes not possible of achievement in view of the conditions under which the project will operate, the support by the government organizations concerned, the inadequacy of the inputs and overoptimism with regard to the time-scale. Much of the sense of lack of fulfilment felt about projects has been due to these two errors in estimate (objectives and time-scale). A rigid form of time-scale of, say, five years, which is frequently set in FAO/UNDP projects, needs to be made more flexible. Setting such a time-scale is not an isolated, decisive act but is related to the variety of factors already mentioned and, if assessment of them is wrong, then the time-scale based on them inevitably will be wrong.

Responsibilities for decisions

While it is recognized that in many instances local circumstances – including political considerations – may call for the enumeration of certain objectives within a certain time-scale, both the governments and the aid agencies concerned should insist on the technical and practical considerations as being of paramount importance. Here, again, the decisive voice has to be that of the government. Delays in implementation of projects are not the outcome of the sins of omission or commission of any one of the partners but of all concerned. A step in the right direction for reducing such delays is the integrated development approach based on each country's national development plan or established priorities. Even so, a degree of judgement is inevitably involved in such matters as determining the objectives relative to the time-scale for the project. In this case, again, the Member Governments must be the chief decision makers since their personnel should, by their knowledge and experience of their own country, be better informed as to the likely pace of progress of any project concerned with development. But, more flexibility should be written into the operational plans for projects, especially in respect of the time-scale, so that progress can be measured over longer periods and can be seen in better perspective. When this approach becomes general, a more practical and realistic evaluation of projects will be possible, as measurement and judgement will be made in relation to clearly attainable objectives within a realistic time-scale. This will, in turn, provide a solid basis for planning and preparing any required follow-up action in good time so as to ensure continuity of momentum and effort.

A New Approach to Technical Assistance in Coastal Fisheries   *S Iibuchi*

Une nouvelle formule en matiere d'assistance technique a la pêche cotiere

L'auteur déclare que la conception actuelle de l'assistance technique est erronée car elle repose essentiellement sur les valeurs en cours dans les pays techniquement avancés et fait surtout intervenir des facteurs économiques. Il esquisse une formule nouvelle, basée sur les systèmes politiques, sociaux et religieux des pays intéressés et tenant compte de l'histoire, des coutumes, des attitudes, des habitudes alimentaires, etc de la population. En particulier, l'auteur propose – sous réserve que les gouvernements bénéficiaires prennent les mesures voulues – un plan convenant aux projets de développement de la pêche côtière.

Nuevo enfoque de la asistencia tecnica a las pesquerias costeras

El autor sostiene que la forma de abordar el problema de la asistencia técnica ha sido errónea, ya que se basaba esencialmente en concepciones propias de los países técnicamente avanzados y primordialmente en factores económicos. En el trabajo se bosqueja un nuevo método basado en los sistemas políticos, sociales y religiosos de los países correspondientes incluidas tradiciones, costumbres, perspectivas, hábitos alimentarios, etc, de la población. En especial, el trabajo propone un sistema adecuado de preparación de proyectos para el desarrollo de las pesquerías costeras, presuponiendo la necesaria intervención por parte de los gobiernos beneficiarios.

The differences in background, outlook, dietary habits and other customs between people of various countries are such that no single plan for technical assistance can be drawn up which would be suitable for all cases. In addition, of course, there are also the differences in the degree of development of the facilities available at fishing ports, and of road and transport infrastructure. Each country, therefore, requires separate study to determine which is the best approach to its development problems.

CONDITIONS REQUIRED FOR SUCCESSFUL TECHNICAL ASSISTANCE

There are several conditions which have to be established if technical assistance is to be successful. One is that social reform must be implemented by the developing countries to bring about a fairer distribution of wealth and a rise in the living standards of the people through increased productivity.

So far as the coastal fisheries are concerned, these embrace a large number of fishermen mainly in the category referred to as artisanal fisheries. If we are to succeed with technical assistance in this sector, then a precondition is that the governments concerned must convey the coastal fishing rights to the fishermen. If this is not done, the fishermen will have to go on working for the benefit of the middlemen, and moneylenders, without a chance of achieving economic independence. Another essential condition is the establishment of effective cooperatives. These cooperatives can only prosper if their members prosper, therefore, the conveyance of coastal fishing rights to the fishermen is necessary for the prosperity of the cooperatives. Moreover, the rights and privileges of the fishermen should be of major concern to the cooperatives. Unfortunately, the traditional social structure of many developing countries, especially in parts of Asia, is so deeply rooted that the fishermen alone have little chance of overturning the old established privileges and vested interests. For this reason, although the necessity may be regrettable, the cooperatives will have to be operated for many years to come under the control of the governments concerned. Perhaps in a generation or two, when better educated and better trained young fishermen, who enjoy economic independence, take over, such official control and support will no longer be required, but for the present time it is virtually inescapable in these countries.

If the fishermen's cooperatives are to be fully effective, they must be of a multi-purpose nature. They must be a source of credit and they must undertake a major role in the development of the fishery industries, from the improvement of boats, gear, equipment and techniques to processing, distribution, marketing and sales promotion. Such responsibilities will include the development of effective transport and communications systems, and the establishment of cold storage and similar facilities. The establishment and growth of the cooperatives, essential for the long-term wellbeing of the fishermen, will arouse the hostility of vested interests, such as, middlemen and moneylenders. These will attack not only the cooperatives but the supporting governments. In many cases, the governments do not feel strong enough to overcome these vested interests through the introduction and implementation of social reforms yet such reforms are essential if the poorer sectors of society, such as the artisanal fishermen and their families, are to be able to attain economic independence and raise their standard of living. The problem as far as fishery administrations and fishery cooperatives are concerned is aggravated by the shortage of well-trained administrators and managers, This represents one of the most critical elements of the problem of the successful development of coastal fisheries and of that of other impoverished sectors of the population of developing countries.

One other important point should be made relative to the provision of technical assistance. Under the present system, there are bilateral and multilateral sources of assistance, both requiring negotiation and agreement between donor and recipient countries. Both fear misunderstanding of motives and intentions because of their different political and other interests, their different backgrounds and ways of thought and so on. It would be in the common interest of everyone concerned, therefore, if all technical assistance was channelled through an international organization. It should be negotiated by the organization and guided by that body through all stages, including implementation and follow-up activities. While such a body could hardly be introduced and set up to take over these responsibilities immediately, it could do so step by step.

THE MISAKI INTERNATIONAL FISHERIES TRAINING CENTRE

On the basis of the aforementioned considerations, the Misaki International Fisheries Training Centre has been established to organize technical cooperation in coastal fisheries. Three main requirements are envisaged: (a) consolidation of laws controlling coastal fisheries; (b) the establishment of Coastal Fishermen's Cooperatives; and (c) the introduction of knowledge and improved techniques and practices required for the development of coastal fisheries

The first two of these steps must essentially be taken by the governments concerned. Our contribution as a donor country is chiefly in the third step. As a practical approach to the problem, we have drawn the plan as shown below:

As the plan indicates, the concentration is on education and training, which we regard as a key to effective development. In the Misaki Centre we are not only providing training in techniques applicable in coastal fisheries but are planning to provide a course in coopera-

Staff members of government and
related organizations in recipient
country

Fishing Gear and Methods
Extension Course

Fisheries Cooperative Course

Misaki International Fisheries Training Centre

Fishing Village Development Centre
in Recipient Country

Youths in Fishing
Village

Branch of Fishing Village
Development Centre

Native Fishing
Village

tives. This will be aimed at training leaders among the fishermen who will, through the cooperatives, spearhead the drive to economic independence. The Fishing Village Development Centres (see chart) will be, in the main, organized and run by fishermen we have trained. They will give technological and professional training to the youths in the fisheries who, in turn, will undertake the organization of cooperatives in their own villages. In order to assist them in this undertaking, Branch Development Centres will be set up in the villages through which technical and professional training can be given and the organization of cooperatives promoted.

An essential aim of this type of technical assistance is that it should lead to self-sustaining growth and spread throughout the coastal fisheries of the country concerned. Of course, for the initial effort, funds are needed over and above those provided by the recipient government both as finance and in the form of facilities, services, personnel and so on. While I appreciate that FAO is concerned with the whole field of fisheries, it would seem that the Organization should give especial attention to this artisanal sector and, in this connexion, could promote the approach and the type of project described. This could be done if FAO would make a determined effort to seek the support of donor countries for such projects and the agreement of recipient countries to accept them, together with the required conditions.

CONCLUSIONS

Technical assistance in the past, whatever form it has taken, has not achieved its ostensible objectives because the approach has been wrong. To emphasize this again, it is only necessary to refer to the fact that the usual request for assistance is to establish fishery universities or capital-intensive, labour-saving industries. The millions of small fishermen in the coastal or artisanal fisheries have generally been overlooked or neglected. Yet, true development on a sustained and expanding basis in fisheries must be concerned with the economic independence and rising standards of living of these masses if such development is to have any real and lasting meaning in terms of the human beings concerned. It is, therefore, up to both the recipient and donor countries to recognize this fact and to take the actions necessary to make this development possible.

British Assistance in the Development of Fish Handling, Processing and Preservation Industries   *D N F Hall and N R Jones*

Aide Britannique au developpement des industries de la manutention, de la transformation et de la conserve du poisson
Exposé succinct des considérations d'ordre politique dont s'inspire le Royaume-Uni dans le choix de ses programmes d'aide et description des divers types d'assistance accordés, notamment dans le domaine des pêches.

Ayuda Britanica para crear industrias de manipulacion, conserva y elaboracion del pescado
En este documento se describen brevemente las consideraciones de tipo político que orientan la selección de programas y proyectos de ayuda del Reino Unido y se determinan las diversas clases de ayuda facilitada, incluida la que se presta a la pesca.

The United Kingdom makes significant contributions to world fisheries development through its extensive home programmes of research and industrial development, its support to the United Nations agencies, and through developmental projects and training programmes with less well developed countries under bilateral assistance arrangements supported through the Overseas Development Administration (ODA) of the Foreign and Commonwealth Office (FCO). The usual criteria against which ODA judges any request for assistance in fisheries, be it a single technical assistance assignment or a complex programme of work; be it research, survey, construction, extension or straightforward training; are that the project in question shall be directly related to the needs of the country concerned, and be likely to benefit the social or economic development within the foreseeable future. In the field of fish processing industry development, the emphasis of the bilateral assistance programme is essentially toward urgent solutions of practical problems, bearing in mind the special problems of individual countries and the development value of individual projects. There is little or no place in the programme for the more esoteric type of research project, or for projects with no reasonable indication of socio-economic benefit. Since the purpose of the British aid programme is to promote social and economic development within the recipient countries, it can be considered to be simply a long-term educational programme, and the aid itself can be considered to have two distinct parts: (a) the provision of funds for essential physical requirements within the infrastructure of the recipient countries and in connexion with such activities as research and the conduct of feasibility studies and pilot projects, and (b) the transfer of skills through the loan of qualified people to the recipient countries and the training in the United Kingdom of developing country nationals.

ATTRACTING COMMERCIAL INVESTMENT

Through various activities in the fields of research and feasibility studies, by providing funds for basic infrastructure projects, and by assisting in the provision of qualified staff to governmental departments and at the request of the government concerned to certain semi-autonomous undertakings, the official United Kingdom aid programme helps to create the climate attractive to commercial investment, although the aid programme does not itself invest directly in commercial undertakings. The ODA also administers three measures for using official aid in direct association with British private investment in developing countries. These comprise a scheme of financial support for pre-investment studies carried out by firms contemplating direct investment in developing countries; the extension of capital aid through recipient governments to local development institutions for use in joint ventures with British firms; and, with the agreement of recipient governments, the use of capital aid to finance essential infrastructure, such as roads, power and water, required for specific British investment projects.[1] The White Paper in which the British Government announced these measures (Command 4656, April 1971) also includes measures operated by other Government Departments. These include in particular a scheme for insuring new British private investment overseas against non-commercial risks, and the negotiation with as many developing countries as possible of bilateral investment protection agreements.

Aid priorities considered

Requests for bilateral technical assistance in fish handling, processing and preservation industries and related research and development projects are received by ODA through the official channels, the Embassy or High Commission concerned, having been considered within the less well developed country or region against the background of other possible aid priorities. Evaluation within the ODA takes into account the thinking, planning and the general developmental programme of the country concerned, and includes also appraisal by the Administration's specialist technical and economic advisory staff. The consideration of requests for the use of capital funds within the aid provision is broadly similar. Where the results of research are likely to be generally applicable and not restricted to the benefit of any single country, separate budgetary arrangements may be made, while requests for training, which are frequently associated with other project proposals, are handled through the British Council. With regard to the fundamental British approach to fish handling and processing problems, the United Kingdom considers that within developing countries first priority should be accorded to the dissemination of good practice in the simplest processing techniques, which are essentially the techniques that can be applied most widely and which are likely to benefit the greatest number of people. These include variations on, and improvements to, existing local techniques, which may be expected to produce a product already well-known and acceptable to the local populations, together with the introduction of ice. Research by the Tropical Product Institute (TPI) has shown that the storage life of tropical species, if they are properly chilled, may be much longer than was believed formerly, with a consequent lessening of the need for freezing techniques, which are expensive in both capital and running costs; but requests for assistance in refrigeration and cold storage projects may be supported if these practices are required by the local conditions. In general terms, however, it is considered that sophisticated processing techniques should be introduced early in development only when a product is destined for a sophisticated (world) market.

TECHNICAL RESOURCES

In order to implement the government-to-government bilateral agreements, the ODA can call upon the considerable technical resources of the British industry which is engaged in a very wide range of commercial processing operations. It has access also to the resources of the semi-governmental Industrial Research Associations and to the Torry Research Station of the Ministry of Agriculture Fisheries and Food, which is well-known for its work at the forefront of processing and preservation research; and it supports directly the work of the Tropical Products Institute, which is a major scientific and technical unit of the ODA with particular interests in tropical artisanal fisheries and in the position of tropical fisheries in integrated food industries in the less well developed countries (this latter aspect is often neglected in wider planning considerations). A most important aspect of United Kingdom bilateral assistance in the field of fish processing industry development is training. Arrangements for this are very flexible, ranging from formal training in food technology or management over a period of years in a university to diploma or degree standard and thereafter to post-graduate degree level at a university or research institution, to shorter-term (normally not less than three months) specialized training in individual industrial techniques. Experience over the years has shown that the greatest care should be taken during the formulation of requests to ensure that the training course selected is truly relevant to the problems that prevail in the trainee's home country. For the training of the generalist fisheries officers, who will be expected to undertake some supervision of artisanal and industrial processing development, attention is drawn to the ODA-supported Diploma (Course) in Fisheries Management which, while based on the College of Technology, Grimsby, nevertheless draws on a wide range of British research, development and industrial organizations.

FUNDING POLICY

A consideration of some importance is the attitude of the British aid programme to multilaterally-funded activities in this field. For a variety of reasons, which are outside the scope of this paper, the United Kingdom prefers generally to maintain some element of distinction between British-funded and multilaterally-funded activities so that, normally, direct British participation in a multilaterally-funded fish processing industry project would be unlikely. However, this does not mean that the United Kingdom is never willing to give assistance in an area where there is already a multilateral project in being and where British aid would be complementary to that project. To take just one example from the field of fisheries ecology, the United Kingdom is funding research in a location and in a situation which would not justify the expenditure if there was not a substantial UNDP/FAO project already operational; the two projects are mutually beneficial. The possibility exists of parallel situations occurring in the field of fish processing and, indeed, it is anticipated that the first such project will shortly become operational. Further, in the past the United Kingdom has endorsed

---

[1]Further data on support for private investment in developing countries can be obtained from the Private Investment & Consultancies Department, Foreign and Commonwealth Office, Overseas Development Administration, Eland House, Stag Place, London SW1E 5DH. (Telephone: (01) 834 2377 Ext. 237)

multilaterally-funded regional programmes which act largely as a means of stimulating and coordinating activities which are individually funded by a variety of means, but, generally, active participation by the United Kingdom within such regional programmes requires the preparation of specific projects which can be funded through the normal British bilateral aid programme.

CONCLUSIONS

In summary, the United Kingdom believes that most situations need to be considered independently, and that the handling, processing and preservation practices most appropriate to the particular situations should be developed, with emphasis on the simplest practices likely to benefit the greatest number of people. The official aid programme can be drawn upon to prepare the way for and directly assist private investment in fish processing industries: in so doing, the aid programme itself can draw upon the expertise within a wide range of organizations, and, through ODA, it funds directly the Tropical Products Institute which includes within its remit the special study of the post-harvest behaviour and treatment of tropical fish.

Acknowledgement

The authors are grateful to their colleagues within ODA and TPI for their helpful criticism of this paper which does not, however, absolve the authors from sole responsibility for any errors.

Research and Development Activities of the International Development Research Centre of Canada in West Africa and the Caribbean *W H L Allsopp*

Activites de recherche et de developpement du Centre International Canadien de recherche en matiere de developpement en Afrique de l'Ouest et dans la region des Caraibes

L'auteur décrit les fonctions et les objectifs du Centre international de recherche en matière de développement (IDRC) de l'Université de la Colombie britannique, au Canada. Le Centre s'emploie à encourager, soutenir et conduire des recherches dans les pays en voie de dévelopment en coopération avec leurs gouvernements et institutions. Les projets halieutiques qui bénéficient de l'aide de l'IDRC en Afrique de l'Ouest et dans les Caraibes sont brièvement décrits pour illustrer les activités du Centre.

Actividades de investigacion y perfeccionamiento del Centro Internacional Canadiense para investigaciones en Africa Occidental y en el Caribe

El autor describe la función y los objetivos del Centro Internacional Canadiense (IDRC) de la Universidad de la Columbia Británica, en el Canadá. El Centro trata de alentar, favorecer, y efectuar investigaciones en los países en desarrollo cooperando con sus administraciones e instituciones. Se hace una breve descripción de los proyectos pesqueros en Africa Occidental y en el Caribe a los que presta ayuda el IDRC y también se ilustran las actividades de este Centro.

Fishery research and development project activities fall within the Division of Agriculture, Food and Nutrition Sciences of the International Development Research Centre (IDRC). Its purpose is:

to initiate, encourage, support and conduct research into the problems of the developing regions of the world and into the means for applying and adapting scientific, technical and other knowledge to the economic and social advancement of those regions, and, in carrying out those objects

(a) to enlist the talents of natural and social scientists and technologists of Canada and other countries;
(b) to assist the developing regions to build up the research capabilities, the innovative skills and the institutions required to solve their problems;
(c) to encourage generally the coordination of international development research; and
(d) to foster cooperation in research on development problems between the developed and developing regions for their mutual benefit.

The selection of expertise for consultancy advice is not restricted to any national source. Similarly, the purchase of required equipment is not confined to any monetary area. With regard to areas of activity, the Centre has given greater emphasis to needs of the semi-arid tropics. In fisheries, the focus has been on the pragmatic problems associated with increased profitability of rural fishing activities. Such a focus, however, endeavours to deal with the problems in as comprehensive a way as possible with realistic objectives but taking account of related factors and liaison with other institutions. This is particularly important in respect of fish product improvement in developing countries since all sectors of the industry are closely integrated and interdependent.

FACTORS IN SEMI-ARID TROPICS

In the countries which are within this broad area, the needs for protein for human consumption can generally be best provided in the cheapest form by fish. Where there is a tradition of fish consumption, the problems are those of price and regularity of supplies of the cheap fish. In many cases also, there are quantities of fish available which are not readily accepted. In both cases, the desirable levels of protein intake are not met, particularly in the youngest age groups. This protein gap is further complicated by losses due to processing, packaging or insect infestation as well as in storage and transport to remoter areas. There is need for an improvement of the traditional products so as to provide a wholesome and palatable product without much change in its appearance or presentation, while improving its food value and keeping it as cheap as possible (maximize nutritive value and minimize costs). There is, too, need for the development of new but acceptable products which are less wasteful of protein and can be prepared in greater bulk for economy and to cope with the quantities available at seasonal glut. This naturally involves questions of the feasibility of investment when acceptable products are developed and find markets. All these factors which tend to help stimulate the efforts from the primary sector of the industry by stabilizing the market for the fish produced can thus enable a profitable diversification of the catching systems and more rational cropping of available fish resources.

Rural fishing, due to vertical integration, stops when the small smoking ovens and storage bins are filled. Efficient processing systems, coupled with adequate storage and effective distribution to markets, are collectively therefore the pivotal factors on which the improvement of small scale rural fishing activity depends. This is particularly the case where there are no wholesale markets and nearby industrial depots of canneries, etc. The socio-economic effect on the primary and secondary sectors of the fishing industry is thus greater in the rural or artisanal fisheries with their low capital investment and labour intensiveness, so there is greater need for efforts to optimize the conditions as far as possible from the governmental viewpoint.

In less developed countries, processing losses between landing and consumption may be as much as 30 per cent by weight and often 60 per cent in food value. Losses are due to protein denaturing (as in charred fish in the hot-smoking systems in West Africa) or mould damage in storage. Insect infestation by beetles and fly maggots as well as breakage damage through rough handling in transportation also account for considerable losses. The pattern is of processing at beach or river bank production centres and the transport of the brittle, light-weight but bulky product packed in bags or mats, to distant markets. The changing pattern in coastal areas is of transport of frozen marine fish to remote centres where it is then processed for localized distribution. Thus the finished product is subject to less handling. In practice, the profitability of the latter system is greater, apart from the constancy and greater bulk of base-supply. The 5-ton transport trucks can carry 8 tons of frozen fish in cartons but only 3 to 4 tons of smoked or dried fish in baskets. The former arrives in perfect condition as a thawing-out block and is easily handled for smoke processing as a better product. The latter is partly broken and damaged and thus less attractive for market. The former supply comes from industrial enterprise and factory ships, the latter from rural enterprise which can only decline under such severe competition unless there is some adjustment to the system. Rural purchasing power is much less than that of the cities. The exception to this generalization occurs at industrial centres such as mines, mills, plantations, etc. Their fish needs are met by supplies of cheaper types of fish products. Once the traditional consumption pattern is established, it becomes difficult to change. Such communities are very conservative in habits and perhaps may only change as their purchasing power increases.

In other tropical areas, such as the Caribbean, the consumption of fresh fish has been so established that markets for chilled or frozen fish are only very gradually being developed in cities where adequate storage permits sales of acceptable products. Very often the fish is exposed for sale in the fresh state and, if unsold, held later in cold storage (about –5°C). Such storage causes a slow freezing of the water in the fish muscle and results in burst fibres and mushy fish when unthawed or cooked. This often happens in areas where cold storage is available but where the fresh fish is not frozen quickly or held at constant low temperatures (say 2° to 5°C). This practice is deterrent to widespread consumption where the consumer is accustomed to eating fish prepared from the fresh state. Such difficulties have occurred in some countries where frozen storage depots have been introduced and are used jointly for meat and fish products at the same temperature.

In most of the countries of interest to IDCR, the fish products consumed are fresh, smoked, salted or canned preparations. Frozen domestic pack preparations, when present in such countries, are consumed by higher income groups and are not the focus of IDRC projects. It has been found that the low-income consumer wants a small quantity of fish per meal for his family use. The purchaser thus buys a fish which weighs no more than 100 to 160 g or, say, a 2–oz (56 g) can of sardines or pilchards for the family meal. This small sized fish is thus in demand not only as a convenient unit to be added to the meal but because it is cheap. In some areas, however, even this is too costly. There is therefore a need for the cheapest hygienic packaging for small unit packs. This is likely to be satisfied by plastic packaging of some traditional products in somewhat dehydrated condition.

Rural fish consumption in remote inland areas is made more difficult by the seasonality of supplies, the variable climate conditions, and the problems of adequate storage. The periods of heavy rain and intense dry heat alternately favour the growth of moulds on the moister smoked products or the multiplication of dermestes beetles and fly maggots in the dried and smoked products. When the fish is treated both by salting and smoking, the losses due to moulds and insects are less in general terms. Such salted/smoked products are contrary to traditional food preparations. It would require much publicity (in difficult and expensive circumstances) to induce acceptance of any varied product which would entail preparatory treatment, such as de-salting by overnight soaking or boiling and discarding the water. The adoption of such a system would alleviate storage losses considerably. However, the total cost of and time involved in having to change the food preparation system and having a product that is totally acceptable to the consumer has prevented its widespread application after experimental demonstrations in Mali, northern Nigeria and Togo. So the problem of effective processing and the packaging of small units for direct consumption still persists. The objective may be realized through economies of scale in bulk processing of the traditional product, individual consumer packs in cheap material that conserves fish in mould-free and insect-free condition, and bulk packaging for rough overland transport. A flexible combination of these circumstances may be the solution in different parts of Africa. Meanwhile, the bulk landings of frozen fish have tended to smooth out fluctuating supplies and to create more dispersed processing centres around each interior township where the frozen cartons are distributed. This offers a better opportunity for innovative change by introducing slightly modified products for these areas even though the consumer tastes will not have changed.

CURRENT IDRC PROJECTS

West African rural fisheries

This project has been conducted since July 1972 in Ghana by the Ghanaian Government Ministry of Agriculture which coordinates the inputs of different departments and research institutes for the study of the interrelated factors for rural fishery improvement. The research objectives are to increase the total landings of fish and improve net earnings of artisanal fishermen particularly in the off season (October to May) and to establish the processing parameters which significantly influence the chemical/physical and nutritional properties of smoked and dried fish products with particular regard to present and future consumer acceptance. The present systems of marketing and distributing fish by and among the fishing and other rural communities will be studied, and the various conditions of the areas under research (ie harvesting, processing and distribution) will be examined, together with the potential cost benefit structure of each of the innovations proposed. The impact of increased protein sources upon the health of the rural peoples will also be studied. Extension activities are implied in the whole programme. Research and testing of suitable extension techniques to be undertaken in the pilot area will facilitate the utilization of results of technical research in the rural communities. Studies are determining the nutritive losses in processing and in storage under normal conditions with the commonly available fish types. The parameters involved in smoking the fish and the entire mechanics of the system as regards fish, ovens, fuels, handling costs, storage and flow of supplies have permitted an appreciation of the factors responsible for quality reduction. Since the traditional oven design does not allow much variation of process control, investigations are being carried out on the effect of varying the smoking parameters on processing efficiency and product acceptability with a view to oven design improvement. At the same time a system has been adopted for standardizing quality assessment of smoked products (in appearance, organoleptic condition and chemical content). Work is also in progress on the development of a sealed-pack storage procedure for use with smoked sardinella of low moisture content. Because the final product must be within the means of the lowest income group, the product must be cheap. Economies of scale must be adapted for coping with the major production season of three months and the bulk of the products must be storable without food-value loss for eight months at least. It is hoped that this work, when completed, can make a significant impact toward stabilizing the production of artisanal fisheries not only in Ghana but in the wider region where conditions are similar. The work is being undertaken by the Food Research Institute of the CSIR of Ghana and the Food Science and Nutrition Department of the University of Ghana, Legon. The duration of the study up to the pilot plant stage should be to 1975.

Processing of cultured oysters (West Africa)

This project is essentially concerned with oyster culture but will be also involved in the depuration for live oyster sales and particularly with the improvement in the traditional smoke-processing and with packaging of the oysters as a hygienic and storable product for regional markets. The project is likely to be based in Gambia with the collaboration of other West African countries in various aspects of the research study.

Fisheries by-products (Caribbean)

The utilization of fisheries by-products and species caught which are at present of uneconomic value is developing as a potential area of emphasis for IDRC support. Discussions are in progress with a number of fisheries research stations, in particular one in British Honduras, where it is proposed to develop marketable products from the discarded heads and legs of the spiny lobsters of which at present only the tails are of economic importance, and a variety of other fish caught in the Caribbean waters by the shrimp trawlers fishing the Guyana banks. This research study is to be done in collaboration with various institutions in the area for specific objectives and organization arrangements are being currently formulated.

AREAS OF SPECIAL POTENTIAL

Some areas of the tropics have a particularly large unsatisfied demand for fish and, while imports have partially met the need, the national objective is self-sufficiency in fish supplies. Some have experimented with the large-scale importation of fresh codfish to be processed as dry salted cod (Jamaica), while others have tried replacing stockfish by local processed products (Nigeria, Cameroon). An essential feature for a profitable process is the combination of cheap fuel for drying and bulk quantities. In the Niger delta area of Nigeria, the fish production has been reduced because of employment offered in the petroleum industry. Frozen fish supplies are imported and distributed in bulk to compensate for this reduced production and increasing demand. However, the flaming jets of natural gas burnt off in this oil prospection zone seem particularly favourable for dehydrating the product to a form similar to stockfish. The demand for fish in Nigeria is expected to amount to 1,200,000 tons by 1985. Considerable investment is to be undertaken in vessels, crew-training, harbours, and cold chain infrastructure to meet this. The abundant supply of natural gas can be used in a processing system for the efficient production of products that are widely accepted while better, and perhaps more desirable products, are being developed and popularized.

In areas where shrimp trawlers operate, all the fish that is caught is discarded because of its much lower market value. This is generally a great bulk of mixed species which include many that are readily eaten in the area. In the case of the trawlers fishing off the Guyanas it is estimated that more than 100,000 tons of edible fish are jettisoned annually by the 400 trawlers operating there, while the Caribbean area is a net importer of fish. Many countries of the region are planning to use this fish and some are said to be now bringing in part of the edible fish caught for experimental marketing. The main problem seems to be one of logistics, of bulk handling, storage and sale where the shore facilities have to be equipped to handle such fish supplies and adequate markets have to be found without harm to the traditional inshore producers. The conversion of these quantities of fish to suitable products in all the major shrimp fisheries may probably be facilitated by the use of the flesh and bone separator machines. These can produce minced flesh from which comestible products, such as sausages, hams, fishburgers, fish pastes, etc., can be made. This seems to be a system that can allow for a great range of products to cater for varied tastes in the more sophisticated consumer markets.

CONCLUSIONS

The main motive in this area of activity of IDRC is to make available more food products by reduction of waste of traditional fish products as well as the development of processes for fish not currently used. While the current scale of the projects is small, it is hoped that their impact, once demonstrated at the pilot plant scale, will have an increasing influence in the country of operation and region. The importance of effectively conserving fish products is considered to be a limiting factor to profitability of tropical fishing enterprises as well as being the eventual basis on which diversification of fishing techniques, prolongation of the season by fishing for other types, and the more effective rational cropping of available fish resources, can be realized.

Technical Note

Peruvian Experience in Joint Ventures

P Andersen, W P Appleyard, P W de Haan, G H Hordijk, E C A van Noort and J A R Souness

Peruvian experience in joint ventures are of two kinds: 'convenios' and mixed enterprises. A 'convenio' is an agreement to operate jointly during the experimental stage of a project. The result of experimental stage will largely decide whether the partners will then form a mixed enterprise. The following examples are of 'convenios' formed by the Empresa Pública de Servicios Pesqueros (EPSEP) and a foreign partner.

EPSEP – Polish Foreign Trade Department (RYBEX)

This convenio between EPSEP and the Polish Foreign Trade Department was signed in November 1972. Originally planned to operate two Polish factory trawlers of the B-15 class (2,300 GRT) during one year, the agreement has been extended for another year increasing the number of vessels to six. Four vessels are already operating in Peruvian waters. EPSEP is responsible for the management and administration of the project and the Polish partner for production and marketing who will make all the payments in hard currency. Operational costs and profits or losses will be evenly shared. Peruvians will form 30 per cent of the crews of the vessels.

Yearly catches of the first two ships are estimated to be around 200,000 tons, mainly merluza, which is processed into the following final products:

2,000 m.t. of merluza fillet blocks, US standard;
1,400 m.t. of merluza fillet blocks, European standard;
3,000 m.t. of dressed merluza;
2,000 m.t. of other fish;
2,000 m.t. of fishmeal;
400 m.t. of fish oil.

EPSEP – Flota Cubana de Pesca (FLOCUBA)

The convenio between EPSEP and FLOCUBA was signed in August 1973 for one year and the two Cuban 2,000-GRT trawlers have started operations. If catches are satisfactory, a third ship will be brought in. The total cost of the project is estimated to be about US$3 million. The partners will share equally the costs and the profits or losses. Again, Peruvians will form 30 per cent of the crews.

The fleet is mainly fishing for merluza and the following production is anticipated (in round figures):

550 m.t. of merluza fillets with V-cut;
550 m.t. of merluza fillets, Cuban standard;
11,000 m.t. of dressed merluza;
4,500 m.t. of other fish;
1,200 m.t. of fishmeal.

Challwa del Perú S.A. or CHALLPESA

A mixed enterprise has been formed by EPSEP with three Japanese companies: Taiyo Fisheries Co. Ltd., Nihon Hogei Co. Ltd. and Mitsubishi Corp. It will operate under the name of Challwa del Perú S.A. (CHALLPESA).

The new company, with a total investment of about US$11 million, will conduct the following activities in two phases and in two different locations:

Phase 1

Fish sausage production in Paita.
Fish canning in Oquendo.
The operation of a 700-GRT trawler.
The first stage is planned to be completed at the end of 1974.

Phase 2

Frozen merluza fillet blocks and fillets production based on a raw material supply of about 50 m.t. daily.
Fish sausage production in Oquendo.

Extended fish canning in Oquendo.

The operation of two trawlers, one of 700 GRT and one of 200 GRT.

The operation of cold storage, freezing and ice-making equipment in Oquendo.

The second stage will be initiated in 1975. It is planned that in the seventh year the company will become fully operational.

Merluza raw material requirements, corresponding to the various stages of production, are estimated to be:

1973 about 3,000 m.t.
1974 about 10,000 m.t.
1975 about 22,000 m.t.
1979 about 16,000 m.t.

Developing the Guyana Shrimp Industry   *F A Peterkin*

Developpement de l'industrie crevettiere de la Guyane

Description de développement de la pêche hauturière de la crevette en Guyane où les pêcheries traditionnelles se bornent à exploiter les eaux côtières. Le rapide essor de la pêcherie des crevettes de grand fond est attribué à trois facteurs principaux: activités de recherche et de pêche exploratoire entreprises en coopération par plusieurs gouvernements; évolution de l'industrie de la pêche qui a créé des installations à terre et fourni des bateaux de pêche; et accueil favorable réservé à la nouvelle industrie par les gouvernements des trois pays intéressés (Guyane, Guyane française et Surinam). En outre, on a immédiatement trouvé ces débouchés pour la crevette. Entre 1960 et 1970, les exportations de crevettes capturées dans les eaux guyanaises sont passées de 1,600 à 5,300 tonnes. L'industrie poursuit son expansion: elle agrandit ses installations à terre et en construit de nouvelles et elle acquiert davantage de bateaux modernes. Le Gouvernement de la Guyane cherche à diversifier les activités halieutiques nationales grâce à l'exploitation des diverses espèces de poissons et de crustacés vivant dan ses eaux et à l'implantation d'un secteur secondaire chargé de la transformation des captures.

Desarrollo de la industria camaronera de la Guyana

En este trabajo se describe el desarrollo de la industria camaronera de media altura en la Guyana, donde tradicionalmente se pescaba sólo en aguas próximas a la costa. El rápido incremento de la pesca del camarón en alta mar se atribuye sobre todo a tres factores: las actividades de investigación y pesca exploratoria de varios gobiernos, en colaboración mutua; la construcción de bases en tierra y la compra de buques pesqueros por parte de la industria pesquera, y la buena acogida concedida a la nueva industria por los gobiernos de los tres países interesados (Guyana, Guayana Francesa y Surinam). También ha contribuido el hecho de que existiera ya un mercado para los camarones. Entre 1960 y 1970 la exportación de camarones capturados en caladeros de la Guyana aumentaron de 1,600 a 5,300 toneladas. La industria está aún en expansión, y se están construyendo nuevas instalaciones en tierra, más amplias, y más buques modernos. El Gobierno de Guyana intenta diversificar las actividades pesqueras del país para explotar las diversas especies de peces y crustáceos que se encuentran en sus aguas y fomentar industrias secundarias basadas en las capturas.

DEVELOPMENT OF FLEET AND PRODUCTION

The presence of good shrimp resources (mainly pink shrimp, *Penaeus brasiliensis*, and brown shrimp, *P. aztecus*) led to the establishment of shrimp bases and fleets. Before this development, the traditional local fisheries of the countries in the region were based on the small inshore species, especially sea-bob (*Xyphopenaeus krøyeri*). Shrimp fishing began in earnest about 1959 in the countries closest to the deeper grounds. Processing plants were built in Parimaribo, Surinam; Georgetown, Guyana; and Cayenne and St. Laurent, French Guiana. While the first large scale fishing was started in Guyana by a combined operation of local boat owners, the United States played an important part in the development of the shrimp fisheries in this area. Later (1967–68) the Japanese appeared, followed by the Koreans and Cubans. Almost all the catch is processed in shore-based plants in the area. During 1968 and 1969 factory ships were reported in the area, but were found to be uneconomical and were withdrawn. It is estimated that the number of boats fishing for shrimp in Guyana, French Guiana and Surinam increased from about 100 in 1961 to some 400 by 1969. Most fleets are standardized to facilitate maintenance and repairs. The boats carry identical engines, auxiliaries, electronic equipment, etc. Lately, the trend is to steel, with some fibreglass hulls. Many of the latest vessels are brine refrigerated but there is still a sizeable fleet of ice-boats. Production of shrimp tails, excluding small shrimp, has increased from about 1,600 tons in 1960 to some 4,100 tons in 1968 and 5,400 tons in 1972. Most of this production is exported. All fishing supplies and equipment imported directly for the industry are exempt from import duty. Freezing and processing plants, however, pay company and property tax. There is also an export tax on the shrimp fixed at an agreed rate of approximately US$0.13/kg. Proposals for 1973 include a Government/owner agreement to bring in fish for sale to the Government at a low price. Hopefully, this is the beginning of another diversification in the national interest.

EXPLOITATION OF THE RESOURCE

The development of the shrimp fishery was due to three factors: research and exploratory fishing by several Governments working in cooperation; follow-up by the fishing industry by establishing shore bases and bringing in modern fishing vessels; and the welcome given to the new industry by the Governments in the three countries. The main thrust in exploration and development came from the United States. Before the offshore beds of large shrimp were discovered, the vast quantities of inshore sea-bobs had long provided a resource for substantial local fisheries. In 1956 the first freezing plant in the area was established in Surinam to process sea-bobs. Although this venture never amounted to a great deal, the plant was ready for use when the offshore fishery was developed and was the first to start production (Croaker, 1967). The enterprises established in the various countries to harvest the shrimp have followed the same general operating pattern. They mostly started as pilot projects and experienced, in particular, difficulties in the preservation of the catch. As a result, there were times when, after much endeavour and rich catches, the shrimp failed to reach the shore station in good condition. Much work, therefore, has gone into the task of preserving the catch, an essential safeguard because most of the fishing grounds are distant from the processing plants.

In this respect, the development of the use of chemical dips (chiefly sodium bisulphite) has been a major breakthrough. However, because of chemical residual problems, constant vigil is necessary to keep the process within limits.

Consideration also had to be given to the existence of shops to supply groceries for the boats, spare parts depots and the proximity to ports, where the catches could be transferred to refrigerated vessels to be shipped to the overseas markets. Shore bases, therefore, are either near to the docks or have their own docking facilities. The shore bases generally utilized existing facilities and buildings but as the industry grew it was necessary to extend these facilities. Unfortunately, most of the expansion was not as carefully planned as it should have been, principally because the investors feared that the resource would become exhausted. Time has proved this fear to be unfounded. To meet the demands of the sustained growth, training programmes for plant workers and fishermen have had to be organized. Ancillary services have had to be introduced and encouraged, and in some cases even subsidized. There are, therefore, the required types of skills now available, although small in volume. Very few of these shore bases are in isolated areas. As can be appreciated, those that are isolated find themselves at a disadvantage in terms of cost for such amenities as living quarters for staff and medical and other welfare services. Also other problems arise, such as getting expatriate skippers and crews in and out as replacements or on rotation. Future plans for expansion, therefore, must take into consideration these various aspects.

In addition, investors are looking for the type of political climate that is not only sympathetic to the industry but encourages its growth, both in terms of earnings and the potential of the resource. At present, there are two schools of political thought about shrimp – as a good dollar-earner and as rich food for the nations in the area. Both of these have to take into consideration that the producers have their home bases in the United States or Japan. They harvest the resource, pay locally for packing, freezing and shipping, and have their own systems of sale and distribution. In some instances, vessel owners have merged and built shore facilities jointly by them, but they market the product under their own label or trade name. Small independent operators have appeared in the last three to four years. They sell their catches outright to the foreign organizations or have marketing agreements with them. The indications are, however, that there will be more Government participation in the industry, not only in terms of vessels and shore facilities but also of domestic market programmes. This, it is hoped, will generate greater confidence between Government and investors, as well as ensure that the countries share in the harvest of their rich natural resources.

The country has always had a small domestic shrimp fishery operated by local fishermen in small open boats. They fish in the estuaries of the Demerara and Berbice. The fine white shrimp are referred to locally as 'white bellies'. The shrimp are sold fresh locally but, when catches are big, some are sun-dried. Part of this production is exported to the Caribbean. Government loans to small cooperative groups to own boats, harvest the shrimp and process them in simple mechanical dryers, are now being given to promote an increase in this trade as there is a big demand for this shrimp, fresh or dried. When dried with salt added it makes a welcome addition to a favourite regional rice dish. Another development is the harvesting and processing of a tiny brown shrimp found in large quantities in the inshore waters along the coast, particularly in the eastern parts. It is estimated that this resource could support a fishery with a catch of 1,800 to 2,300 tons a year. However, it will be necessary to design a small trawler equipped with brine tanks or refrigerated holds to deliver the catch for processing.

OUTLOOK

The shrimp fisheries have contributed immensely to the economic growth of Guyana and planned increased production, therefore, as well as diversification, particularly in the export markets, are essential to ensure continuity of this contribution. This means that future development of exports will require governmental, as well as financial, support. The Guyana Government have made it quite clear that their efforts are directed toward the expansion of the industry and the development of secondary industries, such as for fish products. The country has the potential for such growth because of the proximity of the fishing grounds and the quantities and varieties of species in them. These will be exploited to develop markets, starting in the Caribbean where the shortage of fish is acute, and expanding elsewhere. Some investors have shown great interest in the dried shrimp and in bottling small shrimp in brine for export. A cheap boat, economic in operation and capable of harvesting the small shrimp, has been experimentally produced and is being tested. Consideration is being given to designing processing plants capable of expansion with the industry, particularly for handling fish, including dry salted fish, and fish and shrimp products. The estimated 20 per cent increase in the fleet in 1973 will mean that most of the existing plants will be worked to capacity. Some of the local operators, therefore, have joined forces with the newest overseas owner/investor to open a small processing and freezing plant. A reduction in the number and frequency of refrigerated boats to the United States, Japan, etc., has been negotiated. As a result the country will be able to ship shrimp to areas that could not be serviced before because of lack of shipping facilities. The United Kingdom and Europe are relatively new markets as contact was lost with them in 1960–61 because of the shortage of the commodity and its diversion to high price markets. However, Europe appears once again interested in Guyana shrimp. The Caribbean area can use large quantities of medium and small shrimp at the present market price, particularly during the tourist season. The previous difficulty with this market was the irregularity of supply because of lack of regular transport. Small shipments were sent by air but this was expensive. A new refrigerated boat service will now relieve this situation and open the market.

In developing exports it is necessary to consider the long-term viability of the resources. As already pointed out, the area is rich in these, but there has been a growing fleet fishing them. Some of the countries of the area have, therefore, unilaterally extended their territorial waters to conserve the resources for their developing economies. Efforts are also being made to classify and catalogue the data relative to the resources. Such information will assist in determining measures to maintain the level of the catches to avoid serious fluctuations. The Japanese fleets have cooperated in this respect. They have charted the area and produced data about catches for various fishing grounds at various times of the year. Price resistance has occurred in the United States and Japan because of increased world production and other factors, a situation in which the new markets were quite welcome. In the last six months of 1972 the situation became so adverse that firms from Guyana were compelled to offer their production to less developed markets. Fortunately, the situation is only temporary but it is another reason for developing trade in fish and fish products to cushion any serious set-back in the main shrimp industry. As has been pointed out, the Government are deeply conscious of the value of the industry. However, perhaps what is needed is legislation by the Government to safeguard the right of the sea for the industry based in Guyana. It would be tragic after developing the industry to see it fail because of lack of foresight and the offer of better facilities and conditions in a neighbouring territory. Taking all the circumstances into consideration, present indications are that the climate for investment in Guyana is good, but future development does not rest only on the shoulders of the Government and the industry. It will also be influenced by the increasing sophistication and change in the developed markets of the world. Guyana, in order to maintain and improve her position, must keep abreast of these.

References

CROKER, R S   The shrimp fishery of Central America, the
1967   Caribbean Sea and northern South America, *Foreign Fish,*
       Leafl. US Fish Wildl. Serv., (74):127 p.
NAIDU, K S and BOEREMA, L K The High-sea shrimp resources off
1972   the Guyanas and northern Brazil, *FAO Fish. Circ.*, (141):
       18p.

Discussion on Part VIII

International cooperation, investment and development

The discussion took into consideration the various types of fisheries. A great need for foreign aid exists for small-scale inshore fisheries and it appears that bilateral and multilateral aid organizations could play a key role in the drawing up of programmes for this type of development. The discussion on investment and development focussed on the question of joint ventures.

WATZINGER (FAO) described, in connexion with this whole question, how the Department of Fisheries has been restructured to enable it to play a more direct and intensive role in resource utilization through investment and development. In particular, a Fishery Development Service has been created in the Fishery Industries Division so that maximum effort can be made to promote investment, including joint ventures. A special unit to promote the development of small-scale inshore or artisanal fisheries has been set up in the Service. And as a means of working in closer cooperation with the international banks, a Joint Group has been established in the FAO Investment Centre. Further, as a means to closer cooperation with industry, a Fishery Industry Group has been established with FAO's Industry Cooperative Programme. He explained that the other Service in the Fishery Industries Division (the Fish Production and Marketing Service) will cooperate in the foregoing activities by providing technical services for the Organization's field programmes and continue with its regular programme activities. FAO would work in cooperation with any other UN Agency or other bodies engaged in fisheries development, including joint ventures.

KOMBOT-NAGUEMON (Central African Republic) welcomed the establishment of the Fishery Development Service and expressed the hope that FAO will take into account regional needs as well as those of individual countries in undertaking developmental work.

APPLEYARD (FAO), referring to the general question of development, expressed the conviction that the joint venture approach is a practical way to accelerate progress. FAO's role in joint ventures is that of the 'honest broker' when requested to join negotiations by a Member Government. He felt that there will be increasing use of the joint venture approach and an increasing need for FAO involvement. With regard to the need for identification and formulation of strategic fisheries projects, he suggested that special efforts should be made by governments and by bilateral and multilateral aid agencies to finance the necessary missions.

SOUDAN (France) stressed the difficulties of securing the services of highly skilled personnel needed to assist in fisheries development. Perhaps industry may be able to release specialists, replacing them during their absence, but this situation might be more difficult in the case of research institutes which have a limited number of staff fixed by the government. In both cases, the difficulties that released staff may find on their return must also be taken into consideration. She suggested that one way of coping with the situation might be to form permanent teams for assisting developing countries.

ALLSOPP (IDRC) stated that there is a tendency in development in developing countries to obtain bigger vessels for industrialized fishing. This creates problems of management and of processing and storage. If the results of studies of these problems can be made available to developing countries, they would be of practical help in coping with these problems.

TAYLOR (UK) said that in entering a joint venture a commercial concern, however enlightened, must obtain adequate returns, while a government may wish to achieve a socio-economic objective for which an 'adequate' return in a business sense is not a necessity. In such cases, perhaps the joint venture could be undertaken on the basis of a management/technical agreement from government to government. In any venture, the management responsibility must be clearly defined and should normally be that of the company partner. However, there should be written undertaking in the agreement for the company to train local personnel to take over management responsibilities as soon as practical. So far as the share between joint venture partners is concerned, he suggested that the majority holding should go to the local partner.

SLAVIN (USA) stated that joint ventures may be as useful to developed as to developing countries, especially in relation to coastal fisheries and in the case of under-utilized species. He suggested that FAO should take the lead in this matter by working closely with experts from Member Governments and industry to define resource utilization possibilities. For this purpose, it might perhaps be desirable to set up a working group to provide FAO with advice in this field.

BLACKWOOD (Canada) said that optimum utilization of their fishery resources is under urgent investigation in many countries and FAO should play an effective role in focussing attention on the potential utilization of the world's fishery resources.

VAN IJSSELSTEIN (Netherlands), supporting this view, said there should be world-wide planning for the utilization of marine resources, including an extensive development of aquaculture.

ALLSOPP (IDRC) explained organization and areas of interest of the International Development and Research Centre (IDRC) of Canada. Special attention is being given to the prevention of waste in fish utilization and distribution, to problems of the artisanal fisheries and to aquaculture. IDRC is also interested in sponsoring the development of fish products with good keeping time and which are easy to store and transport in tropical countries.

TAPIADOR (FAO) informed the Conference on the setting up of a Liaison Group on Fish Product Development by the Indo-Pacific Fisheries Council (IPFC). The group met for the first time during the Conference in Tokyo and discussed a programme aimed at cooperative research work in the IPFC region and surveyed fields of interest in cooperation between technological institutes of both developed and developing countries.

KREUZER (FAO) gave as an example of practical cooperation a proposal made by Allsopp at the meeting of the IPFC Liaison Group. He had suggested that the IDRC programme aiming at the development of fish products from underutilized fish species might be carried out jointly by IDRC and IPFC. Allsopp had mentioned that IDRC is prepared to sponsor a permanent consultative panel of experts on product development from developing and developed countries. The first meeting of the panel could be convened in the IPFC region in 1974.

Transfer of technology and problems in establishing fishery products industries

The discussion on these subjects centred on training for development and on quality control.

APPLEYARD (FAO) pointed out that small-scale fisheries produce about 90 per cent of the food fish in the developing countries and it is these fisheries in particular that need to attract financial and technical assistance to achieve development. In view of their scattered nature, they especially need training to improve processing and distribution techniques and the most practical way of reaching them for this purpose is through extension workers. He referred to the increasing attention being given to these small-scale fishery problems by FAO.

HANSEN (FAO) said that the technology of developed countries cannot merely be transferred to developing countries for use in their small-scale fisheries. Training must be based on techniques developed and tried and tested to meet local requirements. For this reason, special funds are required for research and development. As an example of the need, he cited the Danish work in evolving a new box/ice system for use in small-scale tropical fisheries but which has been halted for want of further funds to bring it into practical use.

JONES (UK) declared that training in many ways is required in the artisanal fisheries and this should not be based for tropical countries on 'the dogmas of experts in cold water fish technology'. He went on to list a number of technical problems needing to be solved in the artisanal fisheries, such as the relationship of catching techniques to quality, including the subsequent handling of the fish; the establishment of parameters governing quality and salability of dried and smoked products; the health hazards in certain of the present semi-dried products; and the need for chilling as a superior method to poor cold storage.

CONSTANTINIDES (USA) recounted the training work done by the University of Rhode Island with the help of a grant from the United States Agency for International Development. It has established an International Centre for Marine Resource Development (ICMRD) which is involved in the problems of developing countries in relation to marine resource economics, marine biology, oceanography, ocean engineering, fishermen training, fishing gear research, marine food science and technology, marine and resources extension work, and certain sociological factors related to fishermen. A large part of all this training activity takes place in developing countries. The Centre is the coordinating headquarters of a consortium of five American universities engaged in the development of technology. The consortium is working with foreign and local universities and other aid organizations in a number of developing countries.

BYKOV (USSR) reported on a similar sort of training activity. His country is helping to train technical personnel, is participating in the construction of ice making facilities, cold storage and processing plants, and is assisting in the investigation of resources, catching, handling and processing and training personnel in these fields.

IMAI (Japan) stated that one of the main problems faced by developing countries in their efforts to establish fishery products industries and to channel the output into export trade is that of quality control.

VAN IJSSELSTEIN (Netherlands) and SOUDAN (France) suggested that FAO could assist in this matter by giving more attention to the establishment of international quality standards and fish handling practices. As

449

Soudan pointed out, the joint FAO/WHO Codex Alimentarius Committee is the body to establish quality and hygienic standards and the Conference should request it to give priority to this task.

BLACKWOOD (Canada) suggested that in connexion with the question of quality control FAO should request member countries to provide information about their inspection agencies and a list of their relevant acts and regulations so that FAO may prepare and keep up-to-date a directory of this material for common use. He also suggested similarly making a directory of fisheries research institutions with a reference to their programmes.

JAMES (Australia) supported these proposals, adding that such a listing has already been done for technological laboratories in the IPFC region and could be extended.

YOUSSOUF ALI (Bangladesh) made a plea that all bilateral aid for fisheries development should be made available in non-tied form. He pointed out that any form of tied aid can force developing countries to buy materials, machinery and equipment which may not be the most suitable and may be too expensive. Tied aid also results in developing countries acquiring a great variety of machinery and equipment, which adds to the difficulties of maintenance and service.

At the end of the Session participants from the Latin American countries put forward a proposal that FAO should organize a conference in their region on the evaluation and programming of fisheries.

KOMBOT-NAGUEMON (Central African Republic) supported this suggestion and said there should be such conferences for all regions.

WATZINGER (FAO) explained that FAO has not the substantial additional funds required to finance such an ambitious series of meetings. The funds would have to be raised by the regions. He added, however, that plans for holding seminars in Latin America on planning and development in fisheries and on quality control meet to some extent the objectives of the proposals.

GENERAL AND SPECIFIC INDEXES

General Index

Index of Fish Names[1]

(Raw material)

[1] Wherever possible, the O.E.C.D. Multilingual Dictionary of Fish and Fish Products has been used in preparing the index. A catalogue of fish names in common use in various regions is currently in preparation by FAO, but unfortunately was not sufficiently advanced to be used here.

Index of Shellfish Names

(Raw material)

Index of Processed Fishery Products

461